Analysis of Electric Circuits

McGraw-Hill Electrical and Electronic Engineering Series
FREDERICK EMMONS TERMAN, *Consulting Editor*
W. W. HARMAN and J. G. TRUXAL, *Associate Consulting Editors*

ANALYSIS OF ELECTRIC CIRCUITS

EGON BRENNER, D.E.E.

ASSISTANT PROFESSOR OF ELECTRICAL ENGINEERING
THE CITY COLLEGE OF NEW YORK

MANSOUR JAVID, Ph.D.

ASSISTANT PROFESSOR OF ELECTRICAL ENGINEERING
THE CITY COLLEGE OF NEW YORK

McGRAW-HILL BOOK COMPANY, INC.

New York   Toronto   London

1959

ANALYSIS OF ELECTRIC CIRCUITS

THE MAPLE PRESS COMPANY, YORK, PA.

PREFACE

The subject of linear electrical circuit analysis has been a part of the
curricula of electrical-engineering students since the inception of such
curricula. As the discipline of electrical engineering has developed, it
has been found that the study of circuit analysis must be broadened
correspondingly in order to provide the student with the necessary background. The introduction of the fundamental principles of *pulse circuits,
analogue and digital computers, feedback control systems, network synthesis,
noise and communication theory* in an ever-increasing number of undergraduate curricula requires thorough preparation in analysis. In addition the older disciplines such as *electrical machinery, radio communica-
tions,* and *electronic circuits* are presented in a more analytically oriented
fashion than in the past.

The need for suitable text material in analysis at the earliest possible
level, namely, the sophomore-junior level, has therefore developed. It is
our belief that, for the reasons set forth below, this book may fill this need.

Traditionally the student has been introduced to electrical-circuit
analysis by studying in sequence "d-c circuits," "a-c circuits," and
"transients." This scheme, which was possibly adequate in years past,
does not for several reasons satisfy present-day needs. By a study of
steady-state response alone the student is led to think of voltages and
currents as "voltmeter readings" and "ammeter readings," while for
today's curriculum and for tomorrow's applications it is just as important
(indeed perhaps even more important) that he think of waveforms, or
"oscillograms," in this connection. Second, with the subdivisions mentioned above the "transients" portion is taught too late in the student's
undergraduate career to be of value in corequisite course work. As evidence of this, one need only glance at books on electronic circuits or
servomechanisms and one observes the large number of pages, and indeed
chapters, which are devoted to exposition of linear circuit analysis. This
detracts from the main concepts in those books and causes duplication,
with the corresponding waste of precious classroom time. Third, we
observe that the subdivisions enumerated above lead the student to
believe that he has learned three different subjects, while in fact he has
studied three special areas within a single topic. Thus the traditional

organization becomes an impediment to the integration of the subject matter into a consistent, coherent whole. Finally, because of its fundamental simplicity linear-circuit analysis, when treated in a unified manner, can serve as a vehicle for teaching and developing analytical skills per se.

While the need for integration of subject matter has been evident for some time, the implementation has been the subject of considerable controversy. The conclusion reached by some is that the remedy lies in the introduction of the Laplace transform at the earliest level. The argument used to justify this view is the following: A circuit is described by a linear differential equation. Since the Laplace transform is the "easiest" method for solving such equations, it should be taught at the earliest level.

The authors believe that the application of this view leads to an unsatisfactory result because the number of conceptual difficulties which the student encounters at one time is unreasonably large. In particular, without prior understanding of the complex-frequency domain, the Laplace transform, for the student, is only a somewhat mysterious mechanism which, he is told, leads to correct answers. In other words, the premature introduction of transform methods prevents the student from gaining insight into the behavior of linear systems because he has a mechanical means for arriving at answers. From a pragmatic view one could tolerate this disadvantage (for a while) if it were really true that the transform method is the easiest. It is our contention that in the solution of lumped-parameter linear-circuit problems transform methods do not reduce computational complexity; in fact, if the problem is sufficiently "simple," they complicate the work beyond all reason. The student who uses the Laplace transform for a simple circuit problem finds himself somewhat in the position of the operator of a steam shovel who wishes to use it to pick up a pebble. In addition we would point out that imparting to the student facility in solving examples is neither the only nor the ultimate goal of the study of circuits.

Having rejected the traditional subdivisions and wishing to avoid the premature introduction of the Laplace transform, we have organized this book on the basis of the following specific objectives.

1. The behavior of linear systems is described by means of differential equations in the time domain. This fact forms the central core and starting point for all analysis, and other network descriptions as well as methods of solution must be related to the differential equation.

2. As the student progresses, he must gain insight into the behavior of circuits. In particular the relationships between forced (steady-state) and free (transient) response must be explored fully, culminating in the study of networks through pole-zero configurations.

3. Fundamental principles rather than routine short-cut procedures are to be applied to the solution of problems. Thus, for example, the

student should not get into the habit of writing mesh or node equations for simple series-parallel circuits. Similarly the student, when using complex impedances and voltage and current phasors, should be aware of the fact that he is obtaining a particular solution of a differential equation.

4. Sufficient detail must be presented so that both the "conventional" skills and the more "modern" techniques can be applied to practical problems in corequisite and subsequent course work.

5. The foundation must be laid for advanced network and system study in both analysis and synthesis. A thorough introduction to the (complex-) frequency domain enables the student to study transformation methods, not only with ease, but also with understanding.

To obtain these objectives, we have chosen to approach the subject of linear-circuit analysis in the time domain with special emphasis placed on source and response functions which vary exponentially with time. The R-L-C circuits are used extensively because the fundamental behavior of all circuits can be understood from the thorough study of such simple circuits. In the implementation, the first six (short) chapters are devoted to defining the *general problem of circuit analysis*, to *circuit elements*, and to *Kirchhoff's laws*. Circuit elements are defined through their energy and voltage-current characteristics; the subject of resistance of wires and inductance of coils is left to courses in field theory. It should be mentioned here that, in most of the book, simple round numbers are used (for example, 3 farads). This is justified, not only because the scale-change theorems are eventually taken up, but also because it is desirable to avoid numerical difficulties when conceptual difficulties are to be explained. Experience has shown that the student has no trouble in applying the material to practical numerical situations when the occasion arises.

From the outset, however, waveforms and their rates of change, i.e., the differential relationships, in circuit elements and in circuits are emphasized.

In Chap. 7 the source-free R-L, R-C, and L-C circuits serve to introduce the notions of *time constant* and *natural frequency* as well as to exhibit the importance of *initial conditions*. Chapter 8 deals with *complex numbers* and their relationship to sinusoidal functions. In Chap. 9 the source-free R-L-C circuit serves to introduce the concept of *complex frequency*. Chapters 10 and 11 deal with *sources* and *simple circuits with sources*. The general properties which circuit responses exhibit, with particular emphasis on superposition, are illustrated in connection with response calculations. Throughout, the emphasis on time variations is maintained by means of careful discussions of relevant waveforms.

The differential equation relating a response function to a source function in general form is discussed in Chap. 12; *operational notation* is introduced for this purpose. The relationship between the operational form of the equation and its solution for *exponential source functions* is presented, leading to the concept of the transform network function. Both driving point and transfer functions are considered. *Thévenin's* and *Norton's theorems* are also included in this chapter. In Chap. 13 the response to exponential source functions is related to the *pole-zero configuration* of network functions, and the interdependence of forced and free response is established. These ideas are applied to *sinusoidal steady-state response, frequency response*, and (circular) *locus diagrams* in Chaps. 14 and 15. In Chap. 14 the conventional material on *a-c circuits*, such as phasor diagrams and complex power, is included.

In Chap. 16 the *simultaneous-equation methods* for formulating network functions are presented. The responses of networks, initial conditions, and time and frequency scaling are discussed in detail. A brief introduction to two-terminal-pair networks is included. Chapter 17, dealing with *three-phase circuits*, serves the machinery courses and is presented in the form of an application of the node method. Circuits with *mutual inductance*, the ideal transformer, and the linear transformer are introduced in Chap. 18. In the latter articles of Chap. 18 *tuned-transformer circuits* are introduced with the aid of pole-zero diagrams.

The concluding chapter of the book deals with *Fourier series*. While the matter of calculating Fourier coefficients is treated fully, such topics as mean-squared error, discrete frequency spectra, and frequency analysis as applied to signal transmission are also included.

A large number of problems are given at the end of each chapter. Exercises at all levels of difficulty are provided, ranging from simple applications of the text material to theorems (or similar problems) which are intended to carry the theory forward.

The amount of material in the book exceeds that which can be covered in a year course by about 15 per cent, so that some selection is necessary. There are several articles, particularly in Chaps. 11 and 14 to 16, which consist largely of numerical examples and which can be assigned reading or not as the teacher chooses, but which consume no classroom time in either case. Further there is sufficient overlap between chapters so that continuity is not lost by selection, particularly within Chaps. 15 and 16. Similarly some of the material in Chap. 18 dealing with tuned transformers may be postponed to the next course. In general the first semester's work may be through Chap. 13 or 14, with some selection from Chaps. 2 to 4 and 11. The last five articles of Chap. 13 are generally omitted on the first reading. If it is desired to introduce this material, it can be done conveniently in connection with the first part of Chap. 15. Since each teacher is the best judge of his students' needs, it is expected that considerable variations in emphasis will distinguish various classroom presentations. We have attempted to relieve the teacher of the burden of discussing details of numerical calculations in class by including a large number of worked-out examples. This, as well as the detail with which proofs are presented, accounts in part for the bulk of this volume. General reading lists have been omitted as, in this instance also, we feel that the classroom teacher is the best source of reference material for his students.

This book is based on a set of notes which has been in use at the City College of New York for the past three years. We are grateful to some twenty-five instructors who have taught from these notes and who offered many helpful suggestions. The contributions of Profs. L. Echtman, W. T. Hunt, Jr., S. R. Parker, A. G. Schillinger (now at the Polytechnic Institute of Brooklyn), C. Shulman, R. Stein, Dr. L. Bergstein, Mr. P. M. Brown, Mr. D. Eitzer, and Mr. D. Politis (now at The University of Michigan) deserve special mention.

We wish to express our sincere appreciation to Prof. C. Froehlich for her encouragement and help. We also acknowledge with thanks the continued interest of our department chairman, Prof. H. Taub. We thank Drs. J. G. Truxal and W. W. Harman for their valuable suggestions, particularly in connection with the revisions of the final manuscript.

The help of Mr. D. Eitzer in reading proof is appreciated. Miss S. Silverstein, who typed the manuscript, did her usual outstanding work.

Egon Brenner
Mansour Javid

CONTENTS

xiii

CHAPTER 1

THE CIRCUIT CONCEPT

Electrical engineering deals with the design, construction, utilization, and maintenance of electrical apparatus. The electrical engineer must not only understand the new devices which are continually being introduced: he must also conceive and develop novel equipment. Complete understanding of each device requires specialized knowledge of the branches of electrical engineering. For example, understanding the operation of a radio transmitter requires a knowledge of electronics, and understanding the behavior of electric motors requires a background in the theory of electrical machinery. Yet the same basic tool is employed in the study of all these divers specializations within electrical engineering. This tool is called *circuit theory*.

The reader probably recalls that basic electrical phenomena in physics are described by the laws of electromagnetism as formulated by Coulomb, Oersted, Ampère, Faraday, and Maxwell. None of these laws deals with electrical circuits: they all deal with fields. Although a knowledge of field theory is *not* essential for understanding circuit theory, it is the authors' belief that, at the outset, the reader must be made conscious of the relation between the field and circuit concepts, as well as the aims and limitations of circuit theory.

In this chapter a brief qualitative exposition of basic electromagnetic field concepts is given to serve this purpose. The remaining chapters of the book deal exclusively with circuit concepts and do not require a knowledge of electromagnetic theory.

1-1. Field Concepts. It is assumed that the reader is familiar with the concept of energy and power as introduced in the problems of mechanics. To illustrate the significance of terms used in connection with electricity and magnetism, we shall use examples from mechanics.

Force Field. The concepts of force and mass are closely related. For example, gravitational force presupposes the existence of mass. Similarly, observation of the attraction which a magnet possesses for a piece of iron depends on the existence of the mass of iron to be attracted. Nonetheless, through a process of abstraction, we can think of force as a quality of space without explicit reference to the ultimate cause of the

1

force or to the mass upon which the force will be exerted. *With this understanding, we define a force field as a region of space where a force is associated with its every point.* The gravitational field is a familiar example.

The field intensity at a point in a field is defined as the force applied to some unit quantity placed at that point. For example, in a gravitational field, the intensity at a given point is the force applied to a unit mass placed at that point.

Energy Stored in Space. Consider the motion of a mass in the gravitational field of the earth. Let a mass M, which was at rest at point A, at a height h_1, fall to a point B at the height of h_2. At point B the mass M has acquired a kinetic energy which it did not possess at point A. Where did the energy come from? This question is answered by introducing the concept of potential energy. The potential energy of the mass at point A with respect to point B is $Mg(h_1 - h_2)$, where g is the gravitational constant. Thus, in falling from point A to point B, the mass has lost $Mg(h_1 - h_2)$ of its potential energy and acquired its equivalent in kinetic energy. This argument is a familiar one. However, we may ask another question. At point A the mass had a certain potential energy; where was this energy located? This question is not meaningful unless we are convinced that energy must be located somewhere, and such a conviction can be achieved only if we know what energy is. The questions about the nature of fundamental concepts such as mass, time, length, energy, etc., are outside the domain of natural science and belong to the study of metaphysics. In the field theory of gravitation we *assume* that the potential energy is stored in the space (field) where the gravitational force exists. As a mass "falls" in this field, it "draws" from the potential energy stored in the field and transforms it into other forms of energy. In order to "raise" a mass in a gravitational field, work must be done. The energy spent in raising the mass is stored in the gravitational field and is available in the form of potential energy. Thus a mass "rising" in a gravitational field "delivers" energy to the field.

So far we have discussed only the familiar gravitational field. From our observation of nature we come to the conclusion that there are force fields other than the gravitational field. Two such fields are the *electric* and *magnetic* fields. The arguments given for the storage of energy in a gravitational field can be extended to apply to electric and magnetic fields. This will be discussed in Art. 1-2.

Energy Density. As soon as we accept the concept of energy stored in space, it is logical to inquire about the quantity of energy stored in a unit volume. If an energy distribution is uniform in space, the energy stored in any unit volume will be the same as that stored in any other, regardless of the position of the unit volume. However, most often this distribution is not uniform. For example, in the gravitational field of the earth, the force applied to a mass decreases as the mass moves away from the earth. Since the storage of energy is related to the force, it is plausible to assume that the gravitational energy stored in a unit volume located "far" away from the earth will be smaller than the energy stored in a unit volume "closer" to the earth. Moreover, within a given unit volume, the energy distribution is not uniform. However, as the dimensions of a given volume decrease (approach zero), the variation of energy distribution within that volume becomes smaller (approaches zero). In the limit, as the volume approaches a point, the energy stored in that volume approaches zero, but the ratio of the energy stored to the volume remains finite. Thus we define energy density *at a point* as the ratio of the energy stored in an infinitesimal volume located at that point to the volume.

Field Quantities. With each point of a force field we associate a field intensity (a vector quantity) and an energy density (a scalar quantity). These quantities are called field quantities and may vary from point to point, as well as with time. For a given field we may define various other field quantities which would best describe that field.

Static Field. A field whose field quantities are independent of time is called a static field. In a static field the field quantities may vary from point to point, but at a given point their value is constant for all time.

Dynamic Field. A field whose field quantities vary with time is called a dynamic field.

1-2. Electromagnetic Fields. In this article we shall attempt to present a theory which will explain the phenomena of electricity and magnetism. This presentation is qualitative because we wish to show only the relationship between the fundamental concepts of field and circuit theories without presenting involved analytical derivations.

Electrical Charge. The concepts of electric charge and the associated electric and magnetic fields are introduced in physics to explain and analyze certain observed phenomena. The electric charge is a fundamental quantity and is described by its attributes as follows:

1. The electric charge is always associated with mass.

2. It exists in two forms called the positive and the negative charge, respectively.

3. Two force fields are associated with a moving charge. These fields are called the electric and magnetic fields. The intensity of these fields at a given point of space will depend on the magnitude of the charge, its velocity, its acceleration, the distance of the point under discussion from the charge, and three qualities of the medium—ϵ, μ, and ρ—which are

called the permittivity, permeability, and resistivity of the medium, respectively. The (vector) intensities of the electric and magnetic fields are designated by the letters $\mathcal{E}$ and $\mathcal{H}$, respectively.

Electromagnetic Field Quantities. The field associated with the field intensities $\mathcal{E}$ and $\mathcal{H}$ is called the electromagnetic field. Electromagnetic theory relates the values of $\mathcal{E}$ and $\mathcal{H}$ to each other and to the distribution and motion of the charges in space. The fields associated with charges moving with nonuniform acceleration are dynamic fields, and the relationships between these dynamic field quantities are given by a set of equations called *Maxwell's equations.* Three important assumptions which are postulated in conjunction with Maxwell's equations are of great interest to us and will be given here:

1. The density of energy stored in an electric field at a given point in space[1] is $W_E = \epsilon E^2/2$, where ϵ and E are the permittivity of the space and the magnitude of the electric field intensity, respectively, at the point in question. We shall call the energy stored in an electric field the electric energy.

2. The density of the energy stored in a magnetic field at a given point in space[1] is $W_H = \mu H^2/2$, where μ is the permeability of the space and H the magnitude of the electric field intensity at that point in space. We shall call the energy stored in a magnetic field the magnetic energy.

3. At a point in space where the magnitude of the electric field intensity is E, electric energy will be transformed into heat at a *rate* equal to E^2/ρ per unit volume per second, where ρ is a property of the space at the point under discussion and is called the resistivity of the space at that point. The quantities ϵ, μ, and ρ describe the medium in which the electromagnetic field is established.

1-3. Exchange of Energy between Charge and Fields. *Electromagnetic Energy.* We shall use the term electromagnetic energy whenever we wish to refer to either electric or magnetic energy or both. A charge moving in an electromagnetic field will exchange energy with the field in the same manner as a mass moving in a gravitational field exchanges energy with that field. If the charge is accelerated by the field, then it will abstract energy from the field and transform it into kinetic energy. If it is decelerated, it gives up its kinetic energy, which will be stored in the electromagnetic field. If the medium has finite resistivity, the motion of the charge will be affected by the material in the medium and electromagnetic energy will be converted into heat. The fundamental problem of the electromagnetic theory is the determination of the field quantities and computation of energy distribution and transformation in the space.

---

[1] Details of the conditions under which this statement is valid can be found in advanced texts on electromagnetic theory.

1-4. Circuit Concepts. The solution of a field problem requires the determination of the field quantities $\mathcal{E}$ and $\mathcal{H}$ at every point in space as a function of time, when the initial distribution of charges, their velocities, and accelerations are given. Since these field quantities are functions of three space variables (for example, x, y, z), and time, the solution of field problems is generally quite complex, even with deceptively "simple" geometry.

Any electrical device entails the movement of charges. An exact analysis of the behavior of electrical devices should therefore be made by the use of the field theory. Since such an analysis can be exceedingly complex, it has been found necessary to develop an approximate, but sufficiently accurate, method of dealing with many electrical engineering problems. This method is called *circuit analysis*. The basic problem of circuit analysis is the determination of energy distribution and transformation in *different parts* of a device as a function of time *only*.[1] When an electrical device is functioning, there will be charges distributed in different parts of the device and most often these charges move with nonuniform velocities. Hence, an electromagnetic field is established over all space; energy is dissipated into heat, stored or withdrawn from this field, as the charges move in the device. It follows that, as a result of accelerating or decelerating charges in a device, energy will be transferred from one region of space to other regions. This phenomenon is known as the radiation of energy, and in electromagnetic theory it is shown that the energy is transmitted (radiated) with the velocity of light. (In fact, light itself is an electromagnetic phenomenon.)

When we discuss an electrical device, we assume that charges exist and move in that device. Therefore, the phenomenon stated above, which also entails radiation of energy, will take place when the charges in the device are accelerated or decelerated. However, the ratio of the energy associated with the device and its immediate neighborhood to that associated with the rest of space will depend on the dimensions of the device and the magnitude of the acceleration of the charges. It can be shown that, if the product of the maximum value of the acceleration of the charges in a device and the largest dimension of the device is much smaller than the square of the velocity of light, then the greater part of the energy storage and its transformations will be confined to the device and its immediate vicinity and the distribution and transformation of energy at distant points can be neglected. For devices with dimensions of the order of tens of feet, the acceleration of the charges must be of the order of 10^{16} ft/sec^2 before any appreciable radiation will take

---

[1] It is possible to extend the meaning of the term circuit analysis to apply to systems with distributed parameters, such as transmission lines. In such cases space is also an independent variable. In this book we do not deal with such systems.

place. When radiation can be neglected, then all energy storage and transformation take place in the immediate neighborhood of the device. In addition, we assume that the fields due to the motion of charges in one part of the device are established instantaneously in other parts instead of propagating with the velocity of light.

In the solution of the field problem the energy density at a given point of space was given in terms of the electric field intensity ε and the magnetic field intensity $\mathfrak{JC}$. We have said that the electromagnetic energy stored per unit volume of space is $W_{EM} = (\epsilon E^2 + \mu H^2)/2$ and the rate of transformation of energy into heat is E^2/ρ per unit volume.

In circuit theory, instead of computing the values of ε and $\mathfrak{JC}$ for every point in space as a function of time and evaluating from them the energy density and the energy transformation (into heat), we define two new variables associated with a pair of terminals in the device, and from these compute the energy delivered to a region of the device identified by

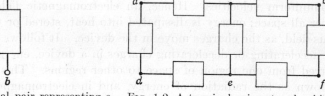

FIG. 1-1. A terminal pair representing a part of a device between two terminals.

FIG. 1-2. A terminal-pair network which may represent a device.

these terminals. Thus, any electrical device is divided into regions or volumes, symbolically shown by boxes or other symbols identified by two terminals and called a terminal pair (see Fig. 1-1). In this way a device is represented by an interconnection of terminal pairs, connected at their accessible terminals and called a terminal-pair network as shown in Fig. 1-2. Such a terminal-pair network is said to be the equivalent network of the device. Instead of discussing energy storage and transformation at all points of the device and computing them from ε and $\mathfrak{JC}$, we focus our attention on the energy storage and transformation within each terminal pair. These processes are computed from two variables which are associated with the terminals of the terminal pair. Thus, field problems, whose variables (ε and $\mathfrak{JC}$) were functions of space (x,y,z) and time (t), have been reduced to circuit problems, whose variables will be functions of time only and refer to the terminals of a given terminal pair.

1-5. Electrical Circuits. We assume that the electric charges which enter one terminal of a terminal pair will come out of the other terminal. Since we have assumed that charges move inside the device, they must be confined to motion through terminal pairs which represent different parts of the device and therefore must move through a closed path formed by terminal pairs connected together. Any such closed path is called a *circuit*. It must be noted that the term circuit may be used to refer to a connection of terminal pairs which is not closed, but it is always implied that such connections will be closed eventually. We shall now proceed to define the two principal variables of circuit theory.

Electric Current. An orderly motion of charges as defined by the (time) rate of flow of positive charges from the terminal a to the terminal b of a terminal pair a-b is called the current flowing from a to b and is shown by the symbol $i_{ab}(t)$. The order of the subscripts ab indicates that the function $i_{ab}(t)$ is the rate of flow of positive charges from a to b. The definition of current implies that, in the terminal pair a-b, $i_{ab}(t) = -i_{ba}(t)$. Thus, if, at one instant of time $t = t_1$, $i_{ab}(t_1)$ is a positive number, then at that instant positive charges are flowing from a to b through the terminal pair. If, at an instant $t = t_2$, $i_{ab}(t_2)$ is a negative number, then at that instant positive charges are flowing from b to a. We emphasize that the current i_{ab} is associated with the terminals a-b, although we may have no information about what is the exact motion of charges inside that particular part of the device which is represented by the terminal pair.

Voltage Function. With the assumption made in the above paragraph, it can be shown that the rate of delivery of energy to a terminal pair can always be given as the product of the current $i_{ab}(t)$ and another function of time associated with the terminals a and b. This function is called the voltage between the two terminals of the terminal pair and is indicated by $v_{ab}(t)$. The order of the subscripts ab indicates that the function $v_{ab}(t)$ is the voltage of point a with respect to point b. Thus, if $p_{ab}(t)$ is the rate of delivery of the energy to the terminal pair a-b, then we can always find a function $v_{ab}(t)$ such that $p_{ab}(t) \equiv v_{ab}(t)i_{ab}(t)$. The above equation may be considered to be the defining equation of the voltage function $v_{ab}(t)$. As in the case of i_{ab}, we understand v_{ab} to be a function of time, and if the voltage between two terminals is not a function of time, we show it with capital V, as in V_{ab}. In general, lower case and capital letters will be used to show time-dependent and time-independent quantities, respectively. Since $v_{ab}(t)$ and $i_{ab}(t)$ are both functions of time and at any given instant of time one may have a positive value and the other a negative value (resulting, at that instant, in a negative value for p_{ab}), we have to interpret the significance of the positive and negative values of p_{ab}. If at a given instant of time $p_{ab}(t)$ is a positive value, by this we understand that energy is being delivered to the terminal pair a-b at the rate given by the magnitude of p_{ab} at that instant. On the other hand, if $p_{ab}(t)$ is negative at another instant of time, by this we understand that the terminal pair is delivering energy to the rest of the circuit at a rate given by the magnitude of p_{ab} at that instant. Consider a terminal pair a-b. By definition, the rate of the delivery of energy to this terminal pair at time t is

$$p_{ab}(t) = v_{ab}(t)i_{ab}(t)$$

and also

$$p_{ba}(t) = v_{ba}(t)i_{ba}(t)$$

Since $p_{ba}(t)$ and $p_{ab}(t)$ refer to the rate of the delivery of energy to the same terminal pair, it follows that

$$p_{ab}(t) = p_{ba}(t)$$

and

$$v_{ab}(t)i_{ab}(t) = v_{ba}(t)i_{ba}(t)$$

Since from the definition of current

$$i_{ba}(t) = -i_{ab}(t)$$

it follows that

$$v_{ba}(t) = -v_{ab}(t)$$

It is noted that the variables, voltage and current, are always associated with a pair of terminals (points). In Chap. 5 it is shown that the methods of circuit analysis may be applied to the study of other systems such as mechanical systems. In such cases $i_{ab}(t)$ may represent the velocity of a (point) mass a with respect to some reference (point) b, and $v_{ab}(t)$ may represent the force applied to a (point) mass a in a reference system designated by b. In this case also, the product of $v_{ab}i_{ab}$ will be power (work done on a per unit time), but the interpretations of the variables are different.

1-6. Idealized Lumped Circuit Elements. In the field problem we discuss the energy density at a given point of space and compute it in terms of the $\mathcal{E}$ and $\mathcal{H}$ variables. In circuit theory we discuss the rate of delivery of energy to a terminal pair or combination of terminal pairs and compute it in terms of the voltage function and the current associated with the terminal pair. In the field theory we saw that energy stored in a unit volume of the magnetic field was $\mu H^2/2$ and that $\epsilon E^2/2$ was the energy stored in the unit volume of the electric field, with E^2/ρ being the rate of transformation of electromagnetic energy into heat per second per unit volume. The factors μ, ϵ, and ρ were the parameters of the space in which the electric and magnetic fields existed. We should be able to find analogous parameters for terminal pairs which would correspond to the permeability, permittivity, and resistivity of the medium in which the fields exist. The latter parameters are called distributed parameters of the medium since their value may change continuously from one point to another in the medium. In circuit theory we are not concerned with values which change from point to point but deal with quantities which are defined in connection with two terminals. When energy is delivered to a terminal pair a-b at the rate $p_{ab} = v_{ab}i_{ab}$, the total energy delivered to the terminal pair between time t_1 and t_2 is $W(t_1,t_2) = \int_{t_1}^{t_2} v_{ab}i_{ab}\,dt$. Part of this energy will be stored in the electric field associated with the terminal pair, another part will be stored in its magnetic field, and the rest of the energy will be transformed into heat. This partition of energy within a terminal pair is shown symbolically in a diagram called a circuit diagram. Such a diagram consists of interconnected symbols called *circuit elements*.[1] The number of such elements and the manner in which they are interconnected are determined by the physical properties of the device or part of the device which the terminal pair represents. Five elements are necessary to represent the energy-storage and -conversion processes in an electrical device. These basic elements describe the following processes:

1. Storage of energy in a magnetic field.
2. Storage of energy in an electric field.
3. Conversion of electromagnetic energy into heat.
4. Transfer of energy from one part of the device (terminal pair) to another part through a magnetic field.
5. Conversion of other forms of energy into electromagnetic energy for delivery to parts of a device, or reception of electromagnetic energy from parts of a device and its transformation into other forms of energy.

In contrast to the "distributed" parameters of the field theory, these elements will be called *idealized lumped circuit elements*. The value attributed to these elements will depend on the geometry of the path of the current between the terminals of the terminal pair and is computed from the dimensions and field properties (ϵ, μ, ρ) of the path. The computation of the values of circuit elements corresponding to a given path of current is not studied in circuit analysis. Instead, we shall define circuit elements in terms of energy-storage and -conversion processes which they represent. It should be noted that this is not the only possible way of defining circuit elements. For example, the voltage-current relationship at the terminals of the elements can be used to define such elements (see Chap. 3). Although the computation of the values of circuit elements is based on field theory, it is possible to determine, by experiment, the values of the elements of a network representing a device.

Inductance. In circuit theory that characteristic of a part of a device (circuit) which accounts for the storage of energy in a magnetic field is called the inductance of that part and will be indicated by the letter L and designated by the symbol shown in Fig. 1-3 with two terminals.

[1] Some authors use the term "parameter" instead of "element."

By analogy with the field expression $\mu H^2/2$ for the magnetic energy density, it is understood that the energy stored in the magnetic field due to a current i_{ab} flowing through the inductance L is $w_M = \frac{1}{2}Li_{ab}^2$. This expression is considered the defining equation for inductance L.

Capacitance. In circuit theory that characteristic of a part of a device which accounts for the storage of energy in an electric field is called the capacitance of that part and will be indicated by the letter C and given the symbol shown in Fig. 1-4 with two terminals. By analogy with the field expression $\epsilon E^2/2$ for the electric energy density, it is understood that the energy stored in the electric field due to a voltage v_{ab} across the capacitance C is $w_E = \frac{1}{2}Cv_{ab}^2$. This expression is considered to be the defining equation of capacitance.

Resistance. In circuit theory that characteristic of a part of a device which accounts for the transformation of electromagnetic energy into heat is called the resistance of that part and will be indicated by the letter

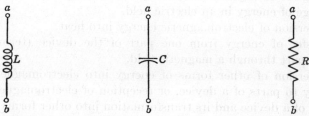

FIG. 1-3. Symbol for in-   FIG. 1-4. Symbol for ca-   FIG. 1-5. Symbol for re-
ductance.   pacitance.   sistance.

R and designated by the symbol shown in Fig. 1-5 with two terminals. By analogy with the field expression E^2/ρ for the rate of transformation of energy into heat, it is understood that the energy is dissipated in a resistance at a rate $p_{ab}(t) = v_{ab}^2/R$.

Mutual Inductance. In circuit theory that characteristic of parts of a device which accounts for the transfer of electromagnetic energy from one region to another through a magnetic field is called mutual inductance. It is designated by the letter M and by its symbolic form as shown in Fig. 1-6. In contrast to R, L, and C, which relate the voltages and currents at a pair of terminals, the mutual inductance relates these variables at two pairs of terminals as shown in Fig. 1-6. The mutual inductance in a circuit represents the effect of the electric field created in one part of a device because of the charges being accelerated in another part of that device. The energy relationships at the two pairs of terminals of a mutual inductance will be discussed in Chap. 18.

Sources. In circuit theory that characteristic of a part of a device which accounts for the conversion of other forms of energy into electromagnetic energy, or absorption of electromagnetic energy for conversion into other forms of energy, is called a source. An *ideal* source is a source which is capable of delivering or absorbing power without limit. Symbolically such an ideal source will be shown by a circle between a pair of terminals as in Fig. 1-7.

The elements R, L, C, M, and sources are called lumped idealized circuit elements. So far we have described these elements in a qualitative manner and have not mentioned the voltage-current relationship of these elements at their terminal. These relationships will be discussed in due course. It is important that the reader should grasp the significance of the above concepts, in a purely descriptive sense, before studying quantitative definitions. Thus the word resistance must become synonymous with the degradation of electromagnetic energy into heat and inductance with storage of energy in the magnetic field. It is true that in elementary courses in physics the symbol used for resistance was

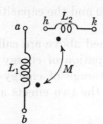

Fig. 1-6. Symbol for mutual inductance.

Fig. 1-7. Symbol for an ideal source.

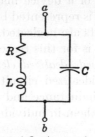

Fig. 1-8. An equivalent circuit of a crystal.

defined in terms of a metallic wire, inductance in connection with a coil, and capacitance in terms of parallel metallic plates. Nonetheless, many parts of an electrical device can be represented by a combination of R, L, and C elements whose actual construction does not contain wires, coils, or parallel plates. A good example of such a device is a crystal used in connection with vacuum-tube oscillators. The behavior of a crystal can be predicted from its equivalent circuit, shown in Fig. 1-8. An actual crystal does not contain a coil or a metallic resistor, but its equivalent circuit will contain resistive and inductive elements.

In effect, the behavior of many mechanical devices may be predicted from their analogous electrical circuits. For example, the problem of the stability of an airplane in flight or the oscillations of a suspension bridge may be solved by the study of their respective analogous circuits. In all cases one should be able to identify the various components of a device with the corresponding element or elements in the equivalent circuit. However, it must be understood that circuit elements are idealized representations and serve as a means to the prediction of the behavior of an actual apparatus.

Any part of an electrical apparatus which carries a current will have all the three characteristics of resistance, inductance, and capacitance. It will be seen that the relative importance of these characteristics will depend on the nature of the variations of the current with time. For example, a part of an electrical device known as a resistor can be represented by a resistance R if the rate of change of the current with time is sufficiently small. In such cases the effect of the inductance and capacitance of the part may be neglected compared with its resistance. However, if the time rate of change of current in this part is sufficiently high, then the inductive or capacitive character of the resistor may become comparable with the resistance of the part, and, in some instances, the dominant characteristic. In such a case a good approximation of the equivalent circuit of a resistor may be a capacitance or an inductance or a combination of the two. The dominant characteristic of some other part of a device may be the inductive characteristic. In this case the part is represented by an inductance, and the resistive and the capacitive effects are neglected.

It is for this reason that the circuit elements defined above are called *lumped idealized elements*. In attributing the dissipation of energy to the idealized circuit element, resistance, and the storage of energy to the inductance and capacitance, we have separated the two effects and put them in individual lumps.

CHAPTER 2

WAVEFORMS

In circuit analysis we deal with currents and voltages which vary with time. The mathematical symbol for the functional relationship between current and time in a terminal pair a-b is $i_{ab}(t)$. If this function is specified, then the value of i_{ab} is known for any given value of t. The

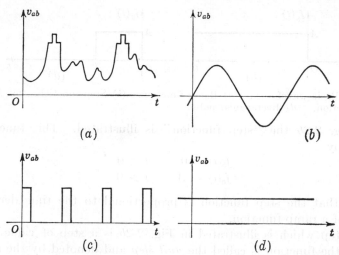

Fig. 2-1. Voltage waveforms. (a) Waveform of a television signal. (b) Waveform of household electricity. (c) Waveform of a train of rectangular pulses such as may be used in a radar modulator. (d) Waveform of a constant voltage (as from a battery).

relationship between i_{ab} and t can be specified either analytically by means of formulas or graphically. In either case we shall refer to the functional relationship by the term "waveform." The time functions which represent the voltages and currents are studied by means of oscillograms which are, in effect, the waveforms of these functions. It is customary to speak of the time derivative of a waveform, meaning either the graphical representation of the derivative of the original function or the analytical form of its derivative. In Fig. 2-1 the waveforms of some familiar voltages are shown.

13

2-1. Basic Waveforms. In the study of circuits certain simple waveforms are of special interest. The "ramp-function" waveform is illustrated in Fig. 2-2a. This waveform is described analytically by the equations

$$f_a(t) = 0 \qquad t < 0$$
$$f_a(t) = at \qquad t \geq 0 \tag{2-1}$$

(The symbol f is used to indicate that the waveform may represent any time variable such as a voltage or a current.)

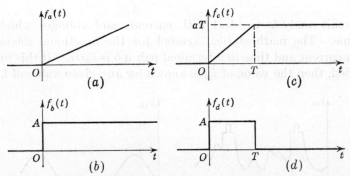

FIG. 2-2. Basic waveforms. (a) Ramp function. (b) Step function. (c) Modified ramp function. (d) Rectangular pulse.

In Fig. 2-2b the "step function" is illustrated. This function is defined by

$$f_b(t) = 0 \qquad t < 0$$
$$f_b(t) = A \qquad t > 0 \tag{2-2}$$

Note that the step function is proportional to the time derivative (slope) of a ramp function.

The step which is illustrated in Fig. 2-2b is a step of value A. If $A = 1$, the function is called the *unit step* and denoted by the symbol $U(t)$ and defined by

$$U(t) = \begin{cases} 0 & t < 0 \\ 1 & t > 0 \end{cases} \tag{2-2a}$$

The ramp-function waveform of Fig. 2-2a represents a time function which increases continuously with increasing time. The modified ramp function shown in Fig. 2-2c is often useful because it does not increase indefinitely. The modified ramp function is defined through the equations

$$f_c(t) = 0 \qquad t \leq 0$$
$$f_c(t) = at \qquad 0 \leq t \leq T \tag{2-3}$$
$$f_c(t) = aT \qquad t \geq T$$

In Eq. (2-3) T is a constant, as shown in Fig. 2-2c.

A "rectangular pulse" of duration T shown in Fig. 2-2d is another waveform which will be used frequently. It is described by the equations

$$f_d(t) = 0 \qquad t < 0 \text{ and } t > T$$
$$f_d(t) = A \qquad 0 < t < T \tag{2-4}$$

Note that the rectangular pulse is proportional to the time derivative (slope) of the modified ramp (Fig. 2-2c).

2-2. Continuous and Discontinuous Waveforms. Because some of the waveforms which are of interest are not continuous, we are often interested in the value of a waveform at an infinitesimal value of time before

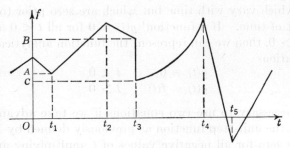

Fig. 2-3. A waveform with discontinuities and corners.

or after a given instant. The following notation is used in such a discussion. Let ϵ be a positive value; then the instant t_1^+ is defined through the limiting process

$$\lim_{\epsilon \to 0} (t_1 + \epsilon) = t_1^+$$

Thus $f(t_1^+)$ is the value of f at t_1 if t_1 is approached from the "right." The instant t_1^- is defined through the limit

$$\lim_{\epsilon \to 0} (t_1 - \epsilon) = t_1^-$$

Referring to the waveform of Fig. 2-3, we note that if the instant $t = t_1$ is approached from the right, such that $t - t_1 = \epsilon$ is a positive value and approaches zero, then in the limit, as ϵ approaches zero, $t = t_1^+$. If the instant $t = t_1$ is approached from the left, so that $t - t_1 = -\epsilon$ is a negative value and approaches zero, then, in the limit, as ϵ approaches zero, $t = t_1^-$.

A function $f(t)$ is said to be continuous at $t = t_1$ if $f(t_1^-) = f(t_1^+) = f(t_1)$. In such cases $f(t_1)$ is defined. Referring to the example of Fig. 2-3, the function shown *is* continuous at $t = t_1$ because the value of the function at $t = t_1$ is the same whether t_1 is approached from the left or the right. This value of $f(t_1) = OA$. On the other hand, this waveform is discontinuous at $t = t_3$ since $f(t_3^-) = OB$ and $f(t_3^+) = OC$ and $OB \neq OC$.

The discontinuity in a waveform is always in the form of a sudden (discontinuous) change in the value of the waveform, shown by a section of infinite slope as at $t = t_3$ in the example in Fig. 2-3. It is noted that $f(t)$ is *not* discontinuous at $t = t_1$ nor t_2 nor t_4 nor t_5. At these instants of time the function $f(t)$ is continuous, but its derivative is discontinuous because the *slope* of the waveform changes abruptly at these instants.

If a waveform has a discontinuity at $t = t_x$, then this discontinuity is measured by the difference $f(t_x^+) - f(t_x^-)$. This value is called the value of the jump at $t = t_x$. The function shown in Fig. 2-3 has a jump of value $OC - OB$ at $t = t_3$, a negative number in this example.

2-3. Multiplication by $U(t)$. In circuit analysis we often deal with waveforms which vary with time but which are zero prior to some arbitrary instant of time. If a function[1] $g(t) \equiv 0$ for all $t < 0$ and is given by $f(t)$ for $t > 0$, then we can represent the function analytically through the two equations

$$\begin{aligned} g(t) &\equiv 0 & t < 0 \\ g(t) &= f(t) & t > 0 \end{aligned} \tag{2-5}$$

It is not necessary to use two equations if we take advantage of the properties of the unit-step function as previously defined by Eqs. (2-2a). Since $U(t)$ is zero for all negative values of t, multiplying any function $f(t)$ by $U(t)$ makes the product zero for all negative values of t. Similarly, since $U(t)$ is unity for positive values of t, the product of any function $f(t)$ and $U(t)$ will be given by $f(t)$ for positive values of t. Hence the function $g(t)$, which was defined by the two equations shown in (2-5), can be defined through the single equation

$$g(t) = f(t)U(t) \tag{2-6}$$

As an example, consider first the straight line defined by

$$f_1(t) = at \tag{2-7}$$

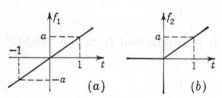

FIG. 2-4. Multiplication by $U(t)$. (a) $f_1(t) = at$. (b) $f_2(t) = atU(t)$.

This function is represented by the waveform shown in Fig. 2-4a. Note that $f_1(t)$ has nonzero values for both positive and negative instants of time. The ramp function shown in Fig. 2-4b can be defined through the equation

$$f_2(t) = f_1(t)U(t) = atU(t) \tag{2-8}$$

In general, the unit-step function can be used to represent a function which has one discontinuity by using the product of a continuous function and a unit-step function. Consider the general functions $g_1(t)$ and $g_2(t)$, and assume that both of these functions are continuous. Then the combination $g(t) = g_1(t) + g_2(t)U(t)$ is discontinuous at

---

[1] The symbol $\equiv$, to be read "is identically," is different from the symbol $=$, "equals," inasmuch as when we write $f(t) = 0$, this means that there exists a value of t for which $f(t)$ is equal to zero; whereas $g(t) \equiv 0$ signifies that $g(t)$ is zero for all values of t (or for a specified range of values of t).

$t = 0$ if $g_2(0)$ is not zero. This follows from the definition of $t = 0^-$ and $t = 0^+$ as stated in the previous section. Since both g_1 and g_2 were defined as continuous functions,

$$g(0^+) = g_1(0^+) + g_2(0^+)U(0^+) = g_1(0) + g_2(0)$$

and $\qquad g(0^-) = g_1(0^-) + g_2(0^-)U(0^-) = g_1(0)$

This representation is illustrated in Fig. 2-5 for the special functions $g_1(t) = 4t$ and $g_2(t) = 3$.

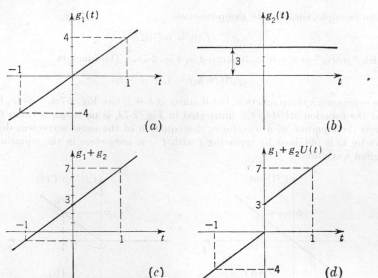

FIG. 2-5. Creation of a discontinuity by multiplication with a step function. (a) $g_1(t) = 4t$. (b) $g_2(t) = 3$. (c) $g_1(t) + g_2(t)$. (d) $g_1(t) + g_2(t)U(t)$.

2-4. Time Displacement.

The reader will recall from analytic geometry that a translation of the axis leaves the shape of the graph of a function unchanged. Thus, for example, the parabola $y = x^2$ has the vertex at the origin, while the curve $y = (x - 1)^2$ represents a parabola of identical shape, but with its vertex at $y = 0$ and $x = 1$.

Applying these ideas to a time function $f(t)$, we note that if, at the instant $t = t_1$, $f(t_1)$ has the value A then the function $f(t - t_d)$ has the value A at $t = t_1 + t_d$. If t_d is a positive number, then the function $f(t - t_d)$ is delayed in time by t_d as illustrated in Fig. 2-6.

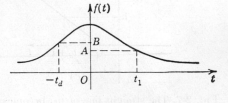

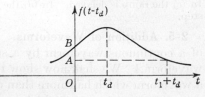

FIG. 2-6. Time displacement. The waveform $f(t - t_d)$ is delayed by t_d with respect to $f(t)$.

Since the unit step is defined as the function

$$U(t) = \begin{cases} 0 & t < 0 \\ 1 & t > 0 \end{cases}$$

the function $U(t - t_d)$ represents a step occurring at $t = t_d$ since

$$U(t - t_d) = 0 \qquad t - t_d < 0$$
$$U(t - t_d) = 1 \qquad t - t_d > 0$$

As an example, consider the ramp function

$$f_1(t) = atU(t)$$

which "starts" at $t = 0$ as illustrated in Fig. 2-7b. The function

$$f_2(t) = a(t - t_d)U(t - t_d)$$

also represents a ramp function, but it starts at $t = t_d$ (see Fig. 2-7c). Note, however, that the function $atU(t - t_d)$, illustrated in Fig. 2-7d, is no longer a ramp function. Given the equation of a waveform, the equation of the same waveform delayed in time by t_d is obtained by replacing t with $t - t_d$ *everywhere* in the equation of the original waveform.

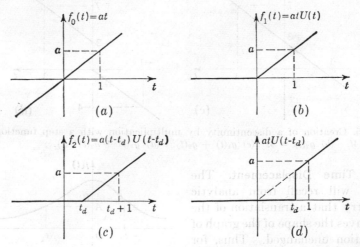

FIG. 2-7. The straight line of (a) becomes the ramp of (b) when multiplied by $U(t)$. In (c) the ramp is delayed. In (d) the ramp of (b) has been multiplied by a delayed step.

2-5. Addition of Waveforms. We have seen that the multiplication of a continuous waveform by a step function results in a discontinuous waveform.[1] We shall now show that it is frequently possible to represent a waveform which has more than one point of discontinuity as the sum of waveforms, each one of which has one discontinuity only.

Suppose that a waveform has a jump of value A at $t = t_1$ and a jump of value $-B$ at $t = t_2$, as illustrated in Fig. 2-8a. Let the original wave-

---

[1] If $f(t)$ is continuous at $t = t_1$, then $f(t)U(t - t_1)$ has a jump at t_1 unless $f(t_1) = 0$.

form, as given by Fig. 2-8a, be called $f(t)$. Consider now the waveform $f_1(t)$, shown in Fig. 2-8b, which is related to $f(t)$ as follows:

$$f_1(t) = f(t) \qquad\qquad t < t_1$$
$$f_1(t) = f(t) - A \qquad\quad t_1 < t < t_2$$
$$f_1(t) = f(t) - A + B \qquad t > t_2$$

From the definition of the displaced step function, we can write

$$f_1(t) = f(t) - A\,U(t - t_1) + B\,U(t - t_2)$$
or
$$f(t) = f_1(t) + A\,U(t - t_1) - B\,U(t - t_2)$$

As an example, consider the addition of the positive step $A\,U(t)$ and the negative step $-A\,U(t - t_1)$ shown in Fig. 2-9a and b. These two waveforms, added up, give the rectangular pulse shown in Fig. 2-9c.

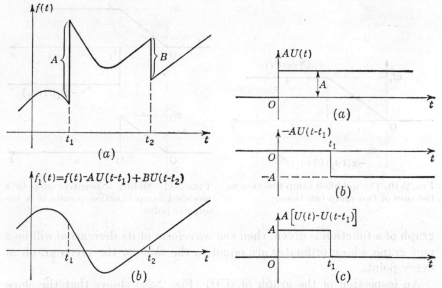

FIG. 2-8. Relating a discontinuous to a continuous waveform.

FIG. 2-9. Adding a positive and a negative displaced step results in a rectangular pulse.

The addition of waveforms can, of course, also be used when the waveforms are continuous but defined sectionally as in the case of the modified ramp function. If we add the ramp function $atU(t)$ to the delayed ramp function $-a(t - t_1)U(t - t_1)$, the modified ramp illustrated in Fig. 2-10 results. As a last example, the triangular pulse shown in Fig. 2-11 is obtained by the addition of two ramps and a step function, i.e., the addition of a negative step to the modified ramp.

The addition process will be useful in the construction of waveforms as well as in the decomposition of complicated waveforms into simpler components.

2-6. Integration and Differentiation of Waveforms. When the step and the ramp functions were defined in Art. 2-1, we pointed out that the step function is proportional to the time derivative of a ramp function. We shall see that waveforms which are related by the process of differentiation or integration are of considerable importance in circuit applications.

When a function $f_1(t)$ is related to $f_2(t)$ through differentiation with respect to time, i.e., if

$$f_2(t) = \frac{df_1}{dt} \qquad (2-9)$$

then the waveform of f_2 is called the derivative of the waveform of f_1. Thus the ramp function $tU(t)$ is the derivative of the parabola $\frac{1}{2}t^2U(t)$, and the step function $U(t)$ is the derivative of the ramp $tU(t)$. If the

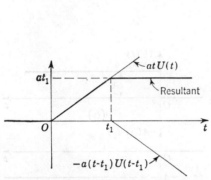

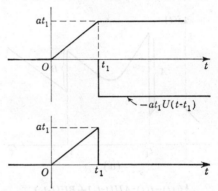

Fig. 2-10. The modified ramp function as the sum of two ramp functions.

Fig. 2-11. Adding a negative step to a modified ramp function results in a triangular pulse.

graph of a function is given, then the waveform of its derivative will be a new graph whose ordinates are equal to the *slope* of the given graph at every point.

An inspection of the graph of $tU(t)$ (Fig. 2-2a) shows that the slope is zero for $t < 0$ and unity for $t > 0$. Hence the derivative of the ramp function $tU(t)$ is the step function $U(t)$. If we use the "product" rule to differentiate $tU(t)$, we have

$$\frac{d}{dt}[tU(t)] = U(t) + t\frac{d}{dt}U(t)$$

In this connection the question about the derivative of the step function arises. We have already stated that at $t = 0$ the "slope" of the step function $U(t)$ is "infinite." If the result obtained from the geometrical study of the slope of the ramp function $tU(t)$ is to agree with the above differentiation, then $(d/dt)U(t)$ must be defined such that $t(d/dt)U(t) \equiv 0$.

Before proceeding further with the derivative of $U(t)$, the *integral* of a waveform will be discussed. If the graph of a function $f_1(t)$ is given, then the waveform of its integral $f_2(t)$ is defined to be a new graph whose ordinate at any point t_1 is equal to the total area under the graph of $f_1(t)$ between $t = -\infty$ and $t = t_1$. The analytical expression for this interpretation of an integral[1] reads

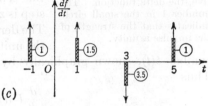

$$f_2(t) = \int_{-\infty}^{t} f_1(\tau)\, d\tau \quad (2\text{-}10)$$

This interpretation differs from that of an indefinite integral, since, as in Eq. (2-10), the constant of integration is determined. The justification for this definition becomes apparent in Chap. 3, when the voltage-current relationship of energy-storing elements is considered.

If $f_1(t)$ is zero prior to some arbitrary time, say, $t = 0$, as, for

FIG. 2-12. (a) A waveform. (b) Integral of the waveform of (a). (c) Derivative of the waveform of (a). The number in each small circle is the strength of the impulse.

example, in the waveform $f_1(t) = f_3(t) U(t)$, then its integral $f_2(t)$ is

$$f_2(t) = \int_{-\infty}^{t} f_3(\tau) U(\tau)\, d\tau = \int_{-\infty}^{0} f_3(\tau) U(\tau)\, d\tau + \int_{0}^{t} f_3(\tau) U(\tau)\, d\tau$$

Since $U(\tau) = 0$ for $\tau < 0$, we define $\int_{-\infty}^{0} f_3(\tau) U(\tau)\, d\tau \equiv 0$. Then

$$f_2(t) = \int_{0}^{t} f_3(\tau) U(\tau)\, d\tau = \int_{0}^{t} f_3(\tau)\, d\tau$$

In Fig. 2-12a and b a waveform and its integral are shown. Note that $f(t)$ has discontinuities at $t = -1$, 1, 3, and 5, while the integral has no discontinuities. Since, in general, the integral of most discontinuous waveforms with which we deal has no discontinuities, we ascribe to the process of integration a *smoothing action* on the waveform. Conversely, differentiation results in discontinuities in the derivative of the waveform at its corners, i.e., points at which the derivative is not continuous.

[1] The integral is written with τ rather than t as the variable of integration because $f_2(t)$ is a function of the upper limit t, and not a function of the variable of integration.

2-7. Impulse Function.   We have already shown that jumps in wave-forms can be accounted for by means of properly placed and scaled step functions (see Art. 2-6).   Therefore, in differentiating waveforms with jumps, the problem of the derivative of a step function must be considered.   From Fig. 2-2b we see that the derivative of a step function is zero except when t is zero, i.e.,

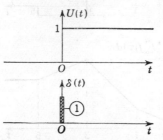

$$\frac{dU(t)}{dt} = 0 \qquad \text{for } t < 0 \text{ and } t > 0$$

FIG. 2-13. A unit step function and the symbol for its deriva-tive, the delta function.   The number 1 in the small circle indicates that the strength of the impulse is unity.

At $t = 0$ the value of the step function is not defined.   We do, however, call the slope at the point of discontinuity "infinite."   In this sense[1] we say that the derivative of the step is zero except at $t = 0$, when it is infinite. The derivative of a unit step function is called the unit impulse function and denoted by the symbol $\delta(t)$, shown graphically by the symbol indicated in Fig. 2-13. Thus

$$\frac{d}{dt} U(t) = \delta(t) \tag{2-11}$$

so that

$$\delta(t) = 0 \qquad t < 0$$
$$\delta(t) = 0 \qquad t > 0$$
$$\delta(t) = \infty \qquad t = 0$$

Now, if we were merely to call the derivative of the step at $t = 0$ infinite, the impulse function would be very poorly defined and quite use-less because the same "value" would be assigned to the derivatives of all steps, regardless of the value of the step.   In order to have a consistent definition, we note that, *if the unit impulse is the derivative of the unit step, then the unit step must be the integral of the unit impulse.*   We therefore supplement the definition of the unit impulse which was stated in (2-11) by the relationship

$$\int_{-a}^{+b} \delta(t)\, dt = 1 \qquad \text{or} \qquad \int_{-\infty}^{t} \delta(\tau)\, d\tau = U(t) \tag{2-12}$$

where a and b are any positive numbers.

In general, the derivative of a waveform at a point of discontinuity is an impulse.   The *strength* of the impulse is defined as the value of the jump at the point of discontinuity.   Applying this definition to the

[1] Strictly speaking, dU/dt at $t = 0$ cannot be discussed since $U(t)$ is undefined at $t = 0$.   Nevertheless, if we regard $U(t)$ as the limit of the modified ramp function shown in Fig. 2-2c as $T \to 0$, we observe that the slope of this function becomes infinite as $T \to 0$.   Hence we "call" dU/dt infinite at $t = 0$.

derivative of the waveform shown in Fig. 2-12a, the derivative shown in Fig. 2-12c results and is given by

$$\frac{df}{dt} = \delta(t + 1) + 1.5\, \delta(t - 1) - 3.5\, \delta(t - 3) + \delta(t - 5)$$

Since a step function can be considered to be the limiting case of a modified ramp function, the study of the derivative of a modified ramp function is useful in illuminating the notion of impulses. Consider the modified ramp function shown in Fig. 2-14a. The derivative of this function is shown in Fig. 2-14b and is seen to be a rectangular pulse of unit area and unit duration. If the slope of the ramp portion of the modified ramp function is now increased so that the rise takes place in one-tenth the original time as shown in Fig. 2-14c, then the derivative

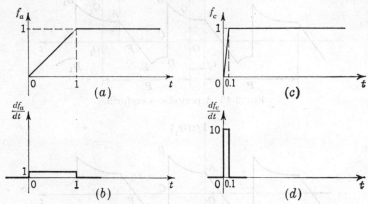

FIG. 2-14. Modified ramp functions and their derivatives.

of the new modified ramp function is the rectangular pulse shown in Fig. 2-14d. Note that this rectangular pulse has ten times the height and one-tenth the duration of the pulse in Fig. 2-14b. In the limit, as the duration of the rise in the modified ramp function is reduced to zero, the modified ramp function becomes the step function and the derivative of the modified ramp function becomes the impulse. Note, however, that the area under the derivative of the modified ramp function remains constant as the limit is approached. This area is the quantity which we have defined as the strength of the impulse.

2-8. Periodic Waveforms. So far in this chapter we have discussed certain waveforms which either were discontinuous or had discontinuous derivatives. In circuit analysis these waveforms are not the only time functions which are of interest. We shall see in subsequent chapters that exponential functions and periodic functions play an important role in circuit analysis. The following is a definition of periodic waveforms:

Let P be a constant value. Then a function (waveform) $f(t)$ which satisfies the condition

$$f(t) = f(t + nP) \qquad n = 1, 2, 3, 4, \ldots$$

is called a periodic function (waveform with period P). In Fig. 2-15 the waveform of a periodic function is shown. Besides the term period, the following terms are used in discussing periodic waveforms.

Cycle. The portion of the waveform in an interval t to $t + P$ is called one cycle of that waveform. In Fig. 2-15 the portion of the waveform

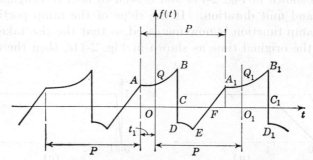

Fig. 2-15. A periodic waveform.

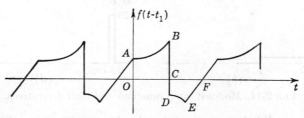

Fig. 2-16. Periodic waveform of Fig. 2-15, retarded by t_1.

between A and A_1 or between B and B_1 constitutes one cycle of the waveform.

Repetition Frequency. The reciprocal of the period is called repetition frequency and is designated by the letter f; $f = 1/P$. It is seen that the repetition frequency of a waveform is equal to the number of cycles of a waveform which occur in one unit of time.

Phase. Each point on a cycle of a periodic waveform is a *phase* of that waveform. In Fig. 2-15 the point A is a phase of the waveform, and it is seen that each phase repeats itself at intervals of one period. Most often we deal with particular phases (points) of a waveform where something special happens to the waveform. For example, at point A the waveform of Fig. 2-15 changes its slope discontinuously, and this is a special phase (point) of the waveform. At B the waveform has its largest value, at C it has a negative-going zero, and at F it has a positive-going zero. All these phases repeat at intervals of one period.

Phase Difference. If $f(t)$ is a periodic function and t_1 is a constant value, then $f(t - t_1)$ will also be a periodic function. Each phase of $f(t)$ will occur in $f(t - t_1)$ at a later time, the difference of occurrence

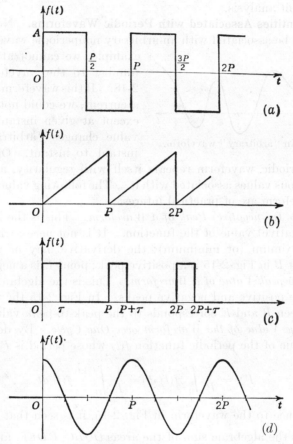

Fig. 2-17. Examples of semiperiodic waveforms. (a) Square wave. (b) Saw-tooth wave. (c) Rectangular pulses. (d) Cosine waveform.

of each phase being t_1. This time is called the phase difference between the functions $f(t)$ and $f(t - t_1)$. If t_1 is a positive value, then $f(t - t_1)$ is said to lag $f(t)$ by t_1 and $f(t)$ is said to lead $f(t - t_1)$ by t_1. It is clear that $f(t + t_1)$ leads $f(t)$ by t_1 and $f(t)$ lags $f(t + t_1)$ by t_1. We also say that $f(t - t_1)$ is obtained from $f(t)$ by retarding it by t_1 and $f(t + t_1)$ is obtained from $f(t)$ by advancing it by t_1. Figure 2-16 shows the waveform of Fig. 2-15 retarded by an amount t_1. It is seen that each phase of the waveform of Fig. 2-16 (such as A or B, etc.) occurs at a time t_1 later than its occurrence in the waveform of Fig. 2-15.

Semiperiodic Waveforms. If $f(t)$ is a periodic waveform, then $f(t)U(t)$ is called a semiperiodic waveform. It is seen that the value of the semi-periodic waveform $f(t)U(t)$ is zero for all $t < 0$ and is periodic for all $t > 0$. Figure 2-17 shows some basic semiperiodic waveforms encountered in circuit analysis.

2-9. Quantities Associated with Periodic Waveforms. No significant number can be associated with an arbitrary nonperiodic waveform. For

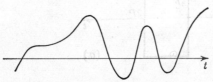

FIG. 2-18. An "arbitrary" waveform.

example, we cannot attribute any number to the waveform in Fig. 2-18. If this waveform represented a current, we could not measure it, except at given instants, since its value changes "arbitrarily" from instant to instant. On the other hand, a periodic waveform repeats itself with regularity, and we may discuss various values associated with it. The following values associated with a waveform are of practical interest:

1. *Positive (or negative) Peak of a Waveform.* This is the largest positive (or negative) value of the function. It is not necessarily a mathematical maximum (or minimum); the derivative may or may not be zero. Point B in Fig. 2-15 is a positive peak; point E is a negative peak.

2. *Peak-to-peak Value of a Waveform.* This is the algebraic difference between the positive and negative peaks. In Fig. 2-15 the vertical distance between B and E corresponds to the peak-to-peak value.

3. *Average Value of the Waveform over One Cycle.* By definition the average value of the periodic function $f(t)$ whose period is P is given by

$$F_{\text{av}} = \frac{1}{P} \int_0^P f(t)\, dt = \frac{1}{P} \int_{t_1}^{P+t_1} f(t)\, dt$$

With reference to the waveform in Fig. 2-15, it is seen that the integral $\int_0^P f(t)\, dt$ is the algebraic sum of the areas $OQBC$, $CDEF$, and $FA_1Q_1O_1$, where the area $CDEF$ has a negative value. Thus the average value of a periodic waveform is the area under one cycle of the waveform divided by its period.

4. *Root-mean-square Value of a Waveform.* In Chap. 1 we have seen that power dissipated in a resistance is proportional to the square of the voltage across it. Or the energy stored in an inductance is proportional to the square of the current in the inductance. It is seen that, in considering power or energy, the square of the functions $v_{ab}(t)$ and $i_{ab}(t)$ will be of interest to us. If the voltage across a resistance is

periodic, $v_{ab}(t) = v_{ab}(t + nP)$, then, by the definition of resistance, the instantaneous power delivered to a resistance R, connected between terminals a-b, is

$$p_{ab}(t) = \frac{[v_{ab}(t)]^2}{R}$$

The average power delivered to a resistance over one period is

$$P_{av} = \frac{1}{P} \int_0^P p_{ab}(t)\, dt = \frac{1}{P} \int_0^P \frac{v_{ab}^2}{R}\, dt$$

The quantity $(1/P) \int_0^P f^2(t)\, dt$ of a periodic function $f(t)$ with period P is called the mean of the square of that function. If the function $f(t)$ is a voltage or a current, then the mean of the square of $f(t)$ will have dimensions of (voltage)^2 or (current)^2, respectively. The root of the mean of the square of a periodic function $f(t)$ will have the same dimensions as the quantity represented by $f(t)$ and is designated by the symbol F_{rms}.

The root of the mean of the square of a function is referred to as the rms value of the function and is used in computations of power and energy with periodic currents and voltages. We note that, although the average value of some periodic functions may be zero, the rms value of no periodic function can be zero. This is due to the fact that, in the integral $\int_0^P f(t)\, dt$, $f(t)$ may have positive or negative values in the interval $0 \le t \le P$ but, in the integral $\int_0^P f^2(t)\, dt$, $f^2(t)$ is always positive.

From the above definition it is seen that

$$F_{rms} = \sqrt{\frac{1}{P} \int_0^P [f(t)]^2\, dt} \qquad (2\text{-}13)$$

If a current with a periodic waveform whose rms value is I_{rms} flows through a resistance R, then the time average of power delivered to R is given by $I_{rms}^2 R$. If a constant current I flows through R, then the power is $I^2 R$. Hence the rms value of a periodic current is also referred to as the "effective" or "heating" value of the current.

Example 2-1. For the current waveform shown in Fig. 2-19a determine the average and the effective value.

For the average value we need the area under the waveform,

$$\text{Area} = 2 \times \frac{P}{2} - 1 \times \frac{P}{2} = \frac{P}{2}$$

The average value is

$$I_{av} = \frac{\text{area}}{\text{base}} = \frac{P/2}{P} = \tfrac{1}{2} \text{ amp}$$

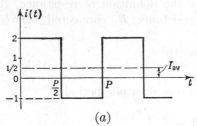
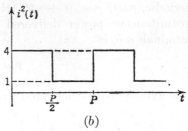

(a) (b)

FIG. 2-19. A semiperiodic waveform. (a) The waveform and its average value. (b) Waveform for calculation of rms value.

To obtain the effective value, we need the area under the curve $[i(t)]^2$. This curve is shown in Fig. 2-19b. By inspection the area is

$$\text{Area} = 4 \times \frac{P}{2} + 1 \times \frac{P}{2} = \tfrac{5}{2}P$$

Hence the effective value is

$$I = \sqrt{\frac{\text{area}}{\text{base}}} = \sqrt{2.5 \, P/P} = \sqrt{2.5} = 1.58 \text{ amp}$$

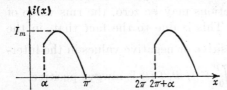

FIG. 2-20. Sinusoidal pulses used in Example 2-2.

Example 2-2. The equations of the waveform shown in Fig. 2-20 are

$$
\begin{array}{ll}
i(x) = 0 & 0 < x < \alpha \\
i(x) = I_m \sin x & \alpha < x < \pi \\
i(x) = 0 & \pi < x < 2\pi \\
i(x) = i(x + 2\pi) &
\end{array}
$$

The average value of $i(x)$ is the area under the curve divided by the period,

$$I_{av} = \frac{1}{2\pi} \int_\alpha^\pi I_m \sin x \, dx = \frac{I_m}{2\pi} \left[-\cos x \right]_\alpha^\pi = \frac{I_m}{2\pi} (1 + \cos \alpha)$$

The effective value is found by applying Eq. (2-13),

$$I_{rms} = I_{eff} = \sqrt{\frac{I_m{}^2}{2\pi} \int_\alpha^\pi \sin^2 x \, dx} = I_m \sqrt{\frac{1}{2\pi} \int_\alpha^\pi \left(\frac{1}{2} - \frac{1}{2} \cos 2x \right) dx}$$

or

$$I = I_m \sqrt{\frac{1}{4\pi} \left[x - \frac{1}{2} \sin 2x \right]_\alpha^\pi}$$

$$I = \frac{I_m}{2\sqrt{\pi}} \sqrt{(\pi - \alpha) + \frac{1}{2} \sin 2\alpha}$$

PROBLEMS

2-1. Sketch the waveform of $f(t) = U(t)U(1 - t)$. *Hint:* To sketch $U(1 - t)$, first let $1 - t = x$.

2-2. Given are two functions $f_1(t) = -t$ and $f_2(t) = t^2$. Sketch, to scale, in the interval $t = -2$ to $t = +2$: (a) $f_1(t) + f_2(t)$; (b) $f_1(t)U(t) + f_2(t)$; (c) $f_1(t) + f_2(t)U(t)$; (d) $[f_1(t) + f_2(t)]U(t)$.

2-3. Sketch the functions: (a) $2tU(t - 1)$; (b) $2(t - 1)U(t - 1)$.

2-4. Write the equation of the waveform of Fig. P2-4 as the sum of three ramp functions.

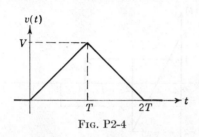

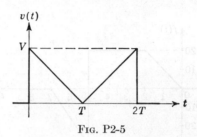

Fig. P2-4   Fig. P2-5

2-5. Use the result of Prob. 2-4 to write the equation for $v(t)$ as shown in Fig. P2-5 by a sum of step and ramp functions.

2-6. (a) For the waveform of Fig. P2-6 state the points of discontinuity and the value of the jumps at those points. (b) Show that the equation of this waveform can be written as $f(t) = tU(t) - (1 + t)U(t - 1) + (9 - 2t)U(t - 3) + 2(t - 4)U(t - 4)$.

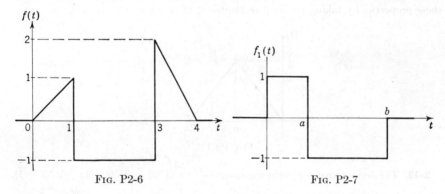

Fig. P2-6   Fig. P2-7

2-7. Let the function $f_1(t)$ be given by its waveform as shown in Fig. P2-7. For the cases (a) $a = 1$, $b = 1$, (b) $a = 2$, $b = 1$, (c) $a = 1$, $b = 2$ sketch the waveform of $f_2(t) = \int_{-\infty}^{t} f_1(\tau) \, d\tau$.

2-8. (a) Integrate $f(t)$, Fig. P2-8, graphically $[f(t) \equiv 0, \ t > 3]$. (b) Verify the result of (a) analytically.

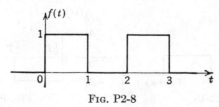

Fig. P2-8

2-9. (*a*) Sketch the waveform of the integral $\int_{-\infty}^{t} v(\tau)\, d\tau$ if $v(t)$ is the function given as in Prob. 2-4 (Fig. P2-4).   (*b*) Sketch the derivative of $v(t)$ if $v(t)$ is given as in Prob. 2-4 (Fig. P2-4).

2-10. For the given waveform (Fig. P2-10), (*a*) sketch, to scale, the waveform of its integral; (*b*) sketch, to scale, the waveform of its derivative.

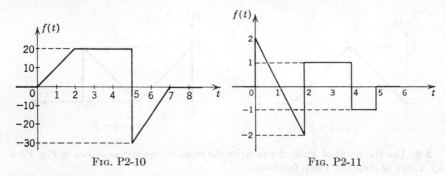

FIG. P2-10   FIG. P2-11

2-11. Integrate and differentiate graphically the function shown in Fig. P2-11.

2-12. (*a*) Show that the unit impulse can be considered the limit of the triangular pulse shown as a approaches zero.   (*b*) Sketch the derivative of $f(t)$.   (*c*) The properties of the derivative of the unit impulse can be obtained from df/dt if $a \to 0$. Obtain these properties by taking the limit of the result of (*b*) as $a \to 0$.

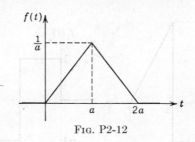

FIG. P2-12

2-13. The derivative of a certain waveform is $\dfrac{df}{dt} = 2U(t) - 2U(t-1) - 2\,\delta(t-1)$.
Find and sketch $f(t)$ if $f(t) = 0$ at $t = 0^{-}$.

2-14. (*a*) A pulse is given by $i(t) = \sin t U(t) + \sin (t - \pi) U(t - \pi)$. Sketch $i(t)$ and the derivative di/dt.   (*b*) A pulse is given by $v(t) = \cos t U(t) + \sin (t - \pi/2) U(t - \pi/2)$. Sketch $v(t)$ and its derivative.

2-15. For the periodic waveform shown in Fig. P2-15, $0 < a < 1$. Calculate the (*a*) average value; (*b*) rms value.

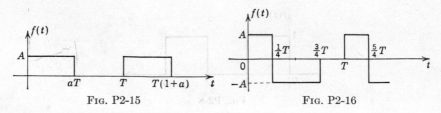

FIG. P2-15   FIG. P2-16

2-16. For the periodic waveform shown in Fig. P2-16, calculate the (*a*) average value; (*b*) rms value.

2-17. Calculate the average and the rms value of the (saw-tooth) waveform given in Fig. P2-17.

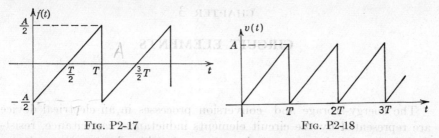

FIG. P2-17   FIG. P2-18

2-18. Use the result of Prob. 2-17 to obtain the rms value of the waveform shown in Fig. P2-18.

2-19. Calculate the rms value of the waveform $v = A \sin t$.

2-20. Sketch the waveforms given in (*a*) and (*b*), and find their average and rms values: (*a*) $f_a(t) = \sin t$, $0 < t < \pi$; $f_a(t) = f(t + \pi)$. (*b*) $f_b(t) = \sin t$, $0 < t < \pi$; $f_b(t) = 0$, $\pi < t < 2\pi$; $f_b(t) = f(t + 2\pi)$.

2-21. (*a*) Calculate the rms value of the periodic waveform shown in Fig. P2-21. (*b*) This waveform represents a voltage $v(t)$ applied to a 10-ohm resistance. What should be the power rating of the resistance to dissipate the generated heat without excessive heating?

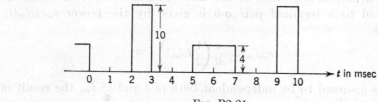

FIG. P2-21

2-22. Sketch the waveform, and calculate the average value of $f(t)$ if $f(t) = e^{-t}$, $0 < t < 1$; $f(t) = f(t + 1)$.

2-23. In Prob. 2-15 take $T = 2\pi$, $a = \frac{1}{2}$. Calculate the average value of the products: (*a*) $f(t) \sin t$; (*b*) $f(t) \cos t$.

2-24. If $f(t)$ is as given in Prob. 2-16 (Fig. P2-16) with $T = 2\pi$, calculate the average value of the products: (*a*) $f(t) \sin t$; (*b*) $f(t) \cos t$; (*c*) $f(t) \cos kt$, k = integer; (*d*) $f(t) \sin kt$, k = integer.

CHAPTER 3

CIRCUIT ELEMENTS

The energy-storage and -conversion processes in an electrical device are represented by the circuit elements inductance, capacitance, resistance, mutual inductance, and sources. In this chapter the voltage-current relation of these elements will be discussed, and the variables which are suitable for the solution of circuit problems will be introduced.

3-1. Voltage-Current Relationship at the Terminals of an Inductance. The circuit element inductance has been defined as an element which accounts for the storage of energy (in magnetic form) in accordance with the equation

$$w_M = \tfrac{1}{2}L i_{ab}^2 \tag{3-1}$$

From the definition of voltage we also know that the rate at which energy is delivered to a terminal pair a-b is given by the power $v_{ab}(t)i_{ab}(t)$. Therefore

$$v_{ab}i_{ab} = \frac{d}{dt}\left(\frac{1}{2}L i_{ab}^2\right)$$

Since L is assumed to be independent both of t and of i_{ab}, the result of the differentiation is

$$v_{ab}i_{ab} = \left(L\frac{di_{ab}}{dt}\right)i_{ab}$$

Thus for an inductance L_{ab}, connected between terminals a-b, the voltage v_{ab} is related to the current i_{ab} by the basic equation

$$v_{ab} = L\frac{di_{ab}}{dt} \tag{3-2}$$

If, from Eq. (3-2), we express the current i_{ab} as a function of the voltage v_{ab}, the result reads

$$i_{ab} = \frac{1}{L}\int v_{ab}\,dt + \text{const} \tag{3-3}$$

The constant can be made explicit if we recognize that the energy stored in the inductance at time t has been delivered over the period of time for which $v_{ab}(t)$ has existed. The current and energy are related by

32

Eq. (3-1), and it is seen that the value of the current at any time t, like the value of the stored energy, will depend on the past history of the voltage across the inductance. This is taken care of by writing the integral expression (3-3) with the lower limit at minus infinity and allowing the integral to be a function of an upper limit t. With this application in mind, in Chap. 2, the integral of a waveform was defined with these limits:

$$i_{ab}(t) = \frac{1}{L} \int_{-\infty}^{t} v_{ab}(\tau) \, d\tau \tag{3-4}$$

It frequently happens that interest is focused on the function i_{ab} beginning at some arbitrary instant of time, usually $t = 0$. In such cases it is convenient to write (3-4) in the form

$$i_{ab}(t) = \frac{1}{L} \int_{-\infty}^{0} v_{ab} \, dt + \frac{1}{L} \int_{0}^{t} v_{ab}(\tau) \, d\tau \tag{3-5}$$

Since the first of the integrals in (3-5) has numerical limits, it represents a number. This number is the value of the current at $t = 0$. Denoting this value by $i(0)$, we have, for an inductance,

$$i_{ab}(t) = i_{ab}(0) + \frac{1}{L} \int_{0}^{t} v_{ab}(\tau) \, d\tau \tag{3-5a}$$

Equation (3-5a) reads, in words

$$\begin{pmatrix} \text{Current in inductance} \\ \text{for all } t > 0 \end{pmatrix} = \begin{pmatrix} \text{current at} \\ t = 0 \end{pmatrix} + \begin{pmatrix} \text{current due to } v_{ab} \\ \text{from } t = 0 \text{ on} \end{pmatrix}$$

The value $i_{ab}(0)$ is usually called the initial value of the current i_{ab}.

3-2. Voltage-Current Relations at the Terminals of a Capacitance.
The energy stored in a capacitance C between terminals a-b is given by the expression

$$w_E = \tfrac{1}{2} C v_{ab}^2 \tag{3-6}$$

The rate of delivery of energy to a capacitance is given by

$$v_{ab} i_{ab} = \frac{dw_E}{dt} = \frac{d}{dt} \left(\frac{1}{2} C v_{ab}^2 \right)$$

If C is independent of t and of v_{ab}, then

$$v_{ab} i_{ab} = \left(C \frac{dv_{ab}}{dt} \right) v_{ab}$$

Thus for a capacitance connected between terminals a-b

$$i_{ab} = C \frac{dv_{ab}}{dt} \tag{3-7a}$$

or, in integral form,

$$v_{ab} = \frac{1}{C} \int_{-\infty}^{t} i_{ab}(\tau)\,d\tau = v_{ab}(0) + \frac{1}{C} \int_{0}^{t} i_{ab}(\tau)\,d\tau \qquad (3\text{-}7b)$$

where $v_{ab}(0)$ is the value of the voltage across the terminals of the capacitance at $t = 0$. This value is called the initial value of the voltage across the capacitance. The reciprocal of capacitance is termed *elastance* and is denoted by $S \equiv 1/C$.

3-3. Charge and Flux Linkages. At the outset we stated that the current i_{ab} is the time derivative of the charge q_a entering terminal a. Hence the voltage-current relation for a capacitance as given by $(3\text{-}7b)$ can be written as

$$v_{ab} = \frac{1}{C}\,q_a \qquad (3\text{-}8)$$

where

$$q_a = \int_{-\infty}^{t} i_{ab}(\tau)\,d\tau$$

In the integral form of the voltage-current relation for an inductance [see Eq. $(3\text{-}4)$], we define the flux linkage Ψ_a as the integral of the voltage, i.e.,

$$\Psi_a(t) = \int_{-\infty}^{t} v_{ab}(\tau)\,d\tau \qquad (3\text{-}9)$$

or

$$i_{ab} = \frac{1}{L_{ab}}\,\Psi_a \qquad (3\text{-}9a)$$

While we have based our field concepts on the assumption of the existence of electric charge and are familiar with its significance, the significance of flux linkage can be discussed only in terms of concepts based on (the surface integral of) magnetic flux density associated with a current. The reader may remember Faraday's law which relates voltage and flux linkages in a circuit through the expression $|v| = |d\Psi/dt| = N|d\phi/dt|$. In circuit analysis we do not need to deal with the concept of "flux," and we consider Eq. $(3\text{-}9)$ to define a quantity which is given the name "flux linkage."

3-4. Voltage-Current Relation in a Resistance. A resistance is defined as that circuit element which accounts for the transformation of electrical energy into heat at the rate given by

$$p_R = \frac{v_{ab}{}^2}{R} = v_{ab}i_{ab} \qquad (3\text{-}10)$$

Thus, for a resistance R connected between terminals $a\text{-}b$,

$$i_{ab} = \frac{v_{ab}}{R} \qquad (3\text{-}11)$$

or

$$v_{ab} = Ri_{ab} \qquad (3\text{-}11a)$$

The reciprocal of resistance is termed *conductance* and is denoted by $G \equiv 1/R$.

3-5. Mutual Inductance. Mutual inductance, which deals not with a pair of terminals but with two such pairs, is discussed in Chap. 18.

3-6. Classification of Elements. In deriving the voltage-current relations for inductance and capacitance, we assumed that these elements were independent of time and of the voltages and currents associated with them. Without an explicit statement, throughout our definitions, we have also assumed that $L_{ab} = L_{ba} = L$, $R_{ab} = R_{ba} = R$, and $C_{ab} = C_{ba} = C$. Elements which satisfy these conditions are called "linear bilateral time-independent elements." These terms will now be explained.

The voltage-current relationship for an inductance, $v_{ab} = L \, di_{ab}/dt$, is a linear relationship because the voltage v_{ab} is proportional to the *first* power of the derivative of the current i_{ab}. Similarly the current through a capacitance is proportional to the first power of the derivative of the voltage across it. For a resistance, voltage and current are proportional to each other. Elements whose voltage-current relation is of the above form are called linear elements. The assumption that the energy stored in an inductance is $w_M = \frac{1}{2}Li^2$ presupposes linearity (if L is assumed constant). Had we assumed $w_M = Ki^3$, then $dw_M/dt = 3Ki^2 \, di/dt$ so that v_{ab} would be given by $v_{ab} = 3Ki_{ab} \, di_{ab}/dt$, which is not a linear relationship since v_{ab} is proportional to the *product* of i_{ab} and di_{ab}/dt.

The term bilateral means that the relationship between v_{ab} and i_{ab} is the same as the relationship between v_{ba} and i_{ba}. Consequently for bilateral elements $R_{ab} = R_{ba}$, etc.

We started by defining circuit elements by equations dealing with energy and from them derived the relationships:

$$\text{For an inductance: } v_{ab} = L \, \frac{d}{dt} i_{ab} \qquad i_{ab} = \frac{1}{L} \int_{-\infty}^{t} v_{ab} \, d\tau \qquad (3\text{-}12a)$$

$$\text{For a capacitance: } i_{ab} = C \, \frac{d}{dt} v_{ab} \qquad v_{ab} = \frac{1}{C} \int_{-\infty}^{t} i_{ab} \, d\tau \qquad (3\text{-}12b)$$

$$\text{For a resistance: } \quad i_{ab} = \frac{1}{R} v_{ab} \qquad\qquad v_{ab} = Ri_{ab} \qquad\qquad (3\text{-}12c)$$

These are linear relationships, while the expressions for stored energy or power are not linear. For this reason we prefer to use Eqs. (3-12) as the defining equations of the circuit elements.

3-7. Units. All relationships which have been so far presented in the various equations hold, of course, in any consistent system of units. In this book we shall use the mks (meter-kilogram-second-ampere) system of units as shown in Table 3-1. In Table 3-2 common prefixes for multiples and decimal fractions of units are shown.

TABLE 3-1. UNITS

Quantity	Units	Abbreviation or symbol†
Energy................	Joules	
Power.................	Watts = joules/second	w
Time.................	Seconds	sec
Voltage..............	Volts	v
Current..............	Amperes = coulombs/second	amp or a
Charge...............	Coulombs	
Flux linkages........	Webers = volt-seconds	
Resistance...........	Ohms	Ω
Inductance..........	Henrys	h
Capacitance........	Farads	f

† In this book the abbreviations w, v, h, f are used only in conjunction with a prefix (see Table 3-2) and on diagrams. The symbol Ω for ohms is used on diagrams only.

TABLE 3-2

Factor	Prefix	Abbreviation	Example
10^6	meg-		5 megohms = 5×10^6 ohms
10^3	kilo-	k	15 kw = 15×10^3 watts
10^{-3}	milli-	m	2.5 ma = 2.5×10^{-3} amp
10^{-6}	micro-	μ	5 μf = 5×10^{-6} farad
10^{-12}	micromicro- or pica-	$\mu\mu$ or p	5 $\mu\mu$f = 5×10^{-12} farad or 5 pf = 5 $\mu\mu$f

3-8. Continuity of the Waveforms of Current in an Inductance and Voltage across a Capacitance.

From the voltage-current relationship

$$v_{ab} = L_{ab} \frac{di_{ab}}{dt}$$

it is seen that a discontinuity in the waveform of i_{ab} would result in an impulse in the voltage v_{ab}. From an energy point of view we note that, since the energy stored in the inductance is given by $w_M = \frac{1}{2}Li^2$, a sudden change in i would require a finite change in the stored energy in zero time. This in turn requires infinite power. Since $p_{ab} = v_{ab}i_{ab}$, for a finite i_{ab} and infinite p_{ab} the voltage v_{ab} must be infinite. We conclude that *in the absence of impulses of voltage the current in an inductance cannot change discontinuously.*

From the voltage-current (or energy) relationship for a capacitance

$$i_{ab} = C_{ab} \frac{dv_{ab}}{dt} \qquad \text{or} \qquad w_E = \frac{1}{2}C_{ab}v_{ab}^2$$

we conclude that *in the absence of impulses of current the voltage across a capacitance cannot change discontinuously.*

Note, however, that *the voltage across an inductance can change abruptly and the current through a capacitance can change abruptly without the occurrence of impulses.* This is seen from the integral relationships

$$i_{ab} = \frac{1}{L_{ab}} \int_{-\infty}^{t} v_{ab}(\tau)\, d\tau \quad \text{and} \quad v_{ab} = \frac{1}{C_{ab}} \int_{-\infty}^{t} i_{ab}(\tau)\, d\tau$$

We recall from Chap. 2 that integration is a "smoothing" operation so that the integrals of discontinuous functions can be continuous.

3-9. Note on an Oversimplification. At this point the authors wish to draw the attention of the reader to a very common oversimplification about the current through a capacitance. In some elementary books on electricity it is mentioned that "current cannot flow through a capacitance." This statement refers to conduction current. In circuit analysis we do not distinguish between conduction and displacement current but use the terminal relationship $i_{ab} = C\, dv_{ab}/dt$. Hence, in accordance with the circuit concept of terminal pairs, it is seen that a current does flow through a capacitance and its value at any instant is proportional to the rate of change of the voltage across its terminals. This current is identically zero when the voltage across the capacitance does not change with time. It must be remembered that i_{ab} in a capacitance depends on the *rate of change* of v_{ab} and not on v_{ab} itself. Thus it is possible to have very large voltages across a capacitance, without any current through it, if the voltage does not change with time. Alternatively it is possible that at any instant the voltage across a capacitance will be zero while current flows through the element at that instant. Similarly the voltage v_{ab} across an inductance does not depend on i_{ab} through it but on the *rate of change* of i_{ab}. Hence, if i_{ab} in an inductance does not change with time, then, regardless of the value of the current, the voltage v_{ab} across the inductance will be zero. Alternatively at a given instant the current in an inductance may be zero, but its rate of change may be nonzero. At such instants there will be a voltage across the inductance without any current through the element. As an example, let the waveform of Fig. 3-1 represent the current through an inductance L_{ab}. At $t = t_1$ the current in the inductance is zero, but $di_L/dt \big|_{t=t_1} > 0$; that is, the slope of the waveform at $t = t_1$ is positive, and therefore at this instant the voltage v_{ab} across L_{ab} will be a positive finite value, whereas the current i_{ab} through L_{ab} is zero. The reader can verify for himself that for the above example the voltage across L_{ab} will be zero in the interval $t_4 < t < t_5$, whereas at $t = t_9$ the current in L_{ab} is zero and v_{ab} across L will be a negative value.

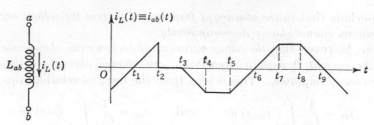

FIG. 3-1. Waveform of a current through an inductance.

3-10. Arrow Notation for Currents.

The double-subscript notation for current is not always suitable when a number of elements are con-

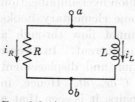

FIG. 3-2. Arrow notation for currents.

nected together between a pair of terminals as shown in Fig. 3-2. In this case, if we talk about the current i_{ab}, we do not refer to the current in any one element shown in this figure. For this reason the currents in R and L are shown as i_R and i_L, respectively, and an arrow is shown with each of the symbols i_R and i_L, to indicate that the waveform $i_R(t)$ represents the rate of flow of positive charges in R from the tail of the arrow to the tip of the arrow, with a similar interpretation for $i_L(t)$. It is noted that the arrow of i_L pointing from a to b (see Fig. 3-2) does not necessarily mean that the positive charges flow from a to b at all times. In Fig. 3-1 a waveform is shown for $i_L(t)$. According to this waveform and the direction of the arrow of $i_L(t)$, for $0 < t < t_1$ the positive charges flow from b to a since $i_L(t)$ is negative during this interval. For $t_1 < t < t_2$ positive charges flow from a to b since $i_L(t)$ is positive during this interval. Therefore from the reference arrow of a current alone we cannot say in which direction the positive charges are flowing. The waveform of the current associated with the arrow must be known before the direction of the flow of the positive charges can be ascertained at a given instant of time. Similarly, if the waveform of i_L is given but a reference arrow is not shown on the circuit, we cannot tell in which direction the positive charges flow at a given instant, although the magnitude of the current at that instant can be found from the waveform.

3-11. Notation for Voltages.

Although the double-subscript notation is quite often the best for indicating which voltage is under discussion, other notations are commonly used. These notations accomplish what the arrow notation accomplishes for the current. The information linking the waveform with the voltage across an element is transferred from the double subscripts to *marks* on the circuit diagram, so that the symbol representing the voltage is interpreted in connection with the circuit diagram. With double-subscript notation the function $v_{ab}(t)$ represented the variation of the voltage of a with respect to b. If we show this function as $v_1(t)$ (see Fig. 3-3), then we must mark the points a and b in such a manner that it is clear that the waveform $v_1(t)$ represents the voltage of point a with respect to point b. We may do this by putting an X mark near a and a 0 mark near b, stating the rule that whenever a waveform $v(t)$ is associated with the terminal pair a-b, marked as above, then the waveform represents the voltage of the point marked X with respect to the point marked 0. The conventional marks used are $+$ and $-$ signs. From Fig. 3-3b, with the waveform and the signs shown, we understand that the waveform $v_1(t)$ represents the voltage of point a (marked $+$) with respect to point b (marked $-$). Thus for $0 < t < t_1$ a is negative with respect to b since during this interval the waveform of $v_1(t)$ has a negative value. For $t_1 < t < t_2$ a is positive with respect to b

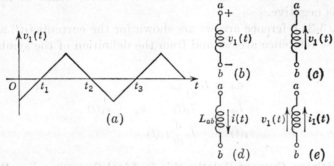

FIG. 3-3. Illustrating arrow notation for voltages.

since during this interval the waveform $v_1(t)$ has a positive value. Thus it is seen that from the $+$ and $-$ signs alone we cannot say whether a is positive or negative with respect to b at a given instant and we need the waveform of $v_1(t)$ to ascertain this fact.

An alternative notation for voltages is the arrow notation. In Fig. 3-3c the arrow shown with $v_1(t)$ indicates that the waveform $v_1(t)$ represents the voltage of the tip of the arrow (point a) with respect to the tail of the arrow (point b). Again the fact that the head of the arrow is at a does not mean that a is always positive with respect to b. To ascertain whether, at a given instant, the head of the arrow (point a) is positive or negative with respect to the tail of the arrow (point b), we must have the waveform of $v_1(t)$. In Fig. 3-3d an inductance L_{ab} is given with the symbol $i(t)$ shown with an arrow reference direction. Some readers may assume that, because the arrow with $i(t)$ is from a to b, this implies that v_{ab} is always a positive value. No such conclusion can be reached from the symbols shown in Fig. 3-3d.

The symbol L_{ab} of this figure is interpreted to mean that

$$v_{ab} = L_{ab} \frac{d}{dt} i_{ab}$$

and the reference arrow is interpreted to mean

$$i(t) \equiv i_{ab}(t)$$

Therefore
$$v_{ab} = L \frac{d}{dt} i(t)$$

Now, if the waveform of $i(t)$ is as shown in Fig. 3-1, then in the interval $t_8 < t < t_9$, di/dt is negative; therefore in this interval v_{ab} is negative. Notice that, in the interval $t_8 < t < t_9$, $i(t)$ is positive, but in an inductance v_{ab} depends not on i_{ab} but on its derivative, which in the above interval is negative.

In Fig. 3-3e reference arrows are shown for the currents $i_1(t)$ and $v_1(t)$. With these reference arrows and from the definition of the symbol L we have

$$v_{ab} = L \frac{d}{dt} i_{ab}$$

$$i_{ab} = -i_1(t) \qquad v_{ab} = v_1(t)$$

Therefore
$$v_1(t) = -L \frac{d}{dt} i_1(t)$$

3-12. Voltage-Current Relationship in Ideal Sources. For R, L, and C the voltage-current relationships were derived from the power and energy relationships associated with these elements. The ideal sources were defined to be capable of delivery or absorption of power without limit. Since there is no restriction placed on the power associated with the ideal source, unlike the case of R, L, and C elements, we cannot restrict the voltage across an ideal source if the current through it is specified. Alternatively, if the voltage across an ideal source is specified, the current through it cannot be restricted.

For this reason two types of ideal sources are defined: (1) an ideal voltage source, where the waveform of the voltage at its terminals is specified but the waveform of the current through it will depend on the nature of the terminal pair connected to the ideal voltage source; (2) an ideal current source, where the waveform of the current at its terminals is specified but the waveform of the voltage across it will depend on the nature of the terminal pair connected to the ideal current source.

3-13. Ideal Voltage Source. An ideal voltage source is said to exist between two terminals a and b if the waveform v_{ab} is specified and is independent of the nature or value of the circuit elements connected between these two terminals. In most ideal voltage sources v_{ab} does vary with time, but by the above definition its waveform is independent of the circuit element connected to it, and therefore independent of the current flowing between its two terminals. The value of v_{ab} at any given instant is predetermined by the waveform $v_{ab}(t)$ which is specified.

In the symbolic representation of an equivalent circuit an ideal voltage source is shown by a circle with some appropriate sign beside it, designating the waveform of $v_{ab}(t)$. Ideal voltage sources are often called "voltage sources" for brevity. They are idealized concepts and do not exist in practice. The voltage between the terminals of all practical sources of voltage will depend on the current flowing through them. However, in circuit analysis the concept of an ideal voltage source is used to advantage. In the literature the term "constant voltage source" is used to designate what we have called "ideal voltage source." The former term is appropriate to sources which do not vary with time. Since we are dealing with time-varying sources, we have used the term ideal rather than constant.

The exact equivalent circuit of an actual source will depend on the nature of the source. It is the subject of study in courses dealing with power supplies, alternators, vacuum-tube oscillators, and other sources. It suffices to say that all practical sources can be represented to a good degree of approximation by a combination of ideal voltage sources and additional circuit elements (R, L, and C).

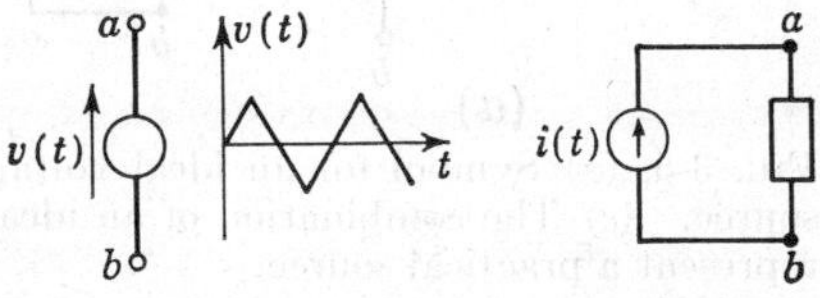

The symbol of an ideal voltage source v_{ab} (see Fig. 3-4a) implies the

Fig. 3-4. Symbols for ideal sources. (a) An ideal voltage source. (b) An ideal current source connected to a terminal pair.

fact that at any given time the voltage of the terminal a with respect to terminal b is independent of the current i_{ab} and is predetermined by the waveform of $v_{ab}(t)$.

3-14. Ideal Current Sources. If a current $i(t)$ flows from terminal a to terminal b of a terminal pair a-b and the waveform of this current is independent of the circuit elements in the terminal pair, an ideal current source $i(t)$ is said to be connected between the two terminals. The current may be a function of time, but the variation of the current with time will not be affected by the nature or the magnitude of the circuit elements connected to the terminals of the source, and hence $i(t)$ will be independent of v_{ab}.

The symbol for an ideal current source is an arrow inside a circle, as shown in Fig. 3-4b.

For certain purposes a phototube or a pentode vacuum-tube amplifier is a good approximation of an ideal current source. In this discussion we are not concerned with the nature of the actual device which is represented by an ideal current source. We are satisfied with the definition which states that the ideal current source $i(t)$ provides a current whose waveform is specified and is independent of the voltage across the terminals of the source.

Practical current sources are represented by an ideal current source, in combination with other circuit elements (R, L, and C), depending on the nature of the source.

3-15. Passive and Active Elements. The circuit elements R, L, C, M, voltage source, and current source are defined in terms of the relationship existing between voltages across them and the currents flowing through them. The elements R, L, C, and M are called passive elements, since voltage and current will exist in them only as a result of their being or having been connected to a source. The voltage source and the

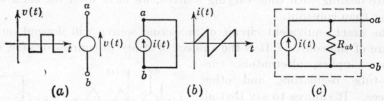

Fig. 3-5. (a) Symbol for an ideal voltage source. (b) Symbol for an ideal current source. (c) The combination of an ideal current source and a resistance shown can represent a practical source.

current source are called active elements, since a voltage or a current, respectively, is associated with them whether or not one or more circuit elements are connected to their terminals. For example, a voltage will exist across the voltage source a-b (Fig. 3-5a) although there is no other circuit element connected to the terminals a and b. Similarly, in accordance with the definition of the current source, a current will flow from a to b, outside the source itself (Fig. 3-5b), regardless of how or whether an element is connected between a and b. The reader will recognize that this is not possible in practice. The concept of ideal voltage or current source is idealized and does not correspond to a practically realizable source. However, it is of great utility in the understanding of practical sources, where a circuit element does exist between the terminals a and b. A practical current source may often be represented as in Fig. 3-5c. If no external circuit elements are placed at the terminals of this source, the current provided by the source flows through the resistive element associated with the source, as shown in Fig. 3-5c. By definition, the waveform of the current provided by the source is independent of the circuit element connected across it. Hence, if the value of R_{ab} shown in Fig. 3-5c is increased indefinitely, the waveform of the current through it will not be altered. An infinite resistance is identical with an open circuit, and the idealized case is reached when the current will flow although there is no circuit element connected between the terminals of the source.

At this stage the reader must associate the ideal current source with a two-terminal circuit element between terminals a and b in which the current i_{ab} is independent of the voltage v_{ab} and is predetermined by the waveform of the source.

3-16. Potential Difference, Voltage Drop, and Electromotive Force. The terms *potential difference, voltage drop,* and *electromotive force* (usually abbreviated emf) are used interchangeably in many introductions to electrical-circuit analysis. In such introductions it has become customary to treat only circuits in which the charges are moving at constant velocity, i.e., circuits in which the currents are constant. The term potential difference is applicable only to such circuits. The reader has undoubtedly noticed that we have avoided using these terms. The reason for this is our interest in time-varying voltages and currents. It is the purpose of this article to show how the above-mentioned terms relate to the term "voltage" as voltage was defined in Chap. 1.

The term *potential difference* has been carried over into circuit analysis from electrostatics. When an electric field in space is a static field, then the potential difference between two points is defined as the work done to carry a (unit) charge from one point to the other. In such static fields the work done in moving the charge is independent of the path through which the charge is moved. When we deal with problems in which the charges are moving with variable velocities (or, in circuit terminology, when the voltages and currents are time-dependent), then the work done in carrying a charge from one point in a region of a dynamic field to another point is no longer independent of the path through which the charge is carried and the original definition of potential difference becomes meaningless. When the variations of voltages and currents with time approach zero, then the term voltage, as defined in Chap. 1, becomes synonymous with the term potential difference. In electrical engineering it has become customary to ignore the original definition of potential difference (which deals with static fields) and use the term as a synonym for voltage even when the voltage is time-dependent. Thus a voltage between terminals a-b, $v_{ab}(t)$, may be referred to as the potential of point a with respect to point b.

As in the case of potential difference, the term *voltage drop* is very descriptive when we deal with time-independent currents. In such a case, if, for example, a current $I_{ab} = 3$ amp flows through a resistance $R_{ab} = 2$ ohms, the voltage V_{ab} will be 6 volts and point a is positive with respect to point b. Hence one may say that in going from a to b the voltage has "dropped" by 6 volts. If, however, through the same resistance, the current i_{ab} is a function of time so that it may be positive or negative at different instants of time, then $v_{ab}(t) = R_{ab}i_{ab}(t)$ and, while at one instant of time a may be positive with respect to b, at another instant of time a may be negative with respect to b. Now it is perfectly permissible to talk about a negative voltage drop between terminals a-b. If we were to say that the voltage drop from a to b is -6 volts, then we would mean that a is 6 volts below b. The authors feel, however, that the term voltage drop from a to b tends to mislead the reader by the excessive use of double negatives. The term voltage drop as commonly used has, however, the same meaning as the term voltage; i.e., the voltage drop or voltage v_{ab} is related to the power flowing into terminals a-b through the product

$$p_{ab}(t) = v_{ab}(t)i_{ab}(t)$$

The term *electromotive force* is introduced in field theory to describe a particular effect which occurs under dynamic field conditions. It is found that if a physical circuit (i.e., materials such as metals) is placed in a region of space in which there are dynamic fields then currents may flow (i.e., charges are set in motion) in this circuit. This effect is attributed to a cause called electromotive force. We shall now qualitatively describe how emf is related to the field intensity and how this phenomenon is represented in circuit analysis.

If we start with a region in space in which there are dynamic fields, then the placing of material into that space will result in a motion of charge (flow of current) which modifies the field distribution in the space. Let us imagine that the material which constitutes the physical circuit is removed and a closed geometrical line replaces the path. In this closed geometrical line there is no longer any current, but an electric field intensity will still exist at any point of the line. At a given instant the line integral of the electric field intensity around the closed line (with the physical circuit removed) will have a value which is called the emf associated with that closed path at that instant.

In the circuit representation this emf (which is associated with a given closed path) is represented by an ideal voltage source. We have said that, when the material circuit is placed back in the path, charges in the material will be set in motion. The distribution of these charges disturbs the original electric field. In the circuit representation the effect of this charge distribution is represented by the circuit element capacitance. Capacitance does not take into account the effect of the motion of the charges. If the charges move with variable velocity, aside from the effect of their distribution they will cause another disturbance in the electric field. The sum total of this disturbance in the *closed* path is represented by the circuit element inductance, and the effect is called the "counter emf of the inductance." Finally the effect of the dissipation of electromagnetic energy into heat along the path of the current is represented by the circuit element resistance. In the light of the above explanation the term lumped circuit element becomes more meaningful. The various effects which take place around a closed path are represented in "lumps." For example, the integral of the electric field intensity around a closed loop is shown as a terminal pair (voltage source for emf, inductance for counter emf); the effect of the existence of charge around a closed path is represented by the terminal pair capacitance. In this way these *field* phenomena are represented by circuit elements. When the voltage source and R, L, and C are connected properly[1] to make a closed circuit, then the current flowing in this closed circuit will, under certain conditions, approximate the actual current flowing in the physical circuit.

In circuit analysis it is common to use the term emf interchangeably with voltage in connection with sources and counter emf interchangeably with voltage across an inductance.

3-17. Circuit Elements and Circuit Components. In elementary physics the idea of resistance is introduced in connection with the properties

---

[1] A detailed discussion of this subject is given in S. Ramo and J. R. Whinnery, "Fields and Waves in Modern Radio," 2d ed., chap. 5, John Wiley & Sons, Inc., New York, 1953.

of metallic materials, inductance is associated with coils, and capacitance is associated with dielectric regions. In this book we have introduced the elements R, L, and C without reference to materials, simply stating the energy process which the elements represent and the voltage-current relationship which is associated with each type of element. Now, when one builds a circuit out of material components (wire, coils, etc.), then the representation of such a circuit in terms of the symbols R, L, and C may require more than one such element for each physical circuit component. Thus a circuit component such as a coil may be represented by several elements, that is, R-L, or a combination of several R-L-C elements. When a coil is placed into a circuit then often the intention is to impart inductance to that circuit. We shall distinguish between the property inductance (as defined by the voltage-current relationship $v_{ab} \equiv L_{ab}\, di_{ab}/dt$) and the component which is placed into the circuit with the intent of imparting inductance to the circuit. This is done by referring to the component in the circuit as an inductor, with the understanding that the component may also introduce other circuit properties. In general the ending "-or" will be used to describe circuit components, and the ending "-ance" will be used to describe the "pure" elements. Thus a resistor is a circuit component whose "dominant" circuit property may be resistance. In every case an "ideal" circuit component is identical with a circuit element. Thus an ideal capacitor is represented on a circuit diagram by a capacitance.

3-18. Variables in Circuit Problems. In field problems the field quantities depend on the distribution, velocities, and acceleration of the charges in space. Analogously one can consider the main variables in circuit problems to be the charge at any point, say, point a, the current flowing from a to b, $i_{ab} = dq_a/dt$, and the second time derivative of the charge, $di_{ab}/dt = d^2 q_a/dt^2$.

Voltage and current are the most commonly used circuit variables, although their derivatives and integrals may also be used.

PROBLEMS

3-1. In a certain physical element 20 joules of energy is stored. Calculate the value of the element if the element is (a) an inductance carrying 2 amp of current (find L); (b) a capacitance with 500 volts across its terminals (find C); (c) a spring stretched 2 cm (find the spring constant); (d) a disk revolving at 10 radians/sec (find the moment of inertia).

3-2. The voltage across an inductance of 10 henrys is given by $2U(t)$. (a) Calculate the current in the inductance at $t = 0$ if it is known that 1.25 joules is stored in the inductance at $t = 2$ sec. (b) Calculate the energy stored at $t = 2$ sec if the current $i(0) = 0$.

3-3. The current in a 4-henry inductance at $t = 0$ is 5 amp. At $t = 2$ sec the current is 4 amp, and at $t = 3$ sec the current is 8 amp. (a) Calculate the energy stored in the inductance at each of these instants of time. (*b*) Calculate the flux linkages associated with the inductance at each instant of time.

3-4. A capacitance has 100 volts across its terminals. To what value should the terminal voltage be increased if the stored energy is to be (*a*) doubled; (*b*) tripled?

3-5. A constant current I_{ab} of 0.3 ma flows through a capacitance of 5 μf. The voltage v_{ab} across the capacitance at $t = t_1$ is 10 volts. Calculate the voltage: (*a*) $v_{ab}(t_1 + 2)$; (*b*) $v_{ab}(t_1 - 2)$.

3-6. The current i_{ab} in a resistance of 10 ohms is given as follows. For each case calculate the energy dissipated in the time interval $t = -1$ sec to $t = 2$ sec: (*a*) $i_{ab} = 3$; (*b*) $i_{ab} = -3$; (*c*) $i_{ab} = 3t + 3$; (*d*) $i_{ab} = 3t - 3$.

3-7. The voltage across a nonlinear resistor between terminals *a-b* is related to the current through the formula $i_{ab} = 10v_{ab}^2$. (*a*) Plot the ratio v_{ab}/i_{ab} as a function of v_{ab}. (*b*) What is the power dissipated by the resistor if (1) $v_{ab} = 10$ volts; (2) $v_{ab} = 20$ volts? (*c*) Assume that a *linear* resistance dissipates the same power as the given nonlinear resistance does when 10 volts is applied to the nonlinear resistance. Calculate the power dissipated by this linear resistance when the voltage across it is 20 volts.

3-8. For the capacitance shown in Fig. P3-8 $v_{ab} = \sin 2\pi t$. Calculate i at the instants (*a*) $t = 0$; (*b*) $t = \frac{1}{4}$; (*c*) $t = \frac{1}{2}$; (*d*) $t = \frac{3}{4}$; (*e*) $t = \frac{7}{8}$; (*f*) $t = 1$.

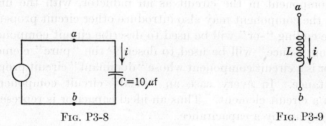

FIG. P3-8   FIG. P3-9

3-9. The current through the inductance shown in Fig. P3-9 is given by $i(t) = (1/L) \cos 2\pi t$. Calculate v_{ab} at the instants (*a*) $t = 0$; (*b*) $t = \frac{1}{2}$; (*c*) $t = \frac{3}{4}$; (*d*) $t = \frac{7}{8}$; (*e*) $t = 1$.

3-10. The graph shown in Fig. P3-10 represents $i(t)$ through the inductance of Prob. 3-9 (Fig. P3-9). The value of L is unity. Calculate v_{ab} at the instants (*a*) $t = 0^+$; (*b*) $t = 2^-$; (*c*) $t = 2^+$; (*d*) $t = 5.5^-$; (*e*) $t = 5.5^+$; (*f*) $t = 6$; (*g*) $t = 6.5^-$; (*h*) $t = 6.5^+$; (*i*) $t = 8^-$.

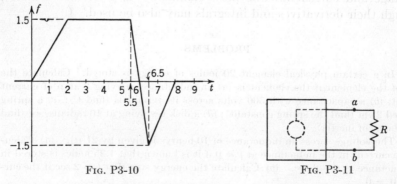

FIG. P3-10   FIG. P3-11

3-11. In Fig. P3-11 it is suspected that a constant ideal source is inside the box. When $R = 1$ ohm, $v_{ab} = 7$ volts. (*a*) If the source is an ideal current source, what should be the value of v_{ab} when (1) $R = 2$ ohms; (2) $R = \frac{1}{2}$ ohm?   (b) If the source is an ideal voltage source, what should v_{ab} be when (1) $R = 2$ ohms; (2) $R = \frac{1}{2}$ ohm?

3-12. Express the terminal relationships for a resistance using as variables (a) charge and voltage; (b) charge and flux linkages; (c) current and flux linkages.

3-13. Express the terminal relationship for an inductance and for a capacitance using as variables (a) current and flux linkages; (b) charge and voltage.

3-14. The element in the terminal pair a-b, Fig. P3-14, is either an inductance or a capacitance.   If $i = 2 \cos 3t$ and $v = \sin 3t$, what is the value of the element if (a) $v = v_{ab}$; (b) $v = v_{ba}$?

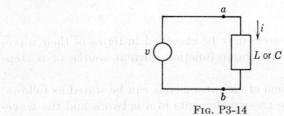

FIG. P3-14

CHAPTER 4

RESPONSE OF SINGLE ELEMENTS

Current and voltage sources may be classified in terms of their waveforms. Thus we speak of a ramp-function current source or a step-function voltage source.

The fundamental problem of circuit analysis can be stated as follows: Given the value of all the passive elements in a network and the waveforms of all the sources in the network, find the waveform of the currents flowing through and the voltages across the elements, and study the process of the energy transfer.

In a network the sources can be considered as cause and the voltages and currents associated with the elements as effect. The network structure and composition will determine the relationship between the cause and effect. Analogous with the terminology used in connection with the nervous system, the sources of the network may be called the excitation and the currents and voltages associated with the passive elements the response.

The analysis of complicated networks may be approached by means of a study of the response of networks of simple and fundamental structure. The simplest electrical network conceivable consists of a single source connected across the terminals of a single passive element. In this chapter the response of such simple networks will be studied.

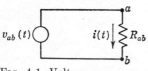

FIG. 4-1. Voltage source applied to a resistance.

4-1. Ideal Sources Applied to Resistances.
Consider the voltage source $v_{ab}(t)$ applied to the resistance R_{ab} as indicated in Fig. 4-1. From the definition of linear resistance it is seen that the current through a resistance and the voltage across it are, at every instant of time, proportional to each other; voltage and current will therefore have exactly the same waveshapes.

Figure 4-2a_1 shows a step waveform,

$$v_{ab}(t) = VU(t)$$

so that the resistance is short-circuited for $t < 0$ and has the constant voltage V across it for $t > 0$. Such a step generator may be thought

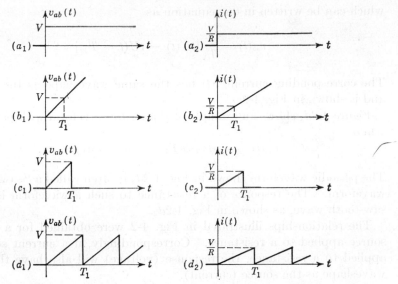

FIG. 4-2. Response of a resistance to different sources.

of as an ideal switch and a constant voltage source as shown in Fig. 4-3. The step is generated at $t = 0$ by throwing the switch from position 1 to position 2. The representation shown in Fig. 4-3 is intended to illustrate that the voltage v_{ab} is zero prior to $t = 0$. This is assured in Fig. 4-3 by means of the ideal connection (short circuit) from point 1 to point b.

Since the resistance R_{ab} is constant, the current i_{ab}, due to the step of value V, will also be a step and equal to V/R_{ab} for $t > 0$. This is illustrated in Fig. 4-2a_2.

The waveform of a ramp-function voltage source is shown in Fig. 4-2b_1. For this source

$$v_{ab}(t) = \frac{V}{T_1} t U(t)$$

where V and T_1 are independent of time. The response of the resistance to this source has the same shape as the source waveform, as illustrated in Fig. 4-2b_2.

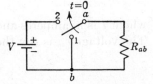

FIG. 4-3. Throwing the switch from position 1 to position 2 at $t = 0$ instantaneously generates a step voltage across terminals a-b.

Figure 4-2c_1 shows a triangular pulse. A pulse lasts for a finite time interval. This particular pulse is defined by the equations

$$v_{ab}(t) = 0 \qquad t < 0$$
$$v_{ab}(t) = \frac{V}{T_1} t \qquad 0 \leq t < T_1$$
$$v_{ab}(t) = 0 \qquad t > T_1$$

which can be written in one equation as

$$v_{ab}(t) = \frac{V}{T_1}[tU(t) - tU(t - T_1)]$$

The corresponding current $i(t)$ has the same waveshape as the voltage and is shown in Fig. 4-2c_2.

Figure 4-2d_1 shows an example of a *periodic* waveform with period T_1, where

$$v_{ab}(t) = v_{ab}(t + nT_1) \qquad n = \text{integer}$$

The periodic waveform shown in Fig. 4-2d_1 is often called a "saw-tooth" waveform. The response of a resistance to such a waveform is also a saw-tooth wave, as shown in Fig. 4-2d_2.

The relationships illustrated in Fig. 4-2 were obtained for a voltage source applied to a resistance. Correspondingly, if a current source is applied to a resistance, the response (voltage) will also have the same waveshape as the source (current).

4-2. Ramp-function Current Source Applied to Inductance. Consider the ramp-function *current source* $i(t)$ applied to an inductance L_{ab} as indicated in Fig. 4-4a. The current through the inductance is the same as the source current shown in Fig. 4-4b, that is,

$$i(t) = \frac{I}{T_1} tU(t)$$

where I is in amperes and T_1 in seconds, both being independent of time. The voltage v_{ab} is (by the definition of inductance)

$$v_{ab} = L_{ab}\frac{di_{ab}}{dt} = L_{ab}\frac{di}{dt}$$

$$v_{ab}(t) = L_{ab}\frac{I}{T_1} U(t)$$

so that the response of the inductance to a ramp current source is a step voltage as shown in Fig. 4-4c. Note that the mathematical process of differentiation which defines inductance is also seen by comparing Fig. 4-4b with Fig. 4-4c. The step function v_{ab} is L_{ab} times the slope of the ramp function $i(t)$.

4-3. Ramp-function Voltage Source Applied to Capacitance. Consider now the ramp-function *voltage source* applied to a capacitance as illustrated in Fig. 4-5a and b:

$$v_{ab} = \frac{V}{T_1} tU(t)$$

It is recalled that the voltage-current relation for a capacitance is

$$v_{ab} = \frac{1}{C_{ab}} \int_0^t i_{ab}\, d\tau + v_{ab}(0)$$

or

$$C_{ab}\frac{dv_{ab}}{dt} = i_{ab}$$

Hence for the circuit of Fig. 4-5a

$$i = C_{ab}\frac{dv_{ab}}{dt}$$

$$= C_{ab}\frac{V}{T_1}U(t)$$

The waveform of the current i is shown in Fig. 4-5c.

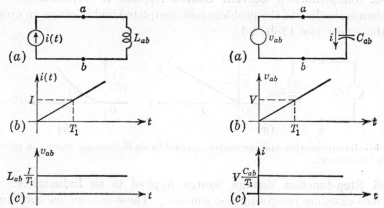

FIG. 4-4. Response of inductance to a ramp-function current source.

FIG. 4-5. Response of capacitance to a ramp-function voltage source.

Duality. The similarity between the responses of the circuit elements in Figs. 4-4 and 4-5 is embodied in the principle of duality, which can be stated as follows: If a voltage of waveform A is applied across a capacitance, resulting in a current of waveform B flowing through it, then the application of a current source of waveform A to an inductance would result in a voltage of waveform B across it. In other words: If the waveform of the current in a capacitance has the same shape as the waveform of the voltage across an inductance, then the waveform of the voltage across the capacitance will have the same shape as the waveform of the current in the inductance. *See 5.8*

4-4. Ramp-function Voltage Source Applied to Inductance. Consider now the ramp-function *voltage source* defined by

$$v_{ab}(t) = \frac{V}{T}tU(t)$$

applied to the inductance L_{ab} as illustrated in Fig. 4-6a. The current i in the inductance is found by application of the basic equation of the inductance,

$$v_{ab} = L_{ab}\frac{di_{ab}}{dt} = L_{ab}\frac{di}{dt}$$

or
$$i = \frac{1}{L_{ab}}\int_{0^+}^{t} v_{ab}\,d\tau + i(0^+)$$

For the given function v_{ab},

$$i = \frac{V}{L_{ab}T}\frac{t^2}{2} + i(0^+) \qquad t > 0$$

This result is illustrated in Fig. 4-6b for the case $i(0^+) = 0$.

4-5. Ramp-function Current Source Applied to Capacitance. This problem is the dual of the problem just completed and is left as an exercise for the reader (see Prob. 4-1).

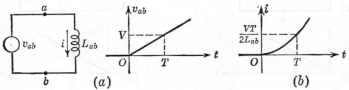

FIG. 4-6. Ramp-function voltage source applied to an inductance results in parabolic current waveform.

4-6. Step-function Voltage Source Applied to an Inductance. The previous cases use ramp-function sources. These sources are continuous, but their derivative is discontinuous at $t = 0$ (that is, they have abrupt changes in slope at $t = 0$). By contrast the step function is itself discontinuous at $t = 0$. It will be recalled that a voltage step function of value V is defined as

$$v(t) = 0 \qquad t < 0$$
$$v(t) = V \qquad t > 0$$

so that the value $v(0)$ is not defined since the slope is infinite at the time $t = 0$. It is necessary, therefore, to be cautious about the value of excitation and response at $t = 0$. For this reason, in time-response problems which involve discontinuous functions, one calculates values "just before" and "just after" the point of discontinuity, choosing the values just before and just after infinitesimally close to the point of discontinuity. If the discontinuity occurs at $t = t_0$, then, as explained before, the instant just before t_0 is denoted by t_0^- and just after t_0 by t_0^+; thus, for the step function voltage applied at $t = 0$, $v(0^-) = 0$ and $v(0^+) = V$.

Let the step function $v_{ab}(t)$ as illustrated in Fig. 4-7a be applied to the inductance L_{ab}; then

$$i = \frac{1}{L_{ab}} \int_0^t v_{ab} \, d\tau + i(0)$$

and

$$i = \frac{V}{L_{ab}} t + i(0) \qquad t > 0$$

If $i = 0$ at $t = 0^+$, the result will be as illustrated in Fig. 4-7b.

4-7. Step-function Current Source Applied to Capacitance. This problem is the dual of the preceding case and is left as an exercise for the reader (see Prob. 4-3).

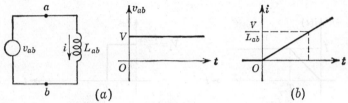

FIG. 4-7. Response of an inductance to a step-function voltage source.

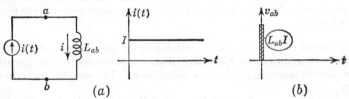

FIG. 4-8. Step-function current source applied to an inductance results in impulse response.

4-8. Step-function Current Source Applied to Inductance. Impulses. Consider now the case of a step-function current source

$$i_{ab}(t) = I U(t)$$

applied to the inductance L_{ab} as illustrated in Fig. 4-8a. The current in the inductance L_{ab} must be the source current $i(t)$. Consequently the voltage v_{ab} must be L_{ab} times the rate of change of this current. Since $i(t) = 0$ for $t < 0$ and $i_{ab} = I = $ const for $t > 0$, the voltage v_{ab} must be zero for $t < 0$ and for $t > 0$. At $t = 0$, however, the rate of change of current is *infinite;* hence the voltage across the inductance is *infinite at $t = 0$ for an infinitesimal time interval.* This infinite voltage, lasting zero time, is precisely the impulse function discussed in connection with the waveforms of Fig. 2-13. The response of this circuit element is of the impulse type because of the idealized nature of the problem; an ideal current source and a dissipationless circuit element were assumed. Since in this idealized arrangement $i(0^-) = 0$ but $i(0^+) = I$, the ideal source transfers finite energy of the amount $\frac{1}{2}LI^2$ in zero time. This constitutes flow of infinite power. In practical devices no such infinite power flow is possible.

Upon recalling the properties of the impulse function from Chap. 2, the solution of this circuit problem may be formulated as follows:

$$v_{ab} = L_{ab}\frac{di_{ab}}{dt} = L_{ab}\frac{di}{dt}$$

$$i(t) = IU(t)$$

Hence $\qquad v_{ab} = L_{ab}I\ \delta(t)$

It is noted that the *area* under the impulse (its strength) is $L_{ab}I$.

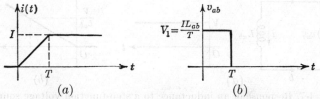

(a)   (b)

Fig. 4-9. If the step-function current source is the limiting case of the modified ramp function as T approaches zero, then the impulse is the limiting case of the rectangular pulse shown in (b).

The same result can be obtained by calculating the limiting case of the response to the modified ramp function of Fig. 4-9a. This demonstration will be carried out by using the current source applied to an inductance. The current-source function is defined by

$$i(t) = 0 \qquad t < 0$$
$$i(t) = \frac{I}{T}t \qquad 0 \le t \le T$$
$$i(t) = I \qquad t > T$$

The response v_{ab} is obtained by multiplying the slope of $i(t)$ by L_{ab}. Hence

$$v_{ab} = 0 \qquad t < 0$$
$$v_{ab} = \frac{L_{ab}I}{T} \qquad 0 < t < T$$
$$v_{ab} = 0 \qquad t > T$$

Note that this response (see Fig. 4-9b) is a rectangular pulse of amplitude $V_1 = IL_{ab}/T$ and duration T. The *area* under this pulse is IL_{ab}, independent of T. If now the duration T of the linear rise of the current source becomes smaller, then V_1 becomes larger but the *area* under the rectangle remains constant. In the limit, as $T \to 0$, the waveform of Fig. 4-9a approaches the step of Fig. 4-8a, and the response of Fig. 4-9b approaches the impulse of Fig. 4-8b. Consequently the impulse of Fig. 4-8b is an impulse of *strength* $L_{ab}I$.

The equation of the response shown in Fig. 4-8b is as before

$$v_{ab}(t) = L_{ab}I\ \delta(t)$$

4-9. Impulse in Capacitance. From the discussion of duality in Art. 4-3 the reader will now expect an impulse current to flow in a capacitance if a step voltage is applied. Indeed, if v_{ab} is defined as

$$v_{ab} = 0 \qquad t < 0$$
$$v_{ab} = V \qquad t > 0$$

then

$$i_{ab} = C_{ab} \frac{dv_{ab}}{dt}$$

and

$$i_{ab} = C_{ab}V \; \delta(t)$$

Exactly as in the previous case the impulse response is obtained because of the ideal nature of the problem. This time the area under the response curve equals the charge on the capacitance. In practical devices *the voltage across the capacitance cannot change abruptly* so that the current through the capacitance will always be finite (though it may change abruptly).

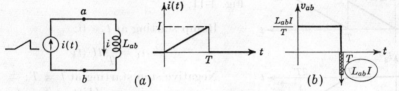

(a)   (b)

FIG. 4-10. Response of inductance to triangular current pulse.

4-10. Examples of Response Calculations for Pulse-type Sources. Superposition. Consider a current source, whose waveform is a triangular pulse, applied to an inductance L_{ab} as illustrated in Fig. 4-10a:

$$i(t) = 0 \qquad t < 0$$
$$i(t) = \frac{I}{T} t \qquad 0 \le t < T$$
$$i(t) = 0 \qquad t > T$$

The voltage v_{ab} is calculated from the definition of inductance,

$$v_{ab} = L_{ab} \frac{di_{ab}}{dt}$$

so that

$$v_{ab} = 0 \qquad t < 0$$
$$v_{ab} = \frac{L_{ab}I}{T} \qquad 0 < t < T$$

In addition, the abrupt current change through the inductance will cause an impulse of voltage of strength $-L_{ab}I$ to occur at $t = T$ so that the complete solution for the voltage v_{ab} is

$$v_{ab} = 0 \qquad\qquad\qquad\quad t < 0$$
$$v_{ab} = \frac{L_{ab}I}{T} \qquad\qquad\quad 0 < t < T$$
$$v_{ab} = -L_{ab}I \; \delta(t - T) \qquad T^- < t < T^+$$
$$v_{ab} = 0 \qquad\qquad\qquad\quad t > T$$

This solution is illustrated in Fig. 4-10b.

This response calculation was carried out piecewise by dealing with sections of the input waveform and calculating the corresponding responses. Another method of obtaining the

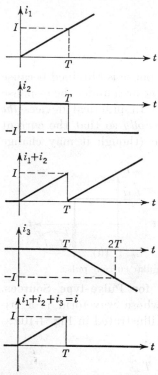

response to pulse types and other waveforms is to use the principle of superposition. Since the relationships defining the circuit elements are linear, <u>the response to several causes applied together is the same as the sum of the response of the individual causes applied separately</u>.

The triangular pulse may be represented as a superposition of step and ramp functions applied at different times as illustrated in Fig. 4-11,

Ramp starting at $t = 0$:
$$i_1 = \frac{I}{T} tU(t)$$

Negative step starting at $t = T$:
$$i_2 = -IU(t - T)$$

Negative ramp starting at $t = T$:
$$i_3 = -\frac{I}{T}(t - T)U(t - T)$$

so that $i = i_1 + i_2 + i_3$. Since the response to step and ramps has already been calculated, the response to the triangular pulse can be obtained by superposing the individual responses, placed properly in time as illustrated in Fig. 4-12.

Fig. 4-11. Representation of a triangular pulse by means of two ramp functions and one step function.

As another case of the use of superposition, consider the same current source (triangular pulse) applied to capacitance C_{ab}. The responses to the step and ramp func-

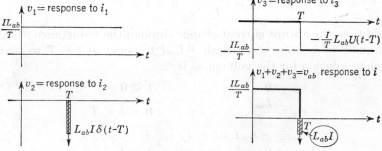

Fig. 4-12. Response of an inductance to a triangular pulse by superposition.

tions are already known (see Fig. 4-5 and Prob. 4-3). The waveform of the response is then constructed as shown in Fig. 4-13. In this figure the triangular pulse $i(t)$ is analyzed into its components i_1, i_2, i_3 as demonstrated in Fig. 4-11. The voltages across C due to the component sources i_1, i_2, and i_3 are shown in Fig. 4-13 as v_1, v_2, and v_3. In the same manner that a point-by-point addition of i_1, i_2, and i_3 gives the triangular pulse $i(t)$, the sum of the components v_1, v_2, and v_3 gives the response v_{ab} across C_{ab} due to the source $i(t)$.

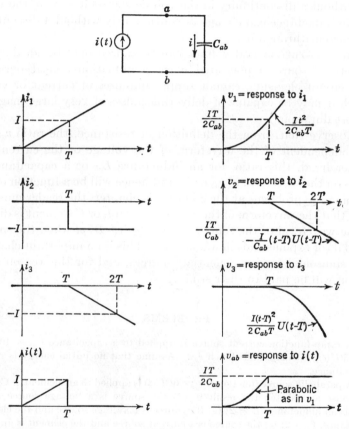

FIG. 4-13. Response of a capacitance to a triangular current pulse by superposition.

In the examples of response calculations the response due to the source is found directly, with less effort than is required by superposition. The foregoing case is introduced to illustrate the significance of superposition (in linear systems) and not merely as a method of solving problems. In the later chapters of this book it is seen that by the application of the principle of superposition certain procedures can be prescribed which facilitate a general discussion of network analysis. Furthermore, it can be shown that any waveform can be represented as a superposition (integral) of an infinite number of infinitesimal (delayed) step functions. Thus, if the response of a network to a step function is known, its response to any other function can be deduced.

4-11. Conclusions. The application of ideal voltage and current sources of various waveforms to the circuit elements demonstrates the fact that a discontinuous current in an inductance requires an impulse of voltage across it. Similarly a discontinuity in the voltage across a capacitance requires an impulse of current through the capacitance. On the other hand, the current through a capacitance can change discontinuously without a discontinuity in the voltage across it. Also, the voltage across an inductance can change discontinuously without a discontinuity in the current through it.

Impulses of current and voltage can be caused only by ideal sources. A "practical" source, represented by the combination of ideal sources and passive circuit elements, cannot supply impulses of current or voltage, although it may be capable of delivering pulses of very large magnitude and short duration.

We observe that, from the definition of resistance, the ratio v_{ab}/i_{ab} in R_{ab} is independent of the waveform of the voltage or the current. On the other hand, this ratio, for an inductance L_{ab} or a capacitance C_{ab}, depends on the waveform of v_{ab} or i_{ab} and hence will be a function of time.

In doing the problems at the end of this chapter, the reader must have noticed that the waveform of the response of an L or C element is different from the waveform of the source applied to it, *except* when the source is sinusoidal (or exponential) in waveform. This is an important characteristic of sinusoidal (and exponential) sources, and for this reason special attention will be paid to their study.

PROBLEMS

4-1. A ramp-function current source is applied to a capacitance $C_{ab} = 10 \ \mu f$. If $i_{ab}(t) = 5tU(t)$, calculate and sketch v_{ab}. Assume that no initial energy is stored in the capacitance.

4-2. A parabolic source function $f(t) = 6t^2U(t)$ is applied to an element. Calculate the response and sketch the result if (a) the source is a voltage source and the element is an inductance, $L = 2$; (b) the source is a voltage source and the element is a capacitance, $C = 2$; (c) the source is a current source and the element is an inductance, $L = 2$; (d) the source is a current source and the element is a capacitance, $C = 2$; (e) the source is a current source and the element is a resistance, $R = 2$.

4-3. Calculate and sketch the voltage response if a 5-ma step-function current source is connected across a 25-μf capacitance at $t = 0$ if the capacitance is uncharged at $t = 0$.

4-4. A source $f(t) = (a_1 + a_2t)U(t)$ is applied to a single element. Calculate the response if $a_1 = a_2 = 10$ and the source and element are given as in Prob. 4-2a to e.

4-5. Repeat Prob. 4-4 if $a_1 = -a_2 = 10$.

4-6. The voltage source whose waveform is shown in Fig. P4-6 is applied to an inductance. If initially the current in the inductance $i_{ab}(0)$ is zero, (a) calculate the instant $t = t_1 > 0$ at which $i = 0$; (b) calculate the instant at which i has its largest positive value.

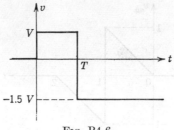

FIG. P4-6

4-7. A 5-μf capacitance connected between terminals a-b has 100 volts across it at $t = 0$ [$v_{ab}(0) = 100$]. A current source given by $i_{ab}(t) = [3 - 5U(t - 2)]$ ma is impressed at $t = 0$. (a) Calculate the instants at which v_{ab} is zero and at which v_{ab} is a maximum. (b) Calculate the maximum value of v_{ab}. (c) Calculate the instant at which v_{ba} has the value which v_{ab} has in (b).

4-8. A modified-ramp-function voltage source is applied to a capacitance at $t = 0$. Calculate the response, and sketch the result.

4-9. Calculate the response of a capacitance C_{ab} to a unit-impulse (a) voltage source; (b) current source.

4-10. Calculate the response of an inductance to a unit-impulse voltage source.

4-11. The triangular pulse shown in Fig. P4-11 represents the waveform of a voltage source v_{ab}. (a) Calculate the response if this source is applied to an inductance of 0.5 henry [$i(0) = 0$]. (b) Calculate the energy stored in the inductance at $t = 1$ and at $t = \infty$. (c) Plot the power $p(t)$. (d) Plot the stored energy $w_L(t)$. (e) What should be the duration of a rectangular voltage pulse which has unit amplitude to store the same final energy?

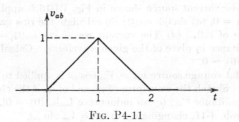

FIG. P4-11

4-12. Assume that the waveform given in Prob. 4-11 (Fig. P4-11) is produced by a current source. (a) Calculate the response if an inductance of 0.5 henry is connected to the source terminals a-b. (b) Calculate the energy stored in the passive element at $t = 1$ and at $t = \infty$. (c) Plot the power $p(t)$. (d) Plot the stored energy $w(t)$. (e) Answer (a) to (d) if the element is a capacitance C_{ab}.

4-13. The waveform given in Prob. 4-11 (Fig. P4-11) represents the current in a 3-ohm resistance. Plot the power delivered to and the energy dissipated by the resistance as a function of time.

4-14. (a) Calculate and sketch the response of an inductance to the voltage waveform shown in Fig. P4-14. (b) Calculate and graph the stored energy as a function of time.

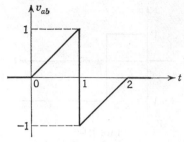

Fig. P4-14

4-15. In the circuit shown in Fig. P4-15 the switch is in position 1 from $t = 0$ to $t = 1$, in position 2 from $t = 1$ to $t = 2$, and in position 3 from $t = 2$ on. If $i(t) = 2t$, (a) calculate and plot v_{ab} [$v_{1b}(0) = 0$]; (b) calculate the energy delivered by the source in the time interval (1) $t = 0$ to $t = 2^-$, (2) $t = 0$ to $t = 2^+$. (c) The source is modified to have the form $i(t) = A + 2t$. Calculate A so that p_{ab} is always finite, and do the calculations required in (a) and (b) for this value of A.

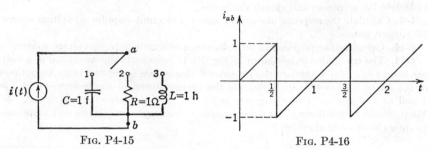

Fig. P4-15   Fig. P4-16

4-16. The periodic current source shown in Fig. P4-16 is applied to a capacitance $C_{ab} = 1$. If $v_{ab}(0) = 0$, (a) sketch $v_{ab}(t)$; (b) calculate the rms value of $i(t)$; (c) calculate the rms value of $v(t)$. (d) The current waveform $i_{ab}(t) = 0.814 \cos 2\pi t$ flows through the capacitance in place of the given waveform. Calculate the rms value of i_{ab} and of v_{ab} if $v_{ab}(0) = 0$.

4-17. A sinusoidal voltage source $v_{ab} = V_m \cos \omega t$ is applied to the terminals a-b of a passive element. Sketch the waveform of v_{ab} and of i_{ab} if the element is (a) a resistance R_{ab}; (b) a capacitance C_{ab}; (c) an inductance $L_{ab}[i_{ab}(0) = 0]$.

4-18. Repeat Prob. 4-17, changing v_{ab} to $v_{ab} = V_m \sin \omega t$.

4-19. Repeat Prob. 4-17, changing v_{ab} to $v_{ab} = Ae^{-st}$.

CHAPTER 5

KIRCHHOFF'S LAWS AND NETWORK EQUATIONS

By combining circuit elements in a proper manner, a circuit can be constructed to represent the behavior of an actual device. For example, under certain conditions the field coil of a generator can be represented as a combination of R and L elements placed end to end as shown in Fig. 5-1.

Referring to the field coil of a generator and its equivalent circuit as shown in Fig. 5-1, the two terminals a and b represent actual terminals of the field coil, but the junction between the two elements (point d) does not correspond to any particular point in the field coil. This is not surprising, since, according to our definitions of the circuit elements, R accounts for the dissipation of energy into heat and L accounts for the storage of energy in the magnetic field whenever a current flows between terminals a-b of the actual field coil. In the actual device the "resistance" and the "inductance" are not separate "parts," but in the equivalent circuit we choose to represent them as such.

Fig. 5-1. Series connection of two elements.

The only true similarity between the response of the actual device and its equivalent circuit is in the correspondence between their voltage-current characteristic at the two terminals a-b. What goes on inside the equivalent circuit may have no counterpart in the actual device. For example, as a result of the flow of current from a to b, a voltage will develop across R (Fig. 5-1). This voltage does not correspond to any voltage which can be *measured* in the actual field coil. On the other hand, voltage and current at terminals a-b of the field coil and of its equivalent circuit will be identical. We may consider the circuit shown in Fig. 5-1 to be a terminal pair a-b representing the actual device. In such a case the terminals a and b are called *accessible* terminals, and the terminal d is called an *inaccessible* terminal.

5-1. Series and Parallel Connections of Elements. Elements connected end to end, such that they carry the *same current*, are said to be in "series." In Fig. 5-1, R and L are connected in series. If at any instant of time there is a current $i_{ad}(t)$ in R, then there will also be a

61

current $i_{db}(t)$ such that $i_{ad}(t) \equiv i_{db}(t) \equiv i$. This result is arrived at from the fundamental assumption that in a terminal pair the charges which enter one terminal must come out from the other terminal. This is called the "assumption of continuity of current."

Elements connected between a pair of terminals are said to be connected in "parallel." Elements connected in parallel will have the *same voltage* across them.

The connection of the elements R and C in Fig. 5-2 is an example of *parallel connection* of two elements. In this circuit the two elements are placed so that the same voltage will always exist across them. While this circuit may correspond to the actual connection of two physical devices, it may also be the equivalent circuit for many practical devices. In this circuit terminals a-b may represent the input terminals of a vacuum-tube amplifier. In that case the capacitance C may not be placed in the circuit intentionally but may represent the combination of certain unavoidable features of the tube. As another example, the same

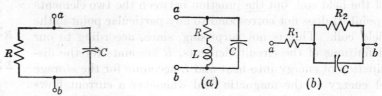

FIG. 5-2. Parallel connection of two elements.   FIG. 5-3. Series-parallel connections of elements.

circuit may, with respect to the voltage-current characteristic at terminals a-b, represent the input to a telephone cable.

The circuit shown in Fig. 5-3a is an example of a "series-parallel" connection of circuit elements. The series connection of R and L is connected in parallel with C. It is interesting to note that this circuit might represent a coil of wire. The resistance and inductance represent the same types of energy conversion as explained in connection with Fig. 5-1. The capacitance C would account for the electric-energy storage in the electric field between the winding of the coil.

The circuit of Fig. 5-3b is another example of a series-parallel circuit. In this circuit the resistance R_1 is in series with the parallel combination of R_2 and C. This circuit, like all the others, may represent the actual combination of several nearly "pure" elements or may be the equivalent circuit of an actual device or a portion of such a device. (Figure 5-3b may represent the input circuit of an oscilloscope probe.)

5-2. Network Terminology. The representation of electrical systems frequently requires the combination of many sources and elements connected in a more complicated manner than the simple series or parallel arrangements just described. Special techniques have been developed for the study of complicated combinations of sources and elements. In connection with this study a number of terms will be defined. The reader is reminded that, in the literature, these terms may be defined in a different fashion from that used here.

Network. An interconnection of circuit elements is called a network. A network may contain both active and passive elements or may consist of passive elements only. In the former case it is called an active network, and in the latter case it is called a passive, or source-free, network. If the elements of a passive network are all of the same type, i.e., resistances, inductances, or capacitances, then the network is called a resistive, inductive, or capacitive network, respectively.

Response of a Network. The waveform corresponding to the current in an element of a network or the voltage across such an element is called a response of the network.

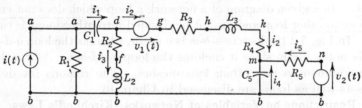

FIG. 5-4. Diagram of a network.

Nodes. We shall call a point in the network common to two or more elements a node. For example, in Fig. 5-4, the points $a, b, d, f, g, h, k, m,$ and n are nodes.

Junctions. We shall call a node common to three or more elements a junction. In Fig. 5-4 the nodes $a, b, d,$ and m are junctions, whereas the nodes $g, h, k,$ and n are not junctions, since each of them is common to two elements only.

Branch. We shall call a single element or a series connection of elements between any two junctions a branch. In Fig. 5-4 the following branches are identified: branch ab, consisting of the current source $i(t)$; the resistive branch ab, consisting of R_1; branch ad, consisting of C_1; branch db, consisting of R_2 and L_2; branch dm, consisting of $v_1(t), R_3, L_3,$ and R_4; branch mb, consisting of C_5; branch mnb, consisting of R_5 and $v_2(t)$. Note that in accordance with our definition, in Fig. 5-4 $km, hkm,$ and df are not branches since they do not connect two junctions.

Passive and Active Branches. If a branch contains no sources, it is called a passive branch; otherwise it is an active branch. In Fig. 5-4 the branch mnb is an active branch, and the branch dfb is a passive branch. The current source $i(t)$ in this figure constitutes a branch by itself.

Branch Current. A current flowing in a branch is called a branch current. The same branch current flows through all the elements in a given branch, since the elements in a branch are in series.

Loop. We shall call any closed path through the circuit elements of a network a loop. In Fig. 5-4 the following loops are identified: loop a-b-a, consisting of R_1 and $i(t)$; loop a-d-f-b-a, consisting of C_1, R_2, L_2, and R_1; loop a-b-f-d-a, consisting of $i(t)$, L_2, R_2, and C_1; loop d-g-h-k-m-n-b-f-d, consisting of $v_1(t)$, R_3, L_3, R_4, R_5, $v_2(t)$, L_2, and R_2. The reader may trace a few more loops as an exercise. If a loop contains one element of a branch, it will contain all the elements of that branch. In Fig. 5-4 the loop a-b-f-d-a, which contains R_2, also contains L_2, which with R_2 forms the branch dfb. In Fig. 5-4 loop a-b-a has two branches, that is, $i(t)$ and R_1; and loop a-b-f-d-a has three branches, R_1, C_1, and dfb. A branch may be common to more than two loops. In Fig. 5-4 the branch R_1 is common to loops a-d-f-b-a, a-d-g-h-k-m-b-a, and others.

Mesh. In a given diagram of a network a loop which does not encircle or enclose another loop and cannot be divided into other loops is called a mesh. In Fig. 5-4 the loop m-n-b-m is a mesh, whereas the loop a-d-g-h-k-m-b-a is not a mesh, since it encloses the loop a-d-f-b-a. A branch may not be common to more than two meshes. The reasons for defining meshes as well as loops are discussed in Chap. 16.

5-3. Restrictions on Variables of Networks: Kirchhoff's Laws. As a result of the interconnection of elements in a network, certain restrictions are placed on the currents and voltages associated with these elements. For example, in the series connection of the R and L elements in Fig. 5-1, the principle of continuity of current requires that $i_{ad} \equiv i_{db}$. In the parallel connection of the R and C elements in Fig. 5-2, the definition of the voltage requires that the same voltages exist across R and C. Therefore, if the current i_{ad} in Fig. 5-1 or the voltage across R in Fig. 5-2 is specified, the current i_{db} in Fig. 5-1 or the voltage across C in Fig. 5-2, respectively, will also be specified. Thus, when we connect elements in series, we place a restriction on the current through them. When we connect elements in parallel, a restriction is established on the voltage across them.

The application of the principles of continuity of current and the law of conservation of energy establishes certain restrictions on the currents and voltages associated with elements in a network. We shall first state these restrictions and then deduce them from the above principles. The treatment of circuit problems can be approached by stating these restrictions as "laws" of circuits. These laws are called, after the physicist Gustav Robert Kirchhoff (1824–1887), Kirchhoff's laws.

Kirchhoff's Voltage Law. At any instant the sum of the voltages around any loop is identically zero.

As an illustration, we shall apply this law to the loop *a-d-f-b-a* in Fig. 5-4:

$$v_{ad} + v_{df} + v_{fb} + v_{ba} = 0$$

Similarly, consider the loop *a-d-g-h-k-m-n-b-a*:

$$v_{ad} + v_{dg} + v_{gh} + v_{hk} + v_{km} + v_{mn} + v_{nb} + v_{ba} = 0$$

To state Kirchhoff's current law in compact form, we shall give two definitions in connection with reference arrows for currents.

If the head of the reference arrow of a current points toward (or away from) a node, we say that the current is entering (or leaving) that node. If a current i enters a node through an element, then a current $-i$ leaves the node through that element.

With these definitions in mind, Kirchhoff's current law is stated as follows:

Kirchhoff's Current Law. At any instant the algebraic sum of the currents *entering* a node is identically zero, or at any instant the sum of the currents *leaving* a node is identically zero.

As an illustration of this law, consider the node m in Fig. 5-4, where $i_2 + i_4 + i_5 = 0$. The reference arrows of the three currents point toward the junction m, and therefore i_2, i_4, and i_5 enter this junction, and their sum is zero. At the junction d, i_2 and i_3 both leave d, but i_1 enters d. If i_1 enters d, then $-i_1$ leaves d and the application of Kirchhoff's current law gives $-i_1 + i_2 + i_3 = 0$. The latter equation may be written as $i_1 = i_2 + i_3$, which can be interpreted as: The sum of currents whose reference arrows enter a node (i_1 entering d) is equal to the sum of currents whose reference arrows leave that node (i_2 and i_3 leaving d).

Notice that, in the branch *dghkm* of Fig. 5-4, i_2 is the branch current and flows through all the elements of that branch. Thus

$$i_{dg} = i_{gh} = i_{hk} = i_{km} = i_2$$

The equation $i_{dg} = i_{gh}$ is itself an expression of Kirchhoff's current law. This is seen from the fact that i_{dg} is the current entering node g, and i_{gh} is the current leaving node g, and they must be identical.

In discussing the series connection of elements, we referred to the assumption of continuity of current. The application of this principle to the junction of elements results in Kirchhoff's current law. If the sum of the currents entering a junction were not equal to the sum of the currents leaving that junction, then there would be an accumulation of charge at that junction. The effect of accumulation of charge is represented by the circuit element capacitance, and accumulation of charge at a terminal has no meaning in terms of the concepts already defined.

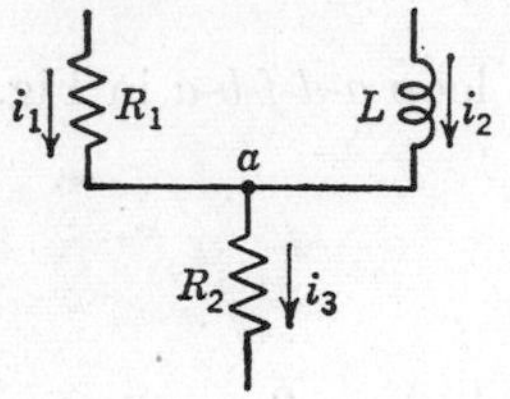

Example 5-1. Let i_1 and i_2 in Fig. 5-5 be given by $i_1 = 8U(t)$ and $i_2 = 3tU(t)$. With these two currents specified we are no longer at liberty to specify $i_3(t)$ since $i_3(t) = i_1 + i_2 = (8 + 3t)U(t)$.

At time t the amount of charge which has entered the junction a is $\int_{-\infty}^{t} (i_1 + i_2) \, d\tau$, and the amount of charge which has left a is $\int_{-\infty}^{t} i_3 \, d\tau$.

FIG. 5-5. Illustration of Kirchhoff's current law: $i_1 + i_2 = i_3$.

If $i_3 \neq i_1 + i_2$, then charge equal to $\int_{-\infty}^{t} (i_1 + i_2 - i_3) \, d\tau$ has accumulated at a. As mentioned above, this is contrary to our concept of terminal pairs, and therefore $i_1 + i_2 = i_3$.

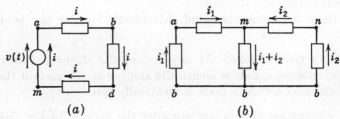

(a)   (b)

FIG. 5-6. (a) Network consisting of one loop. (b) A two-mesh network.

5-4. Derivation of Kirchhoff's Voltage Law from the Current Law and the Law of Conservation of Energy.

In Fig. 5-6a a closed path is shown. Let us assume that the terminal pairs shown in this figure are passive (do not include sources) and that the only source in the path is $v(t)$.

At any instant, power flows to the terminal pairs a-b, b-d and d-m at the rate $v_{ab}i_{ab}$, $v_{bd}i_{bd}$, and $v_{dm}i_{dm}$, respectively. Since $i_{ab} = i_{bd} = i_{dm} = i$, the rate of delivery of energy to the passive elements is

$$v_{ab}i_{ab} + v_{bd}i_{bd} + v_{dm}i_{dm} = i(v_{ab} + v_{bd} + v_{dm})$$

The source delivers energy at the rate iv_{am}, and therefore

$$iv_{am} = i(v_{ab} + v_{bd} + v_{dm})$$

so that

$$v_{am} = v_{ab} + v_{bd} + v_{dm} = -v_{ma} \qquad (5\text{-}1)$$

or

$$v_{ab} + v_{bd} + v_{dm} + v_{ma} = 0 \qquad (5\text{-}2)$$

which is the statement of Kirchhoff's voltage law for this circuit.

Most often, when the circuit contains a source in series with passive terminal pairs, it is more convenient to express Kirchhoff's voltage law in the form of Eq. (5-1), namely, with the source function on one side of the equation, rather than in the form of Eq. (5-2).

The above derivation was made in the special case of a network consisting of one loop. The argument can be extended to apply to any network, regardless of its geometry. In Fig. 5-6b a two-mesh network, without any source, is shown. In conformity with Kirchhoff's current law, the current in branch mb of Fig. 5-6b is $i_1 + i_2$.

By the law of conservation of energy the total power received by all the terminal pairs is zero. (This means that at any given instant some of the terminal pairs receive and others deliver energy.)

$$-v_{ab}i_1 + v_{am}i_1 + v_{mb}(i_1 + i_2) - v_{mn}i_2 - v_{nb}i_2 = 0$$
$$i_1(v_{am} + v_{mb} - v_{ab}) + i_2(v_{mb} - v_{mn} - v_{nb}) = 0 \qquad (5\text{-}2a)$$

In the network of Fig. 5-6b the waveform of i_2 can be changed without any change in the waveform of i_1. This can be achieved by changing the elements in the terminal pairs of the network (for example, terminal pairs m-n, n-b, and m-b). In other words, the only restriction placed by the network on the waveform of the current is that given by $i_{mb} = i_1 + i_2$. This is a restriction on the waveform of i_{mb}. One of the currents i_1 and i_2 can be specified independently of the other.

Returning now to Eq. (5-2a), we note that the form of this equation is

$$i_1(t)f_1(t) + i_2(t)f_2(t) = 0 \qquad (5\text{-}2b)$$

Now, since $i_1(t)$ or $i_2(t)$ can be specified arbitrarily, it follows that $f_1(t) \equiv 0$ and $f_2(t) \equiv 0$. To clarify this argument, let us assume that $i_2(t) \equiv 0$ and $i_1(t) \neq 0$. Then $f_1(t) \equiv 0$. If, on the other hand, we let $i_1(t) \equiv 0$ and choose $i_2(t) \neq 0$, then $f_2(t) \equiv 0$. Hence in Eq. (5-2a) $v_{am} + v_{mb} - v_{ab} = 0$, and $v_{mb} - v_{mn} - v_{nb} = 0$.

These equations correspond to Kirchhoff's voltage law for each of the two meshes a-m-b-a and m-n-b-m.

Although the derivation of Kirchhoff's voltage law has dealt only with particular examples (Fig. 5-6a and b), the result is general and can be proved generally by application of a similar procedure.

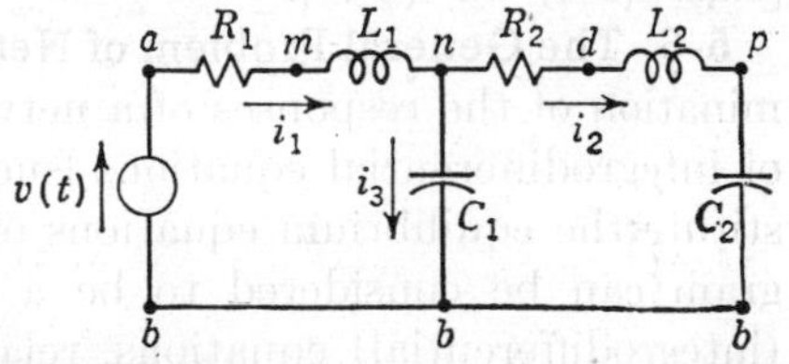

5-5. Equilibrium Equations of a Network. Any equation which is obtained as a result of applying either of Kirchhoff's laws to a network is called an equilibrium equation of that network.

FIG. 5-7. Illustration for the example of Art. 5-5.

In Fig. 5-7 the application of Kirchhoff's voltage law to the mesh a-m-n-b-a will result in

$$v_{am} + v_{mn} + v_{nb} + v_{ba} = 0 \qquad (5\text{-}3)$$

If we express the above voltages in terms of the currents and the circuit elements, we have

$$R_1 i_1 + L_1 \frac{di_1}{dt} + \frac{1}{C_1} \int_0^t i_3 \, d\tau + v_{nb}(0) - v(t) = 0 \tag{5-4}$$

$$R_1 i_1 + L_1 \frac{di_1}{dt} + \frac{1}{C_1} \int_0^t i_3 \, d\tau = v(t) - v_{nb}(0) \tag{5-5}$$

Notice that, by expressing the element voltages in terms of the currents, the number of circuit variables involved in the Kirchhoff-voltage-law equation is reduced.   Thus in Eq. (5-3) there are three variables (v_{am}, v_{mn}, and v_{nb}), while in Eq. (5-5) there are only two variables (i_1 and i_3).

The determination of the waveform of the variables in equilibrium equations such as Eq. (5-4) or Eq. (5-5) is the subject of other chapters in this book.   At this point we shall concern ourselves only with establishing the equilibrium equations of networks.

In Fig. 5-7 another equilibrium equation can be obtained by applying Kirchhoff's voltage law to mesh n-d-p-b-n and expressing the voltages in terms of the branch currents and the circuit elements.   This will result in

$$R_2 i_2 + L_2 \frac{di_2}{dt} + \frac{1}{C_2} \int_0^t i_2 \, d\tau + v_{pb}(0) - \frac{1}{C_1} \int_0^t i_3 \, d\tau + v_{bn}(0) = 0 \tag{5-6}$$

where the initial conditions $v_{pb}(0)$ and $v_{bn}(0) = -v_{nb}(0)$ are usually specified.   Similarly the application of Kirchhoff's current law to the junction n results in

$$i_1 = i_2 + i_3 \tag{5-7}$$

In Eqs. (5-5), (5-6), and (5-7) there are three unknowns i_1, i_2, and i_3. In future chapters we shall see how we can obtain the waveform of the responses (i_1, i_2, and i_3) from the equilibrium equations of the network [Eqs. (5-5) to (5-7)].

5-6. The General Problem of Network Analysis.   In general the determination of the responses of a network will require the solution of a set of integrodifferential equations [such as Eqs. (5-5) to (5-7)], which constitute the equilibrium equations of the network.   In fact a circuit diagram can be considered to be a symbolic representation of a set of (integrodifferential) equations, relating different functions [such as $v(t)$, $i_1(t)$, $i_2(t)$, $i_3(t)$ in Eqs. (5-5) to (5-7)].

In such a case circuit analysis will be a part of applied mathematics, and a circuit will be considered as the graphical representation of relations (equations) between dependent variables of a system, without specifying the system or attributing any significance to its individual variables.   According to this point of view, circuit analysis may be applied to mechanical systems, where the variables will be force, distance, velocity, and acceleration, and the parameters of the system will be coefficients of friction, inertia (mass), elastance, etc.

If the system is a chemical one, the dependent variables may be concentration, temperature, pressure, etc. In an electrical system the variables will be voltages and current with their derivatives and integrals (with respect to time).

Such an approach benefits and suffers at the same time from the usual advantages and disadvantages of generalization. While the generality of the application of the methods of circuit analysis to any (linear) system should be emphasized at the outset, we shall study it using electrical-circuit terminology.

Although our ultimate aim is the study of the response of networks of arbitrary geometry and construction, we shall approach this by the study of relatively simple circuits. We shall see that, from a knowledge

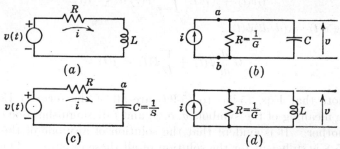

FIG. 5-8. Analogous circuits.

of the behavior of "simple" circuits, we can easily deduce the response of the most complicated networks.

5-7. Analogous Circuits. When two or more circuits are described by equilibrium equations of identical mathematical form, then these circuits are analogous. The four circuits shown in Fig. 5-8 are analogous because they are all described by an equilibrium equation of the form

$$a \frac{d}{dt} y(t) + by(t) = f(t) \qquad (5-8)$$

where a and b are constants. The values of a and b, the response $y(t)$, and the source function $f(t)$ are found for the individual circuits by application of Kirchhoff's laws. For the circuit of Fig. 5-8a the application of Kirchhoff's voltage law gives

$$L \frac{d}{dt} i(t) + Ri(t) = v(t) \qquad (5-9a)$$

Kirchhoff's current law applied to junction a in the circuit of Fig. 5-8b gives the equation

$$C \frac{d}{dt} v(t) + Gv(t) = i(t) \qquad (5\text{-}9b)$$

For the circuit of Fig. 5-8c Kirchhoff's voltage law gives

$$Ri(t) + S \int_{-\infty}^{t} i \, d\tau = v(t)$$

or, using $i = (d/dt)q_a(t)$,

$$R \frac{d}{dt} q_a(t) + Sq_a(t) = v(t) \qquad (5\text{-}9c)$$

Applying Kirchhoff's current law to the circuit of Fig. 5-8d gives

$$Gv(t) + (1/L) \int_{-\infty}^{t} v(\tau) \, d\tau = i(t)$$

or, using $v(t) = (d/dt)\psi(t)$,

$$G \frac{d}{dt} \psi(t) + \frac{1}{L} \psi(t) = i(t) \qquad (5\text{-}9d)$$

We note that Eqs. (5-9a) to (5-9d) are all of the form of Eq. (5-8): only the meaning of the symbols a, b, y, and f distinguishes one equation from another. It is evident that the solution of any one of the circuits of Fig. 5-8 is sufficient for the solution of all these circuits. Thus recognizing analogies enables us to write the solutions for some circuits by inspection.

5-8. Dual Circuits. Two circuits which are analogous are said to be *duals* of each other *provided* that the current and voltage variables in the two equilibrium equations associated with the circuits are interchanged. Thus, if in the equation of one circuit a term contains a voltage $v(t)$, the analogous term in the equation of the other circuit must contain a current variable $i(t)$. As an illustration of duality, we note that the voltage-current relationship for an inductance connected between terminals a-b of a current source $i(t)$ is $v_{ab} = L(d/dt)i(t)$ and that the relationship for a capacitance connected to a voltage source $v(t)$ is $i_{ab} = C(d/dt)v(t)$. It is seen that in these two equations the voltage and current variables are interchanged. Hence these two circuits are duals of each other. Two elements whose voltage-current relationships are duals are called dual elements. Thus the elements inductance and capacitance are dual elements, and a voltage source is the dual of a current source. Referring to the equilibrium equations for the circuits of Fig. 5-8, we note that circuits (a) and (b) are duals of each other and that circuits (c) and (d) are duals of each other. We again point out that the property of duality applies to *special cases* of analogous circuits. Thus all dual circuits are analogous, but only selected analogous circuits are duals.

Referring again to the circuits of Fig. 5-8a and b, we note that the following descriptions and terms correspond in these dual circuits:

Fig. 5-8a	Fig. 5-8b
Voltage source	Current source
Series circuit	Parallel circuit
Series resistance	Parallel conductance
Series inductance	Parallel capacitance
Magnetic-energy storage	Electric-energy storage
Dependent variable $i(t)$	Dependent variable $v(t)$

We have already noted that the elements L and C are dual elements. The tabulation given in connection with the two circuits of Fig. 5-8a and b leads to the general tabulation of dual quantities given in Table 5-1.

TABLE 5-1. DUAL QUANTITIES

Voltage	Current
Current	Voltage
Charge	Flux linkages
Flux linkages	Charge
Inductance	Capacitance
Resistance	Conductance $\frac{1}{R} = G$
Series connection	Parallel connection

5-9. Mechanical Analogues. (In defining analogous circuits it was stated that any two circuits which are described by similar equilibrium equations are analogous. This statement can be extended as follows: Any two *physical systems* which are described by equilibrium equations of the same mathematical form are analogous. A very common application of this concept to mechanical systems results in the establishment of electrical circuits which can represent mechanical (or electromechanical) systems. Such representations are useful both for analysis and for experimental study. It is possible to study (experimentally) an electrical circuit (which can be adjusted with ease) rather than a mechanical model (which may be more cumbersome, expensive to construct, and difficult to adjust), provided that the two systems are analogous.)

(The analogy between electrical and mechanical systems is based on the analogy between Newton's laws in mechanics and Kirchhoff's laws in circuit analysis. Newton's acceleration law states that: The sum of the unbalanced forces (torques) acting on a mass (moment of inertia) is proportional to the acceleration (or angular acceleration) of the body.) Symbolically we write

$$f(t) = M\frac{du}{dt} \quad \text{or} \quad T(t) = J\frac{d\omega}{dt} \tag{5-10}$$

where
$$
\begin{aligned}
f &= \text{force} & T &= \text{torque} \\
M &= \text{mass} & J &= \text{moment of inertia} \\
u &= \text{velocity} & \omega &= \text{angular velocity}
\end{aligned}
$$

We can immediately set up analogies between electrical and mechanical elements. In doing so we shall deal with rotating systems, reserving the translational systems as exercises for the reader (see Prob. 5-9).

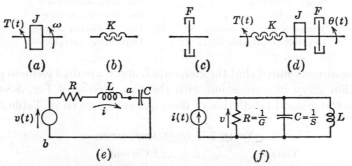

FIG. 5-9. Electrical analogues. (*a–c*) Symbols for mechanical elements. (*d*) A mechanical system. (*e*) Torque-voltage analogue for the system of (*d*). (*f*) Torque-current analogue for the system of (*d*).

The variables in a rotational system, together with the symbols which we shall use, are

$$\text{Torque} = T(t)$$
$$\text{Angular displacement} = \theta$$
$$\text{Angular velocity} \frac{d\theta}{dt} = \omega$$
$$\text{Angular acceleration} \frac{d^2\theta}{dt^2} = \frac{d\omega}{dt}$$

The parameters of such a mechanical system, together with their symbols, are

$$\text{Moment of inertia} = J$$
$$\text{Torsional spring} = K$$
$$\text{Viscous friction} = F$$

The parameter moment of inertia is defined by the equation

$$T(t) = J\frac{d^2\theta}{dt^2} = J\frac{d\omega}{dt} \tag{5-10a}$$

This element will be shown symbolically by the disk symbol of Fig. 5-9*a*. The arrows round the shaft symbol indicate the directions in which the torque and the angular velocity are positive numbers. A torsional spring is an element which exerts a (restoring) torque proportional to the angular displacement, defined by the equation

$$T(t) = K\theta \tag{5-11}$$

The symbol shown in Fig. 5-9b is used to denote such an element.

In mechanics an element is said to furnish *viscous friction* if it creates a frictional torque which is proportional to the velocity. (The reader should not confuse this type of friction with the "static frictional torque" which is the product of coefficient of friction and "normal torque.") Thus viscous friction is defined through the equation

$$T(t) = F\omega = F\frac{d\theta}{dt} \tag{5-12}$$

A symbol for this element is shown in Fig. 5-9c.

Once the mechanical elements are defined, the electrically analogous elements are evident. Recalling the duality which was discussed in the preceding article, we can pair each mechanical element with either of two electrical elements, as is evident by comparing the defining equations for each set of elements in the accompanying tabulation.

Mechanical element	Electrical element	Alternate electrical element
Moment of inertia $T = J\dfrac{d\omega}{dt}$	Inductance $v = L\dfrac{di}{dt}$	Capacitance $i = C\dfrac{dv}{dt}$
Viscous friction $T = F\omega$	Resistance $v = Ri$	Conductance $i = Gv$
Spring $T = K\theta = K\int\omega\,dt$	Capacitance $v = Sq = S\int i\,dt$	Inductance $i = L^{-1}\psi = L^{-1}\int v\,dt$

From this tabulation it is clear that the following types of electrical and mechanical sources are also analogous:

A source of torque corresponds to voltage source or current source.

A source of velocity corresponds to current source or voltage source.

We have, therefore, two analogies. In one, torque is analogous to voltage: in the other, torque is analogous to current. Table 5-2 shows analogous variables and parameters for these two possibilities.

As an example, consider the mechanical system represented in Fig. 5-9d, where a torque $T(t)$ is applied to a moment of inertia through a spring in the presence of viscous friction. The equation of motion for the disk is

$$T(t) - K\theta - F\frac{d\theta}{dt} = J\frac{d^2\theta}{dt^2} \tag{5-13}$$

or

$$T(t) = J\frac{d^2\theta}{dt^2} + F\frac{d\theta}{dt} + K\theta \tag{5-14}$$

TABLE 5-2. MECHANICAL-ELECTRICAL ANALOGUES

Mechanical quantity	Electrical quantity	
	Torque-voltage analogue	Torque-current analogue
Torque	Voltage	Current
Velocity	Current	Voltage
Displacement	Charge	Flux linkages
Momentum	Flux linkages	Charge
Moment of inertia	Inductance	Capacitance
Spring	Reciprocal capacitance	Reciprocal inductance
Viscous friction	Resistance	Conductance
Potential energy	Electric field energy	Magnetic energy
Kinetic energy	Magnetic energy	Electric (field) energy

We may identify this mechanical system with a series R-L-C circuit as shown in Fig. 5-9e, where

$$v(t) = L\frac{d^2 q_a}{dt^2} + R\frac{dq_a}{dt} + Sq_a \tag{5-15}$$

or with the parallel R-L-C circuit shown in Fig. 5-9f, where

$$i(t) = C\frac{d^2\psi}{dt^2} + G\frac{d\psi}{dt} + \frac{1}{L}\psi \tag{5-16}$$

So far we have mentioned only mechanical analogies of electrical circuits. Other systems are also represented by equations which in their mathematical form resemble the equilibrium equations of circuits. For example, thermal, acoustic, and chemical systems have this property. The electrical engineer who is conversant with circuit analysis reaps from this skill an extra bonus, for each circuit diagram which is analyzed can convey information about other systems if analogues are recognized.

PROBLEMS

5-1. In the series R-L-C circuit shown in Fig. P5-1 calculate and sketch $v_{ab}(t)$ if (a) $i(t) = 10^{-3}U(t)$; (b) $i(t) = 10^{-3}tU(t)$; (c) $i(t) = e^{-10^3 t}U(t)$. The capacitance is initially uncharged.

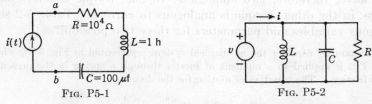

FIG. P5-1   FIG. P5-2

5-2. In the circuit shown in Fig. P5-2 assume that all elements have unit value. Calculate and sketch $i(t)$ if (a) $v(t) = 2U(t)$; (b) $v(t) = 3tU(t)$; (c) $v(t) = e^{-2t}U(t)$. The inductance carries no initial current.

5-3. In the circuit shown in Fig. P5-3 it is known that $i_1(t) = U(t)$. Calculate $v_{ab}(t)$ $[v_{a'b}(0) = 0]$.

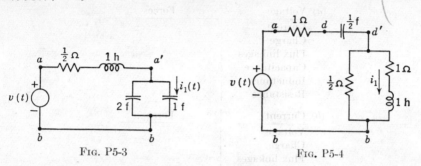

FIG. P5-3   FIG. P5-4

5-4. In the circuit shown in Fig. P5-4 $i_1(t) = tU(t)$. Calculate $v_{ab}(t)$ $[v_{dd'}(0) = 0]$.

5-5. In the circuit shown in Fig. P5-5 it is known that $v_{ab}(t) = t^3U(t)$. Calculate $i(t)$. (All capacitances are initially uncharged.)

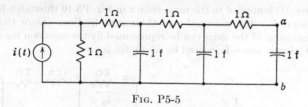

FIG. P5-5

5-6. In the circuit shown in Fig. P5-6 all energy-storing elements are deenergized at $t = 0^-$. It is known that $v_{ab}(t) = t^2U(t)$. Calculate $i(t)$.

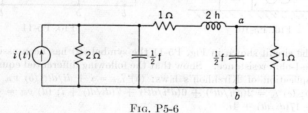

FIG. P5-6

5-7. In the circuit shown in Fig. P5-7 (a) apply Kirchhoff's voltage law to write two simultaneous equations for i_1 and i_2; (b) apply Kirchhoff's current law, and write an equation relating v_{db} to v; (c) write the equation for energy balance.

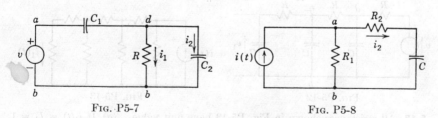

FIG. P5-7   FIG. P5-8

5-8. In the circuit shown in Fig. P5-8 apply Kirchhoff's laws to obtain an equilibrium equation relating $i_2(t)$ to $i(t)$.

5-9. Complete the tables of electromechanical analogues for translational systems.

(a)

Voltage	Force
Current	
Charge	
Flux linkages	
Capacitance	
Inductance	
Resistance	

(b)

Current	Force
Voltage	
Charge	
Flux linkages	
Capacitance	
Inductance	
Resistance	

5-10. A force $f(t)$ is applied to the mass shown in Fig. P5-10 through a linear spring whose elastance is K. It is assumed that there is no friction. Show that the equation for displacement of the mass can be represented by the equation for charge in an analogous L-C circuit which is excited by a voltage source.

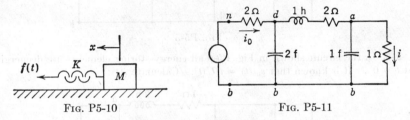

FIG. P5-10   FIG. P5-11

5-11. In the circuit shown in Fig. P5-11 the symbol $i(t)$ has been assigned to the current in the 1-ohm resistance. Show that the following differential equations result from the application of Kirchhoff's laws: (a) $i_{da} = i + di/dt$; (b) $v_{db} = d^2i/dt^2 + 3(di/dt) + 3i$; (c) $i_0 = 2(d^3i/dt^3) + 6(d^2i/dt^2) + 7(di/dt) + i$; (d) $v_{nb} = 4(d^3i/dt^3) + 13(d^2i/dt^2) + 17(di/dt) + 4i$.

5-12. Apply Kirchhoff's laws to the circuit given in Fig. P5-12, and show that (a) $v_{ab} = RC(dv_1/dt) + v_1$; (b) $v_{db} = (RC)^2(d^2v_1/dt^2) + 3RC(dv_1/dt) + v_1$; (c) $v = (RC)^3 (d^3v_1/dt^3) + 5(RC)^2(d^2v_1/dt^2) + 6RC(dv_1/dt) + v_1$.

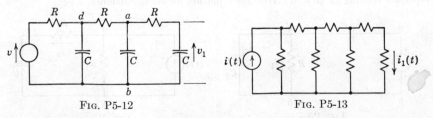

FIG. P5-12   FIG. P5-13

5-13. All resistances shown in Fig. P5-13 have unit value. (a) If $i_1(t) = I_1 = 1$, calculate $i(t) = I$. (b) Use the result of (a) to calculate (1) $i(t)$ when $i_1(t) = 2t$; (2) $i_1(t)$ when $i(t) = 10 \sin 5t$.

CHAPTER 6

CIRCUITS CONTAINING ONLY ONE TYPE OF ELEMENT

When a circuit contains (in addition to sources) only one type of passive element (i.e., only resistance or only inductance or only capacitance), then the analysis of the circuit is particularly simple because the solution of such circuits is carried out without the use of differential equations, only algebra being needed.

When two circuit elements, connected in series or in parallel between two terminals, are of the same type (e.g., both inductances or both capacitances as in Fig. 6-1), then the arrangement, with respect to those two terminals, can be represented by a single circuit element of the same type.

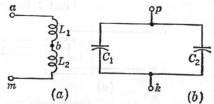

6-1. Series Connection of Capacitances. Consider the series combination of the capacitances C_1 and C_2 shown in Fig. 6-2a. Assume that a current source $i(t)$ is connected between terminals a-b at $t = 0$.

Fig. 6-1. (a) Series connection of two inductances. (b) Parallel connection of two capacitances.

Then the voltage across each capacitance is given by

$$v_{am} = \frac{1}{C_1} q_a(0) + \frac{1}{C_1} \int_0^t i \, d\tau = v_{am}(0) + \frac{1}{C_1} \int_0^t i \, d\tau \qquad (6\text{-}1)$$

and

$$v_{mb} = \frac{1}{C_2} q_m(0) + \frac{1}{C_2} \int_0^t i \, d\tau = v_{mb}(0) + \frac{1}{C_2} \int_0^t i \, d\tau \qquad (6\text{-}2)$$

Now, if Kirchhoff's voltage law is applied between terminals a-b, the voltage v_{ab} is given by the addition:

$$v_{am}(t) + v_{mb}(t) = v_{ab}(t) \qquad (6\text{-}3)$$

Hence

$$v_{ab}(t) = v_{am}(0) + v_{mb}(0) + \left(\frac{1}{C_1} + \frac{1}{C_2} \right) \int_0^t i \, d\tau$$

This relationship can be written as

77

$$v_{ab} = v_{ab}(0) + \frac{1}{C_e} \int_0^t i(\tau)\, d\tau \qquad (6\text{-}4)$$

where
$$\frac{1}{C_e} = \frac{1}{C_1} + \frac{1}{C_2} = \frac{C_1 + C_2}{C_1 C_2} \qquad (6\text{-}5)$$

Using the elastances $(S = 1/C)$

$$S_e = S_1 + S_2 \qquad (6\text{-}6)$$

If we now consider the circuits shown in Fig. 6-2, then the voltage-current characteristics between terminals a-b in Fig. 6-2b are the same as those of Fig. 6-2a; i.e., if the same $v_{ab}(t)$ is applied to each circuit, the same current $i_{ab}(t)$ will flow, and vice versa. Hence Fig. 6-2b is an

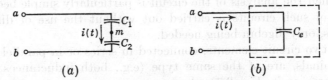

FIG. 6-2. Capacitances in series.

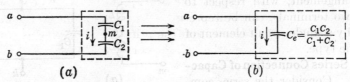

FIG. 6-3. Equivalent capacitance for series capacitances.

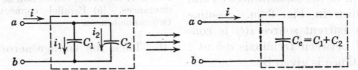

FIG. 6-4. Equivalent capacitance for parallel capacitances.

equivalent circuit of Fig. 6-2a. This is indicated symbolically in Fig. 6-3, *where the equivalence is valid only with respect to terminals a-b.* For example, as a result of impressing a current $i_{ab}(t)$ in Fig. 6-2, a voltage $v_{am} = S_1 \int_{-\infty}^t i_{ab}\, d\tau$ is observed (by connecting an oscilloscope across terminals a-m). In the "equivalent" circuit of Fig. 6-3, however, the point m does not appear, the voltage v_{am} could not be observed, and no equivalence exists for this measurement. Hence the two <u>circuits are equivalent only with respect to the voltage-current relationship at terminals a-b</u>.

6-2. Parallel Connection of Capacitances. Figure 6-4 shows the capacitances C_1 and C_2 connected in parallel between terminals a-b. If a voltage source v_{ab} is connected to terminals a-b, the same voltage $v_{ab}(t)$

exists across each capacitance.   Hence

$$i_1 = C_1 \frac{dv_{ab}}{dt} \qquad (6\text{-}7)$$

and
$$i_2 = C_2 \frac{dv_{ab}}{dt} \qquad (6\text{-}8)$$

Then
$$i_1 + i_2 = (C_1 + C_2) \frac{dv_{ab}}{dt} \qquad (6\text{-}9)$$

But in accordance with Kirchhoff's current law

$$i_1(t) + i_2(t) = i(t) \qquad (6\text{-}10)$$

Hence
$$i(t) = (C_1 + C_2) \frac{dv_{ab}}{dt} \qquad (6\text{-}11)$$

Equation (6-11) gives the voltage-current characteristics of a capacitance which, with respect to terminals a-b, is equivalent to the parallel combination of C_1 and C_2, namely, $C_p = C_1 + C_2$ or $1/S_p = 1/S_1 + 1/S_2$.   This equivalence is indicated symbolically in Fig. 6-4.

6-3. Series and Parallel Connection of Inductances or Resistances. Whereas two capacitances in parallel add up, it can easily be shown that two inductances in series will add up.   This may be shown directly (see Prob. 6-1) or may be deduced from the principle of duality as expressed by the comparison between the voltage-current characteristics of L and C:

$$v = L \frac{di}{dt} \qquad \text{and} \qquad i = C \frac{dv}{dt} \qquad (6\text{-}12)$$

or
$$i = \frac{1}{L} \int_{-\infty}^{t} v \, d\tau \qquad \text{and} \qquad v = \frac{1}{C} \int_{-\infty}^{t} i \, d\tau$$

Similarly, series resistances add up (see Prob. 6-4).   These equivalences are illustrated in Fig. 6-5.

6-4. Combinations of Nonsimilar Elements. In the context of this discussion the term "similar elements" refers to elements which store the same type of energy (Ls or Cs) *or* dissipate energy (i.e., resistances). It is not possible to find single equivalent elements for series or parallel combinations of nonsimilar circuit elements.   For example, in Fig. 6-6, where a voltage source v_{am} is applied to a series arrangement of R and L, it is not possible to replace R and L by a single equivalent circuit element. Kirchhoff's voltage law reads

$$v_{am} = v_{ab} + v_{bm}$$

which, using the definitions of R and L, becomes

$$v_{am} = Ri + L \frac{di}{dt} \qquad (6\text{-}13)$$

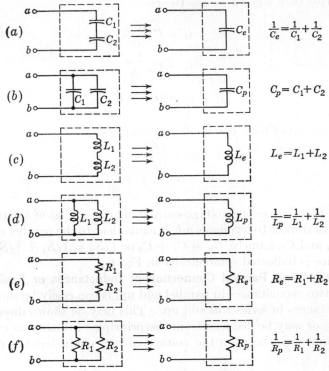

FIG. 6-5. Equivalent elements.

It is noted that this equation contains not only $i(t)$ but also the time derivative of the current. Comparing this to Eqs. (6-1) and (6-2), which are written for the series combination of one type of element (two capacitances), we observe that Eqs. (6-1) and (6-2) combined into one integral because only integrals of the current were involved. In the present case [Eq. (6-13)] the terms Ri and $L(di/dt)$ cannot be combined into a single term for *arbitrary* waveforms $i(t)$, and therefore the circuit cannot be replaced by an equivalent circuit consisting of a single element.

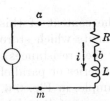

FIG. 6-6. Series connection of resistance and inductance.

There is a clear physical reason for the non-existence of a single equivalent circuit element when two (or more) dissimilar elements are in the original circuit. In such circuits more than one type of energy transformation is involved. The equivalent circuit would have to represent all these types of energy conversions. Since a single element is defined so as to correspond to one type of energy, a circuit containing dissimilar elements cannot be represented by a single equivalent element for all waveforms.

To show how the waveform influences this statement, two examples will be considered briefly. Suppose first that, in Fig. 6-6, $i(t)$ is constant. Then $di_{ab}/dt = 0$, and $v_{ab} = $ const. The arrangement of elements between a and b is then "equivalent" to a resistance R as far as the voltage-current relationship is concerned so long as *no changes* in the current take place.

In general, if the waveform of the current in a network is sinusoidal, then di/dt also is sinusoidal. In that case the combinations of circuit elements can be represented, under certain conditions, by two elements, one representing energy conversion into heat, i.e., resistance, the other representing the "dominant" energy storage, that is, L or C. This is treated in detail in a later chapter.

6-5. Voltage Division across Series Connection of Two Similar Elements. Consider the series connection of the two inductances shown in Fig. 6-7. (While we are formally dealing with only two elements in series, the reader will certainly recognize that each of these two elements may be the equivalent element for a combination of elements.) We desire to formulate the relationship between the voltage across one inductance and the voltage across both inductances.

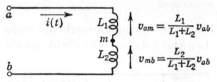

FIG. 6-7. Voltage division for series inductances.

The voltage across L_1 is, at any instant of time,

$$v_{am} = L_1 \frac{di}{dt}$$

and the voltage across L_2 is

$$v_{mb} = L_2 \frac{di}{dt}$$

Hence the ratio v_{am}/v_{mb} is equal to the ratio of the inductances,

$$\frac{v_{am}}{v_{mb}} = \frac{L_1}{L_2} \tag{6-14}$$

In words, when two inductances are connected in series, then the voltage across each inductance is proportional to the value of that inductance.

Since the equivalent inductance of the two elements in series is

$$L_e = L_1 + L_2$$

we may also write

$$\frac{v_{am}}{v_{ab}} = \frac{L_1}{L_1 + L_2} \tag{6-15}$$

Equation (6-15) is the *voltage-division formula* for inductances. In words, this formula states that the ratio of the voltage across one inductance in a series connection of inductances is to the voltage across all the series-connected inductances as the one inductance is to the sum of the inductances.

For the series connection of several resistances the same statement applies if the word inductance is replaced by resistance everywhere. This result is illustrated in Fig. 6-8. The proof is left as an exercise for the reader.

In the case of capacitances we can show that if the same current

$$v_{am} = \frac{R_1}{R_1 + R_2} v_{ab}$$

$$v_{mb} = \frac{R_2}{R_1 + R_2} v_{ab}$$

FIG. 6-8. Voltage division across series resistances.

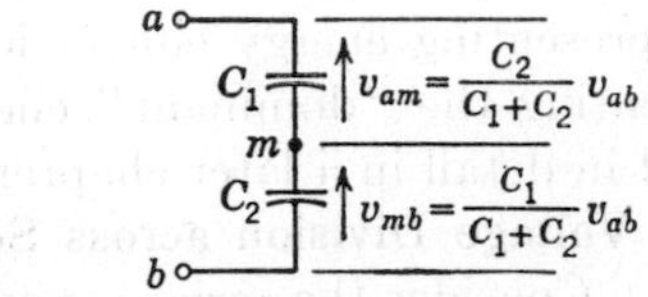

$$v_{am} = \frac{C_2}{C_1 + C_2} v_{ab}$$

$$v_{mb} = \frac{C_1}{C_1 + C_2} v_{ab}$$

FIG. 6-9. Voltage division across series capacitances.

has been flowing through the series-connected capacitances for all time then the voltages will divide as the reciprocals of the capacitances, i.e., proportionally to the elastances, as illustrated in Fig. 6-9. The proof is left as an exercise for the reader (see Prob. 6-11).

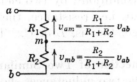

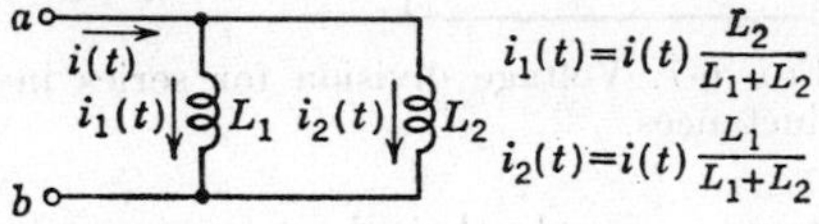

$$i_1(t) = i(t) \frac{L_2}{L_1 + L_2}$$

$$i_2(t) = i(t) \frac{L_1}{L_1 + L_2}$$

FIG. 6-10. Current division in parallel inductances.

6-6. Current Division in Parallel Combinations of Similar Elements. Consider now the parallel inductances L_1 and L_2 shown in Fig. 6-10. The current in each inductance is given, for all $t > 0$, by

$$i_1(t) = i_1(0) + \frac{1}{L_1} \int_0^t v_{ab} \, d\tau \tag{6-16}$$

and

$$i_2(t) = i_2(0) + \frac{1}{L_2} \int_0^t v_{ab} \, d\tau \tag{6-17}$$

If we now assume that the ratio $i_1(0)/i_2(0) = L_2/L_1$ [or that both $i_1(0)$ and $i_2(0)$ are zero], then

$$\frac{i_1(t)}{i_2(t)} = \frac{L_2}{L_1} \tag{6-18}$$

so that (under the assumed conditions) the current in two parallel inductances divides proportionally to the reciprocals of the inductances.

In the case of two parallel resistances (as shown in Fig. 6-11) the current divides proportionally to the conductances (reciprocal resistances), and for parallel capacitances the current divides proportionally to the capacitances as shown in Fig. 6-12. The proof of these statements is left as an exercise for the reader.

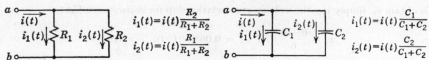

FIG. 6-11. Current division in parallel resistances.

FIG. 6-12. Current division in parallel capacitances.

6-7. Examples of Circuits Containing Similar Elements. Example 6-1.

In the circuit shown in Fig. 6-13a the voltage v_{ab} is applied at $t = 0$ and has the form $v_{ab}(t) = f(t)U(t)$. The voltage across each capacitance is zero before $t = 0$. Calculate the voltage across C_5 and the current $i_5(t)$.

Solution. First reduce the series-parallel combination of the five capacitances to a single capacitance with respect to terminals a-b. Then the voltage- and current-division formulas for capacitances will be applied repeatedly.

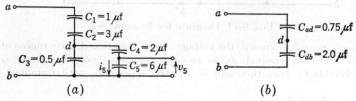

$$(a) \qquad\qquad (b)$$

FIG. 6-13. Diagrams for Example 6-1.

The series combination of C_1 and C_2 can be replaced by the capacitance

$$C_{ad} = \frac{C_1 C_2}{C_1 + C_2}$$

or, using the numbers as given,

$$C_{ad} = \frac{(1)(3)}{1 + 3} = 0.75 \ \mu\text{f}$$

Between terminals d-b we have the parallel combination of C_3 and the equivalent capacitance $C_4 C_5 / (C_4 + C_5)$:

$$C_{db} = 0.5 + \frac{(2)(6)}{2 + 6} = 2.0 \ \mu\text{f}$$

Since C_{ad} and C_{bd} are in series as shown in Fig. 6-13b, C_{ab} can be found from

$$\frac{1}{C_{ab}} = \frac{1}{C_{ad}} + \frac{1}{C_{db}}$$

or

$$\frac{1}{C_{ab}} = 1.33 + 0.50 \qquad (1/\mu\text{f})$$

$$C_{ab} = 0.547 \ \mu\text{f}$$

To find i_5, we shall first find $i_{ab}(t)$ and then apply current division.

$$i_{ab}(t) = C_{ab} \frac{dv_{ab}}{dt} \equiv i(t)$$

or

$$i(t) = 0.547 \frac{df}{dt} U(t) \qquad \mu\text{a}$$

Hence

$$i_5 = 0.547 \frac{C_4 C_5 / (C_4 + C_5)}{C_3 + C_4 C_5 / (C_4 + C_5)} \frac{df}{dt} U(t) = 0.410 \frac{df}{dt} U(t) \qquad \mu\text{a}$$

To obtain v_5, simply use the volt-ampere relationship for capacitance C_5:

$$v_5 = \frac{0.410}{6} f(t) U(t) = 0.068 f(t) U(t) \qquad \text{volts}$$

Alternatively, the voltage division could have been used to find v_{db} first and then v_5; i_5 is then obtained from v_5. This procedure is left as an exercise for the reader.

Example 6-2. In the resistance circuit of Fig. 6-14 the current i_4 is, at some instant of time, 4 amp. Find the value of the voltage v_{ab} at that instant of time. Let all resistances have unit values.

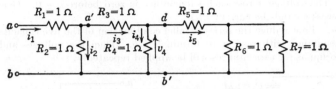

FIG. 6-14. Diagram for Example 6-2.

Solution. Since i_4 is known, the voltage v_4 can be obtained. By representing the circuit to the left of terminals d-b as an equivalent resistance, the current i_5 can be found. Kirchhoff's laws then can be applied repeatedly until terminals a-b are reached.

Since $i_4 = 4$ and $R_4 = 1$,

$$v_{db'} = 4 \text{ volts}$$

The combination of R_5, R_6, and R_7 forms a resistance $R_{db'}$, where

$$R_{db'} = 1 + \tfrac{1}{2} = 1.50$$

Hence
$$i_5 = \frac{v_{db'}}{R_{db'}} = \frac{4}{1.5} = 2.67 \text{ amp}$$

so that
$$i_3 = i_4 + i_5 = 4 + 2.67 = 6.67 \text{ amp}$$

Thus
$$v_{a'd} = 6.67 \cdot R_3 = 6.67 \text{ volts}$$

and
$$v_{a'b} = v_{a'd} + v_{db} = 6.67 + 4 = 10.67 \text{ volts}$$

so that
$$i_2 = \frac{v_{a'b}}{R_2} = 10.67 \text{ amp}$$

and
$$i_1 = 10.67 + 6.67 = 17.34 \text{ amp}$$

Then
$$v_{aa'} = 17.34 \cdot R_1 = 17.34 \text{ volts}$$

and finally
$$v_{ab} = v_{aa'} + v_{a'b} = 17.34 + 10.67 = 28.01 \text{ volts}$$

PROBLEMS

6-1. Show that the equivalent inductance of two inductances in series is the sum of the individual inductances.

6-2. (*a*) Calculate the equivalent inductance L_{ab}, Fig. P6-2, where $i_{ab}(0) = 0$. (*b*) $L_1 = 1$ henry, $L_2 = 1$ henry, L_3 is variable. Calculate the largest and the smallest value which L_{ab} can have. (*c*) L_1 is variable; $L_2 = L_3 = 1$ henry. Calculate the largest and the smallest value which L_{ab} can have.

6-3. A sawtooth-pulse voltage source $v(t) = t U(t) U(a - t)$ is applied to the parallel inductances shown in Fig. P6-3. It is known that $i_1(0) = i_2(0) = 0$. As a further specification, neither i_1 nor i_2 may exceed 2 amp at any instant of time. Calculate (*a*) the largest allowable value of a; (*b*) the maximum allowable value of $i(t)$.

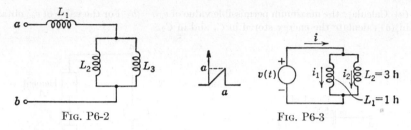

FIG. P6-2   FIG. P6-3

6-4. Prove the equivalences indicated in Fig. 6-5e and f.

6-5. The equivalent resistance of two resistances in series is 10 ohms. When the two resistances are placed in parallel, the equivalent resistance is 2.4 ohms. Calculate the values of the resistances.

6-6. In the two circuits shown in Fig. P6-6 the same current I_0 flows for the same voltage V_{ab}. It is also known that the ratio I_1/I_0 is the same in both circuits. Calculate R_a and R_b.

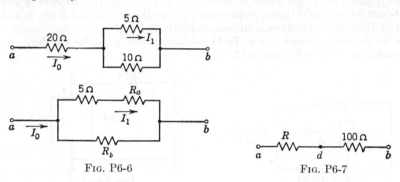

FIG. P6-6   FIG. P6-7

6-7. In the circuit shown in Fig. P6-7 $v_{db} = 50$ mv when $v_{ab} = 150$ volts. Calculate R (voltmeter "multiplier").

6-8. In the circuit shown in Fig. P6-8 $I_1 = 100 \ \mu a$ when $I = 1$ amp. Calculate R (ammeter "shunt").

FIG. P6-8   FIG. P6-9

6-9. (a) Two uncharged capacitances are connected in series as shown in Fig. P6-9. If $C_1 = 1 \ \mu f$ and C_2 is adjustable from 0.01 to 0.1 μf, calculate the maximum and the minimum value of C_{ab}. (b) Calculate the maximum and minimum values of the equivalent capacitance if the two capacitances are placed in parallel.

6-10. The equivalent capacitance of two capacitances in series is 10 μf. When the same capacitances are connected in parallel, the equivalent capacitance is 50 μf. Calculate the values of the individual capacitances.

6-11. Prove the relationships indicated in Figs. 6-8, 6-9, 6-11, and 6-12.

6-12. In the circuit shown in Fig. P6-12 the voltage value indicated below each capacitance value specifies the highest permissible voltage across that capacitance.

(a) Calculate the maximum permissible value of v_{ab}.   (b) For the value of v_{ab} obtained in (a) calculate the energy stored in C_1 and in C_2.

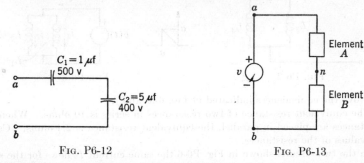

Fig. P6-12

Fig. P6-13

6-13. In the circuit shown in Fig. P6-13 $v_{ab}(t) = 2tU(t)$.   Calculate v_{nb} if (a) the elements A and B are 1- and 3-ohm resistances, respectively; (b) the elements A and B are 1- and 3-henry inductances, respectively; (c) the elements A and B are 1- and 3-farad (initially deenergized) capacitances, respectively.

6-14. In the circuit shown in Fig. P6-14 calculate the ratio i_b/i for the three element conditions specified in Prob. 6-13.

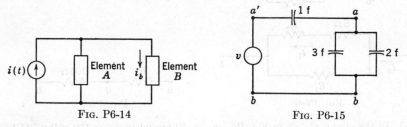

Fig. P6-14

Fig. P6-15

6-15. In the circuit shown in Fig. P6-15 calculate v_{ab}/v.

6-16. In the circuit shown in Fig. P6-16 calculate the energy stored in each capacitance.

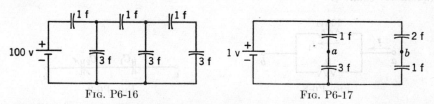

Fig. P6-16

Fig. P6-17

6-17. In the circuit shown in Fig. P6-17 calculate V_{ab}.

6-18. In the circuit shown in Fig. P6-18 calculate V_{ab}.

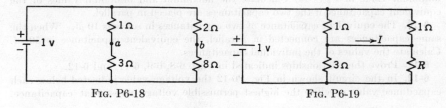

Fig. P6-18

Fig. P6-19

6-19. In the circuit shown in Fig. P6-19 calculate I if (a) $R = 3$ ohms; (b) $R = 6$ ohms.

6-20. Calculate v_{ab} as a function of $v(t)$ in Fig. P6-20.

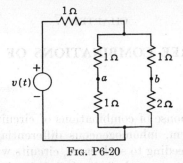

FIG. P6-20

6-21. The energy dissipated in R_6, see Fig. P6-21, in the time interval $t = 0$ to $t = 6$ is 4 joules. Calculate A.

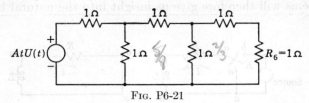

FIG. P6-21

6-22. In the circuit shown in Fig. P6-22, if $v_{ab} = v/2$ and $i_1 = 3i/4$, calculate R_1 and R_2.

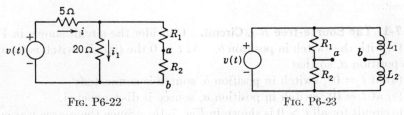

FIG. P6-22   FIG. P6-23

6-23. In the circuit of Fig. P6-23 (a) find the ratio v_{ab}/v. (b) Change the elements L_1 and L_2 to C_1 and C_2, respectively, and calculate v_{ab}/v. (c) Obtain numerical answers for (a) if $R_1 = 1$, $R_2 = 3$ and $L_1 = 1$, $L_2 = 3$; and for (b) if $R_1 = 1$, $R_2 = 3$, $C_1 = 1$, $C_2 = 3$.

CHAPTER 7

SOURCE-FREE COMBINATIONS OF ELEMENTS

To obtain the response of combinations of circuit elements to sources of arbitrary waveform, inhomogeneous differential equations must be solved. Before proceeding to such cases, circuits without sources will be examined. Without sources the behavior of circuits is determined solely by the combination of the passive circuit elements. The solution of such problems will therefore give us insight into the natural behavior of circuits.

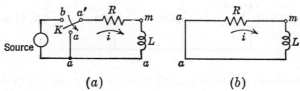

FIG. 7-1. Deenergizing an R-L branch. (a) Switching operation. (b) Source-free circuit.

7-1. The Source-free R-L Circuit. Consider the circuit shown in Fig. 7-1a, with the switch in position b. At $t = 0$ the (ideal) switch is thrown to position a, so that

(a) at $t = 0^-$, switch in position b, source is connected;

(b) at $t = 0^+$, switch in position a, source is disconnected.

The circuit for all $t > 0$ is shown in Fig. 7-1b. Since the source was connected prior to $t = 0$, there will in general be some current flowing in the inductance at $t = 0^-$. Let this current be I_0; that is,

$$i(0^-) = I_0 \tag{7-1}$$

It is desired to find the value of the current at *any* instant of time after $t = 0$, that is, the equation for $i(t)$ for all $t \geq 0^+$.

Since the source is removed at $t = 0$, no new energy can be furnished to the circuit. At $t = 0^-$ energy in the amount $\frac{1}{2}LI_0{}^2$ is stored in the inductance. In an inductance the current cannot change in zero time unless an impulse of voltage takes place. In the circuit which we are considering such an impulse cannot take place. To show this, let us assume a step change of current in the circuit. This results in a step

88

change of the voltage across the resistance (v_{am}); this voltage is also the voltage across the inductance L. But a step change of current in the circuit would require an impulse of voltage across the inductance. It is seen that the assumption of a step change of current leads to a contradiction and therefore is not permissible. We conclude that no impulses take place in this circuit, so that $i(0^+) = i(0^-) = I_0$. The value of $i(0^+)$ is referred to as the *initial* condition (of i), and the statement $i(0^+) = i(0^-)$ is referred to as the *continuity* condition (of i).

Now, for $t > 0$ the current flows in the circuit of Fig. 7-1b; in particular it flows through the resistance. Since this resistance dissipates energy as the current flows through it, the current which at $t = 0^+$ is equal to I_0 must decay toward zero as the initial energy stored in the inductance is converted into heat by the resistance. The current which is associated with the gradual decay of energy stored in the inductance by dissipation of heat in the resistance is called a "transient" current. Transient phenomena occur in all circuits which contain energy-storing elements in addition to resistances.

A quantitative description of the decaying current is obtained by applying Kirchhoff's voltage law:

$$v_{am} + v_{ma} = 0 \quad \text{for } t \geq 0^+ \tag{7-2}$$

or
$$Ri + L\frac{di}{dt} = 0 \quad \text{for } t \geq 0^+ \tag{7-3}$$

Equation (7-3) is a linear homogeneous differential equation with constant coefficients (R and L are constant), of first order (since the highest derivative is the first derivative). Its solution, subject to the initial condition

$$i(0^+) = i(0^-) = I_0 \tag{7-3a}$$

represents the current $i(t)$.

It is instructive to consider the equation in the form

$$\frac{di}{dt} = -\frac{R}{L} i \tag{7-3b}$$

Equation (7-3b) shows that $i(t)$ is a function whose derivative is proportional to the function itself. From elementary differential calculus it is recalled that this is a definition of the *exponential function*. A "trial" solution of Eq. (7-3a) may therefore be written in the form

$$i(t) = Ae^{st} \tag{7-4}$$

In order to find s, we substitute $i(t)$ and

$$\frac{di}{dt} = sAe^{st} \tag{7-4a}$$

into Eq. (7-3b) and obtain

$$sAe^{st} = -\frac{R}{L}Ae^{st}$$

or

$$s = -\frac{R}{L} \tag{7-5}$$

The general solution of Eq. (7-3) is

$$i = Ae^{-(R/L)t} \qquad t \geq 0^+ \tag{7-6}$$

Introducing the initial condition (7-3a) into the general solution, it follows that

$$I_0 = Ae^{-(R/L)0} \qquad \text{or} \qquad A = I_0 \tag{7-7}$$

and therefore the particular solution which satisfies Kirchhoff's law and fits the initial condition of the problem described in Fig. 7-1b is

$$i(t) = I_0 e^{-(R/L)t} \qquad t \geq 0^+ \tag{7-8}$$

Note that the exponent of the solution is negative, indicating that the current decays, as was anticipated. Indeed an exact energy balance is obtained if the energy dissipated in the resistance is calculated in the interval $t = 0$ to $t = \infty$,

$$p_R(t) = i^2 R = I_0^2 Re^{-(2R/L)t} \tag{7-9}$$

$$W = \int_0^\infty I_0^2 Re^{-(2R/L)t}\, dt$$

or

$$W = \frac{I_0^2 Re^{-(2R/L)t}}{-2R/L}\bigg|_0^\infty = \tfrac{1}{2}LI_0^2 \tag{7-10}$$

so that when the current decays to zero (at $t = \infty$) all the energy which was initially stored in the inductance has been used by the resistance.

7-2. Time Constant. Before studying the waveshape of the solution (7-8) in detail, it is of value to examine the exponent $st = -(R/L)t$. This exponent must be dimensionless since the exponential function is otherwise meaningless. This is easily verified since R has the dimensions of (volts/ampere) and the inductance L is dimensionally (volts $\times$ seconds/ampere), and therefore $R/L \sim 1/\text{sec}$. The ratio L/R has thus the dimensions of time. It is called the time constant of the R-L circuit and will be denoted by the capital T:

$$\frac{L}{R} \equiv T \qquad \text{sec} \tag{7-11}$$

Introducing (7-11) in (7-8),

$$i(t) = I_0 e^{-t/T} \qquad t \geq 0^+ \tag{7-12}$$

From inspection of Eq. (7-12) we note that all R-L circuits with the same time constant will give the same waveshape of current when deenergized.

This universality of the parameter T is a matter of considerable importance which is to be explored more fully.

Consider the table of exponentials shown as Table 7-1.

TABLE 7-1

x.............	0	1	2	3	4	5	6
e^{-x}..........	1	0.37	0.14	0.05	0.018	0.0067	0.0025

Using this table in Eq. (7-12), we obtain the values shown in Table 7-2.

TABLE 7-2

t..........	0	T	$2T$	$3T$	$4T$
i..........	I_0	$0.37I_0$	$0.14I_0$	$0.05I_0$	$0.018I_0$

We note that the current decays to 37 per cent of its initial value in a time interval equal to one time constant. After three time constants the current is 5 per cent of its initial value. Since at $t = 3T$ the stored energy is then less than one-fourth of 1 per cent of its initial value (why?), it is common practice ("rule of thumb") to say that (in the absence of other specifications) the deenergizing process, while theoretically lasting to $t = \infty$, is completed for practical purposes in a time equal to three time constants.

To study the waveshape of the current $i(t)$ as given by Eq. (7-12), it is convenient to rewrite the equation in dimensionless form:

$$\frac{i(t)}{I_0} = e^{-t/T} \qquad t \geq 0^+ \qquad (7\text{-}12a)$$

This equation (7-12a) is a dimensionless or "normalized" equation; that is, i/I_0 represents the fraction of the initial value which the current has at any time. Moreover, it is convenient to regard t/T as a time variable in which time is measured not in seconds but in time constants. Introducing this notion explicitly, we may set

$$\frac{i(t)}{I_0} = y = \text{normalized current}$$

and

$$\frac{t}{T} = x = \text{normalized time}$$

Then the equation

$$y = e^{-x} \qquad (7\text{-}13)$$

represents the decay of current in any R-L circuit which is deenergized. This relationship, showing the waveshape of such a decaying current, is plotted to scale in Fig. 7-2. Note that the graph of Fig. 7-2 can be sketched quickly if the numbers $e^{-1} = 0.37$, $e^{-2} = 0.14$, $e^{-3} = 0.05$ are remembered. Since exponential decays are so frequently encountered and since the response waveforms are of such importance, the reader should practice sketching responses involving exponential decays by using the values at $t = T$, $2T$, and $3T$ (this method of sketching exponentials may be termed the "three-time-constant" method, see Prob. 7-3).

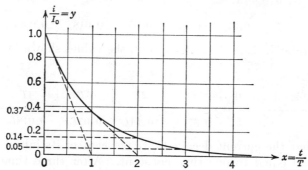

FIG. 7-2. Normalized exponential decay.

Another interpretation of the time constant is possible by considering the initial slope of

$$y = e^{-x} \qquad x \geq 0^+ \tag{7-13}$$

$$\frac{dy}{dx} = -e^{-x} \qquad x \geq 0^+ \tag{7-14}$$

Hence, at $x = 0^+$, $(t = 0^+)$,

$$\frac{dy}{dx}\bigg|_{x=0^+} = -1 \qquad \text{or} \qquad \frac{di}{dt}\bigg|_{t=0^+} = -\frac{1}{T} I_0$$

so that the slope of the normalized response curve is -1 at $x = 0^+$ and the slope of $i(t)$ is $-I_0/T$ at $t = 0^+$. Consequently, *if the current were to decay at its initial rate*, the value zero *would* be reached in a time equal to one time constant (see Prob. 7-4).

7-3. More about Initial Conditions. Consider again the circuit and the switching operation indicated by Fig. 7-1. Let it now be required to solve for the voltage $v_{ma}(t)$. One method of solution is to solve for the current as was done earlier,

$$i_{ma}(t) = I_0 e^{-(R/L)t} \qquad t \geq 0^+ \tag{7-8}$$

and, by using the definition of inductance,

$$v_{ma} = L\frac{di_{ma}}{dt} = -RI_0 e^{-(R/L)t} \qquad t \geq 0^+ \tag{7-15}$$

It is noted that $v_{ma} = -Ri$, so that the formal differentiation is unnecessary. Note also that in this case the product of $v_{ma}i_{ma}$ is negative for the inductance so that the inductance acts as a nonideal source, furnishing energy to the resistance.   For a resistance the power is always positive.

Another important observation must be made here.   In solving for the current the initial value $i(0^+)$ had to be equal to the value $i(0^-)$ because of the initial energy storage in the inductance.   From the solution (7-12) we note that

$$v_{ma}(0^+) \; = \; -RI_0 \; = \; L\left(\frac{di}{dt}\right)_{0^+}$$

but we have *no* information concerning $(di/dt)_{0^-}$.   We conclude again that the rate of change of current in an inductance (or the voltage across it) *can* and *does* change discontinuously.   If, for example, the source in Fig. 7-1 was a constant current source of value I_0 so that $(di/dt)_{0^-} = 0$, we note that $(di/dt)_{0^+} \neq 0$.

While the initial value of di/dt is not the same just before and just after switching, the value of this initial derivative after switching is not arbitrary but is determined by the differential equation *and* by the initial value of the current.   Recalling the differential equation for all $t > 0$,

$$L\frac{di}{dt} \; = \; -Ri \qquad t > 0 \tag{7-3b}$$

At $t = 0^+$, $i(0^+) = I_0$; therefore

$$L\left(\frac{di}{dt}\right)_{t=0^+} \; = \; -RI_0$$

or
$$\left(\frac{di}{dt}\right)_{0^+} \; = \; -\frac{R}{L}I_0 \; = \; -\frac{1}{T}I_0 \tag{7-16}$$

The condition on the initial value of di/dt as obtained above is called a *derived* initial condition.   We use the term derived initial condition to distinguish between initial conditions which depend on continuity and conditions which are deduced from the continuity conditions in conjunction with the Kirchhoff's-law equations for the circuit.   Thus, in the example which is under consideration, the condition $i(0^+) = i(0^-)$ is a continuity initial condition because it follows from the continuity of the stored energy (in the absence of impulses).   The value of the current in the inductance at the instant (0^+) depends *only* on the value of the current in the inductance at the instant (0^-).   On the other hand, the value of the voltage across the inductance (and the value of derivative di/dt) at the instant (0^+) depends both on the value $i(0^+)$ and on the value of the elements, that is, R or L in this example.   Now it is quite clear that in this very simple circuit one can always follow the procedure of solving for $i(t)$ and then differentiating to find di/dt.   However, it is important to recognize, even in this simple example, that the continuity condition can always be used to obtain other initial values; in more complicated circuits derived initial conditions become very useful.

An immediate, though somewhat trivial, application of such a derived initial condition would be the solution of the problem defined by Fig. 7-1 for $v_{ma}(t)$. Recalling that derivatives and integrals of the exponential functions are proportional to each other, instead of assuming a solution of the form $i(t) = Ae^{st}$, one may start with

$$v_{ma}(t) = Be^{st} = L\frac{di}{dt}$$

$$i(t) = \frac{1}{L}\int Be^{st}\,dt$$

$$(7-17)$$

and substitute in the differential equation of the circuit, $Ri + L\,(di/dt) = 0$.

Therefore $$\frac{R}{L}\int Be^{st}\,dt + Be^{st} = 0 \qquad (7\text{-}18a)$$

$$\frac{R}{sL}Be^{st} + Be^{st} = 0$$

$$\frac{R}{sL} + 1 = 0 \qquad (7\text{-}18b)$$

and again $$s = -\frac{R}{L} \qquad (7\text{-}18c)$$

so that $$v_{ma}(t) = Be^{-(R/L)t} = Be^{-t/T} \qquad (7\text{-}19)$$

Using Eq. (7-16),

$$v_{ma}(0^+) = L\left(\frac{di}{dt}\right)_{0^+} = -RI_0 = B \qquad (7\text{-}20)$$

so that the result shown previously in Eq. (7-15) is obtained *directly without first solving for the current*. Note that the waveshape of the voltage v_{ma} is also an exponential decay, and the universal graph of Fig. 7-2 can be used if the y axis is reinterpreted. It is now clear that any electrical quantity in this source-free circuit, or its rate of change, will decay proportionally to $e^{-t/T}$. For this reason the value $s = -1/T$ is called the *characteristic root* of the source-free circuit, and the equation which defines this value [Eq. (7-18b) or Eq. (7-5)] is called the *characteristic equation* for the source-free circuit.

Returning to the subject of initial values, consider again Eq. (7-3b),

$$\frac{di}{dt} = -\frac{1}{T}\,i \qquad t \geq 0^+ \qquad (7\text{-}3b)$$

Since this equation holds for all $t \geq 0^+$, its derivative also holds for all $t \geq 0^+$:

$$\frac{d^2i}{dt^2} = -\frac{1}{T}\frac{di}{dt} \qquad t \geq 0^+ \qquad (7\text{-}21)$$

We may differentiate as often as we like:

$$\frac{d^n i}{dt^n} = -\frac{1}{T}\frac{d^{n-1}i}{dt^{n-1}} \qquad t \geq 0 \qquad (7\text{-}22)$$

Hence, setting $t = 0^+$, we have

$$i(0^+) = I_0$$

$$\left(\frac{di}{dt}\right)_{0^+} = \left(-\frac{1}{T}\right) I_0$$

$$\left(\frac{d^2i}{dt^2}\right)_{0^+} = \left(-\frac{1}{T}\right)^2 I_0$$

$$\cdot \qquad \cdot$$
$$\cdot \qquad \cdot \qquad\qquad\qquad (7\text{-}23)$$
$$\cdot \qquad \cdot$$

$$\left(\frac{d^n i}{dt^n}\right)_{0^+} = \left(-\frac{1}{T}\right)^n I_0$$

The relationships shown in Eqs. (7-23) illustrate that any desired number of derived initial conditions for the rates of change of the unknown (i) can be obtained by combining the differential equation with the original initial condition as obtained from the continuity of the stored energy.

The expressions for these derived initial conditions can be used to illustrate the dependence of the solutions on these initial values.   Equation (7-23) gives the value of a function $i(t)$ at one instant of time ($t = 0^+$) and the value of all the derivatives of this function at $t = 0^+$.   This recalls the special case of Taylor's series, called Maclaurin's series, from mathematics:

$$f(x) = f(0) + f'(0)x + \frac{1}{2!} f''(0)x^2 + \frac{1}{3!} f'''(0)x^3 + \cdot \cdot \cdot \qquad (7\text{-}24)$$

Identifying f with i and x with t,

$$i(t) = I_0 + \left(-\frac{1}{T}\right) I_0 t + \left(-\frac{1}{T}\right)^2 \frac{I_0 t^2}{2!} + \left(-\frac{1}{T}\right)^3 I_0 \frac{t^3}{3!} + \cdot \cdot \cdot \quad (7\text{-}25)$$

Factoring I_0 from (7-25),

$$i(t) = I_0 \left[1 + \left(-\frac{t}{T}\right) + \frac{(-t/T)^2}{2!} + \frac{(-t/T)^3}{3!} + \frac{(-t/T)^n}{n!} + \cdot \cdot \cdot \right]$$
$$(7\text{-}26)$$

The expression in the brackets of Eq. (7-26) is recognized as the power-series definition of the exponential function

$$i(t) = I_0 e^{-t/T} \qquad\qquad\qquad (7\text{-}26a)$$

The example just completed was not intended to illustrate a convenient, practical method of solving the original circuit equation.   It was included here to show how the initial values and all the rates of change at one instant (as defined by the differential equation of the circuit) determine uniquely the value of the variable at *any* subsequent instant of time.

7-4. The Source-free R-C Circuit. Consider the circuit shown in Fig. 7-3. At $t = 0^-$ the switch K is in position b. At $t = 0$ the switch is thrown to position a so that the circuit for $t > 0$ is that shown in Fig. 7-3b. Let it be assumed that, owing to the source, there was at $t = 0^-$ a voltage across the capacitance $v_{ma}(0^-) = V_0$ so that the charge on the m

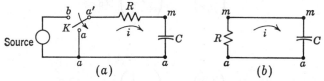

FIG. 7-3. Deenergizing an R-C circuit.

side of the capacitance C at $t = 0^-$ is $CV_0 = Q_0$. The energy stored in (the electric field of) the capacitance is given by

$$w = \tfrac{1}{2}Cv_{ma}^2 = \frac{1}{2C}\,q_m{}^2 \tag{7-27}$$

For a capacitance the general initial condition (in the absence of impulses of current) is

$$q_m(0^-) = q_m(0^+) = Q_0$$
or
$$v_{ma}(0^-) = v_{ma}(0^+) = V_0 \tag{7-28}$$

Let it be required to solve for the charge $q_m(t)$ for all $t \geq 0^+$. With the switch in position a Kirchhoff's voltage law reads

$$v_{am} + v_{ma} = 0 \tag{7-29}$$

or
$$Ri + \frac{1}{C}\,q_m = 0 \tag{7-29a}$$

Since
$$i_{ma} = \frac{dq_m}{dt} \tag{7-30}$$

one obtains the differential equation for the charge q_m,

$$\frac{1}{C}\,q_m + R\frac{dq_m}{dt} = 0 \tag{7-31}$$

subject to the initial condition $q_m(0^+) = q_m(0^-) = Q_0$. Comparing Eq. (7-31) with the equation of the R-L circuit [Eq. (7-3)], one notes that the form is identical but that the dependent variable is now q_m in place of i and the parameters R and L are replaced by $1/C$ and R, respectively.

The solution can be written down by analogy or by using the same formal procedure,

$$q_m = Ae^{st}$$
$$\frac{dq_m}{dt} = sAe^{st} \tag{7-32}$$

so that
$$\frac{1}{C} + sR = 0 \tag{7-33}$$

is the characteristic equation of this source-free circuit. The characteristic root of the source-free circuit is

$$s = -\frac{1}{RC} \equiv -\frac{1}{T}$$

Therefore $\quad\quad\quad\quad q_m = A e^{-t/RC}$ (7-34)

but $\quad\quad\quad q_m(0^-) = q_m(0^+) = Q_0 = A$ (7-35)

so that the final solution is

$$q_m = Q_0 e^{-t/RC} \quad\quad t \geq 0^+ \quad\quad\quad (7\text{-}36a)$$

or $\quad\quad\quad\quad v_{ma} = V_0 e^{-t/RC} \quad\quad t \geq 0^+ \quad\quad\quad (7\text{-}36b)$

Again the graph of Fig. 7-2 may be used to represent a response waveform. The abscissa x is interpreted as t/RC, and the ordinate y is defined as q_m/Q_0 or v_{ma}/V_0.

The current $i(t)$ may be found as dq_m/dt,

$$i(t) = \frac{d}{dt} Q_0 e^{-t/RC} \quad\quad\quad (7\text{-}37)$$

or $\quad\quad\quad i(t) = -\frac{Q_0}{RC} e^{-t/RC} = -\frac{V_0}{R} e^{-t/RC} \quad\quad\quad (7\text{-}38)$

Alternatively a derived initial condition may be used. Since the voltage across C *cannot* change instantaneously (because of the stored energy), the voltage across the resistance $v_{ma}(0^+) = V_0$ and $i_{am}(0^+) = -V_0/R$. The equation for the current is

$$Ri + \frac{1}{C} \int i \, dt = 0 \quad\quad\quad (7\text{-}39)$$

If $\quad\quad\quad\quad i = Be^{st}$ (7-40)

$$R + \frac{1}{sC} = 0 \quad\quad\quad (7\text{-}41)$$

giving again[1]

$$s = -\frac{1}{RC} = -\frac{1}{T} \quad\quad\quad (7\text{-}41a)$$

so that $\quad\quad\quad i = Be^{-t/T} \quad\quad\quad t \geq 0^+$

Since $i(0^+) = -V_0/R = B$,

$$i = -\frac{V_0}{R} e^{-t/T} \quad\quad t \geq 0^+$$

Note again that the current through a capacitance *can* change discontinuously while the voltage across it cannot do so (unless there is an impulse of current). On comparing this statement with the corresponding statement concerning an inductance, the principle of duality is again evident.

Returning to the solution for $i(t) = (-V_0/R)e^{-t/RC}$ for $t > 0$, the reason for the minus sign is evident. It means that, since a positive value for the current in the assumed direction charges the side m with positive

---

[1] The constant of integration which is implicit in $\int Be^{st} \, dt$ is set to zero, since a finite constant cannot satisfy Eq. (7-39).

charge, $i(t)$ must have a negative value (if V_0 is positive) so that the capacitance discharges. For the waveform of the solution the universal curve (Fig. 7-2) again applies with redefined ordinate and abscissa.

7-5. Conclusions Concerning Circuits with One Energy-storing Element. *Initial Conditions.* In the absence of impulses the current through an inductance cannot change instantaneously, while the voltage across it may do so. The voltage (or charge) across a capacitance cannot change instantaneously, while the current through it may do so. The continuity initial condition may always be combined with the Kirchhoff's-law equations to derive other initial values.

Waveshape of Response. The waveshape of the deenergizing response is a decaying exponential curve. The time constant (RC or L/R) is a measure of the speed at which the voltage across a capacitance or the current through an inductance may change. At this point some simple

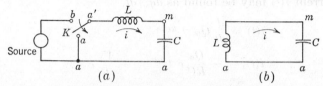

Fig. 7-4. Deenergizing an L-C circuit.

applications of these principles may be mentioned. For example, in an electronic rectifier it is desirable to eliminate fluctuations of current and voltage so as to make the rectifier a constant voltage source. This is accomplished by *series* inductances and *parallel* capacitances, forming a "filter" for a rectifier. On the other hand, in many applications rapid variations of voltage or current are desirable (e.g., television amplifiers). Then the time constants are minimized, and series inductances or parallel capacitances are made as small as is practicable.

7-6. Deenergizing of an L-C Circuit. Since in all electrical devices a certain amount of energy is transformed into heat, a circuit containing no resistive element does not correspond to any physical device. Nevertheless, the study of circuits containing only L and C is instructive because this combination represents the simplest type of circuit in which both types of energy storage are present.

In the circuit shown in Fig. 7-4a the switch K is in position b at $t = 0^-$. At $t = 0$ the switch is thrown to position a. Assume that owing to the source the charge on the m side of the capacitance C is

$$q_m(0^-) = Q_0 \tag{7-42}$$

and that the current in the inductance L is

$$i(0^-) = I_0 \tag{7-43}$$

It is now desired to find $q_m(t)$ and $i(t)$ for all t after $t = 0$.

The stored energy in the inductance just before switching is

$$w_L(0^-) = \tfrac{1}{2}LI_0{}^2$$

and the stored energy in the capacitance at that instant is

$$w_C(0^-) = \frac{1}{2C}Q_0{}^2$$

Neither w_L nor w_C can change in zero time. (Why?) Consequently the correct solution of the circuit problem will have to satisfy the initial conditions

$$i(0^-) = i(0^+) = I_0$$
$$q_m(0^-) = q_m(0^+) = Q_0$$

$$(7\text{-}44)$$

After switching consider the circuit shown in Fig. 7-4b. To find the function $q_m(t)$ apply Kirchhoff's voltage law to this circuit.

$$v_{ma} + v_{am} = 0 \tag{7-45}$$

But
$$v_{ma} = -L\frac{di}{dt} \tag{7-46}$$

where
$$i = \frac{dq_m}{dt} \tag{7-47}$$

so that
$$v_{ma} = -L\frac{d^2q_m}{dt^2} \tag{7-48}$$

Since
$$q_a = -q_m \tag{7-49}$$

$$v_{am} = -\frac{q_m}{C} \tag{7-50}$$

The differential equation for the charge $q_m(t)$ is therefore

$$L\frac{d^2q_m}{dt^2} + \frac{1}{C}q_m = 0 \tag{7-51}$$

or
$$\frac{d^2q_m}{dt^2} + \frac{1}{LC}q_m = 0 \tag{7-51a}$$

Equation (7-51) or (7-51a) is a linear second-order homogeneous differential equation with constant coefficients. Note that $1/LC$ must have the dimensions of (time)$^{-2}$ or (seconds)$^{-2}$ in the mks system of units. Abbreviate

$$\frac{1}{LC} = \omega_0{}^2 \tag{7-52}$$

Then
$$\frac{d^2q_m}{dt^2} + \omega_0{}^2q_m = 0 \tag{7-53}$$

Before proceeding to a formal solution of this differential equation, a physical examination of the energy processes is instructive. Suppose at

$t = 0$ there is no current flowing in the circuit but that there is a voltage across the capacitance; $v_{ma}(0) = V_0$. Since, from $t = 0$ on, the inductance is also connected between terminals a-m, the voltage V_0 will be across the inductance at $t = 0$. Hence the current through the inductance will change because the voltage across an inductance is proportional to the rate of change of the current through it. Now, as the current through the inductance grows, the stored energy in the inductance grows so that the stored energy in the capacitance must decrease, since the total stored energy in the circuit cannot exceed the initial energy in the capacitance. Eventually, a time is reached at which all the energy which was stored in the capacitance at $t = 0$ has been transferred and is stored in the inductance. At that instant v_{ma} will be zero (since w_C will be zero), but the current $i(t)$ will have a value. Hence this current will again carry charges to the capacitance and the stored energy will return from L to C. Now in this energy-transfer process no energy is lost since the circuit contains no resistance (resistance is the only passive element which can make energy unavailable to the rest of the circuit elements). We anticipate, therefore, on physical grounds, that the source-free response of the L-C circuit will involve a periodic interchange of stored energy between inductance and capacitance for all time after $t = 0$.

Returning now to Eq. (7-53), we proceed with the analysis by interpreting the equation in words: The function $q_m(t)$ has the property of having a second derivative which has the same waveshape as the function itself. This is a property not only of the exponential function but also of sine and cosine functions. In the present example it is, at this point, convenient to assume the latter form of solutions.

Let

$$q_m(t) = A \cos \alpha t \qquad \text{or} \qquad q_m(t) = B \sin \beta t \qquad (7\text{-}54)$$

Then
$$\frac{d^2 q_m(t)}{dt^2} = -\alpha^2 A \cos \alpha t \qquad \text{or} \qquad \frac{d^2 q_m}{dt^2} = -\beta^2 B \sin \beta t \qquad (7\text{-}55)$$

Substituting the trial solutions (7-54) and (7-55) in (7-53),

$$-\alpha^2 q_m(t) + \omega_0^2 q_m(t) = 0 \qquad \text{or} \qquad -\beta^2 q_m(t) + \omega_0^2 q_m(t) = 0 \qquad (7\text{-}56)$$

Since (7-56) must hold for all t $[q_m(t) \equiv 0$ is a trivial solution], we have

$$\alpha = \beta = \omega_0 \qquad (7\text{-}57)$$

and the two possible solutions of Eq. (7-53) are

$$q_m(t) = A \cos \omega_0 t \qquad \text{or} \qquad B \sin \omega_0 t \qquad (7\text{-}58)$$

If two functions are solutions of a homogeneous linear differential equation, then any linear combination of these solutions is also a solution. Hence the equation

$$q_m(t) = A \cos \omega_0 t + B \sin \omega_0 t \qquad (7\text{-}59)$$

is a solution of the differential equation (7-53). [The reader should verify this by substituting (7-59) into (7-53).] Note that this solution contains two constants (A and B) which are to be evaluated by means of the two initial conditions.   (Note further that the number of undetermined constants is equal to the number of initial conditions and equal to the order of the differential equation.)

Since the initial conditions involve the current, Eq. (7-59) is differentiated:

$$i(t) = \frac{dq_m}{dt} = -\omega_0 A \sin \omega_0 t + \omega_0 B \cos \omega_0 t \qquad (7\text{-}60)$$

To evaluate A and B, use the initial conditions (7-42) and (7-43) in the solutions (7-59) and (7-60), respectively:

$$Q_0 = A \cos 0 + B \sin 0 = A$$
$$I_0 = -\omega_0 A \sin 0 + \omega_0 B \cos 0 = \omega_0 B \qquad (7\text{-}61)$$

so that $\qquad\qquad A = Q_0 \qquad$ and $\qquad B = \dfrac{I_0}{\omega_0} \qquad (7\text{-}61a)$

The complete solution is now formulated as

$$q_m(t) = Q_0 \cos \omega_0 t + \frac{I_0}{\omega_0} \sin \omega_0 t \qquad (7\text{-}62)$$

and $\qquad\qquad i(t) = -\omega_0 Q_0 \sin \omega_0 t + I_0 \cos \omega_0 t \qquad (7\text{-}63)$

7-7. Waveform of L-C Circuit Response. The form of the solution for the charge and the current is seen to be the sum of two sinusoidal functions.   To study a typical waveform, it is sufficient to consider the example

$$I_0 = 0 \qquad Q_0 \neq 0 \qquad (7\text{-}64)$$

Physically this may represent the case of connecting an inductance across a charged capacitance.   The relations (7-62) and (7-63) then have the form

$$q_m(t) = Q_0 \cos \omega_0 t \qquad t \geq 0^+ \qquad (7\text{-}65)$$
$$i(t) = -\omega_0 Q_0 \sin \omega_0 t \qquad t \geq 0^+ \qquad (7\text{-}66)$$

The waveforms for $q_m(t)$ and $i(t)$ are shown in Fig. 7-5a and b, respectively.   These diagrams show oscillations at a radian frequency ω_0 (or at a frequency $\omega_0/2\pi$ cps).   Referring to Fig. 7-4b at $t = 0$, $q_m(0^+) = Q_0$; hence $v_{ma}(0^+) = Q_0/C = V_0$.   If Q_0 is taken as a positive number, then the initial rate of change of current is found to be negative and is

$$\left.\frac{di}{dt}\right)_{t=0^+} = -\frac{V_0}{L} \qquad (7\text{-}67)$$

Hence positive charges move, at $t = 0^+$, from m to a through the inductance and neutralize the negative charges on the a side of capacitance C.

Referring to Fig. 7-5a and b, from $\omega_0 t = 0$ to $\omega_0 t = \pi/2$ the magnitude of the current rises, and q_m is diminished. Since

$$v_{ma} = \frac{q_m}{C} \tag{7-68}$$

the waveform of v_{ma} is proportional to that of $q_m(t)$ and is shown in Fig. 7-5c. At $\omega_0 t = \pi/2$ the current has reached its minimum but

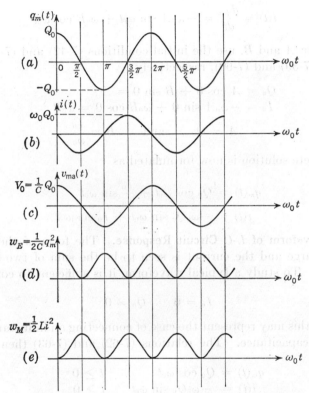

Fig. 7-5. Waveforms in the L-C circuit for $I_0 = 0$, $Q_0 > 0$.

$(v_{ma})_{\omega_0 t = \pi/2} = 0$, since $(q_m)_{\omega_0 t = \pi/2} = 0$ and also $(di/dt)_{\omega_0 t = \pi/2} = 0$. The current in the inductance L will continue to flow, depositing positive charges on the a side of the capacitance C and making v_{ma} negative. The increasing positive charge deposited on side a of the capacitance C causes the magnitude of the current to decrease, and $i = 0$ at $\omega_0 t = \pi$ when $(v_{ma})_{\omega_0 t = \pi} = -V_0$.

Since a is now positive with respect to m and the current in the inductance is zero, the positive charges will start flowing from a to m and the current i becomes positive. Similar reasoning will show that the current will rise to a maximum at $\omega_0 t = 3(\pi/2)$ and fall to zero at $\omega_0 t = 2\pi$, as shown in Fig. 7-5b.

The energy stored in the electric field is

$$w_E = \frac{1}{2}\frac{q_m{}^2}{C} = \frac{1}{2C}\,Q_0{}^2\cos^2\omega_0 t \qquad (7\text{-}69)$$

or

$$w_E = \frac{Q_0{}^2}{4C}\,(1 + \cos 2\omega_0 t) \qquad (7\text{-}70)$$

This is sketched in Fig. 7-5d.   It is noted that the stored energy is always positive and varies with twice the radian frequency of the circuit.

The energy stored in the magnetic field is

$$w_M = \tfrac{1}{2}Li^2(t) = \tfrac{1}{2}L\omega_0{}^2 Q_0{}^2\sin^2\omega_0 t$$

$$= \tfrac{1}{2}L\,\frac{1}{LC}\,Q_0{}^2\sin^2\omega_0 t$$

$$= \frac{Q_0{}^2}{4C}\,(1 - \cos 2\omega_0 t) \qquad (7\text{-}71)$$

The energy stored in the magnetic field is also positive, and its varying component has a radian frequency of $2\omega_0$.   The waveform of (7-71) is shown in Fig. 7-5e.   The total energy stored in the circuit is

$$w_M + w_E = \frac{Q_0{}^2}{2C} \qquad (7\text{-}72)$$

This is equal to the initial value of the energy (which was assumed stored in the capacitance).

Since there is no resistive element in the L-C circuit, there is no time constant associated with such a circuit.   Instead the circuit is characterized by the natural radian frequency $\omega_0 = 1/\sqrt{LC}$ (radians per second). The oscillations of the current and voltage in the circuit are at this natural angular frequency of the circuit.

7-8. A Mechanical Analogue.   At this point it is interesting to recall that sinusoidal oscillations occur commonly in mechanics.   Consider, for example, the mechanical system shown in Fig. 7-6.

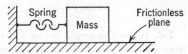

Fig. 7-6. A mechanical analogue of an L-C circuit.

If the mass M is displaced, then the restoring force of the linear spring will act upon it in accordance with Newton's laws:

$$M\,\frac{d^2x}{dt^2} = -Kx \qquad (7\text{-}73)$$

This equation is identical to the equation of the L-C circuit [(7-51)]; only the symbols have different meaning.   This system will oscillate at the radian frequency $\omega_0 = \sqrt{K/M}$. The energy interchange will be between the potential energy stored in the stretched (or compressed) spring and the kinetic energy of the mass.

PROBLEMS

7-1. For a source-free R-L circuit plot on the same set of axes $i(t)/i(0^+)$ and $w_L(t)/w_L(0^+)$ as a function of Rt/L (w_L is the stored energy in the inductance).

7-2. In a source-free R-L circuit what fraction of the initial stored energy is left in the inductance when the current is 50 per cent of its initial value?

7-3. In a source-free R-L circuit $R = 10, L = 3$. At $t = 0.3$ sec the voltage across the inductance is 100 volts. Calculate the initial value of the stored energy.

7-4. (a) An R-L circuit is deenergized at $t = 0$ so that $i(0^+) = I_0$. Show that if the current were to decay at a constant rate, equal to the initial rate, then the value zero could be reached at $t = T = L/R$. (b) If in the circuit of (a), at $t = t_1 > 0$, the current changed from an exponential to a linear decay at a rate equal to $(di/dt)_{t=t_1}$, at which instant would $i = 0$?

7-5. (a) In the circuit of Fig. P7-5 the switch is thrown from position 1 to position 2 at $t = 0$. Calculate $v_{ab}(t)$ for all $t > 0^+$ if $i(0^-) = 1$ amp. (b) In the schematic diagram given in Fig. P7-5 the series combination of the 100-ohm resistance and the 10-henry inductance represents the equivalent circuit of the field coil of a generator. The 10,000-ohm resistance represents a voltmeter rated at 0/150 volts. Comment on the practical suitability of the switching operation, and suggest an alternate method for connecting the voltmeter.

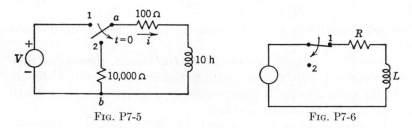

FIG. P7-5   FIG. P7-6

7-6. When a practical device which is represented by an R-L circuit is disconnected from a source at $t = 0$ so that no closed path exists for $t > 0$, an arc will occur across the switch, as shown in Fig. P7-6. Explain.

7-7. In the circuit shown in Fig. P7-7 $i(0^+) = 2$ amp. Switch K is open until $t = 2$. At $t = 2$ the switch is closed. (a) Calculate and plot $i(t)$ for all $t \geq 0^+$. (b) Calculate and plot $v_{ab}(t)$ for all $t \geq 0^+$.

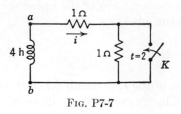

FIG. P7-7

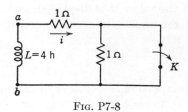

FIG. P7-8

7-8. In the circuit shown in Fig. P7-8 $i(0^+) = 2$ amp. Switch K is closed until $t = 2$. At $t = 2$ the switch is opened. Calculate and plot $i(t)$ and $v_{ab}(t)$ for all $t \geq 0^+$.

7-9. In the circuit shown in Fig. P7-9 $i(0^+) = 1$ amp. Calculate the following initial values: (a) $v_{bn}(0^+)$; (b) $v_{ab}(0^+)$; (c) $i_1(0^+)$; (d) $(di/dt)_{0^+}$.

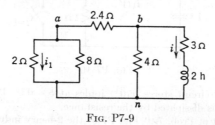

FIG. P7-9

7-10. What is the time constant of the circuit given in Prob. 7-9 (Fig. P7-9)?

7-11. In the circuit shown in Fig. P7-11 $i(0^+) = 2$ amp. (a) Calculate $v_{ab}(0^+)$. (b) Calculate and sketch $v_{ab}(t)$ for all $t \geq 0^+$.

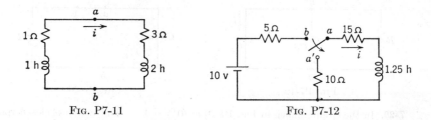

FIG. P7-11   FIG. P7-12

7-12. In the circuit shown in Fig. P7-12 $i(0^+) = 0.5$ amp. The switch is thrown from position b to a' at $t = 0$. Calculate the voltage across the open switch v_{ba} for all $t \geq 0^+$, and sketch the result.

7-13. A capacitance of 10 μf is charged to 100 volts at $t = 0$ and connected across a resistance R. It is desired that at $t = \frac{1}{2}$ sec the voltage across the capacitance be no more than 60 volts and no less than 50 volts. Calculate the allowed range of the value of R.

7-14. In the circuit shown in Fig. P7-14 $v_{ab}(0^+) = 50$. Calculate the initial values: (a) $i(0^+)$; (b) $(dv_{ab}/dt)_{0^+}$; (c) $(d^2v_{ab}/dt^2)_{0^+}$.

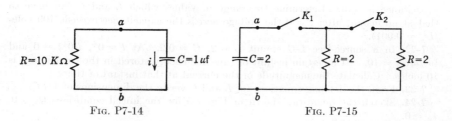

FIG. P7-14   FIG. P7-15

7-15. In the circuit shown in Fig. P7-15 $v_{ab}(0^+) = 10$. Switch K_1 is closed at $t = 0$, switch K_2 is closed at $t = 6$. Calculate and sketch $v_{ab}(t)$ for all $t \geq 0^+$.

7-16. In the circuit shown in Fig. P7-16 $i(t) = 2$ at $t = 1^-$. At $t = 1$ the switch is opened. Calculate and sketch $i(t)$ and $v_{ab}(t)$ for all $t \geq 1^+$.

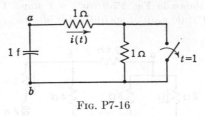

FIG. P7-16

7-17. A series R-C circuit stores $w(0^+)$ joules at $t = 0^+$. Prove that eventually all the stored energy is dissipated by the resistance.

7-18. In the circuit of Prob. 7-9 (Fig. P7-9) the 2-henry inductance is replaced by a 2-farad capacitance. Calculate the time constant of this new circuit.

7-19. In the circuit shown in Fig. P7-19 $v_{ab}(0^+) = V_0$. Obtain the expression for $i_2(t)$ for all $t \geq 0^+$.

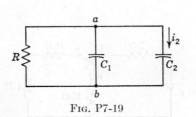

FIG. P7-19

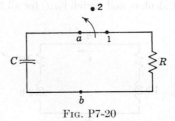

FIG. P7-20

7-20. In the circuit shown in Fig. P7-20 $v_{ab}(0^+) = V_0$. The switch is closed (position 1) at $t = 0$ and opened (position 2) at $t = RC$. Calculate and sketch $v_{ab}(t)/V_0$ for all $t/RC \geq 0^+$.

7-21. (a) In a source-free L-C circuit the initial value of the stored energy in the inductance $w_L(0^+) = W_L$, and the initial value of the stored energy in the capacitance $w_C(0^+) = W_c$. Use the law of conservation of energy to show that the maximum value of the current is $i_{max} = [2(W_L + W_c)/L]^{\frac{1}{2}}$ and the maximum value of the voltage across the capacitance is $v_{max} = [2(W_L + W_c)/C]^{\frac{1}{2}}$. (b) In a source-free L-C circuit the initial value of the voltage across the capacitance is 100 volts, and the initial value of the current is zero. It is desired that $LC = 0.001$ and that at no instant after $t = 0$ the current exceed 0.2 amp. Calculate the range of values which L and C can have. (c) In the circuit of (b), $i(0^+) = 0.5$, and the initial value of the voltage across the capacitance is zero. Determine the range of values which L and C can have so that at no instant after $t = 0$ the voltage across the capacitance exceeds 100 volts ($LC = 0.001$).

7-22. In a source-free L-C circuit $L = 2$, $C = 0.2$. At $t = 0^+$, $i(0^+) = 0$ and $(di/dt)_{0^+} = 10$. At a certain instant of time the energy stored in the capacitance is 10 joules. Calculate the magnitude of the current at that instant of time.

7-23. From the defining equations for L and C verify the dimensions of $1/LC$.

7-24. Sketch the quantities shown in Fig. 7-5 for the initial conditions $Q_0 = 0$, $I_0 \neq 0$.

7-25. In the source-free L-C circuit shown in Fig. P7-25 it is known that $C = 0.4$ and that $v_{ab} = 10 \cos (5t - 30°)$. (a) Calculate $v_{ab}(0^+)$. (b) Calculate $i(0^+)$. (c) Calculate L.

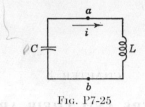

Fig. P7-25

7-26. In an L-C circuit $\omega_0 = 1,000$, $L = 0.5$ henry, the initial values are $Q_0 = 500$ μcoulomb, $I_0 = (dq/dt)_{0^+} = 2$ amp. Calculate (a) the first instant after $t = 0$ when the voltage across C is zero; (b) the maximum value of the voltage across the capacitance; (c) the first instant after $t = 0$ when the condition of (b) occurs. (d) What is the energy stored in each element at (1) $t = 0$; (2) $t = 0.001$ sec; (3) $t = 0.004$ sec?

7-27. In the circuit shown in Fig. P7-27 the switch is in position 1 from $t = 0$ to $t = 1$. At $t = 1$ the switch is thrown to position 2. If $v_{ab}(0^+) = 10$ volts and $i_L = 0$ for $t \leq 1^-$, calculate and sketch $v_{ab}(t)$ for all $t \geq 0^+$.

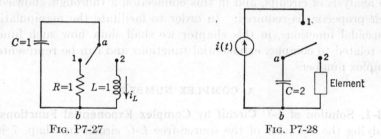

Fig. P7-27   Fig. P7-28

7-28. In the circuit shown in Fig. P7-28 $i(t) = tU(t)$. The switch is in position 1 from $t = 0$ to $t = 3$. At $t = 3$ the switch is thrown to position 2. It is also known that $v_{ab}(0^+) = 0$. Calculate and sketch $v_{ab}(t)$ for all $t \geq 0^+$ if the element is (a) a resistance $R = 1$; (b) an initially deenergized inductance $L = 1$.

7-29. Show that the electrical analogue of a pendulum (for small displacements) is an L-C circuit.

COMPLEX NUMBERS AND THEIR APPLICATION TO SINUSOIDAL TIME FUNCTIONS

In the previous chapter we found that the response of a source-free L-C circuit had a sinusoidal waveform. Sinusoids appear frequently in the analysis of circuits, and in this connection a thorough knowledge of their properties is required. In order to facilitate the manipulation of sinusoidal functions, in this chapter we shall show how such functions are related to complex exponential functions and can be represented by complex numbers.

A. COMPLEX NUMBERS

8-1. Solution of L-C Circuit by Complex Exponential Functions. In studying the behavior of the source-free L-C circuit in Chap. 7 it was mentioned that the solution of the differential equation could be carried through in exponential form.

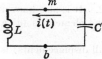

Consider now, as an example, the circuit shown in Fig. 8-1, and assume the special initial conditions

FIG. 8-1. Source-free L-C circuit.

$$q_m(0^+) = Q_0 \qquad (8\text{-}1)$$
$$i(0^+) = 0 \qquad (8\text{-}2)$$

In words, an initially charged capacitance is "discharged" through an inductance. The equilibrium equation for the charge $q_m(t)$ is

$$\frac{d^2 q_m}{dt^2} + \omega_0{}^2 q_m = 0 \qquad (8\text{-}3)$$

Assume the solution of the exponential form

$$q_m(t) = A e^{st} \qquad (8\text{-}4)$$

where s is independent of time. Substituting Eq. (8-4) and its second derivative with respect to time in Eq. (8-3), we obtain

$$s^2 q_m(t) + \omega_0{}^2 q_m(t) = 0 \qquad (8\text{-}5)$$

which results in the characteristic equation

$$s^2 + \omega_0{}^2 = 0 \qquad (8\text{-}6)$$

or
$$s^2 = -\omega_0{}^2 \qquad (8\text{-}7)$$

Since $\omega_0{}^2 = 1/LC$ is a positive number, s^2 must be a negative number. Rewriting,

$$s^2 = (-1)\omega_0{}^2 \tag{8-8}$$

and defining the "imaginary" number j,

$$j^2 = -1 \qquad j = +\sqrt{-1} \tag{8-9}$$

the two solutions of the characteristic equation are

$$s_{1,2} = \pm j\omega_0$$

We now write

$$q_m(t) = Ae^{j\omega_0 t} + Be^{-j\omega_0 t} \tag{8-10}$$

and

$$i(t) = -\frac{dq_m}{dt} = -(j\omega_0 Ae^{j\omega_0 t} - j\omega_0 Be^{-j\omega_0 t}) \tag{8-11}$$

In Eqs. (8-10) and (8-11) the constants A and B are evaluated from the initial conditions

$$Q_0 = A + B$$
$$0 = -j\omega_0 A + j\omega_0 B$$

so that

$$A = B = \tfrac{1}{2}Q_0$$

And so the solution for $q_m(t)$ may be written

$$q_m(t) = Q_0 \frac{e^{j\omega_0 t} + e^{-j\omega_0 t}}{2} \tag{8-12}$$

From the previous chapter we already know that the solution for these initial conditions is given by

$$q_m(t) = Q_0 \cos \omega_0 t \tag{8-13}$$

Regardless of the method of solution, the response of the source-free L-C circuit of Fig. 8-1 must be *unique*. Thus forms (8-13) and (8-12) must be identical. To understand the form of the solution given in (8-12), the meaning of the term $e^{j\omega_0 t}$—an exponential function with "imaginary" exponent—must be investigated.

8-2. Introduction to Complex Numbers. The class of real numbers is defined by certain rules of operation such as addition, division, extracting square roots, etc. When we apply the rule for extracting square roots to negative real numbers, we arrive at a result which cannot be a real number because the square of a real number is always a positive real number. In this sense the class of real numbers is not complete. In other words, we are faced with the situation where some of the operations which were defined in connection with the real numbers cannot be performed. To overcome this difficulty, mathematicians have introduced the class of numbers called "imaginary numbers," which obey the same rules of operation as real numbers but whose squares are always negative real numbers.   The terms "real" and "imaginary" are not used in their colloquial sense but in the mathematical sense.   The choice of the term imaginary is unfortunate because of its colloquial implication.

The concept of real integral numbers is formed through association with objects: the words "two eyes" or "ten fingers" are intuitively meaningful.   The concept of negative numbers, on the other hand, arises from the insistence that the algebraic operations of addition and subtraction always can be performed.   Thus in the statement $x + 5 = 3$ the symbol x cannot represent a number unless we admit negative numbers into the system of numbers.   In terms of such operations, imaginary numbers are introduced in connection with relationships such as Eq. (8-7), where we had

$$s^2 = -\omega_0{}^2$$

If we relate the imaginary number s with the real number ω_0 through the relation

$$s = j\omega_0 \tag{8-14}$$

where j is the unit imaginary number and ω_0 is the real number indicating how many imaginary units there are in the imaginary number s, then, squaring both sides of (8-14), we have

$$s^2 = -\omega_0{}^2 = j^2\omega_0{}^2$$

where
$$j^2 \equiv -1$$
and
$$j \equiv + \sqrt{-1} \tag{8-15}$$

Equation (8-15) may be taken to be the defining equation of the unit imaginary number[1] j.

8-3. Complex Numbers.   We become acquainted with imaginary numbers in the process of extracting the square root of a negative real number. Suppose now we attempt to extract the square root of an imaginary number.   Here we are faced with an operation whose result is neither a real nor an imaginary number.   This difficulty is overcome by introducing another class of numbers called *complex numbers*.   We shall see that both real and imaginary numbers are special cases of complex numbers.   It can be shown that the result of application of all algebraic operations on a complex number is a complex number.   By contrast, this statement could not be made about either real or imaginary numbers.

Let lower-case letters such as a, b, c, d, ... denote real numbers. Then the combination $a + jb$ is called a complex number, denoted by a boldface letter, often capital $\mathbf{A} = a + jb$. a is called the real part and

---

[1] The reader will recall that mathematicians denote the unit imaginary number by the letter i; engineers use j because the symbol i is used for current.

b the imaginary part of the complex number $\mathbf{A}$. Note that by this definition the imaginary part of a complex number is a real number. Symbolically the real and imaginary parts of complex numbers are indicated by the abbreviations Re and Im. Thus for the complex number $\mathbf{A} = a + jb$, we write

$$\mathrm{Re}\,\mathbf{A} = a \quad \text{and} \quad \mathrm{Im}\,\mathbf{A} = b$$

In a numerical case, if $\mathbf{A} = -3 - j6$, $\mathrm{Re}\,\mathbf{A} = -3$, $\mathrm{Im}\,\mathbf{A} = -6$.

8-4. Addition of Complex Numbers. Let

$$\mathbf{A} = a + jb \qquad (8\text{-}16)$$
$$\mathbf{B} = c + jd \qquad (8\text{-}17)$$

Then by definition

$$\mathbf{A} + \mathbf{B} = \mathbf{B} + \mathbf{A} \equiv \mathbf{D}$$

where $\mathbf{D}$ is a complex number such that

$$\mathbf{D} = (a + c) + j(b + d)$$

The sum of two complex numbers is another complex number whose real part is the sum of the real parts and whose imaginary part the sum of the imaginary parts of the components.

Subtraction of Complex Numbers. Subtraction can be taken to be a special case of addition resulting in

$$\mathbf{A} - \mathbf{B} \equiv \mathbf{E}$$
$$\mathbf{E} = (a - c) + j(b - d)$$

where $\mathbf{A}$ and $\mathbf{B}$ are given by (8-16) and (8-17).

8-5. Multiplication of Complex Numbers. In multiplying two complex numbers each number is treated as a binomial. When in the product the term j^2 appears it can be replaced by the number -1.

$$\mathbf{B} \cdot \mathbf{A} = \mathbf{A} \cdot \mathbf{B} = (a + jb)(c + jd) = ac + jad + jbc + j^2bd$$
$$= (ac - bd) + j(ad + bc)$$

Thus the product of two complex numbers results in another complex number.

8-6. Conjugate of a Complex Number. The conjugate of a complex number $\mathbf{A}$, denoted by the symbol $\mathbf{A}^*$, is a complex number whose real part is identical with the real part of $\mathbf{A}$ and whose imaginary part is the negative of the imaginary part of $\mathbf{A}$. Thus if

$$\mathbf{A} = a + jb$$

then

$$\mathbf{A}^* = a - jb$$

The product of a complex number and its conjugate is a real number:

$$\mathbf{A} \cdot \mathbf{A}^* = (a + jb)(a - jb) = a^2 - (jb)^2 = a^2 + b^2$$

Let
$$A = + \sqrt{a^2 + b^2}$$

Then A is called the magnitude of the complex number $\mathbf{A}$. It is clear that the magnitude of $\mathbf{A}^*$ is also A.

8-7. Division of Complex Numbers. The result of dividing two complex numbers is another complex number. To find the ratio $\mathbf{A}/\mathbf{B}$, where $\mathbf{A}$ and $\mathbf{B}$ are complex numbers given by (8-16) and (8-17), the method called "rationalization" is used. This is illustrated in

$$\frac{\mathbf{A}}{\mathbf{B}} = \frac{\mathbf{A}}{\mathbf{B}} \cdot \frac{\mathbf{B}^*}{\mathbf{B}^*} = \frac{\mathbf{A} \cdot \mathbf{B}^*}{B^2}$$

The operation of division of two complex numbers is reduced to multiplication of two complex numbers by multiplying the numerator and denominator of $\mathbf{A}/\mathbf{B}$ by the conjugate of the denominator. Since $\mathbf{B}\mathbf{B}^* = B^2$ is a real number, then $\mathbf{D} = \mathbf{A}/\mathbf{B}$ is a complex number such that

$$\mathbf{D} = \frac{\mathbf{A}}{\mathbf{B}} = \frac{\mathbf{A}\mathbf{B}^*}{B^2} = \frac{(a + jb)(c - jd)}{c^2 + d^2} = \frac{ac + bd}{c^2 + d^2} + j\frac{bc - ad}{c^2 + d^2}$$

8-8. The Complex Plane. The concept of abstract integral numbers such as 3 or 5 without reference to any object is difficult to explain. Even more difficult is the concept of abstract negative real numbers or irrational real numbers or transcendental numbers. In the case of integers we form our understanding of abstract numbers through their association with objects. For other types of numbers this means is not available. For example, the number $e = 2.7183 \cdot \cdot \cdot$, the base of natural logarithms, cannot be associated with objects visually or otherwise. One way of describing such numbers is through the artifice of an axis, called the real-number axis. If a straight line starts from point O and continues indefinitely in a given direction, as in Fig. 8-2, and on this line a given length OA is taken to represent unity, then each and every point on this line will correspond to a positive real number. If $OB = 2(OA)$ then the

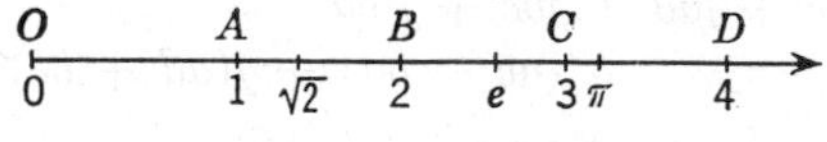

Fig. 8-2. The axis of positive real numbers.

point B corresponds to the number 2. Irrational numbers such as $\sqrt{2}$ or transcendental numbers such as π are also located on this axis.

When the axis of the real numbers is extended on both sides of point O as in Fig. 8-3, then if the part OA and its continuation are taken to contain the set of all positive real numbers the part OM and its continuation will contain the set of all negative real numbers.

We see, therefore, that every real number can be associated with a point on an axis, and vice versa. We now recall that any complex number is defined through two real numbers, namely, the real and the imaginary part of the complex number. A geometrical interpretation of complex numbers can therefore be achieved if we recall that each point in a plane is also defined through two real numbers. Starting with a set of mutually perpendicular axes, if one of these axes is taken to be the axis of the real numbers and the other the axis of the imaginary numbers, then the plane of the two axes is called the *complex plane* and with each point on this plane a complex number can be associated. The coordinate of a point along the real axis will be the real part of the complex number, and its coordinate along the imaginary axis will be the imaginary part.

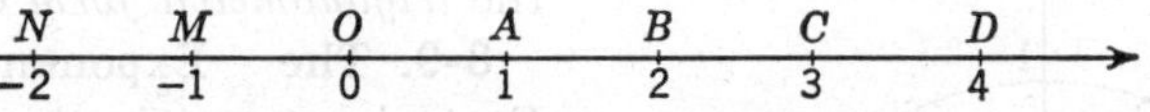

$$
\begin{array}{ccccccc}
N & M & O & A & B & C & D \\
-2 & -1 & 0 & 1 & 2 & 3 & 4
\end{array}
$$

FIG. 8-3. The axis of real numbers.

Often the real and imaginary part of a complex number are designated by x and y, respectively, and the complex number itself by $\mathbf{z}$. Thus $\mathbf{z} = x + jy$. If x and y represent the coordinates of a point in a set of rectangular cartesian coordinates (see Fig. 8-4), then to each point (x,y) in the cartesian plane there may therefore be made to correspond exactly one complex number and the cartesian plane may serve as a representation of all the complex numbers. In this representation all the real numbers ($y = 0$) will be found on the x axis, or "real axis"; the y axis will be the locus for all the purely imaginary numbers and will be called the "imaginary axis." Instead of considering the point (x,y) as the representative of the complex number $\mathbf{z} = x + jy$, we may as well consider the corresponding radius vector as such. And instead of characterizing the complex number by its cartesian coordinates (x,y) we may as well characterize it by its polar coordinates. In that case it is customary among electrical engineers to write

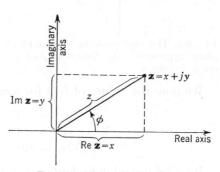

FIG. 8-4. The complex plane.

$$\mathbf{z} = z\underline{/\phi} \qquad \text{(read "z at an angle ϕ")}$$

where z is called the "magnitude," or "absolute value," and ϕ the "argument," or "angle," of the complex number $\mathbf{z}$. The magnitude z is also indicated symbolically by $z = |\mathbf{z}|$.

The following equations relate the polar and rectangular form of a complex number

$$z = \sqrt{x^2 + y^2} \qquad \phi = \tan^{-1} \frac{y}{x}$$

and

$$\operatorname{Re} \mathbf{z} = x = z \cos \phi$$
$$\operatorname{Im} \mathbf{z} = y = z \sin \phi$$

So far we have seen that a complex number may be written in three different forms:

$$\mathbf{z} = z\underline{/\phi} = x + jy = z(\cos \phi + j \sin \phi)$$

where $z\underline{/\phi}$ is called the *polar form* of $\mathbf{z}$, $x + jy$ is called the *rectangular form* of $\mathbf{z}$, and $z(\cos \phi + j \sin \phi)$ is called the *trigonometric form* of $\mathbf{z}$.

8-9. The Exponential Form.

Factoring out z in the trigonometric expression for $\mathbf{z}$, we may write

$$\mathbf{z} = z \cdot f(\phi)$$

where $f(\phi) = \cos \phi + j \sin \phi$

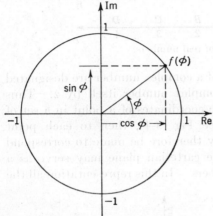

FIG. 8-5. The unit circle in the complex plane represents the function $f(\phi) = \cos \phi + j \sin \phi$.

We see that in the complex plane (see Fig. 8-5) $f(\phi)$ represents a point on a circle whose center is at the origin and whose radius is 1. The abscissa of the point is $\cos \phi$; the ordinate has the length $\sin \phi$. Or we may also say that $f(\phi)$ represents a complex number of magnitude 1 at an angle ϕ: $f(\phi) = 1\underline{/\phi}$.

We note the values of $f(\phi)$ for some particular values of ϕ:

$$f(0) = +1 \qquad f(\tfrac{1}{2}\pi) = +j$$
$$f(\pi) = -1 \qquad f(\tfrac{3}{2}\pi) = -j$$
$$f(2\pi) = f(0) = 1$$

In order to find out whether or not we can identify $f(\phi)$ with one of the functions we know from elementary analysis, we differentiate it with respect to ϕ:

$$\frac{df}{d\phi} = -\sin \phi + j \cos \phi = j(\cos \phi + j \sin \phi)$$

We see that f obeys the differential equation

$$\frac{df}{d\phi} = jf$$

or, in words, f is a function whose derivative is proportional to itself. We know that functions that have this property are the exponential functions and therefore

$$f(\phi) = Ke^{j\phi}$$

Because
$$f(0) = 1$$

it follows that $K = 1$ and therefore

$$f(\phi) = \cos \phi + j \sin \phi = e^{j\phi}$$

This equation shows the close relationship which exists between the trigonometric and the exponential functions. It was discovered by the mathematician Leonhard Euler (1707–1783).

It follows from the previous discussion that $e^{j\phi}$ may be represented in the complex plane by a radius vector of magnitude 1 at an angle ϕ (see Fig. 8-6). Its real part is $\cos \phi$, its imaginary part $\sin \phi$. Some special values of $e^{j\phi}$ are

$$e^{j\pi/2} = j \qquad e^{j\pi} = -1 \qquad e^{j3\pi/2} = -j \qquad e^{j2\pi} = 1$$

We note that

$$e^{j(\phi \pm 2k\pi)} = e^{j\phi} \qquad k = \text{integer}$$

That is, the exponential function with imaginary argument is a periodic function having the period 2π.

We may now write any complex number of magnitude z and argument ϕ in the form

$$\mathbf{z} = ze^{j\phi}$$

which is called the *exponential form*. Strictly speaking, in the exponential form the angle of a complex number must be specified in radians. While this is true, the use of radians is not convenient in numerical work because the slide rules which we all use are marked in degrees. It is therefore permissible to give the angle in exponential and polar

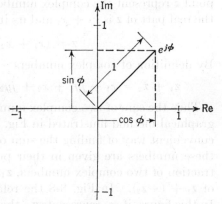

Fig. 8-6. Representation of $e^{j\phi}$ in the complex plane.

forms in degrees, provided that the degree symbol is shown. This symbol ° is then interpreted to mean the factor $\pi/180$, which is used to convert degrees to radians. Thus, for example,

$$6e^{j\pi/4} = 6e^{j45°} = 6e^{j45\pi/180}$$

The reader is cautioned not to omit the degree symbol if degrees are meant since we must interpret a "dimensionless" angle as an angle in radians.

8-10. Graphical Manipulation of Complex Numbers. In Fig. 8-7 two complex numbers $z_1 = x_1 + jy_1$ and $z_2 = x_2 + jy_2$ are shown. We may consider either the point z_1 or the radius vector oz_1 to "represent" the complex number z_1, with a similar representation for z_2. Let oz be the resultant of oz_1 and oz_2 as obtained by the "parallelogram" rule. Let

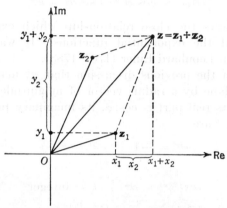

FIG. 8-7. Addition of complex numbers.

point z represent the complex number z. A study of Fig. 8-7 shows that the real part of z is $x_1 + x_2$ and its imaginary part is $y_1 + y_2$. Therefore

$$z = (x_1 + x_2) + j(y_1 + y_2)$$

By definition of complex numbers

$$z_1 + z_2 = x_1 + jy_1 + x_2 + jy_2 = (x_1 + x_2) + j(y_1 + y_2) = z$$

Thus the sum of two complex numbers z_1 and z_2 can be obtained by the graphical method illustrated in Fig. 8-7. This method is often the most convenient way of finding the sum of two complex numbers, especially if these numbers are given in their polar or exponential form. The subtraction of two complex numbers, $z_1 - z_2$, can be treated as the addition of $z_1 + (-z_2)$. In Fig. 8-8 the relation between z_2 and $-z_2$ is shown. In this figure, if oz_2 represents z_2, then oa, which is collinear with oz_2, with $oz_2 = oa$, will represent $-z_2$. In Fig. 8-9 the sum of $z_1 + (-z_2)$ is shown. In this figure om represents $z_1 - z_2$.

Figures 8-7 and 8-9 show that the rule for adding and subtracting complex numbers is identical to the rule for adding two-dimensional vectors in the xy space. This resemblance between vector addition and the addition of complex numbers is responsible for the practice of calling a diagram showing the addition of complex numbers, as in Fig. 8-7, a "vector" diagram. As is evident from the succeeding operations (multi-

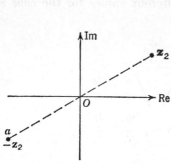

FIG. 8-8. A complex number and its negative.

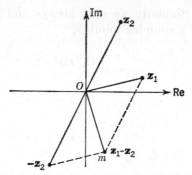

FIG. 8-9. Subtraction of complex numbers.

plication, division), the resemblance between vector algebra and ordinary algebra (which applies to complex numbers) *is restricted to the rule for addition.*

8-11. Use of Exponential Form in Multiplication and Division. Let

$$z_1 = z_1 e^{j\phi_1} = z_1 \underline{/\phi_1} \qquad z_2 = z_2 e^{j\phi_2} = z_2 \underline{/\phi_2}$$

Then

$$z_1 z_2 = z_1 z_2 e^{j\phi_1} e^{j\phi_2} = z_1 z_2 e^{j(\phi_1 + \phi_2)} = z_1 z_2 \underline{/\phi_1 + \phi_2}$$

and

$$\frac{z_1}{z_2} = \frac{z_1 e^{j\phi_1}}{z_2 e^{j\phi_2}} = \frac{z_1}{z_2} e^{j(\phi_1 - \phi_2)} = \frac{z_1}{z_2} \underline{/\phi_1 - \phi_2}$$

In words, the product (quotient) of two complex numbers is a complex number whose magnitude equals the product (quotient) of the magnitudes and whose angle equals the sum (difference) of the angles of the two original complex numbers.

8-12. Powers and Roots. Let $z = z e^{j\phi}$; then

$$z^n = z^n e^{jn\phi} = z^n \underline{/n\phi} = z^n \cos n\phi + jz^n \sin n\phi \qquad (8\text{-}18)$$

In words, the nth power of a complex number is a complex number whose magnitude is the nth power of the magnitude and whose angle is n times the angle of the original complex number. Equation (8-18) is also valid for fractional powers. However, it must be remembered that any integral multiple of 2π may be added or subtracted to ϕ without changing the values of $e^{j\phi}$:

$$e^{j\phi} = e^{j(\phi + 2k\pi)} \qquad k \text{ an integer}$$

Therefore, if we wish to find the *square root* of a complex number z, we shall find *two* values,

$$(\sqrt{z})_1 = z^{\frac{1}{2}} e^{j\phi/2} = \sqrt{z} \underline{\bigg/\frac{\phi}{2}} = \sqrt{z} \cos \frac{\phi}{2} + j \sqrt{z} \sin \frac{\phi}{2}$$

$$(\sqrt{z})_2 = z^{\frac{1}{2}} e^{j(\phi + 2\pi)/2} = \sqrt{z} \underline{\bigg/\frac{\phi}{2} + \pi} = -\sqrt{z} \cos \frac{\phi}{2} - j \sqrt{z} \sin \frac{\phi}{2}$$

Similarly we shall always find *three* different values for the *cube root* of a complex number,

$$(\sqrt[3]{z})_1 = z^{\frac{1}{3}}e^{j\phi/3} = \sqrt[3]{z} \;\underline{/\dfrac{\phi}{3}}$$

$$(\sqrt[3]{z})_2 = z^{\frac{1}{3}}e^{j(\phi+2\pi)/3} = \sqrt[3]{z} \;\underline{/\dfrac{\phi}{3} + \dfrac{2\pi}{3}}$$

$$(\sqrt[3]{z})_3 = z^{\frac{1}{3}}e^{j(\phi+4\pi)/3} = \sqrt[3]{z} \;\underline{/\dfrac{\phi}{3} + \dfrac{4\pi}{3}}$$

As an example, consider the three values of $\sqrt[3]{1}$ illustrated in Fig. 8-10. In this figure it is seen that

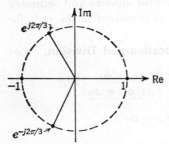

FIG. 8-10. The three cube roots of unity.

$$(\sqrt[3]{1})_1 = 1\underline{/0} = 1 + j0$$

$$(\sqrt[3]{1})_2 = 1 \;\underline{/\dfrac{2\pi}{3}} = -\dfrac{1}{2} + j\dfrac{\sqrt{3}}{2}$$

$$(\sqrt[3]{1})_3 = 1 \;\underline{/\dfrac{4\pi}{3}} = -\dfrac{1}{2} - j\dfrac{\sqrt{3}}{2}$$

8-13. The Logarithm. If $z = ze^{j\phi}$, we have

$$\ln z = \ln (ze^{j\phi}) = \ln z + \ln e^{j\phi} = \ln z + j\phi$$

Again it must be remembered that any integer multiple of 2π may be added to or subtracted from ϕ without changing the value of $e^{j\phi}$. Therefore the logarithm of a complex number is not single-valued since

$$\ln z = \ln z + j(\phi + 2\pi n) \qquad n = 0, \pm 1, \pm 2, \pm 3, \ldots$$

Sometimes a particular value of n such as $n = 0$ is chosen to define a "principal value" of $\ln z$.

8-14. Exponential Form of the Conjugate. The conjugate of

$$z = x + jy$$

is given by

$$z^* = x - jy = ze^{-j\phi} = z\underline{/-\phi}$$

The complex number z and its conjugate z^* are shown in Fig. 8-11. From this figure it is seen that z^* is the "image" of z with respect to the real axis.

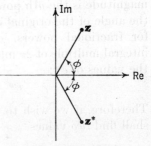

FIG. 8-11. A complex number and its conjugate.

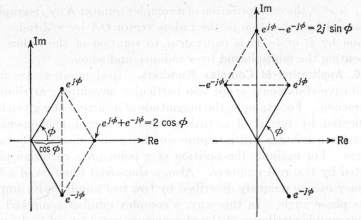

FIG. 8-12. Representation of cos ϕ and sin ϕ by use of complex numbers.

It is seen that the following relations hold:

$$\operatorname{Re} \mathbf{z} = \tfrac{1}{2}(\mathbf{z} + \mathbf{z}^*) \tag{8-19}$$

$$\operatorname{Im} \mathbf{z} = \frac{1}{2j}(\mathbf{z} - \mathbf{z}^*) \tag{8-20}$$

$$z^2 = |\mathbf{z}|^2 = \mathbf{z}\mathbf{z}^* \tag{8-21}$$

In the special case where $\mathbf{z} = e^{j\phi}$, $\mathbf{z}^* = e^{-j\phi}$ Eqs. (8-19) and (8-20) yield the important relations

$$\cos \phi = \tfrac{1}{2}(e^{j\phi} + e^{-j\phi})$$

$$\sin \phi = \frac{1}{2j}(e^{j\phi} - e^{-j\phi})$$

These are illustrated by the diagrams in Fig. 8-12.

8-15. Graphical Representation of Multiplication and Division. The complex number $e^{j\phi}$ has a magnitude of unity and an angle ϕ. Multiplication of the complex number $\mathbf{A} = A e^{j\phi_1}$ by $e^{j\phi_2}$ results in

$$\mathbf{B} = A e^{j\phi_1} e^{j\phi_2} = A e^{j(\phi_1 + \phi_2)}$$

The complex number **B** is obtained by rotating the radius vector OA counterclockwise through an angle ϕ_2 (Fig. 8-13).

It is also noted that

$$e^{j0} = \cos 0 + j \sin 0 = 1 = j^0$$

$$e^{j\pi/2} = \cos \frac{\pi}{2} + j \sin \frac{\pi}{2} = j = j^1$$

$$e^{j\pi} = \cos \pi + j \sin \pi = -1 = j^2$$

$$e^{j3\pi/2} = \cos \frac{3\pi}{2} + j \sin \frac{3\pi}{2} = -j = j^3$$

$$e^{j2\pi} = \cos 2\pi + j \sin 2\pi = 1 = j^4$$

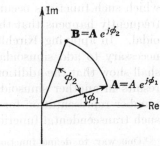

FIG. 8-13. Multiplication of **A** by $e^{j\phi_2}$.

Since $j = e^{j\pi/2}$, the multiplication of a complex number **A** by j is graphically represented by a rotation of the radius vector OA by $\pi/2$ rad. Multiplication by j^2 or (-1) is equivalent to rotation of the radius vector representing the multiplicand by π radians, and so on.

8-16. Application of Complex Numbers. Real numbers are used in quantitative statements about one particular measurable attribute of a phenomenon. For example, the magnitude of a current at a given instant is indicated by means of a real number. Certain phenomena have measurable attributes which require simultaneous indication by two real numbers. For example the position of a point on a cartesian plane is indicated by two real numbers. Also, a sinusoidal function of a known frequency can be uniquely described by two real numbers, its amplitude and its phase angle. In this way, a complex number composed of the two measurable attributes of the phenomenon can be used to describe it. Thus we can indicate a point on the cartesian plane by the complex number $x + jy$ or a sinusoidal function of amplitude A and phase angle θ by the complex number $A/\underline{\theta}$. The latter representation is discussed in Part B of this chapter.

B. SINUSOIDAL FUNCTIONS

Sinusoidal functions are a special type of periodic function which satisfy the differential equations[1] of the form

$$\frac{d^2}{dt^2} f(t) + \omega^2 f(t) = 0$$

where ω is a constant and the solution of the equation is in the form

$$f(t) = A \cos \omega t + B \sin \omega t$$

ω is called the radian frequency of the sinusoidal function.

We have seen that the sinusoidal functions occur as the solutions to the source-free L-C circuit. This is only one example of a circuit problem in which such functions occur. As we shall see in subsequent chapters, it frequently happens that the voltages and currents in a circuit are sinusoidal. In applying Kirchhoff's laws to such circuits it will therefore be necessary to add sinusoidal functions. In this part of the chapter we shall show that the addition of sinusoids which have the same frequency results in another sinusoidal function. Moreover, the use of complex-number representation for such functions transforms the summation of such transcendental functions to algebraic operations.

[1] One way to define functions is to specify them as the solutions of differential equations. For example, the exponential function $e^{-\alpha t}$ is defined as the solution of the equation $(d/dt)f(t) + \alpha f(t) = 0$.

8-17. Basic Properties of Sinusoids.   The function

$$f_1(t) = A \cos \omega t$$

may be visualized, from elementary trigonometry, as having at every instant of time t the value given by the ratio of the adjacent leg to the hypotenuse of a right triangle in which the angle formed by these two legs is increasing with time at the rate ω rad/sec.   A similar visualization can be made for

$$f_2(t') = B \sin \omega t'$$

In this case the opposite leg and the hypotenuse are involved.   Figure 8-14a shows the waveform of $f_1(t) = A \cos \omega t$, and Fig. 8-14b shows

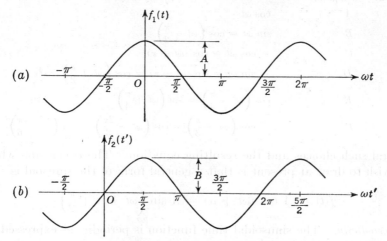

FIG. 8-14. Waveform of sinusoids.

$f_2(t') = B \sin \omega t'$.   With sinsuoidal functions it will often be convenient to normalize the time scale and choose as independent variable ωt instead of t.   In such a case the period P of the function corresponds to $\omega P = 2\pi$. The waveforms of Fig. 8-14 are shown with ωt as the independent variable. Examining the waveshapes of Fig. 8-14a and b, we note that they are identical, the only difference being the choice of location of the y axis, $\omega t = 0$.   For this reason, distinction between sine and cosine functions is often unnecessary, and the term *sinusoidal function* is used to describe either function or a linear combination of both.

Referring to Fig. 8-14, we note that, when $t = 0$, $t' = \pi/2\omega$.   This is an expression of the trigonometric identity concerning complementary angles,

$$\cos \omega t = \sin \left(\omega t + \frac{\pi}{2} \right)$$

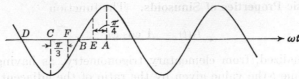

FIG. 8-15. Choice of time reference determines the functional form of the sinusoid as in Table 8-1.

Pursuing this, consider Fig. 8-15, where a sinusoid is sketched without the ordinate axis. The equation which describes this waveform depends on the location of the point where t (or ωt) is zero. Table 8-1 indicates

TABLE 8-1. DATA PERTINENT TO FIG. 8-15

$\omega t = 0$ at point	Time function
A	$\cos \omega t$
B	$\sin \omega t = \cos \left(\omega t - \dfrac{\pi}{2} \right)$
C	$- \cos \omega t = \cos (\omega t + \pi)$
D	$- \sin \omega t = \sin (\omega t + \pi) = \cos \left(\omega t + \dfrac{\pi}{2} \right)$
E	$\cos \left(\omega t - \dfrac{\pi}{4} \right) = \sin \left(\omega t + \dfrac{\pi}{4} \right)$
F	$- \cos \left(\omega t + \dfrac{\pi}{3} \right) = \cos \left(\omega t - \dfrac{2\pi}{3} \right) = \sin \left(\omega t - \dfrac{\pi}{6} \right)$

several such choices and the resulting equation. The conclusion which we wish to draw at present is that a general form of the sinusoid is

$$f(t) = A \cos (\omega t + \alpha) = A \sin \left(\omega t + \alpha + \frac{\pi}{2} \right)$$

Periodicity. The sinusoidal time function is periodic, as expressed by the identity

$$\cos (\omega t + \alpha) = \cos (\omega t + 2n\pi + \alpha) \qquad n = \pm 1, \pm 2, \ldots$$

The relation between its period P and its radian frequency ω is

$$\omega P = 2\pi \qquad \text{or} \qquad P = \frac{2\pi}{\omega}$$

The reciprocal of the period is called the frequency (f), which becomes

$$f = \frac{1}{P} = \frac{\omega}{2\pi}$$

Waveshape Property. From the time-derivative relationships

$$\frac{d}{dt} \sin \omega t = \omega \cos \omega t \qquad \frac{d}{dt} \cos \omega t = -\omega \sin \omega t$$

we observe that *the sinusoid is the only periodic real function which has a derivative of the same shape as the function itself.* It is this particular property of sinusoidal functions which makes them so useful in analysis.

Amplitude.   The function

$$f(t) = A \cos (\omega t + \alpha)$$

reaches the maximum value A when $\omega t + \alpha = 0$ or $2n\pi$; the minimum is $-A$ and occurs at $\omega t + \alpha = (2n - 1)\pi$ (n = integer).   The positive

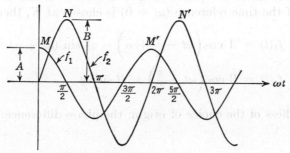

Fig. 8-16. Illustration of phase difference between two sinusoidal functions.   The function f_2 lags the function f_1 by $\pi/2$.

maximum value of the function is called the *amplitude* of the sinusoid. Note that the relationship

$$\cos \omega t = - \cos (\omega t \pm \pi)$$

makes it possible to choose A always as a positive number, e.g.,

$$f(t) = -10 \cos \left(\omega t + \frac{\pi}{3}\right) = 10 \cos \left(\omega t - \frac{2\pi}{3}\right)$$

Phase Angle.   We have already defined phase difference in connection with the periodic functions (see Chap. 2).   Two sinusoidal waveforms of the same frequency can differ only in their amplitude and phase. Figure 8-16 shows the waveforms of $f_1(t) = A \cos \omega t$ and $f_2(t) = B \sin \omega t$. The two waveforms have the same frequency but differ in amplitude and phase.   For example, $f_1(t)$ reaches its maximum at $\omega t = 0$, whereas $f_2(t)$ has its maximum at $\omega t = \pi/2$.   Inspection of Fig. 8-16 shows that every phase of $f_1(t)$ occurs in $f_2(t)$ at exactly $\pi/2$ rad later.   Thus we say that a sine function *lags* a cosine function by $\pi/2$ rad (90°).   It is of course possible to say that the maximum N of $f_2(t)$ occurs earlier than maximum M' of $f_1(t)$ by $3\pi/2$.   We may therefore say, $f_2(t) = B \sin \omega t$ leads $f_1(t) = A \cos \omega t$ by $3\pi/2$ rad (270°).   It is seen that lagging by $\pi/2$ and leading by $3\pi/2$ are identical conditions.   This point is evident from the fact that $\omega t - \pi/2$ differs from $\omega t + 3\pi/2$ by 2π, which is the period of the sinusoid on the ωt scale.

The ideas from the special example of Fig. 8-16 may be generalized to compare any two sinusoids which have the *same frequency*. Thus, in Fig. 8-17, f_1 leads f_2 by α rad (or f_2 leads f_1 by $2\pi - \alpha$) or f_2 lags f_1 by α. This is expressed analytically

$$f_1(t) = A \cos \omega t$$
$$f_2(t) = B \cos (\omega t - \alpha)$$

The angle α is called the phase (angle) difference of the two sinusoids. Note that, if the time reference ($\omega t = 0$) is chosen at K, then

$$f_1(t) = A \cos \left(\omega t - \frac{\pi}{2} + \alpha \right) = A \sin (\omega t + \alpha)$$

$$f_2(t) = B \cos \left(\omega t - \frac{\pi}{2} \right) = B \sin \omega t$$

Thus, regardless of the choice of origin, the phase difference remains the same.

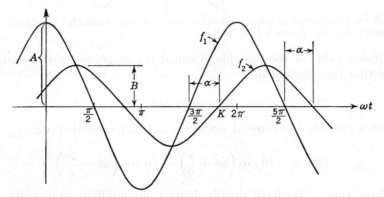

FIG. 8-17. Illustration of phase difference between two sinusoids.

To conclude, it needs to be pointed out that a phase difference on the "angle scale" corresponds to a time difference on the time scale. Thus, if f_2 lags f_1 by α, f_2 is delayed in time by α/ω sec with respect to f_1.

8-18. Addition of Sinusoids. We have already seen (in connection with the L-C circuit) that the sum of two sinusoids may occur in circuit problems. The addition of two or more sinusoidal time functions of the same frequency but with different amplitude and phase is common in circuit analysis; moreover, it is almost always desired to express the sum as a single sinusoidal term.

Consider as an example

$$f(t) = A \cos \omega t + B \sin \omega t \tag{8-22}$$

This function may be reduced to the form

$$f(t) = C \cos (\omega t + \gamma) \tag{8-23}$$

by the method of identities in trigonometry.   Since

$$\cos (\omega t + \gamma) = \cos \omega t \cos \gamma - \sin \omega t \sin \gamma$$

we get

$$f(t) = A \cos \omega t + B \sin \omega t = C \cos \gamma \cos \omega t - C \sin \gamma \sin \omega t \quad (8\text{-}24)$$

If Eq. (8-24) is to hold for all t, by comparison of the coefficient of $\sin \omega t$ and $\cos \omega t$ on both sides of the equation it is seen that

$$\begin{aligned} A &= C \cos \gamma \\ B &= -C \sin \gamma \end{aligned} \quad (8\text{-}25)$$

or

$$\begin{aligned} C &= + \sqrt{A^2 + B^2} \\ \gamma &= \tan^{-1} \frac{-B}{A} \end{aligned} \quad (8\text{-}26)$$

Hence Eq. (8-22) may be rewritten in the desired form,

$$f(t) = \sqrt{A^2 + B^2} \cos \left(\omega t + \tan^{-1} \frac{-B}{A} \right) \quad (8\text{-}27)$$

This result, as well as the addition indicated by Eq. (8-22), is illustrated in Fig. 8-18 for the special case $A = B = 1$.   While the conversion of

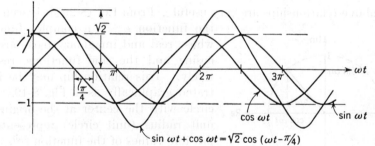

FIG. 8-18. Addition of two sinusoids.

Eq. (8-22) to the form (8-27) is done with little difficulty by trigonometric expansion, the addition of two terms of the form

$$f(t) = A \cos (\omega t + \alpha) + B \cos (\omega t + \beta)$$

or of three terms, e.g.,

$$f(t) = A \cos (\omega t + \alpha) + B \sin (\omega t + \beta) + D \cos (\omega t + \delta)$$

is very cumbersome by this method.   In Art. 8-20 we shall study a graphical method of adding any number of sinusoidal functions.   This graphical method is best understood through a study of the complex function $e^{j\omega t}$.

8-19. The Complex Function $e^{j\omega t}$. Phasors. In Part A of this chapter we had Euler's equation of the form

$$e^{j\phi} = \cos \phi + j \sin \phi \qquad (8\text{-}28)$$

where ϕ was a real number (in radians). We may extend this equation to the case when ϕ is a real function of t such as

$$\phi = \omega t$$

where ω will be in radians per second. Thus we shall have

$$e^{j\omega t} = \cos \omega t + j \sin \omega t \qquad (8\text{-}29)$$

The transition from Eq. (8-28), which is a representation of a complex *number* in two forms (exponential and trigonometric), to Eq. (8-29), relating a complex exponential *function* of the real variable t to two sinusoidal functions of t, is an important step. Recalling the relationship between the real parts of a complex number and its conjugates, and extending this rule to apply to complex functions, we have

$$\cos \omega t = \operatorname{Re} e^{j\omega t} = \tfrac{1}{2}(e^{j\omega t} + e^{-j\omega t})$$
$$\sin \omega t = \operatorname{Im} e^{j\omega t} = \frac{1}{2j}(e^{j\omega t} - e^{-j\omega t}) \qquad (8\text{-}30)$$

The above relationships are very useful. From Eq. (8-29) it is seen that

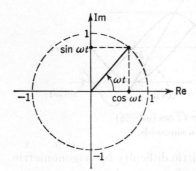

the function $e^{j\omega t}$ is a complex function whose real and imaginary parts are the cosine and the sine functions, respectively. This relationship may be illustrated graphically as in Fig. 8-19. The circle with the center at the origin and unit radius (unit circle) represents all possible values of the function $e^{j\omega t}$.

At any instant of time the value of $e^{j\omega t}$ is found by drawing the radius of the circle at the angle ωt rad with the horizontal. The real part of $e^{j\omega t}$ is the projection of this line on the real axis

FIG. 8-19. Representation of the complex function $e^{j\omega t}$.

(i.e., it is $\cos \omega t$); the imaginary part is the projection on the imaginary axis.

Consider now the two functions

$$f_1(t) = \cos \omega t = \operatorname{Re} e^{j\omega t}$$
$$f_2(t) = \cos (\omega t + \alpha) = \operatorname{Re} e^{j(\omega t + \alpha)}$$

Both these functions have unit amplitude, the same frequency, but f_2 leads f_1 by the angle α. (In the discussion of this problem, it will be assumed that α is an acute positive angle.)   Figure 8-20a shows how the values of f_1 and f_2 are obtained at $t = t_1$; they are the projections of lines OA_1 and OB_1 on the real axis.   Figure 8-20b shows how they may be obtained at $t = t_2 > t_1$.   Figure 8-20c shows how these values are obtained at $t = 0$.   Note that $f_2(t)$ at $t = t_2$ as shown in Fig. 8-20b is

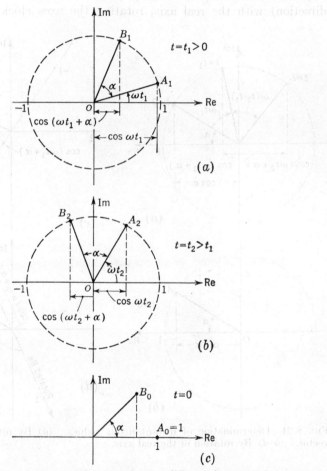

FIG. 8-20. Values of two complex functions at different instants of time.

the projection of OB_2 on the negative real axis; hence $f_2(t_2)$ is a negative number.

Let us again examine the method used to find the value of

$$f(t) = \cos{(\omega t + \alpha)} = \text{Re } e^{j(\omega t + \alpha)}$$

at any instant of time.   We draw the unit radius as in Fig. 8-21a at an angle $\omega t + \alpha$ with the real axis, then take the projection of that radius on the real axis. Figure 8-21a shows three such instants of time. Note that as t increases the radius whose projection is generating $f(t)$ rotates *counterclockwise*.

Alternatively the value of $f(t)$ at any instant of time may be found by drawing the radius at the angle α (in the positive, i.e., counterclockwise, direction) with the real axis, rotating the axes clockwise through the

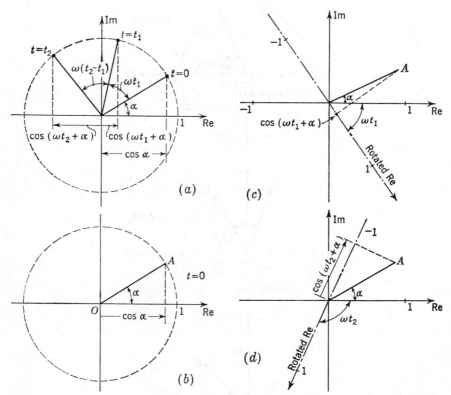

(a)

(b)

(c)

(d)

Fig. 8-21. Determination of instantaneous values.   (a) By rotation of the radius vector.   (b–d) By rotation of the real axis.

angle ωt, and then taking the projection on the rotated real axis as illustrated in Fig. 8-21b, c, and d for the same three instants used in Fig. 8-21a. Since by this method the axes rotate and the radius representing the exponentials remains the *same*, the radius OA in Fig. 8-21b may be taken to *represent* the sinusoid $f(t)$. We may therefore associate with every sinusoidal function a *complex number* which represents the amplitude and phase of the sinusoid with respect to a time (phase) reference. When a complex number is used to represent a sinusoidal time function, then the graphical representation of this complex number is called a *phasor*.[1]

Thus the complex number $1/0°$ may be used to represent the sinusoidal time function $f(t) = \cos \omega t$. The number A/α would then represent the time function $A \cos (\omega t + \alpha)$.

Since in the addition of any two complex numbers the rule

$$\text{Re } \mathbf{z}_1 + \text{Re } \mathbf{z}_2 = \text{Re } (\mathbf{z}_1 + \mathbf{z}_2)$$

applies, the resultant of two sinusoids may be obtained by adding the phasors which represent the two sinusoids. To obtain the value of the resulting time function at any instant of time, the resulting phasor is projected on a properly rotated real axis. Before supplementing the graphical proof which is outlined above by an analytical proof a simple graphical example will be done.

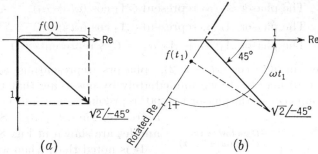

FIG. 8-22. Illustrating addition of two phasors.

Consider

$$f(t) = \cos \omega t + \sin \omega t$$

or

$$f(t) = \cos \omega t + \cos (\omega t - 90°)$$

Since $\cos \omega t = \text{Re } e^{j\omega t}$ and $\sin \omega t = \text{Re } e^{j(\omega t - \pi/2)}$, the value of $f(t)$ at $t = 0$ is given by the projection of the sum $1/0 + 1/-90°$ on the real axis as in Fig. 8-22a. At the instant of time $t = t_1$ the value $f(t_1)$ is illustrated in Fig. 8-22b. It is emphasized that the meaning of the resultant phasor

$$1/0 + 1/-90° = \sqrt{2} \; /-45°$$

is that

$$f(t) = \sqrt{2} \cos (\omega t - 45°)$$

[1] To avoid ambiguity, it is customary to place an arrowhead at the point where the complex number is located. For this reason and because the addition of complex numbers resembles vector addition, the term "vector" is often used to mean phasor. The term "sinor" is also used as a synonym for phasor. It must be noted that we have defined a phasor to be a complex *number*. There is some tendency to confuse the complex *function* $\mathbf{A}e^{j\omega t}$ with the phasor $\mathbf{A}$ which represents (but is not equal to) the real part of that function. The authors, following a suggestion of B. J. Starkey, "Laplace Transforms for Electrical Engineers," Philosophical Library, Inc., New York, 1955, believe that the term "animated phasor" or "activated phasor" may appropriately describe the function $\mathbf{A}e^{j\omega t}$.

8-20. Analytical Proof of Phasor Addition. Consider

$$f(t) = A_1 \cos (\omega t + \alpha_1) + A_2 \cos (\omega t + \alpha_2)$$

We may write

$$f(t) = \mathrm{Re}\ (A_1 e^{j\alpha_1} e^{j\omega t}) + \mathrm{Re}\ (A_2 e^{j\alpha_2} e^{j\omega t})$$

Again recalling the identity for any two complex quantities,

$$\mathrm{Re}\ \mathbf{z}_1 + \mathrm{Re}\ \mathbf{z}_2 = \mathrm{Re}\ (\mathbf{z}_1 + \mathbf{z}_2)$$
$$f(t) = \mathrm{Re}\ [(A_1 e^{j\alpha_1} + A_2 e^{j\alpha_2}) e^{j\omega t}]$$

Defining

$$A_1 e^{j\alpha_1} + A_2 e^{j\alpha_2} = C e^{j\gamma}$$
$$f(t) = C \cos (\omega t + \gamma)$$

Thus the sum $f(t)$ is obtained by the following representations:

The phasor $A_1\underline{/\alpha_1}$ represents $A_1 \cos (\omega t + \alpha_1)$

The phasor $A_2\underline{/\alpha_2}$ represents $A_2 \cos (\omega t + \alpha_2)$

The phasor $A_1\underline{/\alpha_1} + A_2\underline{/\alpha_2} = C\underline{/\gamma}$ represents $f(t)$

Because $\sin \omega t = \cos (\omega t - \pi/2)$, phasors representing a function $B \sin (\omega t + \beta)$ may be drawn immediately by observing that the phasor $1\underline{/0}$ represents $\cos \omega t$, the phasor $1\underline{/-90°}$ represents $\sin \omega t$, and $1\underline{/-90° + \beta}$ represents $\sin (\omega t + \beta)$.   Several examples are shown in Fig. 8-23.

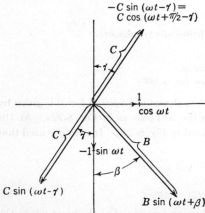

It is noted that, when we say that the phasor $A\underline{/\alpha}$ represents a sinusoidal function, by this we mean that this sinusoidal function is given by

$$\mathrm{Re}\ [A e^{j\alpha} e^{j\omega t}] = A \cos (\omega t + \alpha)$$

We could have just as well used the convention of taking the imaginary part to give

$$\mathrm{Im}\ [A e^{j\alpha} e^{j\omega t}] = A \sin (\omega t + \alpha)$$

This would be equivalent to rotating the imaginary axis by ωt and projecting $A\underline{/\alpha}$ on the rotated imaginary axis.   In this book we choose the

Fig. 8-23. Representations of sinusoidal functions by phasors.

convention that the phasor $1\underline{/\alpha}$ represents $\mathrm{Re}\ e^{j(\omega t + \alpha)}$ rather than $\mathrm{Im}\ e^{j(\omega t + \alpha)}$.

Example 8-1. Express

$$f(t) = 100 \cos (\omega t + 30°) - 60 \sin (\omega t + 45°) - 40 \cos (\omega t - 45°)$$

as a single sinusoid.

Solution. Let

$$100 \cos (\omega t + 30°) \text{ be represented by } 100\underline{/30°}$$

Then $-60 \sin (\omega t + 45°)$ is represented by $60\underline{/+45°} - 90° \pm 180°$

and $-40 \cos (\omega t - 45°)$ is represented by $40\underline{/-45°} \pm 180°$

These representations are illustrated in Fig. 8-24.   We therefore add

$$\mathbf{c} = 100\underline{/30°} + 60\underline{/135°} + 40\underline{/135°}$$
$$= 86.6 + j50 - 70.7 + j70.7 = 15.9 + j120.7$$
$$= 122\underline{/82.5°}$$

or $$f(t) = 122 \cos (\omega t + 82.5°)$$

8-21. Summary of Representation of Sinusoidal Functions by Phasors.

We recall that in Part A of this chapter we mentioned that complex numbers are suitable for representing phenomena with two measurable

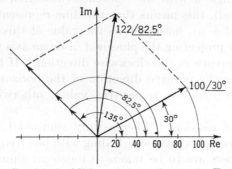

FIG. 8-24. Graphical addition of three phasors for Example 8-1.

attributes.   If the radian frequency of a sinusoidal function is known, then the only other two factors which would completely specify the function are its amplitude and the phase angle.   The phasor (complex number) $A\underline{/\alpha}$ gives these two factors in one complex number.   It must be remembered that the complex number $A\underline{/\alpha}$ *represents* the sinusoidal function $A \cos (\omega t + \alpha)$ but is *not* equal to it.   This is shown by writing

$$A \cos (\omega t + \alpha) \rightarrow A\underline{/\alpha}$$

where the arrow means "represents."   The second statement is shown by

$$A\underline{/\alpha} \neq A \cos (\omega t + \alpha)$$

to indicate that the representation is not mathematical equality.   Similarly, whereas $A\underline{/\alpha} + B\underline{/\beta}$ represents the sum of $A \cos (\omega t + \alpha) + B \cos (\omega t + \beta)$, it is *not* correct to write $A\underline{/\alpha} + B \cos (\omega t + \beta)$ to represent the sum of the two sinusoidal functions.   This is a mixture of two different notations which does not convey the required information.

The justification for adding phasors to represent the sum of their respective sinusoidal functions lies in the fact that

$$A \cos (\omega t + \alpha) = \operatorname{Re} A e^{j(\omega t + \alpha)} = \operatorname{Re} [A e^{j\alpha} e^{j\omega t}]$$
$$B \cos (\omega t + \beta) = \operatorname{Re} B e^{j(\omega t + \beta)} = \operatorname{Re} [B e^{j\beta} e^{j\omega t}]$$

Now, since the phasor method is used to add only sinusoidal functions of the same frequency, the term $e^{j\omega t}$ and the symbol (operator) Re will occur in all linear operations such as additions, subtraction, differentiation, and integration. We may implicitly assume these recurrences and by $A e^{j\alpha}$ may understand that it represents $\operatorname{Re} [A e^{j\alpha} e^{j\omega t}]$ and by $B e^{j\beta}$ may understand that it represents $\operatorname{Re} [B e^{j\beta} e^{j\omega t}]$. Therefore, when we write $A e^{j\alpha} + B e^{j\beta}$, we imply $\operatorname{Re} [A e^{j\alpha} e^{j\omega t}] + \operatorname{Re} [B e^{j\beta} e^{j\omega t}]$, which is $A \cos (\omega t + \alpha) + B \cos (\omega t + \beta)$. In this sense the phasor is a shorthand notation with specified rules of operation.

Finally, when the phasor $A \underline{/\alpha}$ is shown graphically by an arrow of length A at an angle α with the reference (measured counterclockwise from the horizontal), this means that this line represents the sinusoidal function $A \cos (\omega t + \alpha)$, inasmuch as the value of this function at any time t_1 is found by projecting the phasor $A \underline{/\alpha}$ on an axis which makes the angle ωt_1 with reference in the clockwise direction. If the projection of the arrow is along the positive direction of the horizontal axis rotated through ωt_1, then $f(t_1)$ has a positive value; otherwise $f(t_1)$ will be negative.

A final word of caution. Whereas any sinusoidal function *can* be represented by a complex number (dealing with one frequency only), not all complex numbers are to be taken to represent sinusoidal functions. For example, $3 \underline{/\pi/4}$ *may* represent $3 \cos (\omega t + \pi/4)$. On the other hand, it may be just a complex number and have nothing to do with sinusoidal functions.

PROBLEMS

8-1. If **A** and **B** are two complex numbers: (*a*) Prove that Re **A** + Re **B** = Re (**A** + **B**). (*b*) Is the relationship (Re **A**)(Re **B**) = Re (**AB**) true? (*c*) Is the relationship $|\mathbf{A} + \mathbf{B}| = |\mathbf{A}| + |\mathbf{B}|$ true?

8-2. Prove the following relationships for any complex quantity **A**: (*a*) Re **A** = Im $(j\mathbf{A})$; (*b*) Im **A** = Re $(-j\mathbf{A})$; (*c*) Im **A** = Re $(j\mathbf{A}^*)$.

8-3. For the two complex quantities **A** and **B** prove that $\mathbf{A}^*\mathbf{B}^* = (\mathbf{AB})^*$.

8-4. Prove that $e^{j\theta} = \cos \theta + j \sin \theta$ by expanding the functions in a Maclaurin's series.

8-5. Find five distinct solutions of the equation $z^5 = 1$, and express the answers in polar, rectangular, and exponential form.

8-6. If **A** = $3.46 + j2.00$, **B** = $-0.012 + j0.43$, **C** = $126 + j19.0$, express in polar and rectangular form the numbers (*a*) **A** · **B**; (*b*) **A** · **C**/**B**; (*c*) **A** · **B**/**C***; (*d*) **A**^{2}; (*e*) $\sqrt{\mathbf{C}}$.

8-7. Convert to polar form: (*a*) $3.46 + j2.00$; (*b*) $0.346 + j2.00$; (*c*) $0.0346 + j2.00$; (*d*) $-3.46 - j2.00$; (*e*) $0.346 - j2.00$; (*f*) $(-3.46 - j2.00)^2$.

8-8. Convert to rectangular form: (*a*) $4.08 \underline{/105°}$; (*b*) $4.08 \underline{/75°}$; (*c*) $4.08 \underline{/-165°}$; (*d*) $(743 \underline{/14°})(0.635 \underline{/-28°})$; (*e*) $82 \underline{/-87°}$; (*f*) $0.00246 \underline{/-0.3°}$.

8-9. Evaluate A, and express the answer in polar and rectangular form:

(a) $A = \dfrac{(2 + j3)(1 - j4) - 8\underline{/45°}}{(\sqrt{8}\underline{/15°})(1 + j) + 4\underline{/-60°}}$.

(b) $A = \dfrac{(6.46 + j17.3)\ \text{Re}\ (14\underline{/30°}) - \text{Im}\ (27\underline{/-37°})}{(2.92 - j3.73)^2}$.

(c) $A = (4.86 + j47)(3.6 + j37) - (j30)^2$.

8-10. Evaluate Re A if (a) $A = 10\underline{/89°}$; (b) $A = 5e^{3+j4}$; (c) $A = 10e^{-0.2+j0.77}$; (d) $A = \sin (3 + j4)$; (e) $A = j5e^{2+j}$; (f) $A = (4.26 - j3.62)/(2.12 + j8.63)$.

8-11. If Re K = 17 and Re $[(-3 + j6)K] = 4$, find K, and express the answer in polar form.

8-12. If Re K = 3 and Im $[(-5 - j5)K] = 5$, find K in polar form.

8-13. Prove the following identities:

(a) $\sin (x + jy) = \dfrac{e^y + e^{-y}}{2} \sin x + j\dfrac{e^y - e^{-y}}{2} \cos x$.

(b) $\cos (x + jy) = \dfrac{e^y + e^{-y}}{2} \cos x - j\dfrac{e^y - e^{-y}}{2} \sin x$.

(c) Re $e^{x+jy} = e^x \cos y$.

8-14. If the principal value of the angle of A is between zero and 2π, evaluate ln A if (a) $A = j$; (b) $A = -5$; (c) $A = -6 - j6$.

8-15. Perform the following operations graphically if $A = 4.5 + j6$ and $B = 2 + j2$: (a) $A + B$; (b) $A + jB$; (c) $j^2A + jB$; (d) $A - B$; (e) $B - A$; (f) $A^* - B$.

8-16. Solve the equation $100\underline{/0°} + A\underline{/60°} = 173\underline{/\phi}$ for A and ϕ.

8-17. Solve the equation $100\underline{/-60°} + A(1 + j4) = 200\underline{/\phi}$ for A and ϕ.

8-18. If Im $[100\underline{/-50°} + A(1 + j4)] = 0$, find A.

8-19. If $A = (10 + 5\underline{/\phi})/(10 - 5\underline{/\phi})$, find the maximum value of A and the corresponding value of ϕ.

8-20. Show that $|A^j| = 1$ if A is any real number.

8-21. Evaluate (a) $\sqrt{j}$, (b) j^j, (c) $(3 + j4)^j$, and express the answer in polar form.

8-22. Prove that $(\cos \theta + j \sin \theta)^n = (\cos n\theta + j \sin n\theta)$ (De Moivre's theorem).

8-23. In the equation $a_0 + a_1z + a_2z^2 + \cdots + a_nz^n = 0$ the constants a_1, a_2, $\ldots$, a_n are real. Prove that if z is a solution of this equation then z^* is also a solution.

8-24. Sketch on one set of axes, using ωt as the independent variable, (a) $f_1(t) = \cos \omega t$, (b) $f_2(t) = 1.5 \cos (\omega t - 60°)$, (c) $f_1(t) + f_2(t)$, obtained by graphical addition.

8-25. (a) Sketch the function $f(t) = 23 \cos (5,000t - 30°)$. (b) For the function of (a) what are (1) its amplitude; (2) its radian frequency; (3) its frequency? (c) What is the phase relation of the function $f(t)$ to the function (1) $\cos 5,000t$; (2) $\sin 5,000t$; (3) $\sin (5,000t + 60°)$; (4) $\sin (5,000t - 60°)$?

8-26. Prove the following identities:

(a) $\dfrac{d}{dt} \text{Re}\ e^{j\omega t} = \text{Re} \left(\dfrac{d}{dt} e^{j\omega t} \right)$.

(b) $\dfrac{d}{dt} \text{Im}\ e^{j\omega t} = \text{Im} \left(\dfrac{d}{dt} e^{j\omega t} \right)$.

(c) $\dfrac{d}{dt} \text{Re}\ e^{j\omega t} = \text{Im} \left[\dfrac{d}{dt} (je^{j\omega t}) \right]$.

8-27. The following functions are to be represented by phasors: (a) $500 \sin (\omega t + 30°)$; (b) $-80 \cos (\omega t - 45°)$; (c) $-60 \sin (\omega t - 121°)$. What are the phasors which represent these functions if (1) $\cos \omega t$ is represented by $1/\underline{0}$; (2) $\sin \omega t$ is represented by $1/\underline{0}$?

8-28. Use phasor representation to add $f(t) = 72 \cos (\omega t - 14°) + 80 \sin (\omega t + 26°) - 40 \sin \omega t$.

8-29. Use phasor representation to obtain $f(t)$ if $100 \cos \omega t = f(t) + 30 \sin \omega t + 150 \sin (\omega t - 200°)$.

8-30. Solve the following equation for A and ϕ: $100 \cos \omega t + A \cos (\omega t + 60°) = 173 \cos (\omega t + \phi)$.

8-31. The phasor $1/\underline{0°}$ represents the function $\cos \omega t$. The function $f_1(t)$ is represented by $10/\underline{45°}$, and $f_2(t)$ is represented by $12/\underline{-60°}$. The function $f(t)$ is defined by $f(t) = f_1(t) + f_2(t)$. Find the value of $f(t)$ when (a) $\omega t = 0$; (b) $\omega t = \pi/4$; (c) $\omega t = 5\pi/6$; (d) $\omega t = 3\pi/2$.

8-32. Show that the general solution of a source-free L-C circuit can be written as $q(t) = \text{Re} (\mathbf{K}e^{j\omega t})$ if $\omega_0{}^2 = 1/LC$.

8-33. Shown in Fig. P8-33 are two phasors $\mathbf{A}$ and $\mathbf{B}$ which represent the sinusoidal functions $f_a(t)$ and $f_b(t)$, respectively, in accordance with the convention used in this book, that is, $\cos \omega t \rightarrow 1/\underline{0°}$. The frequency is 1,000 cps. Calculate the values of $f_a(t)$, $f_a(t) + f_b(t)$, $f_a(t) - f_b(t)$ at the instants (a) $t = 0$; (b) $t = 2 \times 10^{-4}$ sec; (c) 4×10^{-4} sec; (d) 6×10^{-4} sec.

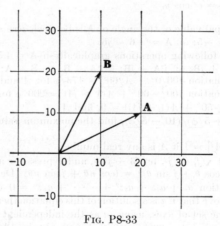

FIG. P8-33

8-34. At the junction shown in Fig. P8-34 $i_1(t) = 5 \cos \omega t$, $i_2(t) = 3 \cos (\omega t - 120°)$. Calculate $i_3(t)$ in the form $i_3(t) = A \cos (\omega t + \phi)$.

FIG. P8-34

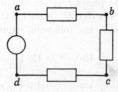

FIG. P8-35

8-35. It is known that in Fig. P8-35 $v_{ab}(t) = 3 \cos \omega t$, $v_{bc}(t) = 4 \sin \omega t$, and $v_{cd}(t) = 5 \cos (\omega t + 37°)$. Calculate $v_{ad}(t)$.

8-36. If $f_1(t) = 6 \cos (\omega t - 72°)$ and $f_2(t) = 12 \sin (\omega t + 150°)$, calculate the maximum value of (a) $f_1(t) + f_2(t)$; (b) $f_1(t) - f_2(t)$.

CHAPTER 9

THE SOURCE-FREE R-L-C CIRCUIT

A circuit consisting of a single resistance, a single inductance, and a single capacitance is the simplest circuit in which energy dissipation as well as electric- and magnetic-energy storage takes place. For this reason the source-free R-L-C circuit does, to a first order of approximation, represent the equivalent circuit of many electrical devices. For example, a receiving or transmitting antenna, cavity resonators and matching devices used in microwave techniques, piezoelectric crystals used in audio- and radio-frequency work, automatic control systems, as well as electromechanical and purely mechanical devices such as galvanometers and vibrating systems can be represented by series or parallel connections of R, L, and C elements. The technique of such representations was briefly discussed in Chap. 5, and the reader will find more extended discussions in textbooks dealing with particular devices. In this chapter we shall study the behavior of the variables (voltages and currents) associated with R-L-C circuits. We shall show that, depending on the relative values of the three elements, any variable $y(t)$ associated with a source-free R-L-C circuit will be of one of the following three forms:

$$y(t) = A e^{-\alpha t} \cos (\omega t + \gamma)$$
$$y(t) = A_1 e^{-(\alpha+\beta)t} + A_2 e^{-(\alpha-\beta)t}$$
$$y(t) = (A_3 + A_4 t) e^{-\alpha t}$$

where α, ω, and β are positive values, independent of time, and are determined by the values of R, L, and C and A, A_1, A_2, A_3, A_4, and γ are also independent of time and their values are determined by the initial conditions of the circuit as well as the values of R, L, and C. The three possible waveforms associated with a source-free R-L-C circuit are shown in Figs. 9-3, 9-5, and 9-6, respectively.

A study of these figures will show that any variable associated with a source-free R-L-C circuit will "decay" to zero, although, as in the case of Fig. 9-3, this decay may be associated with oscillations. Thus the voltage or current associated with an element in an R-L-C circuit (or, in mechanical analogues, the velocity or displacement) will vary with time in accordance with the waveform of one of the above figures. Further-

135

more, in Chap. 16 it will be shown that the variables associated with any connection of passive elements, no matter how complicated, will vary in accordance with a combination of the above-mentioned waveforms.

For this reason a knowledge of the behavior of an R-L-C circuit will enable us to understand the behavior of any "complicated" source-free network.

9-1. Equilibrium Equation for the Source-free Series R-L-C Circuit.

Consider the circuit shown in Fig. 9-1a. Prior to $t = 0$ the switch is in position d. At $t = 0$ the switch is thrown to position a so that for $t \geq 0^+$

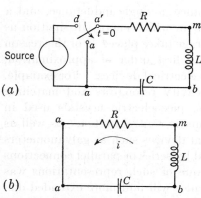

(a)

(b)

Fig. 9-1. Deenergizing a series R-L-C circuit. (a) Switching operation. (b) Source-free circuit.

Fig. 9-1b represents the circuit to be studied. The equilibrium conditions in this circuit can be expressed in terms of any of the variables in the circuit, i.e., the current, the charge at either terminal of the capacitance, or the voltage across any of the elements. While we shall choose the voltage across the capacitance, v_{ab}, as the variable in the bulk of this chapter, the formulation of the equilibrium equation using the other quantities in the circuit as the variables is also instructive. In the following paragraphs the current $i(t)$ will be used as the dependent variable.

Application of Kirchhoff's voltage law to the circuit of Fig. 9-1b gives the equation

$$v_{bm} + v_{ma} + v_{ab} = 0 \tag{9-1}$$

In order to reduce Eq. (9-1) to an equation which contains only one variable, we note that the voltage across the individual elements are all related to the current i, through the voltage-current equations of the elements. Thus

$$v_{bm} = L\frac{di}{dt} \qquad v_{ma} = Ri \qquad v_{ab} = \frac{1}{C}\int_{-\infty}^{t} i\, d\tau \tag{9-2}$$

Using Eqs. (9-2) in (9-1), we obtain the equilibrium equation which has the current as the variable,

$$L\frac{di}{dt} + Ri + \frac{1}{C}\int_{-\infty}^{t} i\, d\tau = 0 \qquad t \geq 0^+ \tag{9-3}$$

This equation is an integrodifferential equation. Differentiating both sides of the equation and dividing by L, we obtain the (second-order linear homogeneous) equation

$$\frac{d^2i}{dt^2} + \frac{R}{L}\frac{di}{dt} + \frac{1}{LC}i = 0 \qquad t \geq 0^+ \qquad (9\text{-}3a)$$

If instead of the current $i(t)$ the voltage across the capacitance, $v_{ab}(t)$, is chosen as the variable, then we note [from Eq. (9-2)] that

$$i = C\frac{dv_{ab}}{dt} \qquad (9\text{-}4a)$$

Hence $\quad v_{ma} = iR = RC\dfrac{dv_{ab}}{dt} \quad$ and $\quad v_{bm} = L\dfrac{di}{dt} = LC\dfrac{d^2v_{ab}}{dt^2} \quad (9\text{-}4b)$

Using Eqs. (9-4a) and (9-4b) in Eq. (9-1), we have the equilibrium equation

$$LC\frac{d^2v_{ab}}{dt^2} + RC\frac{dv_{ab}}{dt} + v_{ab} = 0 \qquad t \geq 0^+$$

or, dividing by LC,

$$\frac{d^2v_{ab}}{dt^2} + \frac{R}{L}\frac{dv_{ab}}{dt} + \frac{1}{LC}v_{ab} = 0 \qquad t \geq 0^+ \qquad (9\text{-}5)$$

It should be clear now that the equilibrium equation for any of the variables in this source-free circuit will have the form

$$\frac{d^2y}{dt^2} + \frac{R}{L}\frac{dy}{dt} + \frac{1}{LC}y = 0 \qquad t \geq 0^+ \qquad (9\text{-}6)$$

where y may be i, v_{ab}, q_a, q_b, v_{ma}, dv_{ma}/dt or any other variable. This follows from the linear relationships between the variables which describe the elements as expressed by Eqs. (9-2).

9-2. Initial Conditions. If we assume that at $t = 0^-$ there was energy stored in the inductance and in the capacitance, then the solution of the equilibrium equations is subject to the continuity conditions,

Because of the inductance: $\quad i(0^-) = i(0^+) \equiv I_0$

and

Because of the capacitance: $\quad v_{ab}(0^-) = v_{ab}(0^+) \equiv V_0$

since, exactly as in the cases of the R-L, R-C, and L-C circuits, no impulses can occur.

In addition to the continuity conditions it is possible to obtain initial conditions for any of the variables of the circuit or their derivatives by using the continuity conditions in the equilibrium equations. Several examples of this procedure will be given below.

Since $v_{ab} = q_a/C$, the (continuity) condition for q_a is $q_a(0^+) = CV_0$. Writing the equilibrium equation (9-5) in terms of the charge q_a, we have

$$\frac{d^2q_a}{dt^2} + \frac{R}{L}\frac{dq_a}{dt} + \frac{1}{LC}\,q_a = 0 \qquad t \ge 0^+ \tag{9-7}$$

or

$$\frac{d^2q_a}{dt^2} = -\left(\frac{R}{L}\frac{dq_a}{dt} + \frac{1}{LC}\,q_a\right) \qquad t \ge 0^+ \tag{9-7a}$$

Now, since $dq_a/dt = i$, we may rewrite Eq. (9-7a) in the form

$$\frac{d^2q_a}{dt^2} = \frac{di}{dt} = -\left(\frac{R}{L}\,i + \frac{1}{LC}\,q_a\right) \qquad t \ge 0^+ \tag{9-7b}$$

Equation (9-7b) is an equilibrium equation which holds for all $t \ge 0^+$; in particular it holds at $t = 0^+$. Substituting $t = 0^+$ in Eq. (9-7b), we obtain the initial value of di/dt,

$$\left(\frac{di}{dt}\right)_{0^+} = -\left[\frac{R}{L}\,i(0^+) + \frac{1}{LC}\,q_a(0^+)\right]$$

or

$$\left(\frac{di}{dt}\right)_{0^+} = -\left(\frac{R}{L}\,I_0 + \frac{1}{L}\,V_0\right) \tag{9-8a}$$

The condition (9-8a) gives the initial value of the first derivative of the current. This condition is *not* a continuity condition; in fact the derivative of the current is generally not continuous at $t = 0$. Hence Eq. (9-8a) gives only $(di/dt)_{0^+}$ and gives *no* information about $(di/dt)_{0^-}$. We recall from Chap. 7 that an initial condition which is *not* a continuity condition is referred to as a *derived* initial condition. We can obtain as many derived initial conditions as we choose by using the continuity conditions in the various forms of the equilibrium equation. If, for example, Eq. (9-7b) is differentiated once with respect to time, we have the relationship (using $dq_a/dt = i$)

$$\frac{d^3q_a}{dt^3} = \frac{d^2i}{dt^2} = -\left(\frac{R}{L}\frac{di}{dt} + \frac{1}{LC}\,i\right) \qquad t \ge 0^+ \tag{9-7c}$$

Hence, substituting $t = 0^+$, we have the initial condition for the second derivative of the current,

$$\left(\frac{d^2i}{dt^2}\right)_{0^+} = -\left[\frac{R}{L}\left(\frac{di}{dt}\right)_{0^+} + \frac{1}{LC}\,i(0^+)\right] \tag{9-8b}$$

The numerical value of $(d^2i/dt^2)_{0^+}$ is obtained by substitution of the result (9-8a) and the continuity condition for i in (9-8b),

$$\left(\frac{d^2i}{dt^2}\right)_{0^+} = -\left[\frac{R}{L}\left(-\frac{R}{L}\,I_0 - \frac{1}{L}\,V_0\right) + \frac{1}{LC}\,I_0\right]$$

$$= -\left[\left(\frac{1}{LC} - \frac{R^2}{L^2}\right)I_0 - \frac{R}{L^2}\,V_0\right] \tag{9-8c}$$

The process of differentiating the equilibrium equation and substituting $t = 0^+$ can be repeated indefinitely and as many initial values for the higher derivatives can be deduced as are desired. While some of these derived initial conditions are subject to immediate physical interpretation [for example $L(di/dt)_{0^+} = v_{bm}(0^+)$], the higher derivatives should generally be looked upon as describing the slopes and curvatures (and their rates of change) of the waveform for the variable.

9-3. The Characteristic Equation. The response of the source-free R-L-C circuit, using the voltage across the capacitance, v_{ab}, as the variable, is determined by the solution of the equilibrium equation

$$\frac{d^2 v_{ab}}{dt^2} + \frac{R}{L}\frac{dv_{ab}}{dt} + \frac{1}{LC} v_{ab} = 0 \qquad t \geq 0^+ \qquad (9\text{-}9a)$$

subject to the initial conditions

$$v_{ab}(0^+) = V_0 \qquad \text{and} \qquad \left(\frac{dv_{ab}}{dt}\right)_{0^+} = \frac{1}{C} I_0 \qquad (9\text{-}9b)$$

The equilibrium equation (9-9a) can be satisfied at every instant of time only if the waveshapes of v_{ab}, its first derivative dv_{ab}/dt, and its second derivative $d^2 v_{ab}/dt^2$ are all similar to each other. In addition we note that at any instant at least one of these terms must have a sign opposite to the others so that the sum of the three terms can be identically zero (for all values of t). This property which is required of the function $v_{ab}(t)$ is also a property of exponential functions. It is recalled that a similar argument was used in obtaining the solution of the first-order homogeneous equation which is associated with a source-free R-L or R-C circuit. In fact, the same argument applies to any homogeneous linear differential equation with constant coefficients. The solution of such an equation will therefore be of the form e^{st}, where s is independent of t. To solve the equilibrium equation (9-9a), we therefore assume the solution of the form

$$v_{ab}(t) = A e^{st} \qquad (9\text{-}10a)$$

and note that

$$\frac{dv_{ab}}{dt} = s A e^{st} = s v_{ab} \qquad (9\text{-}10b)$$

$$\frac{d^2 v_{ab}}{dt^2} = s^2 A e^{st} = s^2 v_{ab} \qquad (9\text{-}10c)$$

$$\frac{d^n v_{ab}}{dt^n} = s^n A e^{st} = s^n v_{ab} \qquad (9\text{-}10d)$$

Substituting the assumed form (9-10a) and the resulting form for the first two derivatives (9-10b) and (9-10c) in the equilibrium equation (9-9a), we have

$$s^2 v_{ab}(t) + \frac{R}{L} s v_{ab}(t) + \frac{1}{LC} v_{ab}(t) = 0 \qquad t \geq 0^+$$

or

$$\left(s^2 + \frac{R}{L} s + \frac{1}{LC}\right) v_{ab}(t) = 0 \qquad t \geq 0^+ \qquad (9\text{-}11)$$

Since $v_{ab}(t)$ cannot be zero for all $t \geq 0^+$, it follows from Eq. (9-11) that the relationship

$$s^2 + \frac{R}{L} s + \frac{1}{LC} = 0 \qquad (9\text{-}12)$$

must hold if the assumed form (9-10a) is to be a solution.

Equation (9-12) is the characteristic equation associated with the equilibrium equation (9-9a). This equation resulted from the equilibrium equation with $v_{ab}(t)$ as its variable. We note now that the equilibrium equation in terms of any other variable of this source-free circuit would have exactly the same form, i.e., the form of Eq. (9-6). The solution for any one of the variables will therefore also have the same form, i.e., the form Ke^{st}, one solution differing from the other solution only in the constant K. Since the same equation (9-12) must be satisfied for any of the variables, this equation is called the *characteristic* equation. The word characteristic is used to imply that the relationship applies to *any variable of the source-free circuit.*

9-4. The Characteristic Roots and Natural Modes of a Circuit. The algebraic equation (9-12) has two roots which are called the characteristic roots of the equation (or of the circuit). Applying the quadratic formula to Eq. (9-12), the two characteristic roots are

$$s_1 = -\frac{R}{2L} + \sqrt{\left(\frac{R}{2L}\right)^2 - \frac{1}{LC}}$$
$$s_2 = -\frac{R}{2L} - \sqrt{\left(\frac{R}{2L}\right)^2 - \frac{1}{LC}} \qquad (9\text{-}13)$$

Either of the terms $A_1 e^{s_1 t}$ and $A_2 e^{s_2 t}$ can therefore satisfy the equilibrium equation. Since the circuit contains two independent energy-storing elements, the solution must contain two, as yet arbitrary, constants to fit the two arbitrarily chosen continuity conditions. The solution is therefore written in the form

$$v_{ab}(t) = A_1 e^{s_1 t} + A_2 e^{s_2 t} \qquad (9\text{-}14)$$

We note again that the solution for any other variable can also be written in the same form, for example,

$$i(t) = B_1 e^{s_1 t} + B_2 e^{s_2 t}$$
$$\text{or} \qquad v_{bm}(t) = D_1 e^{s_1 t} + D_2 e^{s_2 t} \qquad (9\text{-}15)$$

Modes of Response. Each of the time functions $B_1 e^{s_1 t}$ and $B_2 e^{s_2 t}$ in Eq. (9-15) is called a natural mode (mode for brevity) of the source-free series $R\text{-}L\text{-}C$ circuit. In general the number of modes of a source-free circuit is identical with the number of characteristic roots of the characteristic equation associated with the circuit. In the case of an $R\text{-}L$

circuit, which contained one energy-storing element, the characteristic equation was $s + R/L = 0$, resulting in the single characteristic root $s = -R/L$ and its corresponding mode $Ae^{-(Rt/L)}$. The R-L-C circuit, which contains two energy-storing elements, has two characteristic roots, given in Eq. (9-13), and two corresponding modes $A_1e^{s_1t}$ and $A_2e^{s_2t}$. Later we shall see that the number of natural modes of a source-free network is the same as the number of its "independent" energy-storing elements.

Simple and Multiple Characteristic Roots. If the discriminant of the characteristic equation (9-12), namely, $(R/2L)^2 - 1/LC$, is *not* zero, then the two roots s_1 and s_2 are not equal to each other; they are "distinct" and are called simple roots. If $(R/2L)^2 = 1/LC$, then the two roots are identical, since then $s_1 = s_2 = -R/2L = -1/\sqrt{LC}$. This type of root is called a multiple root. With multiple roots the complete solution cannot be of the form (9-14) since, for $s_1 = s_2$,

$$A_1e^{s_1t} + A_2e^{s_2t} = A_1e^{s_1t} + A_2e^{s_1t} = (A_1 + A_2)e^{s_1t} = Me^{s_1t}$$

This form has only one arbitrary constant (M) and therefore cannot be made to fit two (arbitrarily specified) initial conditions. The case for which the discriminant of the characteristic equation is zero is therefore a special case. The special form of the solution in this case will be taken up in Art. 9-13.

9-5. Use of the Initial Conditions. Excluding the case $s_1 = s_2$, the solution for the voltage $v_{ab}(t)$ can be written in the form

$$v_{ab}(t) = A_1e^{s_1t} + A_2e^{s_2t} \qquad s_1 \neq s_2, t \geq 0^+ \qquad (9\text{-}16a)$$

and its first derivative is

$$\frac{dv_{ab}}{dt} = s_1A_1e^{s_1t} + s_2A_2e^{s_2t} \qquad (9\text{-}16b)$$

The constants A_1 and A_2 can now be evaluated by introducing the initial conditions (9-9b),

$$v_{ab}(0^+) = V_0 = A_1e^{s_10} + A_2e^{s_20} = A_1 + A_2$$

$$\left(\frac{dv_{ab}}{dt}\right)_{0^+} = \frac{I_0}{C} = s_1A_1e^{s_10} + s_2A_2e^{s_20} = s_1A_1 + s_2A_2$$

Hence A_1 and A_2 are the solutions of the two simultaneous algebraic equations

$$A_1 + A_2 = V_0 \qquad (9\text{-}17a)$$

$$s_1A_1 + s_2A_2 = \frac{I_0}{C} \qquad (9\text{-}17b)$$

Multiplying Eq. (9-17a) by $-s_2$ and adding the result to Eq. (9-17b), we obtain the solution for A_1 and A_2,

$$A_1 = \frac{I_0/C - s_2 V_0}{s_1 - s_2} \tag{9-18a}$$

$$V_0 - A_1 = A_2 = \frac{s_1 V_0 - I_0/C}{s_1 - s_2} \tag{9-18b}$$

[At this point we note again that the case $s_1 = s_2$ is excluded. If $s_1 = s_2$, then Eqs. (9-18) are meaningless because of the division by $s_1 - s_2$.] The solution for v_{ab} can now be written by substituting the values of A_1 and A_2 in (9-16a),

$$v_{ab}(t) = \frac{1}{s_1 - s_2}\left[\left(\frac{I_0}{C} - s_2 V_0\right)e^{s_1 t} + \left(s_1 V_0 - \frac{I_0}{C}\right)e^{s_2 t}\right] \qquad s_1 \neq s_2,\ t > 0^+ \tag{9-19}$$

If the current $i(t)$ is desired, then we use the relationship $i(t) = C\,dv_{ab}/dt$

$$i(t) = \frac{C}{s_1 - s_2}\left[\left(\frac{s_1 I_0}{C} - s_1 s_2 V_0\right)e^{s_1 t} + \left(s_1 s_2 V_0 - \frac{I_0 s_2}{C}\right)e^{s_2 t}\right] \qquad s_1 \neq s_2,\ t \geq 0^+$$

We again point out that the mathematical form of $v_{ab}(t)$ is identical to the form of $i(t)$.

9-6. Types of Response. The Quality Factor Q_0. In order to study the waveshapes of the solution and to include the case heretofore excluded, three cases, depending on the nature of the characteristic roots, may be distinguished; these cases are defined in Table 9-1. The reasons for the

TABLE 9-1

Condition	Name of case	Nature of the roots
$\left(\dfrac{R}{2L}\right)^2 < \dfrac{1}{LC}$	Underdamped or oscillatory	Complex conjugates with negative real parts
$\left(\dfrac{R}{2L}\right)^2 = \dfrac{1}{LC}$	Critically damped	Negative, real, and equal ($s_1 = s_2$)
$\left(\dfrac{R}{2L}\right)^2 > \dfrac{1}{LC}$	Overdamped	Negative, real, and unequal ($s_1 \neq s_2$)

names which are assigned to these conditions will become clear as each case is discussed in detail. The conditions which lead to these three cases depend on the relative values of two numbers: $R/2L$ and $1/\sqrt{LC}$. In order to show this more explicitly, the following abbreviations are introduced:

$$\omega_0 = \frac{1}{\sqrt{LC}} \qquad \alpha = \frac{R}{2L} \tag{9-20}$$

The meaning of ω_0 is already clear: it is the radian frequency with which the response *would* oscillate *if* the resistance were zero. The term α is interpreted as a "damping" constant since it is the term due to the resistance. With the symbols defined in Eqs. (9-20) the roots of the characteristic equation are

$$s_{1,2} = -\alpha \pm \sqrt{\alpha^2 - \omega_0^2}$$

The critically damped case occurs when $\alpha = \omega_0$, so that in this case $s_1 = s_2 = -\omega_0 = -\alpha$.

It is convenient to define a single number which, for this circuit, indicates the type of response. Since, for critical damping $s_1 = s_2$, $(R/2L)^2 = 1/LC$, it follows that

$$\text{For critical damping:} \frac{1}{2} = \frac{\sqrt{L/C}}{R} = \frac{\omega_0 L}{R}$$

In other words, if the number $\sqrt{L/C}/R = \frac{1}{2}$, the circuit is critically damped. If $\sqrt{L/C}/R < \frac{1}{2}$, then $(R/2L)^2 > 1/LC$ and the circuit is overdamped. The number $\sqrt{L/C}/R$ is denoted by the symbol Q_0 and is called "the Q" ("the cue") of the series R-L-C circuit. The three cases are related to the Q by the relationships

$$Q_0 > \tfrac{1}{2} \qquad \text{underdamped}$$
$$Q_0 = \tfrac{1}{2} \qquad \text{critically damped}$$
$$Q_0 < \tfrac{1}{2} \qquad \text{overdamped}$$

The symbol Q_0 is called the quality factor of the circuit and should not be confused with the symbol for charge (or initial charge). The Q of a circuit is a basic quantity whose value depends on the circuit elements only. The relationship

$$Q_0 = \frac{\sqrt{L/C}}{R} = \frac{\omega_0 L}{R} \tag{9-21}$$

holds only for the series R-L-C circuit. A Q is also defined for other simple R-L-C circuits; the expressions for other such cases will be deduced as these cases are discussed.

9-7. The Underdamped (Oscillatory) Case. When the Q of the circuit is more than $\frac{1}{2}$, then $\omega_0 > \alpha$ and the characteristic roots are the conjugate complex values

$$s_{1,2} = -\alpha \pm \sqrt{(-1)(\omega_0^2 - \alpha^2)}$$

In this case it is convenient to define

$$\omega_d = +\sqrt{\omega_0^2 - \alpha^2}$$

so that the roots can be written as

$$\mathbf{s}_1 = -\alpha + j\omega_d \qquad \text{and} \qquad \mathbf{s}_2 = -\alpha - j\omega_d \qquad (9\text{-}22)$$
$$\mathbf{s}_1 - \mathbf{s}_2 = j2\omega_d \qquad \text{and} \qquad \mathbf{s}_1\mathbf{s}_2 = \alpha^2 + \omega_d{}^2 = \omega_0{}^2$$

The response of the circuit as given by the equation for $v_{ab}(t)$ has the form [see Eq. (9-19)]

$$v_{ab}(t) = \mathbf{A}_1 e^{\mathbf{s}_1 t} + \mathbf{A}_2 e^{\mathbf{s}_2 t} \qquad (9\text{-}23)$$

where
$$\mathbf{A}_1 = \frac{I_0/C - \mathbf{s}_2 V_0}{\mathbf{s}_1 - \mathbf{s}_2}$$
$$\mathbf{A}_2 = \frac{\mathbf{s}_1 V_0 - I_0/C}{\mathbf{s}_1 - \mathbf{s}_2} \qquad (9\text{-}24)$$

where boldface type is used wherever the quantity *is or may be* complex. The form of Eq. (9-23) shows that $v_{ab}(t)$ is the sum of two complex terms; yet we know that $v_{ab}(t)$ is a real function of time, because it is the solution of a differential equation with real variables and real coefficients. We shall now show that $v_{ab}(t)$ can be written in real form and that, *once this general form has been established*, we need not use the complex form (9-23). Since $\mathbf{s}_1$ and $\mathbf{s}_2$ are conjugate complex quantities, $\mathbf{A}_1$ and $\mathbf{A}_2$ are also conjugate complex quantities. This can be shown by substituting the expressions for $\mathbf{s}_1$ and $\mathbf{s}_2$ from Eqs. (9-22) into Eqs. (9-24),

$$\mathbf{A}_1 = \frac{I_0/C - (-\alpha - j\omega_d)V_0}{2j\omega_d} = \frac{I_0/C + \alpha V_0}{2j\omega_d} + \frac{j\omega_d V_0}{2j\omega_d}$$
$$= \tfrac{1}{2}V_0 - j\frac{I_0/C + \alpha V_0}{2\omega_d} \qquad (9\text{-}25a)$$

and

$$\mathbf{A}_2 = \frac{(-\alpha + j\omega_d)V_0 - I_0/C}{2j\omega_d} = \frac{j\omega_d V_0}{2j\omega_d} + \frac{-\alpha V_0 - I_0/C}{2j\omega_d}$$
$$= \tfrac{1}{2}V_0 + j\frac{I_0/C + \alpha V_0}{2\omega_d} \qquad (9\text{-}25b)$$

In Eqs. (9-25a) and (9-25b) we note that

$$\text{Re } \mathbf{A}_1 = \tfrac{1}{2}V_0 = \text{Re } \mathbf{A}_2$$

and
$$\text{Im } \mathbf{A}_1 = -\frac{I_0/C + \alpha V_0}{2\omega_d} = -\text{Im } \mathbf{A}_2$$

Hence $\mathbf{A}_1$ and $\mathbf{A}_2$ are conjugate complex numbers,

$$\mathbf{A}_1^* = \mathbf{A}_2$$

Since $\mathbf{A}_1$ and $\mathbf{A}_2$ are complex numbers, we can write them in polar or exponential form: Let

$$\mathbf{A}_1 = A_1 e^{j\gamma} = A_1\underline{/\gamma}$$

Then
$$\mathbf{A}_2 = \mathbf{A}_1^* = A_1 e^{-j\gamma} = A_1\underline{/-\gamma}$$

Noting that s_1 and s_2 are also conjugate complex numbers, Eq. (9-23) can be written as follows:

$$v_{ab}(t) = \mathbf{A}_1 e^{s_1 t} + \mathbf{A}_1^* e^{s_1^* t} \qquad (9\text{-}26)$$

Now $$\mathbf{A}_1 e^{s_1 t} = A_1 e^{-\alpha t} e^{j(\omega_d t + \gamma)}$$

and $$\mathbf{A}_1^* e^{s_1^* t} = A_1 e^{-\alpha t} e^{-j(\omega_d t + \gamma)} = (\mathbf{A}_1 e^{s_1 t})^* = \mathbf{A}_2 e^{s_2 t}$$

Hence Eq. (9-26) can be written as the sum of the above complex conjugate terms. We now recall that, for any complex quantity $\mathbf{z}$,

$$\mathbf{z} + \mathbf{z}^* = 2 \operatorname{Re} \mathbf{z}$$

Hence the general form of the solution in the underdamped case can be written as

$$v_{ab}(t) = 2 \operatorname{Re} (\mathbf{A}_1 e^{s_1 t})$$

or, letting $\mathbf{K} = 2\mathbf{A}_1$,

$$v_{ab}(t) = \operatorname{Re} (\mathbf{K} e^{s_1 t}) \qquad (9\text{-}27)$$

9-8. Different Forms of the Solution in the Underdamped Case. Concept of Complex Frequency. In Eq. (9-27) the value of the complex number $\mathbf{K} = 2\mathbf{A}_1$ will depend on the initial conditions, as well as the circuit elements [see Eqs. (9-25)]. In example 9-1, below, a detailed numerical example is presented. At any rate $\mathbf{K}$ can be written in the exponential form $\mathbf{K} = K e^{j\gamma}$, where K and γ will be evaluated from Eqs. (9-9b). By convention K is always a positive number, and the value of γ, depending on the initial conditions, may be anywhere between zero and 2π. In contrast s_1 is a complex number whose value is determined by the circuit elements only and is independent of the initial conditions.

$$s_1 = -\frac{R}{2L} + j \sqrt{\omega_0^2 - \alpha^2} = -\alpha + j\omega_d$$

or $$s_1 = \sqrt{\alpha^2 + \omega_d^2} \ \Big/ \tan^{-1} \frac{\omega_d}{-\alpha}$$

Since α and ω_d are both positive numbers, $s_1 = -\alpha + j\omega_d$ will be in the second quadrant of the complex plane. With reference to Fig. 9-7 (page 160), let

$$\delta = \tan^{-1} \frac{\omega_d}{-\alpha} \qquad \frac{\pi}{2} < \delta < \pi \qquad (9\text{-}28)$$

From $\omega_0^2 = \alpha^2 + \omega_d^2$ and the above equations we have the polar form,

$$s_1 = \omega_0 \underline{/\delta} \qquad (9\text{-}29)$$

where ω_0 and δ are both independent of the initial conditions, depending only on the values of the circuit elements.

Using the exponential form of $\mathbf{K}$ in Eq. (9-27), we have

$$
\begin{aligned}
v_{ab}(t) &= \text{Re } [Ke^{j\gamma}e^{(-\alpha+j\omega_d)t}] \\
&= \text{Re } [Ke^{-\alpha t}e^{j(\omega_d t + \gamma)}] \\
&= Ke^{-\alpha t} \cos (\omega_d t + \gamma) \qquad\qquad (9\text{-}30a)
\end{aligned}
$$

Expanding the cosine term in Eq. (9-30a), we have

$$
v_{ab}(t) = e^{-\alpha t}(K_2 \cos \omega_d t + K_3 \sin \omega_d t) \qquad\qquad (9\text{-}30b)
$$

where $\qquad K_2 = K \cos \gamma \qquad$ and $\qquad K_3 = -K \sin \gamma$

Depending on the type of the problem and the required result, one or another of the above forms will be found to be more convenient.

We have already stated that the form of the response for the variables $i(t)$ and $q(t)$ or any of the derivatives of a circuit variable will be of the same form as indicated for $v_{ab}(t)$ in Eqs. (9-27) and (9-30). Thus the waveshape of these variables and their derivatives will be the same (damped oscillatory), and the difference in their waveforms will be in the value of the constant K and the phase angle of the cosine term.

Complex Frequency. The derivatives of circuit variables (v_{ab} and i_{ab}) are of particular interest in circuit analysis. When the mode of response of a circuit is underdamped, the most convenient form for differentiation is the complex form of Eq. (9-27), which is repeated here,

$$
v_{ab}(t) = \text{Re } (\mathbf{K}e^{\mathbf{s}_1 t})
$$

Differentiating with respect to time,

$$
\frac{d}{dt} v_{ab}(t) = \frac{d}{dt} \text{Re } (\mathbf{K}e^{\mathbf{s}_1 t}) = \text{Re } (\mathbf{s}_1\mathbf{K}_1 e^{\mathbf{s}_1 t}) \qquad\qquad (9\text{-}31)
$$

Substituting the exponential forms of $\mathbf{s}_1$ and $\mathbf{K}$ in Eq. (9-31), we have

$$
\begin{aligned}
\frac{d}{dt} v_{ab}(t) &= \text{Re } [\omega_0 e^{j\delta}Ke^{j\gamma}e^{(-\alpha+j\omega_d)t}] \\
&= \omega_0 Ke^{-\alpha t} \cos (\omega_d t + \gamma + \delta) \qquad\qquad (9\text{-}32)
\end{aligned}
$$

A comparison of Eqs. (9-30a) and (9-32) shows that the operation of differentiation on the former has resulted in multiplying Eq. (9-30a) by ω_0 and advancing the phase angle of its cosine term by δ.

If $v_{ab} = \text{Re } (\mathbf{K}e^{\mathbf{s}_1 t})$ is differentiated twice, we have

$$
\begin{aligned}
\frac{d^2}{dt^2} v_{ab}(t) &= \text{Re } (\mathbf{K}\mathbf{s}_1^2 e^{\mathbf{s}_1 t}) \\
&= \text{Re } [Ke^{j\gamma}\omega_0^2 e^{j2\delta}e^{(-\alpha+j\omega_d)t}] \\
&= \omega_0^2 Ke^{-\alpha t} \cos (\omega_d t + \gamma + 2\delta)
\end{aligned}
$$

Thus, to obtain the second derivative of $v_{ab}(t)$, we have only to multiply it by ω_0^2 and advance the phase of its cosine term by 2δ. Similarly the

nth derivative of a damped oscillatory waveform is obtained by multiplying the waveform by $\omega_0{}^n$ and advancing the phase of its oscillatory term by $n\delta$.

$$\frac{d^n}{dt^n} \operatorname{Re} (\mathbf{K}e^{s_1 t}) = \omega_0{}^n K e^{-\alpha t} \cos (\omega_d t + \gamma + n\delta)$$

In the study of sinusoidal functions we saw that

$$\operatorname{Re} e^{j\omega t} = \cos \omega t$$

$$\frac{d}{dt} \cos \omega t = \frac{d}{dt} \operatorname{Re} e^{j\omega t} = \operatorname{Re} (j\omega e^{j\omega t})$$

Since

$$j = e^{j\pi/2}$$

$$\frac{d}{dt} \cos \omega t = \operatorname{Re} (\omega e^{j\pi/2} e^{j\omega t}) = \omega \cos \left(\omega t + \frac{\pi}{2} \right)$$

Thus, in differentiating $\cos \omega t$, its amplitude is multiplied by ω and its phase is advanced by $\pi/2$. Similarly

$$\frac{d^2}{dt^2} \cos \omega t = \omega^2 \cos \left(\omega t + 2\frac{\pi}{2} \right)$$

$$\frac{d^n}{dt^n} \cos \omega t = \omega^n \cos \left(\omega t + n\frac{\pi}{2} \right)$$

Thus $e^{j\omega t}$ is recognized to be a special case of $e^{s_1 t}$ where the factor α is zero. Whereas ω is called the (real) radian frequency of the function $\cos \omega t$, the complex number $s_1 = -\alpha + j\omega_d$ is called the complex radian frequency of the function $e^{s_1 t}$. Complex frequencies are characteristic of damped oscillations and play an important part in the study of circuits. The real part of the complex frequency is the attenuation factor of the natural mode of a source-free circuit, and its imaginary part, ω_d, is the damped radian frequency of the oscillatory term of the mode.

It is noted that $\int e^{st} \, dt = (1/s)e^{st}$, and, by analogy with differentiation,

$$\int e^{-\alpha t} \cos \omega_d t \, dt = \frac{1}{\omega_0} e^{-\alpha t} \cos (\omega_d t - \delta)$$

In words, integration of a mode with complex frequency results in division of its amplitude by ω_0 and delay of the phase of its oscillatory component of δ.

Example 9-1. In the circuit of Fig. 9-1 the switch is thrown from position d to position a at $t = 0$. It is known that, at $t = 0^-$, $v_{ab}(0^-) = 12.5$ volts and $i(0^-) = -0.6$ amp. The numerical values of the elements are

$$R = 3 \text{ ohms} \qquad L = 0.5 \text{ henry} \qquad C = 0.08 \text{ farad}$$

Solve for $v_{ab}(t)$ and $i(t)$ for all $t \geq 0^+$.

Solution. The continuity conditions require that

$$v_{ab}(0^+) = v_{ab}(0^-) = 12.5 \text{ volts}$$

and

$$i(0^+) = i(0^-) = C\left(\frac{dv_{ab}}{dt}\right)_{0^+} = -0.6 \text{ amp}$$

The equilibrium equation for the charge q_a is

$$0.5\frac{d^2}{dt^2}q_a + 3\frac{d}{dt}q_a + \frac{100}{8}q_a = 0$$

so that the characteristic equation is

$$0.5s^2 + 3s + 12.5 = 0$$

or

$$s^2 + 6s + 25 = 0$$

The characteristic roots are

$$s_{1,2} = -3 \pm \sqrt{9-25}$$
$$s_{1,2} = -3 \pm j4$$

The circuit is therefore underdamped. We immediately write the general form of the solution as

$$v_{ab}(t) = \text{Re } [\mathbf{K}e^{(-3+j4)t}]$$

and

$$\frac{dv_{ab}}{dt} = \text{Re } [(-3+j4)\mathbf{K}e^{(-3+j4)t}]$$

We now introduce the initial conditions

$$v_{ab}(0^+) = 12.5 = \text{Re } \mathbf{K}$$
$$\left(\frac{dv_{ab}}{dt}\right)_{0^+} = \frac{i(0^+)}{C} = -\frac{0.6}{8\times 10^{-2}} = \text{Re } [(-3+j4)\mathbf{K}]$$

Now we write $\mathbf{K}$ in *rectangular* form,

$$\mathbf{K} = k + jk'$$

Then

$$12.5 = \text{Re } (k + jk') = k$$

Now

$$\mathbf{K} = 12.5 + jk'$$

Since

$$\text{Re } [(-3+j4)(k+jk')] = -3k - 4k'$$

we have

$$\frac{-0.6}{8\times 10^{-2}} = (-3\times 12.5) - 4k'$$

Then

$$k' = -7.5$$

so that

$$\mathbf{K} = 12.5 - j7.5$$

Now we write $\mathbf{K}$ in *polar* form,

$$\mathbf{K} = 14.6\underline{/-31°}$$

Hence

$$v_{ab}(t) = \text{Re } (14.6\underline{/-31°}\ e^{-3t}e^{j4t})$$

or

$$v_{ab}(t) = 14.6e^{-3t}\cos(4t - 31°)$$

where $4t$ is in radians and 31 is in degrees.

The root s_1 in polar form is

$$s_1 = -3 + j4 = 5\underline{/126.9°}$$

Hence

$$\frac{d}{dt}v_{ab} = 5\times 14.6e^{-3t}\cos(4t - 31° + 126.9°)$$

or

$$\frac{d}{dt}v_{ab} = 73e^{-3t}\cos(4t + 95.9°)$$

Since
$$i = C \frac{dv_{ab}}{dt} = 8 \times 10^{-2} \frac{dv_{ab}}{dt}$$
$$i(t) = 5.84e^{-3t} \cos (4t + 95.9°) \qquad \text{Ans.}$$

9-9. Sketching of Waveforms in the Underdamped Case.

The general forms of solution in the underdamped case are proportional to

$$f(t) = e^{-\alpha t} \cos (\omega_d t + \gamma) \tag{9-33}$$

We shall discuss in this article a reasonably accurate method for sketching $f(t)$ so that elaborate point-by-point computation of values can often be avoided. Such "reasonably accurate" sketches of functions can usually be obtained by locating the instants at which $f(t)$ is zero, has a maximum, or has a minimum. While the maxima and minima of Eq. (9-33) will be discussed, the form of the equation suggests a slightly different method. Equation (9-33) gives $f(t)$ as the *product* of two functions, both of which were discussed in detail in earlier chapters,

$$f(t) = f_1(t)f_2(t)$$
where
$$f_1(t) = e^{-\alpha t}$$
$$f_2(t) = \cos (\omega_d t + \gamma)$$

These functions are sketched in Figs. 9-2a and b, respectively. (In Fig. 9-2b it is assumed that $0 < \gamma < \pi/2$.) We note now that the following points on the product $f(t)$ are evident:

When $\cos (\omega_d t + \gamma) = 0$, then $f(t) = 0$. These instants are denoted by $t = t_z$ in Fig. 9-2.

When $\cos (\omega_d t + \gamma) = \pm 1$, then $f(t) = \pm e^{-\alpha t}$. These instants are denoted by $t = t_e$ in Fig. 9-2.

To sketch the product $f(t)$, the instants $t = t_z$ and $t = t_e$ are located on the t axis, and the curves $+e^{-\alpha t}$ and $-e^{-\alpha t}$ are sketched so that both positive and negative values at $t = t_e$ are readily located. [The curves $+e^{-\alpha t}$ and $-e^{-\alpha t}$ are called the envelopes of $f(t)$.] The curve is now sketched in through the t_e and t_z points. Before discussing the location of maxima and minima of the curve, the location of the values of t_e and t_z will be discussed in the following example.

Example 9-2. Find the values of t_z and t_e for $f(t) = e^{-\alpha t} \cos (\omega_d t + \gamma)$ when $\alpha = 3$, $\omega_d = 4$, and $\gamma = \pi/3$.

Solution. By definition of t_z

$$\cos \left(4t_z + \frac{\pi}{3}\right) = 0$$
Hence
$$4t_z + \frac{\pi}{3} = \frac{\pi}{2}, \frac{3\pi}{2}, \ldots, (2n-1)\frac{\pi}{2}$$

so that the first zero occurs at

$$4t_{z1} = \frac{\pi}{2} - \frac{\pi}{3} = \frac{\pi}{6} \qquad t_{z1} = \frac{\pi}{24}$$

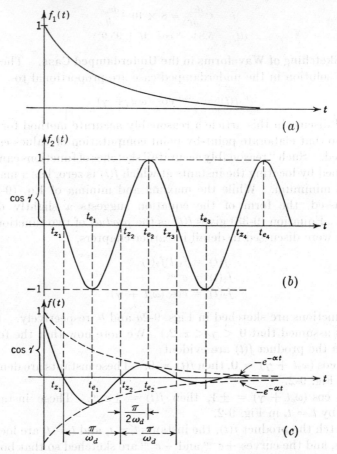

Fig. 9-2. Construction of a waveform in the underdamped case.

The second zero occurs at

$$4t_{z2} = \frac{3\pi}{2} - \frac{\pi}{3} = \frac{7\pi}{6} \qquad t_{z2} = \frac{7\pi}{24}$$

so that the zeros are separated by $\pi/\omega_d = \pi/4$,

$$t_{zn+1} - t_{zn} = \frac{\pi}{\omega_d} = \frac{\pi}{4}$$

All the t_z points can therefore be found if any one t_z point is located. The others are then found by spacing them at the t axis π/ω_d units from each other.

The values of t_e are defined by

$$\cos\left(4t_e + \frac{\pi}{3}\right) = \pm 1$$

Hence $$4t_e + \frac{\pi}{3} = \pi, 2\pi, 3\pi, \ldots, m\pi$$

so that the first value of t_e is given by $4t_{e1} = \pi - \pi/3$; $t_{e1} = \pi/6$, and

$$t_{e2} - t_{e1} = \frac{\pi}{\omega_d} = \frac{\pi}{4}$$

$$t_{e(n+1)} - t_{en} = \frac{\pi}{\omega_d} = \frac{\pi}{4}$$

Note also that a value of t_e is separated from an adjacent value of t_z by $\pi/2\omega_d$. Hence the location of any t_z point or any t_e point together with the number $\pi/2\omega_d$ is sufficient for locating all these points. Figure 9-2 illustrates the example.

Although the location of the maxima and minima of the damped oscillations is not, in general, necessary for the sketching of the waveforms, these values are of interest and will therefore be examined. There is a tendency to think that the maxima and minima of $f(t)$ will occur at the position of the maxima and minima of the cosine function. This, of course, is not true since the maxima of a product $f_1(t)f_2(t)$ are not generally at the same points as the maxima of either factor. The maxima and minima of $f(t)$ occur at the zeros of df/dt. We have seen that if

$$f(t) = e^{-\alpha t} \cos (\omega_d t + \gamma)$$

then
$$\frac{df}{dt} = \omega_0 e^{-\alpha t} \cos (\omega_d t + \gamma + \delta)$$

where ω_0 and δ are connected with the characteristic roots through the relationship

$$^-\alpha + j\omega_d = \omega_0 \underline{/\delta} = 5\underline{/126.9°} = 5\underline{/2.22}$$

The maxima and minima therefore occur when $\cos (\omega_d t + \gamma + \delta) = 0$.

Denoting the instant at which f is a maximum by t_m, we call the first of these instants t_{m1}. Setting $\gamma = \pi/3$, we find that it will be located at

$$(\omega_d t_{m1} + \gamma + \delta) = \left(4t_{m1} + \frac{\pi}{3} + 2.22\right) = \frac{3\pi}{2}$$

and that the nth t_m will be located at

$$t_{mn} = t_{m1} + \frac{(n-1)\pi}{\omega_d}$$

9-10. Energy Relations. An interesting relationship exists between the successive maxima and minima of the voltage across the capacitance, $v_{ab}(t)$. In Fig. 9-3a a curve for $v_{ab}(t)$ in the oscillatory case has been drawn. The successive instants at which $v_{ab}(t)$ is a maximum or a minimum have been identified as $t = t_1, t_2, \ldots$. Now at these instants the current in the circuit is zero because the current is equal to the time derivative of the charge (or proportional to the derivative of voltage across the capacitance). Hence

$$i(t_1) = 0 \qquad i(t_2) = 0 \qquad i(t_3) = 0 \qquad \cdots$$

At the instants when current is zero, the stored energy which remains in the circuit is all stored in the capacitance:

$$w(t_1) = \tfrac{1}{2}C[v_{ab}(t_1)]^2 \qquad w(t_2) = \tfrac{1}{2}C[(v_{ab}(t_2)^2] \qquad \cdots$$

Now
$$v_{ab}(t_1) = Ke^{-\alpha t_1} \cos (\omega_d t_1 + \gamma)$$
$$v_{ab}(t_2) = Ke^{-\alpha t_2} \cos (w_d t_2 + \gamma)$$

.
.   (9-34)
.

$$v_{ab}(t_n) = Ke^{-\alpha t_n} \cos (\omega_d t_n + \gamma)$$

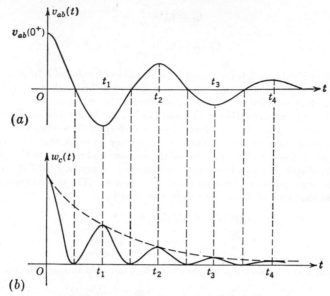

Fig. 9-3. Voltage across capacitance and energy in capacitance as a function of time for an underdamped circuit.

We now recall from the preceding article that each maximum occurs π/ω_d sec after and before the adjacent minimum. Hence

$$t_2 = t_1 + \frac{\pi}{\omega_d}$$

$$t_3 = t_2 + \frac{\pi}{\omega_d}$$

$$t_n = t_{n-1} + \frac{\pi}{\omega_d}$$

Using these relationships in Eqs. (9-34), we may write

$$v_{ab}(t_1) = Ke^{-\alpha t_1} \cos{(\omega_d t_1 + \gamma)}$$

$$v_{ab}(t_2) = Ke^{-\alpha(t_1 + \pi/\omega_d)} \cos{\left[\omega_d \left(t_1 + \frac{\pi}{\omega_d}\right) + \gamma\right]}$$

$$= Ke^{-\alpha t_1}e^{-\alpha \pi/\omega_d} \cos{(\omega_d t_1 + \pi + \gamma)}$$

or $\qquad v_{ab}(t_2) = -v_{ab}(t_1)e^{-\alpha \pi/\omega_d}$

Similarly $\qquad v_{ab}(t_3) = -v_{ab}(t_2)e^{-\alpha \pi/\omega_d}$

and $\qquad v_{ab}(t_n) = -v_{ab}(t_{n-1})e^{-\alpha \pi/\omega_d}$ $\qquad\qquad$ (9-35)

In words, Eq. (9-34) states that the magnitude of the voltage across the capacitance is reduced by the factor $e^{-\alpha \pi/\omega_d}$ between a maximum and a minimum point. In terms of energy storage we note that

$$\tfrac{1}{2}C[v_{ab}(t_n)]^2 = \tfrac{1}{2}C[-v_{ab}(t_{n-1})]^2 e^{-2\pi \alpha/\omega_d}$$

Hence the stored energy between two maxima is reduced by the factor $e^{-2\pi\alpha/\omega_d}$,

$$\frac{w(t_n)}{w(t_{n-1})} = e^{-2\pi\alpha/\omega_d} \qquad (9\text{-}36)$$

This relationship is illustrated in Fig. 9-3b.

The quantity $-2\pi\alpha/\omega_d$, which appears in the exponent of Eq. (9-36), is amenable to physical interpretation: The period of the damped oscillations, P_d, is the reciprocal of the frequency,

$$P_d = \frac{1}{f_d} = \frac{2\pi}{\omega_d}$$

The time constant of the exponential envelope, T, is given by

$$T = \frac{1}{\alpha}$$

Hence $\dfrac{2\pi\alpha}{\omega_d} = \dfrac{P_d}{T} = \dfrac{1}{\rho} \qquad \rho = \dfrac{T}{P_d}$

The quantity $\rho = T/P_d$ gives the number of damped oscillations which occur in one time constant of the decaying envelope.   Now

$$\frac{w(t_n)}{w(t_{n-1})} = e^{-1/\rho}$$

We observe that the waveshape of the response is connected with the decay of the stored energy through the number ρ.   It is left as an exercise for the reader to show that ρ is related to Q_0 by the equation

$$\rho = \frac{1}{2\pi} \sqrt{4Q_0{}^2 - 1} \qquad (9\text{-}37)$$

If $\rho \gg 1$, then the response may be termed highly oscillatory because many cycles of oscillations will elapse before the envelope limits the amplitude to 0.37 per cent of original value.   In Fig. 9-4a such a highly oscillatory response is shown for the case $\rho = 10$.   The waveshape of Fig. 9-4a is drawn with the time scale normalized with respect to T so that the oscillatory decay is shown to $t/T = 3$.   If the oscillations at the beginning of the process are to be observed, then the time scale may be normalized with respect to $P_d = 2\pi/\omega_d$.   This is shown in Fig. 9-4b.   Note that the beginning (first few cycles) of the waveshape as shown in Fig. 9-4b is quite similar to the response of the L-C circuit.   In Fig. 9-4c and oscillatory decays are shown for the case $T = P_d$.

For the case $T < P_d$, as illustrated in Fig. 9-4e, the oscillations are barely noticeable, and the response is quite similar to that of the overdamped case, which will be discussed in the next article.

9-11. The Overdamped Case.   If the characteristic roots are real and unequal, then the response of the source-free circuit is given as the sum of two real exponential functions.   In that case, since

$$s_{1,2} = -\alpha \pm \sqrt{\alpha^2 - \omega_0{}^2} \qquad \alpha > \omega_0$$

it is convenient to define the positive number β,

so that
$$\beta = \sqrt{\alpha^2 - \omega_0{}^2}$$
$$s_1 = -\alpha + \beta \qquad s_2 = -\alpha - \beta$$

The general solution is obtained immediately by substituting the numerical values of s_1 and s_2 in the general solution (9-19). The general result reads

$$v_{ab}(t) = \frac{1}{2\beta}\left\{ \left[\frac{I_0}{C} - (-\alpha - \beta)V_0\right]e^{(-\alpha+\beta)t} + \left[(-\alpha + \beta)V_0 - \frac{I_0}{C}\right]e^{(-\alpha-\beta)t}\right\}$$
$$t \geq 0^+$$

It is of course not necessary to remember the complicated general result. A numerical example will serve to illustrate how to proceed, after solution of the characteristic equation, once it is found that the roots are real and distinct (simple real roots).

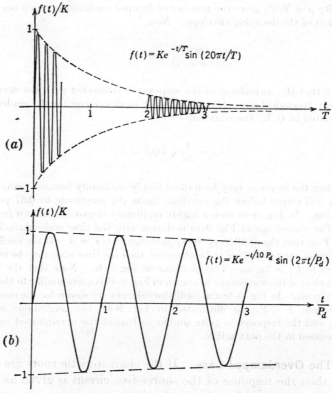

Fig. 9-4. Response waveforms for an underdamped R-L-C circuit. (a, b) Illustration of highly oscillatory response. (c, d) Oscillatory response. (e) Slightly oscillatory response.

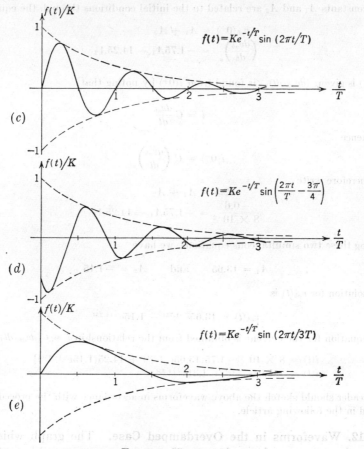

$$f(t) = Ke^{-t/T}\sin(2\pi t/T)$$

(c)

$$f(t) = Ke^{-t/T}\sin\left(\frac{2\pi t}{T} - \frac{3\pi}{4}\right)$$

(d)

$$f(t) = Ke^{-t/T}\sin(2\pi t/3T)$$

(e)

FIG. 9-4. (Continued.)

Example 9-3. In the series R-L-C circuit of Fig. 9-1

$$R = 8 \text{ ohms} \qquad L = 0.5 \text{ henry} \qquad C = 8 \times 10^{-2} \text{ farad}$$

It is known that $v_{ab}(0^+) = 12.5$ volts and $i(0^+) = -0.6$ amp. Find $v_{ab}(t)$ and $i(t)$ for all $t \geq 0^+$.

Solution. The characteristic equation is

$$0.5s^2 + 8s + \frac{10^2}{8} = 0$$

or

$$s^2 + 16s + 25 = 0$$

so that

$$s_{1,2} = -8 \pm \sqrt{64 - 25}$$

and

$$s_1 = -1.75 \qquad s_2 = -14.25$$

Since the roots are real and unequal, we write

$$v_{ab}(t) = A_1 e^{-1.75t} + A_2 e^{-14.25t}$$

$$\frac{dv_{ab}}{dt} = -1.75A_1 e^{-1.75t} - 14.25A_2 e^{-14.25t}$$

The constants A_1 and A_2 are related to the initial conditions through the equations

$$v_{ab}(0^+) = A_1 + A_2$$
$$\left(\frac{dv_{ab}}{dt}\right)_{0^+} = -1.75A_1 - 14.25A_2$$

$v_{ab}(0^+)$ is given; $(dv_{ab}/dt)_{0^+}$ is found from $i(0^+)$ by noting that

$$i = C\frac{dv_{ab}}{dt}$$

and hence

$$i(0^+) = C\left(\frac{dv_{ab}}{dt}\right)_{0^+}$$

We therefore write

$$12.5 = A_1 + A_2$$
$$\frac{-0.6}{8 \times 10^{-2}} = -1.75A_1 - 14.25A_2$$

Solving these two simultaneous equations, we have

$$A_1 = 13.65 \quad \text{and} \quad A_2 = -1.15$$

The solution for $v_{ab}(t)$ is

$$v_{ab}(t) = 13.65e^{-1.75t} - 1.15e^{-14.25t}$$

The equation for the current is obtained from the relationship $i = C(dv_{ab}/dt)$,

$$i(t) = 8 \times 10^{-2}[-1.75(13.65e^{-1.75t}) + 14.25(1.15e^{-14.25t})]$$

or $\quad i(t) = -1.91e^{-1.75t} + 1.31e^{-14.25t}$

The reader should sketch the above waveforms in accordance with the procedure discussed in the following article.

9-12. Waveforms in the Overdamped Case. The graph which corresponds to the waveform of an overdamped response is easily constructed as the sum of two exponential decays with the different time constants $1/(\alpha - \beta)$ and $1/(\alpha + \beta)$. It is convenient to choose as the abscissa $(\alpha - \beta)t$ because the characteristic root whose absolute value is the smaller one represents the longer time constant. The construction of the response curve is shown in Fig. 9-5a and b, with the special initial conditions V_0 positive and $I_0 = 0$. In these graphs the numerical relationship $(\alpha - \beta) = \frac{1}{3}(\alpha + \beta)$ is also assumed. Since α is always larger than β, this corresponds to choosing $\alpha = 2\beta$. Note that the current in Fig. 9-5b is negative because V_0 was assumed to be a positive number and the capacitance discharges in a direction opposite to that of the reference arrow of $i(t)$ as chosen in Fig. 9-1.

9-13. The Critically Damped Case (Multiple Roots). It was pointed out in Art. 9-5 that the case

$$s_1 = s_2 = -\alpha = -\omega_0$$

is a special case because the exponential function gives only one independent mode of the circuit. This case was explicitly excluded from the "general" solution (9-19).

To obtain the complete solution in this case, several procedures may be used. One may start with the solution (9-19) and take the limit as s_1 approaches s_2. One may start with the general solution for the overdamped case and take the limit as β approaches zero. It is also possible

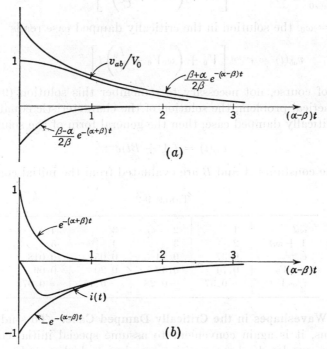

FIG. 9-5. Response waveforms in an overdamped circuit.

to start with the oscillatory case and take the limit as ω_d approaches zero. The last-named method will be used here. The solution for the underdamped case is, for our present purpose, most convenient in the form shown below. This form is obtained by expanding Eq. (9-30a) and using the values for sin γ, cos γ, and K in terms of the initial conditions,

$$v_{ab}(t) = e^{-\alpha t}\left[V_0 \cos \omega_d t + \left(\alpha V_0 + \frac{I_0}{C} \right) \frac{\sin \omega_d t}{\omega_d} \right]$$

We desire to obtain

$$\lim_{\omega_d \to 0} v_{ab}(t) = \lim_{\omega_d \to 0} \left\{ e^{-\alpha t}\left[V_0 \cos \omega_d t + \left(\alpha V_0 + \frac{I_0}{C} \right) \frac{\sin \omega_d t}{\omega_d} \right] \right\}$$

Now

$$\lim_{\omega_d \to 0} \cos \omega_d t = 1$$

and

$$\lim_{\omega_d \to 0} \frac{\sin \omega_d t}{\omega_d} = \lim_{\omega_d \to 0} \left(t \frac{\sin \omega_d t}{\omega_d t} \right) = \lim_{x \to 0} \left(t \frac{\sin x}{x} \right) = t$$

so that

$$\lim_{\omega_d \to 0} v_{ab}(t) = e^{-\alpha t} \left[V_0 + \left(\alpha V_0 + \frac{I_0}{C} \right) t \right]$$

Since $\alpha = \omega_0$, the solution in the critically damped case reads

$$v_{ab}(t) = e^{-\omega_0 t} \left[V_0 + \left(\omega_0 V_0 + \frac{I_0}{C} \right) t \right] \tag{9-38}$$

It is, of course, not necessary to remember this solution (9-38). If, in a numerical problem, the solution of the characteristic equation leads to the critically damped case, then the general form of the solution is

$$v_{ab}(t) = (A + Bt)e^{-\omega_0 t} \tag{9-39}$$

where the constants A and B are evaluated from the initial conditions.

TABLE 9-2

$\omega_0 t$	1	2	3	4
$1 + \omega_0 t$	2	3	4	5
$e^{-\omega_0 t}$	0.37	0.14	0.05	0.018
v_{ab}/V_0	0.74	0.42	0.20	0.09
$i/\omega_0 V_0 C$	−0.37	−0.28	−0.15	−0.072

9-14. Waveshapes in the Critically Damped Case. To study typical waveforms, it is again convenient to assume special initial conditions. As before, we let V_0 be a positive number and choose $I_0 = 0$. The solution for the voltage $v_{ab}(t)$ is then given by

$$v_{ab}(t) = V_0(1 + \omega_0 t)e^{-\omega_0 t} \qquad t \geq 0^+ \tag{9-40}$$

and the current is

$$i(t) = C\frac{dv_{ab}}{dt} = -CV_0\omega_0(\omega_0 t e^{-\omega_0 t}) \qquad t \geq 0^+$$

It is convenient to normalize the time scale with respect to $1/\omega_0$. To sketch the result, we note that Eq. (9-40) is the product of the straight line $1 + \omega_0 t$ and the exponential $e^{-\omega_0 t}$. The values given in Table 9-2 are helpful. The waveshapes are shown in Fig. 9-6.

The minimum value of the current (maximum absolute value) is obtained by differentiating the equation for $i(t)$,

$$\frac{di}{dt} = -\omega_0 C V_0 (e^{-\omega_0 t})(-\omega_0^2 t + \omega_0)$$

so that this value occurs when $\omega_0 t = 1$ and the current there has the value $-0.37(\omega_0 C V_0)$ as indicated in Fig. 9-6b.

9-15. Comparison of the Three Cases. The Complex-frequency Plane, or s Plane. The underdamped, overdamped, and critically

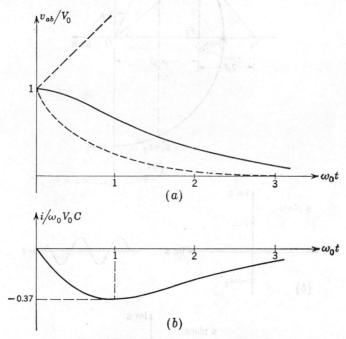

FIG. 9-6. Critically damped response.

damped cases give different response waveshapes as determined by the nature of the characteristic roots. It is recalled that the roots of the characteristic equation are

$$s_{1,2} = -\frac{R}{2L} \pm \sqrt{\left(\frac{R}{2L}\right)^2 - \frac{1}{LC}}$$

or

$$s_{1,2} = -\alpha \pm \sqrt{\alpha^2 - \omega_0^2}$$

An interesting relationship exists between the roots of the characteristic equation. We note that in any case the geometric mean of the roots is the undamped natural radian frequency ω_0,

$$s_1 s_2 = (-\alpha + \sqrt{\alpha^2 - \omega_0^2})(-\alpha - \sqrt{\alpha^2 - \omega_0^2})$$

or

$$s_1 s_2 = \omega_0^2$$

Let us now study the series $R\text{-}L\text{-}C$ circuit with fixed values of L and C

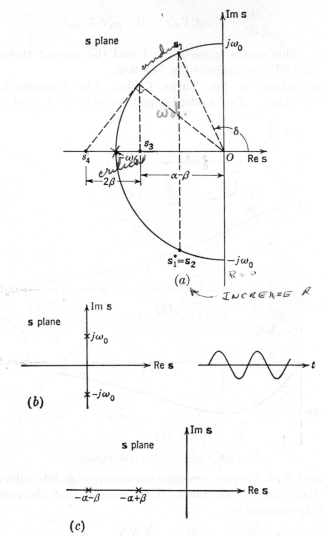

Fig. 9-7. (a) Roots in the s plane. Points s_1 and s_2 are examples of complex roots; s_3 and s_4 are a pair of real roots. (b) A pair of conjugate imaginary roots corresponds to sinusoidal oscillations. (c) The overdamped case gives a pair of real roots in the s plane.

but for all possible values of R. Since L and C are fixed, ω_0 remains constant. Since the roots of the characteristic equation are complex in the underdamped case, these roots may be identified with points in the complex plane. In Fig. 9-7a we have shown a set of rectangular coordinates; the real axis on that diagram corresponds to the real part of s and the imaginary axis shows the imaginary part of s. The plane defined by these axes is then called the s plane. When the roots are complex, then they can be written in polar form as

$$\mathbf{s}_{1,2} = \omega_0\underline{/\pm\delta} = \omega_0\underline{\bigg/\pm\tan^{-1}\frac{\omega_d}{-\alpha}}$$

Hence the locus of the roots for all possible values of R which result in the underdamped case forms the semicircle with the center at the origin and radius ω_0. When the roots are real, they will be located on the negative real axis in the complex plane such that their geometric mean is ω_0. In the critically damped case the two roots are identical and will be designated as a "double" point in the s plane. These relationships are illustrated in Fig. 9-7a.

Now the study of these relationships leads to the following conclusions: When the resistance is zero, then the circuit is undamped (L-C) and the roots are imaginary. In that case the response is undamped; i.e., it consists of periodic sinusoidal oscillations of radian frequency ω_0. Hence *imaginary* roots shown in Fig. 9-7b correspond to sinusoidal oscillations. On the other hand, real roots as shown in Fig. 9-7c correspond to decaying exponentials. We now note that

$$e^{-\alpha t} = e^{j(j\alpha)t}$$

corresponds to exponential damping. We therefore use the term imaginary frequency to describe exponential functions with real exponents. It then follows that the exponentially damped oscillations which occur in the underdamped case may be termed oscillations with complex frequency. It will be recalled that in Art. 9-8 we illustrated some properties of the complex frequency s. The real part of the complex frequency (Re s $= -\alpha$) describes the damping envelope of the response curve, and the imaginary part of the complex frequency (Im s $= \omega_d$) describes the radian frequency of the oscillations. In Fig. 9-7a a multiple root, corresponding to the critically damped case, occurs where the semicircle intersects the real axis at $s = -\alpha = -\omega_0$. We shall further discuss the concept of the complex frequencies and its use in the study of circuits in Chap. 13.

9-16. Solution for Other Variables. We have emphasized throughout the earlier parts of this chapter that the modes of the various voltages and currents in the source-free circuit are identical, so that the general solution for any one of the variables has the same form as the solution for any other variable. This statement implies that, given the initial conditions of the circuit, we can, in any numerical case, solve for only one variable, say, the voltage across C, and then obtain the required function, say, the current through C, by appropriate manipulation, that is, $i = C\ (dv/dt)$. This method is not the most convenient procedure in every numerical case.   In this article we shall show how to use derived initial conditions in a specific example.

Suppose we are given the circuit of Fig. 9-8 with the continuity conditions

$$v_{ab}(0^+) = V_0$$
$$i(0^+) = I_0$$

and suppose further that it is required to solve for the voltage $v_{fb}(t)$ for all $t \geq 0^+$.

We could solve for the voltage v_{ab} first, then differentiate this function and use the relationship $i = C(dv_{ab}/dt)$ to find $i(t)$.   The voltage v_{fb} is then found by application of Kirchhoff's voltage law:

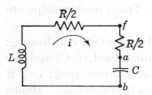

$$v_{fb} = v_{fa} + v_{ab} = i\left(\frac{R}{2}\right) + v_{ab}$$

FIG. 9-8. Circuit used in Art. 9-16.

This procedure may be quite cumbersome, especially if the circuit is underdamped.   Now, since the modes of all the variables in the circuit are the same, we know that

If circuit is underdamped: $v_{fb}(t) = \mathrm{Re}\ (\mathbf{D}e^{s_1t})$

or

If circuit is critically damped: $v_{fb}(t) = (A + Bt)e^{-\omega_0 t}$

or

If circuit is overdamped: $v_{fb}(t) = A_1 e^{s_1 t} + A_2 e^{s_2 t}$

If we have solved the characteristic equation, then we know which one of these forms to use.   Suppose now that we know the initial values $v_{fb}(0^+)$ and $(dv_{fb}/dt)_{0^+}$.   Then the solution could immediately be completed by writing

If underdamped: $v_{fb}(0^+) = \mathrm{Re}\ \mathbf{D}$ $\left(\dfrac{dv_{fb}}{dt}\right)_{0^+} = \mathrm{Re}\ (\mathbf{s_1 D})$

or

If critically damped: $v_{fb}(0^+) = A$ $\left(\dfrac{dv_{fb}}{dt}\right)_{0^+} = -\omega_0 A + B$

or

If overdamped: $v_{fb}(0^+) = A_1 + A_2$ $\left(\dfrac{dv_{fb}}{dt}\right)_{0^+} = s_1 A_1 + s_2 A_2$

The constants $\mathbf{D}$, or A and B, or A_1 and A_2 can then be obtained so that the solution is complete.

To follow the procedure outlined above, we need the initial values $v_{fb}(0^+)$ and $(dv_{fb}/dt)_{0^+}$.   These values can be obtained by using the continuity conditions in the Kirchhoff's-law equations. We write

$$v_{fb} = i \frac{R}{2} + v_{ab} \qquad t \geq 0^+ \tag{9-41}$$

Hence, setting $t = 0^+$ in Eq. (9-41), we have

$$v_{fb}(0^+) = i(0^+) \frac{R}{2} + v_{ab}(0^+) = I_0 \frac{R}{2} + V_0 \tag{9-41a}$$

Differentiating Eq. (9-41) once, we get

$$\frac{dv_{fb}}{dt} = \frac{di}{dt} \frac{R}{2} + \frac{dv_{ab}}{dt} \qquad t \geq 0^+$$

But

$$\frac{dv_{ab}}{dt} = \frac{i}{C}$$

Hence

$$\frac{dv_{fb}}{dt} = \frac{di}{dt} \frac{R}{2} + \frac{i}{C} \qquad t \geq 0^+ \tag{9-42}$$

Setting $t = 0^+$ in Eq. (9-42), we have

$$\left(\frac{dv_{fb}}{dt}\right)_{0^+} = \left(\frac{di}{dt}\right)_{0^+} \frac{R}{2} + \frac{I_0}{C} \tag{9-43}$$

The derived condition $(di/dt)_{0^+}$ can be obtained from the equilibrium equation

$$L \frac{di}{dt} = -Ri - v_{ab}$$

Hence

$$\left(\frac{di}{dt}\right)_{0^+} = \frac{-RI_0 - V_0}{L} \tag{9-44}$$

Inserting (9-44) in (9-43), we have the desired value,

$$\left(\frac{dv_{fb}}{dt}\right)_{0^+} = \left(\frac{-RI_0 - V_0}{L}\right) \frac{R}{2} + \frac{I_0}{C}$$

or

$$\left(\frac{dv_{fb}}{dt}\right)_{0^+} = -\frac{V_0 R}{2L} + \frac{I_0}{C}\left(1 - \frac{R^2 C}{2L}\right) \tag{9-45}$$

The values given by (9-41a) and (9-45) are the desired initial values.

9-17. The Dual Circuit. If the parallel combination of R-L-C shown in Fig. 9-9 is disconnected from a source at $t = 0$, then the differential equation for the voltage v_{ab} is

$$\frac{1}{R} v_{ab} + C \frac{dv_{ab}}{dt} + \frac{1}{L} \int_{-\infty}^{t} v_{ab} \, d\tau = 0 \qquad t \geq 0^+$$

subject to the initial conditions

$$i_L(0^-) = i_L(0^+) \qquad \text{or} \qquad \int_{-\infty}^{0^-} v_{ab} \, dt = \int_{-\infty}^{0^+} v_{ab} \, dt$$

$$v_{ab}(0^-) = v_{ab}(0^+) \qquad \text{or} \qquad q_a(0^-) = q_a(0^+)$$

This problem is an exact dual of the series circuit and is left as an exercise for the reader. A study of the characteristic equation of the parallel R-L-C circuit will show that the Q of the circuit is $R/\omega_0 L$.

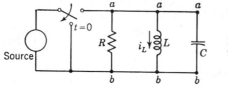

FIG. 9-9. Deenergizing a parallel R-L-C circuit.   FIG. 9-10. A series-parallel source-free R-L-C circuit.

9-18. Other Circuits. The reader should be aware of the fact that the detailed discussion of the series R-L-C circuit which has been presented in this chapter deals with the solution of a linear second-order homogeneous differential equation with constant coefficients of the form of Eq. (9-6). The solution of this equation was subject to certain continuity conditions. It is therefore clear that the methods of solution for any circuit which lead to a second-order equilibrium equation have been discussed. Furthermore, it can be shown that the equilibrium equation of any network containing two independent energy-storing elements and expressed in terms of one network variable will be a second-order differential equation. As an example, we shall consider a series-parallel circuit which leads to a second-order differential equation.

Consider the source-free circuit shown in Fig. 9-10. For this circuit we can write

$$\frac{v_{ab}}{R} + C\frac{dv_{ab}}{dt} + i_L = 0 \qquad \text{or} \qquad i_L = -\frac{v_{ab}}{R} - C\frac{dv_{ab}}{dt} \tag{9-46}$$

and

$$v_{ab} = R_1 i_L + L\frac{di_L}{dt} \tag{9-47}$$

Inserting (9-46) in (9-47), we have the equilibrium equation for v_{ab},

$$v_{ab} = R_1\left(-\frac{v_{ab}}{R} - C\frac{dv_{ab}}{dt}\right) + L\left(-\frac{1}{R}\frac{dv_{ab}}{dt} - C\frac{d^2v_{ab}}{dt^2}\right)$$

or

$$LC\frac{d^2v_{ab}}{dt^2} + \left(R_1 C + \frac{L}{R}\right)\frac{dv_{ab}}{dt} + \left(1 + \frac{R_1}{R}\right)v_{ab} = 0 \qquad t \geq 0^+$$

In addition the continuity conditions are

Because of L: $i_L(0^+) = i_L(0^-)$
Because of C: $v_{ab}(0^+) = v_{ab}(0^-)$

If the initial condition $(dv_{ab}/dt)_{0^+}$ is desired, then it can be obtained from Eq. (9-46). Setting $t = 0^+$ in Eq. (9-46), we have

$$i_L(0^+) = -\frac{v_{ab}(0^+)}{R} - C\left(\frac{dv_{ab}}{dt}\right)_{0^+}$$

or

$$\left(\frac{dv_{ab}}{dt}\right)_{0^+} = -\frac{i_L(0^+)}{C} + \frac{v_{ab}(0^+)}{RC}$$

The method of completing the solution should now be clear to the reader and is left as an exercise.

9-19. An Electromechanical Analogy. As an example of the application of source-free R-L-C circuits, we shall discuss the equivalent circuit of a galvanometer.

It is assumed that the reader is acquainted with the principle of operation of moving-coil meters. Figure 9-11a and b shows a sketch of the essential parts of such a meter. With reference to this figure the relevant values associated with the meter are given below. These values can be given in any consistent system of units, such as mks units.

l = length of frame on which coil of meter is wound
d = width of frame
n = number of turns in coil
B = flux density in which coil moves
k = spring constant
θ = angular displacement of coil round its axis of suspension
f = frictional torque per unit angular velocity
J = moment of inertia of coil with respect to its axis of suspension
R = resistance of coil
i = current in coil which would flow as the result of application of an external source $v(t)$ to coil
L = coil inductance (considered negligible)
$K_1 = nBl\,d$, called the electromechanical-conversion constant

Since the flux density is considered to be radial in direction and constant in magnitude, in accordance with Ampère's law (force $= Bil$),

$$\text{Torque on coil} = nBli\,d = K_1 i$$

As a result of this applied torque the coil will rotate around its axis of suspension such that

(Applied torque) = (inertial torque) + (frictional torque)
                    + (restoring torque due to spring)

$$K_1 i = J\frac{d^2\theta}{dt^2} + f\frac{d\theta}{dt} + k\theta$$

Since the coil is moving in a magnetic field, there will be an induced voltage in the coil, given, according to Faraday's law ($v_i = n\,d\phi/dt$), by

$$v_i = 2nlB\frac{d}{2}\frac{d\theta}{dt} = K_1\frac{d\theta}{dt}$$

It can be shown that the coil moving in the magnetic field given in Fig. 9-11a is equivalent to the terminal pair consisting of the series connection of R, L, and v_i given in Fig. 9-11c. If the effect of the inductance L of the coil is neglected (which is an allowable approximation), then this equiv-

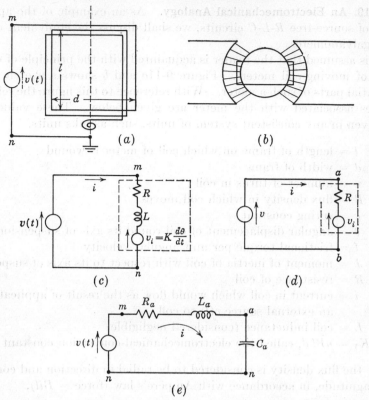

Fig. 9-11. (a, b) Sketch of a galvanometer. (c–e) Equivalent circuits.

alent circuit reduces to the one shown in Fig. 9-11d. From this figure it is seen that

$$v(t) - v_i(t) = iR$$

$$i = \frac{1}{R}\left[v(t) - K_1\frac{d\theta}{dt}\right]$$

$$K_1 i = \frac{K_1}{R}\left[v(t) - K_1\frac{d\theta}{dt}\right] = J\frac{d^2\theta}{dt^2} + f\frac{d\theta}{dt} + k\theta$$

$$v(t) = \frac{RJ}{K_1}\frac{d^2\theta}{dt^2} + \left(\frac{Rf}{K_1} + K_1\right)\frac{d\theta}{dt} + \frac{Rk}{K_1}\theta \qquad (9\text{-}48)$$

From the above equation it is clear that if we consider q_a to represent the angular displacement θ and assume the following analogous elements,

$$L_a \to \frac{RJ}{K_1} \qquad R_a \to \frac{Rf}{K_1} + K_1 \qquad C_a \to \frac{K_1}{Rk}$$

then the circuit of Fig. 9-11e would be the analogous circuit of the galvanometer. The value of such an analogous circuit can be understood by examination of Eq. (9-48). We observe, for example, that the degree of damping of the *mechanical* oscillations can be controlled by adjustment of the *electrical* element (R) in the circuit.

PROBLEMS

9-1. In the circuit shown in Fig. P9-1 obtain the equilibrium equation with (a) the current i as the variable; (b) the voltage v_{ad} as the variable.

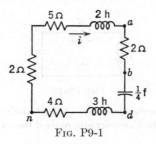

FIG. P9-1

9-2. In the circuit of Prob. 9-1 (Fig. P9-1) $i(0^+) = 2$ amp and $v_{bd}(0^+) = 4$ volts. Calculate the following initial values: (a) $v_{ab}(0^+)$; (b) $v_{ad}(0^+)$; (c) $v_{dn}(0^+)$; (d) $v_{na}(0^+)$; (e) $(dv_{ad}/dt)_{0^+}$; (f) $(d^2v_{ad}/dt^2)_{0^+}$.

9-3. In the circuit shown in Fig. P9-3 $v_{ab}(0^+) = 10$ volts and $i_1(0^+) = 3$ amp. Calculate (a) $i_2(0^+)$; (b) $dv_{ab}/dt)_{0^+}$; (c) $(dv_{an}/dt)_{0^+}$.

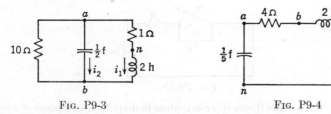

FIG. P9-3   FIG. P9-4

9-4. In the circuit shown in Fig. P9-4, at a certain instant $t = t_1$, $v_{bd}(t_1) = 10$ volts and $v_{dn}(t_1) = -6$ volts. Calculate $v_{na}(t_1)$ and $(dv_{na}/dt)_{t=t_1}$.

9-5. Show that the form $Ae^{-\alpha t} \cos(\omega_d t + \gamma)$, $\alpha = R/2L$, $\omega_d^2 = 1/LC - \alpha^2$, is a solution of the source-free series R-L-C circuit by direct substitution of this form in the equilibrium equation.

9-6. Show that the form $Kte^{-\omega_0 t}$, $\omega_0 = (1/LC)^{\frac{1}{2}}$, is a solution of the source-free R-L-C series circuit, if $R/2L = (1/LC)^{\frac{1}{2}}$, by direct substitution in the equilibrium equation.

9-7. Start with the general solution of the overdamped series R-L-C circuit given in Art. 9-11, and deduce the general solution of the critically damped circuit by taking the limit as β approaches zero.

9-8. In the circuit shown in Fig. P9-8 $i(0^+) = 0$ and $v_{ab}(0^+) = 100$ volts. Calculate $v_{ab}(t)$ and $i(t)$ for all $t \geq 0^+$ if (a) $R = 0$; (b) $R = 0.8$ ohm; (c) $R = 2.4$ ohms; (d) $R = 4$ ohms; (e) $R = 5.66$ ohms; (f) $R = 10.4$ ohms.

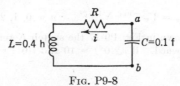

FIG. P9-8

9-9. For each of the cases given in Prob. 9-8 calculate the first maximum value of $i(t)$ which occurs after $t = 0$. In each case state the instant at which the maximum occurs.

9-10. Sketch the waveforms of $i(t)$ and $v_{ab}(t)$ for the various cases given in Prob. 9-8.

9-11. Use the result of Prob. 9-2 to calculate $v_{ad}(t)$ in the circuit of Prob. 9-1 (Fig. P9-1) for all $t \geq 0^+$. Do not solve for $v_{bd}(t)$ or for $i(t)$.

9-12. In the series R-L-C circuit shown in Fig. P9-12 $R = 200$ ohms, $L = 0.1$ henry, $C = 0.1$ μf. For $v_{ab}(0^+) = 100$ v and $i(0^+) = 0$, calculate $v_{ab}(t)$ for all $t \geq 0^+$, and sketch the result.

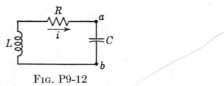

FIG. P9-12

9-13. In a certain R-L-C series circuit the characteristic roots are $s_{1,2} = -3 \pm j100$. What will be the values of the characteristic roots if the values L and C are multiplied by 10^{-4}?

9-14. Sketch the following waveforms: (a) $10e^{-t} \cos 5t$; (b) $10e^{-t} \cos (5t - 120°)$; (c) $5e^{-t} + 10e^{-2t}$; (d) $3 + 2te^{-t}$.

9-15. With reference to Prob. 7-6 we recall that opening of the switch K (see Fig. P9-15) will result in an arc across the switch if C is omitted. Explain how the capacitance C acts as an "arc suppressor."

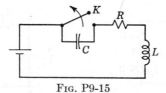

FIG. P9-15

9-16. In servomechanism theory it is convenient to describe the response of a source-free R-L-C circuit using a parameter called the "damping ratio," denoted by ζ. For the series circuit this parameter is defined by the equation

$$\zeta = \frac{R}{2} \sqrt{\frac{C}{L}}$$

(a) Show that $\zeta = \alpha/\omega_0$. (b) Relate ζ to Q_0. (c) In an underdamped series R-L-C circuit the voltage across the capacitance at $t = 0^+$ is V_0, and $i(0^+) = 0$. Show that the voltage across the capacitance for $t \geq 0^+$ is given by

$$v_c = \frac{V_0}{\sqrt{1 - \zeta^2}} e^{-\omega_0 \zeta t} \cos \left(\omega_0 \sqrt{1 - \zeta^2}\, t - \tan^{-1} \frac{\zeta}{\sqrt{1 - \zeta^2}} \right)$$

(d) Show that the maxima and minima of v_c in (c) depend only on the damping ratio and are given by

$$|v|_{\text{extreme}} = V_0 e^{-n\pi\zeta/\sqrt{1-\zeta^2}} \qquad n = 0, 1, 2, \ldots$$

9-17. In the circuit shown in Fig. P9-17 the switch K remains closed until $t = 1$. At $t = 1$ the switch is opened. If $v_{ab}(0^+) = 10$ and $i(0^+) = 0$, calculate and sketch $i(t)$ for all $t \geq 0^+$.

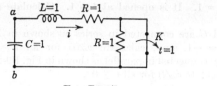

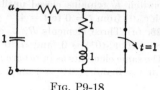

FIG. P9-17

FIG. P9-18

9-18. In the circuit shown in Fig. P9-18 $v_{ab}(0^+) = 10$. The switch is opened at $t = 1$. Calculate and sketch $v_{ab}(t)$ for all $t \geq 0^+$.

9-19. When the resistance of a series R-L-C circuit is 1,000 ohms, the source-free response is overdamped and of the form $K_1 e^{-3,730t} + K_2 e^{-270t}$. (a) Calculate ω_0. (b) Calculate the value of R for critical damping if L and C remain fixed. (c) Calculate the value of R if the circuit is underdamped and if two transient oscillations occur in every time constant of the damping envelope. The values of L and C remain fixed.

9-20. Recalling that the locus of $e^{j\omega t}$ in the complex plane is a unit circle, calculate and plot the locus of $e^{(-1+j6.28)t}$ for $t \geq 0$ in the complex plane.

9-21. For a certain series R-L-C circuit $\omega_0 = 100$. The circuit is underdamped; $\alpha = 60$. Calculate the frequency of the transient oscillations.

9-22. The characteristic roots of a series R-L-C circuit are shown (Fig. P9-22) in the s-plane diagram for $R = 1$. The values of L and C remain fixed. (a) Calculate the value of R necessary for critical damping. (b) Calculate the value of R necessary to have the circuit overdamped so that one root has the value $s_1 = -10$.

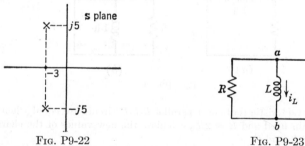

FIG. P9-22

FIG. P9-23

9-23. For the parallel R-L-C circuit shown in Fig. P9-23 obtain the equilibrium equation with (a) the current i_L as the variable; (b) the voltage v_{ab} as the variable.

9-24. In the circuit of Prob. 9-23 (Fig. P9-23) $i_L(0^+) = I_0$, $v_{ab}(0^+) = V_0$. Calculate $(dv_{ab}/dt)_{0^+}$.

9-25. For the parallel R-L-C circuit of Prob. 9-23 (Fig. P9-23) deduce the criteria for the various types of response.

9-26. In the parallel R-L-C circuit of Prob. 9-23 (Fig. P9-23) $R = 0.5$, $C = 1$, and $LC = 1$. Calculate the sketch $v_{ab}(t)$ for all $t \geq 0^+$ if (a) $v_{ab}(0^+) = 10$, $i_L(0^+) = 0$; (b) $v_{ab}(0^+) = 0$, $i_L(0^+) = 2$; (c) $v_{ab}(0^+) = 10$, $i_L(0^+) = 2$.

9-27. In the parallel R-L-C circuit shown in Fig. P9-27 $v_{ab}(0^+) = 1$, $i_L(0^+) = 0$.

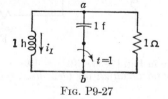

FIG. P9-27

The switch K remains closed until $t = 1$. It is opened at $t = 1$. Calculate and sketch $v_{ab}(t)$ from $t = 0$ to $t = 4$.

9-28. (a) Three elements R, L, and C are connected in series as shown in Fig. P9-28a. If $v_{ab}(0^+) = 0$ and $i_L(0^+) = -1$ amp, calculate $v_{ab}(t)$ for all $t \geq 0^+$. (b) The same elements as in (a) are now connected in parallel as shown in Fig. P9-28b. If $v_{ab}(0^+) = 0$ and $i_L(0^+) = 1$ amp, calculate $v_{ab}(t)$ for all $t \geq 0^+$.

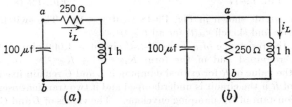

Fig. P9-28

9-29. Given are three elements R, $L = 1$ henry, $C = 1$ farad. These elements are connected either in series or in parallel as shown (Fig. P9-29). (a) Calculate the value of R so that both circuits have the same characteristic roots. (b) There exists a range of values for R, $R_{max} > R > R_{min}$, so that both circuits have the same type of response (i.e., overdamped or underdamped). Calculate R_{max} and R_{min}.

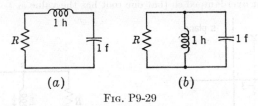

Fig. P9-29

9-30. The characteristic roots of a parallel R-L-C circuit are equal when $R = R_1$. If L and C remain fixed and $R = 2R_1$, calculate the new values of the characteristic roots in terms of L, and C.

9-31. The characteristic roots of a parallel R-L-C circuit are $s_{1,2} = -3 + j4$ when $R = 2$. What should the value of R be so that the circuit is critically damped?

9-32. In the circuit shown in Fig. P9-32 all elements have unit value. Is the circuit overdamped, underdamped, or critically damped?

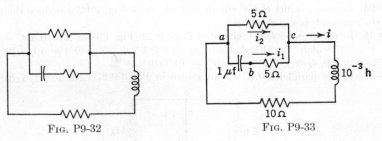

FIG. P9-32   FIG. P9-33

9-33. In the circuit shown in Fig. P9-33 $v_{ab}(0^+) = 10$ volts, $i(0^+) = 1$ amp. Calculate (a) $v_{bc}(0^+)$; (b) $v_{ac}(0^+)$; (c) $(di/dt)_{0^+}$; (d) $(dv_{ab}/dt)_{0^+}$; (e) $i_2(0^+)$; (f) $(di_2/dt)_{0^+}$; (g) $(d^2v_{ab}/dt^2)_{0^+}$.

9-34. In the circuit shown in Fig. P9-34 (a) deduce the second-order differential equation for v_{ab}; (b) if $v_{ab}(0^+) = V_0$ and $i_{ad}(0^+) = I_0$, find an expression for $(dv_{ab}/dt)_{0^+}$; (c) deduce the condition for nonoscillatory response.

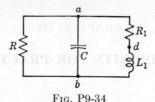

FIG. P9-34

9-35. In a critically damped parallel R-L-C circuit no initial energy is stored in the inductance. If $L = C = 1$ and if the energy stored in the capacitance at $t = 2$ is 2 joules, calculate (a) the energy stored in the inductance at $t = 2$; (b) the energy stored in the capacitance at $t = 0$.

CHAPTER 10

EQUIVALENT CIRCUITS FOR PRACTICAL SOURCES

The reader will recall that in Chap. 1 two *ideal* sources of electrical energy were defined. The *ideal voltage source* (represented by the symbol shown in Fig. 10-1a) has the property of maintaining across its terminals a waveform of voltage $v(t)$ which is independent of any elements connected to its terminals. The *ideal current source* (represented by the

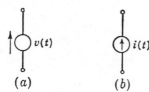

symbol shown in Fig. 10-1b) delivers a current $i(t)$ whose waveform is independent of any element connected to its terminals. Practical sources such as generators, batteries, power supplies, vacuum-tube oscillators, etc., differ from ideal sources in that the waveforms at

FIG. 10-1. Symbols for ideal sources. (a) Ideal voltage source. (b) Ideal current source.

their accessible terminals are influenced by the circuit components which are connected to those terminals. This happens because, in the process of transferring energy from the source to the circuit components connected to it, energy is either dissipated or stored in elements representing certain internal characteristics of the source.

Under certain conditions, which need not be discussed here, practical sources may be represented by a combination of ideal sources and passive

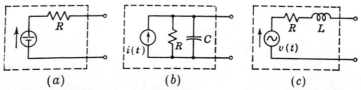

FIG. 10-2. Equivalent circuits for some practical sources. (a) Battery. (b) Vacuum-tube amplifier. (c) Alternator.

elements, i.e., equivalent circuits. For example, the series combination of an ideal constant voltage source and resistance shown in Fig. 10-2a may represent a battery. The connection of current source, resistance, and capacitance shown in Fig. 10-2b may represent a vacuum-tube source.

The series connection of voltage source, resistance, and inductance shown in Fig. 10-2c may represent a generator.

10-1. Resistive Voltage Source.   Because under certain conditions many (but not all) sources may be represented as the combination of an ideal source and a resistance, this case is treated first.   We shall call this type of source a resistive source.   Consider the series combination of an ideal voltage source $v_{mb}(t)$ and a resistance R_s, representing a practical source, delivering energy to a load resistance R_L as shown in Fig. 10-3a. We note that, when $R_s = 0$, the source is ideal and the terminal voltage $v_{ab}(t)$ is independent of R_L, as indicated by the dotted line in Fig. 10-3b.

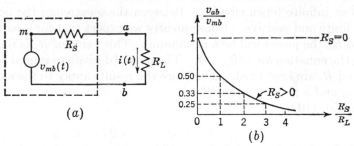

(a)

(b)

Fig. 10-3. A resistive voltage source and its terminal characteristic when the load is a resistance.

To obtain the dependence of terminal voltage on load resistance for finite values of R_s, apply Kirchhoff's voltage law to the circuit of Fig. 10-3a,

$$i(t)R_L + i(t)R_s = v_{mb}(t) \tag{10-1}$$

so that

$$i(t) = \frac{v_{mb}(t)}{R_L + R_s} \tag{10-2}$$

Note that, for an ideal source $R_s = 0$, $i(t)$ tends toward infinity as $R_L \rightarrow 0$.   This indicates that an ideal voltage source is capable of delivering infinite current.   The voltage at the terminals of the resistive source, v_{ab}, is given by

$$v_{ab} = i(t)R_L \tag{10-3}$$

or

$$v_{ab}(t) = v_{mb}(t)\frac{R_L}{R_L + R_s} \tag{10-3a}$$

This expression may be written in normalized form,

$$\frac{v_{ab}(t)}{v_{mb}(t)} = \frac{1}{1 + R_s/R_L} \tag{10-4}$$

This relationship is illustrated in Fig. 10-3b.   Note that the terminal characteristics of the resistive-source–resistive-load combination are independent of the waveform of the source.

The power delivered by the source to the load resistance R_L, at any instant of time, is given by

$$p_L(t) = [i(t)]^2 R_L \qquad (10\text{-}5)$$

Using the result for $i(t)$ given in Eq. (10-2),

$$p_L(t) = [v_{mb}(t)]^2 \frac{R_L}{(R_L + R_s)^2} \qquad (10\text{-}6)$$

Consider now an instant of time at which $v_{mb}(t)$ is not zero. We note then that no power is delivered to the load resistance if its value is zero (short circuit) or infinite (open circuit). Between these extremes the power is always finite and positive. Consequently we expect that for a particular value of R_L the power will be a maximum. This value of R_L is found by solving the equation $\partial p_L / \partial R_L = 0$. The partial derivative is used because $v_{mb}(t)$ and R_s are kept fixed. Therefore the results apply to the case of a given v_{mb} and a given nonzero R_s.

From Eq. (10-6),

$$\frac{\partial p_L}{\partial R_L} = [v_{mb}(t)]^2 \frac{(R_L + R_s)^2 - 2(R_L + R_s)R_L}{(R_L + R_s)^4}$$

Setting this derivative to zero, the load receives maximum power when

$$R_L = R_s \qquad (10\text{-}7)$$

The result obtained in Eq. (10-7) is called the *maximum-power-transfer theorem for resistive sources*. (It will be shown in the next article that the same result applies to both voltage and current sources.) This theorem states: For an adjustable load and fixed source resistances, at all instants of time, maximum power is transferred to a load resistance by a resistive source if the load resistance is made equal to the source resistance.[1] It is noted that for this condition ($R_L = R_s$) the power which is dissipated in the load (R_L) is equal to the power dissipated within the source (R_s). In many applications where the total amount of power or energy involved is sufficiently small, the rather low (50 per cent) efficiency is tolerated for the sake of obtaining the maximum power which the resistive source is *capable* of delivering.

It is instructive to calculate the ratio of the power delivered for any value of R_L to the power delivered when $R_L = R_s$. Substituting Eq.

[1] It is again pointed out that the condition $R_L = R_s$ deals with maximum power transfer to R_L for any value of $v_{mb}(t)$. This condition should not be confused with the maximum instantaneous power, which occurs for any value of R_L at those instants of time at which $v_{mb}(t)$ is a maximum. See Probs. 10-2 and 10-4.

$$_{mb}(t)]^2 \, \frac{1}{4R_s} \tag{10-8}$$

$$\frac{4R_sR_L}{R_s + R_L)^2}$$

$$\frac{4(R_L/R_s)}{\lfloor + R_L/R_s)^2} \tag{10-9}$$

g. 10-4.

oltage source must contain some

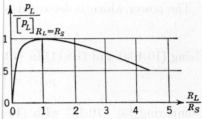

IG. 10-4. Relative power-transfer curve
or a resistive voltage source with resis-
ive load.

practical current source may fre-
l combination of an ideal current

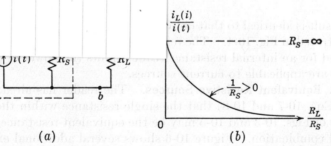

(a)   (b)

FIG. 10-5. Resistive current source supplying a resistive load and its terminal
characteristics.

source and a resistance. Such a current source is shown connected to a
load resistance R_L in Fig. 10-5a. We note that in this case the source is
ideal when R_s is infinite; then $i(t) = i_L(t)$, independently of R_L. This
ideal case is illustrated by the dotted line of Fig. 10-5b.

To obtain the dependence of load current on load resistance for the
case of the practical source, apply Kirchhoff's current law at terminal a,

$$i(t) = \frac{v_{ab}}{R_s} + \frac{v_{ab}}{R_L} \tag{10-10}$$

so that $$v_{ab} = i(t)\,\frac{1}{1/R_L + 1/R_s} \qquad (10\text{-}10a)$$

Since $$i_L(t) = \frac{v_{ab}(t)}{R_L} \qquad (10\text{-}10b)$$

we have the result

$$i_L(t) = i(t)\,\frac{1}{1 + R_L/R_s} \qquad (10\text{-}11)$$

or $$\frac{i_L(t)}{i(t)} = \frac{1}{1 + R_L/R_s} \qquad (10\text{-}11a)$$

The result (10-11a) is illustrated in Fig. 10-5b.

The power which is delivered to the load resistance R_L is

$$p_L(t) = [i_L(t)]^2 R_L = v_{ab}(t)i_L(t) \qquad (10\text{-}12)$$

Using (10-10a) and (10-11) in (10-12),

$$p_L(t) = [i(t)R_s]^2\,\frac{R_L}{(R_L + R_s)^2} \qquad (10\text{-}13)$$

Comparing Eq. (10-13) with (10-6), we note that the result of solving $\partial p_L/\partial R_L$ gives again

$$R_L = R_s \qquad (10\text{-}14)$$

as the condition for maximum power transfer. For this condition the power is

$$[p_L(t)]_{R_L = R_s} = [i(t)]^2\,\frac{R_s}{4} \qquad (10\text{-}15)$$

This result is identical to that obtained for the voltage source [Eq. (10-9)] as illustrated in Fig. 10-4. The remarks at the end of Art. 10-1 regarding the need for an internal resistance, which limits the power of a practical source, are applicable to current sources.

10-3. Equivalent Resistive Sources. The reader has already noticed (from Eqs. 10-7 and 10-8) that the single resistance within the practical sources of Figs. 10-3 and 10-5 may be the equivalent resistance of a series parallel combination. Figure 10-6 shows several additional examples of equivalent sources, i.e., sources which have identical terminal characteristics. Note that in this type of equivalence *voltage* sources with several internal resistances are equivalent to *voltage* sources with a single internal resistance R_s and *current* sources with several internal resistances are equivalent to *current* sources with a single internal resistance.

The similarity between the characteristics of practical voltage and current sources, however, leads one to suspect that there is a general equivalence between these two *types* of sources [compare Figs. 10-3b and 10-5b and Eqs. (10-4) and (10-11a)]. Such an equivalence does indeed exist and will be discussed now. We shall first state this general equivalence:

A voltage source consisting of an ideal voltage source $v(t)$ and a *series* resistance R_s may, *with respect to its output terminals only*, be represented as the *parallel* combination of an ideal current source $i(t) = v(t)/R_s$ and the resistance R_s.   Conversely, a current source consisting of the *parallel* combination of an ideal source $i(t)$ and the internal resistance R_s may,

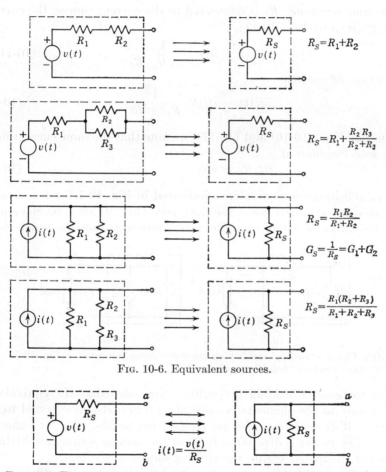

Fig. 10-6. Equivalent sources.

Fig. 10-7. The two sources shown have the same terminal characteristics.

with respect to its output terminals only, be represented as the *series* combination of an ideal voltage source $v(t) = i(t)R_s$ and the resistance R_s. The reader may ask himself why one type of source should be converted into another type.   The answer is to be found in the simplification which can be achieved in some networks when a suitable conversion is made. This point will become clear as we progress.   The equivalences, illustrated in Fig. 10-7, will now be proved.

If a load resistance R_L is connected to the terminals a-b of the voltage source of Fig. 10-7, the current in this resistance is given, by Eq. (10-2),

$$i_L = \frac{v(t)}{R_L + R_s} \qquad (10\text{-}16)$$

If the same resistance R_L is connected to the current source, the current in R_L is given by Eq. (10-11),

$$i_L(t) = i(t)\, \frac{1}{1 + R_L/R_s} \qquad (10\text{-}11)$$

which may be written

$$i_L(t) = i(t)R_s\, \frac{1}{R_L + R_s} \qquad (10\text{-}17)$$

Comparing Eqs. (10-16) and (10-17), we note that the same current flows *in the load resistance* if

$$i(t)R_s = v(t) \qquad (10\text{-}18)$$

thus establishing the equivalence indicated in Fig. 10-7 for a resistance connected to terminals a-b. We note here that R_L may be the equivalent resistance of a series-parallel combination so that the proof above

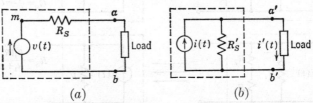

(a)   (b)

Fig. 10-8. Circuits used in establishing the equivalence indicated in Fig. 10-7. The terminal pairs marked "Load" are identical.

applies to resistive loading generally. Note also that the equivalence applies only to the elements connected to terminals a-b external to the sources. *Within* the sources *no* equivalence exists. If, for example, $R_L = \infty$, no power is dissipated in R_s of the voltage source but $i(t)^2R_s$ is the power dissipated within the current source.

We shall now show that the equivalence indicated in Fig. 10-7 applies for *any* combination of elements connected to terminals a-b. Such an arrangement is indicated in Fig. 10-8.

Let the terminal pair shown in Fig. 10-8a connected across the terminals a-b of the resistive voltage source contain an arbitrary combination of circuit elements. The *same* terminal pair is connected across the terminals a'-b' of the resistive current source shown in Fig. 10-8b. If the response of the elements represented by the terminal pair to the two sources is to be identical (so that the sources are equivalent with respect to their output terminals), then the following two conditions must be fulfilled:

$$v_{a'b'}(t) = v_{ab}(t) \qquad (10\text{-}19a)$$

and
$$i'(t) = i_{ab}(t) \qquad (10\text{-}19b)$$

Given these conditions, we are required to find the relation between $v(t)$, $i(t)$, R_s, and R_s'. We cannot evaluate i_{ab} or i' flowing in the loads since the nature and the value of the elements in the load are not known and are arbitrary.

In Fig. 10-8a, independently of the nature of the load, application of Kirchhoff's voltage law gives

$$i_{ab}(t) = \frac{v(t)}{R_s} - \frac{v_{ab}(t)}{R_s} \qquad (10\text{-}20)$$

In Fig. 10-8b application of Kirchhoff's current law gives

$$i'(t) = i(t) - \frac{v_{a'b'}(t)}{R_s'} \qquad (20\text{-}21)$$

The conditions (10-19) must hold for any *arbitrary* time function $v(t)$. Using (10-19b) and (10-21),

$$i(t) - \frac{v_{a'b'}(t)}{R_s'} = \frac{v(t)}{R_s} - \frac{v_{ab}(t)}{R_s} \qquad (10\text{-}19c)$$

If the equivalence is to be valid $v_{a'b'} = v_{ab}$ and Eq. (10-19c) may be written

$$v_{ab}(t) \left(\frac{1}{R_s} - \frac{1}{R_s'} \right) = \frac{v(t)}{R_s} - i(t) \qquad (10\text{-}19d)$$

Now $v(t)$ is an unspecified time function; $v_{ab}(t)$ is arbitrary in the sense that it will depend on the elements in the load as well as on $v(t)$. Equation (10-19d) states that the arbitrary time function $v(t)/R_s - i(t)$ must equal the arbitrary time function $v_{ab}(t)(1/R_s - 1/R_s')$. This is possible only if each side of Eq. (10-19d) is equal to zero.

The conditions for equivalence (with respect to their output terminals) of the two sources shown in Fig. 10-8 are therefore

$$R_s = R_s'$$

and
$$\frac{v(t)}{R_s} = i(t) \qquad (10\text{-}22)$$

We note now that
$$i(t) R_s = v(t)$$

is the voltage across the terminals of either source if *no* elements are connected to those terminals (open circuit) and

$$i(t) = \frac{v(t)}{R_s}$$

is the current which flows from terminal a to b in either circuit if a short circuit is connected between those terminals.

We observe that in converting a resistive voltage source the corresponding current source $i(t)$ has the same waveform as the current which will flow in R_s (see Fig. 10-7) if the terminals of the voltage source are short-circuited together. This is called the short-circuited current of the practical sources. Similarly, if a current source is converted to a voltage source, the waveform of the latter is identical with that of the voltage appearing across R_s' (see Fig. 10-7) if no external element is connected across the terminals of the practical current source. This is called the open-circuited voltage of the resistive sources.

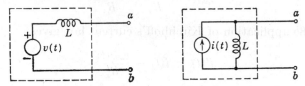

Fig. 10-9. Inductive sources.

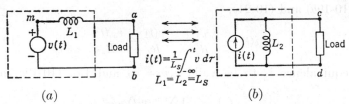

Fig. 10-10. Equivalent inductive sources.

10-4. Inductive Sources. Under certain conditions it is possible to represent practical sources as combinations of ideal sources and inductances as shown in Fig. 10-9. The definition of equivalence between voltage and current sources is the same as before: The same load connected across terminals a-b in Fig. 10-10a and terminals c-d in Fig. 10-10b must draw the same current from either source and will therefore have the same voltage across it: $v_{ab} = v_{cd}$ and $i_{ab} = i_{cd}$. In Fig. 10-10a application of Kirchhoff's voltage law gives

$$L_1 \frac{di_{ab}}{dt} + v_{ab} = v_{mb} = v(t) \tag{10-23}$$

In Fig. 10-10b application of Kirchhoff's current law at point c gives

$$\frac{1}{L_2} \int_{-\infty}^{t} v_{cd} \, d\tau + i_{cd} = i(t) \tag{10-24}$$

If the conditions for equivalence

$$\begin{aligned} v_{cd} &= v_{ab} \\ i_{cd} &= i_{ab} \end{aligned} \tag{10-25}$$

hold, Eq. (10-24) may be written

$$\frac{1}{L_2} \int_{-\infty}^{t} v_{ab} \, d\tau + i_{ab} = i(t) \tag{10-26}$$

Multiplying Eq. (10-26) by L_2 and differentiating with respect to time,

$$L_2 \frac{di_{ab}}{dt} + v_{ab} = L_2 \frac{di}{dt} \tag{10-27}$$

By the argument employed in connection with Eq. (10-19d), the two sources of Fig. 10-10 are equivalent with respect to their terminal characteristics if

$$v(t) = L_s \frac{di}{dt}$$

or

$$i(t) = \frac{1}{L_s} \int_{-\infty}^{t} v \, d\tau \tag{10-28}$$

$$L_1 = L_2 = L_s$$

In connection with Eqs. (10-28) we again note that if terminals a-b are left open then the voltage in each circuit (Fig. 10-10a and b) is the same, and if the terminals are short-circuited then the two short-circuit currents are the same.

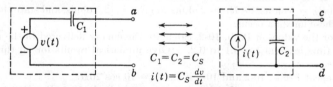

FIG. 10-11. Equivalent capacitive sources.

Example 10-1. Suppose that the voltage source in Fig. 10-10a is a step of value V. Find the equivalent current source.

Solution. The voltage source is defined by

$$\left.\begin{array}{ll} v(t) = 0 & t < 0 \\ v(t) = V & t > 0 \end{array}\right\} \quad \text{or} \quad v(t) = VU(t)$$

The equivalent current source will consist of the inductance L_s, in parallel with an ideal current source whose functional form is

$$i(t) = \frac{1}{L_s} \int_{-\infty}^{t} VU(\tau) \, d\tau = \frac{V}{L_s} t U(t)$$

i.e., a ramp-function current source.

10-5. Capacitive Sources. The equivalence between capacitive voltage and current sources is shown in Fig. 10-11. The proof is left as an exercise for the reader (see Prob. 10-14).

10-6. Other Sources. It happens frequently that practical sources cannot be represented by an ideal source and one element (or combinations of *similar* elements). See, for example, Fig. 10-2b and c. When the source contains dissimilar internal elements, the waveform of their equivalent source will be the sum of a number of waveforms obtained from the original waveform by differentiation, integration, or multiplication by a constant. This subject is studied in Chap. 12.

PROBLEMS

10-1. For the resistive voltage source shown in Fig. P10-1 the efficiency of power transfer is defined as p_{ab}/p_{mb}. Sketch a graph of this efficiency as a function of R_L/R_s.

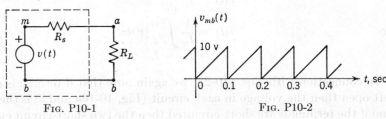

FIG. P10-1   FIG. P10-2

10-2. In the circuit of Fig. P10-1 $v_{mb}(t)$ is given by the graph shown in Fig. P10-2. The value of R_s is 5 ohms. Calculate the maximum instantaneous power delivered to R_L if (a) $R_L = 5$ ohms, (b) $R_L = 2$ ohms, (c) $R_L = 12.5$ ohms, and state the instants at which these maxima occur.

10-3. For the values of Prob. 10-2, calculate the energy delivered to the resistance R_L in the time interval $t = 0.1$ to 0.2. (Give numerical results for all three values of R_L.)

10-4. Repeat Probs. 10-2 and 10-3 if $v_{mb}(t) = 10 \cos 20\pi t$.

10-5. (a) Show that the resistive voltage source of Prob. 10-1 (Fig. P10-1) becomes an ideal current source if $R_s \to \infty$, $v(t) \to \infty$, but $v(t)/R_s$ remains finite. (b) In Prob. 10-1, $R_s = 100$ ohms. The value of R_L varies between 0.1 and 2.0 ohms. Calculate v_{ab}/v_{mb}, and compare this result with the result obtained if the resistance R_L is connected to an ideal current source $i(t) = v_{mb}/100$.

10-6. Show that a resistive current source is a good approximation to (a) an ideal current source if $R_s \gg R_L$; (b) an ideal voltage source if $R_s \ll R_L$.

10-7. For which value of R_L will the resistive source shown in Fig. P10-7 deliver maximum power to R_L?

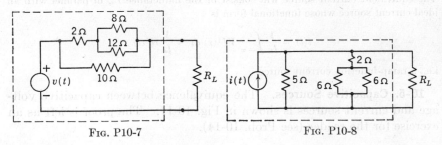

FIG. P10-7   FIG. P10-8

10-8. For which value of R_L will the resistive source shown in Fig. P10-8 deliver maximum power to R_L?

10-9. (*a*) In Fig. P10-9 calculate the value of R_L so that maximum power is transferred to it.   (*b*) The two sources are constant as indicated.   If $R_1 = 5$ ohms, $R_2 = 15$ ohms, obtain an expression for the power delivered to R_L as a function of V, I, and R_L.

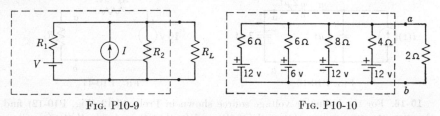

FIG. P10-9   FIG. P10-10

10-10. In Fig. P10-10 convert all voltage sources to current sources, and (*a*) calculate V_{ab}; (*b*) calculate the power delivered by each ideal source.

10-11. Represent the network to the left of terminals *a-b* in Fig. P10-11 as (*a*) a resistive current source; (*b*) a resistive voltage source.

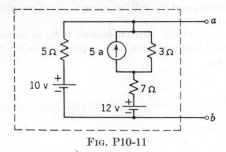

FIG. P10-11

10-12. In Fig. P10-12 the inductive voltage source is to be represented as a current source as shown.   If $i(0^+) = 5$, $v(t) = U(t)$, calculate $i_s(t)$ and $i_1(0^+)$.

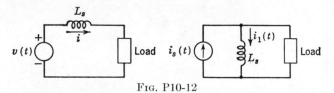

FIG. P10-12

10-13. In the capacitive voltage source of Fig. P10-13 $v_{ma}(0^+) = V_0$.   What is the value of the voltage across C_s (v_{ab}) at $t = 0^+$ in the equivalent current source shown?

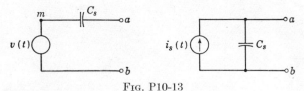

FIG. P10-13

10-14. Prove the relationships indicated in Fig. 10-11.

10-15. (a) In Fig. P10-15 convert the parallel combination of $i(t)$ and the 2-μf capacitance to a voltage source. Let $i(t) = 10^{-3}U(t)$. (b) Represent the elements to the left of terminals a-b as the parallel combination of an ideal current source and a single capacitance. (c) Use the result of (b) to calculate v_{ab}. (d) Calculate v_{ab}, using the current-division and the voltage-division formulas in the circuit as given.

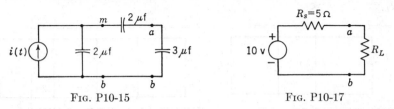

FIG. P10-15   FIG. P10-17

10-16. For the inductive voltage source shown in Prob. 10-12 (Fig. P10-12) find the current-source representation if (a) $v(t) = \delta(t)$; (b) $v(t) = A \sin \omega t U(t)$; (c) $v(t) = A \cos \omega t U(t)$.

10-17. (a) In Fig. P10-17 calculate the power delivered in the 5-ohm resistance as a function of R_L. (b) Represent the 10-volt–5-ohm combination as a current source, and calculate the power delivered to the 5-ohm resistance as a function of R_L in the current-source representation of the voltage source. (c) Comment on the equivalence of the two representations.

10-18. In a resistive circuit the source resistance is R_s, as in Fig. 10-3a. Show that the power delivered to a load resistance kR_L is the same as the power delivered to a load resistance R_s^2/kR_L.

CHAPTER 11

RESPONSE OF CIRCUITS WITH SOURCES

A. GENERAL PRINCIPLES

In several of the preceding chapters, circuits with initial energy storage but without sources were studied. The response of such circuits is characteristic of the structure of the circuit and of the relative values of the passive elements. The response of circuits to sources depends not only on the passive elements connected to the source (or sources) but also on the nature and waveform of the source.

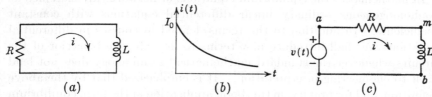

FIG. 11-1. (a) A source-free R-L circuit and (b) its characteristic response. (c) Series R-L circuit with an ideal voltage source.

For example, the current in a source-free R-L circuit will be a decaying exponential (see Fig. 11-1) regardless of the value of the initial current $i(0) = I_0$. But if the series connection of R and L elements contains a source (Fig. 11-1c), then the waveform of the current in the circuit depends on the waveform of the source and may not be exponential.

In the case of simple circuits which we have so far considered, such as the circuit in Fig. 11-1c, the equation describing the behavior of the current has been an integrodifferential or a differential equation. For example, for the circuit of Fig. 11-1c, the differential equation is

$$L \frac{di}{dt} + Ri = v(t) \tag{11-1}$$

In the following chapters it will be shown that the application of Kirchhoff's laws to any circuit containing sources and linear time-invariant passive elements will always result in one or more ordinary linear differential equations with constant coefficients. Equation (11-1) is an example of a linear differential equation with constant coefficients.

Since the solution of a circuit with linear time-invariant elements requires the solution of an ordinary linear differential equation with constant coefficients, we shall study those properties of these equations which help us to find standard methods for their solution.

11-1. Definitions. *Setting of Sources to Zero.* If in a network all ideal voltage sources are removed, each is replaced by a short circuit, and all the ideal current sources are taken out of the network (open-circuited), we say that the sources in the network are set to zero. These operations are identical to making the current sources $i(t)$ and voltage sources $v(t)$ identically equal to zero (for all t).

Equilibrium Equations of a Network. The application of Kirchhoff's laws to a network containing sources and passive elements will result in a system of differential equations relating voltages, currents, and their time derivatives. These differential equations are called the *equilibrium equations of the network*. If the network is linear and time-invariant, we shall call its equilibrium equation a linear constant-coefficient equilibrium equation, or equilibrium equation for brevity.

In mathematics the equilibrium equations of networks are classified as nonhomogeneous ordinary linear differential equations with constant coefficients. In addition to the terms defined in courses in differential equations we shall introduce new terms to describe the behavior of the circuits whenever the standard mathematical terminology does not lend itself to engineering interpretation. It is emphasized that by the above definition, and for brevity, in this book application of the term equilibrium equation is restricted to linear time-invariant networks.

Source-free Equilibrium Equation. If in a network all the ideal voltage and current sources are set to zero, the equilibrium equation of the remaining network is called a source-free equilibrium equation, or source-free equation, for brevity. In mathematics the source-free equation is called a homogeneous equation. In Fig. 11-1c, if the voltage source is set to zero, the remaining circuit will be as shown in Fig. 11-1a. The source-free equilibrium equation of the circuit of Fig. 11-1a is

$$Ri + L\frac{di}{dt} = 0$$

Solution of Source-free Equilibrium Equation. The response of certain source-free circuits was discussed in Chap. 9. The procedure which may be followed in the more general case, when the system of equilibrium equations of the network forms an Mth-order differential equation, is identical to the procedure which was followed in solving the second-order equation of Chap. 9. In Chap. 16 it is shown that the general form of the source-free equilibrium equation of a network can be written, in terms of a given variable such as $i(t)$, as

$$\sum_{m=0}^{M} a_m \frac{d^m}{dt^m} i(t) = 0 \tag{11-2}$$

The procedure for the solution of this equation is to introduce the form

$$i(t) = Ke^{st} \tag{11-3}$$

Substituting (11-3) in (11-2) results in the equation

$$\sum_{m=0}^{M} a_m s^m = 0 \tag{11-4}$$

Equation (11-4) determines the values of s which will allow the form (11-3) to satisfy the source-free equilibrium equation (11-2). Equation (11-4) is the *characteristic equation* of the equilibrium equation (11-2), and the values of s which satisfy the characteristic equation are called the *characteristic roots* of the equilibrium equation.

General Solution of the Source-free Equation. If the M solutions of the characteristic equation (11-4) are all different (i.e., if the M characteristic roots are distinct), then

$$i(t) = \sum_{m=1}^{M} K_m e^{s_m t} \tag{11-5}$$

is called the general solution of the source-free equation (11-2). The term "general" is used because there is no other solution of Eq. (11-2) which is not included in the form (11-5). In mathematical language we say that there is no solution of Eq. (11-2) which is linearly independent of Eq. (11-5).

Modes of Response. In Chap. 9 we saw that the equilibrium equation of a circuit with two energy-storing elements (L and C) was a second-order differential equation and that its response was composed of two modes $e^{s_1 t}$ and $e^{s_2 t}$, where s_1 and s_2 were the roots of the characteristic equation of the circuit. In general a source-free network with M "independent" energy-storing elements will have its equilibrium equation in the form of a differential equation of the Mth order with its corresponding characteristic equation an algebraic equation of the Mth degree. The response of the source-free network will be composed of M modes, corresponding to the M roots of the characteristic equation. In Eq. (11-5) each of the $e^{s_m t}$ terms are a mode of the response of the network whose equilibrium equation is given by Eq. (11-2). The sum of these modes $K_m e^{s_m t}$ forms the general solution of the source-free equation (11-2). The general solution will be identified by the subscript f; thus Eq. (11-5) is written as

$$i_f(t) = \sum_{m=1}^{M} K_m e^{s_m t}$$

Note that $i_f(t)$ contains M undetermined constants $(K_1, K_2, \ldots, K_M)$. If any of the roots of the characteristic equation (11-4) are equal to each other (as in the case of the critically damped R-L-C circuit), the solution of the characteristic equation (11-4) is modified accordingly. Such solutions are discussed in Chap. 13.

Complete Response of a Network. That function which satisfies the equilibrium equation of a network, as well as the initial conditions specified with the network, is called the complete response of the network. For a given network and given initial conditions this is a unique function. For example, let the voltage source in Fig. 11-1c be given by

$$v(t) = atU(t) \tag{11-6}$$

and let the time constant of the circuit be $L/R = T$. The quantities a and T are independent of t. Then an equilibrium equation of the R-L circuit of Fig. 11-1c is

$$Ri + L\frac{di}{dt} = at \qquad t > 0 \tag{11-7}$$

Let the initial condition of the circuit be $i(0^+) = I_0$. We shall subsequently show that the complete response of the circuit is given by the function

$$i(t) = \frac{a}{R}(t - T) + \left(I_0 + \frac{a}{R}T\right)e^{-t/T} \qquad t > 0 \tag{11-8}$$

If $i(t)$ is substituted from Eq. (11-8) into Eq. (11-7), it will be seen that the equilibrium equation will be satisfied. By substituting $t = 0$ in Eq. (11-8) it is seen that the initial condition is also satisfied.

11-2. Properties of Equilibrium Equations and of Network Response. Equation (11-7) is the equilibrium equation of a series connection of R-L elements and the voltage source $v(t) = atU(t)$. A more complicated network containing only one source, designated by $\phi(t)$, will be associated with many response functions, such as currents in every one of its elements or voltages across these elements.

In Chap. 16 we shall discuss a systematic method of relating each of these responses (network variables) with the source function. At this point we shall state that any of the variables of the network (voltage or current associated with an element of the network) denoted by $y(t)$ is related to the single source $\phi(t)$ of the network by an equation of the form

$$a_M \frac{d^M}{dt^M} y(t) + a_{M-1} \frac{d^{M-1}}{dt^{M-1}} y(t) + \cdots + a_1 \frac{d}{dt} y(t) + a_0 y(t)$$

$$= b_N \frac{d^N}{dt^N} \phi(t) + b_{N-1} \frac{d^N}{dt^{N-1}} \phi(t) + \cdots + b_1 \frac{d}{dt} \phi(t) + b_0 \phi(t)$$

or
$$\sum_{m=0}^{M} a_m \frac{d^m}{dt^m} y(t) = \sum_{n=0}^{N} b_n \frac{d^n}{dt^n} \phi(t) \qquad (11\text{-}9)$$

where the range of the summation parameters m and n, as well as the values of the coefficients a_m and b_n, will depend on the structure and elements of the network.   Equation (11-7) is a special case of the above general form.   A plausible argument indicating the validity of Eq. (11-9) can be presented by observing that in a linear network the relation between the voltage and current across an element is obtained by operations of multiplication, as in R, and differentiation, as in L and C.   The application of Kirchhoff's laws to a node or a mesh results in a sum containing a number of such operations.   The application of Kirchhoff's laws to all the nodes and meshes results in a set of simultaneous differential equations.

By a procedure of substitution (as in algebraic simultaneous equations) or by other methods (such as the operational method described in Chap. 12) a set of simultaneous differential equations can be reduced to a single differential equation with one unknown function $y(t)$ as given in Eq. (11-9).   This matter is reviewed in Chap. 12 and treated in detail in Chap. 16.

In Eq. (11-9) it is noted that the source function $\phi(t)$ is specified, and therefore all its derivatives are known.   The right-hand side of Eq. (11-9) is the sum of a number of known functions and can be represented in the form

$$\sum_{n=0}^{N} b_n \frac{d^n}{dt^n} \phi(t) \equiv f(t) \qquad (11\text{-}9a)$$

This is purely a symbolic representation for ease of writing.   Nonetheless it is emphasized that if the source $\phi(t)$ is specified then $f(t)$ is a known function.   The right-hand side of Eq. (11-9), namely, $f(t)$, corresponding to a given source $\phi(t)$, is referred to as the forcing function of the differential equation, and it should *not* be confused with $\phi(t)$, which is the waveform of the source in the circuit.   Equation (11-9) can now be written as

$$\sum_{m=0}^{M} a_m \frac{d^m}{dt^m} y(t) = f(t) \qquad (11\text{-}9b)$$

Equation (11-9b) is the general form of equilibrium equation of a network with one source, written in terms of a chosen network variable $y(t)$.

We now consider the case when the network contains more than one source. In such a case the principle of superposition can be applied. This "principle," which is a direct result of the linearity of the elements of the network (resulting in an equilibrium equation which is a linear differential equation with constant coefficients), may be stated in the form of a theorem.

Superposition Theorem. Let $y_1(t)$ be any arbitrary solution of the Mth-order differential equation,

$$\sum_{m=0}^{M} a_m \frac{d^m}{dt^m} y(t) = f_1(t) \qquad (11\text{-}9c)$$

and let $y_2(t)$ be a solution of

$$\sum_{m=0}^{M} a_m \frac{d^m}{dt^m} y(t) = f_2(t) \qquad (11\text{-}10)$$

that is,

$$\sum_{m=0}^{M} a_m \frac{d^m}{dt^m} y_1(t) = f_1(t) \qquad (11\text{-}9d)$$

and

$$\sum_{m=0}^{M} a_m \frac{d^m}{dt^m} y_2(t) = f_2(t) \qquad (11\text{-}10a)$$

where in Eqs. (11-9) and (11-10), in accordance with the property of linearity of the equations, all a_m are independent of $y(t)$. Then $y_1(t) + y_2(t)$ will satisfy the equation

$$\sum_{m=0}^{M} a_m \frac{d^m}{dt^m} y(t) = f_1(t) + f_2(t) \qquad (11\text{-}11)$$

A general proof of this theorem will not be given here. The theorem will be illustrated by a simple example, and the general proof will be left to the reader, since it follows from the illustration.

Example 11-1. Let $i_1(t)$ satisfy the equilibrium equation

$$\frac{d}{dt} i(t) + \frac{1}{T} i(t) = v_1(t) \qquad (11\text{-}12)$$

that is,

$$\frac{d}{dt} i_1(t) + \frac{1}{T} i_1(t) = v_1(t) \qquad (11\text{-}12a)$$

and let $i_2(t)$ satisfy

$$\frac{d}{dt} i(t) + \frac{1}{T} i(t) = v_2(t) \qquad (11\text{-}13)$$

that is,

$$\frac{d}{dt} i_2(t) + \frac{1}{T} i_2(t) = v_2(t) \qquad (11\text{-}13a)$$

We have to prove that $i(t) = i_1(t) + i_2(t)$ satisfies

$$\frac{d}{dt} i(t) + \frac{1}{T} i(t) = v_1(t) + v_2(t) \qquad \textbf{(11-14)}$$

The proof consists in adding Eqs. (11-12a) and (11-13a) to obtain

$$\frac{d}{dt} [i_1(t) + i_2(t)] + \frac{1}{T} [i_1(t) + i_2(t)] = v_1(t) + v_2(t) \qquad (11\text{-}15)$$

Equation (11-15) states that $i_1(t) + i_2(t)$ is the solution to Eq. (11-14).

The theorem presents the *principle of superposition* which can be expressed as follows:

Principle of Superposition. The response of a linear system to several ideal sources is the sum of its responses to each source acting individually.[1]

Equations (11-12), (11-13), and (11-14) can be identified with the equilibrium equations of the circuits of Fig. 11-2a, b, and c, respectively.

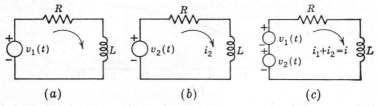

FIG. 11-2. Illustration of superposition.

These equations state that the current in the circuit of Fig. 11-2c, due to two sources $v_1(t)$ and $v_2(t)$, is equal to the sum of the currents due to $v_1(t)$ (see Fig. 11-2a) and to $v_2(t)$ (see Fig. 11-2b). In other words, with reference to Fig. 11-2, the superposition theorem states that $i(t) = i_1(t) + i_2(t)$.

The principle of superposition applies when the elements of the network are linear, i.e., when their value is independent of the voltage or current associated with them. To illustrate this, consider the circuits of Fig. 11-3a, b, and c. In these circuits the value of $R = 3$, independent of the voltage across it, and the principle of superposition applies such that $I = I_1 + I_2 = 2 + 4 = 6$. In Fig. 11-4$a$, b, and c it is assumed that the value of R_{ab} is a function of the voltage across it. In Fig. 11-4d a possible relationship for a nonlinear resistance and the voltage across it is shown.

[1] In the following pages various components of a response are discussed, and the term "full component of the response due to the source" is defined. In the statement of the superposition theorem the term "response" must be interpreted as the full component of the response due to the source.

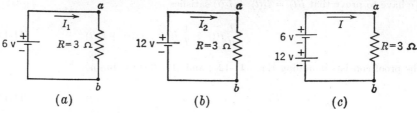

FIG. 11-3. Illustration of superposition in a linear element: $I_1 + I_2 = I$.

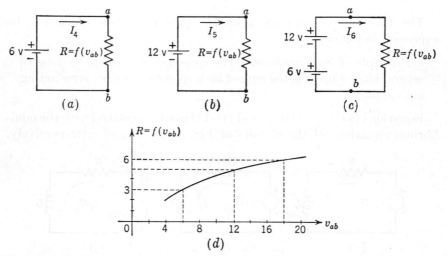

FIG. 11-4. Showing that superposition cannot be used when an element is nonlinear: $I_4 + I_5 \neq I_6$.

It is seen that, for $v_{ab} = 6$, $R = 3$; for $v_{ab} = 12$, $R = 5$; for $v_{ab} = 18$, $R = 6$. With these values and with reference to Fig. 11-4a, b, and c

$$I_4 = \frac{6}{f(6)} = \frac{6}{3} = 2 \qquad I_5 = \frac{12}{f(12)} = \frac{12}{5} = 2.4 \qquad I_6 = \frac{18}{f(18)} = \frac{18}{6} = 3$$

and
$$I_4 + I_5 = 2 + 2.4 \neq I_6$$

Thus the principle of superposition is not applicable to nonlinear elements. The following example indicates an application of the principle of superposition for linear elements.

Example 11-2. The circuit of Fig. 11-5a is used as an "adding circuit" in analogue computers. By the use of the superposition theorem find the response $v_1(t)$ in terms of $v_A(t)$, $v_B(t)$, and $v_C(t)$.

Solution. Let $v_{1A}(t)$ be the response due to source $v_A(t)$ when v_B and v_C are set to zero. The response $v_{1A}(t)$ is computed from Fig. 11-5b, which is obtained from Fig. 11-5a by setting $v_B \equiv 0 \equiv v_C$. From Fig. 11-5b it is seen that

$$v_{1A}(t) = \frac{R_{a'b}}{1 + R_{a'b}} v_A \qquad \frac{1}{R_{a'b}} = 1 + \frac{1}{2} + \frac{1}{2}$$

$$v_{1A}(t) = \frac{\frac{1}{2}}{1 + \frac{1}{2}} v_A = \tfrac{1}{3} v_A(t)$$

From Fig. 11-5c it is seen that

$$v_{1B}(t) = \frac{R_{a''b}}{2 + R_{a''b}} v_B \qquad \frac{1}{R_{a''b}} = 1 + 1 + \frac{1}{2}$$

$$v_{1B}(t) = \frac{\frac{2}{5}}{2 + \frac{2}{5}} v_B = \tfrac{1}{6} v_B(t)$$

Similarly $\qquad v_{1C}(t) = \tfrac{1}{6} v_C(t)$

Using the superposition theorem, the response $v_1(t)$ due to the sources v_A, v_B and v_C acting simultaneously is equal to the sum of the responses due to each source acting individually,

$$\begin{aligned}
v_1(t) &= v_{1A}(t) + v_{1B}(t) + v_{1C}(t) \\
&= \tfrac{1}{3} v_A(t) + \tfrac{1}{6} v_B(t) + \tfrac{1}{6} v_C(t)
\end{aligned}$$

From the expression for $v_1(t)$ it is seen that it is composed of the sum of fractions of the functions v_A, v_B, and v_C. The magnitude of these fractions is determined by the values of the resistances.

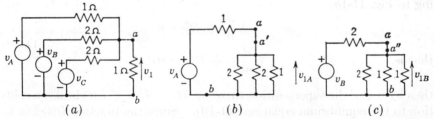

FIG. 11-5. Circuit diagram for Example 11-2.

Complete-response Theorem. This is a special version of the superposition theorem, which can be stated as follows: Let the function $y_s(t)$ satisfy the equation

$$\sum_{m=0}^{M} a_m \frac{d^m}{dt^m} y(t) = f_s(t) \tag{11-16}$$

where f_s is the forcing function. Now let the function $y_f(t)$ be the general solution to the *source-free* equation

$$\sum_{m=0}^{M} a_m \frac{d^m}{dt^m} y_f(t) = 0 \tag{11-17}$$

Then $y_s(t) + y_f(t)$ will also satisfy Eq. (11-16).

Proof. This is a special case of the superposition theorem, as is seen by observing that $f_s(t)$ can be written as

$$f_s(t) = f_s(t) + f_f(t) \qquad f_f(t) \equiv 0 \tag{11-18}$$

Since $y_s(t)$ and $y_f(t)$ are the solutions to the two equations (11-16) and (11-17), respectively, by the superposition theorem $y_s(t) + y_f(t)$ is a solution to the equation

$$\sum_{m=0}^{M} a_m \frac{d^m}{dt^m} y(t) = f_s(t) + f_f(t) = f_s(t)$$

As an example, we may apply this result to the circuit of Fig. 11-1c.

If $i_s(t)$ is a solution to the equilibrium equation of the circuit of Fig. 11-1c,

$$L \frac{di}{dt} + Ri = v(t) \tag{11-19}$$

that is, $L \dfrac{d}{dt} i_s(t) + Ri_s(t) = v(t)$

and if $i_f(t)$ is the general solution to the source-free equation corresponding to Fig. 11-1a,

$$L \frac{di}{dt} + Ri = 0$$
$$\tag{11-20}$$

that is, $L \dfrac{d}{dt} i_f + Ri_f = 0$

then by use of the superposition theorem $i(t) = i_s(t) + i_f(t)$ is also a solution to the equilibrium equation (11-19). Since the function $i_f(t)$ has as many constants of integration as continuity (initial) conditions of the system, its addition to any solution of Eq. (11-19), such as $i_s(t)$, will make it possible for the sum of the two solutions to satisfy the arbitrary initial conditions of the system and thus form the complete response of the circuit.

For example, in the case of Eq. (11-19), let

$$v(t) = at = Ri + L \frac{di}{dt} \tag{11-20a}$$

The general solution of the source-free equation (11-20) is

$$i_f(t) = A e^{-t/T} \tag{11-21}$$

where A is an undetermined constant. A solution of Eq. (11-20a) can be shown to be

$$i_s(t) = \frac{a}{R} (t - T) \tag{11-22}$$

as can be verified by substitution.   (A method for determining this result is discussed in Art. 11-3.)

$$i(t) = i_s(t) + i_f(t) = Ae^{-t/T} + \frac{a}{R}(t - T)   \qquad t \geq 0^+ \quad (11\text{-}23)$$

If A is so chosen that Eq. (11-23) satisfies the initial condition $i(0^+) = I_0$, then Eq. (11-23) will be the complete response of the circuit of Fig. 11-1c. Substituting $t = 0$ in Eq. (11-23) and replacing $i(0^+)$ with I_0, we have

$$A = \frac{a}{R}T + I_0 \qquad\qquad\qquad\qquad\qquad (11\text{-}24)$$

$$i(t) = \frac{a}{R}(t - T) + \left(\frac{a}{R}T + I_0\right)e^{-t/T} \qquad t \geq 0^+ \quad (11\text{-}25)$$

which satisfies Eq. (11-20a) and the initial condition $i(0^+) = I_0$.   The reader who is familiar with mathematical terminology will recognize that the complete response of a circuit is identical with that *special* particular solution of the inhomogeneous differential equation of the circuit which satisfies the particular initial conditions of the circuit problem.

Composition of the Complete Response.   An analysis of the composition of the complete response of a circuit will be undertaken here.   This discussion should not necessarily be taken as a procedure for solving problems; it is rather intended to give insight into the principles which are involved in complete-response computations.

The complete-response theorem states that the complete response of a circuit is composed of a solution of the equilibrium equation and the general solution of the source-free equation, the latter being chosen so that the initial conditions of the circuit problem are satisfied.   The "flow chart" shown in Fig. 11-6 illustrates this statement.

With reference to Eq. (11-25) we note now that the complete response of a circuit can always be written as the sum of several (two or more) terms. Some of these terms are the natural modes of the source-free network and will satisfy the source-free equilibrium equation without, in general, satisfying the equilibrium equation of the active network.   With these points in mind we shall now give the following definitions.

Component of the Response Due to a Source.   The sum of those terms in the complete response of a network which satisfy the equilibrium equation of the active network but do not satisfy the source-free equation is called the component of the response due to the source, or the response due to the source for brevity.   It is seen that all the natural modes of response of the source-free network are excluded from the response due to the source.

In Eq. (11-25) the term $(a/R)(t - T)$ satisfies the equilibrium equation (11-19) but does not satisfy the source-free equation (11-20) and hence is the response due to the source. In general the waveshape of the response due to a source is either identical with the waveshape of the source or can be obtained from it by performing on the source waveshape operations of integration, differentiation, and/or addition. This is seen from the fact that the voltages and currents in a circuit are related by the above-mentioned operations through restrictions placed on them by the circuit elements L, C, and R. The reader can take this as a guide in finding the

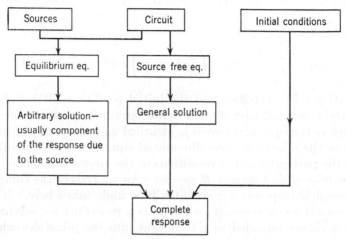

Fig. 11-6. Complete response of network.

response due to a source. In the example cited above the voltage source is a ramp function, and the response due to the source is

$$i_s(t) = \frac{a}{R}(t - T)$$

for $t \geq 0$, which is a ramp function $(a/R)t$ plus a constant value (step function) $-(a/R)T$, the waveform of which can be obtained from the source function by differentiation.

Free Component of the Response. Those terms in the complete response of the circuit which satisfy the source-free equation but do not satisfy the equilibrium equation are called the free component of the response, or free response for brevity. In Eq. (11-25) the term $(aT/R + I_0)e^{-t/T}$ constitutes the free response of the circuit. It is noted that the free component of the response is obtained from the general solution of the source-free equation when its constants are evaluated to fit the initial conditions of the problem. Hence the modes of the free response will be independent of the source, although their magnitude will depend on the source. It is also seen that the free component of the response is composed of the sum of the natural modes of the source-free network.

Steady-state Component of the Response.   If the response due to source is time-invariant or periodic with time, we shall refer to it as the steady-state component of the response, or steady-state response for brevity. In Eq. (11-25), since the response due to the source $(a/R)(t - T)$ is neither time-invariant nor periodic, according to the above definition, it is not called a steady-state response.

Transient Component of the Response.   If the free response of the circuit decays to zero with increasing time, then it is called the transient component of the response; usually the free response of a circuit containing resistance decays to zero as time approaches infinity.   In Eq. (11-25) the free response $(aT/R + I_0)e^{-t/T}$ is a transient response, since it decays to zero as time approaches infinity.

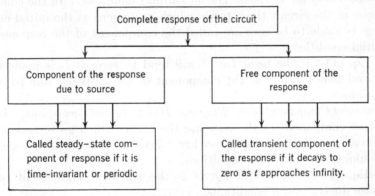

Fig. 11-7. Composition of the complete response of the circuit.

The reader is warned that different writers may define the terms transient and steady state in different ways.   For example, some writers define what we have called the response due to the source to be the steady-state response of the circuit whether or not it is time-invariant or periodic.   According to this definition the term $(a/R)(t - T)$ in Eq. (11-25) is a steady-state response, whereas according to our definition it is not since it is neither time-invariant nor periodic.   Some books define the transient response of a circuit (without the word component) to mean that which we have defined as complete response.   In the absence of standard definitions, in reading other books the subject matter must be interpreted in terms of the writers' definitions.

In Fig. 11-7 the components of the complete response of a circuit are illustrated.

A different approach to the composition of the complete response would be to consider it as the effect of two causes, sources and initial conditions.   It should be clear that sources and initial conditions are the only two possible causes which would produce flow of charges or estab-

lish voltages in a network. With this point of view the following definitions are given.

Full Component of the Response Due to the Source. In the complete
response of the circuit those terms which go to zero as the sources in the
circuit are set to zero are called the full component of the response due to
the source. (This definition is suggested by the authors and does not
appear in the literature.)

Equation (11-25) gives the complete response of an *R-L* circuit to the
voltage source $v(t) = at$. When a goes to zero, the terms $(a/R)(t - T) +
(aT/R)e^{-t/T}$ go to zero and therefore, in this case, $(a/R)(t - T) +
(aT/R)e^{-t/T}$ is the full component of the response of the *R-L* circuit due
to the source $v(t) = at$.

Component of the Response Due to Initial Conditions. In the complete
response of the circuit those terms which go to zero as the initial energy
storage is made to be zero are called the component of the response due
to initial conditions.

In Eq. (11-25) the term $I_0 e^{-t/T}$ will tend to zero as I_0 is made to be
zero, and hence $I_0 e^{-t/T}$ is the component of the response due to initial
conditions.

Transient Component of the Response Due to Initial Conditions. In the
transient component of the response the terms which go to zero as the
initial energy storage is made zero are called the transient component of
the response due to initial conditions.

In Eq. (11-25) the term $I_0 e^{-t/T}$ is the transient component of the
response due to initial conditions.

Transient Component of the Response Due to the Source. If the circuit
contains resistive elements, that part of the full component of the response
which does not satisfy the equilibrium equation is called the transient
component of the response due to the source.

In Eq. (11-25) the term $(aT/R)e^{-t/T}$ is the transient component of the
response due to the source.

Figure 11-8 shows the complete response of a circuit analyzed from the
point of view of the sources and initial conditions. Figure 11-9 shows
the composition of the complete response from two points of view, with
reference made to the example of Eq. (11-25). The figure may be read
either from top to bottom or in the reverse direction.

The Significance of the Transient Components. A familiarity with the
complete response of the network will show that the transient component
of the response acts as a "buffer" between the requirement of sources and
the initial conditions in the network. In the absence of impulses the
initial energy stored in the inductances and capacitances of the circuit
cannot change discontinuously. On the other hand, when a source is
applied to the circuit, it may require the distribution of charges and

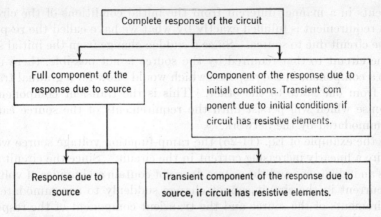

Fig. 11-8. "Bookkeeping" table for complete response of a circuit.

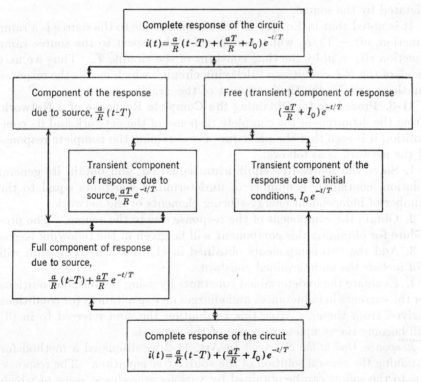

Fig. 11-9. Composition of complete response with reference to the example of Eq. (11-25).

currents in a manner different from the initial conditions of the circuit. This requirement is fulfilled exactly by what we have called the response of the circuit due to source.   Since a sudden change from the initial state of the circuit to that required by the source is not possible, there must exist a component in the response which would allow for a gradual transition from one state to the other.   This is the transient component of response which will persist until the requirements of the source can be accommodated by the network.

In the example of Eq. (11-25) the ramp-function voltage source would require a linearly increasing current in the circuit.   Since the circuit contains an inductance and the source does not contain an impulse of voltage, the current in the circuit cannot change suddenly to accommodate the requirements of the source and the transient component of the response $(I_0 + aT/R)e^{-t/T}$ will compensate the difference.   After many time constants the transient component "dies out," and the response of the circuit, for all practical purposes, will increase linearly with time as dictated by the source.

It is noted that in Eq. (11-25) the response due to the source is a ramp function, $a(t - T)/R$, which is delayed with respect to the source ramp function $v(t) = at$ by the time constant of the circuit, T.   Thus we may think of the R-L circuit as a "delaying circuit" which makes the response lag the source by the time constant of the circuit.

11-3. Procedure for Obtaining the Complete Response of a Network. From the definition of the complete response of the network and its composition it is seen that the procedure for obtaining the complete response of the network is as follows:

1. Solve the source-free equilibrium equation, and obtain its general solution, containing a number of undetermined constants equal to the number of independent energy-storing elements of the network.

2. Obtain the component of the response due to the source.   The procedure for obtaining this component will be given in the following pages.

3. Add the two components obtained in (1) and (2).   This sum will *still include* the undetermined constants.

4. Evaluate the undetermined constants by using the initial conditions for the currents in inductances and charges on capacitances (or conditions derived from these).   After this evaluation the sum referred to in (3) will become the complete response of the network.

Response Due to the Source.   In Art. 11-2 we discussed a method for obtaining the general solution of the source-free equation.   The response due to the source can be obtained by various procedures, some of which will be discussed here.   One method would be to use trial solutions, chosen through the knowledge that, for a given source function, the response due to the source has the same mathematical form as the source function or is related to it by differentiation, integration, and/or addition. Another method is to find the response for one type of source function through a knowledge of the response for another source, related to the first through addition, multiplication, differentiation, or integration.

To illustrate these methods of solution, we begin with the response of an R-L-C circuit to the basic source function $U(t)$. This response can be used as a building block for the response of networks to arbitrary source functions.

The reader who is familiar with Taylor's expansion of functions will realize that if the response of a network to a step function $A_0 U(t)$ is known, and from this the response to $A_1 t U(t)$, $A_2 t^2 U(t)$, $\ldots$, $A_n t^n U(t)$ is obtained, then the response of the network to any arbitrary source $f(t) = \sum_n A_n t^n$ can be found by superposition.

11-4. Response of the R-L-C Circuit to a Step Function. Example 11-3. The voltage source in the circuit of Fig. 11-10 is a step function. At $t = 0$ the initial conditions are $i(0) = I_0$ and $q_n(0) = Q_0$. Find $i(t)$ as a function of time for $t \geq 0^+$.

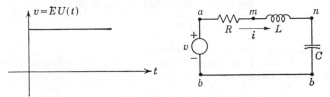

FIG. 11-10. Series R-L-C circuit with a step-function voltage source impressed.

Solution. The equilibrium equation of the circuit of Fig. 11-10 in terms of $q_n(t)$ can be obtained from the application of Kirchhoff's law to the circuit, resulting in

$$R \frac{d}{dt} q_n + L \frac{d^2}{dt^2} q_n + \frac{1}{C} q_n = EU(t) \tag{11-26}$$

$$\frac{d^2}{dt^2} q_n + \frac{R}{L} \frac{d}{dt} q_n + \frac{1}{LC} q_n = \frac{E}{L} U(t) \tag{11-27}$$

The general solution of the corresponding source-free equation, $[q_n(t)]_f$, was discussed in Chap. 9. This response was given as the sum of the two modes,

$$[q_n(t)]_f = A_1 e^{s_1 t} + A_2 e^{s_2 t} \qquad s_1 \neq s_2 \tag{11-28}$$

$$s_{1,2} = -\alpha \pm \sqrt{\alpha^2 - \omega_0^2} \tag{11-29}$$

$$\alpha = \frac{R}{2L} \qquad \omega_0^2 = \frac{1}{LC} \tag{11-30}$$

The response due to the source in Eq. (11-26) can be found by inspection. It is observed that

$$EU(t) = E \qquad t > 0 \tag{11-31}$$

$$EU(t) = 0 \qquad t < 0 \tag{11-32}$$

Hence for $t > 0$

$$\frac{d^2}{dt^2} q_n + \frac{R}{L} \frac{d}{dt} q_n + \frac{1}{LC} q_n = \frac{E}{L} \qquad t > 0 \tag{11-33}$$

Let the response due to the source be $(q_n)_s$. Since the source is independent of time for $t > 0$, it is reasonable to expect that $(q_n)_s$ may be independent of time. If the expected solution $(q_n)_s$ is indeed independent of time, then in Eq. (11-33) the terms $(d^2/dt^2)(q_n)_s$ and $(d/dt)(q_n)_s$ are zero and Eq. (11-33) reduces to

$$\frac{1}{LC}(q_n)_s = \frac{E}{L} \qquad (q_n)_s = CE \tag{11-34}$$

The addition of CE to the right hand side of Eq. (11-28) will result in

$$q_n(t) = CE + A_1 e^{s_1 t} + A_2 e^{s_2 t} \tag{11-35}$$

When A_1 and A_2 in Eq. (11-35) are evaluated to satisfy the initial conditions, the resulting function will be the complete response of the circuit. Substitution of $(q_n)_s$ from (11-34) into (11-27) confirms that (11-34) is a solution of Eq. (11-27). Furthermore, since in Eq. (11-35) CE does not satisfy the source-free equation, it is the response due to the source. Since it is time-invariant, it is the steady-state response of the circuit.

The response due to the source can also be obtained by observing that, after the source-free current in the circuit has decayed to a negligible value, the capacitance C will be charged to $v_{nb} \to E$. Under this condition the voltage $v_{an} = 0$, and the circuit has reached a steady state.

$$\lim_{t \to \infty} v_{nb}(t) = E \qquad \text{but} \qquad v_{nb} = \frac{q_n}{C} \tag{11-36}$$

Therefore
$$(q_n)_s = CE \tag{11-37}$$

which is a steady-state solution, independent of t.

The values of A_1 and A_2 are found by the use of initial conditions, as was done in Chap. 9 for the source-free case,

$$q_n(0^+) = CE + A_1 + A_2 = Q_0 \tag{11-38}$$

$$i(t) = \frac{d}{dt} q_n(t) = s_1 A_1 e^{s_1 t} + s_2 A_2 e^{s_2 t} + 0 \tag{11-39}$$

$$i(0^+) = s_1 A_1 + s_2 A_2 = I_0 \tag{11-40}$$

A_1 and A_2 are found, from Eqs. (11-38) and (11-40), to be

$$A_1 = \frac{s_2(Q_0 - CE) - I_0}{s_2 - s_1} \qquad s_2 \neq s_1 \tag{11-41}$$

$$A_2 = \frac{s_1(Q_0 - CE) - I_0}{s_1 - s_2} \qquad s_2 \neq s_1 \tag{11-42}$$

The above procedure illustrates the trial method (inspection method) of finding the response due to the source. It is already evident that, if for a certain circuit,

i_s is the component of the response due to the source of $v(t)$

then

Ki_s is the component of the response due to the source $Kv(t)$ *if* K is time-invariant

We shall now see how the response of a circuit to various sources can be obtained from its response to a step function. This method is based on the theorem discussed in the next article.

11-5. Related-sources Theorem. For a given equilibrium equation of the form

$$\sum_{m=0}^{M} a_m \frac{d^m}{dt^m} i(t) = \sum_{n=0}^{N} b_n \frac{d^n}{dt^n} v(t) \qquad t > 0 \qquad (11\text{-}43)$$

If $i(t)$ is the full component of the response due to the only source of the network, $v(t)$, then the replacement of $v(t)$ by another source of the form $v_1(t) = (d/dt)v(t)$ or $v_2(t) = \int_0^{\tau=t} v(\tau)\, d\tau$ will result in a full component of the response given by $i_1(t) = (d/dt)i(t)$ or $i_2(t) = \int_0^t i(\tau)\, d\tau$, respectively. A complete proof of this theorem will not be given here. It is pointed out only that differentiation of both sides of Eq. (11-43) results in

$$\sum_{m=0}^{M} a_m \frac{d^m}{dt^m}\left[\frac{d}{dt} i(t)\right] = \sum_{n=0}^{N} \frac{d^n}{dt^n} b_n \left[\frac{d}{dt} v(t)\right] \qquad t > 0 \qquad (11\text{-}44)$$

Replacing $(d/dt)v(t)$ and $(d/dt)i(t)$ by $v_1(t)$ and $i_1(t)$, respectively, we have

$$\sum_{m=0}^{M} a_m \frac{d^m}{dt^m} i_1(t) = \sum_{n=0}^{N} \frac{d^n}{dt^n} b_n v_1(t) \qquad t > 0 \qquad (11\text{-}45)$$

Equation (11-45) is interpreted to state that the full component of response due to the source $v_1(t) = (d/dt)v(t)$ is given by $i_1(t) = (d/dt)i(t)$. A similar argument can be made for

$$v_2(t) = \int_0^t v(\tau)\, d\tau \qquad \text{and} \qquad i_2(t) = \int_0^t i(\tau)\, d\tau$$

In the application of the related-sources theorem the following points must be observed:

1. If in Eq. (11-43) the time functions have discontinuities, the impulse functions that are produced by the differentiations must be taken into account.

2. The related-sources theorem in the form stated here applies to *full* component of the response due to the source. It is recalled that this is equal to the complete response if the continuity conditions of the network are zero.

3. The theorem can be applied to the component of the response due to the source in the case of differentiation if the source $v(t)$ is continuous for $t > 0$. This means that, if $i_s(t)$ is the response due to a source for the source $v(t)$, then $(d/dt)i_s(t)$ will be the response due to the source $(d/dt)v(t)$.

4. In the case of integration the theorem may be applied to the response due to the source subject to evaluation of a constant of integration. This will be illustrated in Example 11-4.

The related-sources theorem gives an "engineering" version of the method of "undetermined coefficients." In the study of differential equations it is shown that if

$$\sum_{m=0}^{M} a_m \frac{d^m}{dt^m} f(t) = \sum_{n=0}^{N} b_n t^n \qquad (11\text{-}46)$$

then the function

$$f(t) = \sum_{n=0}^{N} K_n t^n$$

will satisfy the differential equation. The values of the constants K_n is obtained by substituting $\displaystyle\sum_{n=0}^{N} K_n t^n$ for $f(t)$ in the differential equation and comparing the coefficients of the like powers of t on each side of the equation. Application of the related-sources theorem results, of course, in the same response as given by the foregoing method. However, the statement of the theorem is worded in such a manner as to emphasize the possibility of finding the response of a circuit due to a number of sources if its response to a step function is known.

Example 11-4 illustrates the use of the related-sources theorem.

Example 11-4. The voltage source in a series $R\text{-}C$ circuit shown in Fig. 11-11a is a ramp function $(E/a)tU(t)$, where E and a are independent of time and E/a is the slope of the ramp. The continuity condition of the circuit is $q_n(0^+) = Q_0$. Find $q_n(t)$ for $t > 0$.

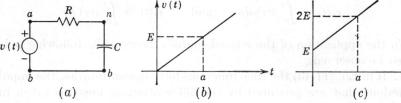

(a)   (b)   (c)

FIG. 11-11. (a) Series $R\text{-}C$ circuit with ideal voltage source. (b) Waveform of a ramp-function source. (c) Waveform of a step- plus ramp-function source.

Solution. The complete response of the $R\text{-}C$ circuit to a step source $(E/a)U(t)$ is given as

$$q_n(t) = \frac{CE}{a}(1 - e^{-t/RC}) + Q_0 e^{-t/RC} \qquad (11\text{-}47)$$

The full component of the response due to the step source, designated by $[q_n(t)]_{fs}$, is

$$[q_n(t)]_{fs} = \frac{CE}{a}(1 - e^{-t/RC}) \qquad (11\text{-}48)$$

The full component of the response due to the ramp source

$$v_2(t) = \frac{E}{a}tU(t) = \int_0^t \frac{E}{a} U(\tau) \, d\tau \qquad (11\text{-}49)$$

is

$$[q_n(t)_2]_{fs} = \int_0^t \frac{CE}{a}(1 - e^{-\tau/RC})\, d\tau = \frac{CE}{a}[(t - RC) + RCe^{-t/RC}] \qquad t > 0 \quad (11\text{-}50)$$

The component of the response due to the source is

$$[q_n(t)_2]_s = \frac{CE}{a}(t - RC) \qquad\qquad\qquad\qquad\qquad\qquad (11\text{-}51)$$

Notice that if the component of the response due to the step source, (CE/a), is integrated this will result in

$$\int_0^t q_n(\tau)\, d\tau = \int_0^t \frac{CE}{a}\, d\tau = \frac{CE}{a}\, t \qquad\qquad\qquad\qquad (11\text{-}52)$$

This result differs from that of Eq. (11-50) by the constant $(-CE/a)RC$. This is the constant of integration referred to in item 4 above.

With the aid of the related-sources theorem and the superposition theorem the response of the circuit to many sources can be found in terms of the circuit response to a step function. Example 11-5 illustrates the application of the superposition theorem to the solution of a problem.

Example 11-5. The voltage source in the series R-C circuit of Fig. 11-11a has the waveform

$$v(t) = EU(t) + \frac{E}{a}tU(t) \qquad\qquad\qquad\qquad\qquad (11\text{-}53)$$

as shown in Fig. 11-11c. Determine the charge component $[q_n(t)]_s$.

Solution. The response due to the source given in Eq. (11-53) is obtained by observing that $v(t)$ can be analyzed as the sum of $EU(t)$ and $(E/a)tU(t)$.

We have already found the response of the R-C circuit due to $EU(t)$ and due to the source $(E/a)t$. Therefore the response to $v(t) = EU(t) + (E/a)tU(t)$ is obtained from superposition by adding these two responses. This results in

$$[q_n(t)]_s = CE\left(1 + \frac{t - RC}{a}\right) \qquad\qquad\qquad\qquad (11\text{-}54)$$

11-6. Networks with Constant Sources (D-C Sources).

The abbreviation d-c refers to direct current. Throughout the literature this abbreviation is used to indicate a source which is independent of time, for all values of time between $-\infty$ and $+\infty$.

Effect of Inductance and Capacitance on the Steady-state Response of Networks with D-C Sources. A network with d-c sources approaches its steady state after few time constants. In d-c steady state the voltages and currents of the network elements are independent of time. Since the voltage across an inductance is proportional to the rate of change of the current in the inductance $[v_{ab} = L(d/dt)i_{ab}]$, the flow of a d-c current in an inductance will result in zero voltage across the inductance. Hence in the d-c steady state we have a circuit element L_{ab} wherein there is a current I_{ab} but voltage $V_{ab} = 0$. As far as the d-c steady state is concerned, the inductance L_{ab} can be replaced by a line (short circuit) as shown in Fig. 11-12a. The d-c voltages and currents at the terminals a-b of the L_{ab} and the short circuit a-b are identical when the current I_{ab} is independent of time. Similarly the current through a capacitance is proportional to the rate of change of the voltage across the capacitance $[i_{ab} = C(dv_{ab}/dt)]$. If v_{ab} is independent of time, then the current i_{ab} is equal to zero. Since in the d-c steady state there is no current through C_{ab}, it can be taken out of the circuit (open-circuited) without any change in the currents or voltages of the network. In Fig. 11-12b this equivalence is shown. Therefore, when the steady-state response of a network with d-c sources is required, all the capacitances in the network can be open-circuited and all inductances short-circuited.

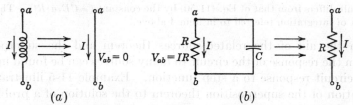

(a) $\qquad\qquad\qquad\qquad$ (b)

FIG. 11-12. Direct-current equivalents for the elements L and C.

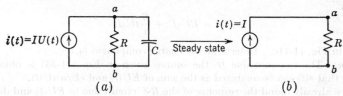

(a) $\qquad\qquad\qquad\qquad$ (b)

FIG. 11-13. A d-c-circuit calculation. (a) Original circuit. (b) Direct-current equivalent.

Example 11-6. In Fig. 11-13a find the steady-state response for v_{ab} when $i(t) = IU(t)$.

Solution. The complete response of this circuit can be shown to be

$$v_{ab}(t) = Ae^{-t/RC} + IR$$

where A will be evaluated from the initial conditions of $v_{ab}(0^+)$. If $v_{ab}(0^+) = 0$, then

$$v_{ab}(t) = IR(1 - e^{-t/RC}) = IR - IRe^{-t/RC} \qquad t \geq 0^+$$

The steady-state component of v_{ab} is IR. We can arrive at this steady-state response by open-circuiting (removing) the capacitance C, which leaves the circuit of Fig. 11-13b. From this figure it is seen that the d-c steady-state response is

$$V_{ab} = IR$$

Example 11-7. In Fig. 11-14a find the d-c steady-state response for v_{ab}.

Solution. The steady-state equivalent circuit of Fig. 11-14a is shown in Fig. 11-14b. From this figure it is seen that the steady-state response for v_{ab} is $V_{ab} = IR/2$.

11-7. Initial-condition Generators.

We have so far discussed the procedure for obtaining the complete response of a circuit which is subject to a set of given initial conditions. These initial conditions were used to determine the constants which are associated with the source-free component of the response. In this article we shall show that it is always possible to determine the complete response of a circuit by first obtaining the complete response, assuming that the initial-energy storage is zero, and then adding the response due to the initial-energy storage. This procedure is a result of the fact that the initial-energy storage in a circuit can always be represented by ideal sources. The ideal sources which are placed into the circuit to represent the initial-energy storage are called "initial-condition generators," or ICGs. While the utility of these initial-condition generators in the solution of *particular* examples is doubtful, we shall see in Chap. 12 that the replacement of the initial-energy storage by these ideal sources results in considerable simplification of the development of general analytical techniques.

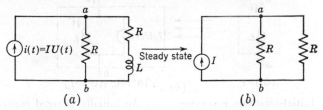

FIG. 11-14. A circuit and its d-c equivalent.

In a *practical* circuit the transfer of a finite amount of energy in zero time is not possible because no practical source is capable of transferring (or absorbing) infinite power. For the present we shall restrict the discussion of initial conditions to energy-storing elements which are incorporated in practical circuits. Therefore the basic initial condition which must be satisfied if a switching operation occurs at $t = t_0$ is

$$w_{\text{stored}}(t_0^-) = w_{\text{stored}}(t_0^+) \tag{11-55}$$

(We shall choose the time of switching to be $t = 0$.) The continuity of the stored energy through a switching operation as expressed by Eq. (11-55) is reformulated for simple elements as follows: In an *inductance* the value of the *current* must be the same just before and just after switching, and across a *capacitance* the *voltage* must be the same just before and just after switching. Based on these relationships we shall show that an initially charged capacitance as shown in Fig. 11-15a can be represented, with respect to its terminals, as a series combination of a step-function voltage source and an initially uncharged capacitance. Similarly an inductance with initial current can be represented as the parallel combination of a step-function current source and an inductance with no initial current as indicated in Fig. 11-15b.

Initially Charged Capacitance. Consider first the capacitance C connected between terminals a-b as shown in Fig. 11-15a on the left side. The voltage-current relationship for a capacitance is given by

$$v_{ab} = \frac{1}{C} \int_{-\infty}^{t} i_{ab} \, d\tau \qquad (11\text{-}56a)$$

where the limits, from $-\infty$ to t, mean that we wish to define q_a as *all* the charge carried to the a side of the capacitance up to the instant of time t.

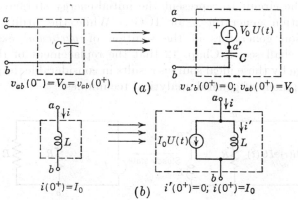

$$v_{ab}(0^-) = V_0 = v_{ab}(0^+) \qquad (a) \qquad v_{a'b}(0^+) = 0; \; v_{ab}(0^+) = V_0$$

$$i(0^+) = I_0 \qquad (b) \qquad i'(0^+) = 0; \; i(0^+) = I_0$$

Fig. 11-15. Initial-condition generators. (a) An initially charged capacitance and its voltage-source equivalent. (b) An initially energized (charged) inductance and its current-source equivalent.

Now, in view of the linearity of the capacitance, we may rewrite Eq. (11-56a) as

$$q_a(t) = q_a(0^+) + q'(t) \qquad (11\text{-}56b)$$

where

$$q_a(0^+) = \frac{1}{C} \int_{-\infty}^{0^+} i_{ab} \, dt$$

and

$$q'(t) = \frac{1}{C} \int_{0^+}^{t} i_{ab} \, d\tau$$

The quantities $q_a(0^+)$ and $q'(t)$ are easily interpreted. By $q_a(0^+)$ we mean the charge on the a side of the capacitance at the instant $t = 0^+$. The symbol $q'(t)$ stands for the additional charge which the current $i_{ab}(t)$ carries to the a side of the capacitance after $t = 0^+$ until time t. Upon substituting Eq. (11-56b) in Eq. (11-56a), the voltage-current relationship for the capacitance reads: For all time $t \geq 0^+$

$$v_{ab} = \frac{1}{C} q_a(0^+) + \frac{1}{C} q'(t) \qquad t \geq 0^+$$

or, recognizing $q_a(0^+)/C = v_{ab}(0^+) \equiv V_0$,

$$v_{ab} = v_{ab}(0^+) + \frac{1}{C} q'(t) \qquad t \geq 0^+ \qquad (11\text{-}57)$$

Since we specify that the problem starts at $t = 0^+$, we may write Eq. (11-57), employing the step function $U(t)$, as

$$v_{ab} = V_0 U(t) + \frac{q'(t)}{C} \tag{11-57a}$$

Equation (11-57a) can be interpreted as representing the circuit shown on the right side in Fig. 11-15a, if we set $q_{a'}(t)$ equal to the charge on the a' side of the capacitance C in that circuit. The equation relating v_{ab} and i_{ab} in the circuit on the right side of Fig. 11-15a reads

$$v_{ab} = V_0 U(t) + \frac{1}{C} \int_{0^+}^{t} i_{ab} \, d\tau$$

where $\qquad \frac{1}{C} \int_{0^+}^{t} i_{ab} \, d\tau = q_{a'}(t) = q'(t)$

It follows that the two circuits shown in Fig. 11-15a are equivalent with respect to the terminals a-b. The charge on the capacitance in the circuit on the right, $q_{a'}(t)$, represents the additional charge which the current i_{ab} carries to either capacitance after $t = 0^+$. The step-function voltage source $V_0 U(t)$ represents the initial voltage across the original capacitance.

It is concluded that the series combination of a step-function voltage source and a series capacitance which is uncharged at $t = 0^+$ can be used to represent a capacitance with initial charge for all $t \geq 0^+$. Note that the correspondence has been established only for the voltage-current relationship[1] after $t = 0$.

If we wish to calculate the complete response of a circuit in which there are initially charged capacitances, we may therefore represent each of the capacitances as the series combination of source and initially uncharged capacitance and calculate the complete response by superposing the responses due to the individual sources, treating a source which represents an initial condition exactly as any other ideal source.

Inductance with Initial Current. We now consider an inductance L connected between terminals a-b as shown on the left side of Fig. 11-15b. The voltage-current relationship for an inductance may be written as

$$i_{ab} = \frac{1}{L} \int_{-\infty}^{t} v_{ab} \, d\tau$$

Exactly as in the case of the analogous integral for a capacitance, we may attach meaning to $\int_{-\infty}^{t} v_{ab} \, d\tau$. When we write $\int_{-\infty}^{t} v_{ab} \, d\tau$, we mean the total

---

[1] Energy relations must be calculated by using the total charge $q_a(t)$ because the energy stored in a capacitance is not linearly related to the charge.

flux linkages which link the inductance,[1] $\Psi(t)$. Since in a practical circuit the current in an inductance must satisfy the continuity condition

$$i_{ab}(0^-) = i_{ab}(0^+) \qquad \text{or} \qquad L i_{ab}(0^-) = L i_{ab}(0^+)$$

we may write

$$i_{ab}(t) = \frac{1}{L} \int_{-\infty}^{0^+} v_{ab}\, dt + \frac{1}{L} \int_{0^+}^{t} v_{ab}\, d\tau \qquad t \geq 0^+ \qquad (11\text{-}58)$$

We now note that the term $\displaystyle\int_{-\infty}^{0^+} v_{ab}\, dt$ represents the flux linkages at the time $t = 0^+$. Hence

$$\frac{1}{L} \int_{-\infty}^{0^+} v_{ab}\, dt = i(0^+)$$

Using this result in Eq. (11-58), we have the following voltage-current relationship for an inductance with initial current:

$$i_{ab}(t) = i_{ab}(0^+) + \frac{1}{L} \int_{0^+}^{t} v_{ab}\, d\tau \qquad t \geq 0^+ \qquad (11\text{-}59)$$

If we define

$$i'(t) = \frac{1}{L} \int_{0^+}^{t} v_{ab}\, d\tau \qquad t \geq 0^+$$

then Eq. (11-59) becomes

$$i_{ab}(t) = i_{ab}(0^+) U(t) + i'(t) \qquad (11\text{-}59a)$$

But Eqs. (11-59) and (11-59a) represent the relationships for the circuit on the right side of Fig. 11-15b. Thus with respect to its terminals an inductance which carries an initial current can be represented as the parallel combination of a step-function current source and an inductance which carries no initial current. The current source which represents the initial condition may be treated exactly as any other ideal source in the analysis of a circuit.

11-8. Impulse Sources for Initial Conditions. In the previous article we showed that an initially charged capacitance and an initially energized inductance can be represented by step-function sources combined with initially uncharged elements as shown in Fig. 11-15. By conversion of voltage and current sources a second representation, employing impulse sources, is possible.

In Fig. 11-16a the equivalent circuit for an initially charged capacitance using a step-function voltage source is shown. By the results of Chap. 10 the circuit of Fig. 11-16b is equivalent to that of Fig. 11-16a with respect

---

[1] Since $v_{ab} = L(di_{ab}/dt)$, in a linear inductance where $|v| = N(d\phi/dt)$ we define the flux linkages $N\phi = \Psi = Li$, hence $\Psi = \displaystyle\int_{-\infty}^{t} v\, d\tau$.

to terminals a-b. Similarly the parallel combination of the current source and inductance, shown in Fig. 11-16c, which represents an initially energized inductance, is equivalent, with respect to its terminals a-b, to the impulse voltage source and inductance shown in Fig. 11-16d.

We conclude that the initial-energy storage in an inductance or a capacitance may be correctly represented by either step- or impulse-function sources as shown in Figs. 11-15 and 11-16.

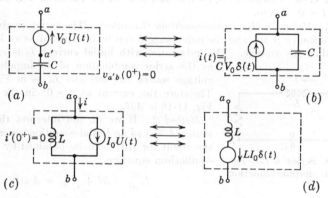

(a)   (b)   (c)   (d)

Fig. 11-16. The step-function initial-condition generators and their impulse-function equivalents.

11-9. Response to Impulse Sources. The equivalences which have been demonstrated in the two preceding articles are not only useful for the purpose of calculating the contribution (to a complete response) of the initial conditions but may also be used to *interpret and study* the response to step and impulse sources. If, for example, a step-function voltage $V U(t)$ in series with a capacitance C, as shown at the right in Fig. 11-17, or an impulse-function voltage source $A \delta(t)$ in series with L is *applied* to a passive terminal pair, then the effect of such a source is exactly the same as the effect of connecting the element C or L, with the respective initial conditions, to the terminal pair; i.e., the response will be identical to the response of a source-free circuit! The same statement applies if the equivalent current sources are impressed.

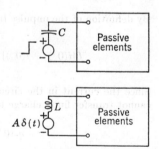

Fig. 11-17. The ideal sources shown can be considered initial-condition generators for the purpose of studying response.

A very simple physical argument may serve to illustrate the mathematical conclusions which have been reached. An impulse function, while having infinite amplitude, lasts for zero time. Hence it represents a theoretical mechanism for transferring finite energy in zero time.

Moreover, if the impulse occurs at $t = 0$, then it has passed (i.e., its value is zero) at $t = 0^+$. Any response which is observed from $t = 0^+$ onward must therefore be the source-free response since the circuit, for $t \geq 0^+$, is indeed source-free.

11-10. Illustrative Examples. To show how initial-condition generators (ICGs) can be used, examples are worked out in this article.

Example 11-8. Calculate the current at $t = 0^+$ in the circuit of Fig. 11-18. The current at $t = 0^-$ is zero.

Solution. Method 1 (By Initial-condition Generator). The series combination of the impulse source $A \delta(t)$ and the inductance L can be interpreted as an inductance with initial-energy storage. The inductance with initial current I_0 is represented as the series combination of an impulse-function voltage source $LI_0 \delta(t)$ and L, as in Fig. 11-16d. Therefore the current at $t = 0^+$ in the circuit of Fig. 11-18 is A/L.

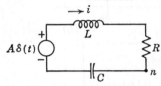

FIG. 11-18. Series R-L-C circuit with impulse-function source.

Method 2. If we do not interpret the impulse source $A \delta(t)$ as an initial-condition generator, then the result for $i(0^+)$ can be obtained by use of the equilibrium equation

$$L \frac{di}{dt} + Ri + \frac{1}{C} q_n = A \delta(t)$$

Now let us integrate this equation from $t = 0^-$ to $t = 0^+$,

$$\int_{0^-}^{0^+} L \frac{di}{dt} \, dt + R \int_{0^-}^{0^+} i \, dt + \frac{1}{C} \int_{0^-}^{0^+} q_n \, dt = \int_{0^-}^{0^+} A \delta(t)$$

By definition of the impulse function, $\int_{0^-}^{0^+} A \delta(t) = A$; hence, integrating,

$$L[i(0^+) - i(0^-)] + R[q_n(0^+) - q_n(0^-)] + \frac{1}{C} \int_{0^-}^{0^+} q_n \, dt = A$$

Since the current in the circuit is at all times *finite*, it follows that a finite current cannot transfer finite charge to the capacitance in zero time.

$$q_n(0^+) = q_n(0^-) \qquad \int_{0^-}^{0^+} q_n \, dt = 0$$

If the equilibrium equation is to be satisfied at $t = 0$, the current i must experience a jump. Hence

$$L[i(0^+) - i(0^-)] = A$$

and since $i(0^-)$ was given as zero, $i(0^+) = A/L$.

Example 11-9. The circuit shown in Fig. 11-19a is in the d-c steady state before $t = 0$. At $t = 0$ the value of the source is abruptly changed from 150 to 120 volts. Find the values of v_{an} and v_{bn} at the instants $t = 0^-$ and $t = 0^+$.

Solution. No steady-state current can flow through the capacitances owing to the constant source. Hence the voltage $v_{bn}(0^-) = 0$. To calculate $v_{an}(0^-)$, the circuit of Fig. 11-19b can be used (because the voltage across each resistance is zero). Circuits containing only one type of passive element were discussed in Chap. 6. Combining the 0.2-μf and the 0.3-μf capacitances into an equivalent, we arrive at the circuit of Fig. 11-19c. Since the voltage across capacitances divides proportional to the elastances (reciprocal capacitances), $v_{an}(0^-) = 150(1/1.5) = 100$ volts. On replacing the charge on each capacitance with ICGs the circuit of Fig. 11-19d will result. (Note that the sum of the voltages in each loop adds to zero with zero current in each resistance; this serves as a check on the work so far.) In this circuit $v_{a'a}$, $v_{a''n'}$, and $v_{ab'}$ are all zero. Hence the circuit of Fig. 11-19e applies *at the instant* $t = 0^+$. In this circuit $v_{a'a}$, $v_{ab'}$, and $v_{a''n'}$ are also zero (at $t = 0^+$). Hence *the equivalent circuit at* $t = 0^+$ *can be drawn* as in Fig. 11-19f, with those voltages which we know to be zero replaced by short circuits. To obtain the desired initial values $v_{an}(0^+)$ and $v_{bn}(0^+)$, we can now solve the d-c circuit, Fig. 11-19f, and use the result at $t = 0^+$ as the answer to the original circuit problem. Combining the 120- and the 50-volt source, we obtain the circuit of Fig. 11-19g. Converting each voltage source to a current source, we have the circuit of Fig. 11-19h. This circuit is equivalent to the circuit of Fig. 11-19f with respect to terminals a-n. In this circuit $V_{an} = (700 + 100 + 200) \times 10^{-6}R$, where $1/R = 1/10^5 + 1/10^6 + 2/10^6$, or $R = 10^6/13$; hence $V_{an} = 1{,}000/13 = 76.9$ volts. It follows from Fig. 11-19f that $V_{bn} = 76.9 - 100 = -23.1$ volts. Hence in the original problem $v_{an}(0^+) = 76.9$ volts, $v_{bn}(0^+) = -23.1$ volts.

To return to the original circuit, the value of the current in each resistance at $t = 0^+$ can now be calculated. This is left as an exercise for the reader.

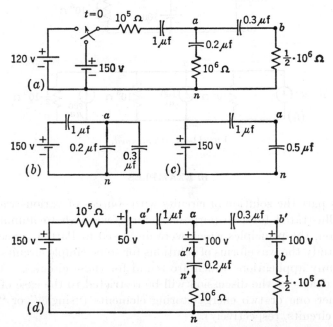

Fig. 11-19. Pertinent to Example 11-9. (a) Original circuit and switching operation. (b) Circuit at $t = 0^-$. (c) Equivalent to (b) with respect to terminals a-n. (d) Circuit at $t = 0^-$. The initial-condition generators are shown; hence the voltages $v_{a'a}$, $v_{a''n'}$, and $v_{ab'}$ are zero. (e) Circuit at $t = 0^+$. This circuit differs from the circuit (d) only in the new value of the source. (f) Equivalent circuit at $t = 0^+$. (g) Equivalent to (f). (h) Circuit equivalent to (g) at terminals a-n.

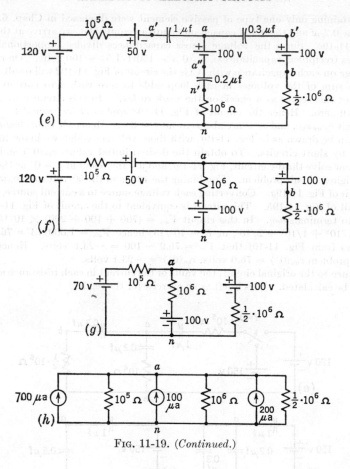

FIG. 11-19. (*Continued.*)

B. EXAMPLES

In this part the solution of circuits with sources of various waveforms will be illustrated for two purposes. First, we wish to illuminate, by application, the principles which were discussed in Part A. Second, we wish to study the waveforms of solutions for some simple circuits because of the many applications which are found for these circuits. As in the previous chapters, the discussion will be restricted to the case of circuits with either one or two energy-storing elements ("single-" or "double-energy" circuits, respectively).

11-11. Single-energy Circuits; Series R-C Circuit with Step-function Voltage Source. Consider as the first example the series R-C circuit shown in Fig. 11-20. Assume that $v(t)$ is the step-function voltage source

$$v(t) = VU(t)$$

and let it be assumed that

$$q_m(0^-) = Q_0 = Cv_{mb}(0^-) = CV_0$$

is a known condition (i.e., the capacitance is initially charged to the value V_0 from a source which is connected to the circuit prior to $t = 0$ and is not shown on the diagram). Let it be required to solve for $v_{mb}(t)$ for all $t \geq 0^+$. The application of Kirchhoff's voltage law gives the equilibrium equation

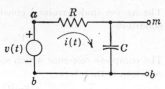

FIG. 11-20. Series R-C circuit with voltage source.

$$R\frac{dq_m}{dt} + \frac{1}{C}q_m = V \qquad t \geq 0^+ \qquad (11\text{-}60)$$

which is to be solved, subject to the initial condition

$$q_m(0^+) = q_m(0^-) = Q_0$$

or

$$v_{mb}(0^+) = v_{mb}(0^-) = V_0 = \frac{Q_0}{C}$$

By using the relationship $q_m = Cv_{mb}$ and identifying the time constant $T = RC$, the differential equation (11-60) may be written with $v_{mb}(t)$ as the unknown,

$$T\frac{dv_{mb}}{dt} + v_{mb} = V \qquad t \geq 0^+ \qquad (11\text{-}60a)$$

In order to obtain the complete response, we need to add the two components $(v_{mb})_f$, the source-free component, and $(v_{mb})_s$, the component due to the source. The source-free component is the solution of the homogeneous equation

$$T\frac{d(v_{mb})_f}{dt} + (v_{mb})_f = 0 \qquad (11\text{-}60b)$$

which is given by the exponential form

$$(v_{mb})_f = Ae^{st} \qquad (11\text{-}61)$$

Substituting (11-61) in (11-60b) gives the now familiar characteristic equation for this circuit,

$$sT + 1 = 0 \qquad \text{or} \qquad s = -\frac{1}{T}$$

so that

$$(v_{mb})_f = Ae^{-t/T}$$

In order to obtain the component of the response due to the source, we make use of the linearity of the equation and assume a solution of the same form as the source; i.e., we let

$$(v_{mb})_s = K = \text{const}$$

Substituting this "trial" solution in Eq. (11-60a) gives

$$K = V$$

so that the complete response is found by adding the components

$$v_{mb}(t) = (v_{mb})_f + (v_{mb})_s$$

namely,

$$v_{mb}(t) = V + Ae^{-t/T} \qquad t \geq 0^+ \qquad (11\text{-}62)$$

The as yet undetermined constant A in Eq. (11-62) is evaluated from the initial condition

$$V_0 = V + A \qquad A = V_0 - V$$

The complete response which satisfies both the initial condition and the equilibrium equation is therefore

$$v_{mb}(t) = V + (V_0 - V)e^{-t/T} \tag{11-63}$$

The form of Eq. (11-63) is the sum of two terms, the component due to the source (in this case a steady-state value V) and the free component $(V_0 - V)e^{-t/T}$. It is sometimes convenient to regroup the terms as follows:

$$v_{mb}(t) = V(1 - e^{-t/T}) + V_0 e^{-t/T}$$

In this form the two terms may be interpreted differently:

$$v_{mb}(t) = \begin{pmatrix} \text{complete response if} \\ \text{capacitance is initially} \\ \text{uncharged, } V_0 = 0 \end{pmatrix} + \begin{pmatrix} \text{component of response} \\ \text{due to initial charge} \\ \text{on capacitance} \end{pmatrix}$$

This is the form in which the solution would have been found if the initial voltage across the capacitance had been represented by an initial-condition generator. The

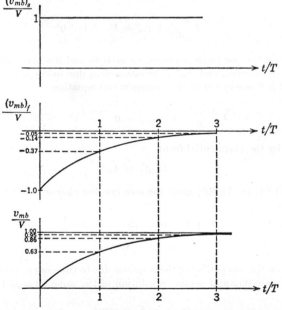

FIG. 11-21. Step response of an initially deenergized R-C circuit obtained by superposition of the component of response due to the source and the source-free component.

reader should solve the problem by the method of ICGs and verify this result. To study the waveforms of the response, it is convenient to work with the form of Eq. (11-63), normalizing $v_{mb}(t)$ with respect to the value of the source, V,

$$\frac{v_{mb}(t)}{V} = 1 + \left(\frac{V_0}{V} - 1 \right) e^{-t/T}$$

As an example, consider the case $V_0 = 0$.   (The case $V_0 = V$ is trivial because in this case no change in stored energy and therefore no transient occurs.)   The construction of the waveform for the case $V_0 = 0$ is illustrated in Fig. 11-21, where the two components $(v_{mb})_s$ and $(v_{mb})_f$ are added.

Note that the value V is approached exponentially so that the response is within 5 per cent of this value after a time equal to three time constants has elapsed.   The complete response for two nonzero values of V_0 is illustrated in Fig. 11-22.   In each

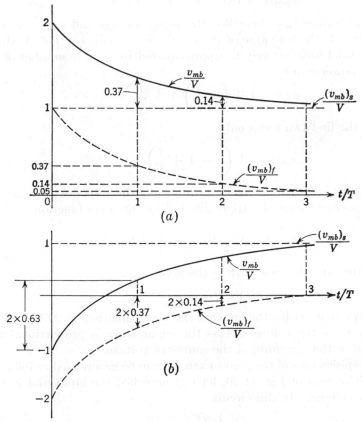

FIG. 11-22. Step response of the series R-C circuit for two nonzero initial values of voltage across the capacitance.   (a) $V_0/V = 2$.   (b) $V_0/V = -1$.

case the resultant starts from its initial value and approaches the final value in such a way that after an interval equal to one time constant the difference between the resultant and the final value is reduced by 37 per cent.

$$V - v_{mb}(0^+) = V - V_0$$
$$V - v_{mb}(T) = (V - V_0) \times 0.37$$
$$V - v_{mb}(2T) = (V - V_0) \times 0.14$$
$$V - v_{mb}(3T) = (V - V_0) \times 0.05$$

Since the output voltage (across the capacitance) will approach (after three time constants) the step input, another way of describing the response of the R-C circuit is to say that it furnishes a *time delay*.

11-12. Integrating Property of the R-C Circuit. An interesting and exceedingly useful property of the R-C circuit is noticed if the response is examined in the time interval $0 < t < T$, that is, at the beginning of the transient. Consider the case in which the capacitance of Fig. 11-20 is initially deenergized so that, for a step voltage source, the response is given by

$$v_{mb}(t) = V(1 - e^{-t/T}) \qquad t \geq 0^+$$

Let the voltage $v_{ab}(t)$ be called the input voltage and $v_{mb}(t)$ the output voltage. If the *beginning* of the transient is studied, $t/T \ll 1$, then the exponential function may be approximated by a finite number of terms in the power series

$$e^{-t/T} = 1 + \left(-\frac{t}{T}\right) + \frac{(-t/T)^2}{2!} + \cdots$$

Using the first two terms only,

$$v_{mb}(t) \approx V\left(1 - 1 + \frac{t}{T}\right)$$

so that for sufficiently "small" values of t the response (voltage across the capacitance) may be approximated by the *ramp* function

$$v_{mb}(t) \approx V\frac{t}{T}U(t) \qquad t \ll T$$

Since the input to the circuit is the step

$$v(t) = VU(t)$$

it follows that, within the limits of the approximation ($t^2/2T^2 \ll t/T$), the waveform of the voltage across the capacitance is proportional to the integral of the waveform of the source of voltage.

The special case of the above example can be generalized as follows: In the R-C circuit of Fig. 11-20, let $v(t)$ be called the input and $v_{mb}(t)$ the output voltage. In this circuit

$$v_{mb}(t) = \frac{1}{C}\int_{0^+}^{t} i\, d\tau + v_{mb}(0^+)$$

Let $v_{mb}(0^+) = V_0$; then

$$v_{mb}(t) - V_0 = \frac{1}{C}\int_0^t i\, d\tau = \frac{1}{C}\int_0^t \frac{v - v_{mb}}{R}\, d\tau = \frac{1}{T}\int_0^t (v - v_{mb})\, d\tau$$

$$v_{mb}(t) - V_0 + \frac{1}{T}\int_0^t v_{mb}\, d\tau = \frac{1}{T}\int_0^t v\, d\tau \qquad\qquad (11\text{-}64)$$

If the conditions are such that for any given time t

$$v_{mb}(t) \gg \frac{1}{T}\int_0^t v_{mb}\, d\tau \qquad\qquad (11\text{-}65)$$

then Eq. (11-64) can be written as

$$v_{mb}(t) - V_0 \approx \frac{1}{T} \int_0^t v \, d\tau \qquad (11\text{-}66)$$

The inequality (11-65) is most often satisfied for $t/T \ll 1$. Under such conditions, and in the interval of time $t \ll T$, Eq. (11-66) is a good approximation. Furthermore, if the initial condition $v_{mb}(0^+) = 0 = V_0$, then

$$v_{mb}(t) \approx \frac{1}{T} \int_0^t v \, d\tau \qquad (11\text{-}66a)$$

These relationships state that in a series R-C circuit for values of $t \ll T$, and to a first order of approximation, the waveform of the voltage across the capacitance is the integral of the waveform of the voltage across the R and C elements plus the initial value of the voltage across the capacitance.

Thus the R-C circuit can be used to produce, approximately, the integral of a waveform. The inequality (11-65) is the necessary and sufficient condition for an R-C circuit to have the above-mentioned integrating property. The form of this inequality is not very helpful since it refers to the voltage across the capacitance, which is not usually given but is to be found. When the voltage source and R-C circuit are specified and a judgment is required as to whether the voltage across the capacitance is the integral of the applied voltage, we can say that in most cases this is true for values of $t \ll T$. No further generalizations are made beyond this if the source is not specified. For an exact condition the inequality of (11-65) should be satisfied.

In Fig. 11-23a the actual voltage across the capacitance of Fig. 11-23b due to a step-function input voltage is shown with the integral of the input voltage, i.e., a ramp function. Note that in this case the difference between the output voltage and the integral of the input voltage is 37 per cent at $t = T$ but only 0.5 per cent at $t = 0.1T$. The integrating property of the R-C circuit will be illustrated again in a later article of this chapter for other specific input waveforms.

11-13. Differentiating Property of the R-C Circuit. Suppose that in the circuit of Fig. 11-23b, with the step voltage applied, it is required to find the current in the circuit, $i(t)$, or the voltage across the resistance, $v_{am}(t)$. Since we have the solution for $v_{mb}(t)$, we could apply the equation $q_m = C v_{mb}$ and find i from dq_m/dt. Alternatively we could solve for $i(t)$ directly by use of a derived initial condition for $i(0^+)$. Here it is convenient to apply Kirchhoff's voltage law,

$$v_{am} + v_{mb} = v = VU(t) \qquad v_{mb}(0^+) = V_0$$

Using the solution for the voltage across the capacitance, we obtain

$$v_{am}(t) = V - [V + (V_0 - V)e^{-t/T}] \qquad t \geq 0^+$$

or
$$v_{am}(t) = (V - V_0)e^{-t/T} \qquad t \geq 0^+ \qquad (11\text{-}67)$$

Also,
$$i(t) = \frac{V - V_0}{R} e^{-t/T} \qquad t \geq 0^+$$

The solution is seen to be the familiar exponential decay shown in Fig. 11-23c. We note that the shape of this response could have been predicted from the curves shown in Figs. 11-21 and 11-22; since $i = dq/dt$, Fig. 11-23c is proportional *to the slope* of the curves shown in Figs. 11-21 and 11-22. Referring to Fig. 11-23c, we note that the voltage across R is

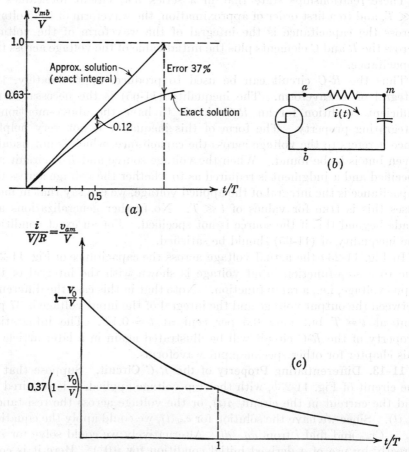

FIG. 11-23. (a) Illustration of integration property of the R-C circuit for step-function source. (b) Series R-C circuit with step-function voltage source. (c) Illustration of differentiation property of the series R-C circuit: voltage across resistance for step input. This voltage approaches zero as t increases.

less than 5 per cent of its initial value after three time constants; i.e., it is "practically" zero or equal to the *slope* of the input voltage.   For this reason, the R-C circuit is called a *differentiating* circuit when the "output" is considered to be the voltage across the resistance, and for $t > 3T$.

The results illustrated in this example can be generalized by noting that in the R-C circuit of Fig. 11-23b

$$v_{am} = Ri = RC \frac{d}{dt} v_{mb}(t)$$

$$= T \frac{d}{dt} [v(t) - v_{am}(t)] \tag{11-67a}$$

If for all values of t under consideration

$$\left| \frac{dv_{am}}{dt} \right| \ll \left| \frac{dv}{dt} \right| \tag{11-68}$$

then $$v_{am} \approx T \frac{dv}{dt} \tag{11-69}$$

The condition (11-69) requires that the rate of change of the source voltage be much larger than that of the voltage across the resistance. This condition, which is necessary, is misleading when stated alone, because it appears that the inequality will best be fulfilled when the source function has a jump ("infinite" rate of change).   We must recall, however, that because of the continuity of the voltage across the capacitance a discontinuity in $v(t)$ will result in an equal discontinuity in the voltage across the resistance.   It is therefore useful to examine the equation of the R-C circuit in a slightly different form.

We start with $v_{mb} = v(t) - v_{am}$
Since

$$v_{mb} = \frac{1}{C} \int_{-\infty}^{t} i \, d\tau = \frac{1}{T} \int_{-\infty}^{t} v_{am} \, d\tau$$

we observe that if

$$|v(t)| \gg |v_{am}| \tag{11-70}$$

then $$v_{mb} = \frac{1}{T} \int_{-\infty}^{t} v_{am} \, d\tau \approx v(t)$$

or, differentiating both sides,

$$v_{am} \approx T \frac{dv}{dt} \tag{11-69}$$

We therefore conclude that both conditions, (11-68) and (11-70), must be fulfilled for the approximation (11-69) to hold.   Thus the source function must be larger than the voltage across the resistance and the rate of change of the source function must be much larger than the rate of change of the voltage across the resistance to obtain (approximate) differentiating action in an R-C circuit. These conditions are often fulfilled more than three time constants after the source has had a jump. The result of this paragraph and the preceding paragraphs may be summarized as follows:

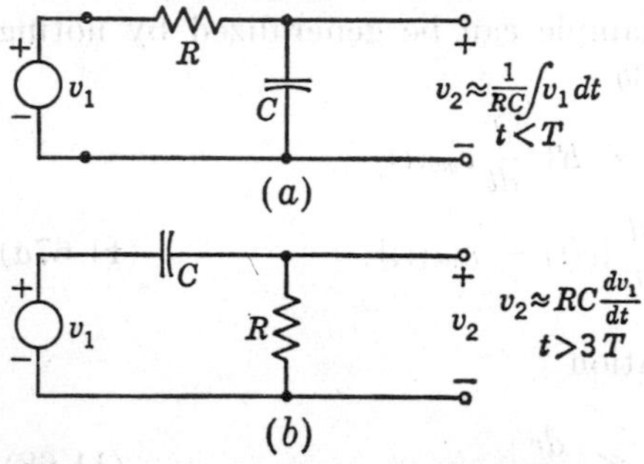

Under certain conditions the series R-C circuit can furnish an output voltage which is *approximately* the *integral* of the impressed voltage if the voltage across the capacitance is considered the "output" and if the beginning of the time response ($t < T$) is considered only (see Fig. 11-24a).

$$v_2 \approx \frac{1}{RC}\int v_1 \, dt$$
$$t < T$$

(a)

$$v_2 \approx RC \frac{dv_1}{dt}$$
$$t > 3T$$

(b)

FIG. 11-24. Integrating and differentiating circuits. In addition to the condition stated on the diagram inequality (11-65) or (11-68) and (11-70) must be satisfied. (a) Integrating circuit. (b) Differentiating circuit.

Under certain conditions the series R-C circuit can furnish an output voltage which is *approximately* the *derivative* of the impressed voltage if the voltage across the resistance is considered the "output" voltage (see Fig. 11-24b).

11-14. Impulse Response. Let us consider again the equation of the current in the R-C circuit for step input of value $v_1(t) = VU(t)$ (see Fig. 11-23b),

$$i(t) = \frac{V - V_0}{R} e^{-t/T} \qquad t \geq 0^+ \tag{11-71}$$

The *area* under the curve of the current [Eq. (11-71)] until any time t represents the charge carried to the m side of the capacitance in the time interval $t = 0^+$ to the arbitrary time chosen,

$$q(t) - Q_0 = \int_{\tau=0}^{\tau=t} i \, d\tau = \frac{V - V_0}{R}(-T)e^{-\tau/T}\Big|_{\tau=0}^{\tau=t} = C(V - V_0)(1 - e^{-t/T})$$

where $T = RC$. Let us assume now that $Q_0 = 0$ ($V_0 = 0$); then the area under the curve represented by Eq. (11-71) is $Q = CV$ if we consider the time interval from $t = 0$ to $t = \infty$. This result is independent of the resistance R. Consider now the four examples of response curves for $i(t)$ shown in Fig. 11-25 with *non*normalized axes. If curve 1 represents the current response for a certain R-C circuit when C is fixed and R is adjusted to a value R_1, then curve 2 represents the response of the same circuit if $R = \frac{1}{2}R_1$, curve 3 represents the response when $R = \frac{1}{3}R_1$, and curve 4 represents the response when $R = \frac{1}{5}R_1$. As R is decreased, the value of the current $i(t)$ at $t = 0^+$ *increases but the area under the curve remains constant and equal to* CV. In the *limit*, as R is reduced to zero, the time constant becomes zero, the initial value of the current $i(0^+) = I_0$ becomes infinite, *but the area under the curve which is independent of R remains CV*. We recall that this type of infinite pulse, lasting zero time but with finite area, defines an impulse function

$$\lim_{R \to 0} \frac{V}{R} e^{-t/RC} U(t) = VC \, \delta(t)$$

$$\lim_{T \to 0} \frac{e^{-t/T}}{T} U(t) = \delta(t)$$

Therefore, if the resistance is zero, the capacitance will charge to the value of the impressed voltage in zero time and an impulse of current will occur to transfer this finite charge. In practice such a situation is impossible because of the ever-present

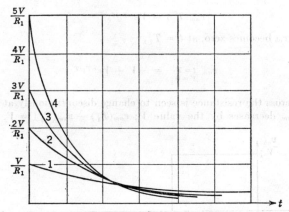

FIG. 11-25. Current response of step-excited R-C circuit as the resistance is decreased.

"residual" resistance. The present discussion is nevertheless of great value since it emphasizes the possibility of obtaining large-amplitude current pulses with this circuit in spite of the fact that no constant (direct) current can flow. This property may be useful (as in pulse-forming networks) or undesirable (as in gas-tube rectifiers).

11-15. Rectangular Pulse Applied to R-C Circuit. Consider now the rectangular pulse

$$\begin{aligned} v(t) &= 0 & t &< 0 \\ v(t) &= V & 0 &< t < T_1 \\ v(t) &= 0 & t &> T_1 \end{aligned}$$

applied to an initially deenergized R-C circuit as shown in Fig. 11-26. The response may be found either by solving the problem first in the time interval from $t = 0$ to $t = T_1$, then to $t = \infty$, or by superposition of the responses to two step functions. Both methods will be illustrated.

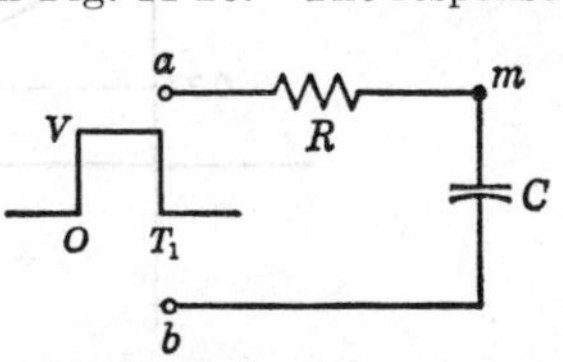

If we consider the time interval $t = 0$ to $t = T_1$, then the response is given by the step response [Eq. (11-63) or Eq. (11-67)] with $V_0 = 0$. (There is no loss in generality in taking this case since the case $V_0 \ne 0$ can be included easily by using the notion of initial-condition generators.)

FIG. 11-26. Rectangular pulse applied to R-C circuit.

$$\begin{aligned} v_{mb}(t) &= V(1 - e^{-t/T}) & 0^+ &\le t \le T_1 \\ \text{or} \qquad v_{am}(t) &= V e^{-t/T} & 0^+ &< t < T_1 \end{aligned} \qquad (11\text{-}72)$$

At $t = T_1^-$ the voltage across the capacitance is $v_{mb}(T_1^-) = V(1 - e^{-T_1/T})$. Since the voltage across the capacitance cannot change in zero time, $v_{mb}(T_1^-) = v_{mb}(T_1^+)$.

Now consider the new time scale, $t' = t - T_1$. When $t' = 0$, the terminals a-b become short-circuited and the voltage across the capacitance will decay exponentially to zero,

$$v_{mb}(t') = V(1 - e^{-T_1/T})e^{-t'/T} \qquad t' > 0$$

since, for $t' > 0$, $v_{mb} + v_{am} = 0$,

$$v_{am}(t') = -V(1 - e^{-T_1/T})e^{-t'/T} \qquad t' > 0$$

Note that the voltage across the resistance just before $v_{ab} = 0$, at $t = T_1^-$, is

$$v_{am}(T_1^-) = Ve^{-T_1/T}$$

and just after v_{ab} becomes zero, at $t = T_1^+$,

$$v_{am}\bigg|_{\substack{t=T_1^+ \\ t'=0^+}} = -V + Ve^{-T_1/T}$$

The voltage across the resistance is seen to change discontinuously at $t = T$; in fact the voltage v_{am} decreases by the value V; $v_{am}(T_1^-) - v_{am}(T_1^+) = V$. This can be

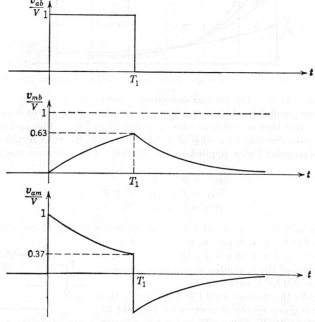

FIG. 11-27. Response of R-C circuit to rectangular pulse, $T_1 = T$.

reasoned immediately from the following considerations: At $t = T_1$ the impressed voltage decreases abruptly. Since the voltage across C cannot change discontinuously, the impressed voltage jump appears across the resistance at $t = T_1$. These results are illustrated in Fig. 11-27 for the case $T_1 = T$. Figure 11-28 shows the case $T_1 \gg T$, and Fig. 11-29 shows the case $T_1 \ll T$. Examining Fig. 11-28b, we note that when the time constant of the circuit is short *compared* with the duration of the pulse then the voltage across the capacitance is a "good" reproduction of the input pulse, while the voltage across the resistance (except near $t = 0$ and near $t = T_1$) is approximately proportional to the derivative of the rectangular pulse (i.e., zero) (Fig. 11-28c).

Referring to Fig. 11-29, note that when the time constant of the R-C circuit is large *compared* with the duration of the pulse then the voltage across the resistance is a "good" reproduction of the input waveform, while the voltage across the capacitance is proportional (approximately) to the integral of the rectangular pulse (i.e., modified ramp function). The reader should compare these results with the requirements of condition (11-65).

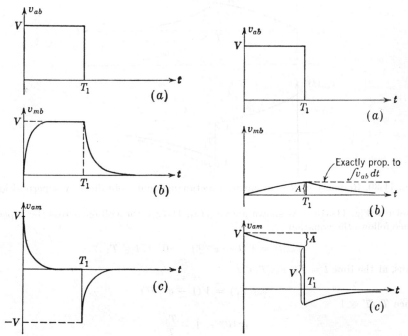

FIG. 11-28. Response of R-C circuit to rectangular pulse, $T_1 \gg T$.

FIG. 11-29. Response of R-C circuit to rectangular pulse, $T_1 \ll T$.

As was stated above, the response to the rectangular pulse may also be obtained by superposition. The input pulse is represented as the sum of two steps,

$$v_{ab}(t) = VU(t) - VU(t - T)$$

so that the responses are

$$v_{mb}(t) = V(1 - e^{-t/T})U(t) - V(1 - e^{-(t-T_1)/T})U(t - T_1)$$
and $\quad v_{am}(t) = Ve^{-t/T}U(t) - Ve^{-(t-T_1)/T}U(t - T_1)$

This procedure is illustrated for the case $T = T_1$ in Fig. 11-30.

An interesting result concerning the analytical utility of impulses may be obtained if a rectangular pulse of very short duration compared with the time constant of the circuit is studied. Consider a rectangular pulse of amplitude V and duration $T_1 \ll T$,

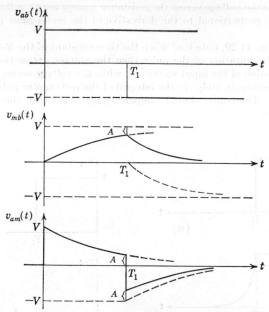

FIG. 11-30. Response of R-C circuit to a rectangular pulse obtained by superposition.

shown in Fig. 11-31a. As shown above [(Eq. 11-72)], the voltage across the capacitance follows the equation

$$v_{mb}(t) = V(1 - e^{-t/T}) \qquad 0^+ \leq t \leq T_1$$

Thus, at the time $t = T_1^-$, $v_{mb}(T_1^-)$ is

$$v_{mb}(T_1^-) = V(1 - e^{-T_1/T})$$

Since $T_1/T \ll 1$

$$e^{-T_1/T} \approx 1 - \frac{T_1}{T}$$

or

$$v_{mb}(T_1^-) \approx V\frac{T_1}{T}$$

For $t > T_1$ the capacitance will discharge exponentially through the resistance

$$v_{mb}(t) = v_{mb}(T_1^+)e^{-(t-T_1)/T} \qquad t \geq T_1^+$$

Since $v_{mb}(T_1^+) = v_{mb}(T_1^-)$, the equation for the discharge of the capacitance is given approximately by

$$v_{mb}(t) \approx V\frac{T_1}{T} e^{-(t-T_1)/T} \qquad t \geq T_1^+$$

This result is illustrated in Fig. 11-31b.

Consider now an impulse of voltage applied to the circuit as indicated in Fig. 11-31c,

$$v(t) = A \, \delta(t)$$

Because of the impulse the voltage across the capacitance will be changed discontinuously, and for $t \geq 0^+$ there will be a voltage across it although no energy was stored in it at $t = 0^-$. The change in voltage across the capacitance is found from the equation

$$T \frac{dv_{mb}}{dt} + v_{mb} = A \, \delta(t)$$

Since at $t = 0$ the impulse is infinite, v_{mb} will be insignificant compared with its time derivative. Hence

$$v_{mb}(t) \Big|_{0-}^{0+} = \frac{A}{T} \int_{0-}^{0+} \delta(t) \, dt = \frac{A}{T}$$

and the capacitance will charge to the voltage A/T and then (for $t > 0^+$) discharge exponentially through the resistance as indicated in Fig. 11-31d.

On comparing Fig. 11-31b with Fig. 11-31d it is noted that if we adjust the area of the rectangular pulse (Fig. 11-31a) so that $VT_1 = A$ the response for $t > T_1$ (Fig. 11-31b) will differ only slightly from the response to an impulse (Fig. 11-31d).

11-16. Ramp-function Voltage Source Applied to the Series R-C Circuit. If the ramp function (Fig. 11-32a)

$$v(t) = \frac{V}{T_1} t U(t)$$

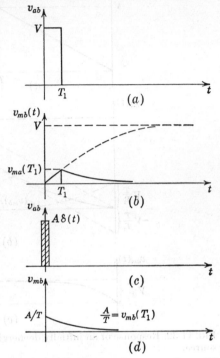

Fig. 11-31. Response to pulse and to impulse.

is applied to the R-C circuit of Fig. 11-26, then the equation for the voltage across the capacitance is

$$T \frac{dv_{mb}}{dt} + v_{mb} = \frac{V}{T_1} t U(t) \qquad t \geq 0^+$$

For the purposes of this illustration, we will assume that the capacitance is initially uncharged so that $q(0^-) = 0$ or $v_{mb}(0^-) = 0$, hence $v_{mb}(0^+) = 0$.

The complete response is of the form

$$v_{mb}(t) = [v_{mb}(t)]_s + A e^{-t/T} \qquad T = RC, \, t \geq 0^+ \qquad (11\text{-}73)$$

In Eq. (11-73) the free component of the response is written with the undetermined constant A. The component of the response due to the source $[v_{mb}(t)]_s$ must now be found. When a step was applied (Art. 11-11), the component due to the source was a constant. Since we now apply a waveform which is proportional to the integral of the step, we may assume a solution of the form

$$[v_{mb}(t)]_s = K_1 + K_2 t \qquad (11\text{-}74)$$

and

$$\frac{d(v_{mb})_s}{dt} = K_2$$

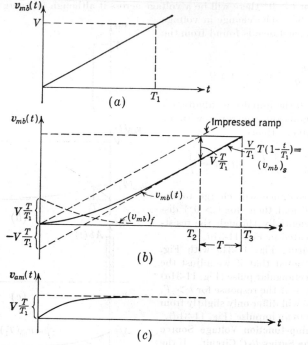

Fig. 11-32. Response of an initially deenergized R-C circuit to a ramp-function voltage source.

Substituting the "trial" solution (11-74) in the equilibrium equation, we obtain

$$TK_2 + K_1 + K_2 t = \frac{V}{T_1} t$$

or

$$TK_2 + K_1 + t\left(K_2 - \frac{V}{T_1}\right) = 0 \qquad (11\text{-}75)$$

Since Eq. (11-75) must apply at all instants of time after $t = 0$, it follows that

$$K_2 = \frac{V}{T_1} \qquad \text{and} \qquad K_1 = -TK_2 = -\frac{VT}{T_1}$$

so that the complete response at this point is

$$v_{mb}(t) = \frac{VT}{T_1}\left(-1 + \frac{t}{T}\right) + Ae^{-t/T} \qquad t \geq 0^+ \qquad (11\text{-}76)$$

The constant A in Eq. (11-76) is evaluated from the initial condition,

$$v_{mb}(0^+) = v_{mb}(0^-) = 0 = \frac{VT}{T_1}(-1 + 0) + Ae^0$$

or

$$A = \frac{VT}{T_1}$$

The complete response is therefore

$$v_{mb}(t) = \frac{VT}{T_1}\left(-1 + \frac{t}{T} + e^{-t/T}\right) \qquad t \geq 0^+ \tag{11-77}$$

This solution is illustrated in Fig. 11-32b. We note that after the free component has decayed ($t > 3T$) the voltage across the capacitance has the same shape as the input voltage but is delayed in time. The difference between the input and the voltage across the capacitance is seen to be VT/T_1. The time delay is calculated as follows: At some time $t = T_2 > 3T$ the input is VT_2/T_1. Voltage across the capacitance is $VT_2/T_1 - VT/T_1$. The voltage across the capacitance will have the value VT_2/T_1 at $t = T_3$,

$$V\frac{T_2}{T_1} = \frac{VT}{T_1}\left(-1 + \frac{T_3}{T}\right)$$

or

$$T_2 + T = T_3$$

It is therefore seen that the time delay introduced by the R-C circuit is (after the exponential has decayed) equal to the time constant of the R-C circuit.

The voltage across the resistance may be found by subtraction,

$$v_{am} = v_{ab} - v_{mb}$$

so that

$$v_{am}(t) = \frac{VT}{T_1}(1 - e^{-t/T}) \qquad\qquad t \geq 0^+$$

The result is illustrated in Fig. 11-32c. Note that the voltage across the resistance after a time equal to three time constants will be within 5 per cent of $T(V/T_1)$ so that the voltage across the resistance (for $t > 3T$) is T times the slope of the input ramp.

The integrating property of the circuit for this impressed waveform can be seen by studying the voltage across the capacitance [Eq. (11-77)] for $t < T$. The expansion of the exponential function

$$e^{-t/T} = 1 - \frac{t}{T} + \frac{(t/T)^2}{2!} + \cdots$$

is substituted in Eq. (11-77),

$$v_{mb}(t) \approx \frac{VT}{T_1}\left(-1 + \frac{t}{T} + 1 - \frac{t}{T} + \frac{t^2}{2T^2} - \cdots\right)$$

Using the first nonzero term in the result,

$$v_{mb}(t) \approx \frac{V}{2T_1 T}t^2 \qquad 0^+ < t < T \tag{11-78}$$

Equation (11-78) is the equation of a parabola, the integral of the ramp function.

11-17. Exponentially Decaying Voltage Applied to the Series R-C Circuit.

As a final example in the study of the R-C circuit, consider the voltage

$$v(t) = Ve^{-t/T_1}U(t)$$

illustrated in Fig. 11-33a, applied to the series R-C circuit. The equation for the voltage across the capacitance is

$$T \frac{dv_{mb}}{dt} + v_{mb} = Ve^{-t/T_1} \qquad t \geq 0^+$$

The complete response in this case is again written in the form

$$v_{mb}(t) = [v_{mb}(t)]_s + Ae^{-t/T}$$

The component of the response due to the source, $[v_{mb}(t)]_s$, may be found by assuming a solution of the same form as the impressed waveform,

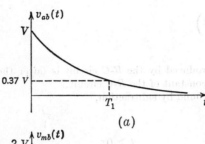

$$[v_{mb}(t)]_s = Ke^{-t/T_1} \qquad (11\text{-}79)$$

Substituting Eq. (11-79) in the equilibrium equation results in

$$-\frac{T}{T_1} Ke^{-t/T_1} + Ke^{-t/T_1} = Ve^{-t/T_1}$$

$$(11\text{-}80)$$

Since the common factor e^{-t/T_1} in Eq. (11-80) is not zero at any (finite) time, we may divide Eq. (11-80) by this factor and solve for K,

$$\left(-\frac{T}{T_1} + 1\right) K = V$$

so that (provided that T/T_1 is *not* unity)

$$K = \frac{V}{1 - T/T_1} \qquad T \neq T_1$$

The complete response at this point is written

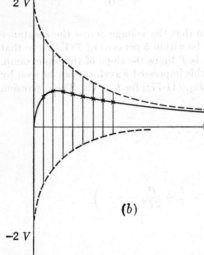

(b)

FIG. 11-33. Exponentially decaying voltage applied to an R-C circuit. In (b) the construction of a response waveform is shown.

$$v_{mb}(t) = \frac{V}{1 - T/T_1} e^{-t/T_1} + Ae^{-t/T}$$
$$\frac{T}{T_1} \neq 1, t \geq 0^+$$

The value of A is found from the initial condition

$$v_{mb}(0^-) = v_{mb}(0^+) = V_0$$

or

$$V_0 = \frac{V}{1 - T/T_1} + A$$

so that the solution (for $T \neq T_1$) is

$$v_{mb}(t) = \frac{V}{1 - T/T_1} (e^{-t/T_1} - e^{-t/T}) + V_0 e^{-t/T} \qquad T \neq T_1, t \geq 0^+ \quad (11\text{-}81)$$

This solution is illustrated in Fig. 11-33b for the case $T = \frac{1}{2}T_1$, $V_0 = 0$.

An interesting case results if one seeks the solution for $T = T_1$ when the time constant of the impressed decay is equal to the ("natural") time constant of the R-C circuit. In this exceptional case the solution can be obtained by taking the limit of Eq. (11-81) as T approaches T_1.

Define $x = T_1/T$, and consider

$$\lim_{T \to T_1} \frac{e^{-t/T_1} - e^{-t/T}}{1 - T/T_1} = \lim_{x \to 1} \frac{e^{-t/T_1} - (e^{-x})^{t/T_1}}{1 - 1/x}$$

Since the fraction whose limit we seek is in the form 0/0, we apply L'Hôpital's rule,

$$\lim_{x \to 1} \frac{e^{-t/T_1} - e^{-x(t/T_1)}}{1 - 1/x} = \lim_{x \to 1} \frac{\dfrac{d}{dx}(e^{-t/T_1} - e^{-x(t/T_1)})}{\dfrac{d}{dx}[1 - (1/x)]} = \lim_{x \to 1} \frac{\dfrac{t}{T_1} e^{-x(t/T_1)}}{1/x^2}$$

$$= \frac{t}{T_1} e^{-t/T_1} = \frac{t}{T} e^{-t/T}$$

Hence the complete response in this special case is

$$v_{mb}(t) = V \frac{t}{T} e^{-t/T} + V_0 e^{-t/T} \qquad T = T_1, t \geq 0^+ \quad (11\text{-}82)$$

It is seen that the component of the response due to the source is $V(t/T)e^{-t/T}$.

11-18. The Parallel R-C Circuit. The equilibrium equation of the parallel R-C circuit shown in Fig. 11-34a with the current source $i(t)$ is

$$\frac{1}{R} v_{ab} + C \frac{dv_{ab}}{dt} = i(t) \qquad v_{ab}(0^+) = v_{ab}(0^-) \quad (11\text{-}83)$$

This equation is identical in form to the equation of the series circuit and may be treated exactly as in the preceding examples.

Note further that, if the resistive current source of Fig. 11-34a is converted to a voltage source as in Fig. 11-34b, the equilibrium equation of the series circuit (Fig. 11-34b) is

$$RC \frac{dv_{ab}}{dt} + v_{ab} = v(t) = i(t)R \quad (11\text{-}84)$$

Equation (11-84) is identical to Eq. (11-83).

While the solution for the voltage across the capacitance, v_{ab}, will be the same for the two circuits of Fig. 11-34, the equivalence does *not* extend to the current in (or voltage across) the resistance R. The voltage v_{da} in Fig. 11-34b has *no* counterpart in the circuit of Fig. 11-34a, and the current in $R, (v_{ab}/R)$, in Fig. 11-34a has *no* counterpart in Fig. 11-34b because the two circuits are equivalent only with respect to the element (C) connected between terminals a-b.

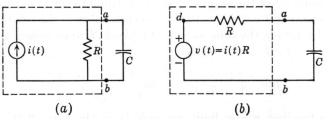

(a)   (b)

FIG. 11-34. Parallel R-C circuit with a current source and its series equivalent.

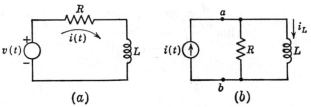

(a)   (b)

FIG. 11-35. Series and parallel R-L circuits with sources.

11-19. R-L Circuit. The equilibrium equations of the two circuits of Fig. 11-35a and b (which can be made equivalent with respect to two terminals by conversion of the sources) are

$$\text{Fig. 11-35}a: \qquad Ri + L\frac{di}{dt} = v(t) \qquad i(0^+) = i(0^-) \qquad (11\text{-}85)$$

$$\text{Fig. 11-35}b: \qquad \frac{v_{ab}}{R} + \frac{1}{L}\int_{-\infty}^{t} v_{ab}\, d\tau = i(t)$$

or

$$\frac{1}{R}\left(L\frac{di_L}{dt}\right) + i_L = i(t) \qquad i_L(0^+) = i_L(0^-) \qquad (11\text{-}86)$$

Equations (11-85) and (11-86) are again first-order linear differential equations so that the procedures for solution are identical to those for the R-C circuit. Attention is called to the fact that in the inductance the current cannot change abruptly (unless impulse voltages are impressed), while for a capacitance the voltage cannot change abruptly (unless impulse currents are impressed).

11-20. Other Single-energy Circuits. Consider the circuit of Fig. 11-36. Let it be required to solve for $v_{ab}(t)$. While it is possible to solve directly the two simultaneous Kirchhoff's law equations

$$\frac{v_{da}}{R_1} = C\frac{dv_{ab}}{dt} + \frac{v_{ab}}{R}$$
$$v(t) = v_{da} + v_{ab}$$

it is often more convenient to consider the series combination of R_1 and $v(t)$ a resistive source and obtain the circuit of Fig. 11-37.   These circuits are equivalent with respect to $a\text{-}b$.   Inspection of the circuit of Fig. 11-37

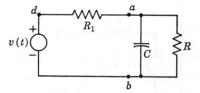

FIG. 11-36. A series-parallel $R\text{-}C$ circuit.

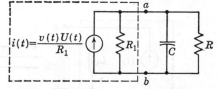

FIG. 11-37. Current-source equivalent of Fig. 11-36.

shows that the circuit is equivalent to a parallel $R\text{-}C$ circuit, the equivalent resistance is $R_1 R/(R_1 + R)$, so that the time constant is

$$T = \frac{R_1 R}{R_1 + R}\,C$$

Completion of the problem for various functions $v(t)$ is left as an exercise for the reader.

As a second example consider the initially deenergized circuit shown in Fig. 11-38; the source $i(t)$ is given as the ramp function,

$$i(t) = \frac{I}{T_1}\,tU(t)$$

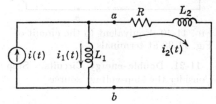

FIG. 11-38. Series-parallel $R\text{-}L$ circuit.

The solution may most conveniently be accomplished by converting the parallel combination of $i(t)$ and L_1 to a voltage source as shown in Fig. 11-39.   With respect to terminals $a\text{-}b$ the equivalent circuit shown in Fig. 11-40 results.   The differential equation for $i_2(t)$ is

$$(L_1 + L_2)\frac{di_2}{dt} + Ri_2 = \frac{L_1 I}{T_1} \qquad t \geq 0^+ \qquad (11\text{-}87)$$

This equation applies to the circuit of Fig. 11-40 only, since the current in the element L_1 in this circuit is identical with the current i_2, while in the original circuit L_1 carries the current i_1.   Therefore we use Eq. (11-87) to find the component of i_2 due to the source.

The complete response has the form

$$i_2(t) = \frac{L_1 I}{R T_1} + A e^{-t/T} \qquad t \geq 0^+$$

where
$$T = \frac{L_1 + L_2}{R}$$

This value is obtained from the source-free circuit. Note that the source-free circuit is independent of the source conversion. The value of A is

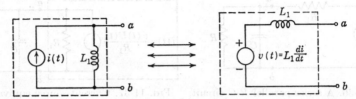

FIG. 11-39. Source conversion.

found from the initial condition $i_2(0^+) = 0$; hence

$$i_2(t) = \frac{LI}{R T_1} (1 - e^{-t/T}) \qquad t \geq 0^+$$

If, in the original problem (Fig. 11-38), it was required to solve for $i_1(t)$, we could still first solve for $i_2(t)$ and then apply Kirchhoff's current law at terminal a,

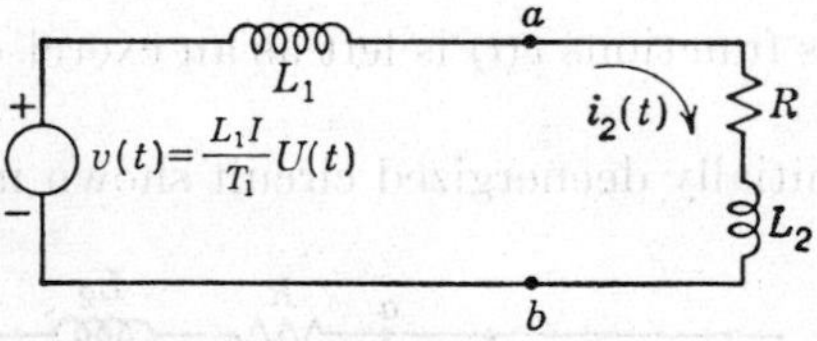

$$i_1(t) = i(t) - i_2(t)$$

Note again that the current in L_1 in Fig. 11-40 is not the same as the current in that element in Fig. 11-38.

FIG. 11-40. Equivalent to the circuit of Fig. 11-38 at terminals a-b.

11-21. Double-energy Circuits. Step Voltage Applied to Series R-L-C Circuit. Consider the step-voltage source

$$v_{ab}(t) = V U(t)$$

applied to a series R-L-C branch as shown in Fig. 11-41.

Application of Kirchhoff's voltage law results in the equation

$$L \frac{d^2 q_m}{dt^2} + R \frac{dq_m}{dt} + \frac{1}{C} q_m = V \qquad t \geq 0^+$$

and the initial conditions are

$$q_m(0^+) = q_m(0^-) = Q_0$$
$$i(0^+) = i(0^-) = I_0$$

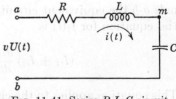

FIG. 11-41. Series R-L-C circuit.

To obtain the complete response, we again write

$$q_m(t) = (q_m)_s + (q_m)_f$$

The form of the free component of the solution depends on the natural mode of the circuit response; i.e., it depends on whether the circuit is underdamped, overdamped, or critically damped.   If, for example, we assume critical damping, then

$$(q_m)_f = (A + Bt)e^{-\omega_0 t} \qquad \alpha = \frac{R}{2L} = \omega_0 = \frac{1}{\sqrt{LC}}$$

The component of the solution due to the source is seen to be constant:

$$(q_m)_s = CV$$

so that in the critically damped case the solution is

$$q_m(t) = CV + (A + Bt)e^{-\omega_0 t} \qquad\qquad t \geq 0^+$$

and $\qquad \dfrac{dq_m}{dt} = i(t) = e^{-\omega_0 t}(-\omega_0 A - \omega_0 Bt + B) \quad t \geq 0^+$

Using the initial conditions, we obtain the two equations for A and B,

$$Q_0 = CV + A$$
$$I_0 = -\omega_0 A + B$$

The complete response for the charge is therefore

$$q_m(t) = CV + (e^{-\omega_0 t})[Q_0 - CV + (I_0 + \omega_0 Q_0 - \omega_0 CV)t] \qquad t \geq 0^+$$

If the circuit is overdamped, then the free component of the response has the form

$$(q_m)_f = Ae^{s_1 t} + Be^{s_1 t}$$
$$s_{1,2} = -\alpha \pm \sqrt{\alpha^2 - \omega_0^2} \qquad \alpha > \omega_0$$
$$\alpha = \frac{R}{2L} \qquad \omega_0^2 = \frac{1}{LC}$$

The complete response has the form

$$q_m(t) = CV + Ae^{s_1 t} + Be^{s_2 t}$$

where the constants are evaluated from the initial conditions.   If the circuit is underdamped, we write any of the forms for $(q_m)_f$ in Chap. 9; for example,

$$(q_m)_f = Ke^{-\alpha t} \cos{(\omega_d t + \gamma)} = \operatorname{Re} \mathbf{K}e^{(-\alpha + j\omega_d)t} \qquad \omega_d = \sqrt{\omega_0^2 - \alpha^2}, \, \omega_0 > \alpha$$

form the complete response (the constants $\mathbf{K}$ or K and γ are evaluated from the initial conditions).   The graphical construction for the complete response is identical in procedure to that outlined in Chap. 9, only $(q_m)_s$ must be added to $(q_m)_f$.

11-22. Ramp Function Applied to Series R-L-C Circuit.   If the ramp function

$$v(t) = \frac{V}{T_1} t U(t)$$

is applied to the circuit of Fig. 11-41, the complete response will differ in form from the step-function case only in $(q_m)_s$.   To find $(q_m)_s$, the form

$$(q_m)_s = K_1 + K_2 t$$

may be assumed and substituted in the equation

$$L \frac{d^2(q_m)_s}{dt^2} + R \frac{d(q_m)_s}{dt} + \frac{1}{C} (q_m)_s = \frac{V}{T_1} t$$

which gives

$$L(0) + RK_2 + \frac{1}{C} K_1 + \frac{K_2 t}{C} = \frac{V}{T_1} t \qquad (11\text{-}88)$$

If Eq. (11-88) is to hold for all $t \geq 0^+$, it follows that

$$RC = - \frac{K_1}{K_2}$$

and

$$K_2 = \frac{VC}{T_1}$$

so that

$$(q_m)_s = VC \left(- \frac{RC}{T_1} + \frac{t}{T_1} \right)$$

The value of the inductance does not affect this component of the solution because the current (dq_m/dt) is constant after the transient has decayed.

11-23. Evaluation of Response by Means of Derived Initial Conditions. Exactly as in the case of source-free circuits, it is sometimes convenient to solve for the current (or for the voltage across the inductance) without first solving for the charge or for the voltage across C. Consider the general type of source $v(t)$ impressed on the series R-L-C branch,

$$L \frac{d^2 q_m}{dt^2} + R \frac{dq_m}{dt} + \frac{1}{C} q_m = v(t) \qquad t \geq 0^+$$

For all times after $t = 0$ one may write

$$\frac{di}{dt} = \frac{d^2 q_m}{dt^2} = \frac{v(t) - q_m/C - Ri}{L} \qquad t \geq 0^+ \qquad (11\text{-}89)$$

Now, if $q(0^+) = Q_0$ and $i(0^+) = I_0$, we may apply Eq. (11-89) at $t = 0^+$ to obtain a derived initial condition for di/dt,

$$\frac{di}{dt} \bigg|_{t=0^+} = \frac{v(0^+) - Q_0/C - RI_0}{L}$$

Upon differentiating Eq. (11-89) and putting $t = 0^+$, the derived initial condition for di^2/dt^2 is found,

$$\left(\frac{d^2 i}{dt^2} \right)_{0^+} = \frac{(dv/dt)_{0^+} - I_0/C - R(di/dt)_{0^+}}{L}$$

If we desire to solve for $i(t)$ directly, we may write

$$i(t) = (i)_s + (i)_f \qquad (11\text{-}89a)$$

and

$$\frac{di}{dt} = \frac{di_s}{dt} + \frac{di_f}{dt} \qquad (11\text{-}89b)$$

The constants in the solution are then evaluated by putting $t = 0$ in

Eqs. (11-89*a*) and (11-89*b*),

$$I_0 = i_s(0^+) + i_f(0^+)$$

$$\left(\frac{di}{dt}\right)_{0^+} = \left(\frac{di_s}{dt}\right)_{0^+} + \left(\frac{di_f}{dt}\right)_{0^+}$$

Similarly we might solve for $L(di/dt)$ directly, using the initial values $(di/dt)_{0^+}$ and $(d^2i/dt^2)_{0^+}$.

11-24. Other R-L-C Circuits. By conversion of sources it is often possible to reduce other combinations of resistance, inductance, and capacitance to series or

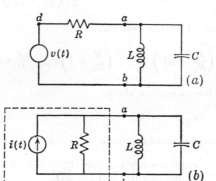

FIG. 11-42. Series-parallel R-L-C circuit and an equivalent.

parallel R-L-C circuits. The series-parallel circuit shown in Fig. 11-42*a* may be changed to the parallel circuit of Fig. 11-42*b* if

$$i(t) = \frac{v(t)}{R}$$

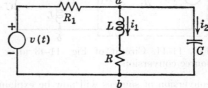

FIG. 11-43. A series-parallel circuit.

The circuit of Fig. 11-42*b* is equivalent to the original circuit with respect to terminals *a*-*b*. Details of the solution are left as an exercise for the reader.

As a final example, consider the circuit shown in Fig. 11-43. This circuit may be solved directly by application of Kirchhoff's laws:

$$v_{ab} = Ri_1 + L\frac{di_1}{dt} \tag{11-90a}$$

$$C\frac{dv_{ab}}{dt} = i_2 \tag{11-90b}$$

$$v_{ab} = v(t) - (i_1 + i_2)R_1 \tag{11-90c}$$

The initial conditions are

$$v_{ab}(0^+) = v_{ab}(0^-) = V_0$$
$$i_1(0^+) = i_1(0^-) = I_0$$

If it is desired first to solve for $v_{ab}(t)$, we eliminate i_1 and i_2 from Eqs. (11-90). Solving Eq. (11-90*c*) for i_1,

$$R_1i_1 = v(t) - v_{ab}(t) - i_2R_1 \tag{11-90d}$$

Substitute (11-90b) in (11-90d),

$$i_1 = \frac{v(t) - v_{ab}(t)}{R_1} - C\frac{dv_{ab}}{dt} \tag{11-90e}$$

Differentiate (11-90e),

$$\frac{di_1}{dt} = \frac{1}{R_1}\left(\frac{dv}{dt} - \frac{dv_{ab}}{dt}\right) - C\frac{d^2v_{ab}}{dt^2} \tag{11-90f}$$

Now substitute Eqs. (11-90f) and (11-90e) in (11-90a),

$$v_{ab} = \frac{R}{R_1}[v(t) - v_{ab}(t)] - CR\frac{dv_{ab}}{dt} + \frac{L}{R_1}\left(\frac{dv}{dt} - \frac{dv_{ab}}{dt}\right) - LC\frac{d^2v_{ab}}{dt^2} \tag{11-91}$$

Collecting terms in Eq. (11-91), we obtain

$$LC\frac{d^2v_{ab}}{dt^2} + \left(\frac{L}{R_1} + RC\right)\frac{dv_{ab}}{dt} + \left(\frac{R}{R_1} + 1\right)v_{ab} = \frac{R}{R_1}v(t) + \frac{L}{R_1}\frac{dv(t)}{dt} \tag{11-92}$$

The initial condition for v_{ab} is given above,

$$v_{ab}(0^+) = V_0$$

It is convenient to derive an initial condition for dv_{ab}/dt. Using Eq. (11-90c) at $t = 0^+$,

$$v_{ab}(0^+) = v(0^+) - i_1(0^+)R_1 - i_2(0^+)R_1$$

so that
$$R_1 i_2(0^+) = v(0^+) - V_0 - R_1 I_0$$

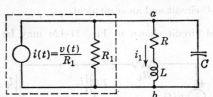

FIG. 11-44. Circuit of Fig. 11-43 after source conversion.

Substituting in (11-90b) at $t = 0^+$ gives

$$\left(\frac{dv_{ab}}{dt}\right)_{0^+} = \frac{i_2(0^+)}{C} =$$
$$\frac{v(0^+) - V_0 - R_1 I_0}{CR_1}$$

Hence Eq. (11-92) can be solved for $v_{ab}(t)$.

An alternate method which involves conversion of sources will now be explained. The circuit of Fig. 11-44 is equivalent to the circuit of Fig. 11-43 with respect to terminals a-b. The Kirchhoff's-law equations are

$$\frac{v_{ab}}{R_1} + C\frac{dv_{ab}}{dt} + i_1 = \frac{v(t)}{R_1} \tag{11-93a}$$

and
$$v_{ab} = Ri_1 + L\frac{di_1}{dt} \tag{11-93b}$$

Equation (11-92) is then obtained from Eqs. (11-93) by eliminating i_1 from Eqs. (11-93a) and (11-93b).

PROBLEMS

11-1. The differential equation of a series circuit is $2(di/dt) + 10i = v(t)$. It is known that $i(0^+) = 3$. Calculate the initial value $(di/dt)_{0^+}$ if (a) $v(t) = U(t)$; (b) $v(t) = (3t + 10)U(t)$; (c) $v(t) = 30\cos 2tU(t)$; (d) $v(t) = 30\sin 2tU(t)$; and (e) $v(t) = 50\cos(2t - 53.1°)U(t)$; (f) $v(t) = 6e^{-3t}$.

11-2. In the circuit shown in Fig. P11-2 $R = 5$ ohms and $L = 3$ henrys. It is known that $i_L(0^+) = 2$ amp, $i_R(0^+) = 3$ amp. Calculate: (a) $i(0^+)$; (b) $v_{ab}(0^+)$; (c) $(di/dt)_{0^+}$ if $(dv_{ab}/dt)_{0^+} = 0$.

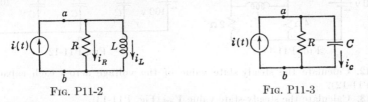

FIG. P11-2   FIG. P11-3

11-3. In the R-C circuit shown in Fig. P11-3 $R = 10^5$, $C = 10^{-6}$. It is known that $v_{ab}(0^+) = 10$ volts. Calculate $i_c(0^+)$ if (a) $i(t) = 10^{-4}$; (b) $i(t) = 5 \times 10^{-4}e^{-0.1t}$; (c) $i(t) = 25 \times 10^{-6} \cos (\omega t - 60°)$.

11-4. A series R-L circuit is defined by the equation $di/dt + i = v(t)$. The complete response is given as $i(t) = 5e^{-t} + t + 2e^{-4t}$. (a) Calculate $v(t)$. (b) What is the component of the response due to the source?

11-5. The complete response of a circuit defined by the equation $dv/dt + v = 5e^{-t}$ is given by $v = 5te^{-t} + 10e^{-t}$. (a) Verify the complete response by substitution in the equilibrium equation. (b) Identify the component of the response due to the source (which does not satisfy the source-free equation).

11-6. The complete response of a circuit defined by the equilibrium equation $di/dt + i = 10e^{-2t}$ is to have the form $i(t) = Ae^{-2t}$. (a) Calculate $i(0^+)$ and A. (b) What is the value of the source-free component of the complete response? (c) What is the equation for the complete response $i(t)$ if $i(0^+) = 20$ amp?

11-7. In the circuit shown in Fig. P11-7 what is the free mode of the response at the source terminals if the source is (a) an ideal voltage source; (b) an ideal current source?

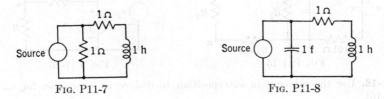

FIG. P11-7   FIG. P11-8

11-8. Discuss the free component of the response of the source terminals for the circuit shown in Fig. P11-8 if the source is (a) an ideal voltage source; (b) an ideal current source.

11-9. Calculate the steady-state value V_{ab} (Fig. P11-9).

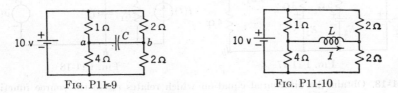

FIG. P11-9   FIG. P11-10

11-10. Calculate the steady-state value I (Fig. P11-10).

11-11. Calculate the steady-state value I (Fig. P11-11).

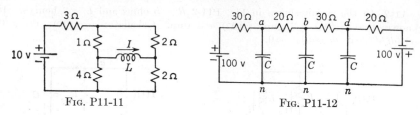

FIG. P11-11   FIG. P11-12

11-12. Calculate the steady-state value of the voltage across each capacitance (Fig. P11-12).

11-13. Calculate the steady-state value V_{an} (Fig. P11-13).

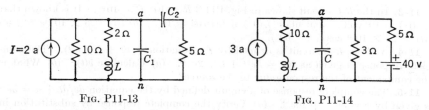

FIG. P11-13   FIG. P11-14

11-14. Calculate the steady-state value V_{an} (Fig. P11-14). *Hint:* Represent the resistive voltage source as a current source.

11-15. In the circuit shown in Fig. P11-15 the power dissipated by R_1 in the steady state is 4,500 watts. The steady-state value of the voltage V_{dn} is 90 volts. Calculate the following steady-state values: (a) V_{ab}; (b) I; (c) the power delivered to R_2; (d) the power delivered by the 100-volt source.

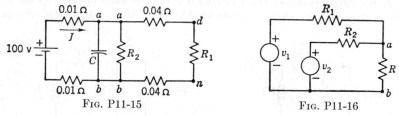

FIG. P11-15   FIG. P11-16

11-16. Use the principle of superposition to deduce an expression for v_{ab} (Fig. P11-16).

11-17. In the circuit shown in Fig. P11-17, E_1, E_2, and E_3 have certain fixed values. When $E_4 = 0$, $V_{ab} = 30$ volts. Calculate E_4 so that $V_{ab} = 20$ volts.

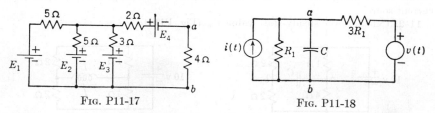

FIG. P11-17   FIG. P11-18

11-18. Obtain the differential equation which relates v_{ab} to the source functions $i(t)$ and $v(t)$ (Fig. P11-18). Show how the principle of superposition applies in this problem.

11-19. The circuit shown in Fig. P11-19 is in the steady state at $t = 0^-$ with the switch in position 1. At $t = 0$ the switch is thrown to position 2. Draw the circuit for $t > 0$, representing all initial-energy storage by means of (a) ideal voltage sources; (b) ideal current sources.

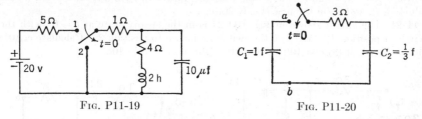

FIG. P11-19   FIG. P11-20

11-20. In Fig. P11-20 the capacitance C_1 is initially charged to 100 volts; C_2 is initially uncharged. The switch is closed at $t = 0$. (a) Calculate $v_{ab}(t)$ for all $t \geq 0^+$. (Use an initial-condition generator.) (b) Calculate the energy stored on C_1 at $t = 0$. (c) Calculate the total energy stored on C_1 and C_2 at $t = \infty$. (d) Account for the difference between total initial stored energy and total final stored energy by calculating the total energy dissipated in the 3-ohm resistance between $t = 0$ and $t = \infty$. (e) The 3-ohm resistance is replaced by an arbitrary resistance R. Show that the energy dissipated by R between $t = 0$ and $t = \infty$ is independent of the value of R.

11-21. The circuit shown in Fig. P11-21 is in the steady state until $t = 0$ with the switch in position 1. At $t = 0$ the switch is thrown to position 2. (a) Calculate $i(t)$ for all $t \geq 0^+$. The initial value of the current in L_2 is zero. *Hint:* Represent the initial energy stored in L_1 by an ideal current source. (b) Calculate the energy stored in L_1 and L_2 at $t = 0$ and at $t = \infty$. (c) Calculate the total energy delivered to R in the interval $t = 0$ to $t = \infty$. (d) Compare the results of this problem with the results of Prob. 11-20.

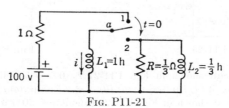

FIG. P11-21

11-22. The circuit shown in Fig. P11-22 is in the steady state before $t = 0$ with $V = 40$ volts. At $t = 0$ the value of V is abruptly changed to 60 volts. Calculate: (a) $v_{ab}(0^-)$; (b) $v_{bn}(0^-)$; (c) $v_{ab}(0^+)$; (d) $v_{bn}(0^+)$; (e) $i(0^-)$; (f) $i(0^+)$; (g) the new steady-state values of v_{ab} and v_{bn}.

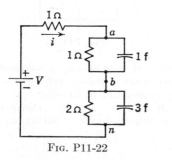

FIG. P11-22

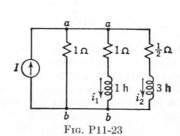

FIG. P11-23

11-23. The circuit shown in Fig. P11-23 is in the steady state before $t = 0$ with $I = 40$ amp. At $t = 0$ the value of I is abruptly changed to 60 amp. Calculate: (a) the values i_1, i_2, and v_{ab} at $t = 0^-$; (b) the values i_1, i_2, and v_{ab} at $t = 0^+$; (c) the values i_1, i_2, and v_{ab} in the new steady state.

11-24. The circuit shown in Fig. P11-24 is in the steady state at $t = 0^-$ with the switch in position 1. At $t = 0$ the switch is thrown to position 2. Calculate $v_{an}(0^+)$ and $(dv_{an}/dt)_{0^+}$ if (a) $v = 10t$; (b) $v = 10 - 10t$; (c) $v = 5 - 10t$.

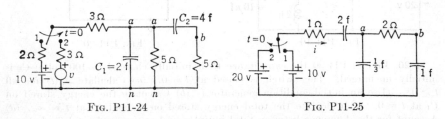

FIG. P11-24   FIG. P11-25

11-25. The circuit shown in Fig. P11-25 is in the steady state with the switch in position 1. At $t = 0$ the switch is thrown to position 2. Calculate $i(0^+)$ and $v_{ab}(0^+)$.

11-26. The circuit shown in Fig. P11-26 is in the steady state with the switch in position 1. At $t = 0$ the switch is thrown to position 2 so that an impulse of current flows and the voltages across the capacitances change abruptly. Represent the steady-state condition for $t < 0$ by ideal voltage sources, and calculate $v_{an}(0^+)$, using superposition.

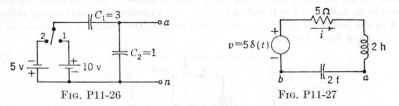

FIG. P11-26   FIG. P11-27

11-27. In the circuit shown in Fig. P11-27 $v_{ab}(0^-) = 5$ volts. Calculate $i(0^+)$, $v_{ab}(0^+)$, and $(dv_{ab}/dt)_{0^+}$ if (a) $i(0^-) = 0$; (b) $i(0^-) = 2.5$ amp; (c) $i(0^-) = -2.5$ amp.

11-28. In the circuit shown in Fig. P11-28 calculate $v_{ab}(0^+)$ if (a) $v_{ab}(0^-) = 0$; (b) $v_{ab}(0^-) = 10$ volts.

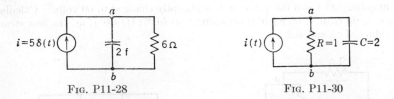

FIG. P11-28   FIG. P11-30

11-29. When a step voltage of 50 volts is impressed on an initially deenergized series R-C circuit at $t = 0$, the voltage across the capacitance is 30 volts at $t = 0.3$ sec. At which instant of time will the voltage across the capacitance be 40 volts?

11-30. In the circuit shown in Fig. P11-30 $v_{ab}(0^+) = 20$ volts. Calculate and sketch to scale $v_{ab}(t)$ for all $t \geq 0^+$ if (a) $i(t) = 10U(t)$; (b) $i(t) = 20U(t)$; (c) $i(t) = 40U(t)$.

11-31. A ramp-function voltage source $v(t) = Vt/T_1$ is applied to a series R-C circuit. The initial value of the voltage across the capacitance is V_0. Calculate the value of V_0 (and show the reference directions on a circuit diagram) if the free component of the response is zero.

11-32. The rectangular voltage pulse shown in Fig. P11-32 is impressed on the series R-C circuit. Calculate and sketch $v_{ab}(t)$ and $i(t)$ for all $t \geq 0^+$ if (a) $v_{ab}(0^+) = 0$; (b) $v_{ab}(0^+) = 5$ volts; (c) $v_{ab}(0^-) = -5$ volts. *Hint:* It is convenient to represent the initial-energy storage by an equivalent ideal voltage source and use the principle of superposition.

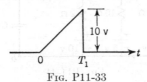

FIG. P11-32

11-33. The triangular pulse shown in Fig. P11-33 represents the voltage waveform v of the source in the circuit of Prob. 11-32 (Fig. P11-32). Calculate and sketch carefully to scale $v_{ab}(t)$ and $v_{ma}(t)$ if $v_{ab}(0^+) = 0$ and (a) $T_1 = 1$; (b) $T_1 = 10$; (c) $T_1 = 0.1$.

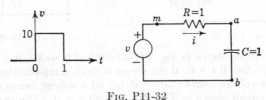

FIG. P11-33

11-34. Analyze the results of Prob. 11-33 with the integrating and differentiating property of R-C circuits in mind; i.e., compare the waveforms obtained with those which are obtained from an ideal integrator and differentiator.

11-35. Show that an R-L circuit has (approximate) integrating and differentiating properties by deducing the appropriate inequalities, and illustrate your result, using a ramp-function source with no initial-energy storage.

11-36. Calculate the current response of a series R-L circuit to a voltage source which is a rectangular pulse of duration T_1, for the following cases: (a) $T_1 = L/R$; (b) $T_1 = 10L/R$; (c) $T_1 = L/5R$. Assume no initial-energy storage.

11-37. In the circuit shown in Fig. P11-37 calculate $v_{ab}(t)$ for all $t \geq 0^+$, and sketch the result if (a) $i(0^+) = 0$; (b) $i(0^+) = 10$ amp. (c) Repeat the calculation required in (a) if the source is the ramp function $30tU(t)$.

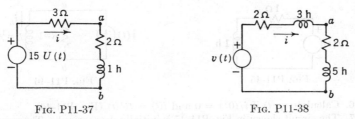

FIG. P11-37   FIG. P11-38

11-38. In the circuit shown in Fig. P11-38 $i(0^+) = 0$. Calculate $v_{ab}(t)$ for all $t \geq 0^+$ if (a) $v(t) = 10tU(t)$; (b) $v(t) = 10U(t)$; (c) $v(t) = (5 + 6t)U(t)$.

11-39. In the circuit shown in Fig. P11-39 the source waveform $v(t)$ is a rectangular pulse of 0.5 sec duration and unit amplitude. Calculate $v_{ab}(t)$ for all $t \geq 0^+$, and sketch the result if the capacitance is initially uncharged.

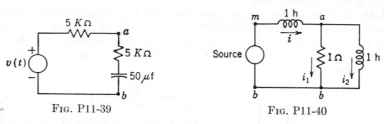

FIG. P11-39   FIG. P11-40

11-40. In the circuit shown in Fig. P11-40 $i(0^-) = 0$, and $i_2(0^-) = 0$. Calculate $i(t)$, $i_1(t)$, and $i_2(t)$ for all $t \geq 0^+$ if the source is (a) a ramp-function current source $i(t) = tU(t)$; (b) a voltage source $v_{mb}(t) = tU(t)$; (c) a voltage source $v(t) = U(t)$.

11-41. In the circuit shown in Fig. P11-41 $v_{ab}(0^-) = 0$. The switch is closed at $t = 0$. Calculate $v_{ab}(t)$ for all $t \geq 0^+$. *Hint:* Represent all voltage sources as current sources.

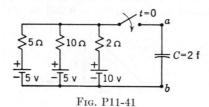

FIG. P11-41

11-42. The 2-farad capacitance of Prob. 11-41 (Fig. P11-41) is replaced by an initially deenergized series combination of R and L. If $L = 2$ henrys and R is chosen for maximum power transfer in the steady state, calculate (a) $v_{ab}(0^+)$; (b) $v_{ab}(t)$ for all $t \geq 0^+$.

11-43. In Prob. 11-41 calculate the function which represents the power dissipated by the 2-ohm resistance for all $t \geq 0^+$.

11-44. A source $v(t) = 10e^{-t}$ is impressed on an initially deenergized series R-L circuit. Use $R = 2$ and calculate $i(t)$ if (a) $L/R = 2$; (b) $L/R = 1$.

11-45. The R-L circuit shown in Fig. P11-45 is initially deenergized. (a) Show that, if $v(t) = \sqrt{2} \cos (t - 45°)$, $i_s(t) = \sin t$. (b) Show that, if $v(t) = e^{-t} \sin t$, $i_s(t) = -e^{-t} \cos t$. (c) Obtain the complete response if $i(0^+) = 0$ and $v(t) = e^{-t} \sin t$.

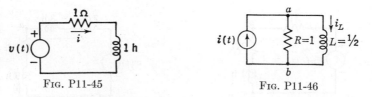

FIG. P11-45   FIG. P11-46

11-46. Calculate $v_{ab}(t)$ if $i_L(0^+) = 0$ and $i(t) = tU(t)$ (Fig. P11-46).

11-47. The circuit shown in Fig. P11-47 is initially deenergized. The source is the step function $v(t) = 10U(t)$. Calculate, and sketch carefully to scale, $v_{ab}(t)$ if (a) $R = 0$; (b) $R = 0.4$ ohm; (c) $R = 2$ ohms; (d) $R = 5.2$ ohms.

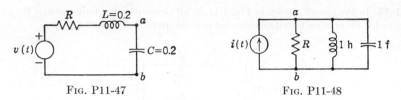

FIG. P11-47   FIG. P11-48

11-48. The circuit shown in Fig. P11-48 is initially deenergized. Calculate $v_{ab}(t)$ for all $t \geq 0^+$ if $i(t) = 5tU(t)$ and (a) $R = \infty$; (b) $R = 1$ ohm; (c) $R = \frac{1}{2}$ ohm; (d) $R = \frac{1}{4}$ ohm.

11-49. In the circuit shown in Fig. P11-49 $v_{ab}(0^-) = 1$ volt, and $i(0^-) = 0$. If $v(t) = U(t)$, calculate $v_{bn}(t)$ for all $t \geq 0^+$.

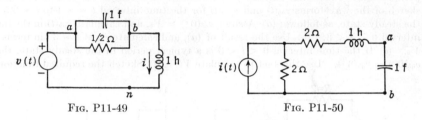

FIG. P11-49   FIG. P11-50

11-50. The circuit shown in Fig. P11-50 is initially deenergized. Calculate $v_{ab}(t)$ if $i(t) = U(t)$.

11-51. In Fig. P11-51 the R-L-C branch is initially deenergized. The switch is closed at $t = 0$. Calculate $i(t)$ for all $t \geq 0^+$.

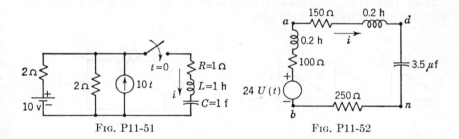

FIG. P11-51   FIG. P11-52

11-52. The circuit shown in Fig. P11-52 is initially deenergized. Calculate: (a) $v_{ab}(0^+)$; (b) $(dv_{ab}/dt)_{0^+}$; (c) $v_{ab}(t)$ for all $t \geq 0^+$. Solve for v_{ab} directly, without finding $v_{dn}(t)$ or $i(t)$.

11-53. A series R-L-C circuit has the equilibrium equation $d^2i/dt^2 + 2(di/dt) + i = e^{-t}$. Show that the form $i = (At^2 + K_1t + K_2)e^{-t}$ is the complete response, and calculate A.

11-54. An L-C circuit has $L = 1$ and $C = 1$. A source $v(t) = \cos t$ is impressed. Show that $v_c = At \sin t$ is a solution of the equilibrium equation for the voltage across the capacitance, and find A.

11-55. In the circuit of Fig. 11-42a, $v_{ab}(0^+) = 10$, and the initial energy stored in the inductance is zero. Calculate $v_{ab}(t)$ and $v_{da}(t)$ for all $t \geq 0^+$ if $v(t) = 40U(t)$ and $R = 2$, $L = 1$, $C = 1$.

11-56. In the circuit shown in Fig. P11-56 all elements have unit value. If $v(t) = U(t)$ and if there is no initial-energy storage, calculate $v_{ab}(t)$ for all $t \geq 0^+$.

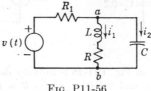

FIG. P11-56

11-57. The periodic source function is applied to the series R-C circuit as shown in Fig. P11-57. In Chap. 19 it is shown that the component of a response due to a periodic source function is periodic. Assume this statement to be true, and obtain a sketch of the waveforms $v_{ab}(t)$ and $v_{ma}(t)$ for the time interval $t = -1$ to $t = 3.5$ in the steady state, as follows: (a) Assume $v_{ab}(0^+) = V_0$, and calculate $v_{ab}(t)$ in the time interval $0 < t < 3$. (b) Use the result of (a), and calculate v_{ab} at $t = 3^-$ in terms of V_0. (c) If the time interval $0 < t < 3$ is a typical period in the steady state, then $v_{ab}(0^-) = v_{ab}(3^-)$. Use this fact to calculate V_0. (d) Sketch the required functions.

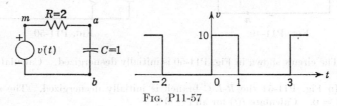

FIG. P11-57

11-58. Perform the calculations required in Prob. 11-57 if $v(t)$ is the periodic sawtooth waveform shown in Fig. P11-58.

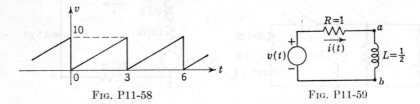

FIG. P11-58   FIG. P11-59

11-59. In the circuit shown in Fig. P11-59 $v(t)$ is the periodic waveform of Prob. 11-57. Assume (as in Prob. 11-57) that the steady-state condition has been reached at $t = 0$. Use $i(0^+) = I_0$, and calculate $i(3^-)$; then obtain I_0, and sketch $i(t)$ and $v_{ab}(t)$ in the time interval $-\frac{1}{2} < t < 3\frac{1}{2}$.

CHAPTER 12

NETWORK FUNCTIONS

In Chap. 11 we stated that in a network containing a single source $\phi(t)$ any response function $y(t)$ is related to the source function through a linear differential equation of the general form

$$\sum_{m=0}^{M} a_m \frac{d^m}{dt^m} y(t) = \sum_{n=0}^{N} b_n \frac{d^n}{dt^n} \phi(t) \qquad (12\text{-}1)$$

In that chapter the solution of differential equations of above form was discussed, but, except for the case of series or parallel connection of elements, the general procedure for establishing an equilibrium equation of the form (12-1) was not indicated. To establish an equilibrium equation in terms of a single network variable $y(t)$, we start with the application of Kirchhoff's laws to the nodes and loops of the network. This will result in a set of simultaneous equations containing different voltages and currents as unknowns. By substitution of all the unknown functions in terms of the single unknown variable $y(t)$ and its derivatives an equation of the form (12-1) is obtained.

If a network contains only one type of passive element (see Chap. 6), then the set of equilibrium equations of that network are algebraic equations and for such a network the procedure of repeated substitutions outlined above is a simple one. However, for networks containing resistive as well as energy storing elements the equilibrium equations will be a set of simultaneous differential equations, and the amount of required substitutions grows to an enormous degree as the complexity of the network increases. One of the purposes of this chapter is to introduce an "operational" notation which will greatly facilitate the manipulation of a set of simultaneous differential equations. We shall also examine the behavior of networks when the source function is an exponential function of time. This consideration will lead to the study of network response by algebraic means in the "complex-frequency" domain.

Before proceeding with a discussion of the operational method and its significance, an example will be given to illustrate the amount of work required for establishing a differential equation of the form of Eq. (12-1), when "substitution" methods are used.

12-1. Example of Simultaneous Differential Equations. In Fig. 12-1 find a differential equation relating the response $v(t)$ to the source $i(t)$.

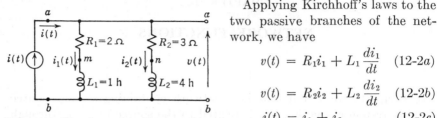

FIG. 12-1. Circuit used to illustrate how simultaneous equations arise in network analysis.

Applying Kirchhoff's laws to the two passive branches of the network, we have

$$v(t) = R_1 i_1 + L_1 \frac{di_1}{dt} \quad (12\text{-}2a)$$

$$v(t) = R_2 i_2 + L_2 \frac{di_2}{dt} \quad (12\text{-}2b)$$

$$i(t) = i_1 + i_2 \quad (12\text{-}2c)$$

To obtain an equation relating $v(t)$ to $i(t)$, the unknown variables i_1 and i_2 and their derivatives must be eliminated from Eqs. (12-2). Substituting for i_2 from (12-2c) in (12-2b), we have

$$v(t) = R_2 i + L_2 \frac{di}{dt} - R_2 i_1 - L_2 \frac{di_1}{dt} \quad (12\text{-}3a)$$

Multiplying Eq. (12-3a) by L_1 and Eq. (12-2a) by L_2 and adding, we have

$$(L_1 + L_2)v(t) = R_2 L_1 i + L_1 L_2 \frac{di}{dt} - (R_2 L_1 - R_1 L_2)i_1 \quad (12\text{-}3b)$$

We have so far succeeded in eliminating i_2 and its derivative as well as the derivative of i_1, but i_1 itself still remains in Eq. (12-3b).

For the special case when the value of $R_2 L_1 = R_1 L_2$ or $L_1/R_1 = L_2/R_2$, the coefficient of i_1 in Eq. (12-3b) will be zero and the equation reduces to

$$(L_1 + L_2)v(t) = R_2 L_1 i + L_1 L_2 \frac{di}{dt} \quad (12\text{-}4)$$

We note that L_1/R_1 and L_2/R_2 are the time constants of the two branches of the network of Fig. 12-1. Thus, if the two time constants are equal, Eq. (12-4) will be the desired equilibrium equation relating the response $v(t)$ with the source $i(t)$. However, this is a special case, and in general $R_1 L_2 \neq R_2 L_1$. With this condition we can find i_1 from Eq. (12-3b) as

$$i_1 = \frac{1}{R_2 L_1 - R_1 L_2} \left[R_2 L_1 i + L_1 L_2 \frac{di}{dt} - (L_1 + L_2)v(t) \right] \quad (12\text{-}5a)$$

Differentiating Eq. (12-5a), we have

$$\frac{di_1}{dt} = \frac{1}{R_2 L_1 - R_1 L_2} \left[R_2 L_1 \frac{di}{dt} + L_1 L_2 \frac{d^2 i}{dt^2} - (L_1 + L_2) \frac{dv}{dt} \right] \quad (12\text{-}5b)$$

Substituting for i_1 and di_1/dt from Eq. (12-5) in Eq. (12-2a), rearranging the terms, and introducing the symbols

$$a_0 = R_1 + R_2 \qquad a_1 = L_1 + L_2$$
$$b_0 = R_1 R_2 \qquad b_1 = R_1 L_2 + R_2 L_1 \qquad b_2 = L_1 L_2 \qquad (12\text{-}6)$$

we have the desired equilibrium equation in the form

$$a_1 \frac{d}{dt} v(t) + a_0 v(t) = b_2 \frac{d^2}{dt^2} i(t) + b_1 \frac{d}{dt} i(t) + b_0 i(t) \qquad (12\text{-}7)$$

Here the following points are noted:

1. This equilibrium equation, which relates the response $v(t)$ to the source $i(t)$, is of the general form given in Eq. (12-1).

2. Even in the case of the simple network of Fig. 12-1, a considerable number of substitutions are required before the final result is obtained.

The reader can verify that addition of another branch to the network of Fig. 12-1 would make the required work almost prohibitive.

12-2. Introduction to Operational Method. The example of Art. 12-1 has demonstrated the need for a more compact method of manipulation of simultaneous differential equations. The operational method, described below, is a mathematical technique which satisfies this need. It consists in considering the differential coefficient d/dt as an "operator" designated by a symbol[1] such as p and treating this operator as an algebraic quantity.[2] Thus

$$p \equiv \frac{d}{dt} \qquad p^2 \equiv \frac{d^2}{dt^2} \qquad p^n \equiv \frac{d^n}{dt^n} \qquad (12\text{-}8a)$$

$$pf(t) \equiv \frac{d}{dt} f(t) \qquad p^n f(t) \equiv \frac{d^n}{dt^n} f(t) \qquad (12\text{-}8b)$$

For the purpose of elimination of variables a set of simultaneous differential equations can be written in operational form and treated as a set of algebraic simultaneous equations. We shall illustrate the validity of this method by use of the example treated in Art. 12-1. The set of differential equations of Eq. (12-2) were reduced to Eq. (12-7) by direct substitution. We shall now use the operational method and arrive at the same result with a great deal of saving in the number of substitutions. Equations (12-2a) to (12-2c) are written below in operational form

$$v(t) = R_1 i_1 + p L_1 i_1 = (R_1 + p L_1) i_1 \qquad (12\text{-}9a)$$
$$v(t) = R_2 i_2 + p L_2 i_2 = (R_2 + p L_2) i_2 \qquad (12\text{-}9b)$$
$$i(t) = i_1 + i_2 \qquad (12\text{-}9c)$$

[1] In many books the symbol D is used.

[2] An algebraic manipulation which does not always apply to the symbol p is commutation in multiplication. For example, $5pt = 5$, but $tp5 = 0$.

In accordance with the rules of the operational method Eqs. (12-9a) and (12-9b) can be treated as algebraic equations. Therefore

$$i_1 = \frac{v(t)}{R_1 + pL_1} \quad \text{and} \quad i_2 = \frac{v(t)}{R_2 + pL_2} \quad (12\text{-}10a)$$

Substituting from Eqs. (12-10a) in Eq. (12-9c), we have

$$\frac{v(t)}{R_1 + pL_1} + \frac{v(t)}{R_2 + pL_2} = i(t) \quad (12\text{-}10b)$$

Multiplying both sides of Eq. (12-10b) by $(R_1 + pL_1)(R_2 + pL_2)$, we have

$$(L_1 + L_2)pv(t) + (R_1 + R_2)v(t) = L_1L_2p^2i(t) + (R_1L_2 + R_2L_1)pi(t) \\ + R_1R_2i(t) \quad (12\text{-}10c)$$

With reference to Eqs. (12-6) it is seen that Eq. (12-10c) is the operational form of Eq. (12-7), arrived at through substitution. The above example was discussed to demonstrate the advantages and the simplicity of the operational method. It is not presented as a proof of the validity of the method. In general (by the use of the method of Laplace transformation) it can be shown that the result obtained by the operational method is always the same as that obtained by the method of substitution.

It is noted that *operational notation does not solve* the differential equations. *It is used to reduce a set of simultaneous differential equations to one equation containing a single dependent variable.*

12-3. Operational Immittance[1] for Single Elements. In the previous article the operational method was considered from a mathematical point of view, with the aim of reducing a set of simultaneous differential equations to an equation in terms of one dependent variable. In this article we introduce the network concept of "operational immittance," associated with the circuit elements. The introduction of this concept leads to the following important results:

1. With the aid of operational procedures and the introduction of the concept of immittance certain basic network principles can be conveniently studied in their general form.

2. The component of the response due to sources with exponential waveform can be obtained by inspection of the equilibrium equation of the network in operational form. Since the sinusoidal functions are a special form of exponential functions (see Chap. 8), the operational method provides a very simple method for finding the response to such sources.

[1] Immittance is a generic word synthesized from the words *im*pedance and ad*mittance*.

To introduce the concept of immittance, we start with a study of the voltage-current relations of the circuit elements R, L, and C. These elements were defined by equations:

$$v_{ab} = R_{ab}i_{ab} \qquad \text{or } i_{ab} = G_{ab}v_{ab} \qquad G_{ab} = \frac{1}{R_{ab}} \qquad (12\text{-}11a)$$

$$v_{ab} = L_{ab}\frac{d}{dt}\,i_{ab} \qquad \text{or } i_{ab} = \frac{1}{L_{ab}}\int_0^t v_{ab}\,d\tau + i_{ab}(0) \qquad (12\text{-}11b)$$

$$v_{ab} = \frac{1}{C_{ab}}\int_0^t i_{ab}\,d\tau + v_{ab}(0) \qquad \text{or } i_{ab} = C_{ab}\frac{d}{dt}\,v_{ab} \qquad (12\text{-}11c)$$

In Chap. 11 it was shown that the initial conditions $i(0)$ for the inductance and $v(0)$ for the capacitance can be "replaced" by ideal sources which we have called "initial-condition generators." In this chapter we assume that all these initial conditions (i.e., all continuity conditions) are replaced by initial-condition generators and that therefore the initial values $i_{ab}(0^+)$ [in Eq. (12-11b)] and $v_{ab}(0^+)$ [in Eq. (12-11c)] can be taken as zero. We remark that the result of this assumption does not imply that initial-condition generators must be used in the solution of problems.

Returning to Eqs. (12-11), we observe that one dependent variable (voltage or current) is obtained by performing a mathematical operation on the other dependent variable (current or voltage). In the case of resistance this operation is multiplication. In the case of a capacitance C_{ab} the current i_{ab} is obtained by performing the operation of differentiation with respect to time on v_{ab} and multiplying the result by the number C_{ab}. Thus for a capacitance C_{ab} the current i_{ab} is given by performing the operation $C_{ab}(d/dt)$ on the voltage v_{ab}. The symbol d/dt has meaning only if it is followed by the function which is to be differentiated. It was with this understanding that in Art. 12-2 the differential coefficient d/dt was replaced by the operator p.

The voltage v_{ab} across a capacitance C_{ab} is found by performing the operation of integration on i_{ab} and multiplying the result by $1/C_{ab}$. Symbolically we may define an integral operator by using for example the symbol $\left[\int_0^t d\tau\right]$. This symbol means that the integrand is the function which is written immediately after the symbol. Thus for a capacitance C_{ab} the voltage is given as $v_{ab} = 1/C_{ab}\left[\int_0^t d\tau\right]i_{ab}$.

By analogy with the choice of the symbol p for d/dt we choose the symbol $1/p$ for the operator $\int_0^t d\tau$ such that by definition

$$\frac{1}{p} \equiv \int_0^t d\tau \qquad (12\text{-}12a)$$

With the above definition of the operator $1/p$ it is seen that

$$\frac{d}{dt}\left[\int_0^t f(\tau)\, d\tau\right] = f(t) \equiv p\left[\frac{1}{p} f(t)\right]$$

Therefore $p(1/p) \equiv 1$. Similarly

$$\int_0^t \left[\frac{d}{d\tau} f(\tau)\right] d\tau = f(t) - f(0) \qquad (12\text{-}12b)$$

We have already assumed that in networks all initial (continuity) conditions either are zero or are replaced by initial-condition generators. Therefore, if $f(t)$ represents a network variable, we may consider $f(0) \equiv 0$ and Eq. (12-12b) can be written as

$$\int_0^t \left[\frac{d}{d\tau} f(\tau)\right] d\tau = f(t) \equiv \frac{1}{p}\, pf(t) \qquad (12\text{-}12c)$$

We conclude that, with the assumption of zero initial conditions,

$$\frac{1}{p}\, p \equiv 1 \equiv p\,\frac{1}{p} \qquad (12\text{-}12d)$$

We have seen that if a current source is applied to an element the voltage across that element is considered to be its response. Similarly, if the source is a voltage source, the current through the element is its response.

Element Immittance	Resistance R	Inductance L	Capacitance C
Impedance	$R=1/G$	pL	$1/pC$
Admittance	$G=1/R$	$1/pL$	pC

Fig. 12-2. Operational immittance functions of the elements.

In each case the response function is obtained from the source function through a certain operation which is characteristic of the element and independent of the source function. We call the operator which operates on the source function to produce the element's response function the operational immittance (or, for brevity, immittance) of that element. When the source is a current source, then the response of the element is voltage and its immittance is referred to as an *operational impedance*. For example, the operational impedance of an inductance L_{ab} is $L_{ab}p$ because $L_{ab}p$ operates on i_{ab} to give $L_{ab}pi_{ab} \equiv L_{ab}(di_{ab}/dt) = v_{ab}$.

When the source is a voltage source, then the response of the element is a current and its immittance is referred to as an *operational admittance*. The admittance of an inductance is $1/L_{ab}p$. Note that the operator $1/p$

represents the integral with the limits 0 to t. Hence the response function $i = (1/pL_{ab})v_{ab}$ does not include $i(0)$. If it is assumed that v_{ab} is applied at $t = 0$, then $i = (1/pL_{ab})v_{ab}$ is the component of the response due to the source v_{ab}.

The operational immittance for three basic elements is shown in the tabulation of Fig. 12-2. It is noted that the admittance of an element is the reciprocal of its impedance.

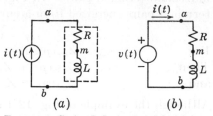

Fig. 12-3. Series R-L circuit with (a) current source, (b) voltage source.

12-4. Driving-point Impedance of Series Connection of Elements.

Consider the series R-L circuit shown in Fig. 12-3a, energized from a current source. The equilibrium equation of this circuit is

$$v_{ab} = Ri + L\frac{di}{dt} = Ri + pLi \qquad (12\text{-}13a)$$

where v_{ab} is the response and $i(t)$ is the source. The above equation can be written in the form

$$v_{ab} = (R + pL)i \qquad (12\text{-}13b)$$

We are already familiar with the differential and integral operators p and $1/p$. In Eq. (12-13b) we have a new operator $R + pL$ which operates on the source function $i(t)$ to produce the response v_{ab}. Upon extending the definition of operational immittance (defined for a single element) to apply to terminal pairs the operator $R + pL$ becomes the operational impedance of the terminal pair a-b since it operates on a current source applied to the terminal pair a-b to give the response v_{ab}. The expression $R + pL$ can be considered to be a function of p. With the symbolism for algebraic functions the operational impedances are denoted by the symbol $Z(p)$ with appropriate subscripts and are referred to as *impedance functions*. The impedance $R + pL$ relates the source and the response of the terminal pair at its *driving points* (i.e., terminals connected to source). For this reason it is called a *driving-point* impedance. Thus the driving-point impedance function of the terminal pair of Fig. 12-3 is $Z_{ab}(p) = R + pL$ and $v_{ab} = Z_{ab}(p)i(t)$. The operator $Z_{ab}(p) = R + pL$ is a symbolic form of the statement: To obtain the response v_{ab} in Fig. 12-3, multiply the source function $i(t)$ by R, and add the result to L times the first derivative of $i(t)$.

We note that the driving-point impedance of the terminal pair a-b consisting of a series connection of elements R and pL is the sum of the impedances of these two elements. This statement can be generalized by saying that the driving-point impedance of a series connection of a number of terminal pairs is equal to the sum of the impedances of the individual terminal pairs. In Fig. 12-4 a series connection of two single terminal pairs energized from a current source is shown. In this circuit

$$v_{ab} = v_{am} + v_{mb}$$

But $$v_{am} = Z_{am}(p)i(t) \qquad v_{mb} = Z_{mb}(p)i(t)$$

Then $$v_{ab} = [Z_{am}(p) + Z_{mb}(p)]\,i(t) = Z_{ab}(p)i(t)$$

and $$Z_{ab}(p) = Z_{am}(p) + Z_{mb}(p)$$

Although the example of Fig. 12-4 is for two terminal pairs connected in series, it is clear that each of these may consist of two or more terminal pairs connected in series.

12-5. Driving-point Admittance of Parallel Connection of Elements. The symbol used for the driving-point admittances is $Y(p)$. In Fig.

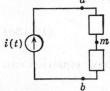

12-5a two elements are connected in parallel and are energized from a voltage source. Application of Kirchhoff's current law results in

$$i = i_1 + i_2 = Gv(t) + Cpv(t)$$
$$= (G + Cp)v(t) = Y_{ab}(p)v(t)$$

In the above equation $Y_{ab}(p) = G + Cp$ is an operator which operates on the source $v(t)$ to give the response i at the terminals of the source. Therefore $G + Cp$ is the driving-point admittance of the parallel combination of elements G and C. It is left to the reader to show that in Fig. 12-5b the admittance $Y_{ab}(p)$ is the sum of the two admittances $Y_1(p)$ and $Y_2(p)$.

FIG. 12-4. Series connection of driving-point immittances.

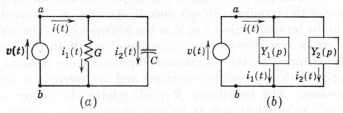

FIG. 12-5. Parallel circuits.

12-6. Relationship between Driving-point Admittance and Impedance of a Terminal Pair. Consider the circuit of Fig. 12-3b, and compare it with the circuit of Fig. 12-3a. In Art. 12-4 we found that, for the series connection of R and L, the driving-point impedance is $Z_{ab} = R + pL$. The fact that we are discussing a driving-point impedance function assumes that the source is a current source as in Fig. 12-3a. In Fig. 12-3b the source is a voltage source and the equilibrium equation is $Ri + L(di/dt) = v(t)$, or

$$(R + pL)i(t) = v(t) \tag{12-14}$$

In this equation the source function $v(t)$ is specified, and the response $i(t)$ is to be found. Hence in Eq. (12-14) the operator which operates on the source function $v(t)$ to produce the response $i(t)$ is not explicitly specified. From the discussion of Art. 12-4 we know that the driving-point impedance of the series connection of R and L elements is $R + pL$. From the discussion of the immittance function of single elements we know that the impedance and admittance of single elements are "reciprocals" of each other. With these ideas in mind we may rewrite the differential equation (12-14) in the form

$$i(t) = \frac{1}{R + pL} v(t) \tag{12-15}$$

Now the operator $1/(R + pL)$ operates on the source $v(t)$ to give the response $i(t)$. Therefore this operator is the admittance function of the terminal pair a-b,

$$Y_{ab}(p) = \frac{1}{R + pL} = \frac{1}{Z_{ab}(p)} \tag{12-15a}$$

By "dividing" both sides of Eq. (12-14) by $R + pL$ we arrive at the conclusion that the driving-point admittance of a series connection of elements is identical with the reciprocal of the driving-point impedance of that series connection.

Although this conclusion is permissible, the form of equation

$$i(t) = \frac{1}{R + pL} v(t)$$

requires interpretation. For the single-element inductance the admittance function was $1/pL$, and the equation $i(t) = (1/pL)v(t)$ was interpreted to mean $i(t) = 1/L \int_0^t v \, d\tau$. We cannot find a simple analogous interpretation for $i(t) = [1/(R + pL)]v(t)$. However, $i(t) = (1/pL)v(t)$ can also be interpreted to mean $pLi(t) = v(t)$ or $v(t) = L(di/dt)$. The analogous interpretation of $i(t) = [1/(R + pL)]v(t)$ is $(R + pL)i(t) = v(t)$, which is the original equilibrium equation of Fig. 12-3b. Thus the operation of division by $R + pL$ which took us from the equilibrium equation (12-14) to Eq. (12-15) must be interpreted in the light of the above discussion.

Prior to the introduction of the concept of immittance functions we introduced the operational method as a means of reduction of a set of simultaneous differential equations to an equilibrium equation relating a single response to the source. Applying the operational procedure to the example of Fig. 12-1, we eliminated i_1 [Eq. (12-10a)] by equating it to $[1/(R_1 + p_1L)]v(t)$. We now recognize $1/(R_1 + p_1L)$ as the operational admittance function of the series connection of R_1 and L_1. The similarity between the above expression $i_1 = [1/(R_1 + p_1L)]v(t)$ and $i = (1/R)v(t)$ for a resistance clarifies the motivation of the concept of immittance functions.

We recall that in a resistive network all the equilibrium equations are algebraic. The introduction of the concept of operational immittance functions enables us to manipulate equilibrium equations of any network as if it were a resistive network. It must be remembered that, regardless of the procedure used, the response of a network containing R, L, and C elements is finally obtained by solving a differential equation. For a given source $v(t)$ and a response expressed as $i = 1/(R + pL)v(t)$ we still have to solve the differential equation $Ri + pLi = v(t)$ to obtain the response.

12-7. Operational Elements. Frequently we symbolize driving-point immittances by the symbol of a terminal pair as shown in Fig. 12-6a. The

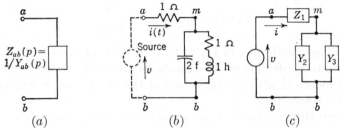

$$Z_{ab}(p) = 1/Y_{ab}(p)$$

(a) (b) (c)

FIG. 12-6. Terminal-pair networks. (a) A single terminal pair. (b, c) Series-parallel circuits.

combination of passive elements indicated by this symbol is referred to as a *passive terminal-pair network*. When operational notation is used to analyze a network, we shall also use the term *operational element* or *p element* to describe a passive terminal-pair network. Since operational driving-point impedances (admittances) in series (parallel) add, we can consider a p element as a "building block" of a network, exactly as the elements R-L-C are the building blocks of a p element. The following examples illustrate this concept.

Example 12-1. Calculate the driving-point immittance for the network of Fig. 12-6b, and interpret the result.

Solution. To calculate the driving-point immittance, we consider a source connected to terminals a-b as indicated in Fig. 12-6b and deduce the relationship between v and i.

The network between terminals a-b can be shown as a connection of p elements, as in Fig. 12-6c. Between terminals m-b we have a parallel connection of $Y_2 = 2p$ and $Y_3 = 1/(1 + p)$ such that

$$Y_{mb}(p) = 2p + \frac{1}{1 + p} = \frac{2p^2 + 2p + 1}{1 + p}$$

Hence $Z_{mb} = \dfrac{1+p}{2p^2 + 2p + 1}$

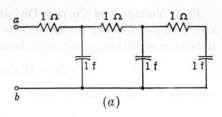

(a)

But $Z_{ab}(p) = Z_{am}(p) + Z_{mb}(p)$

$$= 1 + \frac{1+p}{2p^2 + 2p + 1} = \frac{2p^2 + 3p + 2}{2p^2 + 2p + 1}$$

$$(12\text{-}16a)$$

This result is interpreted to mean

$$(2p^2 + 2p + 1)v(t) = (2p^2 + 3p + 2)i(t)$$

It is noted that even though we manipulate the p-element network as if it were a resistive network the final result is a differential equation.

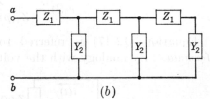

(b)

Example 12-2. Calculate $Z_{ab}(p)$ for the circuit of Fig. 12-7a.

Solution. The circuit can be drawn as in Fig. 12-7b, where $Z_1(p) = 1$ and $Y_2(p) = p$. In Fig. 12-7c we have redrawn the circuit as the series combination of $Z_1(p)$ and an impedance $Z_3(p)$. Hence

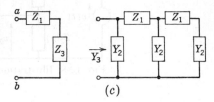

(c)

$$Z_{ab}(p) = Z_1(p) + Z_3(p) = Z_1(p) + \frac{1}{Y_3(p)}$$

Inspection of Fig. 12-7d reveals that the p element $Y_3(p)$ can be regarded as the parallel combination of Y_2 and Y_4, where Y_4 is defined in Fig. 12-7d. Hence

$$Y_3(p) = Y_2(p) + Y_4(p) = Y_2(p) + \frac{1}{Z_4(p)}$$

and $Z_{ab}(p) = Z_1(p) + \dfrac{1}{Y_2(p) + 1/Z_4(p)}$

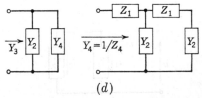

(d)

The process is continued[1] until the last element is reached. Then

FIG. 12-7. A ladder-type network and its representation as a combination of p elements.

$$Z_{ab}(p) = Z_1(p) + \cfrac{1}{Y_2(p) + \cfrac{1}{Z_1(p) + \cfrac{1}{Y_2(p) + \cfrac{1}{Z_1(p) + \cfrac{1}{Y_2(p)}}}}}$$

After some algebra

$$Z_{ab}(p) = \frac{Z_1{}^3 Y_2{}^3 + 5 Z_1{}^2 Y_2{}^2 + 6 Z_1 Y_2 + 1}{Y_2(Z_1{}^2 Y_2{}^2 + 4 Z_1 Y_2 + 3)}$$

or, using the particular functions for $Z_1(p)$ and $Y_2(p)$ given in Fig. 12-7a,

$$Z_{ab}(p) = \frac{p^3 + 5p^2 + 6p + 1}{p(p^2 + 4p + 3)} \tag{12-16b}$$

[1] This form of presentation of a driving-point immittance function is called a "Stieltjes-continued-fraction" presentation and is used as a means for synthesizing driving-point network functions.

12-8. Voltage and Current Division.   Consider a source impressed on two series-connected p elements as shown in Fig. 12-8.   Applying the definition of driving-point impedance,

$$v(t) = [Z_1(p) + Z_2(p)]i(t)$$

Since $v_2(t) = Z_2(p)i(t)$, we have

$$v_2(t) = \frac{Z_2(p)}{Z_1(p) + Z_2(p)} \, v(t) \qquad (12\text{-}17)$$

Equation (12-17) is referred to as the *operational voltage-division formula.*   By analogy with the voltage-division formula associated with

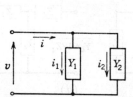

FIG. 12-8. Illustration of voltage division.

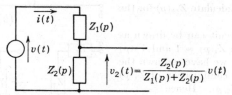

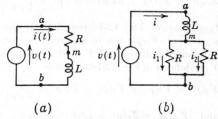

(a)   (b)

FIG. 12-9. Illustration of current division, $i_2(t) = \{Y_2(p)/[Y_1(p) + Y_2(p)]\}i(t)$.

FIG. 12-10. Circuits used to illustrate transfer functions.

series connection of similar elements (see Chap. 6) we may consider the p elements of Fig. 12-8 to be "similar" elements and may state that the voltage across a series connection of p elements "divides" proportionally to the impedance functions.   However, it must be remembered that the "division" in this case has the meaning assigned to it in Art. 12-6 and that Eq. (12-17) must be interpreted as the differential equation

$$[Z_1(p) + Z_2(p)]v_2(t) = Z_2(p)v(t)$$

Consider the parallel connection of two operational admittances shown in Fig. 12-9.   Since

$$i(t) = [Y_1(p) + Y_2(p)]v(t)$$

and

$$i_2(t) = Y_2(p)v(t)$$

we have

$$i_2(t) = \frac{Y_2(p)}{Y_1(p) + Y_2(p)} \, i(t) \qquad (12\text{-}18)$$

In words, at a junction of several admittances the current "divides" proportionally to the admittances. This result is called the *operational current-division formula.*

The voltage- and current-division formulas can be extended to any number of series or parallel p elements, respectively.

12-9. Introduction to Network Functions. So far we have been concerned with the voltage-current equation at a pair of terminals, i.e., the driving points of the p elements. Applying the voltage-division formula to the series connection of R and L elements shown in Fig. 12-10a, we have

$$v_{mb} = \frac{pL}{R + pL} \, v(t) \tag{12-19}$$

By definition a driving-point immittance function relates voltage with current at the *same* pair of terminals. In Eq. (12-19) the operator $pL/(R + pL)$ operates on the source function $v(t)$ applied at terminals a-b to produce the response v_{mb} at *another* pair of terminals, i.e., terminals m-b. Thus this operator is not a driving-point immittance function. In Fig. 12-10b application of voltage- and current-division formulas results in

$$i_2(t) = \frac{\frac{1}{2}}{R/2 + pL} \, v(t) = \frac{1}{R + 2pL} \, v(t) \tag{12-20}$$

In this equation the operator $1/(R + 2pL)$ operates on the source $v(t)$ applied at terminals a-b to result in the response $i_2(t)$ associated with terminals m-b. This operator, too, cannot be classified as a driving-point immittance function. Furthermore it differs from the operator $pL/(R + pL)$ inasmuch as the latter relates a *voltage* response to a *voltage* source at different pairs of terminals, whereas $1/(R + 2pL)$ relates a *current* response to a *voltage* source at different pairs of terminals. Nonetheless the above two operators, as well as driving-point immittance functions, have one common property: they relate a response function to a source function. Operators which relate the source and response functions of a network are important in the analysis and synthesis of networks. *In general, in a network containing a single source, that operator which relates a response of the network to the source is called an operational network function.* The need for limitation of the network to a single source will become apparent in Chap. 16. This is not a serious limitation, since, if the network contains more than one source, through the superposition theorem we can consider one source at a time and add their corresponding responses.

In the definition of network functions we did not specify the nature of the response which is related to the source by the network function. From the examples at the beginning of this article it should be clear that we require different terms to describe different types of network functions. These are defined below.

An *operational immittance function* is a network function which relates a voltage response to a current source or a current response to a voltage source. In the example of Fig. 12-10b the operator $1/(R + 2pL)$ relates response i_2 to the source $v(t)$ and is an immittance function. In Fig. 12-10a the operator $1/(R + pL)$, which relates the response i to the source $v(t)$, is also an operational immittance function.

A *driving-point (operational) immittance function* is an immittance function which relates voltages and currents at the same pair of terminals, i.e., at the terminals of the source. In the example of Fig. 12-10a $1/(R + pL)$ is a driving-point immittance. Notice that in Fig. 12-10b the operator $1/(R + 2pL)$, which relates i_2 to $v(t)$, is an immittance function but not a driving-point immittance, since $i_2(t)$ is not the current at the terminals of the source.

A *transfer function* is a network function which relates the response at a given pair of terminals to a source applied at another pair of terminals. In the example of Fig. 12-10b the response i_2 associated with the terminals m-b is related to the source at the terminals a-b by the network function $1/(R + 2pL)$. Therefore this network function (which was not a driving-point immittance) is a transfer function. Similarly in Fig. 12-10a the response v_{mb} is related to the source $v_{ab}(t)$ by the network function $pL/(R + pL)$. Therefore this network function is a transfer function.

A *gain function* is a transfer function which relates a voltage response to a voltage source or a current response to a current source. In the example of Fig. 12-10a the transfer function $pL/(R + pL)$ relating v_{mb} to the source $v_{ab}(t)$ is a voltage gain function.

Impedance and Admittance. An immittance function can be a driving point or a transfer function. If an immittance function (driving point or transfer) relates a voltage response to a current source, it is called an operational impedance function (driving point or transfer) and is denoted by the symbol $Z(p)$ for driving-point impedance and $z(p)$ for transfer impedance. If the source is a voltage source, then the immittance function is called an admittance and is denoted by $Y(p)$ for driving point or $y(p)$ for transfer admittance function.

The above definitions are summarized in the tabulation of Fig. 12-11.

12-10. General Form of Network Functions. We have illustrated the general relationship[1]

$$\sum_{m=0}^{M} a_m p^m y(t) = \sum_{n=0}^{N} b_n p^n \phi(t) \qquad (12\text{-}21)$$

[1] In the preceding articles we have shown that this relationship applies for series-parallel circuits. A general proof is given in Art. 16-15.

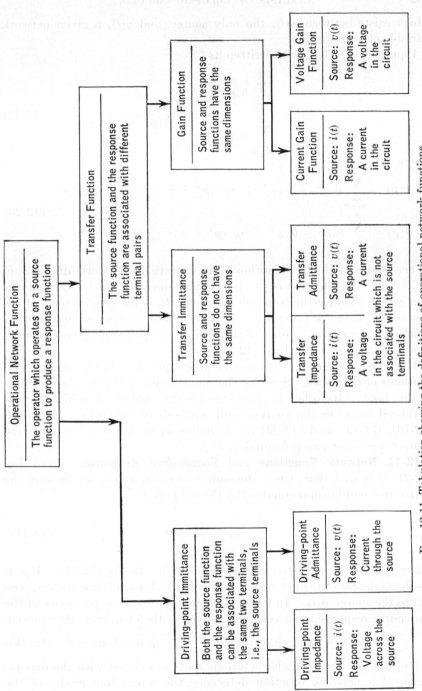

Fig. 12-11. Tabulation showing the definitions of operational network functions.

which exists between $\phi(t)$, the only source, and $y(t)$, a given network variable of a network.

Equation (12-21) can be written as

$$y(t) = \frac{\displaystyle\sum_{n=0}^{N} b_n p^n}{\displaystyle\sum_{m=0}^{M} a_m p^m} \, \phi(t) = \frac{B(p)}{A(p)} \, \phi(t) \tag{12-22}$$

where

$$\begin{aligned} A(p) &= \sum_{m=0}^{M} a_m p^m = a_M p^M + a_{M-1} p^{M-1} + \cdots + a_1 p + a_0 \\ B(p) &= \sum_{n=0}^{N} b_n p^n = b_N p^N + b_{N-1} p^{N-1} + \cdots + b_1 p + b_0 \end{aligned} \tag{12-23}$$

In accordance with the definition of the operational network functions, in Eq. (12-22) the operator $B(p)/A(p)$, which operates on the source function $\phi(t)$ to produce the response function $y(t)$, is the general form of the operational network functions. It is seen that an operational network function is always in the form of the ratio of two polynomials in p, such as $B(p)$ and $A(p)$ given in Eqs. (12-23).

The above statement is of fundamental importance in the analysis and synthesis of networks. Some of the implications of this fact are studied in this book. Its other implications are the subject of study of more advanced topics in the analysis and synthesis of networks. Equations (12-16), (12-19), and (12-20) are examples of network functions in the form of a ratio of two polynomials in p.

12-11. Network Functions and Source-free Response. From Eq. (12-21) it is seen that, when the source function $\phi(t)$ is set to zero, the source-free equilibrium equation of the network is

$$\sum_{m=0}^{M} a_m p^m y_f(t) = 0 \tag{12-24a}$$

where $y_f(t)$ is the source-free component of $y(t)$. In Eq. (12-24a), $A(p)$ is the denominator of the network function $B(p)/A(p)$, relating the response $y(t)$ to the source $\phi(t)$. In Chap. 11 it was shown that the modes of the source-free response are given by the roots of the characteristic equation

$$A(s) = a_M s^M + a_{M-1} s^{M-1} + \cdots + a_1 s + a_0 = 0 \tag{12-24b}$$

We conclude that the characteristic roots associated with the denominator of a network function determine the source-free modes of the response of the network. This is a very important property of network functions and will be dealt with in more detail in Chap. 13. The following examples illustrate the application of this result.

Example 12-3. In Fig. 12-12a the network of Fig. 12-7a is shown energized from a voltage source $v(t)$. Find the source-free component of the response $i(t)$.

Solution. The network function which relates the response $i(t)$ to the source $v(t)$ is the driving-point admittance function $Y_{ab}(p)$. From Eq. (12-16b) this function is found to be

$$Y_{ab}(p) = \frac{p(p^2 + 4p + 3)}{p^3 + 5p^2 + 6p + 1}$$

Therefore the source-free modes of the response i will be given by the roots of the characteristic equation

$$s^3 + 5s^2 + 6s + 1 \approx (s + 0.2)(s + 1.62)(s + 3.18) = 0$$
$$s_1 \approx -0.2 \qquad s_2 \approx -1.62 \qquad s_3 \approx -3.18$$
$$i_f = A_1 e^{-0.2t} + A_2 e^{-1.62t} + A_3 e^{-3.18t} \tag{12-25}$$

The roots of the above cubic equation were obtained by an approximation.

The source-free network of Fig. 12-12a, obtained by setting the voltage source $v(t)$ to zero, is shown in Fig. 12-12b. Equation (12-25) gives the time function for i (Fig. 12-12b).

Example 12-4. In Fig. 12-12c a current source is applied to the terminals a-b. Find the source-free component of the response $v_{ab}(t)$.

Solution. The network function which relates the response $v_{ab}(t)$ to the source $i(t)$ is $Z_{ab}(p)$. In Eq. (12-16b) this was found to be

$$Z_{ab}(p) = \frac{p^3 + 5p^2 + 6p + 1}{p(p^2 + 4p + 3)}$$

The characteristic equation associated with the denominator of this network function is

$$s(s^2 + 4s + 3) = s(s + 1)(s + 3) = 0$$
$$s_1 = 0 \qquad s_2 = -1 \qquad s_3 = -3$$
$$(v_{ab})_f = B_1 + B_2 e^{-t} + B_3 e^{-3t}$$

Figure 12-12d shows the source-free network of Fig. 12-12c when the source $i(t)$ is set to zero. It is noted that this network is different from the source-free network arrived at when the source was a voltage source. In Fig. 12-12d, $(v_{ab})_f$ and $(v_{mb})_f$ are identical.

The modes of the response of Fig. 12-12b, that is, $i(t)_f$, differ from the modes

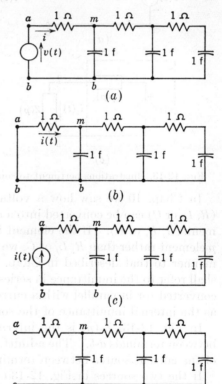

FIG. 12-12. (a) Network with voltage source. (b) The source-free network corresponding to (a). (c) Network with current source. (d) The source-free network corresponding to (c).

of $v_{ab}(t)_f$ in Fig. 12-12d. This is due to the fact that setting the current source $i(t)$ to zero in Fig. 12-12c leaves the terminals a-b open and R_{am} does not affect the source-free modes. The mode corresponding to $s_1 = 0$ is the constant B_1. From Fig. 12-12d it is seen that a constant voltage can exist across C_{mb} and the other two capacitances of the network when the modes e^{-t} and e^{-3t} have died out.

12-12. Conversion of Sources with p-element Internal Immittances.

So far we have seen how the use of operational notation simplifies the formulation of the differential equations which relate source and response functions in series-parallel circuits. We will now use the idea of a terminal pair network represented by a driving point immittance to deduce some useful network theorems.

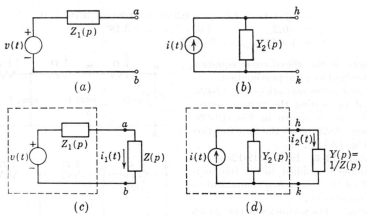

FIG. 12-13. Illustrations pertinent to source conversion with internal p elements.

In Chap. 10 we saw how a voltage source in series with an element (R, L, or C) can be converted into a current source in parallel with an element (R, L, or C). If the element in series with the voltage source is a p element rather than R, L, or C, we can make the conversion in a similar manner to that described in Chap. 10. In the following discussion we shall refer to the immittance in series with a voltage source which is being converted (or in parallel with a current source which is being converted) as the internal immittance of the source.

In Fig. 12-13, $Z_1(p)$ is the internal impedance of the voltage source between terminals a-b. The admittance $Y_2(p)$ is the internal admittance of the current source between terminals h-k.

If the two sources in Fig. 12-13a and b are to be equivalent between their respective terminals a-b and h-k, then if we connect a p element given by $Z(p) = 1/Y(p)$ at either of these terminals the current through this p element must be identical in both cases. In Fig. 12-13c

$$i_1(t) = \frac{1}{Z(p) + Z_1(p)} v(t) \tag{12-26}$$

From Fig. 12-13d

$$i_2(t) = \frac{Y(p)}{Y(p) + Y_2(p)} i(t) \qquad (12\text{-}27)$$

Assuming that the two practical sources are equivalent at their terminals [i.e., that they deliver the same current to the same load immittance $Z(p) = 1/Y(p)$], we set $i_1 = i_2$,

$$\frac{1}{Z(p) + Z_1(p)} v(t) = \frac{Y(p)}{Y(p) + Y_2(p)} i(t) \qquad (12\text{-}28)$$

or

$$i(t) = \frac{Y(p) + Y_2(p)}{Z(p)Y(p) + Z_1(p)Y(p)} v(t) \qquad (12\text{-}29)$$

Since $Z(p)Y(p) = 1 = Z_1(p)Y_1(p)$, we have

$$i(t) = \frac{Y(p) + Y_2(p)}{Z_1(p)[Y(p) + Y_1(p)]} v(t) \qquad (12\text{-}30)$$

The expression (12-30) is the condition for equivalence. However, the two sources must be equivalent *independent* of the load admittance $Y(p)$. This condition can be fulfilled only if $Y_2(p) = Y_1(p)$. Then

$$i(t) = \frac{1}{Z_1(p)} v(t) \quad \text{or} \quad i(t) = Y_1(p)v(t) \quad \text{or} \quad v(t) = Z_1(p)i(t) \qquad (12\text{-}31)$$

Equations (12-31) can then be used to convert a voltage source with a series p-element immittance to a current source with a parallel p-element immittance, and vice versa. It is emphasized that, exactly as in the case of source conversion with single internal elements, the two sources are equivalent only at their "accessible" terminals.

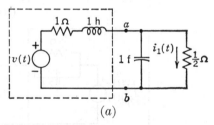

(a)

Example 12-5. Convert the voltage-source-series-impedance combination of Fig. 12-14a to the left of terminals a-b to a current source. Use the result to obtain the transfer impedance which relates $i_1(t)$ to $v(t)$.

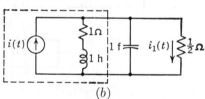

(b)

Fig. 12-14. Circuits for Example 12-5.

Solution. The converted source is shown in Fig. 12-14b. In this circuit $i(t) = [1/(1 + p)]v(t)$. Using the current-division formula,

$$i_1(t) = \frac{2}{(2 + p) + 1/(1 + p)} i(t) \qquad (12\text{-}32)$$

or

$$i_1(t) = \frac{2}{(2 + p) + 1/(1 + p)} \frac{1}{1 + p} v(t) \qquad (12\text{-}33)$$

Hence

$$i_1(t) = \frac{2}{p^2 + 3p + 3} v(t) \qquad (12\text{-}34)$$

Example 12-6. In the circuit of Fig. 12-15a use source conversion to relate $v_{mb}(t)$ to the two source functions $i_1(t)$ and $v_2(t)$.

Solution. The current source to the left of terminals a-b is converted to a voltage source as shown in Fig. 12-15b. Upon adding the two ideal sources in Fig. 12-15b the circuit of Fig. 12-15c is obtained. Using voltage division,

$$v_{mb}(t) = \frac{Z(p)}{Z(p) + 2 + p + 1/(2 + 2p)} \left[\frac{1}{2 + 2p} i_1(t) + v_2(t) \right]$$

or $v_{mb}(t) = \dfrac{Z(p)}{2p^2 + 6p + 5 + Z(p)(2 + 2p)} i_1(t) +$

$$\frac{(2 + 2p)Z(p)}{(2 + 2p)Z(p) + 2p^2 + 6p + 5} v_2(t) \quad (12\text{-}35)$$

This form of the solution could also have been obtained by applying the principle of superposition directly. Note that in Eq. (12-35) the response v_{mb} is related to the source $i_1(t)$ by one transfer function and to the source $v_2(t)$ by a different transfer function.

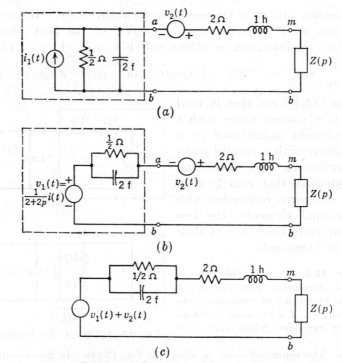

FIG. 12-15. Circuits for Example 12-6.

Initial Conditions. In discussing the conversion of sources we have not discussed the initial energy which may be stored in the source immittance. If this initial energy is represented by equivalent ideal sources (initial-condition generators), then the source conversion is carried out with several sources (some of them being initial condition generators) as in Example 12-6. It is, however, not necessary to consider the initial-condition generators explicitly, provided that we use the correct initial conditions at the terminals of the source.

Thus, using source conversion, we obtain the differential equation which relates an impressed source to the response. The differential equation is independent of the initial conditions and can be solved completely if the initial value of the response function and a sufficient number of its initial derivatives (derived initial conditions) are known. These derived initial conditions are obtained from the circuit before source conversion. The following example illustrates this point.

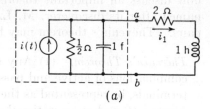

(a)

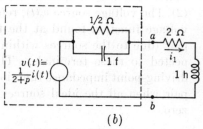

(b)

Fig. 12-16. Circuits for Example 12-7.

Example 12-7. In the circuit of Fig. 12-16a use source conversion as indicated in Fig. 12-16b, and obtain the complete response for $i_1(t)$ if $i(t) = U(t)$, $v_{ab}(0^+) = 2$, $i_1(0^+) = 0$.

Solution. From Fig. 12-16b

$$i_1(t) = \frac{1}{\dfrac{1}{2+p} + 2 + p} \frac{1}{2+p} i(t)$$

Hence

$$(p^2 + 4p + 5)i_1(t) = U(t)$$

The component of the response due to the source is the d-c steady-state value $i_{1s} = \frac{1}{5}$. The characteristic equation is

$$s^2 + 4s + 5 = 0 \qquad s = -2 \pm \sqrt{4-5} = -2 \pm j$$

Hence the complete response is

$$i_1(t) = \tfrac{1}{5} + \mathrm{Re}\,[\mathbf{K}e^{(-2+j)t}]$$

Since $i_1(0^+)$ is known, we need $(di_1/dt)_{0^+}$. Referring to Fig. 12-16a, $v_{ab}(0^+) = 2 = 2i_1(0^+) + 1(di_1/dt)_{0^+}$ so that $(di_1/dt)_{0^+} = 2$. Hence the complex constant $\mathbf{K}$ can be determined from the equations

$$i_1(0^+) = \frac{1}{5} + \mathrm{Re}\,\mathbf{K} = 0 \qquad \left(\frac{di_1}{dt}\right)_{0^+} = \mathrm{Re}\,[(-2+j)\mathbf{K}] = 2$$

$$\mathbf{K} = -\frac{1}{5} - j\frac{8}{5} \qquad\qquad i_1 = 0.2 + 1.61e^{-2t}\cos{(t - 97.1°)} \quad (12\text{-}36)$$

12-13. Thévenin's Theorem. We have seen that many passive terminal pairs can be represented by an operational immittance function $Z(p)$ or $Y(p)$. In Chap. 16 we shall show that all terminal pairs can be represented by such an operator. Further, we have seen that any ideal voltage source in series with an operational element can be converted to a current source in parallel with that element, and vice versa. We shall now discuss an important theorem in circuit analysis. This theorem, named after its discoverer, M. L. Thévenin, deals with active terminal pairs. Thévenin's theorem may be stated in two parts as follows:

Thévenin's Theorem. (1) Any active terminal pair a-b composed of combinations of active and passive elements can, with respect to its terminals, be represented as the series connection of an ideal voltage source $v_o(t)$ and an operational element $Z_s(p)$ between terminals a-b. (2) The voltage source $v_o(t)$, referred to in (1) of the theorem, is the voltage function found at the terminals a-b of the active terminal pair (due to the sources within it), with no external elements connected to these terminals. The impedance function $Z_s(p)$ is the driving-point impedance function at the terminals a-b of the terminal pair when all the ideal sources within the terminal pair are set to zero.

In the above statement of Thévenin's theorem the voltage v_o is the full component of the response due to the internal sources (representing initial conditions by initial-condition generators). It also applies when the component of the response due to the internal sources is studied, for example in steady-state calculations. Most frequently the theorem is used for the latter purpose.

Thus Thévenin's theorem states that the active terminal pair shown in Fig. 12-17a can be represented with respect to terminals a-b as shown in Fig. 12-17b. The function $v_o(t)$ is given by $v_{ab}(t)$ in Fig. 12-17a, when no external elements are connected to the "box," which represents the active terminal pair. We refer to the series combination of Fig. 12-17b as "Thévenin's equivalent source."

Proof of Theorem. We shall not prove the first part of this theorem. We shall, however, show that for every network there is a function $v_o(t)$ and an impedance $Z_s(p)$ which satisfies the condition of equivalence with respect to the selected terminal pair.

Consider the active network shown in Fig. 12-17d, connected to the series combination of an ideal voltage source $v(t)$ and an impedance $Z_T(p)$. The current $i(t)$ which flows in the impedance Z_T can be calculated by superposition as follows:

$$i(t) = [i(t) \text{ due to } v(t)] + [i(t) \text{ due to sources within network}] \quad (12\text{-}37)$$

We shall now consider the waveform of source $v(t)$ as adjustable and adjust $v(t)$ until the total current $i(t) \equiv 0$. The special function $v(t)$ which makes $i(t) \equiv 0$ in Eq. (12-37) will be denoted by $v_1(t)$, as indicated

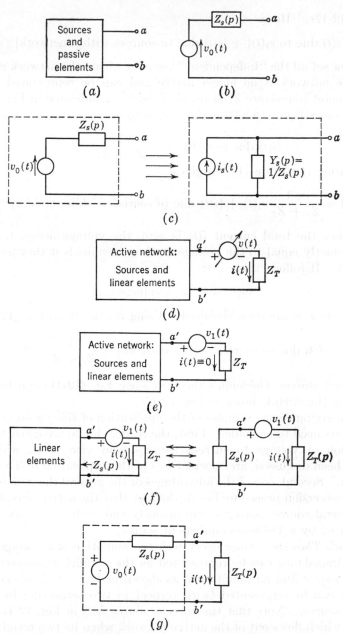

FIG. 12-17. Illustrations for Thévenin's theorem. (a) Active terminal-pair network. (b) Thévenin's equivalent. (c) Conversion to Norton's equivalent. (d) Active terminal pair with voltage source and terminating impedance. (e) The voltage source is adjusted to the special function $v_1(t)$, which gives the result $i(t) \equiv 0$. Under this condition $v_{a'b'}$ is the open-circuit voltage. (f) When the sources in the active terminal pair are set to zero, the terminal pair is represented by an immittance function. (g) Thévenin's equivalent circuit.

in Fig. 12-17e.   Hence

$$0 \equiv [i(t) \text{ due to } v_1(t)] + [i(t) \text{ due to sources within network}] \quad (12\text{-}38)$$

If we now set all the "independent"[1] sources within the network equal to zero, the network is no longer active and can be represented by the driving-point impedance Z_s at terminals $a'\text{-}b'$, as indicated in Fig. 12-17f. The current $i(t)$ due to $v_1(t)$ is then given by

$$[i(t) \text{ due to } v_1(t)] = -\frac{1}{Z_s + Z_T} v_1(t) \quad (12\text{-}39)$$

Substituting (12-39) in (12-38) gives

$$0 \equiv \frac{-1}{Z_s + Z_T} v_1(t) + [i(t) \text{ due to sources within network}] \quad (12\text{-}40)$$

Now, since the total current $i(t)$ is zero, the voltage across terminals $a'\text{-}b'$ is exactly equal to the voltage at those terminals if they are open-circuited.   It follows that

$$v_1(t) = v_o(t) = \text{voltage } v_{a'b'}$$

if terminals $a'\text{-}b'$ are open-circuited.   Using this result in Eq. (12-40),

$$[i(t) \text{ due to sources within network}] = \frac{1}{Z_s + Z_T} v_o(t) \quad (12\text{-}41)$$

This result proves Thévenin's theorem since Eq. (12-41) can be represented by the circuit shown in Fig. 12-17g.

Before giving some examples of the application of this theorem several statements need to be made.   First, the reader should recognize that the conversion of voltage to current sources, and vice versa, which has already been discussed, are special cases of the application of Thévenin's theorem.   Second, one of the advantages of the general theorem over the source-conversion procedure lies in the fact that the active network may have several sources acting simultaneously and such a network may be represented by a Thévenin equivalent source.

Norton's Theorem.   Since every series combination of a voltage source and an impedance can be represented as the parallel combination of a current source and an admittance as shown in Fig. 12-17c every active network can be represented (with respect to two terminals) by such a current source.   Note that the current source $i_s(t)$ in Fig. 12-17c is the current which flows out of the active network when its two terminals are shorted.   It is therefore possible to calculate this short-circuit current and obtain Norton's equivalent circuit *without* first obtaining Thévenin's voltage-source circuit.   We also note that the impedance Z_s is related to

---

[1] Independent sources are ideal sources.   Dependent sources are defined in Chap. 16.

the two circuits by the equation

$$Z_s(p)i_s(t) = v_o(t)$$

so that either Thévenin's or Norton's equivalent circuit can be obtained from a knowledge of the open circuit voltage and the short circuit current.

Output Impedance. In electronic circuits the term output impedance is used as a synonym for the internal impedance of Thévenin's equivalent circuit of a device such as an oscillator. Thus, if a device is represented as an active network between a pair of output terminals, then the output impedance of the device is the operator which operates on a current source applied to the "output" terminals to give the voltage at those terminals when all the *ideal* sources in the network are set to zero.

The following examples illustrate the application of Thévenin's and Norton's theorems.

Example 12-8. In Fig. 12-18a obtain Thévenin's equivalent circuit with respect to terminals *a-b*, and use the result to determine (*a*) the value of a resistance R to be connected between terminals *a-b* so that R receives maximum power from the active terminal pair; (*b*) the value of the maximum power delivered to R.

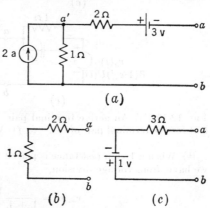

Solution. In the circuit of Fig. 12-18a $v_{a'b} = 2$ and $v_{aa'} = -3$; hence $v_{ab} = v_o = -1$ volt. If the sources are set to zero as in Fig. 12-18b, $Z_{ab} = R_{ab} = 3$ ohms. Hence Thévenin's equivalent circuit is the circuit shown in Fig. 12-18c. For maximum power transfer $R = 3$. The maximum power is $(\frac{1}{6})^2 \times 3 = \frac{3}{36} = 0.0833$ watt.

Example 12-9. (*a*) Replace the circuit of Fig. 12-19a by a Thévenin equivalent (the capacitance is initially uncharged). (*b*) Use the result of (*a*) to calculate the

FIG. 12-18. An active terminal pair and the development of Thévenin's equivalent circuit for this network.

complete response if a load is connected across terminals *a-b* and this load is (1) a 1-ohm resistance or (2) the series impedance $(1 + p)$ (initially deenergized).

Solution. (*a*) Applying Thévenin's theorem to the left of terminals *a'-b'* (see Fig. 12-19b), from Kirchhoff's current law we have

$$-\frac{v_{a'b'}}{2} + 6 + \frac{4 - v_{a'b'}}{2} = 0$$

or

$$v_{a'b'} = 8 \text{ volts}$$

and $Z_{a'b'} = 1$ ohm when the sources are set to zero. The complete response $v_{ab}(t)$ for Fig. 12-19c is found to be $v_{ab}(t) = 8(1 - e^{-t})$ for $t \geq 0^+$. Hence Thévenin's equivalent for the circuit of Fig. 12-19a is the circuit shown in Fig. 12-19d.

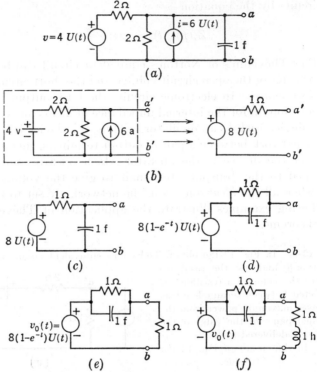

FIG. 12-19. (a) An active terminal pair. (b–d) Development of Thévenin's equivalent for the terminal pair of (a). (e, f) Applications of Thévenin's equivalent circuit.

(b) When a 1-ohm resistance is placed across terminals a-b, as shown in Fig. 12-19e, we have, from voltage division,

$$v_{ab}(t) = \frac{1}{1 + 1/(1+p)} [8(1 + e^{-t})] \qquad t \geq 0^+$$

or
$$(2 + p)v_{ab}(t) = (1 + p)[8(1 - e^{-t})] \qquad t \geq 0^+$$

Since
$$(1 + p)(1 - e^{-t}) = 1 - e^{-t} + 0 + e^{-t} = 1$$
$$(2 + p)v_{ab}(t) = 8$$

Hence
$$v_{ab} = 4 + Ke^{-2t}$$

The initial value of v_{ab} is equal to the initial value of v_0, which is zero. [Note also that $v_{ab}(0^+) = 0$ in Fig. 12-19a.] Hence

$$v_{ab}(t) = 4(1 - e^{-2t}) \qquad t \geq 0^+$$

When the deenergized impedance $1 + p$ is placed across terminals a-b, the circuit of Fig. 12-19f results. In this circuit

$$v_{ab} = \frac{1 + p}{1 + p + 1/(1+p)} v_0$$

or
$$(p^2 + 2p + 2)v_{ab} = (1 + p)^2 [8(1 - e^{-t})] \qquad t \geq 0^+$$

Since $(1 + p)^2(1 - e^{-t}) = (p^2 + 2p + 1)(1 - e^{-t}) = 1 - e^{-t} + 2e^{-t} - e^{-t} = 1$

the equilibrium equation is

$$(p^2 + 2p + 2)v_{ab} = 8$$

Now $v_{ab} = (v_{ab})_f + (v_{ab})_s$. By inspection $(v_{ab})_s = 4$. $(v_{ab})_f$ is the solution of

$$(p^2 + 2p + 2)(v_{ab})_f = 0$$

Hence the characteristic equation is $s^2 + 2s + 2 = 0$. The roots are $s = -1 \pm j$. Now

$$v_{ab} = 4 + \text{Re} \, [\mathbf{K}e^{(-1+j)t}] \qquad t \geq 0^+$$

and

$$\frac{dv_{ab}}{dt} = \text{Re} \, [\mathbf{K}(-1 + j)e^{(-1+j)t}]$$

We have $v_{ab}(0^+) = 0$ and $i_{ab}(0^+) = 0$. At junction a we observe that $(1 + p)(v_o - v_{ab}) = i_{ab}$; hence

$$v_o(0^+) + (dv_o/dt)_{0^+} - v_{ab}(0^+) - (dv_{ab}/dt)_{0^+} = i_{ab}(0^+)$$

Hence $(dv_{ab}/dt)_{0^+} = (dv_o/dt)_{0^+} + v_o(0^+)$. Since $v_o(0^+) = 0$ and $(dv_o/dt)_{0^+} = 8$, it follows that $(dv_{ab}/dt)_{0^+} = 8$. Hence Re $\mathbf{K} = -4$, Re $[\mathbf{K}(-1 + j)] = 8$, and $\mathbf{K} = -4 - j4$, so that $v_{ab}(t) = 4[1 + \sqrt{2}e^{-t} \cos (t - 135°)]$ for $t \geq 0^+$.

This example illustrates the convenience of using Thévenin's theorem when a given active terminal-pair network is applied to several loads in turn.

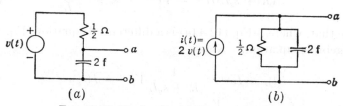

FIG. 12-20. Illustration of Norton's theorem.

Example 12-10. For the circuit shown in Fig. 12-20a obtain Norton's equivalent circuit with respect to terminals a-b.

Solution. When $v(t)$ is set to zero, $Y_{ab}(p) = 2 + 2p$. When terminals a-b are short-circuited, the current through the short circuit is $i_s = v(t)/\frac{1}{2} = 2v(t)$. Norton's circuit is shown in Fig. 12-20b. The same result can of course be obtained by converting the series connection of the $\frac{1}{2}$-ohm resistance and $v(t)$ to a current source.

12-14. Exponential Sources and Transform Network Functions.

The use of operational network functions enables us to compute the component of the response due to an exponential source by a very simple procedure. In Fig. 12-21 let the voltage source be exponential and of the form

$$v(t) = Ve^{s_g t} \qquad (12\text{-}42a)$$

where V and s_g are independent of t and the subscript g in s_g indicates that it is associated with the source (generator).

The equilibrium equation of the circuit of Fig. 12-21 is

$$v(t) = (R + pL)i = Ve^{s_g t} \qquad (12\text{-}42b)$$

Since the source in the circuit is exponential, the component of response due to source is also exponential and of the form

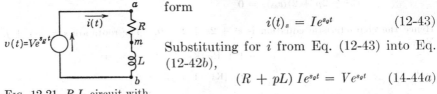

FIG. 12-21. *R-L* circuit with exponential source.

$$i(t)_s = Ie^{s_g t} \qquad (12\text{-}43)$$

Substituting for i from Eq. (12-43) into Eq. (12-42b),

$$(R + pL)Ie^{s_g t} = Ve^{s_g t} \qquad (14\text{-}44a)$$

But $pe^{s_g t} = s_g e^{s_g t}$, and in general

$$p^n e^{s_g t} \equiv \frac{d^n}{dt^n} e^{s_g t} = s_g{}^n e^{s_g t} \qquad (14\text{-}44b)$$

From this we conclude that in an equilibrium equation relating an exponential source (with exponent $s_g t$) and an exponential response the operator p can be replaced by the *number* s_g. In accordance with this rule Eq. (12-44a) can be written as

$$(R + s_g L)Ie^{s_g t} = Ve^{s_g t} \qquad s_g \neq -\frac{R}{L} \qquad (12\text{-}44c)$$

We note that, whereas Eq. (12-44a) is a differential equation, Eq. (12-44c) is an algebraic equation. Now

$$i(t)_s = Ie^{s_g t} = \frac{1}{R + s_g L} Ve^{s_g t} = I(s_g)e^{s_g t} \qquad (12\text{-}45a)$$

where

$$I(s_g) = \frac{V}{R + s_g L} \qquad R + s_g L \neq 0 \qquad (12\text{-}45b)$$

Since operational network functions are symbolic forms of differential equations, we could have started with expressing $i(t)$ in terms of the admittance function $1/(R + pL)$ operating on $v(t)$ to give

$$i(t) = \frac{1}{R + pL} v(t) = \frac{1}{R + pL} Ve^{s_g t} \qquad (12\text{-}46a)$$

If we substitute s_g for p in Eq. (14-46a), the result will be the component of $i(t)$ due to the source $Ve^{s_g t}$. This is

$$i(t)_s = \frac{1}{R + s_g L} Ve^{s_g t} \qquad R + s_g L \neq 0 \qquad (12\text{-}46b)$$

which is identical with the result of Eq. (12-45a).

We have noted that, in dealing with exponential sources of the form $e^{s_g t}$ and the corresponding component of the response due to source, p^n can be replaced by $s_g{}^n$. Thus in general if the source is of the form

$$\phi(t) = e^{s_g t} \tag{12-47a}$$

for a response $y(t)$ related to the source $\phi(t)$ by

$$y(t) = \frac{b_N p^N + b_{N-1} p^{N-1} + \cdots + b_1 p + b_0}{a_M p^M + a_{M-1} p^{M-1} + \cdots + a_1 p + a_0} \phi(t) \tag{12-47b}$$

the component of $y(t)$ due to the source $e^{s_g t}$ is

$$y(t)_s = \frac{b_N s_g{}^N + b_{N-1} s_g{}^{N-1} + \cdots + b_1 s_g + b_0}{a_M s_g{}^M + a_{M-1} s_g{}^{M-1} + \cdots + a_1 s_g + a_0} e^{s_g t} \tag{12-47c}$$

$$y(t)_s = \frac{\displaystyle\sum_{n=0}^{N} b_n s_g{}^n}{\displaystyle\sum_{m=0}^{M} a_m s_g{}^m} e^{s_g t} = \frac{B(s_g)}{A(s_g)} e^{s_g t} = H(s_g) e^{s_g t} \tag{12-47d}$$

where $B(s_g)$ and $A(s_g)$ are polynomials in s_g and $A(s_g) \neq 0$.

We note that, when the source is exponential, then the differential equation relating the source and response [see Eq. (12-46a)] is *transformed* into an algebraic equation [see Eq. (12-46b)] relating the source and component of the response due to the source. In this transformed equation the *ratio* of the component of response due to the source, to the source function is a function of s_g (as well as the network elements) and is called a transform[1] network function. The transform network function is obtained from the operational network function by replacing p with s_g.

Example 12-11. In the circuit of Fig. 12-21 the source is $v(t) = 20e^{-3t}$, and $R = 1$, $L = 2$. Find the component of $i(t)$ due to the source.

Solution. The operational admittance of the series connection of R and L is $1/(R + pL)$. The corresponding transform admittance is $1/(R + s_g L)$ such that

$$i(t)_s = \frac{1}{R + s_g L} v(t) = \frac{20e^{-3t}}{1 - (3)(2)} = -4e^{-3t}$$

We note that, if a transform network function such as $1/(R + s_g L)$ is specified, then, in addition to the component of the response due to the source, the source-free modes can also be found. This is seen from the fact that for a network function $1/(R + s_g L)$ the characteristic equation associated with the denominator of the network function is $R + sL = 0$, resulting in the characteristic root $s = -R/L$ and the source-free mode $Ae^{st} = Ae^{-(R/L)t}$. The following example illustrates this point.

[1] The concept of transform network functions is approached from a more general point of view when transformation calculus is studied.

Example 12-12. A transform network function relating the source $v(t) = V e^{s_g t}$ and the response $v_{mb}(t)_s$ is given as $s_g L / (R + s_g L)$. Find the complete response $v_{mb}(t)$.

Solution. The network function specified above is the voltage gain function of the circuit of Fig. 12-21 when v_{mb} is considered to be the "output." From the definition of the transform network function

$$v_{mb}(t)_s = \frac{s_g L}{R + s_g L} V e^{s_g t} \qquad R + s_g L \neq 0 \qquad (12\text{-}48a)$$

The source-free equilibrium equation corresponding to Eq. (12-48a) is

$$(R + pL)v_{mb}(t)_f = 0 \qquad (12\text{-}48b)$$

$$v_{mb}(t)_f = A e^{-(R/L)t} \qquad (12\text{-}48c)$$

$$v_{mb}(t) = A e^{-(R/L)t} + \frac{s_g L}{R + s_g L} V e^{s_g t} \qquad (12\text{-}48d)$$

Substituting numerical values, let $R = 1$, $L = 2$, $V = 20$, and $s_g = -3$, we have

$$v_{mb}(t) = A e^{-t/2} + 24 e^{-3t} \qquad (12\text{-}48e)$$

The value of A is found to fit the continuity conditions of the circuit.

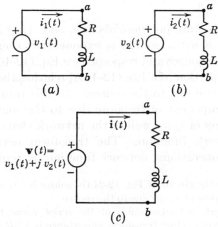

Fig. 12-22. Development of R-L circuit with complex exponential source function.

12-15. Complex Exponential Sources. In the examples treated above the number s_g is real and negative. The same procedure applies if s_g is a positive number (rising exponential source). We now note that a step source $V U(t)$ can be considered to be an exponential source $V e^{s_g t}$ applied at $t = 0$ with $s_g = 0$. Similarly in Chaps. 8 and 9 we saw that a sinusoidal source or a source with a damped oscillatory waveform may be considered[1] as

$$\cos \omega t = \mathrm{Re}\, e^{st} \qquad \mathbf{s} = j\omega \qquad (12\text{-}49a)$$

or

$$e^{-\alpha t} \cos \omega t = \mathrm{Re}\, e^{st} \qquad \mathbf{s} = -\alpha + j\omega \qquad (12\text{-}49b)$$

[1] In the study of transformation calculus it is shown that any function $f(t)$ can be expressed in terms of (an integral containing) exponential functions of the form e^{st}.

Therefore, if we find the component of the response due to a "source" of the form e^{st}, the real part of this response will be due to the source given by Re e^{st}. The following example illustrates this point.

Example 12-13. In the circuit of Fig. 12-22a let $v_1(t) = Ve^{-\alpha t} \cos (\omega t + \gamma)$. Find $i_1(t)_s$.

Solution. Consider a source

$$v_2(t) = Ve^{-\alpha t} \sin (\omega t + \gamma) \tag{12-50a}$$

applied to the R-L circuit as shown in Fig. 12-22b. Let the component of the response due to this source be $i_2(t)_s$. If we consider a "source" with the complex waveform

$$\mathbf{v}(t) = v_1(t) + jv_2(t) \tag{12-50b}$$

applied to the R-L circuit, as shown in Fig. 12-22c, then by superposition the response $\mathbf{i}(t)_s$ in this circuit is

$$\mathbf{i}(t)_s = i_1(t)_s + ji_2(t)_s \tag{12-51a}$$

We note that $\mathbf{v}(t)$ does not correspond to any "physical" source. The concept of a source which is composed of real and imaginary parts is used because of the simplifications it offers. In the case of this example we have

$$\mathbf{v}(t) = v_1(t) + jv_2(t) = Ve^{-\alpha t}[\cos (\omega t + \gamma) + j \sin (\omega t + \gamma)]$$
$$\mathbf{v}(t) = Ve^{-\alpha t}e^{j(\omega t + \gamma)} = Ve^{j\gamma}e^{(-\alpha + j\omega)t} = \mathbf{V}e^{st} \tag{12-50c}$$

where $\mathbf{V} = Ve^{j\gamma}$ and $\mathbf{s} = -\alpha + j\omega$. Now in Fig. 12-22c, by the use of transform admittance, we have

$$\mathbf{i}(t)_s = \frac{1}{R + sL} \mathbf{V}e^{st} = i_1(t)_s + ji_2(t)_s \tag{12-51a}$$

Therefore $\qquad i_1(t)_s = \text{Re } \mathbf{i}(t)_s = \text{Re} \left(\frac{1}{R + sL} \mathbf{V}e^{st} \right) \tag{12-51b}$

If numerical values $R = 12$, $L = 2$, $\alpha = 3$, $\omega = 4$, $V = 20$, and $\gamma = 30°$ are used, we find that the response $i_1(t)_s$ for the source

$$v_1(t) = 20e^{-3t} \cos (4t + 30°)$$

is $\qquad i_1(t)_s = \text{Re} \left(\frac{20/\!\!\underline{30°}}{12 + 2(-3 + j4)} e^{-3t}e^{j4t} \right)$

$$= \text{Re} \left(\frac{20/\!\!\underline{30°}}{10/\!\!\underline{53°}} e^{-3t}e^{j4t} \right) = 2e^{-3t} \cos (4t - 23°)$$

Another justification for the use of the complex source function of the form $\mathbf{v}(t) = \mathbf{V}e^{st}$ is the fact that the real function $v_1(t) = \text{Re } [\mathbf{v}(t)]$ can be expressed as

$$v_1(t) = \text{Re } (\mathbf{V}e^{st}) = \tfrac{1}{2}(\mathbf{V}e^{st} + \mathbf{V}^*e^{s^*t})$$

where $\mathbf{V}^*e^{s^*t}$ is the conjugate of $\mathbf{V}e^{st}$. This is seen from the relationship Re $\mathbf{z} = \tfrac{1}{2}(\mathbf{z} + \mathbf{z}^*)$, where $\mathbf{z}^*$ is the conjugate of $\mathbf{z}$. Therefore the response due to the source $v_1(t) = \text{Re } (\mathbf{V}e^{st})$ will be given by

$$i_1(t) = \tfrac{1}{2}Y(\mathbf{s})\mathbf{V}e^{st} + \tfrac{1}{2}Y(\mathbf{s}^*)\mathbf{V}^*e^{s^*t}$$

Since the coefficients in the polynomials $A(s)$ and $B(s)$ in Eq. (12-47d) are real (see Prob. 8-23), it follows that $Y(\mathbf{s^*}) = [Y(\mathbf{s})]^*$ and

$$i_1(t)_s = \tfrac{1}{2}[\mathbf{i}(t)_s + \mathbf{i^*}(t)_s] = \operatorname{Re}[\mathbf{i}(t)_s]$$

Most often a source given by the real part of a complex exponential is treated as two sources of complex exponential form, one source function being the conjugate of the other source. The following examples illustrate the use of complex source functions.

Example 12-14. In the circuit of Fig. 12-23 calculate the component of v_{ab} due to $v(t)$ if $v(t) = \operatorname{Re}(Ve^{st})$ when (a) $V = 4$, $s = -1$; (b) $V = 4$, $s = +1$; (c) $V = 4$, $s = j$; (d) $V = 4$, $s = -2 + j$.

Solution. Using the voltage-division formula,

$$v_{ab} = \frac{1/(1 + p)}{(1 + p) + 1/(1 + p)}\, v(t)$$

or

$$v_{ab} = \frac{1}{p^2 + 2p + 2}\, v(t)$$

so that the transform network function for this problem is $1/(s^2 + 2s + 2)$.

(a) When $s = -1$, the network function is $1/[(-1)^2 - 2 + 2] = 1$. Hence $(v_{ab})_s = 4e^{-t}$.

(b) When $s = +1$, the network function is $1/(1 + 2 + 2) = \tfrac{1}{5}$. Hence $(v_{ab})_s = \tfrac{4}{5}e^{+t}$.

(c) When $s = j$, the network function is $1/(j^2 + 2j + 2) = 1/(1 + j2)$. Hence $(v_{ab})_s = \operatorname{Re}\{[4/(1 + j2)]e^{jt}\} = 1.79\cos(t - 63.4°)$.

(d) When $s = -2 + j$, $s^2 + 2s + 2 = 1 - j2$, so that $(v_{ab})_s = \operatorname{Re}[4e^{(-2+j)t}/(1 - j2)]$ or $(v_{ab})_s = 1.79e^{-2t}\cos(t + 63.4°)$.

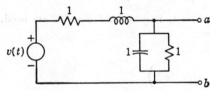
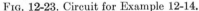
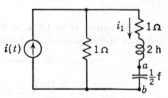

FIG. 12-23. Circuit for Example 12-14.   FIG. 12-24. Circuit for Example 12-15.

Example 12-15. In the circuit of Fig. 12-24 $i(t) = 2 + 2e^{-t} + 2\cos(t + 20°)$. Calculate the component of v_{ab} due to $i(t)$.

Solution. Using the current division formula,

$$i_1(t) = \frac{1}{1 + 1 + 2p + 2/p}\, i(t)$$

Because $v_{ab} = (2/p)i_1(t)$,

$$v_{ab}(t) = \frac{2/p}{2 + 2p + 2/p}\, i(t)$$

or

$$v_{ab}(t) = \frac{1}{p^2 + p + 1}\, i(t)$$

so that the transform transfer impedance is $1/(s^2 + s + 1)$. We now regard the source $i(t)$ as three sources. Using first the source $i(t) = 2$, we set $s = 0$, and v_{ab} due to this source is 2. For the source $2e^{-t}$, $s = -1$, for $2\cos t$, $s = j$. Hence

$$(v_{ab})_s = 2 + \frac{2e^{-t}}{(-1)^2 - 1 + 1} + \text{Re}\left(\frac{2}{j^2 + j + 1} e^{jt+j20\pi/180°}\right)$$

or
$$(v_{ab})_s = 2 + 2e^{-t} + 2\cos(t + 20° - 90°)$$

Example 12-16. The time constant of a certain series R-C circuit is 2 sec. When a voltage source $v(t) = 10e^{-3t}$ is applied, the component of the current due to the source is $2e^{-3t}$. Calculate the component of the current due to a source $v(t) = 10\cos \frac{1}{2}t =$ Re $(10e^{jt/2})$.

Solution. For a series R-C circuit the transform driving-point admittance is $Y(s) = 1 / \left(R + \dfrac{1}{sC}\right) = sC/(sRC + 1)$. Since $RC = 2$, $Y(s) = sC/(2s + 1)$. Now it is given that

$$2e^{-3t} = \left(\frac{sC}{2s + 1}\right)_{s=-3} \times 10e^{-3t}$$

or
$$2(-6 + 1) = -3C \times 10 \qquad 3C = 1$$

Hence $Y(s) = s/(6s + 3)$. When $s = j\frac{1}{2}$, $Y(s) = j\frac{1}{2}/(3j + 3)$. The source $v(t) = 10\cos \frac{1}{2}t$ therefore produces the response component $i(t)_s$, where

$$i(t)_s = \text{Re}\left(\frac{10j}{6 + j6} e^{jt/2}\right) = 1.18\cos\left(\frac{1}{2}t + 45°\right)$$

12-16. Poles and Zeros of Transform Network Functions. In the previous article we saw that the general form of a transform network function was $B(s)/A(s)$, where $B(s)$ and $A(s)$ are polynomials in s. As an example, consider the network of Fig. 12-7a. In Eq. (12-16b) the operational driving-point admittance of this network was given as

$$Y_{ab}(p) = \frac{p(p^2 + 4p + 3)}{p^3 + 5p^2 + 6p + 1} \approx \frac{p(p + 1)(p + 3)}{(p + 0.2)(p + 1.62)(p + 3.18)}$$

If a voltage source with the exponential waveform Ve^{st} is applied to this network, the current in the terminal pair, $i_{ab}(t)_s$ is given by

$$[i_{ab}(t)]_s = \frac{s(s + 1)(s + 3)}{(s + 0.2)(s + 1.62)(s + 3.18)} Ve^{st} \qquad (12\text{-}52a)$$

The transform driving-point admittance function of terminal pair a-b is

$$Y_{ab}(s) = \frac{B(s)}{A(s)} \qquad (12\text{-}52b)$$

$$B(s) = s(s + 1)(s + 3) \qquad (12\text{-}52c)$$

$$A(s) = (s + 0.2)(s + 1.62)(s + 3.18) \qquad (12\text{-}52d)$$

If the source function is such that s in its exponent is one of the zeros of the numerator of the network function (in this case 0, -1, or -3), then the component of the response due to the source is zero. For example, if the voltage source $v(t) = e^{-3t}$ is applied to the terminal pair $a\text{-}b$ of Fig. 12-7a, then the component of the current due to this source, $i_{ab}(t)_s$, will be identically zero. The same statement is true of sources of the form e^{-t} or e^{-0t}, the latter being a constant value for $t > 0$, that is, a step function. The results for a step function are verified by inspection of the network of Fig. 12-7a. The steady-state component of the current response due to a step voltage source for this network is zero, since it is an open circuit for a d-c source. We recall that the roots of a polynomial equation such as $A(s) = 0$ are called the zeros of the polynomial $A(s)$. With this in mind we define as follows:

The zeros of the *numerator* of a transform network function are called the *zeros* of that network function. The reason for this terminology should be clear from the above discussion.

The zeros of the *denominator* of a transform network function are called the *poles* of that network function. The reason for this terminology is probably the fact that, for exponential sources where s_g is a zero of the denominator of the network function, the value of the network function is infinity (goes up the pole).

12-17. Coincidence of Poles of the Network Function and Exponent of the Exponential Source. In Art. 12-16 we have seen that, when the exponent s of the exponential source e^{st} is identical with one of the zeros of the network function, both the network function and the component of the response due to the source will be zero. If s takes up the value of one of the poles of the network function, the network function will become infinite but the component of the response due to the source need not necessarily become infinite. In such cases the component of the response due to the source is proportional to $t^n e^{st}$. A general treatment of such a case is given in Art. 13-7. In this article we shall illustrate the case by the following example.

Example 12-17. In a series circuit $R = 2$, $L = 1$, and the voltage source is $v(t) = e^{-2t}$. Find $i(t)_s$.

Solution. The transform admittance function which relates $i(t)_s$ to the source e^{-2t} is $1/(R + sL)$. For $R = 2$, $L = 1$, and $s = -2$ the value of transform admittance is infinity. However, the equilibrium equation of the circuit is

$$Ri + L\frac{di}{dt} = e^{-2t} \qquad \text{or} \qquad 2i + \frac{di}{dt} = e^{-2t} \qquad (12\text{-}53)$$

A trial solution of $i = te^{-2t}$ will show that this function satisfies the differential equation. This is seen from the fact that

$$\frac{d}{dt} te^{-2t} = t(-2e^{-2t}) + e^{-2t}$$

$$2i + \frac{di}{dt} = 2te^{-2t} - 2te^{-2t} + e^{-2t} = e^{-2t}$$

which agrees with the equilibrium equation (12-53).

In the above example it is seen that, although for $s = -2$ the admittance function $1/(2 + s)$ goes to infinity, the response due to the source is not infinite, since te^{-2t} is always finite. The case when the response due to the source approaches infinity is discussed in Chap. 15.

In Art. 13-7 it is shown that, if m of the poles of a network function are identical with the exponent s of the source e^{st}, then the component of the response due to the source is of the form

$$y_s(t) = Kt^m e^{st}$$

PROBLEMS

12-1. In Fig. P12-1 show, without the use of operators, that the equilibrium equations for v_{an} and v_{bn} are

$$2\frac{d^2 v_{an}}{dt^2} + 7\frac{dv_{an}}{dt} + 2v_{an} = 3\frac{di}{dt} + 2i$$

and

$$2\frac{d^2 v_{bn}}{dt^2} + 7\frac{dv_{bn}}{dt} + 2v_{bn} = 2\frac{di}{dt}$$

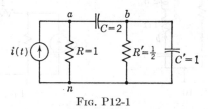

Fig. P12-1

12-2. Deduce the equilibrium equations required in Prob. 12-1 with the aid of operators.

12-3. Perform the indicated operations: (a) $(p^2 + 1)e^{-t}$; (b) $(p + 2) \cos t$; (c) $(1/p)e^{-2t}$; (d) $(6 + 5p)[e^{(-3+j4)t} + e^{(-3-j4)t}]$.

12-4. A differential equation is given in the form $(a_n p^n + a_{n-1}p^{n-1} + \cdots + a_1 p + a_0)y(t) = f(t)$. (a) Show that "multiplication with p" of both sides of the equation is permitted. (b) Show that the procedure of (a) will introduce an arbitrary constant in the solution of the differential equation.

12-5. If $f(t) = [1/(1 + p)]t$, find $f(t)$.

12-6. Use the operational voltage-division formula to obtain the equilibrium equation which relates v_{bn} to $v(t)$, and solve for the case $v(t) = tU(t); i(0^+) = 0$ (Fig. P12-6).

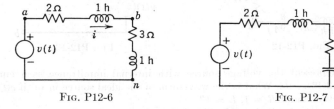

Fig. P12-6   Fig. P12-7

12-7. Use the operational voltage-division formula to relate $v_2(t)$ to $v(t)$ (Fig. P12-7).

12-8. Use the operational voltage- and current-division formulas to find the network function which relates $i(t)$ to $v(t)$ (Fig. P12-8).

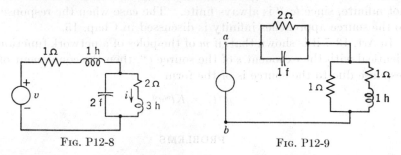

FIG. P12-8   FIG. P12-9

12-9. Calculate the driving-point admittance $Y_{ab}(p)$ for the circuit of Fig. P12-9.

12-10. Obtain the voltage gain function which relates $v(t)$ to $v_{ab}(t)$, and write the corresponding differential equation (Fig. P12-10).

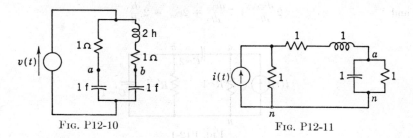

FIG. P12-10   FIG. P12-11

12-11. Write the differential equation which relates $v_{an}(t)$ to the source $i(t)$ by use of operational immittance functions (Fig. P12-11).

12-12. Figure P12-12 shows a source-free network. (a) Calculate the characteristic roots of the given network. (b) Calculate the free modes of v_{dn} if an ideal voltage source is inserted between terminals a-a'. (c) Calculate the free modes of v_{dn} if an ideal voltage source is connected between (1) terminals a-b; (2) terminals b-d. (d) Are there any nonzero free modes for v_{dn} if an ideal current source is inserted between terminals a-a'?

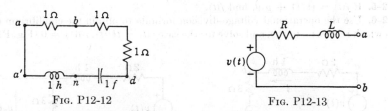

FIG. P12-12   FIG. P12-13

12-13. (a) Represent the voltage source with internal immittance as a current source (Fig. P12-13). (b) What is the waveform of the ideal source in (a) if $v(t)$ is a unit ramp function and if $R = 1$, $L = 1$?

12-14. Redraw the circuit shown in Fig. P12-14, representing all voltage sources as current sources.

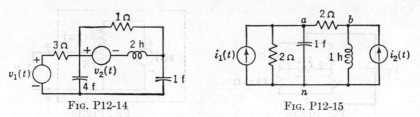

FIG. P12-14   FIG. P12-15

12-15. In the circuit shown in Fig. P12-15 represent current sources as voltage sources, and (a) obtain the differential equation which relates v_{ab} to the source functions. (b) What is the operational transfer impedance which relates v_{ab} to $i_1(t)$? (c) What is the operational transfer impedance which relates v_{ab} to $i_2(t)$?

12-16. In the circuit shown in Fig. P12-16 (a) calculate V_{ab} (switch open); (b) calculate the current i_{ab} if terminals a-b are short-circuited (switch closed). (c) Deduce Thévenin's equivalent circuit with respect to terminals a-b (switch open) from the results of (a) and (b). (d) A 2-farad capacitance is placed across terminals a-b at $t = 0$. Calculate the complete response for the voltage $v_{ab}(t)$ if the capacitance is uncharged at $t = 0$. (e) The capacitance of (d) is removed and replaced by a $\frac{1}{4}$-henry inductance at $t' = 0$. The initial current in this inductance is zero. Calculate $i_{ab}(t')$ for all $t' \geq 0^+$.

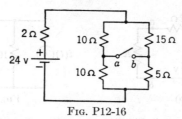

FIG. P12-16

12-17. Represent the circuit of Fig. P12-17a in the form shown in Fig. P12-17b by application of Thévenin's theorem at terminals a-b. (a) State the relationship between v_o and $v(t)$, and give the value of R_s. (b) If $L = 2.4$ henry and both R and C are adjustable, find the relationship between R and C which will keep the circuit critically damped.

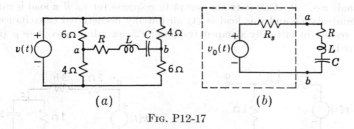

(a)   (b)

FIG. P12-17

12-18. Consider the Wheatstone-bridge circuit shown in Fig. P12-18 when $x = 0$, $I_g = 0$. (a) Obtain Thévenin's equivalent circuit with respect to terminals a-b. (b) Show that $I_g = -x/(8 + 5x)$ and is therefore proportional to x if $5x \ll 8$. (c) Explain how the result of (b) can be used to make measurements with an unbalanced bridge.

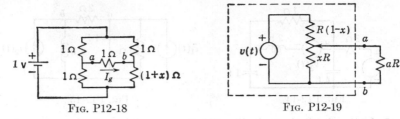

FIG. P12-18   FIG. P12-19

12-19. The circuit shown in Fig. P12-19 is a potentiometer with load resistance aR. (a) Represent the circuit to the left of terminals a-b as a series circuit, using Thévenin's theorem. (b) Show that $v_{ab}/v = xa/[x(1 - x) + a]$. (c) If a is infinite, $v_{ab}/v = x$, and the circuit acts as a voltage divider in the sense that v_{ab} is proportional to x. Hence, if the potentiometer is a linear slide wire, x can be considered the displacement of the slide. From (b) it follows that the under load v_{ab}/v is *not* proportional to x. Consider $(v_{ab}/v) - x$ as the deviation from linearity, and plot this function for $a = 1$ and $a = 5$.

12-20. (a) Use Thévenin's theorem to calculate the value of R for maximum power transfer to R (Fig. P12-20). (b) Set R to the value of (a), and calculate the power delivered to each of the resistances in the *given* circuit.

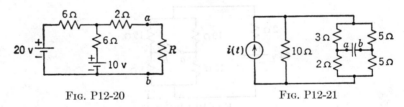

FIG. P12-20   FIG. P12-21

12-21. In the circuit shown in Fig. P12-21 $v_{ab}(0^+) = 0$. (a) Use Norton's theorem to calculate $v_{ab}(t)$ for all $t \geq 0^+$ if $i(t)$ is given as (1) $i(t) = U(t)$, (2) $i(t) = tU(t)$, (3) $i(t) = e^{-t}$ and C has the value which results in a 2-sec time constant. (b) What is the value of C in (a)? *Hint:* Calculate $Z_s = R_s$ by calculating the relationship between v_o and i_s.

12-22. In the circuit shown in Fig. P12-22 $v(t)$ is the ramp function $tU(t)$ and the initial-energy storage is zero. (a) Obtain Thévenin's equivalent circuit with respect to terminals a-b. (b) Calculate the complete response for v_{ab} if a load is connected across terminals a-b and this load is (1) an initially deenergized capacitance whose value C results in critically damped response; (2) an admittance $1 + p$ (initially deenergized).

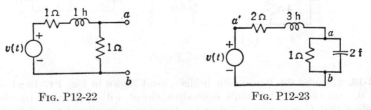

FIG. P12-22   FIG. P12-23

12-23. In the circuit shown in Fig. P12-23 $v_{ab}(t) = e^{st}$. Calculate $v_{a'b}(t)$ if (a) $s = -1$; (b) $s = -\frac{2}{3}$; (c) $s = -\frac{1}{2}$.

12-24. In the circuit of Prob. 12-23 (Fig. P12-23) (a) calculate the transform network function which relates v_{ab} to $v(t)$; (b) use the result of (a) to calculate $(v_{ab})_s$ if $v(t)$ is given as (1) $v(t) = e^{-t}$, (2) $v(t) = e^{-t} + e^{-2t}$, (3) $v(t) = e^{jt} + e^{-jt}$.

12-25. In the circuit shown in Fig. P12-25 the source $i(t)$ has the form $i(t) = Ie^{s_g t}$. Calculate the value of s_g so that the component of v_{ab} due to the source is $5Ie^{s_g t}$.

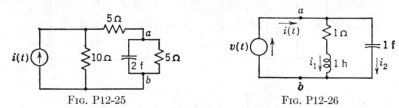

FIG. P12-25   FIG. P12-26

12-26. In the circuit shown in Fig. P12-26 (a) calculate the transform driving-point admittance $Y_{ab}(s)$. (b) What should the waveform of $v(t)$ be so that the component of $i(t)$ due to $v(t)$ is zero? (c) For $v(t)$ as in (b) calculate $i_{1s}(t)$ and $i_{2s}(t)$.

12-27. In the circuit of Prob. 12-22 (Fig. P12-22) $v(t) = 3e^{-2t} \cos t$. Calculate the complete response for $v_{ab}(t)$ if $v_{ab}(0^+) = 0$.

12-28. In the circuit shown in Fig. P12-28 $i(t) = 2e^{-t} + 5e^{-2t} \cos t$. If $v_{ab}(0^+) = 0$, calculate the complete response $v_{ab}(t)$.

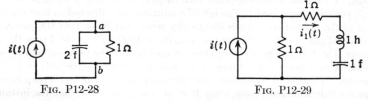

FIG. P12-28   FIG. P12-29

12-29. In the circuit shown in Fig. P12-29 $i(t) = 5 + 2e^{-t/2} + 3 \cos 2t$. Calculate the complete response for $i_1(t)$ if the initial-energy storage is zero.

12-30. In the circuit shown in Fig. P12-30 $v_1(t) = e^{s_1 t}$, $v_2(t) = e^{s_2 t}$. Calculate (a) the transform transfer function which relates $v_{ab}(t)$ to $v_1(t)$; (b) the transform transfer function which relates $v_{ab}(t)$ to $v_2(t)$. (c) Calculate the components of v_{ab} due to the sources if (1) $s_1 = -2$, $s_2 = 0$; (2) $s_1 = 0$, $s_2 = -2$.

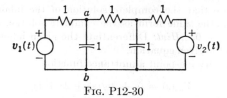

FIG. P12-30

12-31. A certain transform network function is

$$H(s) = \frac{s + 2}{(s + 1)^2 (s + 3)(s^2 + s + 5)}$$

(a) Calculate the component of the response due to a source $\phi(t)$ if (1) $\phi(t) = e^{-4t}$; (2) $\phi(t) = e^{-2t}$; (3) $\phi(t) = \cos t = \frac{1}{2}e^{jt} + \frac{1}{2}e^{-jt}$. (b) What are the free modes of the complete response? (c) Write the differential equation which relates the response $y(t)$ to a source $\phi(t)$.

12-32. (a) Calculate $(v_{ab})_s$ in the circuit of Fig. P12-32a.   (b) Calculate $(i_{ab})_s$ in the circuit of Fig. P12-32b.   (c) It is desired to calculate $(v_{ab})_s$ in Fig. P12-32c.   Use the results of (a) and (b) in conjunction with Thévenin's theorem to calculate $(v_{ab})_s$ if (1) $Z(s) = 1 + s$; (2) $Z(s) = 1 + s + 1/s$.

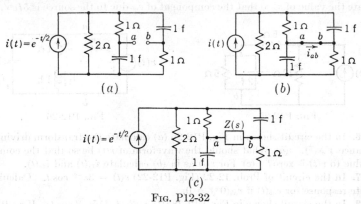

FIG. P12-32

12-33. Use the results of Prob. 12-11 to calculate $v_{an}(t)_s$ if $i(t) = 5e^{-2t}$ in Fig. P12-11.

12-34. A transform driving-point admittance $Y_{ab}(s)$ has a voltage source $Ve^{+\alpha t}$ (α real, positive) impressed.   The initial conditions are adjusted so that the free component of the current response is identically zero.   (a) Show that the power input to the terminal pair a-b from the source is $p_{ab}(t) = V^2 Y(\alpha)e^{2\alpha t}$.   (b) From the result of (a) prove that $Y(\alpha)$ is a positive number for positive α if the terminal pair is passive.

12-35. A transform admittance $Y(s)$ has a voltage source $v(t) = \frac{1}{2}e^{s_g t} + \frac{1}{2}e^{s_g^* t}$ impressed.   The initial conditions are adjusted so that the free component of the response $i(t)$ is identically zero.   (a) If $\mathbf{s}_g = -\alpha \pm j\omega$, show that the instantaneous power delivered to the admittance is

$$p(t) = \frac{1}{2}e^{-2\alpha t}\{\mathrm{Re}\,[Y(\mathbf{s}_g)]\} + \frac{1}{2}e^{-2\alpha t}\,\mathrm{Re}\,[Y(\mathbf{s}_g)e^{j2\omega t}]$$

(b) If $\mathbf{s}_g = j\omega$, show that the average power $P = (\omega/2\pi)\int_0^{2\pi/\omega} p(t)\,dt$ is given by $P = \frac{1}{2}\,\mathrm{Re}\,[Y(j\omega)]$.   Note that this proves that $\mathrm{Re}\,[Y(j\omega)] > 0$ for passive terminal-pair networks.   Compare this result with that of Prob. 12-34.

12-36. Demonstrate that the complete solution of the inhomogeneous equation $(p + 1)y(t) = e^{-t}$ has the same form as the complete solution of the homogeneous equation $(p + 1)^2 y(t) = 0$.   *Hint:* Differentiate the given inhomogeneous equation, and add the result to the given equation.

12-37. A transform driving-point admittance function is

$$Y_{ab}(s) = (s + 2)/(s^2 + 2s + 1)$$

Either a voltage source $v(t) = Ve^{s_g t}$ or a current source $i(t) = Ie^{s_g t}$ is impressed at the terminals a-b of the network.   Under what circumstances (state type of source and values of s_g) will the complete response include a term or terms proportional to (a) e^{-t}; (b) te^{-t}; (c) $t^2 e^{-t}$; (d) te^{-2t}; (e) $e^{-2t} + e^{-4t}$; (f) $te^{-t} + e^{-4t}$?

CHAPTER 13

POLES AND ZEROS OF NETWORK FUNCTIONS

In the preceding chapter we showed how transform network functions enable us to find, through algebraic operations, the response due to an exponential source. In this chapter we shall investigate the properties of transform network functions which, in addition to determining the component of the response due to exponential sources, are also characteristic of the complete response.

13-1. Nature of the Denominator of Network Functions. In every linear network a response function $y(t)$ is related to a source function $\phi(t)$ through a differential equation of the form

$$D(p)y(t) = N(p)\phi(t) \tag{13-1}$$

or
$$y(t) = \frac{N(p)}{D(p)}\phi(t) \tag{13-1a}$$

where $N(p)$ and $D(p)$ are polynomials in p, that is,

$$N(p) = b_N p^N + b_{N-1}p^{N-1} + b_{N-2}p^{N-2} + \cdots + b_1 p + b_0$$
$$D(p) = a_M p^M + a_{M-1}p^{M-1} + a_{M-2}p^{M-2} + \cdots + a_1 p + a_0$$

We recall that the superposition property which characterizes linear networks makes a discussion of a network which includes only one source perfectly general because any statement which applies to a network with one source applies to a network with several sources. To review the terminology used in connection with network functions, consider the network shown in Fig. 13-1. For this network the driving-point admittance at the terminals of the source is

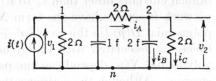

FIG. 13-1. A network used to illustrate network functions.

$$Y_{1n}(p) = \frac{1}{2} + p + \frac{1}{2 + 1/(\frac{1}{2} + 2p)}$$

or
$$Y_{1n}(p) = \frac{8p^2 + 12p + 3}{4 + 8p} \tag{13-2}$$

Hence the voltage $v_1(t)$ is related to $i(t)$ through the equation

$$(8p^2 + 12p + 3)v_1(t) = (4 + 8p)i(t)$$

The transfer impedance which relates $v_2(t)$ to $i(t)$ can be found from the voltage-division formula,

$$v_2(t) = v_1(t) \frac{1/(\frac{1}{2} + 2p)}{2 + 1/(\frac{1}{2} + 2p)}$$

Introducing Eq. (13-2), we have

$$v_2(t) = \frac{8p + 4}{8p^2 + 12p + 3} \frac{1}{4p + 2} i(t)$$

or $\qquad$ $v_2(t) = \frac{2}{8p^2 + 12p + 3} i(t)$

Since $i_C = v_2/2$ and $i_B = 2pv_2$, $i_A = i_B + i_C = (2p + \frac{1}{2})v_2$, the following network functions have now been deduced: The driving-point impedance at the source terminals is

$$v_1 = Z_{d_1}(p)i \qquad Z_{d_1} = \frac{4 + 8p}{8p^2 + 12p + 3}$$

The transfer impedance relating v_2 to $i(t)$ is

$$v_2 = z_{t_{12}}(p)i \qquad z_{t_{12}}(p) = \frac{2}{8p^2 + 12p + 3}$$

The current gain function relating i_A to $i(t)$ is

$$i_A = G_A(p)i \qquad G_A(p) = \frac{1 + 4p}{8p^2 + 12p + 3}$$

It is evident that other network functions can be defined in connection with Fig. 13-1. Thus, for example, we can define a transfer impedance which relates $v_A = v_1 - v_2$ to $i(t)$ and current gain functions which relate branch currents other than i_A to $i(t)$. In every case we observe that all network functions have the form $N(p)/D(p)$ and that the denominator polynomial $D(p)$ (in this case $8p^2 + 12p + 3$) is the same for all network functions associated with the given source terminals. The numerator polynomial $N(p)$ depends on the particular network function under discussion. Although these observations are the result of examining a relatively simple network, the conclusions apply generally.[1]

13-2. The Free Component of the Response. If the source function is set to zero, the equilibrium equation for any network variable $y(t)$ has the same form: $D(p)y(t) = 0$. This linear homogeneous equation with constant coefficients can be solved by introducing the modes Ke^{st} so that the characteristic roots are given by solution of the algebraic equation

---

[1] A general proof is given in Chap. 16.

$D(s) = 0$. The polynomial $D(s)$ can be factored. If the roots are $s = s_1, \ldots, s_M$, then $D(s)$ can be written in the form

$$a_M s^M + a_{M-1} s^{M-1} + \cdots + a_1 s + a_0$$
$$= a_M (s - s_1)(s - s_2) \cdots (s - s_M) \quad (13\text{-}3)$$

In this connection the symbolic use of the product symbol Π is useful. We write

$$\prod_{k=1}^{M} (s - s_k) \equiv (s - s_1)(s - s_2) \cdots (s - s_M)$$

This symbol serves to indicate the multiplication of factors exactly as the symbol Σ signifies addition. Thus

$$\sum_{n=1}^{5} n = 1 + 2 + 3 + 4 + 5 = 15$$

while

$$\prod_{n=1}^{5} n = (1)(2)(3)(4)(5) = 120$$

The characteristic equation can therefore be written in the form

$$\prod_{k=1}^{M} (s - s_k) = 0$$

If no two roots of this equation are equal, the free component of the response is

$$y(t)_f = \sum_{k=1}^{M} K_k e^{s_k t}$$

If m' of the M roots are equal and denoted by s_1, the characteristic equation has the form

$$(s - s_1)^{m'}(s - s_{m'+1})(s - s_{m'+2}) \cdots (s - s_M) = 0$$

or

$$(s - s_1)^{m'} \prod_{m'+1}^{M} (s - s_k) = 0$$

In this case the free component of the response has the form

$$y(t)_f = \sum_{k=1}^{m'} K_k t^{k-1} e^{s_1 t} + \sum_{k=m'+1}^{M} K_k e^{s_k t}$$

or

$$y(t)_f = (K_1 + K_2 t + K_3 t^2 + \cdots + K_{m'} t^{m'-1}) e^{s_1 t}$$
$$+ K_{m'+1} e^{s_{m'+1} t} + \cdots + K_M e^{s_M t}$$

To prove the above statement, we note that in the source-free equation, $D(p)y(t) = 0$, if m' of the roots of $D(p)$ are identical and equal to s_1, then

$$D(p) = (p - s_1)^{m'} D_1(p) = D'(p) D_1(p)$$

where
$$D'(p) = (p - s_1)^{m'}$$

We shall now show that a function of the form

$$f(t) = \sum_{k=1}^{m'} K_k t^{k-1} e^{s_1 t}$$

satisfies the differential equation

$$D'(p)f(t) = (p - s_1)^{m'} f(t) = 0$$

and therefore is a solution to the equation

$$D(p)y(t) = [D'(p) D_1(p)]y(t) = 0$$

For this purpose we note that for any function $h(t)$

$$p[e^{st}h(t)] = se^{st}h(t) + e^{st}ph(t) = e^{st}(p + s)h(t)$$
$$p^2 e^{st}h(t) = pe^{st}(p + s)h(t)$$
$$= se^{st}(p + s)h(t) + e^{st}p(p + s)h(t)$$
$$= e^{st}[s(p + s)h(t) + p^2 h(t) + sph(t)]$$
$$= e^{st}(p + s)^2 h(t)$$

or in general[1]

$$p^k[e^{s_1 t}h(t)] = e^{s_1 t}(p + s_1)^k h(t) \tag{13-4}$$

Now for a polynomial $D'(p) = \sum_{k=1}^{m'} a_k p^k$, we have

$$D'(p)[e^{s_1 t}h(t)] = \sum_{k=1}^{m'} a_k p^k[e^{s_1 t}h(t)] = \sum_{k=1}^{m'} e^{s_1 t} a_k (p + s_1)^k h(t)$$

$$= e^{s_1 t} D'(p + s_1)h(t) \tag{13-5}$$

For
$$D'(p) = (p - s_1)^{m'} \tag{13-6a}$$
$$D'(p + s_1) = (p - s_1 + s_1)^{m'} = p^{m'} \tag{13-6b}$$

---

[1] To prove Eq. (13-4), we observe that

$$pe^{s_1 t}h(t) = e^{s_1 t}(p + s_1)h(t)$$

Now if we assume that Eq. 13-4 is true,

$$p^k[e^{s_1 t}h(t)] = e^{s_1 t}(p + s_1)^k h(t) \tag{13-4}$$

then, differentiating the left-hand side,

$$p^{k+1}e^{s_1 t}h(t) = p^k[pe^{s_1 t}h(t)] = p^k[e^{s_1 t}(p + s_1)h(t)]$$

But from Eq. (13-4), replacing $h(t)$ by $(p + s_1)h(t)$, we have

$$p^k[e^{s_1 t}(p + s_1)h(t)] = e^{s_1 t}(p + s_1)^k(p + s_1)h(t)$$

Hence, if Eq. (13-4) is true for any value k, it is also true for $k + 1$. Since we have shown that Eq. (13-4) is true for $k = 1$, it is true for all values of k.

Equation (13-5) is general and applies to any function $h(t)$. We shall now consider a special case when

$$h(t) = \sum_{k=1}^{m'} K_k t^{k-1} = K_0 + K_1 t + \cdots + K_{m'-1} t^{m'-1} \qquad (13\text{-}7)$$

From Eqs. (13-5) and (13-6b) we have

$$D'(p)[e^{s_1 t} h(t)] = e^{s_1 t} D'(p + s_1) h(t) = e^{s_1 t} p^{m'} h(t) \qquad (13\text{-}8)$$

Now, if $h(t)$ is of the form given in Eq. (13-7), its highest power of t being $t^{m'-1}$, it is seen that

$$p^{m'} h(t) \equiv 0 \qquad (13\text{-}9)$$

Let

$$f(t) = e^{s_1 t} h(t) = \sum_{k=1}^{m'} K_k t^{k-1} e^{s_1 t} \qquad (13\text{-}10)$$

From Eqs. (13-8) and (13-9) we have

$$D'(p) f(t) = 0 \qquad (13\text{-}11)$$

which shows that the right-hand side of Eq. (13-10) is part of the general solution of the source-free equation $D(p)y(t) = 0$.

13-3. Exponential Source Functions. We have already shown in Chap. 12 that the component of the response due to an exponential source function can be obtained directly from the operational network function [when $D(s_g) \neq 0$]. Thus, if a source function is the complex function

$$\phi(t) = e^{s_g t}$$

Then the component of the response due to the source function is

$$\mathbf{y}(t)_s = \frac{N(\mathbf{s}_g)}{D(\mathbf{s}_g)} \phi(t) \qquad D(\mathbf{s}_g) \neq 0$$

We also recall that complex source and response functions do not correspond to a physical source or response but can be used to calculate the response due to physically meaningful cases where the time functions are real. If a source function is

$$\phi(t) = \phi(t) + \phi^*(t)$$

then, if $\mathbf{y}(t)$ is the response to $\phi(t)$, $\mathbf{y}^*(t)$ is the response to $\phi^*(t)$ and by superposition $y(t) = \mathbf{y}(t) + \mathbf{y}^*(t) = 2 \operatorname{Re}[\mathbf{y}(t)]$. Similarly if

$$\phi(t) = \operatorname{Re} \phi e^{s_g t}$$

$$y(t) = \operatorname{Re}\left[\frac{N(\mathbf{s}_g)}{D(\mathbf{s}_g)} \phi e^{s_g t}\right] \qquad D(\mathbf{s}_g) \neq 0$$

In this connection it is convenient to recall the notion of complex frequency which was introduced in Chap. 9. A function of the form e^{st} represents sinusoidal oscillations when $\mathbf{s}$ is imaginary and exponential damping when s is real and negative. For complex values of $\mathbf{s}$ the real part of e^{st} has an exponentially damped (or rising) oscillatory waveform. In this case $\mathbf{s}$ is referred to as the complex frequency of the waveform. Thus the functions $f(t) = 5e^{-3t}\cos(5t - 30°)$ and $7e^{-3t}\sin(5t + 10°)$ are functions with the complex frequency $-3 + j5$ since

$$5e^{-3t}\cos(5t - 30°) = \mathrm{Re}\,[5e^{-j\pi/6}e^{(-3+j5)t}]$$

and $\qquad 7e^{-3t}\sin(5t + 10°) = \mathrm{Re}\,[7e^{-j80\pi/180}e^{(-3+j5)t}]$

Therefore the component of the response of a network, due to a sinusoidal source or a source with damped oscillatory or exponential waveform, can be obtained directly from the appropriate transform network function.

13-4. Relation between Poles and Zeros of the Network Function and Response Due to an Exponential Source. Operational network functions are the ratios of polynomials in p. These polynomials can be written in factored form:

$$\frac{N(p)}{D(p)} = \frac{b_N p^N + b_{N-1}p^{N-1} + \cdots + b_1 p + b_0}{a_M p^M + a_{M-1}p^{M-1} + \cdots + a_1 p + a_0}$$

$$= H\frac{(p - s_A)(p - s_B)\cdots(p - s_N)}{(p - s_1)(p - s_2)\cdots(p - s_M)} \qquad (13\text{-}12)$$

where $H = b_N/a_M$ is a real number and the poles $s_1, \ldots, s_M$ and zeros $s_A, \ldots, s_N$ are in general complex. The transform network function is obtained by replacing p by[1] s,

$$\frac{N(s)}{D(s)} = H\frac{(s - s_A)(s - s_B)\cdots(s - s_N)}{(s - s_1)(s - s_2)\cdots(s - s_M)} \qquad (13\text{-}13)$$

From Chap. 12 we recall that the zeros of the denominator, $s_1, s_2, \ldots, s_M$, which determine the source-free modes, are called the *poles* of the network function. Similarly the zeros of the numerator, $s_A, s_B, \ldots, s_N$, are called the *zeros* of the network function. We now come to a very important conclusion: For any source function e^{st} the component of the response due to the source is determined by the *differences* between s and the zero and pole values of the network function. In Art. 13-8 it is shown how this fact is used to simplify the evaluation of response components due to exponential sources. We also recall that when the value of s in the source function e^{st} is identical with a zero of the network function then the *component* of the response due to the source as well as the network function is zero.

Example 13-1. In the circuit of Fig. 13-2 determine the type of current source for which $v_s(t) \equiv 0$.

---

[1] Although s may be real or complex, boldface type will *not* be used to indicate general values of s in the remainder of this chapter.

Solution. In Fig. 13-2,

$$v(t) = \frac{(1+p)/p}{1+p+1/p}\, i(t)$$

or

$$v(t) = \frac{p+1}{p^2+p+1}\, i(t)$$

$N(s)/D(s) = (s+1)/(s^2+s+1)$. Hence a source $i(t) = Ae^{-t}$ will produce zero component of the response $v(t)$. It should be noted that in this example the result, zero, applies only to the component of the response due to the source for the particular response function under discussion. In Fig. 13-2, for example, $i_1(t) = [1/(p^2+p+1)]i(t)$, and $i_{1s} \neq 0$ when $i(t) = Ae^{-t}$.

13-5. Graphical Interpretation of Zeros and Poles. The general form of a transform network function $H(s)$ is given by Eq. (13-13),

$$H(s) = H\, \frac{(s-s_A)(s-s_B)\,\cdots\,(s-s_N)}{(s-s_1)(s-s_2)\,\cdots\,(s-s_M)}$$

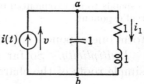

FIG. 13-2. Circuit for Example 13-1.

where the zeros and poles may be real, imaginary, or complex. In any event the value of $H(s)$ for any given value of s is completely specified if all zero and pole locations are specified and if the (real) numerical constant H is known. Since the zero and pole values are generally complex, they can be made to correspond to points in the complex plane. Thus, if the zeros and poles of a (transform) network function are given in the complex-frequency plane, the function is specified except for the multiplying factor H. We shall follow the practice of marking the poles by a cross (x) and the zeros by a small circle (o) in the s plane as shown in Fig. 13-3.

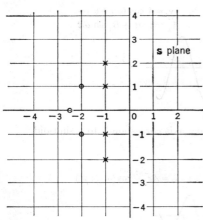

FIG. 13-3. Pole-zero locations for a network function.

The location of zeros and poles in Fig. 13-3 gives the following information:

$$H(s) = H\, \frac{(s+2.5)(s+2-j)(s+2+j)}{(s+1-j)(s+1+j)(s+1-j2)(s+1+j2)}$$

It is seen that, from the location of the poles alone, we know that the free component of the response to any source function is

$$y(t)_f = K_1 e^{(-1+j)t} + K_2 e^{(-1-jt)} + K_3 e^{(-1+j2)t} + K_4 e^{(-1-j2)t}$$

or

$$y(t)_f = \mathrm{Re}\,(2K_1 e^{-t}e^{jt}) + \mathrm{Re}\,(2K_3 e^{-t}e^{j2t})$$

We can correlate the location of poles and the free modes as follows:

1. Pole on the real axis (Fig. 13-4).   The free mode is an exponential function with real exponent.

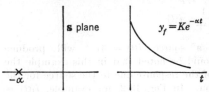

2. A pair of conjugate poles on the imaginary axis at $s = \pm j\omega$ (Fig. 13-5).   The free modes form one sinusoid.

3. A pair of conjugate poles in the left half plane with conjugate complex values (Fig. 13-6) of $s = -\alpha \pm j\omega$.   The two free modes

FIG. 13-4. A pole on the real axis corresponds to an exponential function with real exponent.

form one exponentially damped sinusoid.

Multiplicity.   So far we have assumed that all the poles arise from simple roots of the characteristic equation; i.e., in the equation

$$(s - s_1)(s - s_2) \cdots (s - s_M) = 0$$

$s_j \neq s_k$; that is, no two factors are identical.   We know already (e.g., from the critically damped R-L-C circuit) that it is possible for two or

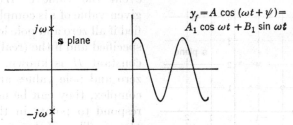

FIG. 13-5. A pair of poles on the imaginary axis corresponds to a sinusoid.

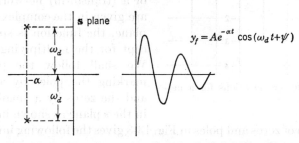

FIG. 13-6. A pair of poles in conjugate locations in the left-half s plane corresponds to an exponentially damped sinusoid.

more poles to coincide.   Such poles are called *multiple poles*.   Graphically we shall represent such multiple poles by a cross together with a roman numeral to indicate the multiplicity of the pole.   We can classify multiple poles as follows:

1. Double pole on the negative real axis (Fig. 13-7a) at $s = -\alpha$.

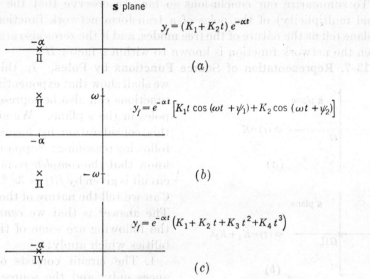

$$y_f = (K_1 + K_2 t)\, e^{-\alpha t}$$

(a)

$$y_f = e^{-\alpha t}\left[K_1 t \cos(\omega t + \psi_1) + K_2 \cos(\omega t + \psi_2)\right]$$

(b)

$$y_f = e^{-\alpha t}\left(K_1 + K_2 t + K_3 t^2 + K_4 t^3\right)$$

(c)

Fig. 13-7. Multiple poles and their significance.

This corresponds to a factor $(s + \alpha)^2$ in the characteristic equation. Hence the free modes corresponding to this are $y_f = (K_1 + K_2 t)e^{-\alpha t}$.

2. Double poles at complex conjugate values of s as shown in Fig. 13-7b. Since a double pole at $s = -\alpha + j\omega$ corresponds to the modes $(A_1 + A_2 t)e^{(-\alpha + j\omega)t}$, the two complex conjugate double poles correspond to the four modes $A_1 e^{(-\alpha+j\omega)t} + A_1^* e^{(-\alpha-j\omega)t} + A_2 t e^{(-\alpha+j\omega)t} + A_2^* t e^{(-\alpha-j\omega)t}$ or

$$y_f = e^{-\alpha t}[K_1 t \cos(\omega t + \psi_1) + K_2 \cos(\omega t + \psi_2)]$$

3. **Higher multiplicity.** The interpretation for multiplicity of orders higher than II should now be clear. For example, the fourth-order pole shown in Fig. 13-7c corresponds to the response component

$$y_f(t) = (K_1 + K_2 t + K_3 t^2 + K_4 t^3)e^{-\alpha t}$$

13-6. The Origin in the s Plane. A mode $e^{-\alpha t}$ corresponds to a pole $s = -\alpha$ in the s plane. If $\alpha \to 0$, the pole moves to the origin. Hence a simple pole at the origin corresponds

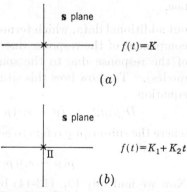

Fig. 13-8. Poles at the origin of the s plane.

to a constant term in the free response as illustrated in Fig. 13-8a. Similarly a double pole at the origin corresponds to the $\lim_{\alpha \to 0} (K_1 + K_2 t)e^{-\alpha t}$ as illustrated in Fig. 13-8b.

To summarize our conclusions so far, we observe that the location (and multiplicity) of the poles of a transform network function in the s plane tell us the nature of the free modes, and if the zeros also are known, then the network function is known to within a factor H.

13-7. Representation of Source Functions by Poles.

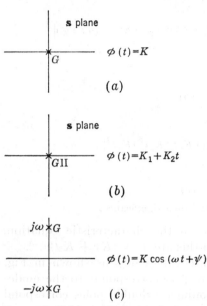

FIG. 13-9. Poles marked with the letter G represent modes of the source function.

In this article we shall show that exponential source functions can also be represented by poles in the s plane. We are led to this consideration by means of the following reasoning: Suppose that we know that the *complete* response of a circuit is given by $f(t) = 3e^{-t} + 4e^{-2t}$. Can we tell the nature of the circuit? The answer is that we *cannot* since the following are some of the possibilities which apply:

1. The circuit consists of resistances only, and the source has the form $Ae^{-t} + Be^{-2t}$.

2. The circuit is an R-L circuit *or* an R-C circuit with time constant either 1 or $\frac{1}{2}$, and the source is either Be^{-2t} or Ae^{-t}.

3. The circuit is a source-free R-L-C circuit.

It is therefore clear that in the complete response we cannot tell, without additional data, which terms are free modes and which terms form the component of the response due to an exponential source (the component of the response due to the source is also called the sum of the *forced modes*). To show how this situation arises mathematically, consider the equation

$$D(p)y(t) = (p - s_1)(p - s_2) \cdots (p - s_n)y(t) = e^{s_g t} \qquad (13\text{-}14)$$

where the subscript g refers to generator. If Eq. (13-14) is differentiated, we have

$$p(p - s_1)(p - s_2) \cdots (p - s_n)y(t) = s_g e^{s_g t} \qquad (13\text{-}15)$$

Now we multiply Eq. (13-14) by $-s_g$ and add to (13-15),

$$(p - s_g)D(p)y(t) = 0 \qquad (13\text{-}16)$$

Consequently the inhomogeneous equation (13-14) is equivalent to the homogeneous equation (13-16). The forced mode $Ae^{s_g t}$, which forms the component of the response due to the source in Eq. (13-14), is a free mode of Eq. (13-16).

This discussion indicates that we can represent the exponential sources in the s plane by poles in the same manner as a free mode is characterized by a pole. To distinguish these poles from the poles of the network function, the letter G will appear near the pole symbol. Thus a d-c source is represented by the pole at the origin as shown in Fig. 13-9a. A ramp-plus a step-function source is illustrated in Fig. 13-9b. A sinusoidal source is represented by the two poles on the axis of imaginaries as shown in Fig. 13-9c.

In order to avoid confusion, the poles of the network function are sometimes marked; we shall use the letter F (for free) to mark poles of the network function.

At this point it is clear what happens if a pole of the network function coincides with a pole of the source function: the complete response will have a term due to a double pole. Thus, in Fig. 13-10a, the complete response is $K_1 e^{-\alpha t} + K_2 e^{s_g t}$, where $K_1 e^{-\alpha t}$ is the free mode and $K_2 e^{s_g t}$ is the forced mode. In Fig. 13-10b the source was changed so that $s_g = -\alpha$. In this case the complete response is $(K_1 + K_2 t)e^{-\alpha t}$, where $K_2 \equiv 0$ if the source is set to zero. Hence $K_2 t e^{-\alpha t}$ is the component of the response due to the source. If a source $A e^{-\alpha t}$ is impressed on a network which has a double pole at $s = -\alpha$ (see Fig. 13-10c), a triple pole results; the forced mode (i.e., the component of the response due to the source) is $K_3 t^2 e^{-\alpha t}$.

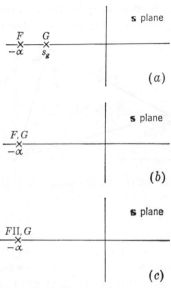

FIG. 13-10. Poles which represent the complete response. (a) The network has a simple pole on the real axis, and the source is an exponential function whose time constant is not the time constant of the network. (b) The mode of the network and of the source coincide to give rise to a double pole. (c) If the network has a double pole and the pole of the source function coincides with this point, then a triple pole results.

13-8. Graphical Determination of Forced Modes. We have seen that, if a source function $\phi(t) = A e^{s_g t}$ is impressed on a network, then, if s_g is not a pole of the network function, the response component due to the source (forced mode) is

$$y(t)_s = \frac{N(s_g)}{D(s_g)} A e^{s_g t} = H(s_g) A e^{s_g t}$$

or
$$y(t)_s = H \frac{(s_g - s_A)(s_g - s_B) \cdots (s_g - s_N)}{(s_g - s_1)(s_g - s_2) \cdots (s_g - s_M)} A e^{s_g t}$$

Hence the evaluation of the complete response depends on the evaluation of products of the form $\prod_k (s_g - s_k)$.   Since each term $s_g - s_k$ may be a complex number, it is convenient to carry out the multiplication and division in polar form.   The values of the factors $s_g - s_k$ can be obtained with ease, in polar form, from the s-plane diagram.

Suppose we wish to find the factor $s_g - s_1$, where s_g and s_1 are as

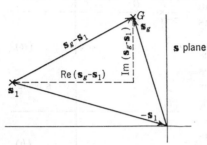

shown in Fig. 13-11; that is, we wish to subtract two complex numbers. Since the subtraction of complex numbers is identical to vector subtraction, the vector drawn from the origin to s_g represents s_g.   The vector *from* s_1 *to* the origin represents $-s_1$. Hence the line *from* s_1 *to* s_g represents the complex number $s_g - s_1$. The transform network function can therefore be evaluated as follows:

FIG. 13-11. The line from s_1 to s_g represents the factor $s_g - s_1$.

1. Join all zero points to the s_g point, and determine the factors in the numerator ($s_g - s_A$, $s_g - s_B$, . . .).

2. Join all pole points to the s_g point, and determine the factors in the denominator ($s_g - s_1$, $s_g - s_2$, . . .).

3. Multiply the factors of (1), and divide by the product of the factors in (2).   Multiply the result by H.

This method applies only when s_g is not a pole of the network function.

Example 13-2.   In a network, current source $i(t)$ produces response $v(t)$ such that

$$v(t) = \frac{p}{p^2 + p + 1} i(t)$$

Use the graphical method to determine the component of the response due to (a) a sinusoidal source $i(t) = 10 \cos (t + 30°)$; (b) a source $i(t) = 10e^{-t} \cos t$.

Solution.   The network function is

$$H(s) = \frac{s}{s^2 + s + 1} = \frac{s}{\left[s + \dfrac{(1 - j\sqrt{3})}{2} \right] \left[s + \dfrac{(1 + j\sqrt{3})}{2} \right]}$$

The poles and zeros are located in Fig. 13-12a at $s_A = 0$ a zero, $s_1 = -\frac{1}{2} + j(\sqrt{3}/2)$ a pole, $s_2 = -\frac{1}{2} - j(\sqrt{3}/2)$ a pole.

(a) The sinusoidal source $10 \cos (t + 30°)$ can be written as $10 \operatorname{Re} e^{j(t+\pi/6)}$; hence we consider the source $e^{j(t+\pi/6)}$.   This source is represented by a pole at $s = j$ as marked in Fig. 13-12a.   The numerator is $s_g - 0 = s_g = j$.   The denominator is $(s - s_1)(s - s_2)$. Measuring, $|s_g - s_1| = 0.52$, $\theta_1 = 15.0°$, $|s_g - s_2| = 1.93$, $\theta_2 = 75°$.   Hence

$$\frac{N(s_g)}{D(s_g)} = \frac{1\underline{/90°}}{(0.52)(1.93)\underline{/90°}} = 1\underline{/0}$$

Hence $v_s = 10 \cos (t + 30°)$.

(b) When the source is $i(t) = 10e^{-t} \cos t$, it is represented by a pole at $s = -1 + j$ as shown in Fig. 13-12b. Now $s_g - s_1 = 0.52\underline{/165°}$, $s_g - s_2 = 1.93\underline{/105°}$, $D(s_g) = 1\underline{/270°}$, $N(s_g) = 1.41\underline{/135°}$, $H(s_g) = 1.41\underline{/-135°}$, $v_s(t) = 14.1e^{-t} \cos (t - 135°)$.

It is clear that the graphical procedure is completely equivalent to the analytical procedure but can result in a considerable saving of effort when the transfer function has many factors. We observe, however, that the

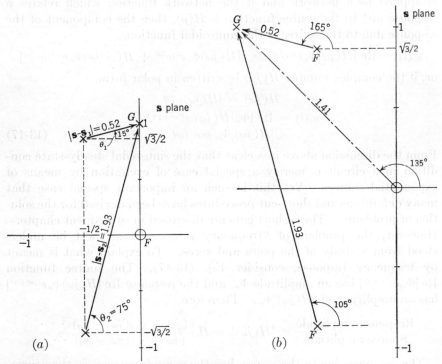

FIG. 13-12. Examples of graphical construction of the component of the response due to an exponential source.

graphical procedure makes it *necessary* to factor $N(s)$ and $D(s)$; this algebraic procedure is not necessary with the analytical method.

13-9. An Application of the Pole-Zero Diagram. *A-C Steady-state Response.* We have seen that specification of the pole-zero locations (and the scale factor H) of a network function is equivalent to specifying the differential equation which relates a response of that network to a source function. As a result, in Example 13-2 we observed that components of response due to exponential sources can be calculated directly if the poles and zeros (as well as the scale factor H) are specified. In the following articles and chapters there are numerous occasions to return to these concepts. This article deals with an application of pole-zero diagrams, namely, the evaluation of the component of response due to a sinusoidal source.

A sinusoidal source can be considered the superposition of two sources of the form $e^{j\omega t}$ and $e^{-j\omega t}$, that is, two sources of the form $e^{s_g t}$, where s_g is imaginary. Hence, if a source

$$\phi(t) = \Phi_m \cos(\omega t + \gamma) = \text{Re}\,(\Phi_m e^{j\gamma} e^{j\omega t}) = \tfrac{1}{2}\Phi_m(e^{j\gamma} e^{j\omega t} + e^{-j\gamma} e^{-j\omega t})$$

is applied to a network and if the network function which relates a response $y(t)$ to the source function is $H(p)$, then the component of the response due to the source is the sinusoidal function,

$$y_s(t) = \text{Re}\,[H(j\omega)\Phi_m e^{j\gamma} e^{j\omega t}] = \tfrac{1}{2}[H(j\omega)\Phi_m e^{j\gamma} e^{j\omega t} + H(-j\omega)\Phi_m e^{-j\gamma} e^{-j\omega t}]$$

or, if the complex number $H(j\omega)$ is written in polar form,

$$H(j\omega) = |H(j\omega)|\,\underline{/\theta}$$
$$y_s(t) = \text{Re}\,[\Phi_m |H(j\omega)| e^{i(\omega t + \gamma + \theta)}]$$
$$= |H(j\omega)|\Phi_m \cos(\omega t + \gamma + \theta) \qquad (13\text{-}17)$$

From the discussion above it is clear that the sinusoidal steady-state condition in a circuit is merely a special case of excitation by means of exponential sources. Yet this is such an important special case that many definitions and short-cut procedures have been devised for the solution of problems. These short cuts are discussed in subsequent chapters. However, the problem of "frequency response" can best be understood from a study of the poles and zeros. To explain what is meant by frequency response, consider Eq. (13-17). The source function $\text{Re}\,[\Phi_m e^{i(\omega t + \gamma)}]$ has an amplitude Φ_m, and the response $\text{Re}\,[H(j\omega)\Phi_m e^{(j\omega t + \gamma)}]$ has an amplitude of $|H(j\omega)|\Phi_m$. Therefore

$$\frac{\text{Response amplitude}}{\text{Source amplitude}} = |H(j\omega)| = H \left| \frac{(j\omega - s_A)(j\omega - s_B)\,\cdots}{(j\omega - s_1)(j\omega - s_2)\,\cdots} \right|$$

The response due to the source has the same frequency as the source. Hence, if we know the ratio of the amplitudes of these two functions (as well as their phase angle), we have complete information about the response. To study the effect of changing the frequency on this "response ratio," we note that in the above expression the absolute value of products is the same as the product of the absolute values. The study of the effect of variation of frequency can be accomplished by examining each of the factors $|j\omega - s_k|$. If such a factor is in the numerator and increases, the response ratio will increase; if it is in the denominator, the response ratio will decrease. Because the magnitude of each factor $j\omega - s_k$ is represented in the s plane by the line joining the point s_k to the point $j\omega$, the variation of this magnitude can often easily be seen from an inspection of the pole-zero diagram. Similarly, if the radian frequency of the source, ω, remains fixed, the effect of changing the pole-zero locations of the network can be predicted. As we have stated, subsequent chapters will deal with many general problems of this type; in this article several simple examples will serve to illustrate the basic idea.

Example 13-3. A voltage source $V_m \cos (\omega t + \gamma)$, whose amplitude V_m is constant, is applied to the series R-L circuit as shown in Fig. 13-13a. Discuss the amplitude variation of $i_s(t)$ as the radian frequency ω is increased.

Solution. The transform admittance of the circuit is

$$Y(s) = \frac{1}{R + sL} = \frac{1}{L}\frac{1}{s + R/L}$$

For $s_g = j\omega$, $Y(s_g) = Y(j\omega) = (1/L)[1/(j\omega + R/L)]$. For a frequency ω_1 corresponding to the point $s = j\omega_1$ the factor $j\omega + R/L$ is represented in the s plane by the line from F to G_1. If the radian frequency is increased to G_2, the factor $|j\omega + R/L|$ is given by the length FG_2. We observe that, as ω increases, the distance FG increases, so that the magnitude of the factor $j\omega + R/L$ increases. Since this factor is in the denominator of the transform network function, the amplitude of $i(t)$ decreases with increasing frequency.

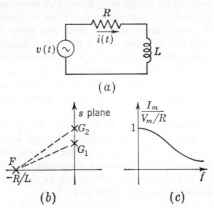

(a)

(b)

(c)

Fig. 13-13. (a) An R-L circuit in the sinusoidal steady state and (b) the corresponding admittance pole-zero diagram at two frequencies (corresponding to poles at G_1 and G_2). In (c) the variation of the response ratio as a function of frequency is shown.

Example 13-4. In the circuit of Fig. 13-14, $v(t)$ is a variable-frequency source. Discuss the ratio of the response amplitude of v_{ab} to the source amplitude.

Solution. From voltage division

$$v_{ab}(t) = \frac{1 + 1/p}{4 + 1/p} v(t)$$

Hence the transform network function under consideration is

$$H(s) = \frac{1}{4}\frac{s + 1}{s + \frac{1}{4}}$$

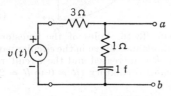

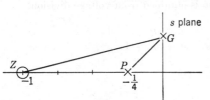

Fig. 13-14. Study of the transfer function which relates the amplitude of v_{ab} to the amplitude of $v(t)$ and the corresponding pole-zero diagram.

When $s_g = 0$ (d-c), the transform network function is 1. (This can also be deduced by observing that the capacitance is an open circuit for the d-c steady-state condition.) As the radian frequency of the source increases to G, with reference to Fig. 13-14, we observe that the distance PG increases more rapidly than the distance ZG. It follows that the amplitude ratio decreases with increasing frequency.

Example 13-5. A certain transform network function is given as

$$H(s) = \frac{s + 1}{(s + 1 - j3)(s + 1 + j3)}$$

Discuss the amplitude response ratio in the sinusoidal steady state.

Solution. Referring to the pole-zero diagram of Fig. 13-15, we observe that the distance from Z to G is a minimum when $\omega = 0$. As ω increases, the G point moves upward on the $j\omega$ axis; hence P_1G decreases, and P_2G and ZG increase. The situation is evidently more complex than in Example 13-4. Nevertheless, near $\omega = 3$, P_1G decreases more rapidly than the other two factors increase. We therefore expect that the response ratio will reach a maximum as the G point moves close to P_1. By taking the limit as $s \to \infty$ we observe that $H(s)$ approaches zero for frequencies far beyond $\omega = 3$. A curve of $|H(j\omega)|$ can easily be constructed by *measuring* the distances P_1G, P_2G, ZG for several values of ω. Then for each value of ω the response ratio is the quotient $ZG/(P_1G)(P_2G)$.

Example 13-6. In the series R-L-C circuit of Fig. 13-16a, R is adjustable, and L and C are unity. When a sinusoidal source of radian frequency 1 is impressed, show that the voltage v_{ab} and the source voltage are in phase, independently of the value of R.

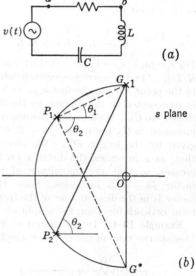

(a)

(b)

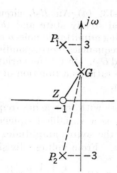

FIG. 13-15. Pole-zero diagram for Example 13-5.

FIG. 13-16. Poles of the transform admittance move in the circular path as R is increased and the circuit remains oscillatory ($R = 0$ to $R = 2$).

Solution. The transform network function is obtained from voltage division,

$$H(s) = \frac{R}{R + s + 1/s} = \frac{sR}{s^2 + sR + 1}$$

or

$$H(s) = R\frac{s}{(s - s_1)(s - s_2)}$$

where $s_{1,2} = -\frac{1}{2}R \pm \sqrt{\frac{1}{4}R^2 - 1}$. Now, when $R^2 < 4$, the roots are complex conjugates which move on the (unit radius) semicircle shown in Fig. 13-16b as R is varied (see Art. 9-15). The transform network function has a zero at $s = 0$. The line $0G$ makes a right angle with the horizontal. Hence the angle in the numerator of $H(j\omega)$ is 90°. The angle in the denominator is $\theta_1 + \theta_2$. Hence the angle of the network function for $s_g = j$ is $90° - \theta_1 - \theta_2$. Constructing line P_1G^*, we observe that P_1GG^* and P_2GG^* are congruent triangles. Hence angle GP_1G^* is $\theta_1 + \theta_2 = 90°$. It follows that the angle of $H(j1) = 0$ for $R^2 \le 4$. Proof of this fact for $R^2 > 4$ is left as an exercise for the reader.

In the examples above we have seen how the pole-zero diagram gives information about the network behavior under various conditions. The following are several conclusions which we can draw from these examples. First, we note that those zeros and poles which are closest to the pole which represents the source function have the largest influence on response changes because the corresponding distances will vary most "rapidly." This useful fact can be developed into an approximation scheme when only dominant poles and zeros are considered. This is discussed in Chap. 15.

In the above paragraphs we have briefly discussed the frequency response of a network. In some cases, as in Example 13-6, the frequency of a source is fixed, but one or more of the passive elements of the network may be changed. In such cases it is of interest to study the effect of such a change on a given component of the response due to the source.

We note that every one of the pole-zero locations in a network depends on all its passive elements. Thus, for example, both poles in Fig. 13-16b change location when one element, R, is varied. This fact complicates the study of networks from pole-zero diagrams when element values are changed, because a change in a single element value changes all pole-zero locations. For this reason a slightly different approach to the problem of element variation is introduced; this matter is also discussed in Chap. 15. One of the procedures used in the synthesis of networks is to choose "desirable" pole-zero locations to obtain a desired frequency response. The "rules" of such procedure will not be discussed here, but it is evident that application of such a procedure requires a knowledge of the regions in which the poles and zeros of a network function may be located. An introduction to the solution of this problem is dealt with in Arts. 13-12 to 13-14.

13-10. Response Due to Source Functions Which Are Represented by Multiple Poles. In the preceding articles it has been shown how the transform network function may be used to study the component of the response due to an exponential source function $e^{s_g t}$ provided that s_g is not a pole of the network function. Thus, if a response $y(t)$ is related to a source $\phi(t)$ through the equation

$$y(t) = \frac{N(p)}{D(p)} \phi(t)$$

then if $\phi(t) = e^{s_g t}$ and if $D(s_g) \neq 0$,

$$y_s(t) = \frac{N(s_g)}{D(s_g)} e^{s_g t} = H(s_g)e^{s_g t} \qquad (13\text{-}18)$$

It has also been shown that the component of the response due to a constant source of unit value is given by Eq. (13-18) with s_g set to zero.

We now consider the problem of calculating the component of the response due to a source of the form te^{st}; this form includes the ramp function as a special case, that is, $te^{st} = t$ when $s = 0$. For a source[1] $\phi(t) = te^{st}$ the general equilibrium equation is

$$D(p)y(t) = N(p)(te^{st}) \tag{13-19}$$

We observe that if the source is of the form e^{st} then Eq. (13-18) is a solution of the equilibrium equation. Hence if (13-18) is substituted in the equilibrium equation, it satisfies this equation, i.e.,

$$D(p)[H(s)e^{st}] = N(p)e^{st} \tag{13-20}$$

In Eq. (13-20) the independent variable is t, and s is a parameter. We may, however, *consider s to be an independent variable* and let t be a parameter. This corresponds to asking the question: How does the response at a given instant t depend on the value of s? Considering s to be the independent variable, Eq. (13-20) is now differentiated with respect to s,

$$\frac{d}{ds}\{D(p)[H(s)e^{st}]\} = \frac{d}{ds}[N(p)e^{st}]$$

or
$$D(p)\left\{\frac{d}{ds}[H(s)e^{st}]\right\} = N(p)\left(\frac{d}{ds}e^{st}\right) = N(p)[te^{st}]$$

Hence
$$y_s = \frac{d}{ds}[H(s)e^{st}] \tag{13-21}$$

is a solution of the equation

$$D(p)(y) = N(p)(te^{st})$$

This result may be extended to show that

$$y_s = \frac{d^n}{ds^n}[H(s)e^{st}]$$

is a solution of the equation

$$y = H(p)(t^n e^{st})$$

Example 13-7. Calculate the component of the response due to the source $v(t) = at$ in an R-L circuit which is defined by the equation

$$(p + 5)i = v(t) = at$$

Solution. We recognize that $at = (ate^{st})_{s=0}$. Hence

$$i_s = \left[\frac{d}{ds}\left(\frac{ae^{st}}{s + 5}\right)\right]_{s=0}$$

[1] In the development which follows it is necessary to consider s, the location of the source pole, a variable. In the final result s_0 will, as is customary, denote a specific numerical value of s.

Since
$$\frac{d}{ds}\left(\frac{e^{st}}{s+5}\right) = \frac{(s+5)t-1}{(s+5)^2}e^{st}$$

$$i_s = \left[\frac{(s+5)t-1}{(s+5)^2}ae^{st}\right]_{s\to 0} = a\frac{(0+5)t-1}{(0+5)^2}e^{0t}$$

or
$$i_s = \frac{a}{25}(-1+5t)$$

Example 13-8. In a certain network a response y is related to a source $\phi(t)$ through the equation

$$y(t) = \frac{p+1}{6p+5}\phi(t)$$

Calculate the component of the response due to the source if (a) $\phi(t) = 100t$; (b) $\phi(t) = te^{-t}$; (c) $\phi(t) = 50t\cos t$.

Solution. The transform network function is $(s+1)/(6s+5)$. We shall first find the response due to a source te^{st},

$$y_s(t) = \frac{d}{ds}\left(\frac{s+1}{6s+5}e^{st}\right)$$

and
$$y_s(t) = \frac{(6s+5)[(s+1)te^{st}+e^{st}] - (s+1)e^{st}(6)}{(6s+5)^2}$$

Simplifying,
$$y_s = \frac{-1 + (6s^2+11s+5)t}{(6s+5)^2}e^{st}$$

For (a) the source scale factor $\Phi_0 = 100$, and $s_g = 0$. Hence

$$y_s = 100\frac{-1+5t}{25} = -4+20t \qquad\qquad Ans.\ (a)$$

For (b), $\Phi_0 = 1$, and $s_g = -1$; hence

$$y_s = \frac{-1+(6-11+5)t}{(-1)^2}e^{-t} = -1e^{-t} \qquad\qquad Ans.\ (b)$$

In this answer the coefficient of the te^{-t} term is zero. This is explained by observing that the source is represented by a double pole at $s = s_g = -1$, while the transform network function has a zero at $s = -1$. The result is that the response has the form which would result if there were a simple pole at $s = -1$. This matter is discussed further in the next article.

For (c), $\Phi_0 = 50$, and $s_g = j$. We find the response to $50te^{jt}$ and take the real part of the result,

$$y_s = \text{Re}\left[50\frac{-1+(-6+j11+5)t}{(6j+5)^2}e^{jt}\right]$$

or
$$y_s = \text{Re}\left[-\frac{50}{(6j+5)^2}e^{jt} + 50\frac{-1+j11}{(6j+5)^2}te^{jt}\right]$$

and
$$y_s = 0.82\cos(t+79.6°) + 9.06t\cos(t-5.2°) \qquad Ans.\ (c)$$

Another method of showing how the component of the response due to the source is obtained in Eq. (13-19) consists in introducing into it as solution a linear combination of the source function and its derivatives, i.e.,

$$y_s = (K_1 + K_2t)e^{st}$$

Hence the values of K_1 and K_2 are found from the equation

$$D(p)[(K_1 + K_2t)e^{st}] = N(p)(te^{st}) \qquad\qquad (13\text{-}22)$$

Evidently $D(p)(K_1 e^{st}) = D(s)K_1 e^{st}$.   Consider now a term of the form

$$A(p)te^{st}$$

where $A(p)$ is the linear operator

$$A(p) = a_0 + a_1 p + \cdots + a_n p^n$$

The operation which is required consists in forming the nth time derivative of the function te^{st}.   We observe the following:

$$p(te^{st}) = e^{st} + ste^{st}$$
$$p^2(te^{st}) = 2se^{st} + s^2 te^{st}$$
$$p^3(te^{st}) = 3s^2 e^{st} + s^3 te^{st}$$

Hence it appears that

$$p^k(te^{st}) = ks^{k-1}e^{st} + s^k te^{st} \tag{13-23}$$

If Eq. (13-23) is true, then k may be replaced with $k + 1$ or

$$p^{k+1}(te^{st}) = (k + 1)s^k e^{st} + s^{k+1}te^{st} \tag{13-24}$$

The same result should be obtained if Eq. (13-23) is differentiated, i.e.,

$$p[p^k(te^{st})] = ks^k e^{st} + s^{k+1}te^{st} + s^k e^{st} \tag{13-25}$$

Since the result expressed in Eq. (13-25) is identical to the result expressed in Eq. (13-24), the hypothesis, (13-23), if true for $k = 1$, is by induction true for all k.   It has already been shown that Eq. (13-23) is true for $k = 1$; hence it is a correct formula. This result is now applied to the operation

$$(a_0 + a_1 p + a_2 p + \cdots + a_k p^k + \cdots + a_n p^n)(te^{st}) = A(p)(te^{st})$$

Thus

$$A(p)(te^{st}) = (a_1 + 2a_2 s + \cdots + ka_k s^{k-1} + \cdots + na_n s^{n-1})e^{st}$$
$$+ (a_0 + a_1 s + a_2 s^2 + \cdots + a_k s^k + \cdots + a_n s^n)te^{st} \tag{13-26}$$

In Eq. (13-26) we recognize that since

$$A(s) = a_0 + a_1 s + a_2 s^2 + \cdots + a_k s^k + \cdots + a_n s^n$$
$$\frac{d}{ds}A(s) = a_1 + 2a_2 s + \cdots + ka_k s^{k-1} + \cdots + na_n s^{n-1}$$

Consequently
$$A(p)(te^{st}) = \left[\frac{d}{ds}A(s) + A(s)t\right]e^{st} \tag{13-27}$$

Observing that both $N(p)$ and $D(p)$ have the form of $A(p)$, Eq. (13-27) is now substituted in Eq. (13-22).   For convenience the prime is used to denote *differentiation with respect to s*, for example, $dN(s)/ds \equiv N'(s)$.   Thus

$$D(p)[(K_1 + K_2 t)e^{st}] = D(s)(K_1 + K_2 t)e^{st} + D'(s)K_2 e^{st} \tag{13-28}$$
$$N(p)(te^{st}) = [N(s)t + N'(s)]e^{st} \tag{13-29}$$

Equating Eqs. (13-28) and (13-29),

$$D(s)K_1 e^{st} + D'(s)K_2 e^{st} + K_2 D(s)te^{st} \equiv N'(s)e^{st} + N(s)te^{st} \tag{13-30}$$

Since Eq. (13-30) must hold for all t, the coefficients of te^{st} and of e^{st} on each side, are, respectively, set equal,

$$K_2 D(s) = N(s) \tag{13-31a}$$
$$K_1 D(s) + K_2 D'(s) = N'(s) \tag{13-31b}$$

Solving (13-31a), $K_2 = N(s)/D(s)$. Substituting this result in (13-31b), we have

$$K_1 = \frac{N'(s)D(s) - D'(s)N(s)}{D^2(s)}$$

which we recognize as the derivative of the transform network function $H(s)$ with respect to s,

$$K_1 = \frac{d}{ds} H(s)$$

The component of the response due to a source te^{st} is therefore given by

$$y_s = \left[\frac{d}{ds} H(s) + H(s)t\right] e^{st} \qquad (13\text{-}32)$$

Equation (13-32) can be simplified further. Consider *the derivative with respect to s* of $H(s)e^{st}$, that is,

$$\frac{d}{ds} [H(s)e^{st}] = [H'(s) + tH(s)]e^{st}$$

Thus the desired response component has the form

$$y_s = \frac{d}{ds} [H(s)e^{st}] \qquad (13\text{-}33)$$

It must be pointed out that, if the function y_s is desired for a particular value $s = s_g$, then the differentiation indicated in (13-33) must be performed before the numerical value of s is substituted.

The result of the above discussion is summarized as follows: The component of the response due to a source $\phi(t) = \Phi_0 t e^{s_g t}$ may be obtained from the transform network function which relates the desired response to the source by the formula

$$y_s(t) = \Phi_0 \left\{\frac{d}{ds} [H(s)e^{st}]\right\}_{s=s_g} \qquad (13\text{-}34)$$

provided that s_g is not a pole of $H(s)$.

13-11. Complete Response to Exponential Sources from the Pole–Zero Location. In Art. 13-7 we have shown that a pole in the s plane can represent either a free mode or a forced mode, and we have used this result to study forced modes; in particular, we used this idea to study the effect of impressing a source which is also a free mode. Now we shall show how the same kind of reasoning can be used to *evaluate* the free component of the response. We start by recalling the component of the response due to an exponential source with unity scale factor $e^{s_g t}$,

$$y_s(t) = H(s_g)e^{s_g t} \qquad (13\text{-}35)$$

where $H(s_g) = HN(s_g)/D(s_g)$, $D(s_g) \neq 0$ and the transform network function is

$$H(s) = H \frac{(s - s_A)(s - s_B) \cdots (s - s_N)}{(s - s_1)(s - s_2) \cdots (s - s_M)} = H \frac{\displaystyle\prod_{k=A}^{N} (s - s_k)}{\displaystyle\prod_{k=1}^{M} (s - s_k)}$$

The term $H(s_g)e^{s_g t}$ is the component of the response due to the source in the equation

$$D(p)y(t) = N(p)e^{s_g t}$$

It is also a solution of the equation

$$(p - s_g)D(p)f(t) = 0$$

i.e., the equation

$$(p - s_g) \prod_{k=1}^{M} (s - s_k)f(t) = 0 \tag{13-36a}$$

Let $D_1(p) = (p - s_g)D(p)$. The component of the response which corresponds to the mode s_g is given by Eq. (13-35) according to the following rule:

$$y_s(t) = \frac{N(s_g)e^{s_g t}}{[D_1(s_g)/(s - s_g)]_{s=s_g}} = \frac{N(s_g)}{D(s_g)} e^{s_g t} \tag{13-36b}$$

Now it is reasonable to ask why the result, Eq. (13-36b), applies only to $s = s_g$. Should it not apply to all poles of the network function? By advanced methods (transformation calculus) it can be shown that this result, Eq. (13-36b), applies to all poles and hence the full component of the response can be obtained by considering each pole to be due to a source function in turn and superposing the result. If the continuity conditions are not zero, then the initial-energy storage should be represented by initial-condition generators and the full components of the response due to the initial-condition generators are added to the full component of the response. The procedure for obtaining the complete response due to an exponential source is illustrated in the following examples.

Example 13-9. A source $v(t) = 3e^{-2t}$ is applied to a series R-L circuit. If $R = 1$, $L = 1$, calculate the complete response $i(t)$ if $i(0^+) = 0$.

Solution. The equilibrium equation is

$$(p + 1)i = 3e^{-2t} \qquad i = \frac{3}{p + 1} e^{-2t}$$

The pole of the network function is $s_1 = -1$, corresponding to the free component $K_1 e^{-t}$. The forced component is $K_2 e^{-2t}$, corresponding to $s_g = -2$. From the above discussion

$$D_1(s) = (s - s_g)D(s) = (s + 2)(s + 1)$$

$$i_s = \left[\frac{3}{D_1(s)/(s - s_g)} e^{st} \right]_{s=s_g} = \left(\frac{3}{s + 1} e^{st} \right)_{s=-2} = -3e^{-2t}$$

and $\qquad i_f = \left[\frac{3}{D_1(s)/(s - s_1)} e^{st} \right]_{s=s_1} = \left(\frac{3}{s + 2} e^{st} \right)_{s=-1} = 3e^{-t}$

Hence the full component of the response is $3(e^{-t} - e^{-2t})$.

Example 13-10. Obtain the full component of the response of the equation

$$(p + 1)(p + 3)f(t) = (p + 2)e^{-4t}$$

Solution. Since $D_1(s) = (s + 4)(s + 1)(s + 3)$, we have

$$f(t) = \frac{-4 + 2}{(-4 + 1)(-4 + 3)} e^{-4t} + \frac{-1 + 2}{(-1 + 4)(-1 + 3)} e^{-t} + \frac{-3 + 2}{(-3 + 4)(-3 + 1)} e^{-3t}$$

or

$$f(t) = -\tfrac{2}{3}e^{-4t} + \tfrac{1}{6}e^{-t} + \tfrac{1}{2}e^{-3t}$$

The general procedure is summarized in the following formula: The full component of the response of the equation

$$f(t) = \frac{N(p)}{D(p)} A e^{s_g t}$$

(where $A e^{s_g t}$ is the source and the network function has M distinct poles) is

$$f(t) = \frac{N(s_g)}{D(s_g)} e^{s_g t} + \sum_{k=1}^{M} \left[\frac{(s - s_k) N(s)}{(s - s_g) D(s)} \right]_{s = s_k} e^{s_k t}$$

if $D(s_g) \neq 0$.

13-12. Introduction to Network Synthesis and Physical Realizability.

When the value of the passive elements and the waveform of the sources in a network are known, the response of the network is obtained through the computation of the relevant network function.   The computation of the network function and determination of the response of the network are the subject matter of *network analysis*.

In problems of design the network is not known.   Instead the source and response are specified, and the proper network is to be "synthesized" to provide the desired response.   In the case of analysis, for a given source and network the response is unique and can always be computed. In synthesis, when the source and the desired response are specified there is no guarantee of the existence or uniqueness of the network, nor is there a standard method for establishing the structure of the desired network and the value of its elements.

Since the source and response are related by a network function, the problem of synthesis is that of design of a network with a specified network function.[1]   For example, the problem may be the design of a terminal pair whose transform impedance function is specified to be $as/(s + b)$.   A little thought shows that this is a parallel connection of a resistance and an inductance.   Alternatively a transfer function such as $a/(s + b)$ may be specified, and the design of a corresponding network may be required.

There are many procedures which give either approximate or, in some cases, exact solutions of a synthesis problem.   Before application of any one of these procedures, it must be established that the passive elements required for the synthesis of the network are R, L, C, or M elements whose values are positive and real numbers.   This requirement is referred to as the "realizability" of the network function.   For example, an impedance function $s/(s + 1)$ can be realized by connecting a 1-ohm resistance in parallel with a 1-henry inductance.   On the other hand, an

---

[1] In the study of transformation calculus it is shown that if the source $\phi(t)$ and response due to the source $y(t)$ are specified then the network function relating the source and response can be uniquely determined.

impedance function of the form $s/(s - 1)$ cannot be realized with passive elements.

13-13. Realizability of Driving-point Immittances. In this article a brief introductory treatment of the properties of driving-point immittance functions is presented. Some results are stated without proof, some with a plausible argument.[1]

From our study of network analysis we know that in a linear network with lumped elements the transform network functions are ratios of polynomials in s. Therefore the first requirement for the realizability of such a network function is that it be the ratio of two polynomials. Now, if the driving-point impedance of a terminal pair a-b is $Z_{ab} = A(s)/B(s)$, then if a current source $i(t)$ is applied to this terminal pair, the response is

$$v_{ab}(t) = Z_{ab}(p)i(t) = \frac{A(p)}{B(p)} i(t)$$

The source-free component of v_{ab} is given by $B(p)v_{ab}(t)_f = 0$, and the modes of this component of response are determined by the characteristic equation $B(s) = 0$. Since the source-free modes of a network must decay exponentially or be sinusoidal, it follows that the location of zeros of $B(s)$ in the s plane must be in the left half side of the plane, or on the imaginary axis. If a voltage source $v(t)$ is applied to the terminal pair a-b, then the current i_{ab} is given by $i_{ab}(t) = Y_{ab}(p)v(t)$, and since $Y_{ab} = 1/Z_{ab} = B(p)/A(p)$ the source-free modes of $i_{ab}(t)$ are given by $A(p)i_{ab}(t)_f = 0$. The roots of the characteristic equation $A(s) = 0$ determine these source-free modes and therefore must be located in the left half plane, or on the imaginary axis. Since the zeros of $B(s)$ and $A(s)$ are the poles and zeros of the driving-point immittance function, it follows that, for realizability, the poles and zeros of a driving point immittance function must be located in the left half plane, or on the imaginary axis.

It can be shown that if the poles and zeros of the network function are to be in the left half plane, or on the imaginary axis, then the coefficients of powers of s in both $A(s)$ and $B(s)$ must be positive.

The complex poles and zeros of a network function must occur as conjugates; otherwise, for a single characteristic root $s = -\alpha + j\omega$, the corresponding mode will be $e^{-\alpha t}e^{j\omega t}$, a complex function of time. This is not admissible since the physical response must be a real function of time.

Multiple poles may occur in the left half plane since a double pole at $s = -\alpha$ on the real axis corresponds to free responses of the form $te^{-\alpha t}$ and $e^{-\alpha t}$, which decay and therefore are permissible. Similarly double complex conjugate poles at $s = -\alpha \pm j\omega$ correspond to the modes of the

---

[1] A complete treatment of this subject may be found in E. A. Guillemin, "Synthesis of Passive Networks," John Wiley & Sons, New York, 1957.

form $te^{-\alpha t} \cos \omega t$ and $e^{-\alpha t} \cos \omega t$. These also decay and therefore are permissible.

A pair of simple poles at $s = \pm j\omega$ corresponds to free responses of sinusoidal form. This occurs when there is no dissipation of energy. However, a double pole at $s = \pm j\omega$ corresponds to source-free modes of the form $t \cos \omega t$. Such a mode increases with time and is not permissible as a free mode. Therefore, when the poles of a network function are located on the imaginary axis, they must be simple conjugate poles.

Another realizability condition for a driving-point immittance function is that the degree of the numerator and denominator polynomial cannot differ by more than 1. Thus, if

$$A(s) = \sum_{m=0}^{M} a_m s^m \quad \text{and} \quad B(s) = \sum_{n=0}^{N} b_n s^n$$

then $|M - N| \leq 1$. This means that either $M = N$ or they differ by 1.[1]

The conditions for physical realizability for driving-point immittances discussed in the paragraphs above are all deduced from the properties of the source-free response, in particular from the fact that the total initially stored energy, which is finite, cannot produce a response which increases without bound. These properties show that a passive lumped-element driving-point immittance function must satisfy the following requirements:

[1] To prove this statement we start with

$$Z_{ab}(s) = \frac{a_n s^n + a_{n-1} s^{n-1} + \cdots + a_1 s + a_0}{b_n s^n + b_{n-1} s^{n-1} + \cdots + b_1 s + b_0}$$

so that either $m = n$ or $m \neq n$. Now if $m = n$, then

$$Z_{ab}(s) = \frac{a_m s^m + a_{m-1} s^{m-1} + \cdots + a_1 s + a_0}{b_n s^n + b_{n-1} s^{n-1} + \cdots + b_1 s + b_0}$$

$$= \frac{a_n + \dfrac{a_{n-1}}{s} + \dfrac{a_{n-2}}{s^2} + \cdots + \dfrac{a_1}{s^{n-1}} + \dfrac{a_0}{s^n}}{b_n + \dfrac{b_{n-1}}{s} + \cdots + \dfrac{b_1}{s^{n-1}} + \dfrac{b_0}{s^n}}$$

so that $\lim_{s \to \infty} Z_{ab}(s) = a_n/b_n$ if $n = m$. Hence the point $s = \infty$ is neither a zero nor a pole of $Z_{ab}(s)$. Now if $n \neq m$, then $\lim_{s \to \infty} Z_{ab}(s) = 0$ or approaches infinity. Hence we have either a zero or a pole at infinity. Now it is an axiom that infinity in the s plane is a single point; i.e., if we imagine the s plane to be on the surface of a large (infinite) sphere with the origin at the "south pole," then infinity is at the "north pole." The imaginary axis which passes through this south pole also passes through the north pole. But zeros and poles on this axis must be simple. Hence the degree of the polynomial $A(s)$ cannot differ from the degree of the polynomial $B(s)$ by more than unity.

1. It is the ratio of polynomials with real positive coefficients.

2. The degree of the numerator polynomial may be the same as the degree of the denominator polynomial or may differ by unity.

3. No poles or zeros may be in the right-half s plane.

4. Poles and zeros on the imaginary axis must be simple.

5. Complex poles and zeros must occur in conjugate pairs.

"*Positive Real*" *Property.* The conditions enumerated above are necessary, but not sufficient. For example,

$$F(s) = \frac{s + 4}{s^2 + 2s + 5} = \frac{s + 4}{[s - (-1 + j2)][s - (-1 - j2)]}$$

satisfies the conditions stated above, but it is not a transform driving-point immittance. This is seen from the fact that, at a radian frequency $\omega = 5$, $F(j\omega) = (j5 + 4)/(-5^2 + j10 + 5)$, or

$$F(j\omega) = \frac{\sqrt{41}\ \underline{/51.4^\circ}}{10\ \sqrt{5}\ \underline{/153.4^\circ}} = 0.285\underline{/-102^\circ} = -0.06 - j0.28$$

If $F(s)$ were a driving-point immittance, then at $s = j5$ its negative real part would represent *negative* resistance, since, in the sinusoidal steady state, the average power input to a terminal-pair network has the same sign as the real part of the driving-point immittance (see Prob. 12-35b). Hence, if this function were an immittance function, the network would deliver electromagnetic energy to the source, without bound, instead of converting the energy supplied by the source into heat or storing it. Since a passive network is not capable of delivering energy without bound, it is evident that $F(s) = (s + 4)/(s^2 + 2s + 5)$ cannot be a driving-point function.

It can be shown that a necessary condition for $H(s) = A(s)/B(s)$ as a driving-point immittance function is the requirement that Re $H(s) \geq 0$ when Re $s \geq 0$. A function which satisfies this condition is referred to as a "positive real function."

Example 13-11. Show that $Z(s) = (s + 1)/(s + 5)$ is a positive real function.

Solution. Let $s = \sigma + j\omega$, where $\sigma = $ Re $s > 0$; then $Z(s) = (\sigma + 1 + j\omega)/(\sigma + 5 + j\omega)$. Rationalizing,

$$Z(\sigma + j\omega) = \frac{(\sigma + 1)(\sigma + 5) + \omega^2 + j4\omega}{(\sigma + 5)^2 + \omega^2}$$

$$\text{Re } [Z(\sigma + j\omega)] = \frac{(\sigma + 1)(\sigma + 5) + \omega^2}{(\sigma + 5)^2 + \omega^2} > 0 \qquad \text{for} \qquad \sigma \geq 0$$

Therefore $Z(s) = (s + 1)/(s + 5)$ is a positive real function. From the definition of positive real functions it is seen that the condition Re $[H(s)] \geq 0$ for Re $s = 0$, that is, Re $[H(j\omega)] \geq 0$, is a necessary condition. It is noted that the function $F(s) = (s + 4)/(s^2 + 2s + 5)$ is such that Re $[F(s)] < 0$ for certain imaginary values of s (Re $s = 0$).

13-14. Realizability of Transfer Functions. Transfer functions differ from driving-point immittance functions in that a transfer function which, for example, relates a response to a voltage source does not apply when a current source is substituted for the voltage source. In contrast, a driving-point immittance and its reciprocal relate either type of source to response.

If a source function $\phi(t)$ is related to a response function $y(t)$ through the equation

$$y(t) = \frac{N(p)}{D(p)} \phi(t)$$

then the source-free response is given by $D(p)y_f(t) = 0$. Hence $D(s)$ cannot have zeros in the right-half s plane or multiple zeros on the imaginary axis. If $N(p)/D(p)$ is a driving-point immittance function, then $D(p)/N(p)$ is also a driving-point immittance function and therefore the zeros of $N(s)$ must be located in the left half plane.

If $N(p)/D(p)$ is a transfer function, then $D(p)/N(p)$ is *not* a transfer function of the same network and the above-mentioned restrictions on the poles of a transfer function will not be applicable to its zeros. However, it can be shown that the degree of $N(s)$ cannot *exceed* the degree of $D(s)$ by more than unity. Thus for transfer functions the restrictions for pole-zero locations are:

1. They are the ratio of polynomials in s.
2. No poles may be in the right-half s plane.
3. Simple poles may be on the imaginary axis.
4. The degree of the numerator polynomial cannot exceed the degree of the denominator polynomial by more than unity.

There is no restriction in the location of the zeros of the transfer functions. In Prob. 13-17 a network which has a zero in the right half s plane is shown. Note also that the restriction on $N(s)$ states only that the degree of this polynomial cannot *exceed* the degree of $D(s)$ by more than unity. This implies of course that the degree of $N(s)$ can be less than the degree of $D(s)$ by any integer.

Example 13-12. In the circuit of Fig. 13-17 find the transform gain function which relates v_2 to v.

Solution. From voltage division

$$v_2(t) = \frac{1/p}{1 + p + 1/p} v(t)$$

Hence $\qquad v_2 = \dfrac{1}{p^2 + p + 1} v(t)$

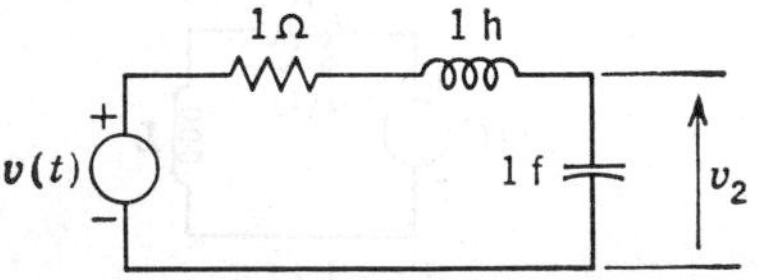

FIG. 13-17. In the transfer function which relates v_2 to v, the degree of $D(s)$ exceeds the degree of $N(s)$ by 2.

The transform gain function is $1/(s^2 + s + 1)$. $N(s) = 1$, $D(s) = s^2 + s + 1$. Hence the degree of $N(s)$ is 0, and the degree of $D(s)$ is 2.

PROBLEMS

13-1. Substitute the function $t^n e^{-t}$ in the equation $(p + 1)^3 y(t) = 0$ as a "trial solution," and show that only the integral values $n = 0, 1, 2$ satisfy the differential equation.

13-2. Locate the poles of the network function in the s plane if the free-response component is (a) $y_f = e^{-t} - te^{-t} + te^{-2t} + e^{-3t} \cos 4t$; (b) $y_f = t^2 e^{-2t} + e^{-2t}$; (c) $y_f = e^{-3t} + 4e^{-3t} \cos (4t - 30°)$.

13-3. When a voltage source $v(t) = 2e^{-3t}$ is impressed on a circuit under certain initial conditions, then the complete response for a voltage $v_2(t)$ is $v_2(t) = 2te^{-3t} + 2e^{-3t} \sin 3t$. Where are the poles of the network function that relates v_2 to $v(t)$ located in the s plane?

13-4. The poles of a network function are simple and are located at $s_1 = -2$ and $s_{2,3} = -5 \pm j6$. What is the form of the free response?

13-5. It is known that a network function has two zeros and two poles, all at real (and negative) values of s. A source $\phi(t) = e^{st}$ is impressed, and the complete response $y(t)$ is analyzed. The following results are noted: When $s = -1$, $y(t) = \frac{1}{2}(e^{-2t} + e^{-4t})$. When $s = -2$, $y(t) = \frac{1}{4}(e^{-2t} - 2te^{-2t} + 3e^{-4t})$. When $s = -3$, $y(t) = \frac{1}{2}(-e^{-2t} + 3e^{-4t})$. When $s = -4$, $y(t) = \frac{1}{4}(-e^{-2t} - 6te^{-4t} + 5e^{-4t})$. (a) Deduce the form of the network function; specify numerically the location of all zeros and poles. (b) Write the differential equation which relates $y(t)$ to $\phi(t)$. (c) Calculate the complete response $y(t)$ if the source is given as $\phi(t) = e^{-5t}$. Use $H = 1$, $y(0^+) = 1$, $(dy/dt)_{0^+} = 4$.

13-6. In the circuit shown in Fig. P13-6, when $i(t) = e^{st}$, the complete response is $v_{ab}(t) = 10e^{st} - 10e^{-0.1t}$. (a) Calculate s. (b) Calculate the complete response for v_{ab}

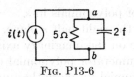

Fig. P13-6

if $v_{ab}(0^+) = 0$ and (1) $i(t) = 2e^{-0.3t}$; (2) $i(t) = 3e^{-0.05t}$; (3) $i(t) = e^{-0.1t}$; (4) $i(t) = \sqrt{2} \cos (0.1t - 30°)$.

13-7. A voltage source $v(t)$ is applied to a series R-L circuit as shown in Fig. P13-7. The component of $i(t)$ due to the source is given for two source functions as follows: $v(t) = 5U(t)$, $i_s(t) = 2$; $v(t) = 5 \cos 2t$, $i_s(t) = A \cos (2t - 45°)$. Calculate (a) R; (b) L; (c) A; (d) the component i_s if $v(t) = 5e^{-t}$.

Fig. P13-7   Fig. P13-8

13-8. In the circuit shown in Fig. P13-8 $v(t) = e^{-\alpha t}$, and $i_s(t) = Ae^{-\alpha t}$. Use a pole-zero diagram to obtain a graph of A versus α.

13-9. A source $v(t) = \text{Re } e^{j\omega t}$ is applied to a critically damped R-L-C series circuit. Use the pole-zero diagram of the transform driving-point admittance to show that $i_s(t)$ is a sinusoid which is in phase with $v(t)$ when $\omega = \omega_0 = 1/\sqrt{LC}$.

13-10. In a certain network a response $y(t)$ is related to a source $\phi(t)$ through the equation $(p^2 + 2p + 17)y(t) = (p^2 + 2p + 5)\phi(t)$. (a) Locate the zeros and poles of the transform network function which corresponds to this differential equation. (b) Use the pole-zero diagram to deduce the component of $y(t)$ due to $\phi(t)$ by the graphical method of Art. 13-8, if $\phi(t)$ is (1) e^{-2t}; (2) e^{-4t}; (3) $2e^{-t}\cos t$; (4) $5\cos 3t$.

13-11. In the circuit shown in Fig. P13-11 calculate the transform network function which relates the following response functions to $i(t)$: (a) v_{ab}; (b) v_{db}; (c) v_{ad}.

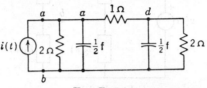

FIG. P13-11

13-12. In the circuit of Prob. 13-11 (Fig. P13-11) if it is desired that the component of v_{ad} due to $i(t)$ be zero, what should be the form of $i(t)$?

13-13. A certain transform network function which relates $y(t)$ to a source $\phi(t) = \phi e^{st}$ is $H(s) = (s + 1)/[(s + 2)^2(s^2 + 2s + 5)]$. Calculate $y_s(t)$ *graphically* if (a) $\phi(t) = e^{-3t}$; (b) $\phi(t) = 10\cos t$; (c) $\phi(t) = 10\cos(t - 30°)$; (d) $\phi(t) = e^{-2t}\cos 2t$.

13-14. In the circuit shown in Fig. P13-14 $v(t) = V_m \cos \omega t$, and in the steady state $v_{ab} = (V_{ab})_m \cos(\omega t - \theta)$. (a) Find the transform network function which relates v_{ab} to $v(t)$. (b) Plot a curve of $(V_{ab})_m/V_m$ versus ω. (c) Plot a curve of θ versus ω.

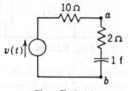

FIG. P13-14

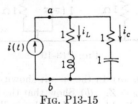

FIG. P13-15

13-15. In the circuit shown in Fig. P13-15 (a) obtain the transform network functions which relate v_{ab}, i_L, and i_c to $i(t)$; (b) if $i(t) = \text{Re } e^{j\omega t}$, use the appropriate pole-zero plot to sketch the response amplitudes of the sinusoids v_{ab}, i_L, and i_c as a function of frequency.

13-16. For the following transform network functions state which are not physically realizable as driving-point immittance functions, and give your reason(s): (a) $H(s) = s^2$; (b) $H(s) = (s - 1)/(s + 2)$; (c) $H(s) = s^2/(s^2 + 2)$; (d) $H(s) = (s + 1)/(s + \frac{1}{2})$.

13-17. (a) Show that the transfer function which relates v_2 to v_1 of the network given in Fig. P13-17 has a zero in the right-half s plane. (b) If $s = j\omega$, show that $|H(j\omega)| = 1$. (c) Show that the phase difference between a sinusoidal $v_1(t)$ and the steady state $v_2(t)$ is $2\tan^{-1}\omega RC$.

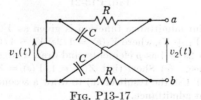

FIG. P13-17

13-18. (*a*) In Fig. P13-18 show that the transform network function which relates $v_{ab}(t)$ to $v(t)$ is $H(s) = [Z_2(s) - Z_1(s)]/[Z_1(s) + Z_2(s)]$. (*b*) Locate the zeros and poles of $H(s)$ if (1) $Z_1 = 1$, $Z_2 = s$; (2) $Z_1 = 1 + s$, $Z_2 = 1/(1 + s)$; (3) $Z_1 = s + s^{-1}$, $Z_2 = 1$.

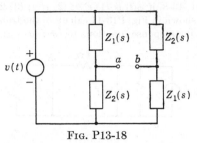

FIG. P13-18

13-19. In the circuit shown in Fig. P13-19 obtain the transform transfer function for the following cases: (*a*) An ideal current source is placed across terminals *a-b*, and the response is v_{cd}. (*b*) An ideal voltage source is placed across terminals *a-b*, and the response is v_{cd}. (*c*) An ideal voltage source is placed across terminals *c-d*, and the response is v_{ab}.

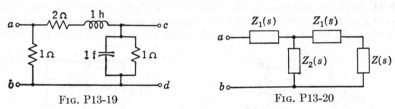

FIG. P13-19   FIG. P13-20

13-20. (*a*) In the circuit shown in Fig. P13-20 prove that if $Z^2(s) = Z_1{}^2 + 2Z_1Z_2$ then $Z_{ab} = Z$. (*b*) Show that the driving-point immittance Z is not in general physically realizable. (*c*) Is Z physically realizable if $Z_2 = kZ_1$, where k is a real constant? Explain and illustrate your answer.

13-21. (*a*) Show that the driving-point impedance of the terminal pair shown in Fig. P13-21*a* has a pole at $s = -1/RC$. (*b*) Show that the series connection of n different R-C circuits as shown in Fig. P13-21*b* forms a driving-point impedance with n poles (at $1/R_1C_1$, $1/R_2C_2$, . . . , $1/R_nC_n$). (Assume $R_kC_k \neq R_jC_j$.)

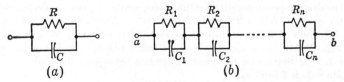

(*a*)   (*b*)

FIG. P13-21

13-22. A driving-point admittance function is given as $Y(s) = (s + 1)/s(s + 2)$. (*a*) Show that $Y(s) = Y_1 + Y_2$, where $Y_1(s) = 1/2s$; $Y_2 = 1/(2s + 4)$. (*b*) Identify $Z_1(s) = 2s$ and $Z_2(s) = 2s + 4$ as *p* elements, and draw a circuit which has the given driving-point admittance. (*c*) Show that $Z(s) = 1/Y(s) = Z_1 + Z_2$, where $Z_1 = s$; $Z_2 = 1/(1 + 1/s)$. (*d*) Use the result of (*c*) to draw a second circuit which has the prescribed driving-point admittance.

13-23. A driving-point impedance is given as

$$Z(s) = \frac{(s + 2)(s + 4)}{(s + 1)(s + 3)(s + 5)}$$

(a) Expand $Z(s)$ by the method of partial fractions into the form

$$Z(s) = \frac{A}{s + 1} + \frac{B}{s + 3} + \frac{C}{s + 5}$$

(b) Use the result of (a) to sketch a network with the prescribed $Z(s)$. Specify the numerical value of all elements.

13-24. Prove the following statements: When a source $\phi(t) = Ae^{\alpha t} \cos(\omega t + \varphi)$ is impressed on a driving-point immittance, the component of the response at the source terminals due to the source cannot have the form $Kte^{\alpha t} \cos(\omega t + \delta)$ if $\alpha > 0$. The component of the response due to the source has the form $Be^{\alpha t} \cos(\omega t + \delta)$, and B cannot be zero.

13-25. In the circuit shown in Fig. P13-25 (a) calculate $Z_{ab}(s)$ as a function of C; (b) locate the zeros and poles of $Z_{ab}(s)$ if (1) $C = \frac{1}{3}$ farad, (2) $C = 1$ farad, (3) $C = \frac{1}{10}$ farad; (c) locate the zeros and poles of the transfer function which relates v_{db} to v for the three cases of (b).

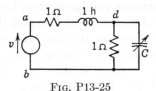

FIG. P13-25

13-26. (a) It has been shown that a transform driving-point immittance has the form

$$Z(s) = H \frac{\displaystyle\prod_{z=0}^{z=Z} (s - s_z)}{\displaystyle\prod_{p=0}^{p=P} (s - s_p)}$$

where $P - Z = 0, +1$, or -1. Show that the angle of the complex factor $s - s_a$ cannot exceed 90° in magnitude if $\operatorname{Re} s \geq 0$ provided that $\operatorname{Re} s_a \leq 0$. (b) Using the positive real property of driving-point immittance functions and the result of (a), show that $P - Z = 0, +1$, or -1.

13-27. In a network the response v_2 is related to the source v by

$$v_2(t) = [p/(p^2 + p + 1)] v(t).$$

Calculate (a) the component of the response due to the source if $v(t)$ is (1) t, (2) te^{-t}, (3) $t \cos t$; (b) the complete response v_2 if the network is initially deenergized and if $v(t) = t$.

CHAPTER 14

CIRCUITS IN THE SINUSOIDAL STEADY STATE

In the preceding chapters we have discussed the component of the response due to a source which varies exponentially with time. In this chapter we shall concentrate on a special case of exponential source function, namely, the sinusoidal source. Before proceeding with the exposition of sinusoidal steady-state analysis, it is appropriate to discuss briefly the reasons for the importance of this special case.

In elementary physics the reader has probably studied circuits consisting of resistances and constant voltage sources (such as batteries). Such circuits and sources are of very limited use, and the advance of electrical technology has made it necessary to study the response of circuits containing energy-storing elements to sources whose waveform varies with time. Among the time-varying sources the sinusoidal source is an exceedingly important (if not the most important) source, for the reasons enumerated below:

1. The sinusoidal function is periodic. From the point of view of consumer of electrical energy the periodic waveform is practical since its time variations are predictable.

2. Sinusoidal sources can be constructed to furnish large amounts of power with ease when compared with sources furnishing other waveforms.

3. The sinusoidal function is the only real periodic function which has an integral and a derivative of the same waveform as the function itself. In any linear circuit this means that the steady-state response to a sinusoidal source will be sinusoidal regardless of the types or number of circuit elements which are interconnected.

4. The analysis of circuits with nonsinusoidal periodic sources can often be carried out conveniently by representing the nonsinusoidal function as a sum of sinusoids and using superposition.

5. The steady-state response of a circuit to sinusoidal sources furnishes information about the response to other waveforms. This follows from the fact that sinusoidal functions can be represented as the sum of exponential functions; and the responses to exponential source functions are related to the pole-zero locations of the network function. Once the poles and zeros of a network function are established, both the free component of the response and the response to exponential source functions

can be determined. Thus the study of circuits with sinusoidal sources is important, not only because many practical systems use such sources (power stations, lights and appliances in homes, radio and television transmitters, electrical machinery, etc.), but also because many basic properties of circuits become evident through analysis or experimentation with sinusoidal sources *even if the circuit is not intended for use with such sources.*

In colloquial engineering terminology the steady-state analysis of circuits with a sinusoidal source is called *alternating-current* (a-c) circuit analysis.

14-1. Single Elements in the Sinusoidal Steady State. *Inductance.* If a current source with the sinusoidal waveform

$$i(t) = I_m \cos \omega t = \operatorname{Re}(I_m e^{j\omega t}) \tag{14-1}$$

is applied to an inductance L, as shown in Fig. 14-1a, the response of this element will be the voltage v. The transform network function which

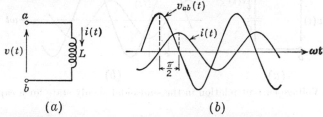

(a) (b)

FIG. 14-1. Voltage-current relation in the sinusoidal steady state for an inductance.

relates the response v to the exponential source $\operatorname{Re}(I_m e^{j\omega t})$ is the impedance sL, where in this case $s = j\omega$. Therefore

$$v(t) = \operatorname{Re}(j\omega L I_m e^{j\omega t}) = \operatorname{Re}(\omega L I_m e^{j(\omega t + \pi/2)})$$

or
$$v(t) = \omega L I_m \cos\left(\omega t + \frac{\pi}{2}\right) \tag{14-2}$$

In Chap. 8 we saw that the sinusoidal functions can be represented by complex numbers, i.e., phasors. For Eq. (14-1) the phasor representing $i(t)$ is $\mathbf{I}_m = I_m\underline{/0}$, and for Eq. (14-2) the phasor representing $v(t)$ is $\mathbf{V}_m = \omega L I_m\underline{/90°}$. The ratio of these two phasors is

$$\frac{\mathbf{V}_m}{\mathbf{I}_m} = \omega L\underline{/90°} = j\omega L$$

Thus the transform impedance for the case $s = s_g = j\omega$ is the ratio of the phasor which represents the voltage to the phasor which represents the current. We further conclude from Eqs. (14-1) and (14-2) that, in the sinusoidal steady state, a sinusoidal current through an inductance produces a sinusoidal voltage. The amplitude of the voltage ($\omega L I_m$) is proportional to the amplitude of the current, and in L_{ab} the current sinusoid i_{ab} *lags* the voltage v_{ab} by 90°, as illustrated in Fig. 14-1*b*.

Capacitance. Since, for a capacitance C, the transform *admittance* is sC, a voltage

$$v_{ab} = V_m \cos (\omega t + \gamma) = \text{Re} (\mathbf{V}_m e^{j\omega t}) \qquad \mathbf{V}_m = V_m e^{j\gamma}$$

produces a current

$$i_{ab}(t) = \text{Re} (j\omega C \mathbf{V}_m e^{j\omega t}) = \omega C V_m \cos \left(\omega t + \gamma + \frac{\pi}{2} \right)$$

Thus the voltage phasor $\mathbf{V}_m$ is related to the current phasor $\mathbf{I}_m$ through the equation

$$j\omega C \mathbf{V}_m = \mathbf{I}_m \qquad \text{or} \qquad \omega C V_m e^{j(\gamma + \pi/2)} = \mathbf{I}_m$$

Hence in a capacitance C_{ab} a sinusoidal voltage current i_{ab} *leads* the sinusoid v_{ab} by 90°. This relationship is illustrated in Fig. 14-2.

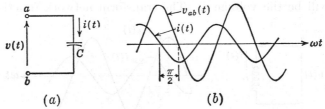

(a)   (b)

Fig. 14-2. Voltage-current relation in the sinusoidal steady state for a capacitance.

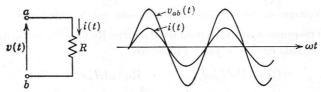

Fig. 14-3. Voltage-current relation in the sinusoidal steady state for a resistance.

Resistance. Since, for a resistance $v_{ab} = i_{ab}R$, a sinusoidal current $i_{ab} = I_m \cos (\omega t + \psi)$ results in the sinusoidal voltage

$$v_{ab} = I_m R \cos (\omega t + \psi)$$

that is, the voltage v_{ab} and the current i_{ab} are *in phase*. This situation is illustrated in Fig. 14-3.

14-2. Complex Immittance. In general, the component of the response $\mathbf{y}_s(t)$ due to a source $\phi e^{s_g t}$ is given through the transform network function $H(s)$ by the relationship

$$\mathbf{y}_s(t) = H(\mathbf{s}_g)\boldsymbol{\phi} e^{s_g t}$$

In the sinusoidal case, $s_g = j\omega$; hence, if $\phi(t) = \text{Re} (\boldsymbol{\phi}_m e^{j\omega t})$,

$$y_s(t) = \text{Re} [H(j\omega)\boldsymbol{\phi}_m e^{j\omega t}]$$

The special value which $H(s)$ assumes when s is imaginary $(s = j\omega)$ is called the *complex network function*. Thus the complex network function is the ratio of the phasor which represents the response sinusoid to the phasor which represents the source sinusoid. In all network functions the term complex is substituted for transform when $s = j\omega$. (Occasionally, when an entire discussion revolves round the sinusoidal steady state, the word complex is omitted. Thus, for example, the term impedance is often used to indicate complex impedance, $Z(j\omega)$). For the elements R, L, and C the complex immittances are:

For an inductance: $\mathbf{Z} = j\omega L = \omega L\underline{/90°}$ $\qquad$ $\mathbf{Y} = \dfrac{1}{j\omega L} = \dfrac{1}{\omega L}\underline{/-90°}$

For a capacitance: $\mathbf{Z} = \dfrac{1}{j\omega C} = \dfrac{1}{\omega C}\underline{/-90°}$ $\quad$ $\mathbf{Y} = j\omega C = \omega C\underline{/90°}$

For a resistance: $\quad$ $\mathbf{Z} = R = R\underline{/0°}$ $\qquad\qquad$ $\mathbf{Y} = \dfrac{1}{R} = \dfrac{1}{R}\underline{/0°}$

These relationships are summarized in Table 14-1.

14-3. Reactance and Susceptance. Since for any terminal pair a-b the (complex) impedance is always a complex number, it can be written in rectangular form,

$$\mathbf{Z}_{ab} = \operatorname{Re} \mathbf{Z}_{ab} + j \operatorname{Im} \mathbf{Z}_{ab} \tag{14-3}$$

Similarly for complex admittance

$$\mathbf{Y}_{ab} = \operatorname{Re} \mathbf{Y}_{ab} + j \operatorname{Im} \mathbf{Y}_{ab} \tag{14-4}$$

Since $\mathbf{Y} \equiv 1/\mathbf{Z}$,

$$\operatorname{Re} \mathbf{Y}_{ab} + j \operatorname{Im} \mathbf{Y}_{ab} = \frac{1}{\operatorname{Re} \mathbf{Z}_{ab} + j \operatorname{Im} \mathbf{Z}_{ab}} \tag{14-5}$$

Rationalizing the right side of Eq. (14-5),

$$\operatorname{Re} \mathbf{Y}_{ab} + j \operatorname{Im} \mathbf{Y}_{ab} = \frac{\operatorname{Re} \mathbf{Z}_{ab} - j \operatorname{Im} \mathbf{Z}_{ab}}{Z_{ab}^{2}} \tag{14-6}$$

$$\operatorname{Re} \mathbf{Y}_{ab} = \operatorname{Re} \frac{\mathbf{Z}_{ab}}{Z_{ab}^{2}} \tag{14-6a}$$

$$\operatorname{Im} \mathbf{Y}_{ab} = -\operatorname{Im} \frac{\mathbf{Z}_{ab}}{Z_{ab}^{2}} \tag{14-6b}$$

The following terms are used in connection with complex immittance:

Reactance. The imaginary part of a complex impedance is called the reactance of the impedance (or reactance for brevity) and is denoted by the symbol X.

Inductive Reactance of an Inductance. The impedance of an inductance is $j\omega L$. Since $\operatorname{Im} j\omega L = \omega L$, the product ωL is called the inductive reactance of L and is denoted by the symbol X_L. Thus for an inductance the complex impedance is given by $\mathbf{Z} = jX_L$.

Table 14-1. Sinusoidal Response of the Basic Passive Elements

Element	Equations	Amplitude	Phase relation	Phasor form $i = \text{Re}\,[I_m e^{j\omega t}]$ $v = \text{Re}\,[V_m e^{j\omega t}]$	Phasor diagram	Time relationship
R	$i = I_m \cos(\omega t + \alpha)$ $v = V_m \cos(\omega t + \alpha)$	$\dfrac{V_m}{I_m} = R$	i and v are in phase	$\dfrac{V_m}{I_m} = R = Z$ $\mathbf{Y} = G = 1/R$		
L	$i = I_m \cos(\omega t + \alpha)$ $v = V_m \cos\!\left(\omega t + \alpha + \dfrac{\pi}{2}\right)$	$\dfrac{V_m}{I_m} = \omega L = X_L$	i lags v by 90°	$\dfrac{V_m}{I_m} = j\omega L = Z$ $= jX_L$ $\dfrac{-j}{\omega L} = jB_L$ $\mathbf{V}_m = \omega L I_m \Big/\!\underline{\dfrac{\pi}{2}}$		
C	$i = I_m \cos(\omega t + \alpha)$ $v = V_m \cos\!\left(\omega t + \alpha - \dfrac{\pi}{2}\right)$	$\dfrac{V_m}{I_m} = \dfrac{1}{\omega C} = -X_c$	i leads v by 90°	$\dfrac{V_m}{I_m} = \dfrac{1}{j\omega C} = Z$ $= jX_c$ $\mathbf{Y} = j\omega C = jB_c$ $\mathbf{V}_m = \dfrac{1}{\omega C} I_m \Big/\!\underline{-\dfrac{\pi}{2}}$		

Capacitive Reactance of a Capacitance. The complex impedance of a capacitance is $1/j\omega C$. Since Im $(1/j\omega C) = -1/\omega C$, the quantity $-1/\omega C$ is called the capacitive reactance of C and is denoted by the symbol X_C. Thus for a capacitance the complex impedance is given by $\mathbf{Z} = jX_C$.

Susceptance. The imaginary part of a complex admittance is called the susceptance (of the admittance) and is denoted by the symbol B.

Inductive Susceptance of an Inductance. For an inductance, $\mathbf{Y} = 1/j\omega L$. The inductive susceptance of such an element is defined as $-1/\omega L$ and is denoted by the symbol B_L. Hence the admittance of an inductance can be written $\mathbf{Y} = jB_L$.

Capacitive Susceptance. For a capacitance, $\mathbf{Y} = j\omega C$. The capacitive susceptance of such an element is ωC and is denoted by the symbol B_C. Hence the admittance of a capacitance is $\mathbf{Y} = jB_C$.

We observe that for a single inductance or for a single capacitance the susceptance is the negative reciprocal of the reactance. It must be emphasized that in view of Eq. (14-6) this statement *does not* apply generally to any terminal pair but applies only to the single elements. The definitions $X = \text{Im } \mathbf{Z}$ and $B = \text{Im } \mathbf{Y}$ *do* apply generally.

Resistance and Conductance. The resistance R of a complex impedance is defined as the real part of the impedance. The conductance G of an admittance is the real part of the admittance. While, for the element R, $G = 1/R$, for a terminal pair a-b, $G_{ab} = \text{Re } \mathbf{Y}_{ab}$ is given by Eq. (14-6a) and is *not* the reciprocal of Re $\mathbf{Z}_{ab}$.

14-4. Power and Energy Relations in Single Elements. *Energy-storing Elements.* It was shown in the preceding articles that a sinusoidal voltage of the form

$$v_{ab}(t) = V_m \cos(\omega t + \alpha) \tag{14-7a}$$

applied either to an inductance or to a capacitance, produces a current

$$i_{ab}(t) = \frac{V_m}{X} \cos\left(\omega t + \alpha - \frac{\pi}{2}\right) \tag{14-7b}$$

where $X = X_L = \omega L$ for an inductance and $X = X_C = -1/\omega C$ for a capacitance. The power which is delivered *to* such an energy-storing element at every instant of time is given by the product $v_{ab}i_{ab}$. Thus the equation for the power at any instant of time is given by

$$p_{ab} = v_{ab}i_{ab} = \frac{V_m^2}{X} \cos(\omega t + \alpha) \cos\left(\omega t + \alpha - \frac{\pi}{2}\right) \tag{14-8}$$

Since $\cos(\omega t + \alpha - \pi/2) = \sin(\omega t + \alpha)$ and since, for any angle x, $2 \sin x \cos x = \sin 2x$, Eq. (14-8) reduces to

$$p_{ab}(t) = \frac{V_m^2}{2X} \sin(2\omega t + 2\alpha) \tag{14-9}$$

The result expressed in Eq. (14-9) is illustrated in Fig. (14-4a). In this figure it is assumed that X is a positive number, that is, $X = X_L$. We note first that the power oscillates at *twice* the frequency of the voltage or the current. Studying one complete cycle of the power oscillations is instructive: referring to Fig. 14-4a, in the interval $\omega t = A$ to $\omega t = B$, $p(t)$ is positive. This means that power is being furnished by the source to the inductance. The inductance is storing the energy (in its associated

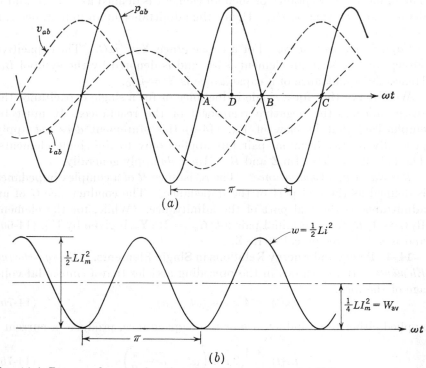

(a)

(b)

FIG. 14-4. Power and energy functions for an inductance. (a) Voltage, current, and power as functions of time. (b) Energy as a function of time.

magnetic field), and at point B the energy which has been transferred to the inductance up to that time is equal to the area under the power curve. In the interval from B to C the power is negative. This means that at point B the power flow has reversed and the inductance is now furnishing energy to the source. At point C the total energy which is stored in the inductance is the same as at point A. We conclude, therefore, that the power supplied to an inductance averaged over one period of the voltage or current is zero, since at the end of every cycle no net energy has been transferred to the inductance. There exists, however, a periodic interchange of energy between the source and the inductance.

An interesting relationship is obtained by comparing the maximum stored energy with the maximum instantaneous power which flows.   The maximum energy which is stored in the inductance could be calculated by integrating the expression for the power from point A to point B (Fig. 14-4a); it is more convenient to use the equation

$$w_L = \tfrac{1}{2}Li^2 = \tfrac{1}{2}LI_m^2 \sin^2(\omega t + \alpha) \qquad I_m = \frac{V_m}{X_L}$$

Since for any angle x, $2\sin^2 x = 1 - \cos 2x$,

$$w_L = \tfrac{1}{4}LI_m^2[1 - \cos 2(\omega t + \alpha)]$$

The waveform of w_L is shown in Fig. 14-4b.   Since the energy is a maximum when the current is a maximum,

$$(w_L)_{\text{max}} = \tfrac{1}{2}LI_m^2$$

We note from Fig. 14-4a that the value of the maximum power (point D) is

$$[p(t)]_{\text{max}} = \tfrac{1}{2}V_mI_m = \tfrac{1}{2}\omega L I_m^2$$

so that the ratio of the maximum power to the maximum stored energy is the radian frequency ω (independent of voltage or current amplitude). Analogous relationships can be deduced for the capacitance.

   Resistance.   For a resistance R between terminals a-b a voltage v_{ab} will produce a current $i_{ab} = v_{ab}/R$.   Hence, under sinusoidal conditions, if $v_{ab} = V_m \cos(\omega t + \alpha)$, the power delivered to the resistance is given by

$$p_{ab} = V_m \cos(\omega t + \alpha)\,\frac{V_m}{R}\cos(\omega t + \alpha)$$

or $\qquad\qquad p_{ab} = V_mI_m \cos^2(\omega t + \alpha) \qquad I_m = \dfrac{V_m}{R}$

For any angle x, the identity $2\cos^2 x = 1 + \cos 2x$ holds.   Hence

$$p_{ab}(t) = \frac{V_mI_m}{2}[1 + \cos(2\omega t + 2\alpha)] \qquad\qquad (14\text{-}10)$$

The result of Eq. (14-10) is illustrated in Fig. 14-5.   Note that the power delivered to the resistance is either positive or zero at every instant of time.   The equation for the power consists of a constant term and a sinusoidal term.   Note that the frequency of the sinusoidal term is twice the frequency of the voltage or the current.   Studying one cycle of the power oscillations, starting at A (Fig. 14-5) and ending at B, we see that the area under the power curve in the interval A to B is $\tfrac{1}{2}V_mI_m(B - A)$, so that the average value of the power over any complete cycle (or any number of complete cycles) is

$$P_{\text{av}} = \frac{V_mI_m}{2} = P$$

[It is common usage, in discussing circuits in the sinusoidal steady state, to call the average power over one period simply the "power" and use the symbol P (capital, no special subscript).]

The energy which has been delivered to the resistance in any time

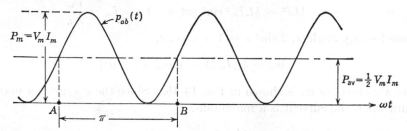

FIG. 14-5. Power as a function of time in a resistance R_{ab}.

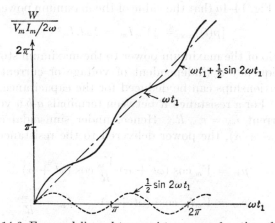

FIG. 14-6. Energy delivered to a resistance as a function of time.

interval $t = t_0$ to $t = t_1$ is found by integrating the expression for the power,

$$W = \int_{t_0}^{t_1} p_{ab}(t)\, dt \tag{14-11}$$

Substituting (14-10) in (14-11) and integrating,

$$W = \frac{V_m I_m}{2\omega} \left[\omega t_1 + \frac{1}{2} \sin (2\omega t_1 + 2\alpha) \right] - K$$

where K is the result of substituting the lower limit of the integral. This result is graphically presented in Fig. 14-6. In this figure the value of K has been chosen as zero and the arbitrary phase angle α also chosen as zero. The axes are normalized as indicated. Figure 14-6 shows that the energy which has been dissipated by the resistance is increasing monotonically, but not at a constant rate.

14-5. Effective Values.   In sinusoidal steady-state calculations it is customary to specify voltages and currents in terms of their "effective," or "root-mean-square," values.   The reader will recall that rms values of periodic functions were discussed in Chap. 2.   For a periodic function $f(t)$ with period T, $[f(t) = f(t + T)]$, the rms value is defined through the relationship

$$F_{rms} = \sqrt{\frac{1}{T} \int_0^T f^2(t) \, dt} \qquad (14\text{-}12)$$

Applying this definition to a sinusoidal function

$$f(t) = F_m \cos (\omega t + \alpha)$$

the rms value is $F_{rms} = F_m/\sqrt{2} = 0.707 F_m$.   It is customary *not* to use a subscript to denote effective (rms) value for voltages and currents.   Thus the current $i(t) = I_m \cos (\omega t + \alpha)$ has the effective value $I = I_m/\sqrt{2}$. The utility of defining such an rms value is clear if we recall the formula for the power which is dissipated in a resistance R due to a current $i(t)$,

$$p(t) = [i(t)]^2 R \qquad (14\text{-}13)$$

The average power which is dissipated per cycle is

$$P = P_{av} = \frac{1}{T} \int_0^T [i(t)]^2 R \, dt \qquad (14\text{-}14)$$

If, instead of the current $i(t)$, a constant current I were to flow through the same resistance R, then the power dissipated by the resistance would be

$$P = I^2 R \qquad (14\text{-}15)$$

We note therefore that the *effective* value of a periodic current is that value which, when used in Eq. (14-15), will give the correct answer for the average power,

$$I_{eff} = \sqrt{\frac{P_{av}}{R}} \qquad (14\text{-}15a)$$

Using this definition for effective current in Eq. (14-12),

$$I_{eff} = \sqrt{\frac{1}{T} \int_0^T [i(t)]^2 \, dt}$$

so that the *effective* value of the current is the same as the rms value. This value of current is also referred to as the "heating" value.   The reason for this term should be clear.   A periodic current whose effective value is I will, when flowing through a resistance, convert electric energy into heat at an average rate equal to the rate at which constant current I converts electric energy into heat in the same resistance.

The relationship between amplitude and effective value for a sinusoid $(F = F_m/\sqrt{2})$, which is stated above, can be deduced without the formal integration indicated by Eq. (14-12). We start with the equation for power delivered to a resistance R_{ab} [Eq. (14-10)],

$$p_{ab}(t) = \frac{V_m I_m}{2} [1 + \cos (2\omega t + 2\alpha)]$$

Since the average value of a cosine wave is zero,

$$P_{av} = \frac{V_m I_m}{2} = \frac{I_m^2}{2} R$$

Using the definition of effective value (14-15a), the effective value of a *sinusoidal* current is

$$I = \frac{1}{\sqrt{2}} I_m = 0.707 I_m \qquad (14\text{-}15b)$$

This result may, of course, be verified by carrying out the integration which is indicated above. It must be emphasized that the result expressed in Eq. (14-15b) applies *only* to *sinusoidal* currents (or voltages). For any other waveshape the definition [Eq. (14-12)] of rms values must be applied directly (see Chap. 2).

In earlier parts of this chapter we have represented sinusoidal voltages and currents by complex numbers, i.e., phasors. Thus, if

$$v(t) = V_m \cos (\omega t + \alpha) \qquad \text{and} \qquad i(t) = I_m \cos (\omega t + \psi)$$

we represented $v(t)$ by the phasor $\mathbf{V}_m = V_m\underline{/\alpha}$ and $i(t)$ by the phasor $\mathbf{I}_m = I_m\underline{/\psi}$. The voltage and current phasors are then related by the complex immittance,

$$\mathbf{V}_m = \mathbf{Z}\mathbf{I}_m \qquad \text{or} \qquad \mathbf{I}_m = \mathbf{Y}\mathbf{V}_m \qquad (14\text{-}16)$$

Since $V_m = \sqrt{2}\, V$ and $I_m = \sqrt{2}\, I$, where V and I are effective values, we can define the complex numbers $\mathbf{V}$ and $\mathbf{I}$ by the relations

$$\mathbf{V} = \frac{1}{\sqrt{2}} \mathbf{V}_m \qquad \text{and} \qquad \mathbf{I} = \frac{1}{\sqrt{2}} \mathbf{I}_m \qquad (14\text{-}17)$$

Introducing (14-17) into (14-16), we note that $\mathbf{V}$ and $\mathbf{I}$ are related through the same complex immittances which relate V_m and I_m,

$$\mathbf{V} = \mathbf{Z}\mathbf{I} \qquad \text{or} \qquad \mathbf{I} = \mathbf{Y}\mathbf{V} \qquad (14\text{-}18)$$

We now observe that the numbers $\mathbf{V}$ and $\mathbf{I}$ are the phasors representing $(1/\sqrt{2})v(t)$ and $(1/\sqrt{2})i(t)$, respectively. Yet it is customary to say that $\mathbf{V}$ and $\mathbf{I}$ represent $v(t)$ and $i(t)$. To avoid confusion, the following terminology is introduced: The function

$$v(t) = V_m \cos (\omega t + \alpha) = \sqrt{2}\, V \cos (\omega t + \alpha)$$

may be represented by the *amplitude phasor* $\mathbf{V}_m = V_m\underline{/\alpha}$ or by the *effective phasor* $\mathbf{V} = V\underline{/\alpha}$. *In this book, from this point on, the term phasor will be used synonymously with the term effective phasor.*

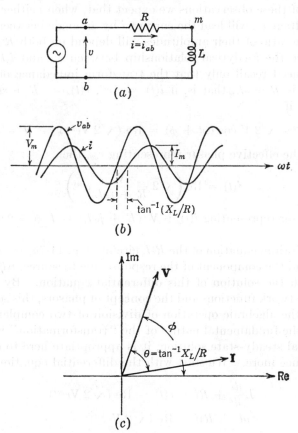

FIG. 14-7. Series $R\text{-}L$ circuit in the sinusoidal steady state.   (a) Circuit diagram. (b) Time-domain relationship between v and i.   (c) Phasor diagram.

14-6. A Series Circuit.   Before studying series and parallel combinations of elements, the series $R\text{-}L$ circuit will be analyzed, because much can be learned about the essentials of a-c circuit analysis from a simple two-element combination.   Consider, therefore, the circuit shown in Fig. 14-7a.   We wish to find the component of $i(t)$ due to a sinusoidal source $v_{ab}(t)$ as indicated in Fig. 14-7a.   Before proceeding to the analytical treatment of this circuit, the following observations are appropriate (see Fig. 14-7a and b):

1. When the inductance L is zero, then the voltage v_{ab} and the current i are in phase and the ratio of their amplitudes (or of their effective values) is given by $V_m/I_m = V/I = R$.

2. When the resistance R is zero (and the inductance is not zero), then the voltage v_{ab} leads the current i by 90° and the ratio of their effective values is given by $V/I = V_m/I_m = X_L$.

Because of these observations we expect that, when neither R nor L is zero, the voltage v_{ab} will lead the current i by an angle between 0 and 90° and that the ratio of their amplitudes will depend on both R and X_L.

To deduce the analytical relationship between v_{ab} and $i(t)$ (see Fig. 14-7a), we need recall only that the transform impedance of the series R-L circuit is $R + sL$, that is, if $i(t) = Ae^{st}$, $v(t)_s = (R + sL)Ae^{st}$. It follows that if

$$v_{ab}(t) = \sqrt{2}\, V \cos (\omega t + \phi) = \mathrm{Re}\,(\sqrt{2}\, \mathbf{V}e^{j\omega t}) \qquad \mathbf{V} = Ve^{j\phi}$$

where $\mathbf{V}$ is the effective phasor representing v_{ab}, then

$$i(t) = \mathrm{Re}\left(\sqrt{2}\, \frac{\mathbf{V}}{R + j\omega L}\, e^{j\omega t} \right) \tag{14-19}$$

and the phasor representing $i(t)_s$ is $\mathbf{V}/(R + j\omega L) = I\underline{/\phi - \theta}$ as shown in Fig. 14-7c.

The equilibrium equation of the R-L circuit (Fig. 14-7a) is a differential equation, and the component of the response due to source, $i(t)_s$, is evaluated through the solution of this differential equation. By the use of transform network functions and the concept of phasors, this solution was reduced to the algebraic operation of division of two complex numbers. Because of the fundamental nature of the "transformation" which gives the sinusoidal steady-state solution, it is appropriate here to discuss the procedure once more. We start with the differential equation

$$L\frac{di}{dt} + Ri = v(t) = \mathrm{Re}\,(\sqrt{2}\, \mathbf{V}e^{j\omega t})$$

or
$$(pL + R)i = \mathrm{Re}\,(\sqrt{2}\, \mathbf{V}e^{j\omega t})$$

and seek the component of the response $i(t)$ due to the source. Since

$$v_{ab} = \mathbf{v}_1 + \mathbf{v}_1^*$$

where $\mathbf{v}_1 = (\sqrt{2}/2)\mathbf{V}e^{j\omega t}$, using superposition we know that

$$i(t) = \mathbf{i}_1 + \mathbf{i}_1^* \tag{14-20}$$

where $\mathbf{i}_1$ is the component of the response due to $\mathbf{v}_1$. Since $\mathbf{v}_1$ is an exponential time function, then

$$(j\omega L + R)\mathbf{i}_1 = \frac{\sqrt{2}}{2}\, \mathbf{V}e^{j\omega t} \tag{14-21}$$

Solving Eq. (14-21) and using (14-20), the result, Eq. (14-19), is obtained. From this result we observe that

$$i(t) = \text{Re}\,(\sqrt{2}\,\mathbf{I}e^{j\omega t})$$

where
$$(R + j\omega L)\mathbf{I} = \mathbf{V}$$

Thus we point out again that the complex impedance $R + j\omega L$ is the ratio of the phasor which represents the voltage to the phasor which represents the current.   The complex impedance can be written in polar form,

$$\mathbf{Z} = R + j\omega L = Z\underline{/\theta}$$

where
$$Z = \sqrt{R^2 + X_L{}^2} \qquad \theta = \tan^{-1}\frac{X_L}{R}$$

Hence the ratio of the effective values (or amplitudes) $V/I\,(= V_m/I_m) = Z$, and the voltage v_{ab} leads the current $i(t)$ by θ,

$$i(t) = \frac{\sqrt{2}\,V}{Z}\cos\,(\omega t + \phi - \theta)$$

The same result can be obtained from a slightly different point of view. As we know, a sinusoidal voltage produces a sinusoidal current.   If this current in the $R\text{-}L$ circuit of Fig. 14-7a is represented by $\mathbf{I}$, that is,

$$i(t) = \text{Re}\,(\sqrt{2}\,\mathbf{I}e^{j\omega t})$$

then the phasor which represents the voltage v_{am} is $\mathbf{I}R$ and the phasor which represents v_{mb} is $j\mathbf{I}X_L$, that is,

$$v_{am} = \text{Re}\,(\sqrt{2}\,\mathbf{I}Re^{j\omega t}) \qquad v_{mb} = \text{Re}\,(\sqrt{2}\,\mathbf{I}jX_Le^{j\omega t})$$

The phasor which represents the sum of two sinusoids can be obtained by adding the phasors which represent the individual time functions,

$$\mathbf{V} = \mathbf{V}_{am} + \mathbf{V}_{mb}$$

or
$$\mathbf{V} = \mathbf{I}R + j\mathbf{I}X_L = (R + jX_L)\mathbf{I}$$

This phasor addition is illustrated in Fig. 14-8.

A diagram which shows the addition of voltage phasors in a circuit is called a *voltage phasor diagram* or, because the addition of phasors resembles the addition of vectors, a *voltage vector diagram*.

As a final remark concerning the series $R\text{-}L$ circuit we observe that the transform impedance $Z(s)$ is

$$Z(s) = R + sL = L\left(s + \frac{R}{L}\right)$$

Hence the transform impedance has a scale factor L and a zero at $-R/L$ in the s plane.   In Fig. 14-9 this zero is shown.   For the sinusoidal case s_g, $+R/L$ is represented by the line joining $(-R/L)$ to G.   Note that the angle which this line makes with the horizontal is the angle of $\mathbf{Z}$, that is, $\tan^{-1}[\omega/(R/L)] = \tan^{-1}(\omega L/R)$. Thus, if the phase angle between $\mathbf{V}$ and $\mathbf{I}$ can be measured at a known frequency, the time constant L/R of the circuit, which characterizes the free response, can be inferred. It is this type of relationship between sinusoidal steady-state response and free response which extends the usefulness of a-c circuit analysis beyond the solution of specific steady-state problems.

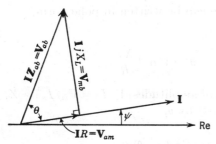

FIG. 14-8. Phasor addition of voltages in the series R-L circuit of Fig. 14-7a.

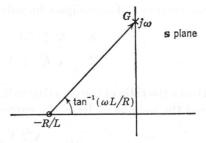

FIG. 14-9. Relating the complex imped-ance of the series R-L circuit to the pole-zero diagram of the transform impedance.

14-7. Series and Parallel Circuits. If elements are connected in series to form a terminal-pair network, the complex impedance of the series combination is the sum of the individual impedances. This is evident, not only because complex impedance is a special case of transform imped-ance, but also because the addition of sinusoidal time functions can be carried out with phasors. Thus, if we consider the circuit of Fig. 14-10, the terminal pair marked $\mathbf{Z}_1$ implies that $\mathbf{V}_{am} = \mathbf{I}\mathbf{Z}_1$; similarly $\mathbf{V}_{mb} = \mathbf{I}\mathbf{Z}_2$; hence, from Kirchhoff's voltage law $\mathbf{V}_{ab} = \mathbf{I}(\mathbf{Z}_1 + \mathbf{Z}_2)$. Thus the phasor ratio $\mathbf{V}_{ab}/\mathbf{I}$, which defines the com-plex driving-point impedance $\mathbf{Z}_{ab}$, is given as the sum of $\mathbf{Z}_1$ and $\mathbf{Z}_2$.

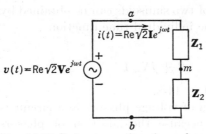

FIG. 14-10. Series connection of complex impedances.

We need to point out that the addition of complex (or transform) impedances represents a large step forward in our treatment of circuits, because we have specified the two im-pedances of the circuit of Fig. 14-10, not by the element values, but rather by the voltage-current relationships, $\mathbf{V} = \mathbf{I}\mathbf{Z}$, in the sinusoidal steady state. Thus, in the phasor method, we have introduced a "new" approach to the analysis of circuits, namely, the specification of the combination of circuit elements by giving their response to a particular waveform, in this case the sinusoidal waveform. This is seen from the fact that, when we say that the complex impedance of a terminal pair a-b is $\mathbf{Z}_{ab}$, by this we mean $\mathbf{V}_{ab} = \mathbf{Z}_{ab}\mathbf{I}_{ab}$ or, when i_{ab} is a sinusoidal current of unit effective value, then $\mathbf{V}_{ab} = \mathbf{Z}_{ab}$. Thus at a given frequency the complex impedance of a terminal pair is identical with the *phasor* representing the response (voltage) across the terminal pair, owing to the passage of a sinusoidal current of unit value.

Voltage-division Formula. Applying the operational or transform voltage-division formula to the a-c case, in Fig. 14-10,

$$\frac{\mathbf{V}_{mb}}{\mathbf{V}} = \frac{\mathbf{Z}_2}{\mathbf{Z}_1 + \mathbf{Z}_2} \tag{14-22}$$

Thus the voltage phasors in a series circuit "divide" across the complex impedances in proportion to the values of these impedances.

Parallel Elements. Consider now the parallel branches shown in Fig. 14-11, where each terminal pair is specified through its complex admittance,

$$\mathbf{I}_1 = \mathbf{Y}_1\mathbf{V}_{ab} \qquad \mathbf{I}_2 = \mathbf{Y}_2\mathbf{V}_{ab}$$

Application of Kirchhoff's current law gives

$$\mathbf{I} = \mathbf{Y}_1\mathbf{V}_{ab} + \mathbf{Y}_2\mathbf{V}_{ab} = \mathbf{V}_{ab}(\mathbf{Y}_1 + \mathbf{Y}_2)$$

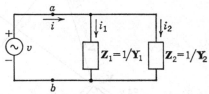

FIG. 14-11. Parallel connection of complex impedances.

so that the driving-point admittance of parallel connected elements is the sum of the admittances. We note further that

$$\frac{\mathbf{I}_1}{\mathbf{I}} = \frac{\mathbf{V}_{ab}\mathbf{Y}_1}{\mathbf{V}_{ab}(\mathbf{Y}_1 + \mathbf{Y}_2)} = \frac{\mathbf{Y}_1}{\mathbf{Y}_1 + \mathbf{Y}_2} \tag{14-23}$$

so that the complex *current-division formula* states: In a parallel circuit the current phasors divide through the admittances, in proportion to the values of the complex admittances. Comparison of Eq. (14-23) and Eq. (14-22) shows that the voltage-division and current-division formulas are duals of each other.

Terminology. In sinusoidal steady-state calculation the use of phasors and complex impedance is so common that the phrase "the phasor representing the current $i(t)$" is often omitted and the phasor $(\mathbf{I})$ is referred to as "the current" in the circuit. Similarly one speaks of a (complex) voltage $\mathbf{V}$, meaning the phasor representing the voltage

$$v(t) = \text{Re} \, (\mathbf{V} \, \sqrt{2} \, e^{j\omega t})$$

14-8. Examples, Use of Phasor Diagram. Example 14-1. Series Circuit. In the series circuit shown in Fig. 14-12a calculate $i(t)$ in the steady state, and draw a voltage phasor diagram.

Solution. Let the voltage $v_{ab}(t) = v(t)$ be represented by the phasor $\mathbf{V} = 100\underline{/0°}$; then $i(t)$ will be represented by the phasor $\mathbf{I} = I\underline{/-\theta}$, where $+\theta$ is the angle of the

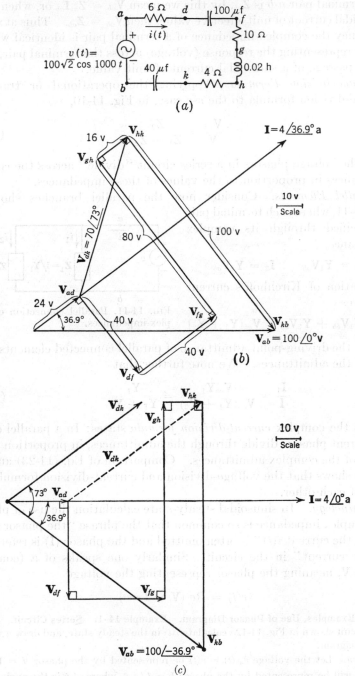

FIG. 14-12. Illustration for Example 14-1. (a) Circuit diagram. (b) Phasor diagram with V_{ab} as reference. (c) Phasor diagram with I as reference.

impedance Z_{ab} and $I = V/Z_{ab}$. To calculate the complex impedance, we need the reactances of the energy-storing elements at the radian frequency of the source $(\omega = 1,000)$.

$$X_{df} = -\frac{1}{1,000 \times 100 \times 10^{-6}} = -10 \text{ ohms}$$
$$X_{gh} = 1,000 \times 0.020 = +20 \text{ ohms}$$
$$X_{kb} = -\frac{1}{1,000 \times 40 \times 10^{-6}} = -25 \text{ ohms}$$

Between terminals a-b the complex impedance is now obtained as the sum of the impedances as follows:

$$Z_{ab} = 6 - j10 + 10 + j20 + 4 - j25 = (20 - j15) \text{ ohms}$$
or $\qquad Z_{ab} = 25\underline{/-36.9°} \text{ ohms}$

The phasor I is given as the ratio of V/Z,

$$I = \frac{100\underline{/0°}}{25\underline{/-36.9°}} = 4\underline{/36.9°}$$

and the solution for $i(t)$ is

$$i(t) = 4\sqrt{2} \cos (1,000t + 36.9°) \text{ amp}$$

The phasor diagram shown in Fig. 14-12b shows the addition of the voltage phasors across the individual elements. The "polygon" method of vector addition is used. Thus the tail of the next phasor in the sum is placed at the head of the preceding one. In Fig. 14-12b the voltage phasor V_{ab} is the reference phasor as stated in the problem. In Fig. 14-12c the phasor diagram is drawn with the current phasor as reference. This choice of reference is sometimes preferred in series connections of elements because the various voltage phasors for the elements are then drawn either horizontally or vertically; moreover, since the current in all parts of a series circuit is the same, it is natural to use the current phasor as the reference.

To illustrate the use of the phasor diagram, suppose that it is desired to find the voltage V_{dk}. Since $V_{dk} = V_{df} + V_{fg} + V_{gh} + V_{hk}$, the phasor V_{dk} can be located by drawing a phasor from the tail of V_{df} to the head of V_{hk}. Performing this construction on Fig. 14-12b, we obtain the length of V_{dk} as 70 and the angle of V_{dk} with respect to the horizontal (V_{ab}) as 73° leading. Hence

$$V_{dk} = 70\underline{/73°} \qquad \text{or} \qquad v_{dk}(t) = 70\sqrt{2} \cos (1,000t + 73°)$$

Upon performing the same construction on Fig. 14-12c, the angle with the horizontal is 36°. But in this diagram I is reference, and the angle with V_{ab} is found by placing the phasor V_{dk} and V_{ab} tail to tail. Note that the resulting angle is 73° as before.

The same result can be obtained analytically. Since

$\qquad\qquad V_{dk} = IZ_{dk}$
and $\qquad Z_{dk} = -j10 + 10 + j20 + 4 = 14 + j10 = 17.2\underline{/35.6°}$
hence $\qquad V_{dk} = (4\underline{/36.9°})(17.2\underline{/35.6°})$
$\qquad\qquad\quad = 68.8\underline{/72.5°}$
so that $\qquad v_{dk}(t) = 68.8\sqrt{2} \cos (1,000t + 72.5°)$

This result is sufficiently close to the graphical answer to constitute a correct check.

While in this particular example the phasor diagram is used merely as a check, we shall see in Example 14-2 that the phasor diagram can be a valuable tool in the solution of problems.

Example 14-2. Series Circuit. In the circuit shown in Fig. 14-13a the following *magnitudes* are known:

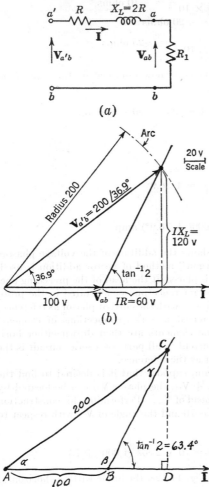

$$V_{ab} = 100 \qquad V_{a'b} = 200 \qquad I = 20 \text{ amp}$$

In addition it is known that $X_L = 2R$. Solve for $Z_{a'a}$ and $V_{a'a}$.

Solution. We shall first show how the solution of this problem is obtained without reference to the phasor diagram. Since Z_{ab} is a resistance R_1, V_{ab} and I are in phase. If we let

$$I = 20/\underline{0°}$$

then $$V_{ab} = 100/\underline{0°}$$

Hence $R_1 = \frac{100}{20} = 5.0$ ohms. At terminals $a'b$ the magnitude of the impedance is $\frac{200}{20} = 10$ ohms. Hence

$$|Z_{a'b}| = 10 = |5.0 + R + j2R|$$

or $$[(5.0 + R)^2 + 4R^2]^{\frac{1}{2}} = 10$$

and, squaring,

$$4R^2 + R^2 + 10R + 25 = 100$$

so that $$5R^2 + 10R - 75 = 0$$

The solutions for R from this equation are $R = 3.0$ and $R = -5.0$. The negative value of R is discounted as extraneous. This value was introduced into the solution when $|Z_{a'b}|$ was squared. Hence $R = 3.0$ ohms, $X_L = 6.0$ ohms, and $Z_{a'a} = 3.0 + j6.0$ ohms. As a check we calculate $Z_{a'b}$. $Z_{a'b} = 3.0 + j6.0 + 5.0 = 8.0 + j6.0 = 10/\underline{+36.9°}$ so that the magnitude is 10 as given. The voltage $V_{a'a}$ is given by $V_{a'a} = IZ_{a'a}$; hence

$$V_{a'a} = 20(|3 + j6|)$$

$$= (20 \times 6.71) = 134.2 \text{ volts}$$

The solution of the quadratic equation can be avoided if a phasor diagram showing the voltage addition is drawn. In Fig. 14-13b, V_{ab} is drawn in phase with I. The magnitude of $V_{a'a}$ is unknown,

Fig. 14-13. Illustration for Example 14-2. (a) Circuit diagram. (b) Phasor diagram, constructed to scale. (c) Freehand sketch of phasor diagram.

Since $V_{a'a} + V_{ab} = V_{a'b}$, we need to add $V_{a'a}$ to V_{ab}. The magnitude of $V_{a'a}$ is unknown, but we know that $V_{a'a}$ will lead I by the angle of $Z_{a'a}$. This angle is given and is equal to $\tan^{-1} 2$ ($= 63.4°$). We therefore draw a line from the end of the phasor V_{ab} making the angle $63.4°$ with the horizontal (I) and of indefinite length. Now the sum $V_{a'a} + V_{ab}$ must have a magnitude of 200; we swing an arc of radius 200 from the tail of the V_{ab} phasor. The intersection of this arc with the line at $\tan^{-1} 2$ must give the end point of both $\mathbf{V}_{a'b}$ and $\mathbf{V}_{a'a}$. We can now measure $\mathbf{V}_{a'a}$ and obtain its angle with respect to $\mathbf{I}$ to obtain $\mathbf{Z}_{a'a}$. Alternatively IR and IX_L can be measured to obtain $\mathbf{Z}_{a'a}$.

We have explained the use of the phasor diagram on the assumption that the diagram has been drawn to scale. If this is inconvenient, one can draw the phasor diagram approximately to scale (i.e., freehand) and calculate the length and angles of the phasors by trigonometry. Such a sketch is shown in Fig. 14-13c. To avoid quadratic equations, the law of sines is used repeatedly.

Since β is the supplement of 63.4°, $\beta = 180° - 63.4° = 116.6°$. Hence γ can be determined,

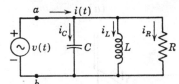

$$\frac{\sin \gamma}{\sin 116.6°} = \frac{100}{200}$$

and
$$\gamma = 26.5°$$

Hence

$$\alpha = 180° - 116.6° - 26.5° = 36.9°$$

Now BC can be calculated by using the law of sines again ($BC/AC = \sin \alpha / \sin \beta$), or CD is obtained: $200 \sin \alpha = 200 \times 0.6 = 120$. The solution is now virtually complete ($CD = 120 = IX_L$, $X_L = 6$, $R = 3$).

Example 14-3. A Parallel Circuit. For the circuit shown in Fig. 14-14 calculate $i(t)$. The source voltage $v(t)$ is given as

$$v(t) = 156 \cos 377t$$

The element values are $R = 100$ ohms, $L = 0.20$ henry, $C = 20$ μf.

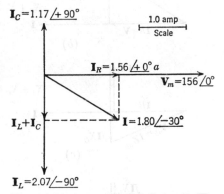

FIG. 14-14. A parallel R-L-C circuit (Example 14-3) and the corresponding current phasor diagram.

Solution. Since $v(t) = 156 \cos 377t$, $V_m = 156$; eventually we shall need I_m so that amplitude phasors will be used. Let

$$\mathbf{V}_m = 156\underline{/0}$$

To calculate $i(t)$, the complex admittance $\mathbf{Y}_{ab}$ is needed. Since

$$B_L = -\frac{1}{\omega L} \qquad B_L = -\frac{1}{377 \times 0.20} = -13.26 \times 10^{-3}\,\text{mho}$$

and
$$B_C = \omega C \qquad B_C = 377 \times 20 \times 10^{-6} = 7.54 \times 10^{-3}\,\text{mho}$$

and
$$G = \frac{1}{R} \qquad G = 0.01 = 10 \times 10^{-3}\,\text{mho}$$

The complex admittance is

$$\mathbf{Y}_{ab} = (10 - j13.26 + j7.54) \times 10^{-3}\,\text{mho}$$
or
$$\mathbf{Y}_{ab} = 11.5 \times 10^{-3}\underline{/-30°}\,\text{mho}$$

Hence
$$\mathbf{I}_m = 156\underline{/0°} \times 11.5 \times 10^{-3}\underline{/-30°} = 1.8\underline{/-30°}\,\text{amp}$$
or
$$i(t) = 1.8 \cos (377t - 30°)\,\text{amp}$$

14-9. The Series and the Parallel R-L-C Circuit. The phase relations between voltage and current in the series and in the parallel R-L-C circuit

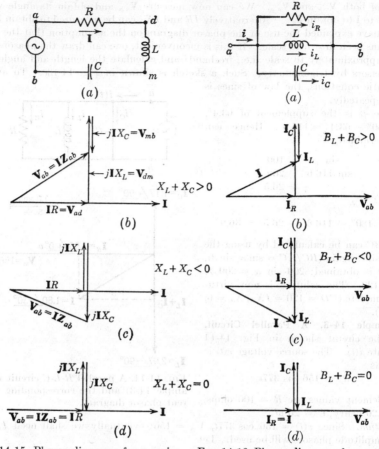

FIG. 14-15. Phasor diagrams for a series
R-L-C circuit. (a) Circuit diagram.
(b) Voltage phasor diagram for $X > 0$.
(c) Voltage phasor diagram for $X < 0$.
(d) Voltage phasor diagram for $X = 0$.

FIG. 14-16. Phasor diagrams for a parallel
R-L-C circuit. (a) Circuit diagram.
(b) Current phasor diagram for $B > 0$.
(c) Current phasor diagram for $B < 0$.
(d) Current phasor diagram for $B = 0$.

are particularly interesting because of their various possibilities. The
series R-L-C circuit shown in Fig. 14-15 has the complex impedance

$$\mathbf{Z}_{ab} = R + jX \qquad X = X_L + X_C$$

so that if

$$v_{ab}(t) = \sqrt{2}\, V \cos{(\omega t + \phi)}$$

$$i_{ab}(t) = \sqrt{2}\, \frac{V}{Z} \cos{(\omega t + \phi - \theta)}$$

where

$$\theta = \tan^{-1}\frac{X}{R}$$

We may now observe the following possible phase relations between v_{ab}
and i:

(1) $X_L + X_C > 0$ $\omega L > \dfrac{1}{\omega C}$ current i lags voltage v_{ab}

(2) $X_L + X_C < 0$ $\omega L < \dfrac{1}{\omega C}$ current i leads voltage v_{ab}

(3) $X_L + X_C = 0$ $\omega L = \dfrac{1}{\omega C}$ current i in phase with voltage v_{ab}

These possibilities are illustrated with the aid of voltage phasor diagrams in Fig. 14-15b, c, and d.   Condition (3), $X = 0$, is of particular interest and will be discussed in detail in Chap. 15.

For the parallel R-L-C circuit shown in Fig. 14-16a the admittance is

$$\mathbf{Y}_{ab} = G + jB \qquad B = B_L + B_C \qquad G = \dfrac{1}{R}$$

Hence, if the current $i(t)$ is given by

$$i(t) = \sqrt{2}\, I \cos(\omega t + \psi)$$

then

$$v_{ab}(t) = \sqrt{2}\, \frac{I}{Y} \cos\left(\omega t + \psi - \tan^{-1}\frac{B}{G}\right)$$

We again observe three possibilities:

(1) $B_L + B_C > 0$ $\dfrac{1}{\omega L} < \omega C$ v_{ab} lags i

(2) $B_L + B_C < 0$ $\dfrac{1}{\omega L} > \omega C$ v_{ab} leads i

(3) $B_L + B_C = 0$ $\dfrac{1}{\omega L} = \omega C$ v_{ab} in phase with i

These three possibilities are illustrated with the aid of current phasor diagrams in Fig. 14-16b, c, and d.

14-10. Series Admittances and Parallel Impedances, Notation.   We have defined the complex impedance between two terminals a-b as being the ratio of the phasors, $\mathbf{V}_{ab}/\mathbf{I}_{ab} = \mathbf{Z}_{ab}$; the complex admittance between these two terminals is defined by $\mathbf{Y}_{ab}\mathbf{Z}_{ab} = 1$.   We shall reserve the symbol θ (Greek letter theta) for the angle of impedance; that is, θ is the angle by which the voltage v_{ab} *leads* the current i_{ab}.   Hence in polar form

$$\mathbf{Z}_{ab} = Z_{ab}\underline{/\theta}$$

and

$$\mathbf{Y}_{ab} = Y_{ab}\underline{/-\theta}$$

As indicated in Fig. 14-17, it is sometimes desired to calculate the admittance of a series circuit in which the complex admittances are specified or the impedance of a parallel circuit in which the complex impedances are specified.

Referring to Fig. 14-17a, we note that for the series circuit

$$\mathbf{Z}_{ab} = \frac{1}{\mathbf{Y}_A} + \frac{1}{\mathbf{Y}_B} = \frac{\mathbf{Y}_A + \mathbf{Y}_B}{\mathbf{Y}_A \mathbf{Y}_B}$$

or $\qquad\qquad \mathbf{Y}_{ab} = \dfrac{\mathbf{Y}_A \mathbf{Y}_B}{\mathbf{Y}_A + \mathbf{Y}_B}$ $\qquad\qquad\qquad$ (14-24)

For the parallel circuit shown in Fig. 14-17b

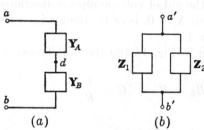

$$\mathbf{Y}_{a'b'} = \frac{1}{\mathbf{Z}_1} + \frac{1}{\mathbf{Z}_2} = \frac{\mathbf{Z}_1 + \mathbf{Z}_2}{\mathbf{Z}_1 \mathbf{Z}_2}$$

or

$$\mathbf{Z}_{a'b'} = \frac{\mathbf{Z}_1 \mathbf{Z}_2}{\mathbf{Z}_1 + \mathbf{Z}_2} \qquad (14\text{-}25)$$

Although Eq. (14-25) appears to be very popular with many readers, the calculation of parallel circuits in a numerical example is usually expedited by obtaining the complex admittances in rectangular form and then adding. This is especially valid when more than two impedances are in parallel.

(a) $\qquad\qquad$ **(b)**

FIG. 14-17. (a) Admittances in series. (b) Impedances in parallel.

14-11. Series-Parallel Circuits. It should be clear now that an equivalent complex immittance can be found for any series-parallel connection of circuit elements by repeated replacement of series and parallel

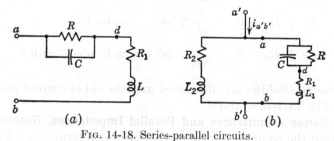

FIG. 14-18. Series-parallel circuits.

combinations with their equivalent immittances. Consider, for example, the circuit shown in Fig. 14-18a. For this circuit

$$\mathbf{Z}_{ab} = \mathbf{Z}_{ad} + \mathbf{Z}_{db}$$

But $\qquad\qquad \mathbf{Z}_{db} = R_1 + j\omega L$

and $\qquad\qquad \mathbf{Z}_{ad} = \dfrac{1}{\mathbf{Y}_{ad}} = \dfrac{1}{1/R + j\omega C}$

Hence $\qquad \mathbf{Z}_{ab} = R_1 + j\omega L + \dfrac{1}{1/R + j\omega C}$ $\qquad\qquad$ (14-26)

For any particular value of ω the complex number $\mathbf{Z}_{ab}$ can be evaluated, and hence the relationship between v_{ab} and i_{ab} in the steady state is determined. If now the elements which form $\mathbf{Z}_{ab}$ are placed in parallel with a second set of elements as illustrated in Fig. 14-18b, the relationship between the sinusoids $v_{a'b'}$ and $i_{a'b'}$ is determined through the admittance $\mathbf{Y}_{a'b'}$,

$$\mathbf{Y}_{a'b'} = \mathbf{Y}_{ab} + \mathbf{Y}_2$$

$$\mathbf{Y}_2 = \frac{1}{R_2 + j\omega L_2}$$

$$\mathbf{Y}_{ab} = \frac{1}{\mathbf{Z}_{ab}}$$

and $\mathbf{Z}_{ab}$ is given by Eq. (14-26). Several numerical examples will serve to illustrate the solution of problems.

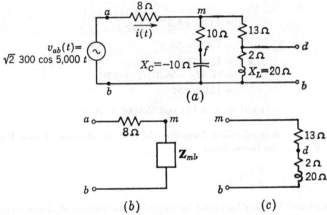

FIG. 14-19. A series-parallel circuit (see Example 14-4).

Example 14-4. A Series-Parallel Circuit. In the circuit shown in Fig. 14-19a, $v_{ab}(t)$ is given by

$$v_{ab}(t) = \sqrt{2}\ 300 \cos 5{,}000t$$

Calculate $i(t)$ and $v_{db}(t)$ in the sinusoidal steady state.

Solution. We shall first obtain $\mathbf{Z}_{ab}$. Several procedures for obtaining $v_{ab}(t)$ will then be discussed.

To obtain $\mathbf{Z}_{ab}$, we shall first obtain $\mathbf{Z}_{mb}$. Since $\mathbf{Y}_{mb} = \mathbf{Y}_{mfb} + \mathbf{Y}_{mdb}$, we calculate

$$\mathbf{Y}_{mfb} = \frac{1}{10 - j10} = 0.05 + j0.05$$

and

$$\mathbf{Y}_{mdb} = \frac{1}{13 + 2 + j20} = \frac{1}{15 + j20} = \frac{1}{25\underline{/53.1^\circ}} = 0.04\underline{/-53.1^\circ}$$

$$= 0.024 - j0.032$$

$$\mathbf{Y}_{mb} = 0.05 + j0.05 + 0.024 - j0.032 = 0.074 + j0.018$$

$$= 0.076\underline{/+13.7^\circ}\ \text{mho}$$

$$\mathbf{Z}_{mb} = \frac{1}{0.076\underline{/+13.7^\circ}} = 13.2\underline{/-13.7^\circ} = 12.8 - j3.12\ \text{ohms}$$

Hence

$$\mathbf{Z}_{ab} = 8 + 12.8 - j3.12 = 20.8 - j3.12 = 21.0\underline{/-8.5^\circ}\ \text{ohms}$$

Let $v_{ab}(t)$ be represented by the (effective) phasor

$$\mathbf{V}_{ab} = 300\underline{/0^\circ} \text{ volts}$$

Then

$$\mathbf{I} = \frac{300\underline{/0^\circ}}{21.0\underline{/-8.5^\circ}} = 14.3\underline{/+8.5^\circ} \text{ amp}$$

Hence

$$i(t) = \sqrt{2}\, 14.3 \cos(5{,}000t + 8.5^\circ) \qquad Ans.$$

To calculate the phasor $\mathbf{V}_{db}$, we may use either the voltage-division formula or the current-division formula. Using the current-division formula and defining $\mathbf{I}_{mdb} = \mathbf{I}_2$,

$$\frac{\mathbf{I}_2}{\mathbf{I}} = \frac{\mathbf{Y}_2}{\mathbf{Y}_1 + \mathbf{Y}_2}$$

where $\mathbf{Y}_2 = \mathbf{Y}_{mdb}$ and $\mathbf{Y}_1 = \mathbf{Y}_{mfb}$. Hence

$$\mathbf{I}_2 = 14.3\underline{/+8.5^\circ} \times \frac{0.04\underline{/-53.1^\circ}}{0.076\underline{/+13.7^\circ}}$$

$$= 7.52\underline{/-58.3^\circ}$$

Thus

$$\mathbf{V}_{db} = \mathbf{I}_2 \times \mathbf{Z}_{db}$$

$$= (7.52\underline{/-58.3^\circ})(2 + j20)$$

$$= 151\underline{/+26^\circ}$$

and

$$v_{db}(t) = \sqrt{2}\, 151 \cos(5{,}000t + 26^\circ) \qquad Ans.$$

The use of the voltage-division formula will now be illustrated (see Fig. 14-19b). The phasor $\mathbf{V}_{mb}$ may be found from

$$\mathbf{V}_{mb} = \frac{\mathbf{Z}_{mb}}{\mathbf{Z}_{ab}} \mathbf{V}_{ab}$$

The voltage phasor $\mathbf{V}_{db}$ may be found by applying the voltage-division formula to the branch mdb (see Fig. 14-19c),

$$\mathbf{V}_{db} = \mathbf{V}_{mb} \times \frac{\mathbf{Z}_{db}}{\mathbf{Z}_{mdb}}$$

Substituting,

$$\mathbf{V}_{db} = 300\underline{/0^\circ} \times \frac{13.2\underline{/-13.7^\circ}}{21.0\underline{/-8.5^\circ}} \times \frac{2 + j20}{15 + j20} = 151\underline{/26^\circ}$$

The reader will recognize that the operations indicated for $\mathbf{V}_{db}$ above are exactly identical to those used when the current-division formula was applied. The voltage $\mathbf{V}_{mb}$ could also be found by application of Kirchhoff's voltage law in the form $\mathbf{V}_{mb} = \mathbf{V}_{ab} - \mathbf{V}_{am}$. There is no reason to consider any of these minor variations in approach to the problem superior to any other variation.

Example 14-5. Series-Parallel Ladder-type Circuit. Consider the circuit shown in Fig. 14-20a. Assume that all the elements marked R are equal to 1.0 ohm and that all the elements marked X_C are equal to -1.0 ohm. Assume that the phasor $\mathbf{V}_{db}$ is known and that the expression for $\mathbf{V}_{ab}$ in terms of $\mathbf{V}_{db}$ is desired.

Solution. $\mathbf{V}_{gb}$ is found by applying voltage division to the branch gdb as shown in Fig. 14-20b,

$$\mathbf{V}_{gb} = \mathbf{V}_{db} \times \frac{1 - j}{-j}$$

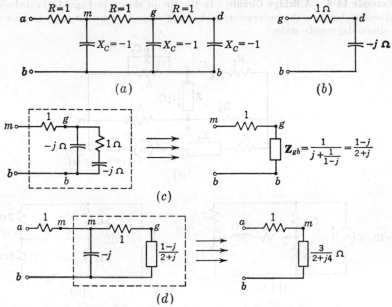

FIG. 14-20. A ladder-type series-parallel circuit.

Now $\mathbf{V}_{mb}$ is found by applying the voltage-division formula to the portion of the circuit shown in Fig. 14-20c,

$$\mathbf{V}_{mb} = \mathbf{V}_{gb} \cdot \frac{1 + \dfrac{1-j}{2+j}}{\dfrac{1-j}{2+j}}$$

Simplifying,

$$\mathbf{V}_{mb} = \mathbf{V}_{gb} \cdot \frac{3}{1-j}$$

Using the result for $\mathbf{V}_{gb}$,

$$\mathbf{V}_{mb} = \mathbf{V}_{db} \cdot \frac{1-j}{-j} \cdot \frac{3}{1-j}$$

$\mathbf{V}_{ab}$ is now found by applying the voltage-division formula to the circuit as drawn in Fig. 14-20d,

$$\mathbf{V}_{ab} = \mathbf{V}_{mb} \cdot \frac{1 + \dfrac{3}{2+4j}}{\dfrac{3}{2+4j}} = \mathbf{V}_{mb} \times \frac{5+4j}{3}$$

Hence, using the previous result for $\mathbf{V}_{mb}$ in terms of $\mathbf{V}_{db}$, we have the desired result,

$$\mathbf{V}_{ab} = \mathbf{V}_{db} \cdot \frac{1-j}{-j} \cdot \frac{3}{1-j} \cdot \frac{5+4j}{3} = \mathbf{V}_{db} \cdot \frac{5+4j}{-j}$$

or $\qquad \mathbf{V}_{ab} = \mathbf{V}_{db} \cdot 6.4 \underline{/128.6°}$

Example 14-6.   A Bridge Circuit.   In the circuit shown in Fig. 14-21a deduce the relationship between the parameters which will cause the current $i_{ab}(t)$ to be zero in the sinusoidal steady state.

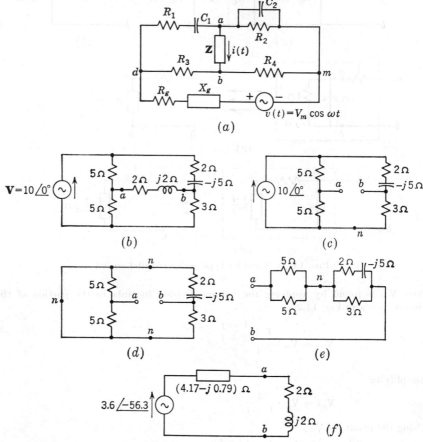

Fig. 14-21. Circuits for Examples 14-6 and 14-7. (a) A bridge type circuit (Example 14-6). (b) An unbalanced bridge (Example 14-7). (c) Calculation of open-circuit voltage for the circuit of (b). (d, e) Calculation of $\mathbf{Z}_s$ for the circuit of (b). (f) Thévenin's equivalent circuit with respect to terminals a-b for the circuit of (b).

Solution.   If $i_{ab}(t) = 0$, $\mathbf{I}_{ab} = 0$ and $\mathbf{V}_{ab} = 0$ regardless of the value of $\mathbf{Z}$.   Applying Kirchhoff's voltage law to loops d-a-b-d and a-m-b-a,

$$\mathbf{V}_{da} + \mathbf{V}_{ab} + \mathbf{V}_{bd} = 0$$

and

$$\mathbf{V}_{am} + \mathbf{V}_{mb} + \mathbf{V}_{ba} = 0$$

Since $\mathbf{V}_{ba}$ must be zero,

and

$$\mathbf{V}_{da} + \mathbf{V}_{bd} = 0$$
$$\mathbf{V}_{am} + \mathbf{V}_{mb} = 0 \tag{14-27}$$

But

$$\mathbf{V}_{da} = \mathbf{I}_{da}\mathbf{Z}_{da}$$
$$\mathbf{V}_{db} = \mathbf{I}_{db}\mathbf{Z}_{db}$$
$$\mathbf{V}_{am} = \mathbf{I}_{am}\mathbf{Z}_{am}$$
$$\mathbf{V}_{mb} = \mathbf{I}_{mb}\mathbf{Z}_{mb} \tag{14-28}$$

Since I_{ab} must be zero,

$$I_{da} = I_{am}$$

and $$I_{db} = I_{bm} \tag{14-29}$$

Substituting Eqs. (14-28) in (14-27) and using (14-29),

$$I_{da}Z_{da} = -I_{bd}Z_{bd} \tag{14-30a}$$

and $$I_{da}Z_{am} = -I_{bd}Z_{mb} \tag{14-30b}$$

Dividing (14-30a) by (14-30b),

$$\frac{Z_{da}}{Z_{am}} = \frac{Z_{bd}}{Z_{mb}} \tag{14-31}$$

This is the desired equation. Note that the result is independent of V_m, R_g, and X_g. For the impedances specified in this example, Eq. (14-31) becomes

$$Z_{da}Y_{am} = \frac{Z_{bd}}{Z_{mb}}$$

$$\left(R_1 + \frac{1}{j\omega C_1}\right)\left(\frac{1}{R_2} + j\omega C_2\right) = \frac{R_3}{R_4}$$

$$\frac{R_1}{R_2} + j\omega\left(C_2R_1 - \frac{1}{R_2C_1\omega^2}\right) + \frac{C_2}{C_1} = \frac{R_3}{R_4}$$

Hence $i_{ab}(t)$ is zero if

$$\frac{C_2}{C_1} = \frac{R_3}{R_4} - \frac{R_1}{R_2}$$

$$\omega^2 = \frac{1}{R_1R_2C_1C_2}$$

Note that this final result involves ω, the radian frequency of the source.

Example 14-7. Use of Thévenin's Theorem. Use Thévenin's theorem to calculate the phasor V_{ab} in the circuit of Fig. 14-21b.

Solution. Since V_{ab} is required, the branch a-b is disconnected and we calculate V_{ab} in Fig. 14-21c. This phasor will be V_o for the Thévenin equivalent circuit. In Fig. 14-21c the voltage-division formula is applied twice,

$$V_{an} = 10\underline{/0} \times \frac{5}{5+5} = 5\underline{/0°} = 5 + j0$$

$$V_{bn} = 10\underline{/0} \times \frac{3}{5-j5} = 4.24\underline{/45°} = 3 + j3$$

Hence $$V_{ab} = V_{an} - V_{bn} = V_o = 5 - 3 - j3 = 2 - j3 = 3.6\underline{/-56.3°}$$

To obtain the complex impedance Z_s, the source V is set to zero and Z_{ab} in Fig. 14-21d is calculated. Drawing the circuit as in Fig. 14-21e, we have

$$Z_{an} = \tfrac{5}{2} = 2.50 + j0 \text{ ohms}$$

$$Y_{nb} = \frac{1}{3} + \frac{1}{2-j3} = 0.49 + j0.23 = 0.54\underline{/25.2°}$$

$$Z_{nb} = \frac{1}{0.54\underline{/25.2°}} = 1.85\underline{/-25.2°} = 1.67 - j0.79$$

Hence Thévenin's equivalent circuit (for this sinusoidal steady-state condition) is represented by a voltage source whose phasor is $3.6\underline{/-56.3°}$ and an impedance $Z_s = 2.50 + 1.67 - j0.79 = 4.17 - j0.79$ ohms as shown in Fig. 14-21f. Replacing the load, V_{ab} in the original circuit is found by application of the voltage-division formula to Fig. 14-21f,

$$V_{ab} = 3.6\underline{/-56.3°} \times \frac{2+j2}{6.17+j1.21} = 1.62\underline{/-0.2°} \text{ volts} \quad Ans.$$

14-12. Equivalent Circuits. At this point it should be clear that the voltage-current relationship (driving-point immittance) for any passive terminal pair in the sinusoidal steady state at any one frequency is com-

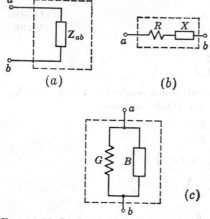

pletely characterized by the complex immittance of the terminal pair. In any numerical case this means that the complex number

$$\mathbf{Z}_{ab} = R + jX$$

or

$$\mathbf{Y}_{ab} = G + jB$$

may represent a passive terminal pair at the input terminals a-b as indicated in Fig. 14-22.

As is indicated in Fig. 14-22, this means that *at any one frequency* we can represent a terminal pair as a series or a parallel combination of only two elements. We shall now present several examples to illustrate this equivalent representa-

FIG. 14-22. In the sinusoidal steady state the complex immittance specifies a terminal pair.

tion. In every case it must be remembered that we are obtaining equivalent representations only with respect to the input terminals and only at one frequency in the sinusoidal steady state. The equivalent representations which are deduced on this basis will serve to obtain *not* the complete response of the original circuit but *only* the component of the response

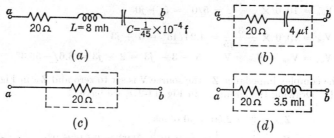

FIG. 14-23. A series R-L-C circuit and its two-element representation at three frequencies.

(at the input terminals) to a sinusoidal source of the frequency at which the calculations are carried out.

Example 14-8. For the series R-L-C circuit shown in Fig. 14-23a deduce equivalent circuits with respect to terminals a-b consisting of two elements at the frequencies (a) $f_1 = 796$ cps; (b) $f_2 = 1.5 \times 796$ cps; (c) $f_3 = 2 \times 796$ cps.

Solution. (*a*) At the frequency $f_1 = 796$ cps the radian frequency is

$$\omega_1 = 2\pi f_1 = 6.28 \times 796 = 5{,}000 \text{ rad/sec}$$

Hence $\qquad X_L = 5{,}000 \times 8 \times 10^{-3} = 40$ ohms

and $\qquad X_C = -\dfrac{1}{\frac{1}{45} \times 5{,}000 \times 10^{-4}} = -90$ ohms

so that $\qquad \mathbf{Z}_{ab} = 20 + j40 - j90$
$$= 20 - j50 \qquad \text{at } \omega = \omega_1$$

This impedance can be interpreted as the series combination of a 20-ohm resistance and a -50-ohm capacitive reactance. Since the equivalent capacitive reactance is -50 ohms, the series capacitance $C = 1/(50 \times 5{,}000) = 4$ μf. This result is shown in Fig. 14-23b.

(*b*) At the frequency $\omega_2 = 1.5\omega_1$

$$X_L = 1.5 \times 40 = 60 \text{ ohms}$$

$$X_C = -\frac{90}{1.5} = -60 \text{ ohms}$$

Hence $\qquad \mathbf{Z}_{ab} = 20 + j60 - j60 = 20 + j0$ ohms $\qquad$ at $\omega = \omega_2$

This result is illustrated in Fig. 14-23c.

(*c*) At the frequency $\omega = 2\omega_1$

$$X_L = 2 \times 40 = 80 \text{ ohms}$$
$$X_C = -\tfrac{1}{2} \times 90 = -45 \text{ ohms}$$

Hence $\qquad \mathbf{Z}_{ab} = 20 + j35 \qquad$ at $\omega = \omega_3$

This result can be interpreted as the series combination of a 20-ohm resistance and a $3.5 \times 10^{-3} [= 35/(2 \times 5{,}000)]$ henry inductance as indicated in Fig. 14-23d.

Figure 14-23b to d shows three circuits which at the three frequencies given have the same complex value $\mathbf{Z}_{ab}$ as the original circuit of Fig. 14-23a. It must be emphasized that each of these equivalent currents at the frequency at which they are equivalent has *the same sinusoidal steady-state response*, i.e., the same component of the response due to the source. These equivalent circuits have *neither* the same equilibrium equation *nor* the same complete response as the original circuit.

Example 14-9. For the circuit of Example 14-8 at the radian frequency $\omega = 5{,}000$ rad/sec deduce a parallel equivalent circuit, and discuss other equivalent circuits.

Solution. The impedance of the circuit at the frequency stated was found to be

$$\mathbf{Z}_{ab} = 20 - j50 \text{ ohms}$$

To obtain a parallel equivalent circuit, we shall find the complex admittance $\mathbf{Y}_{ab}$,

$$\mathbf{Y}_{ab} = \frac{1}{\mathbf{Z}_{ab}} = \frac{1}{20 - j50} = \frac{1}{10} \frac{1}{2 - j5}$$

$$= 0.1 \frac{1}{5.38 / -68.2^\circ} = 0.0185 / +68.2^\circ$$

or, in rectangular form,

$$\mathbf{Y}_{ab} = 0.0069 + j0.0172 \text{ mho}$$

This admittance may be interpreted as the parallel combination of a 0.0069-mho conductance and a $+0.0172$-mho susceptance (capacitive). A 0.0172-mho susceptance corresponds at 5,000 rad/sec to a capacitance of $0.0172/5{,}000 = 3.45$-μf capacitance. A 0.0069-mho conductance corresponds to a $1/0.0069 = 145$-ohm resistance.

These results are illustrated in Fig. 14-24. Again we must emphasize that the equivalence which has been established applies only at the radian frequency of 5,000 in the sinusoidal steady state between terminals a-b. The current in the 145-ohm resistance or in the 3.45-μf capacitance of the equivalent parallel circuit has no meaning in the original circuit. The sum of these currents will, however, equal i_{ab} in the original circuit in the stady state if v_{ab} is the same sinusoidal voltage at the correct frequency.

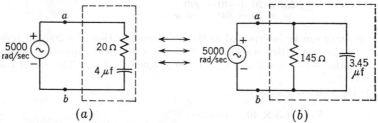

FIG. 14-24. Series and parallel two-element representations in the sinusoidal steady state at a particular frequency.

Other equivalents are easily established. (An infinite variety is possible if more than two elements are allowed.) We may, for example, write

$$\mathbf{Z}_{ab} = 5 + 15 - j50$$

and define

$$\mathbf{Z}_1 = 15 - j50$$

Then

$$\mathbf{Y}_1 = \frac{1}{15 - j50} = 0.0192\underline{/73.3^\circ} = 0.00550 + j0.0183$$

This admittance may be interpreted as the parallel combination of a $181(= 1/0.0055)$ ohm resistance and a $3.66(= 0.0183/5,000)\mu$f capacitance. Since $\mathbf{Z}_{ab} = 5 + \mathbf{Z}_1$, another equivalent circuit may be shown as indicated in Fig. 14-25.

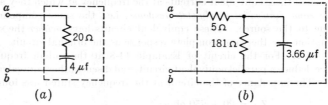

FIG. 14-25. Terminal pairs which have the same complex immittance at a particular frequency.

Immittance for Two Elements. Since a terminal pair, at a fixed frequency in the sinusoidal steady state, is completely specified by its complex immittance, it is possible to represent such a terminal pair either as a series or as a parallel combination of two elements.

A parallel G-B_C combination is shown in Fig. 14-26a. For this circuit the admittance is

$$\mathbf{Y}_{ab} = G + jB_C$$

and the complex impedance is

$$\mathbf{Z}_{ab} = \frac{1}{G + jB_C}$$

In rectangular form $\mathbf{Z}_{ab}$ is written as

$$\mathbf{Z}_{ab} = \frac{1(G - jB_C)}{(G + jB_C)(G - jB_C)} = \frac{G}{G^2 + B_C{}^2} + j\frac{-B_C}{G^2 + B_C{}^2}$$

Consider now the series R-C circuit shown in Fig. 14-26b. For this circuit the impedance is

$$\mathbf{Z}_{a'b'} = R' + jX_C'$$

If we set

$$R' = \frac{G}{G^2 + B_C{}^2} \qquad\qquad (14\text{-}32a)$$

and

$$X_C' = \frac{-B_C}{G^2 + B_C{}^2} \qquad\qquad (14\text{-}32b)$$

then the circuits of Fig. 14-26a and b are equivalent (*in the sinusoidal steady state, at the frequency at which B_C was calculated with respect to terminals a-b and a'-b'*) if Eqs. (14-32) apply.

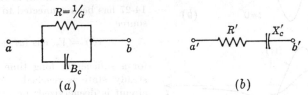

FIG. 14-26. Parallel and series two-element combinations.

Note that the equivalence was established by setting $R' = \mathrm{Re}\ \mathbf{Z}_{ab}$ and $X' = \mathrm{Im}\ \mathbf{Z}_{ab}$. In particular note that R' is *not* the reciprocal of G; it is the real part of the complex impedance. We feel it necessary to warn the reader explicitly that the statement

$$\mathrm{Re}\ \frac{1}{a + jb} = \frac{1}{a} \text{ is not true unless } b \text{ is zero}$$

If it is desired to "convert" the configuration of Fig. 14-26b into that of Fig. 14-26a, we should start with

$$\mathbf{Z}_{a'b'} = R' + jX_C'$$

Hence

$$\mathbf{Y}_{a'b'} = \frac{1}{R' + jX_C'} = \frac{R'}{R'^2 + X_C'^2} + j\frac{-X_C'}{R'^2 + X_C'^2}$$

If $\mathbf{Y}_{a'b'} = \mathbf{Y}_{ab}$, then

$$G = \frac{R'}{R'^2 + X_C{}^2}$$

and

$$B_C = \frac{-X_C'}{R'^2 + X_C'^2}$$

It must be emphasized again that the equivalence is limited to the steady-state terminal relations already cited. The conversion of other two-element circuits is left as an exercise for the reader (see Prob. 14-27).

14-13. Complete Response with Sinusoidal Source.

We have so far dealt exclusively with the calculations of voltages and currents in the sinusoidal steady state. At this point it is instructive to pause and restate a basic aim of the phasor method. The phasor method for solving a-c circuit problems is a method for obtaining the component of the response due to a sinusoidal source. In Chap. 11 we have already discussed the complete response of certain circuits to different waveforms. In that chapter the sinusoidal source was avoided; now we are prepared to deal with problems involving such sources. Several examples will suffice to illustrate complete-response calculations.

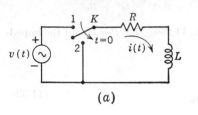

(a)

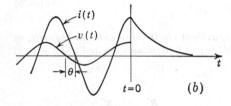

(b)

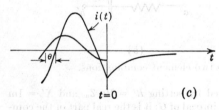

(c)

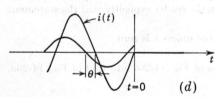

(d)

FIG. 14-27. Deenergizing an R-L circuit from a sinusoidal source. (a) Switching operation. (b) Response if $i(0^-)$ is positive. (c) Response if $i(0^-)$ is negative. (d) Response if $i(0^-)$ is zero.

Example 14-10. Deenergizing an R-L Circuit. An R-L circuit as shown in Fig. 14-27 has been connected to a sinusoidal source

$$v(t) = V_m \cos (\omega t + \phi)$$

for a sufficiently long time so that the steady state is reached. At $t = 0$ the circuit is deenergized; i.e., the switch K is thrown from position 1 to position 2. Solve for $i(t)$ for all $t \geq 0^+$.

Solution. Since the circuit is source free for $t \geq 0^+$, the solution for $i(t)$ is given by the familiar form

$$i(t) = i(0^+)e^{-t/T} \qquad T = \frac{L}{R}, \ t \geq 0^+$$

$$(14\text{-}33)$$

Because of the inductance we have the continuity condition

$$i(0^+) = i(0^-)$$

The value $i(0^-)$ is found by solving for the steady-state alternating current prior to

$t = 0$ and setting $t = 0$ in the equation for $i(t)$.
Since

$$v(t) = \text{Re} \ [V_m e^{j(\omega t + \phi)}]$$

$$i(t) = \text{Re} \left[\frac{V_m}{\mathbf{Z}} e^{j(\omega t + \phi)} \right]$$

where $\qquad \mathbf{Z} = R + j\omega L = Z/\underline{\theta}$

Hence $\qquad i(t) = \frac{V_m}{Z} (\cos \omega t + \phi - \theta) \qquad t \leq 0^-$

and $\qquad i(0^-) = \frac{V_m}{Z} \cos (\phi - \theta)$

Substituting in (14-33), we have

$$i(t) = \left[\frac{V_m}{Z} \cos (\phi - \theta) \right] e^{-t/T} \qquad t \geq 0^+$$

We observe now that the response for $t \geq 0^+$ depends on $\phi - \theta$, *the phase of the steady-state current* at $t = 0$. Several possibilities are shown in Fig. 14-27. Note in particular Fig. 14-27d. In that diagram ϕ is chosen so that $\phi - \theta = \pi/2$ and $i(t) = 0$ for $t \geq 0^+$. If, in a practical problem, the angle ϕ is not known, then one cannot determine the value $i(0^+)$ numerically: one can only delimit the value as at present, where $i(0^+)$ is at most V_m/Z and may be as small as zero.

Example 14-11. Impressing an A-C Source on an R-C Circuit. The circuit shown in Fig. 14-28a is in the steady state with the switch in position 1. At $t = 0$ the switch is thrown to position 2. Calculate $v_{ab}(t)$ for all $t \geq 0^+$.

Solution. Since the circuit is in the steady state for $t < 0$, the current before switching is zero and the voltage across the capacitance is $v_{ab}(0^-) = V_0$. Because of the continuity of the stored energy in the capacitance (impulse currents cannot flow), we have the initial condition

$$v_{ab}(0^+) = v_{ab}(0^-) = V_0$$

For $t \geq 0^+$ the equilibrium equation is

$$RC \frac{dv_{ab}}{dt} + v_{ab} = V_m \cos (\omega t + \phi)$$

or $\qquad\qquad (pRC + 1)v_{ab} = V_m \cos (\omega t + \phi)$

Hence the component of the response due to the source can be found by representing it by the amplitude phasor $(\mathbf{V}_{ab})_m$, replacing p by $j\omega$, and using the source voltage phasor $\mathbf{V}_m$,

$$(j\omega RC + 1)(\mathbf{V}_{ab})_m = \mathbf{V}_m$$

or $\qquad\qquad (\mathbf{V}_{ab})_m = \dfrac{\mathbf{V}_m}{j\omega RC + 1}$

Hence the component of v_{ab} due to the source is

$$[v_{ab}(t)]_s = \mathrm{Re} \left(\frac{\mathbf{V}_m}{j\omega RC + 1} e^{j\omega t} \right)$$

or $\qquad\qquad [v_{ab}(t)]_s = \mathrm{Re} \left(\dfrac{V_m e^{j\phi} e^{j\omega t}}{\sqrt{\omega^2 R^2 C^2 + 1}\, e^{j \tan^{-1} \omega RC}} \right)$

Hence $\qquad\qquad [v_{ab}(t)]_s = \dfrac{V_m}{\sqrt{\omega^2 R^2 C^2 + 1}} \cos (\omega t + \phi - \tan^{-1} \omega RC)$

Before proceeding with the free component an alternate method for calculating the component of v_{ab} due to the source will be presented. Using phasors

$$\mathbf{I}_m = \frac{\mathbf{V}_m}{\mathbf{Z}} \qquad \mathbf{Z} = R + \frac{1}{j\omega C} = \frac{1}{j\omega C} (j\omega RC + 1)$$

$$(\mathbf{V}_{ab})_m = jX_c \mathbf{I}_m$$

Hence $\qquad\qquad (\mathbf{V}_{ab})_m = \dfrac{\mathbf{V}_m (j\omega C)}{j\omega RC + 1} \cdot \dfrac{1}{j\omega C} = \dfrac{\mathbf{V}_m}{j\omega RC + 1}$

exactly as obtained "directly" before.

The free component of the response is found from the equation

$$(pRC + 1)(v_{ab})_f = 0$$

Thus $\qquad (v_{ab})_f = Ke^{st} \qquad sRC + 1 = 0 \qquad s = -\dfrac{1}{RC} = -\dfrac{1}{T}$

The complete response is the sum of the two components,

$$v_{ab}(t) = [v_{ab}(t)]_f + [v_{ab}(t)]_s$$

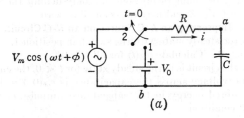

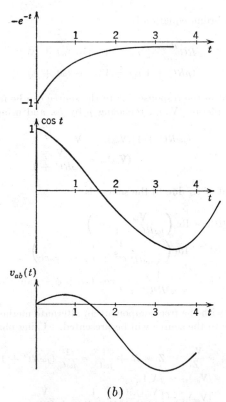

Fig. 14-28. Energizing an R-C series circuit from an a-c source.   (a) Switching operation.   (b) Construction of the complete response [cos $(t) - e^{-t}$].

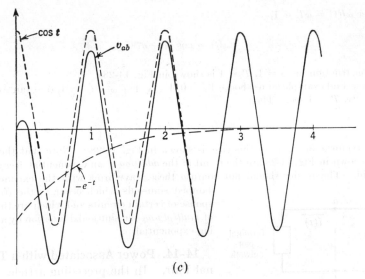

FIG. 14-28 (*continued*).   (*c*) Complete response, $v_{ab} = \cos 2\pi t - e^{-t}$.

With our results this gives the formula

$$v_{ab}(t) = \frac{V_m}{\sqrt{\omega^2 R^2 C^2 + 1}} \cos (\omega t + \phi - \tan^{-1} \omega RC) + K e^{-t/T}$$

Introducing the initial condition,

$$v_{ab}(0^+) = V_0 = \frac{V_m}{\sqrt{\omega^2 R^2 C^2 + 1}} \cos (\phi - \tan^{-1} \omega RC) + K$$

Hence $v_{ab}(t) = \dfrac{V_m}{\sqrt{\omega^2 R^2 C^2 + 1}} \cos (\omega t + \phi - \tan^{-1} \omega RC)$

$$+ \left[V_0 - \frac{V_m}{\sqrt{\omega^2 R^2 C^2 + 1}} \cos (\phi - \tan^{-1} \omega RC) \right] e^{-t/T} \quad (14\text{-}34)$$

We observe again that it is possible to have a free (transient) component which is zero provided that the value of the steady-state component of the voltage across the capacitance at the instant of switching is equal to the initial value,

$$K = 0 \quad \text{if } V_0 = \frac{V_m}{\sqrt{\omega^2 R^2 C^2 + 1}} \cos (\phi - \tan^{-1} \omega RC) \text{ or } V_0 = [v_{ab}(0)]_s$$

To illustrate the waveform of the solution (14-34), several numerical examples will be used.   Let $V_0 = 0$, $\omega RC = 1$, $V_m = \sqrt{2}$.   The solution for v_{ab} in this case becomes

$$v_{ab}(t) = \cos (\omega t + \phi - 45°) - e^{-t/T} \cos (\phi - 45°) \qquad t \geq 0^+$$

The response consists of the *sum* of an exponential term and a sinusoidal term.   Again the importance of ϕ, the phase of the source at the instant of switching, is apparent. First we shall construct response waveforms for $\phi = 45°$ so that the transient component is maximized.

$$v_{ab}(t) = \cos \omega t - e^{-t/T} \qquad\qquad t \geq 0^+$$

or since $\omega RC = \omega T = 1$,

$$v_{ab}(t) = \cos \frac{t}{T} - e^{-t/T}$$

The construction for $\omega = 1$, $T = 1$ is shown in Fig. 14-28b.

As a second example let us choose $V_0 = 0$, $V_m/\sqrt{1 + \omega^2 R^2 C^2} = 1$, $\phi - \tan^{-1} \omega RC = 0$, $\omega = 2\pi$, $T = 1$ sec. Then

$$v_{ab}(t) = \cos 2\pi t - e^{-t}$$

The waveform for $v_{ab}(t)$ in this case is shown in Fig. 14-28c. Note that the waveforms shown in Fig. 14-28 are the result of the *addition* of an exponential decay and a sinusoid. The reader should not confuse these waveforms with the exponentially damped sinusoids which occur in the (free) response of certain circuits and which are the result of *multiplying* the sinusoidal function by a decaying exponential.

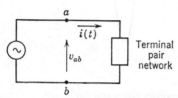

FIG. 14-29. Terminal-pair network with a sinusoidal source.

14-14. Power Associated with a Terminal Pair.

In the preceding articles it has been shown that for the purpose of *sinusoidal steady-state calculations* the relationship between voltage and current for a single-terminal-pair network is completely characterized by the complex immittance. For such a terminal pair, with the reference directions for voltage and current as shown in Fig. 14-29, let

$$v_{ab} = \mathrm{Re}\,(\sqrt{2}\,\mathbf{V}e^{j\omega t}) \qquad \mathbf{V} = Ve^{j\phi}$$

Then $\quad i(t) = \mathrm{Re}\,(\sqrt{2}\,\mathbf{I}e^{j\omega t}) \qquad \mathbf{I} = \mathbf{V}Y_{ab} = \dfrac{\mathbf{V}_{ab}}{\mathbf{Z}_{ab}} \qquad \mathbf{Z}_{ab} = Z\underline{/\theta}$

Upon applying the definitions of voltage and current, the expression for the power which flows into the terminal pair at any instant of time is given by the product of v_{ab} and i,

$$p_{ab}(t) = v_{ab}(t)i(t) \tag{14-35}$$

or $\qquad p_{ab}(t) = [\mathrm{Re}\,(\mathbf{V}\,\sqrt{2}\,e^{j\omega t})][\mathrm{Re}\,(\mathbf{I}\,\sqrt{2}\,e^{j\omega t})] \tag{14-35a}$

The form of this expression is not convenient because the product of the real parts of two complex expressions is *not* the real part of the product. For this reason we introduce a result of the definition of the conjugate of a complex number, namely, if $\mathbf{z}$ is a complex number and $\mathbf{z}^*$ is its conjugate, then

$$\mathrm{Re}\,\mathbf{z} = \tfrac{1}{2}(\mathbf{z} + \mathbf{z}^*) \tag{14-36}$$

Using (14-36), we may write v_{ab} and i as follows:

$$v_{ab}(t) = \mathrm{Re}\,(\sqrt{2}\,\mathbf{V}e^{j\omega t}) = \tfrac{1}{2}\sqrt{2}\,\mathbf{V}e^{j\omega t} + \tfrac{1}{2}\sqrt{2}\,(\mathbf{V}e^{j\omega t})^* \tag{14-37a}$$

and $\qquad i(t) = \mathrm{Re}\,(\sqrt{2}\,\mathbf{I}e^{j\omega t}) = \tfrac{1}{2}\sqrt{2}\,\mathbf{I}e^{j\omega t} + \tfrac{1}{2}\sqrt{2}\,(\mathbf{I}e^{j\omega t})^* \tag{14-37b}$

We now note that for any two complex numbers z_1 and z_2 one can write

$$(z_1 z_2)^* = z_1^* z_2^*$$

because if $z_1 = z_1 \underline{/\alpha_1}$ and $z_2 = z_2 \underline{/\alpha_2}$, then

$$(z_1 z_2 \underline{/\alpha_1 + \alpha_2})^* = z_1 z_2 \underline{/-\alpha_1 - \alpha_2}$$

Hence

$$(\mathbf{V}e^{j\omega t})^* = \mathbf{V}^*(e^{j\omega t})^* = \mathbf{V}^* e^{-j\omega t}$$

and

$$(\mathbf{I}e^{j\omega t})^* = \mathbf{I}^*(e^{j\omega t})^* = \mathbf{I}^* e^{-j\omega t}$$

Equations (14-37a) and (14-37b) can now be rewritten in the form

$$v_{ab}(t) = \tfrac{1}{2}\sqrt{2}\,\mathbf{V}e^{j\omega t} + \tfrac{1}{2}\sqrt{2}\,\mathbf{V}^* e^{-j\omega t} \tag{14-38a}$$

$$i(t) = \tfrac{1}{2}\sqrt{2}\,\mathbf{I}e^{j\omega t} + \tfrac{1}{2}\sqrt{2}\,\mathbf{I}^* e^{-j\omega t} \tag{14-38b}$$

Upon introducing (14-38a) and (14-38b) into Eq. (14-35a), the power flowing into the terminal pair may be written as

$$p_{ab}(t) = \left(\frac{1}{\sqrt{2}}\,\mathbf{V}e^{j\omega t} + \frac{1}{\sqrt{2}}\,\mathbf{V}^* e^{-j\omega t}\right)\left(\frac{1}{\sqrt{2}}\,\mathbf{I}e^{j\omega t} + \frac{1}{\sqrt{2}}\,\mathbf{I}^* e^{-j\omega t}\right)$$

or, multiplying out,

$$p_{ab}(t) = \tfrac{1}{2}\mathbf{VI}^* + \tfrac{1}{2}\mathbf{V}^*\mathbf{I} + \tfrac{1}{2}\mathbf{VI}e^{j2\omega t} + \tfrac{1}{2}\mathbf{V}^*\mathbf{I}^* e^{-j2\omega t} \tag{14-39}$$

Now if, as was stated at the outset,

$$\mathbf{V} = Ve^{j\phi} \qquad \text{then } \mathbf{V}^* = Ve^{-j\phi}$$

and

$$\mathbf{I} = Ie^{j(\phi-\theta)} \qquad \text{then } \mathbf{I}^* = Ie^{j(\theta-\phi)}$$

where θ is the angle of the impedance $\mathbf{Z}_{ab}$, then

$$\tfrac{1}{2}\mathbf{V}^*\mathbf{I} = \tfrac{1}{2}Ve^{-j\phi}Ie^{j(\phi-\theta)} = \tfrac{1}{2}VIe^{-j\theta}$$

and

$$\tfrac{1}{2}\mathbf{VI}^* = \tfrac{1}{2}Ve^{j\phi}Ie^{j(\theta-\phi)} = \tfrac{1}{2}VIe^{j\theta} = \tfrac{1}{2}VI(e^{-j\theta})^*$$

Hence $\tfrac{1}{2}(\mathbf{V}^*\mathbf{I} + \mathbf{VI}^*) = \tfrac{1}{2}\mathbf{V}^*\mathbf{I} + \tfrac{1}{2}(\mathbf{V}^*\mathbf{I})^* = \mathrm{Re}\,(\mathbf{V}^*\mathbf{I}) = \mathrm{Re}\,(\mathbf{VI}^*)$

We further note that

$$\tfrac{1}{2}\mathbf{VI}e^{j2\omega t} = \tfrac{1}{2}(\mathbf{V}^*\mathbf{I}^* e^{-j2\omega t})^*$$

Hence the expression for $p_{ab}(t)$ reduces to

$$p_{ab}(t) = \mathrm{Re}\,(\mathbf{V}^*\mathbf{I}) + \mathrm{Re}\,(\mathbf{VI}e^{j2\omega t}) \tag{14-40}$$

In trigonometric form this expression reads

$$p_{ab}(t) = VI\cos\theta + VI\cos(2\omega t + 2\phi - \theta) \tag{14-41}$$

In an article below we return to a study of Eq. (14-40); for the present we wish to examine the result in the form (14-41).

We note first that the value of the power delivered to the two-terminal pair a-b in the sinusoidal steady state consists of two terms: a constant, $VI\cos\theta$, and a sinusoidal oscillation with radian frequency 2ω and amplitude VI. It is recalled here that in the case of single elements it was also observed that the fluctuating term in the expression for instantaneous power was a sinusoid of twice the frequency of the voltage or the current. Next we observe that Eq. (14-41) reduces to the expressions for single elements which were deduced in Art. 14-4 if the appropriate conditions are imposed. If the terminal pair consists, for example, of an inductance L_{ab}, then $\theta = \pi/2$ and Eq. (14-41) reduces to Eq. (14-9). If an element R_{ab} is connected between terminals a-b, then $\theta = 0$ and the expression (14-41) reduces to the special case given in Eq. (14-10).

A graph of the expression p_{ab} as a function of t or ωt is instructive. This time dependence is illustrated in Fig. 14-30. We observe that the oscillations of amplitude VI fluctuate about the average value $VI \cos \theta$ so that

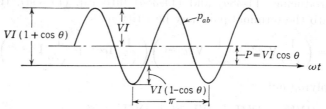

FIG. 14-30. Instantaneous power for a terminal pair under sinusoidal steady-state conditions.

the maximum value of the instantaneous power is $VI(1 + \cos \theta)$. We note, moreover, that during part of each cycle (if $\cos \theta$ is not unity) negative power flows to terminals a-b. Since the condition $\cos \theta \neq 1$ means that the total susceptance or reactance between terminals a-b is not zero, this negative power flow is readily interpreted: during the time interval when $p_{ab}(t)$ is negative, the energy-storing elements in the "box" a-b (i.e., the reactances) are returning stored energy to the source.

In the entire discussion so far it has been tacitly assumed that θ is in the first or fourth quadrant, i.e., that θ is an angle whose magnitude is between 0 and 90°. This assumption means also that $\operatorname{Re} \mathbf{Z}_{ab} > 0$. We now conclude that this assumption is indeed necessary if the terminal pair a-b represents a combination of passive elements. If $\cos \theta$ were a negative number, then $VI \cos \theta$ would be negative and the *average* power flow *into* terminals a-b would be negative so that the box a-b would represent a source of energy, i.e., an active terminal pair. The condition $\operatorname{Re} \mathbf{Z}_{ab} \geq 0$ is a special case of the "positive real" property of driving-point immittance functions which is discussed in Art. 13-13.

14-15. Average Power. The average power delivered to the terminal pair a-b in the sinusoidal steady state is obtained from Eq. (14-41) by observing that the time average value of the sinusoidal component is zero. Hence

$$P_{av} = P_{ab} = VI \cos \theta \qquad (14\text{-}42)$$

We recall here that V is the effective value of v_{ab}, I is the effective value of the current $i(t)$, and θ is the phase angle by which the voltage v_{ab} leads the current $i(t)$. The "average power" is used so commonly that this quantity is usually referred to simply as the "power." When the time function $p(t)$ is meant, a phrase like "instantaneous power" is used. The symbol for average power is the capital letter P, and no subscripts are employed except when it is necessary to identify the terminal pair in question.

Several formulas are equivalent to Eq. (14-42), and these will now be deduced. Since $\cos \theta$ is defined by the angle of the complex impedance (or admittance) between terminals a-b,

$$\cos \theta = \frac{R_{eq}}{|Z_{ab}|} \tag{14-43}$$

It must be emphasized that the term R_{eq} in Eq. (14-43) refers to the *real part of the complex impedance* between terminals a-b. (We recall that Re Z_{ab} may depend on all the elements connected between terminals a-b.) Using Eq. (14-43) in (14-42),

$$P = VI\, \frac{R_{eq}}{Z_{ab}} \tag{14-44}$$

Since $V/Z_{ab} = I$, the expression (14-44) may be rewritten in the form

$$P = I^2 R_{eq} \tag{14-45}$$

Alternatively, upon using the admittance and equivalent conductance between terminals a-b, $\cos \theta = G_{eq}/|Y_{ab}|$, so that we may write

$$P = V^2 G_{eq} \tag{14-46}$$

It must be emphasized that the equivalent conductance between terminals a-b is the real part of the complex admittance. For a terminal pair a-b the quantity G_{ab} is therefore *not*, in general, the reciprocal of R_{ab}. We rather note the relationship [setting (14-45) equal to (14-46)]

$$G_{eq}V^2 = R_{eq}I^2$$

so that
$$G_{eq}\frac{V^2}{I^2} = R_{eq}$$

Hence
$$G_{eq}|Z|^2 = R_{eq} \quad \text{or} \quad G_{eq} = R_{eq}|Y|^2 \tag{14-46a}$$

The reader is reminded that the relationship expressed in Eq. (14-46a) was discussed in Art. 14-12 when equivalent impedances and admittances were discussed.

14-16. Apparent Power, Power Factor. The expression for the average power in the sinusoidal steady state is given by any of the equivalent relations

$$P = VI \cos \theta = V^2\, \text{Re } Y = I^2\, \text{Re } Z \tag{14-47}$$

It is now recalled that *if* V and I were *not* the effective values of sinusoidal time functions but were a constant voltage across a terminal pair and a constant (direct) current flowing into the terminal pair, then the power which would be delivered to the terminal pair would be given by $P = VI$. For this reason the quantity VI is termed the "apparent power"; i.e., the result of multiplying the effective value of the voltage by the effective value of the current would give the correct answer for the power *if* direct current were flowing into a purely resistive terminal pair. In the present instance the quantity VI is not the power; we shall see that it can be interpreted physically and that it can also be an important auxiliary quantity in the solution of certain problems. For this reason we shall use the symbol P_a to denote the volt-ampere product, i.e., the apparent power,

$$P_a = VI = I^2|\mathbf{Z}| = V^2|\mathbf{Y}| \qquad (14\text{-}48)$$

Dimensionally the apparent power is (volts $\times$ amperes) = watts. To assure that this quantity is not confused with the average power, it is customary, in electrical engineering, not to refer to P_a as watts but simply as "volt-amperes," abbreviated va. Thus

$$P_a = VI \qquad \text{va}$$
and
$$P = VI \cos \theta \qquad \text{watts}$$

The quantity $\cos \theta$ which when multiplied by the apparent power gives the correct answer for the average power is referred to as the "power factor" (abbreviated as pf), and is sometimes multiplied by 100 and expressed as a percentage:

$$\cos \theta = \frac{P}{P_a} = \frac{R}{|\mathbf{Z}|} = \frac{G}{|\mathbf{Y}|} = \text{power factor} = \text{pf}$$
$$\text{pf} \times 100 = 100 \cos \theta = \text{power factor} \qquad \% \qquad (14\text{-}49)$$

Since the cosine of an angle θ is the same as the cosine of the negative angle θ, a statement of the power factor alone does not include information about the sign of the angle θ. It is customary to state that the power factor is *lagging* if the current i_{ab} *lags* the voltage v_{ab} so that θ (the angle of the impedance, the angle of voltage lead) is positive. In an "inductive" circuit, therefore, the power factor is lagging. In a capacitive circuit the current i_{ab} *leads* the voltage v_{ab}, and the power factor is *leading*. The angle of impedance in that case is negative.

We return now to the interpretation of $VI = P_a$. Note from Fig. 14-30 and from Eq. (14-41) that the maximum value of the instantaneous power is

$$(p_{ab})_{\max} = VI(1 + \cos \theta) = P_a(1 + \cos \theta) \qquad (14\text{-}50)$$
and
$$p_{ab}(t) = P_a \cos (2\omega t + 2\phi - \theta) + P$$

It is therefore possible to interpret the term apparent power by stating that the apparent power is the amplitude of the oscillating component of the instantaneous power.

14-17. Complex Power, Reactive Power. We now return to the expression for instantaneous power in complex form as given by Eq. (14-40),

$$p_{ab}(t) = \text{Re} \,(\mathbf{V}^*\mathbf{I}) + \text{Re} \,(\mathbf{V}\mathbf{I}e^{j2\omega t})$$

The quantity $\mathbf{V}^*\mathbf{I}$, written in exponential form is

$$\mathbf{V}^*\mathbf{I} = VIe^{-j\theta} = P_a e^{-j\theta} = I^2 \mathbf{Z}^* = V^2 \mathbf{Y}$$

We shall call the complex quantity $P_a e^{-j\theta}$ the "complex power"[1] in the circuit and denote it by the symbol $\mathbf{P}_a$. We can now state that the absolute value of the complex power equals the apparent power and the real part of the complex power is equal to the average power. The following question naturally arises: Does the imaginary part of the complex power have any physical interpretation?

The imaginary part of the complex power is given by the formula

$$\text{Im} \,(\mathbf{V}^*\mathbf{I}) = \text{Im} \,\mathbf{P}_a = VI \sin \,(-\theta)$$

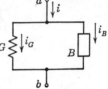

This quantity is denoted by the symbol Q and called the reactive power,

$$Q = -VI \sin \theta \qquad (14\text{-}51)$$

FIG. 14-31. Representation of a terminal pair by two elements in parallel.

While dimensionally the units of reactive power are watts, the use of the unit watt is reserved for the average of instantaneous power and the units of reactive power are called "reactive volt-amperes," abbreviated var. To find physical meaning for reactive power, consider the terminal pair a-b represented as the parallel combination of a conductance G and a susceptance B ($G = \text{Re } \mathbf{Y}_{ab}$ and $B = \text{Im } \mathbf{Y}_{ab}$) as shown in Fig. 14-31. If the voltage v_{ab} is given as before by

$$v_{ab} = \text{Re} \,(\mathbf{V} \,\sqrt{2}\, e^{j\omega t})$$

then the current in the susceptance B is given by

$$i_B(t) = \text{Re} \,(j B\mathbf{V} \,\sqrt{2}\, e^{j\omega t})$$

Hence the complex power which flows *to the susceptance B* is

$$(\mathbf{P}_a)_B = jV^2 B$$

[1] Some authors define complex power as $\mathbf{V}\mathbf{I}^*$. In that case, since $\text{Re} \,(\mathbf{V}\mathbf{I}^*) = \text{Re} \,(\mathbf{V}^*\mathbf{I})$, the real part of the complex power is also equal to the average power but $\text{Im} \,(\mathbf{V}\mathbf{I}^*) = -\text{Im} \,(\mathbf{V}^*\mathbf{I})$ so that the sign of the imaginary part is opposite with this alternate definition. It will become apparent that the difference between the two definitions is trivial.

Since the instantaneous power to any element (or combination of elements) is given by

$$p(t) = \text{Re } \mathbf{P}_a + \text{Re } (\mathbf{P}_a e^{j2\omega t})$$

the instantaneous power flow to the susceptance B is

$$p_B(t) = V^2 B \cos\left(2\omega t + \frac{\pi}{2}\right)$$

Now $V^2 B = \text{Im } (V^2 \mathbf{Y}) = Q$. Hence the reactive power Q is the maximum power which flows from the source to the element which represents all the energy-storing elements in the circuit during the course of a cycle. It is noted that this is an equivalent element whose value is a function of the value of all the circuit elements, as well as the frequency of the source.

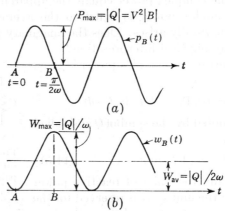

Fig. 14-32. Power and energy as a function of time in a susceptance B.

We can now write the complex power as follows,

$$\mathbf{P}_a = \mathbf{V}^*\mathbf{I} = P + jQ$$

or, in words,

    Complex power = av power $\pm j$(max power to storage elements)

Another interpretation of reactive power is possible. Since the power which flows to the energy-storing elements, represented by the susceptance B, is

$$p_B = Q \sin 2\omega t$$

the waveform of this power is the "double-frequency" sinusoid shown in Fig. 14-32a. The maximum *energy* which is delivered to the susceptance B is given by the area under the curve from point A to point B. (In the time interval from $t = \pi/(2\omega)$ to $t = \pi/\omega$ this energy is returned to the source.) Since the frequency of the power fluctuations is twice the frequency of the voltage or current variations, a half cycle of power oscillations lasts from $\omega t = 0$ (point A) to $\omega t = \pi/2$ (point B). The maximum energy delivered to the susceptance B is therefore given by

$$W_{\max} = \int_0^{\pi/2\omega} Q \sin 2\omega t \; dt = -\frac{Q}{2\omega} \cos 2\omega t \Big|_0^{\pi/2\omega}$$

or $\qquad W_{\max} = \dfrac{|Q|}{\omega}$ $\hfill (14\text{-}52)$

The result of Eq. (14-52) may be stated in words,

$$|\text{Reactive power}| = \omega(\text{max value of stored energy})$$

The variation of the stored energy with time is shown in Fig. 14-32b. We observe that the reactive power is given by

$$|Q| = 2\omega(\text{av stored energy in terminal pair})$$

A summary of the power relations is given in Table 14-2. Not all the formulas given here have been proved in the text; the reader is encouraged to prove these formulas independently.

TABLE 14-2. POWER RELATIONS IN A TERMINAL PAIR

Symbol or abbreviation	Name	Formulas	Comments
p_{ab}	Instantaneous power	$v \cdot i = \operatorname{Re}(\mathbf{V}^*\mathbf{I}) + \operatorname{Re}(\mathbf{V}^*\mathbf{I}e^{j2\omega t})$	
P	Power	$P = VI \cos\theta = \operatorname{Re}(\mathbf{V}^*\mathbf{I}) = I^2 \operatorname{Re}\mathbf{Z} = V^2 \operatorname{Re}\mathbf{Y}$	Time average power
Q	Reactive power	$Q = -VI \sin\theta = \operatorname{Im}(\mathbf{V}^*\mathbf{I}) = I^2 \operatorname{Im}\mathbf{Z}^* = V^2 \operatorname{Im}\mathbf{Y}$	Peak values of power to energy-storing elements
P_a	Apparent power	$P_a = VI = V^2Y = I^2Z = |\mathbf{V}^*\mathbf{I}|$	Peak value of oscillating component of $p(t)$
$\mathbf{P}_a$	Complex power	$\mathbf{P}_a = P + jQ = VI\cos\theta - jVI\sin\theta = V^2\mathbf{Y} = I^2\mathbf{Z}^*$	
pf	Power factor	$\text{pf} = \cos\theta = \dfrac{R}{Z} = \dfrac{G}{Y} = \dfrac{P}{P_a}$	Lagging for positive θ
rf	Reactive factor	$\text{rf} = -\sin\theta = \dfrac{-X}{Z} = \dfrac{B}{Y} = \dfrac{Q}{P_a}$	Lagging for positive θ

14-18. Use of Complex Power. *Admittances in Parallel.* Consider two complex admittances, $\mathbf{Y}_1$ and $\mathbf{Y}_2$, connected in parallel across terminals a-b as shown in Fig. 14-33a. The total admittance $\mathbf{Y}_{ab}$ is

$$\mathbf{Y}_{ab} = \mathbf{Y}_1 + \mathbf{Y}_2$$

and the current $\mathbf{I}$ is given by

$$\mathbf{I} = \mathbf{V}_{ab}(\mathbf{Y}_1 + \mathbf{Y}_2) \hfill (14\text{-}53)$$

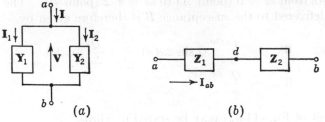

FIG. 14-33. (a) Admittances in parallel. (b) Impedances in series.

With $\mathbf{V}_{ab}$ as reference the phasor diagram which shows the addition of $\mathbf{I}_1$ to $\mathbf{I}_2$ to give $\mathbf{I}$ is drawn in Fig. 14-34a. In this diagram it is assumed that $\mathbf{Y}_1$ is inductive (negative imaginary part) and $\mathbf{Y}_2$ is capacitive (positive imaginary part).

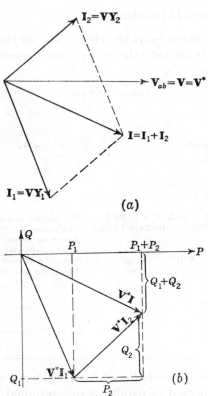

(a)

(b)

FIG. 14-34. Illustration of the addition of complex power.

Let us now multiply Eq. (14-53) by $\mathbf{V}_{ab}^*$. Since $\mathbf{V}_{ab}\mathbf{V}_{ab}^* = V_{ab}^2$, we obtain

$$\mathbf{V}^*\mathbf{I} = V_{ab}^2(\mathbf{Y}_1 + \mathbf{Y}_2)$$

or

$$\mathbf{V}^*\mathbf{I} = V_{ab}^2\mathbf{Y}_1 + V_{ab}^2\mathbf{Y}_2 \tag{14-54}$$

Equation (14-54) states that *for parallel admittances the complex power for the combination is the sum of the individual complex powers.* This relationship is particularly useful in problems in which the admittances are not explicitly specified but the power and power factor (and therefore the complex powers) of each parallel branch are known. The addition of the complex powers is shown in Fig. 14-34b. Note that the real axis represents power and the imaginary axis represents reactive power (since complex power is $P + jQ$). In Fig. 14-34b it is again assumed that $\mathbf{Y}_1$ is inductive and that $\mathbf{Y}_2$ is capacitive.

Impedances in Series. We shall now show that the addition of complex powers gives the correct result for calculating the complex power of impedances in series such as are shown in Fig. 14-33b.

The complex power for the circuit is given by

$$\mathbf{V}_{ab}^*\mathbf{I}_{ab} = [(\mathbf{I}_{ab}\mathbf{Z}_1)^* + (\mathbf{I}_{ab}\mathbf{Z}_2)^*]\mathbf{I}_{ab}$$

Using the rules for manipulations of complex numbers,

$$\mathbf{V}_{ab}^{*}\mathbf{I}_{ab} = I_{ab}{}^{2}(\mathbf{Z}_{1}^{*} + \mathbf{Z}_{2}^{*}) = I_{ab}{}^{2}(\mathbf{Z}_{1} + \mathbf{Z}_{2})^{*}$$

so that the addition of the complex powers gives the complex power for the combination of series impedances.

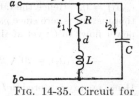

14-1. Illustrative Examples. Example 14-12. A sinusoidal voltage $v_{ab}(t) = 100\sqrt{2}\cos 1{,}000t$ is applied to the terminal pair shown in Fig. 14-35. Use the values

$$R = 3 \text{ ohms} \qquad L = 4 \text{ mh} \qquad C = 200 \ \mu\text{f}$$

FIG. 14-35. Circuit for Example 14-12.

Calculate $i(t)$, $i_1(t)$, $i_2(t)$, and study the power relations.

Solution. Let $v_{ab}(t)$ be represented by the phasor $100\underline{/0^{\circ}}$. The admittances are calculated,

$$B_C = 1{,}000 \times 200 \times 10^{-6} = 0.2 \text{ mho}$$

Hence Y_C, the admittance of the C branch, is

$$\mathbf{Y}_C = j0.2 \text{ mho}$$

The phasor $\mathbf{I}_2$ is

$$\mathbf{I}_2 = 100(j0.2) = j20$$

and

$$i_2(t) = 20\sqrt{2}\cos\left(\omega t + \frac{\pi}{2}\right)$$

The impedance of the R-L branch is

$$\mathbf{Z}_L = 3 + j4 \times 10^{-3} \times 10^{3} = 3 + j4 = 5\underline{/53.1^{\circ}} \text{ ohms}$$

$$\mathbf{Y}_L = \frac{1}{5\underline{/53.1^{\circ}}} = 0.2\underline{/-53.1^{\circ}} = 0.12 - j0.16 \text{ mho}$$

Hence

$$\mathbf{I}_1 = 100(0.2\underline{/-53.1^{\circ}}) = 20\underline{/-53.1^{\circ}} = 12 - j16$$

$$i_1(t) = 20\sqrt{2}\cos(1{,}000t - 53.1^{\circ})$$

The phasor $\mathbf{I}$ is obtained by application of Kirchhoff's current law,

$$\mathbf{I} = \mathbf{I}_1 + \mathbf{I}_2 = j20 + 12 - j16 = 12 + j4 = 12.65\underline{/18.5^{\circ}}$$

and

$$i(t) = 12.65\sqrt{2}\cos(1{,}000t + 18.5^{\circ})$$

The complex power is

$$\mathbf{V}^{*}\mathbf{I} = (100\underline{/0^{\circ}})(12.65\underline{/18.5^{\circ}}) = 1{,}265\underline{/18.5^{\circ}}$$

The power is

$$P = \text{Re }(\mathbf{V}^{*}\mathbf{I}) = 1{,}265\cos 18.5^{\circ} = 1{,}200 \text{ watts}$$

As a check

$$P = I_1{}^{2} \times 3 = 20^{2} \times 3 = 1{,}200 \text{ watts}$$

The equation for $p_{ab}(t)$ is

$$p_{ab} = 1,200 + \text{Re } (1,265\underline{/18.5°}\ e^{j2,000t})$$

or $$p_{ab} = 1,200 + 1,265 \cos (2,000t + 18.5°)$$

To study the energy transfer, the power flow at several instants of time is interesting. Consider first the instant $1,000t = \pi/2$; let that instant be $t = t_1$. At $t = t_1$, $v_{ab}(t_1) = 0$. Hence the rate at which energy flows into the circuit from the source at that instant is zero since $p_{ab}(t_1) = 0$. At that instant no energy is stored in C, and no power flows to C; yet at that instant i_1 is not zero:

$$i_1(t_1) = 20\ \sqrt{2} \cos \left(\frac{\pi}{2} - 53.1°\right) = 20\ \sqrt{2} \times 0.8 = 22.6\ \text{amp}$$

Hence energy is stored in L, in the amount $\frac{1}{2}Li^2(t_1)$. Moreover, at that instant power is flowing into R at the rate $i^2(t_1)R$. This power is flowing out of L since $iL(di/dt)$ at that instant is negative. Hence $t = t_1$ is an instant at which the inductance is furnishing power to the resistance.

This example illustrates that the energy-transfer situation in the "steady" state is a dynamic process. Choosing other instants of time, we would find that energy is continuously interchanged between the storage elements and the source. The calculation of average values tends to obscure the dynamics, and the reader is urged to continue this example to obtain other instantaneous conditions.

Example 14-13. Three loads are connected in parallel across 660-volt a-c lines. These loads are specified as follows:

Load 1, 15 kw, 0.6 pf (lagging).
Load 2, 20 kw, 0.707 pf (leading).
Load 3, 10 kw, 0.4 pf (lagging).

The loads are connected to a substation by means of cables having a resistance of 1.1 ohms for the circuit and negligible reactance. Calculate the voltage at the substation.

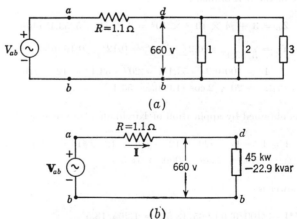

FIG. 14-36. Circuits for Example 14-13.

Solution. A schematic diagram is drawn as shown in Fig. 14-36a. Since for each load the power, power factor, and line voltage are given, the complex admittance can be calculated. For example, for load 1, $15,000 = 660 \times I_1 \times 0.6$. Then $\mathbf{Y}_1 = (I_1/660)\underline{/-\cos^{-1} 0.6}$ or $\mathbf{Z}_1 = (660/I_1)\underline{/\cos^{-1} 0.6}$.

However, it is not necessary to calculate the impedances. The three loads can be combined into one equivalent load by the "complex-power method." The total power dissipated by the three loads is $P_{db} = P_1 + P_2 + P_3 = 15 + 20 + 10 = 45$ kw. The reactive powers are

$$Q_1 = -15 \tan (\cos^{-1} 0.6) = -20 \text{ kvar}$$
$$Q_2 = +20 \tan (\cos^{-1} 0.707) = +20 \text{ kvar}$$
$$Q_3 = -10 \tan (\cos^{-1} 0.4) = -22.9 \text{ kvar}$$

Hence the combination of the three loads, at terminals d-b, is equivalent to a single load which receives 45 kw and -22.9 kvar (see Fig. 14-36b).

The apparent power for the load is

$$P_a = \sqrt{P^2 + Q^2} = 50.5 \text{ kva}$$

Hence the magnitude of the current I_{ad} is

$$I_{ad} = |\mathbf{I}_{ad}| = \frac{50.5 \times 10^3}{660} = 76.5 \text{ amp}$$

[Since $\tan^{-1} (22.9/45) = 27°$, $\mathbf{I}_{ad}$ lags $\mathbf{V}_{ab}$ by $27°$.]

The voltage V_{ab} may be found in several ways. Continuing the use of power relations,

$$P_{ad} = 76.6^2 \times 1.1 = 6.46 \text{ kw}$$

Hence, since $Q_{ad} = 0$,

$$P_{ab} = 45 + 6.46 \approx 51.5 \text{ kw}$$
$$Q_{ab} = -22.9$$

The apparent power at terminals a-b is $\sqrt{51.5^2 + 22.9^2} = 56.3$ kva. Hence the voltage V_{ab} is, in magnitude,

$$V_{ab} = \frac{56,300}{76.5} = 736 \text{ volts} \qquad\qquad Ans.$$

In this example the use of complex power was illustrated. The reader should check the results by other methods (calculation of admittances and impedances, solution by voltage phasor diagram, etc.).

PROBLEMS

14-1. In Fig. P14-1 the terminal pair a-b consists of a single element. Calculate the nature and the value of this element if the waveform marked v is (a) v_{ab}; (b) v_{ba}.

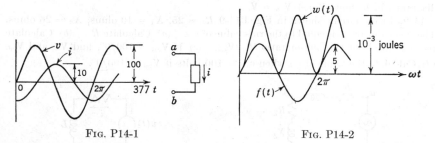

FIG. P14-1   FIG. P14-2

14-2. Figure P14-2 shows a sinusoidal source function $f(t)$ and a curve of the energy which this source function delivers to an element. Calculate the nature and the value of this element if (a) $f(t) = v(t)$; (b) $f(t) = i(t)$.

14-3. A sinusoidal current $i_{ab} = \cos 4t$ flows through an element which is either an inductance $(L = 2)$ or a capacitance $(C = \frac{1}{2})$. Calculate the value of the energy stored in this element in each case (L and C) at an instant when (a) $i = 0$; (b) $i = \frac{1}{2}$; (c) $i = 1$.

14-4. The voltage across a capacitance has the form $v(t) = V_m \cos \omega t$. At $\omega t = \pi/3$ the energy stored in the capacitance is 5 joules. (a) What is the maximum value of the energy stored in the capacitance? (b) If $C = 10^{-3}$, calculate V_m.

14-5. In the circuit shown in Fig. P14-5 the source $i(t)$ is the sinusoid $i(t) = 5 \cos 10t$. In the steady state $v_{ab}(t) = \cos (10t - 53.1°)$. (a) Calculate R and C. (b) Write the differential equation which relates $v_{ab}(t)$ to $i(t)$. (c) The source $i(t)$ is changed to be $i(t) = 5 \cos 5t$; calculate the steady-state response $[v_{ab}(t)]_s$.

FIG. P14-5   FIG. P14-6

14-6. The circuit shown in Fig. P14-6 is in the steady state. The rms value of v_{ab} is 100 volts, and the rms value of v_{ac} is 200 volts. Calculate (a) the rms value of v_{bc}; (b) the phase angle between v_{bc} and v_{ac}. (c) If v_{ac} is in phase with the function $\cos \omega t$, write the functions v_{ac}, v_{bc}, and v_{ab}.

14-7. The circuit shown in Fig. P14-7 is in the sinusoidal steady state. The rms value of i is 5 amp, and the rms value of i_1 is 3 amp. (a) Calculate the rms value of i_2. (b) Calculate the value of i_2 when (1) $i_1 = 3\sqrt{2}$ amp; (2) $i_1 = 3$ amp; (3) $i_1 = 0$; (4) $i = 0$; (5) $i = 5\sqrt{2}$ amp.

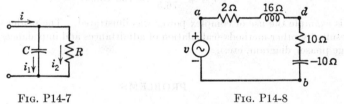

FIG. P14-7   FIG. P14-8

14-8. In the circuit shown in Fig. P14-8 $v_{db} = 100\sqrt{2} \cos 5{,}000t$. (a) Represent v_{db} as a phasor. (b) Calculate the phasor $\mathbf{V}_{ab}$. (c) Write $v_{ab}(t)$. (d) Draw a phasor diagram which shows $\mathbf{V}_{ad} + \mathbf{V}_{db} = \mathbf{V}_{ab}$.

14-9. In the circuit shown in Fig. P14-9 $R_1 = 25$, $X_1 = 10$ ohms, $X_2 = 26$ ohms. The rms value of v_{ab} is equal to the rms value of v_{bd}. (a) Calculate R_2. (b) Calculate the magnitude of the phasor ratio $\mathbf{V}_{ab}/\mathbf{V}_{ad}$. (c) If $\mathbf{V}_{ad} = 100\underline{/0°}$, find $\mathbf{V}_{ab}$ and $\mathbf{V}_{bd}$. (d) Calculate the value of v_{ab} when $v_{ad} = 100$ volts if $\mathbf{V}_{ad} = 100\underline{/0°}$.

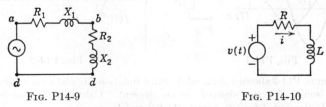

FIG. P14-9   FIG. P14-10

14-10. The circuit shown in Fig. P14-10 is in the steady state, $v(t) = 6 + 10 \cos 2t$, $i_s(t) = 2 + A \cos (2t - 53.1°)$. Use the principle of superposition to calculate

(a) R; (b) L; (c) A; (d) the steady-state equation for $i(t)$ if $v(t) = 10 + 5 \cos t + 5 \cos 2t$.

14-11. In Fig. P14-11, in the steady state $i = 5\sqrt{2}\cos \omega t$. The rms value of v_{ab} is 50 volts, and the rms value of $v(t)$ is 105.8 volts. It is known that $3R = X_L$. (a) Use a voltage phasor diagram drawn to scale to determine R and X_L. (b) Calculate the phase angle between (1) $v(t)$ and v_{ab}; (2) $v(t)$ and i.

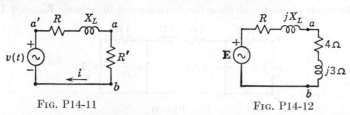

FIG. P14-11   FIG. P14-12

14-12. In the circuit shown in Fig. P14-12 $V_{ab} = 100$ volts, and $E = 200$ volts. Calculate R and X_L if (a) $X_L/R = 1$; (b) $X_L/R = 10$.

14-13. In the circuit shown in Fig. P14-13 $V_{ab} = 100$ volts, and X_c is variable. Use a voltage phasor diagram to determine the smallest value of E for which the voltage $V_{ab} = 100$ volts.

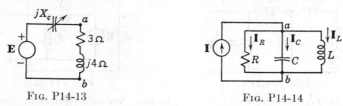

FIG. P14-13   FIG. P14-14

14-14. In the circuit shown in Fig. P14-14 $V_{ab} = 100$ volts, $I = 5$ amp, $I_R = 2$ amp, $I_C = 10$ amp. Calculate R, L, and C if $\omega = 400$.

14-15. In the circuit shown in Fig. P14-15 $R_1 = 6$, and $R_2 = 8$. It is known that $I_1 = I_2 = 10$ and $V_{ab} = 100$ volts. Calculate X_1, X_2, and I.

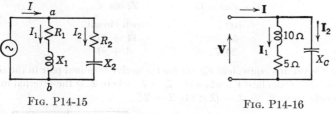

FIG. P14-15   FIG. P14-16

14-16. In the circuit shown in Fig. P14-16 (a) calculate the value of X_C if $\mathbf{V}$ and $\mathbf{I}$ are in phase. (b) If X_C has the value of (a), calculate $\mathbf{I}_1$ and $\mathbf{I}_2$ if $\mathbf{I} = 1\underline{/0°}$. Illustrate your answer with the aid of a phasor diagram.

14-17. In Fig. P14-17, if $X = -R$, calculate the phasor ratio $\mathbf{V}_{ab}/\mathbf{V}$.

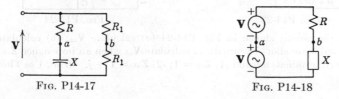

FIG. P14-17   FIG. P14-18

14-18. In the circuit shown in Fig. P14-18 the two sources have equal amplitudes and are in phase. Calculate the phasor ratio $\mathbf{V}_{ab}/\mathbf{V}$ if (a) $R = X$; (b) $3R = X$; (c) $3R = -X$; (d) $3X = -R$.

14-19. In the circuits of Prob. 14-17 and Prob. 14-18 (Figs. P14-17 and P14-18) show that the magnitude ratio V_{ab}/V is independent of the ratio X/R.

14-20. In the circuit shown in Fig. P14-20 (a) calculate $\mathbf{I}_0$ and $\mathbf{V}_{ab}$ if $\mathbf{I} = 1\underline{/0°}$. (b) Use the result of (a) to calculate the driving-point impedance $\mathbf{Z}_{ab}$. (c) Use the

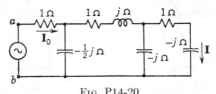

FIG. P14-20

result of (a) to determine the value of V_{ab} which gives $I = 2.5$ amp. (d) Use the result of (a) to determine the value of $\mathbf{I}$ when $\mathbf{V}_{ab} = 10\underline{/0°}$ volts.

14-21. In Fig. P14-21 (a) calculate the radian frequency at which $\mathbf{V}_2/\mathbf{V}$ is $1/\sqrt{8}$; (b) find the angle by which $\mathbf{V}_2$ lags $\mathbf{V}$ at the frequency of (a).

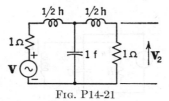

FIG. P14-21

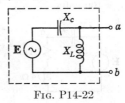

FIG. P14-22

14-22. In Fig. P14-22, if $X_L = -X_c$, deduce Norton's equivalent circuit with respect to terminals a-b.

14-23. The active terminal-pair network shown in Fig. P14-23 contains sinusoidal sources of the same frequency, in addition to R and L elements, and the steady-state conditions only are studied. The following data are obtained:

V_{ab}, rms volts	$\mathbf{Z}$, ohms
100	Open circuit
55	$11 + j0$
26.7	$4 + j0$

(a) Deduce Thévenin's equivalent circuit for the active terminal pair in the sinusoidal steady state. (b) Calculate V_{ab} when (1) $\mathbf{Z} = \mathbf{Z}_s$, where $\mathbf{Z}_s$ is the internal impedance of the Thévenin source; (2) $\mathbf{Z} = |\mathbf{Z}_s|$; (3) $\mathbf{Z} = \mathbf{Z}_s^*$.

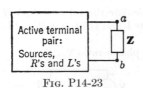

FIG. P14-23

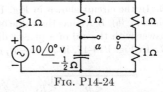

FIG. P14-24

14-24. In the circuit shown in Fig. P14-24 (a) calculate $\mathbf{V}_{ab}$; (b) calculate $\mathbf{I}_{ab}$ if terminals a and b are short-circuited; (c) calculate $\mathbf{V}_{ab}$ when an impedance $\mathbf{Z}_{ab}$ is connected between terminals a-b and (1) $\mathbf{Z}_{ab} = 1$; (2) $\mathbf{Z}_{ab} = 1 + j$. *Hint:* Use Thévenin's theorem.

14-25. Deduce the equation of balance for each of the bridge circuits shown in Fig. P14-25 (i.e., the relationship between the parameters so that $\mathbf{V}_{ab} = 0$).

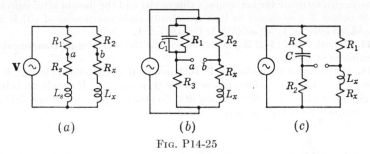

(a)   (b)   (c)

FIG. P14-25

14-26. For the terminal pair shown in Fig. P14-26 (a) calculate $\mathbf{Y}_{ab}$ and $\mathbf{Z}_{ab}$; (b) represent the terminal pair as the series combination of R' and C' if $\omega = 1$; (c) show that if the series representation of (b) is to apply for all values of ω then R' and C' must be functions of frequency; (d) sketch $R'(\omega)$ and $C'(\omega)$ as obtained in (c) as functions of the radian frequency.

FIG. P14-26   FIG. P14-28

14-27. Represent the complex driving-point immittance $\mathbf{Z}_{ab}$ of Prob. 14-20 (Fig. P14-20) as (a) the series connection of two elements; (b) the parallel connection of two elements. Use $\omega = 2$.

14-28. The series circuit shown in Fig. P14-28 is to be represented as the parallel combination of R' and X'_L. Plot R' as a function of X_L and X'_L as a function of X_L.

14-29. Calculate the complete response $v_{ab}(t)$ in the circuit of Prob. 14-5 (Fig. P14-5) if $R = 6$, $C = 0.025$, and (a) $i(t) = 10 \cos 5t$, $v_{ab}(0^+) = 0$; (b) $i(t) = 10 \cos 5t$, $v_{ab}(0^+) = 30$; (c) $i(t) = 10 \cos 5t$, $v_{ab}(0^+) = -30$.

14-30. In Fig. P14-30 the circuit is in the steady state with the switch in position 2. At $t = 0$ the switch is thrown to position 1. If $v(t) = 5 \cos(3t + \phi)$ and $E = 6$, calculate $i(t)$ for all $t \geq 0^+$, and sketch the result for (a) $\phi = 0$; (b) $\phi = -\pi/2$.

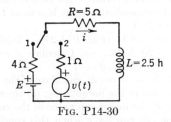

FIG. P14-30

14-31. In the circuit of Prob. 14-30 (Fig. P14-30) assume that steady state has been reached with the switch in position 1. At $t = 0$ the switch is thrown to position 2. Calculate and sketch $i(t)$ if $E = 18$, $v(t) = 14 \cos(3t + \phi)$, and sketch the result for (a) $\phi = 0$; (b) $\phi = -\pi/2$.

14-32. An initially deenergized R-C parallel circuit is connected across an ideal current source $i(t) = I_m \cos (\omega t + \phi)$ at $t = 0$. From a sketch of the voltage across the source, $v(t)$, estimate the maximum value of $v(t)$ and the instant after switching at which it occurs if ϕ is chosen so that the steady-state component of $v(t)$ is zero at $t = 0$ and (a) $\omega RC \ll 1$; (b) $\omega RC \gg 1$; (c) $\omega RC \approx 1$.

14-33. Repeat Prob. 14-32 if ϕ is chosen so that the steady-state component of $v(t)$ is a maximum at $t = 0$.

14-34. In the circuit shown in Fig. P14-34 assume that all elements have unit value. The source function has the form $v(t) = 15 \cos (t + \phi) U(t)$. If the circuit is initially deenergized, calculate (a) $v_2(0^+)$; (b) $(dv_2/dt)_{0^+}$; (c) the complete response $v_2(t)$ if $\phi = 0$; (d) the complete response $v_2(t)$ if $\phi = -\pi/2$.

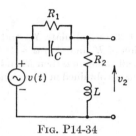

FIG. P14-34

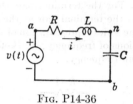

FIG. P14-36

14-35. In the circuit of Prob. 14-34 (Fig. P14-34), $C = 1$, $R_1 = \frac{1}{3}$, $L = 1$, $R_2 = 1$. Calculate the complete response $v_2(t)$ if $v(t) = 10 \cos 2t U(t)$ and if the initial-energy storage is zero.

14-36. In Fig. P14-36 $v(t)$ has the form $v(t) = V_m \cos (\omega t + \phi) U(t)$, the circuit is initially deenergized. (a) Show that $(di/dt)_{0^+}$ has the value $(V_m \cos \phi)/L$. (b) Assume that $\omega_0 \equiv 1/\sqrt{LC}$ satisfies the inequality $\omega_0 \leq 10\omega$, and show that the complex impedance of the circuit is approximately $Z_{ab} \approx R + j\omega L$. (c) Show that if the assumption of (b) applies and if in addition the circuit is "highly" oscillatory, then $Z_{ab} \approx j\omega L$. (d) Show that, if the assumptions of (b) and (c) apply, then the complete response $i(t)$ can be *approximated* for sufficiently small t by $i(t) = \text{Re } K e^{j\omega_0 t} + I_m \cos (\omega t + \phi - \pi/2)$. (e) Using all the assumptions stated above, *estimate* the largest value of $|i(t)|/I_m$ after $t = 0$, during the transient, if (1) $\phi = 0$; (2) $\phi = \pi/2$.

14-37. In the circuit of Fig. P14-36 the initial-energy storage is zero. Assume that $\omega_0 \geq 10\omega$ ($\omega_0{}^2 = 1/LC$) and $(R/2L) \ll \omega_0$. Let $v(t) = V_m \sin (\omega t + \phi) U(t)$. Use the procedure outlined in Prob. 14-36 to estimate the largest value of $i(t)/I_m$ if ϕ is chosen so that (a) the steady-state component of $v_{nb}(t)$ is zero at $t = 0$; (b) the steady-state component of $i(t)$ is zero at $t = 0$.

14-38. The circuit of Prob. 14-24 (Fig. P14-24) is initially not energized. The source is the function $v(t) = 20 \cos 2t$. (a) Calculate the value of the capacitance. (b) Calculate the complete response $v_{ab}(t)$.

14-39. In Fig. P14-39, if $v(t) = 10 \cos 2t$, calculate in the steady state (a) the maximum value of the energy stored in the inductance; (b) the values $v(t)$ can have when the condition of (a) occurs; (c) the maximum value of the energy stored in the capacitance and the values which $v(t)$ can have when this condition occurs. (d) At the instant $t = \pi/4$ calculate (1) the power flowing out of the source; (2) the power flowing into each passive element; (3) the energy stored in the inductance and in the capacitance.

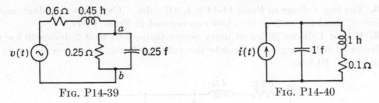

FIG. P14-39

FIG. P14-40

14-40. In Fig. P14-40, if $i(t) = \cos t$, calculate in the steady state (a) the average energy stored by the inductance; (b) the average energy stored by the capacitance; (c) the energy dissipated by the resistance in one cycle ($t = 0$ to $t = 2\pi$).

14-41. The R-L circuit shown in Fig. P14-41 is initially deenergized. The source is adjusted so that $v(t) = V_m \cos (\omega t + \theta)$, $\theta = \tan^{-1} (\omega L/R)$. (a) Show that the complete response $i(t)$ is given by

$$i(t) = I_m (\cos \omega t - e^{-Rt/L}) \qquad I_m = \frac{V}{Z}, \, t \geq 0^+$$

(b) Deduce an expression for the energy delivered to the inductance as a function of time. (c) Calculate the average energy stored in the inductance during the time interval $t = 0$ to $t = 2n\pi/\omega$, and show how the result is related to the reactive power as n increases to very large values.

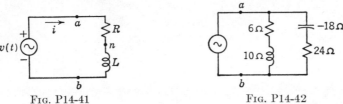

FIG. P14-41

FIG. P14-42

14-42. In Fig. P14-42 (a) calculate the effective value of v_{ab} if the average power delivered to the 6-ohm resistance is 500 watts; (b) for v_{ab} as in (a) calculate P_{ab}, Q_{ab}, the power, and the reactive power for each element.

14-43. The average power delivered to a load at 120 volts is 14.4 kw. The power is delivered through the 0.10-ohm resistance as shown in Fig. P14-43. Calculate and

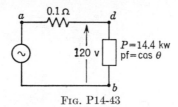

FIG. P14-43

graph the efficiency of transmission (P_{db}/P_{ab}) $\times$ 100 per cent as a function of load power factor and as a function of the angle which corresponds to the various load power factors.

14-44. A certain load draws 60 kw at a power factor of 0.5 lagging. A second load is connected in parallel. Calculate the complex power drawn by the second load if the parallel combination draws 60 kw at a power factor of (a) 0.6 lagging; (b) 0.8 lagging; (c) 0.9 lagging; (d) unity; (e) 0.9 leading.

14-45. The line voltage in Prob. 14-44 is 1,300 volts.   Calculate the admittance of the "second" load for each of the cases enumerated in Prob. 14-44.

14-46. If load 1 draws 30 kw at unity power factor and load 2 draws 30 kw at a power factor of 0.45 (lagging), calculate the value of E and the power factor at terminals a-b (Fig. P14-46).

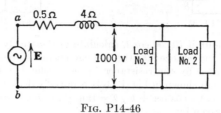

Fig. P14-46

14-47. The voltage phasor across a terminal-pair network has the form $\mathbf{V}_{ab} = \mathbf{V}_1(1 + \mathbf{\Gamma})$, where $\mathbf{\Gamma}$ is a complex number and the current entering the a terminal is given by the phasor $\mathbf{I}_{ab} = (\mathbf{V}_1/R)(1 - \mathbf{\Gamma})$.   Show that the power and the reactive power delivered to the terminal pair are given by the expressions $P_{ab} = V_1^2(1 - \Gamma^2)/R$, and $Q_{ab} = -jV_1^2(\mathbf{\Gamma}^* - \mathbf{\Gamma})/R$.

CHAPTER 15

ADJUSTABLE CIRCUITS IN THE SINUSOIDAL
STEADY STATE

In Chap. 14 we discussed the techniques which are used to solve series-parallel a-c circuit problems. In each example we assumed that both the element values and the frequency of the source were uniquely specified. In this chapter we shall combine the techniques which were introduced in Chap. 14 with the pole-zero diagram to study circuits which are in the sinusoidal steady state but which are "adjustable." By an adjustable circuit we mean a circuit in which either the value of one (or more) element is changed *or* the frequency is changed *or* both are changed. It must be emphasized at the outset that we are not concerned with time-varying parameters. Rather we shall consider circuits in which the change of the value of element (or frequency) is made in steps (possibly "small" steps) but after each change the steady state *only* is calculated. Thus we shall not be concerned with the transition (i.e., the transient) which occurs between the steady-state conditions as the element or the frequency is varied.

The importance of this subject matter in the analysis of electrical circuits may be understood through the following observations:

1. In many circuits the elements actually have different values at various times; for example, the load on a motor or generator is usually not fixed.

2. The study of the adjustment of element values or frequency in the circuit can eventually lead us to the design of circuits which will have a desired response.

3. In many practical instances several sinusoidal sources of different frequency may be impressed on a circuit (either intentionally or unintentionally). A knowledge of circuit response over an appropriate range of frequencies makes it possible to analyze such a situation. As an example, consider the antenna circuit of a radio (or television) receiver. All stations (i.e., frequencies) are "picked up" by the antenna, but only the desired station is to be selected for listening.

4. The laboratory testing of circuits in the sinusoidal steady state at various frequencies can give information about the complete response of the circuit under various conditions. This follows from the fact that

the pole-zero locations which characterize the complete response of a circuit to any source also determine the value of the complex network function. Consequently it is possible to infer the pole-zero locations of a network function from the sinusoidal steady-state response at various frequencies.

15-1. Adjustable Circuits. *Introduction.* If we wish to study the effect of varying one element on the sinusoidal steady-state response of a circuit, then we need to evaluate quantitatively the effect which the particular element has on the complex network function relating the source phasor to the response phasor. In two-element combinations this effect is easy to evaluate. Consider, for example, the series R-L circuit shown in Fig. 15-1a. In this circuit the resistance is adjustable (in general the

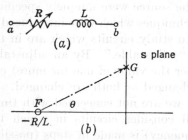

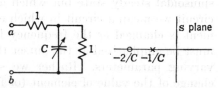

FIG. 15-1. (*a*) Series R-L branch with adjustable resistance. (*b*) Pole-zero diagram for determining the complex impedance.

FIG. 15-2. In the series-parallel circuit shown both the location of the zero and the location of the pole of $Z_{ab}(s)$ depend on the value of C.

adjustable elements are indicated on the circuit diagram by means of the arrow through the element symbol). In this circuit $Z_{ab}(s) = L(s + R/L)$; that is, the driving-point impedance has a zero at $s = -R/L$, as shown in Fig. 15-1b. Since a sinusoidal source is represented by a pole on the imaginary axis as at G, we observe that as R is increased the F point in Fig. 15-1b moves to the left so that the distance FG increases and θ decreases. Thus we have determined the effect of varying R on the sinusoidal steady-state response, since the foregoing statement is equivalent to saying that the magnitude of the impedance increases and its phase angle decreases.

Considering circuits which consist of more than two elements, we recall that a change in the value of a single element generally influences all the pole-zero locations of the network function. For example, in the circuit of Fig. 15-2, the transform impedance at terminals a-b is

$$Z_{ab}(s) = 1 + \frac{1}{1 + sC} = \frac{s + 2/C}{s + 1/C}$$

Hence both the location of the zero (at $s = -2/C$) and the location of the pole (at $s = -1/C$) are changed if C is changed.

We conclude from this discussion that the "migration" of the poles and zeros in the complex-frequency plane which arises from a change in element value may be quite complex so that the corresponding effect on the complex network function may require a considerable number of calculations. For this reason the effect of element variation is often studied by analyzing the complex network function itself rather than its pole-zero representation. This procedure is discussed in the later articles of this chapter.

If, on the other hand, the frequency of the *source* is adjusted, then the s-plane diagram can be used conveniently because for fixed element values the pole-zero locations of the network function ("F points") remain fixed. As the source frequency varies, only the location of the pole at $s = j\omega$ varies. We have already illustrated the interpretation of G-point migration in Chap. 13 by studying the influence which this pole has on the factors $s_g - s_F$ of the network function. In the following articles a more detailed study of this problem is made.

15-2. Frequency Response. *An R-C Circuit.* As the first example of a circuit with fixed elements, consider the parallel R-C circuit with a sinusoidal source of adjustable frequency shown in Fig. 15-3a. The arrow through the source labeled f is intended to indicate that the frequency of the source is adjustable but that the amplitude of the source remains fixed. We shall study the admittance function $\mathbf{Y}_{ab}$, that is, the ratio of the phasors $\mathbf{I}/\mathbf{V}$ as a function of frequency. Again it is necessary to emphasize that we are concerned only with the steady-state response at the various frequencies—we shall not consider the (exceedingly difficult) problem of the transient which occurs while the frequency is changing.

The transform admittance of this circuit is

$$Y_{ab}(s) = \frac{1}{R} + sC = C\left(s + \frac{1}{RC}\right) \tag{15-1}$$

Hence we have a zero at $s = -1/RC$, as shown in Fig. 15-3b. As the radian frequency of the sources increases, the G point moves up as indicated by the arrow. Hence the admittance of the circuit increases in magnitude from $1/R$ at $s = 0$ to infinite value at infinite frequency. The magnitude of the complex impedance correspondingly decreases from R to 0. The angle of the admittance is ϕ and is seen to increase from 0 to $\pi/2$ with increasing frequency.

It is customary to give the information concerning the frequency dependence of the network function by means of graphs which show how the absolute value of the network function and its angle depend on frequency. Such graphs are known as *frequency-response curves*. A curve which shows the magnitude of the network function as a function of frequency shows the amplitude (or effective value) of the response phasor when the amplitude (or effective value) of the source phasor is unity. If a current source of 1 amp is applied, then the voltage across an impedance **Z** is **Z** volts. Curves that give the magnitude of the network function as a function of frequency are called *amplitude-response curves of the frequency response*, or *amplitude-response curves* for brevity. Curves which

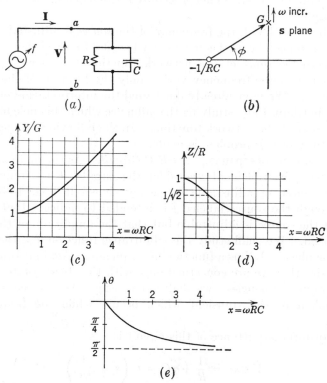

FIG. 15-3. (*a*) Parallel *R-C* circuit with adjustable-frequency sinusoidal source. (*b*) Pole-zero diagram for calculation of **Y**(*jω*). (*c*) Normalized admittance as a function of normalized frequency. (*d*) Normalized impedance as a function of normalized frequency. (*e*) Angle of the complex impedance as a function of frequency.

give the angle of the network function as a function of frequency are called *phase-response curves* (of the frequency response). While the frequency-response curves for complex networks are generally obtained point by point from the pole-zero diagram, this is not necessary in the present example; for the parallel *R-C* circuit the admittance, in polar form, is

$$\mathbf{Y} = \sqrt{\frac{1}{R^2} + \omega^2 C^2} \; \underline{/\tan^{-1} \omega RC} \qquad (15\text{-}2)$$

It is convenient to normalize the admittance with respect to the conductance $G = 1/R$,

$$\mathbf{Y}R = \frac{\mathbf{Y}}{G} = \sqrt{1 + \omega^2 R^2 C^2} \,\underline{/\tan^{-1} \omega RC} \tag{15-3}$$

Then the complex impedance, normalized with respect to R, is

$$\frac{1}{\mathbf{Y}R} = \frac{\mathbf{Z}}{R} = \frac{1}{\sqrt{1 + \omega^2 R^2 C^2}} \,\underline{/-\tan^{-1} \omega RC} \tag{15-4}$$

In these equations we notice that the radian frequency ω in both the magnitude and the angle is always multiplied by RC, the time constant of the R-C circuit. This fact again illustrates that the free response of the circuit (i.e., the time constant) is related to the sinusoidal steady-state response.

For the purpose of drawing the frequency-response curves, it is convenient to introduce a new normalized frequency, say, x, where

$$x = \omega RC$$

(Since $\omega = 2\pi f$, $x = 2\pi \times$ ratio of time constant to period of source.) Using this variable,

$$\frac{\mathbf{Y}}{G} = \sqrt{1 + x^2} \,\underline{/\tan^{-1} x}$$

and

$$\frac{\mathbf{Z}}{R} = \frac{1}{\sqrt{1 + x^2}} \,\underline{/-\tan^{-1} x}$$

Figure 15-3c and d shows the amplitude curves for the admittance and the impedance function, respectively. The phase-response curve giving θ, the angle of the impedance, is shown in Fig. 15-3e.

The frequency-response curves suggest an interesting and frequently useful possibility. Suppose we were to apply a current source to the parallel R-C circuit of Fig. 15-3a and adjust the frequency until, in the steady state, v_{ab} lags $i(t)$ by 45°. At that frequency $\omega RC = 1$. Since we presumably know the frequency, we could use this measurement to determine the time constant RC. Now notice that if RC is known then the free component of the complete response is known to be of the form $Ae^{-t/RC}$. Consequently, at least for this circuit, we can obtain sufficient information for calculation of the complete response for any type of source applied by making measurements in the sinusoidal steady state.

Studying the graph of Z/R, we note that at the frequency

$$f_1 = \frac{1}{2\pi RC}$$

(which corresponds to $x = 1$), $Z = R/\sqrt{2}$. Hence, if an adjustable-frequency current source is applied to a parallel combination of R-C elements at the frequency f_1 the voltage V_{ab} will have an effective value which is 70.7 per cent of the value at direct current. If now a current source at fixed effective value, I, is applied to the R-C circuit, then at $\omega = 0$ (d-c) the power delivered to the circuit is I^2R. When $\omega_1 = 1/RC$, the power delivered to the circuit is $(V_{ab}/R)^2 = (0.707IR)^2/R = \frac{1}{2}I^2R$. Hence the frequency $f_1 = 1/2\pi RC$ is called the "half-power frequency" of the R-C circuit.

15-3. The Parallel R-C Circuit as a Filter. In this article we shall use the example of a parallel R-C circuit to illustrate the filtering property of circuits which contain energy-storing elements. In circuit analysis the term "filtering property of a circuit" means the characteristics of the circuit which result in different sinusoidal steady-state response amplitudes for a given fixed amplitude of the applied source and adjustable frequency.

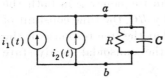

FIG. 15-4. Parallel R-C circuit with two ideal sources.

Let us assume that the two current sources impressed on the parallel R-C circuit of Fig. 15-4 have the following forms: a d-c source

$$i_1(t) = I \tag{15-5}$$

and a sinusoid of amplitude I, radian frequency ω

$$i_2(t) = I \cos \omega t \tag{15-6}$$

The response, in the steady state, may by superposition be written as

$$v_{ab}(t) = (v_{ab})_1 + (v_{ab})_2$$

where $(v_{ab})_1$ is the steady-state response due to i_1 and $(v_{ab})_2$ is due to i_2. Evidently

$$(v_{ab})_1 = IR \tag{15-7a}$$

Since the impedance of the parallel R-C circuit at the radian frequency ω is

$$\mathbf{Z}_{ab} = \frac{1}{\mathbf{Y}_{ab}} = \frac{1}{1/R + j\omega C} = \frac{R}{\sqrt{1 + R^2\omega^2C^2}} \underline{/- \tan^{-1} \omega RC}$$

we have

$$(v_{ab})_2 = IR \frac{1}{\sqrt{1 + R^2\omega^2C^2}} \cos (\omega t - \tan^{-1} \omega RC) \tag{15-7b}$$

Hence

$$v_{ab}(t) = IR \left[1 + \frac{1}{\sqrt{1 + R^2\omega^2C^2}} \cos (\omega t - \tan^{-1} \omega RC) \right] \tag{15-8}$$

Several numerical illustrations are useful. These are shown in Fig. 15-5, where the steady-state response waveforms are shown for four values of ωRC. [In these illustrations the time reference and therefore the phase angles of $(v_{ab})_2$ with respect to i_2 are *not* shown.] Figure 15-5 shows that the sinusoidal component of the response waveform becomes less pronounced as the frequency is adjusted to larger values. This effect may be desirable (as it is in filters for rectifiers) if we do not want the steady-state response to be oscillatory; or it may be undesirable (as in a sound system) when we wish to transmit all frequencies with equal fidelity.

Integrating and Differentiating Properties of the R-C Circuit in the A-C Steady State. The frequency response of the R-C circuit can be related to the integrating and differentiating property of such circuits, as discussed in Chap. 11. Since in that chapter the series R-C circuit was used, we shall now discuss the frequency response

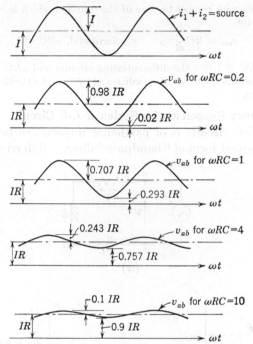

FIG. 15-5. Steady-state response of the circuit of Fig. 15-4 if $i_1(t)$ is a d-c source and $i_2(t)$ is sinusoidal. The result is shown for several values of the frequency of $i_2(t)$.

of the series R-C circuit of Fig. 15-6. For this circuit, in the sinusoidal steady state the voltage across the capacitance is represented by the phasor

$$\mathbf{V}_{mb} = \mathbf{V}_{ab} \times \frac{1/j\omega C}{R + 1/j\omega C} = \frac{1}{j\omega RC + 1} \mathbf{V}_{ab} \qquad (15\text{-}9)$$

If the radian frequency is sufficiently large so that $|j\omega RC| \gg 1$, then (approximately)

$$\mathbf{V}_{mb} \approx \frac{1}{j\omega RC} \mathbf{V}_{ab} \qquad \omega RC \gg 1 \qquad (15\text{-}10)$$

Since division of a phasor by $j\omega$ represents integration with respect to time of the function represented by the phasor, we can write

$$v_{mb} \approx \frac{1}{RC} \int v_{ab}\, dt \qquad v_{ab} \text{ sinusoidal, } \omega RC \gg 1 \quad (15\text{-}11)$$

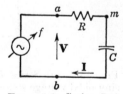

FIG. 15-6. Series R-C circuit with adjusta-ble-frequency con-stant-amplitude volt-age source.

We observe that, when the product $\omega RC \gg 1$, the voltage across the capacitance is approximately proportional to the time integral of the source voltage. Similarly the voltage across the resistance, v_{am}, represented by the phasor $\mathbf{V}_{am}$, is given by $\mathbf{V}_{am} = [(R/(R + 1/j\omega C)]\mathbf{V}_{ab}$, or

$$\mathbf{V}_{am} = \frac{j\omega RC}{1 + j\omega RC} \mathbf{V}_{ab}$$

so that, if $\omega RC \ll 1$, $\mathbf{V}_{am} \approx j\omega RC\mathbf{V}_{ab}$. Since multiplication of a phasor by $j\omega$ represents differentiation with respect to time of the function which is represented by the phasor, we can write

$$v_{am} \approx RC \frac{d}{dt} v_{ab} \qquad v_{ab} \text{ sinusoidal, } \omega RC \ll 1 \qquad (15\text{-}12)$$

The conditions $\omega RC \ll 1$ (for the differentiating circuit) and $\omega RC \gg 1$ (for the integrating circuit) correspond to the inequalities (11-70) and (11-65) if the time functions are sinusoidal.

15-4. Frequency Response of a Series R-L-C Circuit. The frequency response of R-L-C circuits is of particular importance because such circuits are the simplest form of "bandpass" filter. Referring to Fig. 15-7a,

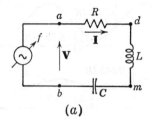

(a)

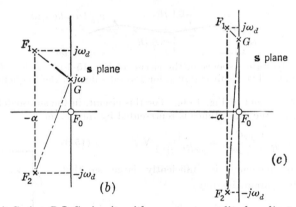

(b)

(c)

Fig. 15-7. (a) Series R-L-C circuit with constant-amplitude adjustable-frequency sinusoidal voltage source. (b) Pole-zero plot for calculating $\mathbf{Z}_{ab}(j\omega)$ for the circuit of (a). (c) Pole-zero diagram for $\mathbf{Z}_{ab}(j\omega)$ in a highly oscillatory case.

we observe that, if the source is a constant-amplitude voltage source, the current will have zero steady-state value at $\omega = 0$, because of the capacitance, and zero steady-state value as ω approaches infinity, because of the inductance. For this circuit the transform admittance is

$$Y(s) = \frac{1}{R + sL + 1/sC} = \frac{1}{L} \frac{s}{s^2 + (R/L)s + 1/LC} \qquad (15\text{-}13)$$

Setting $\alpha = R/2L$, $\omega_0{}^2 = 1/LC$,

$$Y(s) = \frac{1}{L} \frac{s}{s^2 + 2\alpha s + \omega_0{}^2}$$

or, in factored form,

$$Y(s) = \frac{1}{L} \frac{s}{(s - s_1)(s - s_2)}$$

where

$$s_{1,2} = -\alpha \pm \sqrt{\alpha^2 - \omega_0^2}$$

If we assume that the circuit is underdamped, $\alpha < \omega_0$, then we define $\omega_d = (\omega_0^2 - \alpha^2)^{\frac{1}{2}}$ and $s_{1,2} = -\alpha \pm j\omega_d$. Hence $Y(s)$ has a zero at $s = 0$ and poles at $s = s_1$ and $s = s_2$. A sinusoidal source is represented by a pole at $s = j\omega$. The zeros and poles are shown in Fig. 15-7b. The magnitude of the complex admittance is given by the quotient of the products of the following distances:

$$Y = \frac{1}{L} \frac{F_0 G}{(F_1 G)(F_2 G)} \tag{15-14}$$

Since $s = 0$ is a zero of $Y(s)$, $Y(0) = 0$. Since both $F_1 G$ and $F_2 G$ as well as $F_0 G$ approach infinity for infinite frequency, $Y(\infty) = 0$. Since $|Y(j\omega)|$ is a continuous function of ω, we expect a maximum value for some value of ω. It is seen that, if $\alpha \ll \omega_d$, then, as ω increases, in the neighborhood of $\omega = \omega_d$ the ratio of $F_0 G / F_2 G$ changes very "slowly," but $F_1 G$ has a "large" percentage variation, having its minimum value at $\omega = \omega_d$. Thus we expect $Y(j\omega)$ to have a maximum *near* $\omega = \omega_d$ if $\alpha \ll \omega_0$, that is, in the highly oscillatory case. This can be verified by inspecting the pole-zero diagram for a highly oscillatory case as shown in Fig. 15-7c. The ratio of $F_0 G$ to $F_2 G$ changes very little as ω moves from G toward ω_d, while $F_1 G$ changes "rapidly."

From the study of the pole-zero diagram we conclude that the curve of $|Y(j\omega)|$ as a function of ω will have a maximum and that this maximum will be near $\omega = \omega_d$ in the highly oscillatory case. The exact frequency response of this circuit can be obtained either by constructing the graph of $|Y(j\omega)|$ by measuring the distances $F_0 G$, $F_1 G$, and $F_2 G$ for various ω and using Eq. (15-14) or by studying the complex admittance function analytically. The latter procedure is given in the next section.

15-5. The Series R-L-C Circuit. *Resonance.* The exact analysis of the series R-L-C circuit is of interest for several reasons. First of all, this circuit finds considerable application inasmuch as many simple physical systems or devices can be represented by such a circuit. Second, we wish to compare the approximate answers of the preceding article with the exact answers. Finally, the manner in which the analysis is carried out is also applicable to other circuits.

For the series R-L-C circuit of Fig. 15-7a the complex impedance is

$$\mathbf{Z}_{ab}(j\omega) = R + j\omega L + \frac{1}{j\omega C} = R + jX$$

Since $X = \omega L - 1/\omega C$, we have $X = 0$ at $\omega^2 = 1/LC = \omega_0^2$. Hence, since $Z_{ab} = (R^2 + X^2)^{\frac{1}{2}}$, at $\omega = \omega_0$, Z_{ab} is a minimum. When the condition $\omega = \omega_0$ is satisfied, the circuit is said to be in "resonance." For the resonant condition, the following observations are made:

1. In resonance the complex impedance and the complex admittance of the series R-L-C circuit are real numbers. The complex impedance has the value R; the admittance has the value $1/R$.

2. In resonance the magnitude of the impedance of the series R-L-C circuit is a minimum, and the magnitude of its admittance is a maximum. Hence, if a constant-amplitude adjustable-frequency voltage source is impressed on this circuit, the amplitude of the current at resonance will be larger than at any other frequency.

3. The power factor at terminals a-b (Fig. 15-7a) is unity, since the voltage $v_{ab}(t)$ and the current $i_{ab}(t)$ will be in phase when $\omega = \omega_0$ (see also Example 13-5).

4. A study of the pole-zero diagram of the series R-L-C circuit (Fig. 15-7c) indicates that, when $\omega_d \approx \omega_0$, the impedance Z_{ab} has a minimum in the neighborhood of $\omega = \omega_d$. The results of the foregoing exact analysis show that this minimum occurs at $\omega = \omega_0$. Thus our study of the pole-zero diagram has enabled us to arrive at fairly good approximations.

In general the term "resonance" is used to describe three possible conditions.

1. By analogy with the series R-L-C circuit, a terminal pair is in *series* resonance when the magnitude of the driving-point *admittance* is a *maximum*.

2. By analogy with the parallel R-L-C circuit (see Art. 15-9) *parallel* resonance is defined as that condition for which the magnitude of the *impedance* is a *maximum*. To contrast the series with the parallel R-L-C circuit the term *antiresonance* is also used as a synonym for parallel resonance.

3. *Unity-power-factor*, or *resistive*, resonance is that condition for which the driving-point immittance is real.

Although in the series (or parallel) R-L-C circuits the unity-power-factor condition occurs at the same frequency as the series (or parallel) resonant condition, for other terminal-pair networks these conditions generally occur at distinct frequencies.

Power and Energy Relations at Resonance. A study of the power and energy-storage conditions at resonant frequency is useful because the term "resonance" is thus clarified. Let us assume that a sinusoidal voltage source is applied to a series R-L-C circuit and that the frequency of the source is identical with the resonant frequency of the terminal pair.

Let this voltage be

$$v_{ab}(t) = \sqrt{2}\, V \cos \omega_0 t$$

represented by the phasor $\mathbf{V}_{ab} = V\underline{/0}$. The current in the circuit is then given by

$$i(t) = \sqrt{2}\, I_0 \cos \omega_0 t, \text{ represented by the phasor } \mathbf{I} = I_0\underline{/0°}$$

where $I_0 = V/R$. The subscript zero refers to the resonant condition.

The average power in the circuit at resonance, denoted by the symbol P_0, is given by

$$P_0 = \frac{V^2}{R} = I_0{}^2 R$$

Since the rms value (or the amplitude) of the current at resonance is larger than at any other frequency (because the magnitude of the admittance is a maximum), the average power dissipated in the resistance R is a maximum at resonance.

In Chap. 14 we saw that at resonance the steady-state equivalent circuit with respect to terminals a-b (of the series R-L-C circuit) is a resistance R. This equivalence is due to the fact that the voltage across L, v_{dm} in Fig 15-7a, and the voltage across the capacitance, v_{mb}, are equal in amplitude and differ in phase by exactly 180°. To understand the role which the reactive elements play in resonance, the stored energy in each of these elements will be calculated. Using the current phasor as reference, $\mathbf{I} = I_0\underline{/0°}$, we have

$$\mathbf{V}_{mb} = \frac{I_0}{j\omega_0 C}$$

These phasors correspond to the time functions

$$i(t) = \sqrt{2}\, I_0 \cos \omega_0 t \quad \text{and} \quad v_{mb} = \sqrt{2}\,\frac{I}{\omega_0 C} \cos\left(\omega_0 t - \frac{\pi}{2}\right) = \frac{\sqrt{2}\, I}{\omega_0 C} \sin \omega_0 t$$

In a time interval t_1 to t_2 the energy which has been delivered to the inductance Δw_L is given by

$$\Delta w_L = \tfrac{1}{2}L[i(t_2)]^2 - \tfrac{1}{2}L[i(t_1)]^2 = LI_0{}^2 \cos^2 \omega_0 t_2 - LI_0{}^2 \cos^2 \omega_0 t_1 \tag{15-15}$$

In the same time interval the energy which has been delivered to the capacitance is given by

$$\Delta w_C = \tfrac{1}{2}C[v(t_2)]^2 - \tfrac{1}{2}C[v(t_1)]^2 = \frac{I^2}{\omega_0{}^2 C} \sin^2 \omega_0 t_2 - \frac{I_0{}^2}{\omega_0{}^2 C} \sin^2 \omega_0 t_1 \tag{15-16}$$

In Eq. (15-16) we note that $\omega_0{}^2 = 1/LC$ so that

$$\frac{I_0{}^2}{\omega_0{}^2 C} = \frac{I_0{}^2 LC}{C} = LI_0{}^2 \tag{15-17}$$

Now we substitute Eq. (15-17) in Eq. (15-16) and add the result to Eq. (15-15) to obtain the total energy Δw which has been delivered to the energy-storing elements in the circuit in the time interval from t_1 to t_2,

$$\Delta w = LI_0{}^2[\cos^2 \omega_0 t_2 + \sin^2 \omega_0 t_2 - (\cos^2 \omega_0 t_1 + \sin^2 \omega_0 t_1)] \tag{15-18}$$

Since $\cos^2 x + \sin^2 x = 1$, Eq. (15-18) reads

$$\Delta w = 0$$

Since t_2 and t_1 are arbitrary instants of time, we conclude that, with $\omega = \omega_0$, the L-C combination receives no energy from the source at any time during the steady state.

Let us now examine again the individual expressions for Δw_L and Δw_C at certain time intervals. If we choose t_1 to be an instant of time at which $i(t)$ is zero, for example, $t_1 = -\pi/2\omega_0$, and t_2 an instant of time at which $i(t)$ is a maximum, for example, $t_2 = 0$, then for this time interval the inductance has received energy in the amount $LI_0{}^2$ and the capacitance has received energy in the amount $-LI_0{}^2$; the minus sign indicates that the capacitance has delivered energy to the other elements in the circuit. We conclude, therefore, that in the resonant condition there exists a continuous interchange of energy between inductance and capacitance and that the source is not involved in this energy transfer. At any instant of time the *total* stored energy is $LI_0{}^2 = \frac{1}{2}L(\sqrt{2}\,I_0)^2$ or $\frac{1}{2}C(I_0\,\sqrt{2}/\omega_0 C)^2$.

We must emphasize that the process of energy exchange which has been described is a steady-state phenomenon. The total energy stored by the energy-storing elements is supplied by the source during the transient time interval.

15-6. Selectivity, Half-power Points, and Bandwidth. In the preceding article we concentrated on the resonant condition in the series R-L-C circuit, i.e., the sinusoidal steady state at the frequency $\omega = \omega_0 = 1/\sqrt{LC}$. In this article we shall discuss the frequency-response curves of the series R-L-C circuit. While in any numerical case these curves can be obtained from a pole-zero diagram, it is instructive to deduce the shape of the admittance and impedance curves analytically. We start with the expression for the complex impedance $\mathbf{Z}_{ab}$,

$$\mathbf{Z}_{ab} = R + jX = R + j\left(\omega L - \frac{1}{\omega C}\right) \tag{15-19}$$

In order to make the results of this analysis more generally useful, it is convenient to normalize the complex impedance with respect to its minimum absolute value, that is, R, and to introduce a normalized frequency variable μ, which represents the ratio of any frequency to the series-resonant frequency. Thus

$$\mu = \frac{\omega}{\omega_0} = \frac{f}{f_0} = \omega\,\sqrt{LC} \tag{15-20}$$

Introducing μ into Eq. (15-19) and dividing by R, we have

$$\frac{\mathbf{Z}_{ab}}{R} = 1 + j\,\frac{1}{R}\left(\mu\omega_0 L - \frac{1}{\mu\omega_0 C}\right) \tag{15-21}$$

In Eq. (15-21) it is convenient to factor $\omega_0 L$ from the reactance term,

$$\frac{\mathbf{Z}_{ab}}{R} = 1 + j\,\frac{\omega_0 L}{R}\left(\mu - \frac{1}{\mu\omega_0{}^2 LC}\right) \tag{15-21a}$$

Using the definition of ω_0 in Eq. (15-21a), we obtain the form

$$\frac{\mathbf{Z}_{ab}}{R} = 1 + j\,\frac{\omega_0 L}{R}\left(\mu - \frac{1}{\mu}\right) \tag{15-21b}$$

At this point we recognize $\omega_0 L/R$ to be the quality factor Q_0 of the series

R-L-C circuit discussed in Chap. 9. The symbol Q_0 should *not* be confused with the symbol for reactive power.

$$Q_0 = \frac{\omega_0}{2\alpha} = \frac{\sqrt{L/C}}{R} = \frac{\omega_0 L}{R}$$

$$= \text{quality factor of } \textit{series } R\text{-}L\text{-}C \text{ circuit} \quad (15\text{-}22)$$

Introducing Q_0 in Eq. (15-21b), we have the following form for the complex impedance $\mathbf{Z}_{ab}$ of the series R-L-C circuit:

$$\frac{\mathbf{Z}_{ab}}{R} = 1 + jQ_0\left(\mu - \frac{1}{\mu}\right) \quad (15\text{-}23)$$

To obtain the expression for the absolute value of the impedance or admittance, we write Eq. (15-23) in polar form:

$$\frac{\mathbf{Z}_{ab}}{R} = \sqrt{1 + Q_0{}^2\left(\mu - \frac{1}{\mu}\right)^2} \; \Big/ \tan^{-1}\left[Q_0\left(\mu - \frac{1}{\mu}\right)\right] \quad (15\text{-}24)$$

Equation (15-24) embodies a very important conclusion: The shapes of the curves of the normalized impedance (absolute value) and the angle of the impedance θ, as a function of frequency, depend only on the value of Q_0. Thus for the purpose of *comparing* the frequency responses of two R-L-C series circuits we shall need to compare only the values of Q_0. We shall now discuss the curves of Z_{ab}/R, $Y_{ab}R$, and θ as a function of normalized frequency μ.

We have:

Normalized absolute value of impedance:

$$\frac{Z_{ab}}{R} = \sqrt{1 + Q_0{}^2\left(\mu - \frac{1}{\mu}\right)^2} \quad (15\text{-}25)$$

Normalized absolute value of admittance:

$$Y_{ab}R = \frac{1}{\sqrt{1 + Q_0{}^2(\mu - 1/\mu)^2}} \quad (15\text{-}26)$$

Angle of impedance:
$$\theta = \tan^{-1} Q_0\left(\mu - \frac{1}{\mu}\right) \quad (15\text{-}27)$$

To plot Eqs. (15-25) and (15-26), we note that Z_{ab}/R is infinite at $\mu = 0$ and $\mu = \infty$. Similarly $Y_{ab}R$ is zero at these extremes. At resonance $\mu = 1$, and Z_{ab} and Y_{ab} have a minimum and a maximum, respectively. Curves for three values of Q_0 are shown in Fig. 15-8a and b. The curves of θ as a function of μ are shown in Fig. 15-8c. The curves of admittance or impedance as a function of frequency as shown in Fig. 15-8 are frequently used and are commonly referred to as "resonance curves."

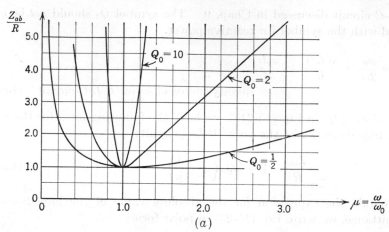

Fig. 15-8a. Normalized impedance of the series R-L-C circuit as a function of normalized frequency with Q_0 as a parameter.

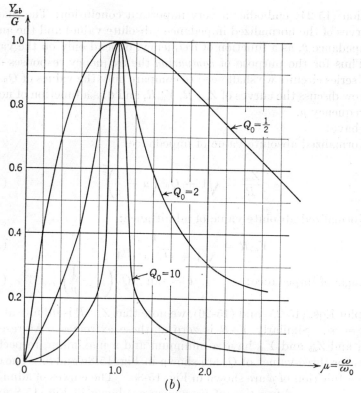

(b)

Fig. 15-8b. Normalized admittance of the series R-L-C circuit as a function of normalized frequency with Q_0 as a parameter.

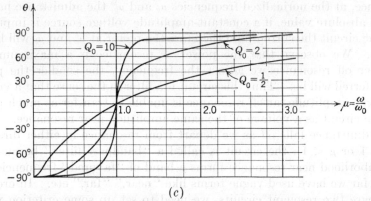

(c)

FIG. 15-8c. Angle of the impedance of the series R-L-C circuit as a function of normalized frequency with Q_0 as a parameter.

Power and Energy Relations. We shall now deduce energy and power relationships from an admittance curve such as that shown in Fig. 15-9.

If a constant-amplitude adjustable-frequency voltage source is applied to the series R-L-C circuit, then the effective value or the amplitude of the current at resonance ($\mu = 1$) is larger than at any other frequency because the circuit at resonance has maximum admittance. From the previous discussion we know that the power delivered to R at resonance is $P_0 = I_0{}^2 R$, where $I_0 = V/R$. From Fig. 15-9 we observe that there are two values of frequency for which the admittance is a given fraction of $1/R$. We shall now show that these two frequencies have a geometric mean which is the resonant frequency, that is, $\mu_a \mu_b = 1$ or $\omega_a \omega_b = \omega_0{}^2$.

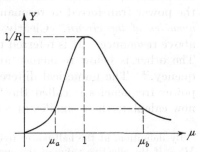

FIG. 15-9. Admittance as a function of frequency for a series R-L-C circuit. Two frequencies at which the admittance has the same absolute value are indicated.

To prove this, we need recall only that, if Y is the same at the two frequencies, Z is also the same. Since $\mathbf{Z} = R + jX$, we conclude that the magnitude of the reactance is identical at the two frequencies. Now

$$\frac{X}{R} = Q_0 \left(\mu - \frac{1}{\mu} \right)$$

Hence

$$\mu_a - \frac{1}{\mu_a} = - \left(\mu_b - \frac{1}{\mu_b} \right)$$

or

$$\mu_a{}^2 \mu_b - \mu_b = -\mu_b{}^2 \mu_a + \mu_a$$

or

$$\mu_a \mu_b (\mu_a + \mu_b) = \mu_a + \mu_b$$

so that

$$\mu_a \mu_b = 1 \tag{15-28}$$

Since, at the normalized frequencies μ_a and μ_b, the admittance has the same absolute value, if a constant-amplitude voltage source is impressed on the circuit the current and therefore the power at μ_a and μ_b will be the same. We observe that the power at resonance is a maximum: the farther off resonance we adjust the frequency, the smaller the power transferred will be. Thus this circuit is a filter in the sense that a voltage of given amplitude far off resonance is unable to transfer as much power to the circuit as a voltage of the same amplitude near resonance. Since the admittance falls off as we depart from resonance in either direction ($\mu > 1$ or $\mu < 1$), the circuit is called a "bandpass filter" because the neighborhood near resonance forms a band of "favored" frequencies.

So far we have used vague terms like "near," "far," etc. In order to compare two resonant circuits, we need to set up some criterion which defines the "passed" frequencies. An arbitrary definition which is commonly accepted is the following: If a fixed-amplitude voltage source with adjustable frequency is impressed on the series R-L-C circuit, then those frequencies for which the power transferred to R is more than *half the power transferred at resonance* form the *passband* of the circuit. The extreme frequencies at which the power transferred to R is *exactly half* the power transferred at resonance are referred to as the *half-power frequencies of the circuit*. Clearly one of these half-power frequencies is above resonance. It is referred to as the "upper half-power frequency." The other is below resonance and is called the "lower half-power frequency." The numerical difference between the upper and lower half-power frequencies is called the "bandwidth" of the circuit. We shall now calculate these significant values.

By definition, at the half-power frequencies, the power delivered to the circuit is $\frac{1}{2}P_0$. If the effective value of the current at these frequencies is I_1 and the effective value of the current at resonance is I_0, we have

$$I_1{}^2 R = \tfrac{1}{2}I_0{}^2 R$$

Hence
$$I_1 = \frac{1}{\sqrt{2}} I_0$$

Since the current at the half-power frequencies is $1/\sqrt{2}$ of the current at resonance,[1] the magnitude of the admittance at the half-power frequencies is $1/\sqrt{2}$ of the magnitude at resonance. Denoting by f_1 and f_2 the lower and upper half-power frequencies, respectively, we see that Y at f_1 and f_2 is $1/\sqrt{2} R$; the absolute value of the impedance at the half-power frequencies is $\sqrt{2} R$. Denoting the impedance at the half-power frequencies by $Z_{1,2}$ we have

$$|Z_{1,2}| = \sqrt{2} R = |R + jX_{1,2}| \tag{15-29}$$

---

[1] The reader must be careful not to confuse this relationship, which involves $\sqrt{2}$, with the relationship between I_m and I at any one frequency.

where $X_{1,2}$ denotes the reactance at f_1 or f_2. We note that Eq. (15-29) reads

$$\sqrt{2}\,R = \sqrt{R^2 + X_{1,2}^2}$$

Solving,

$$X_{1,2} = \pm R$$

The half-power frequencies are therefore determined from the equations

$$\omega_1 L - \frac{1}{\omega_1 C} = -R \tag{15-30a}$$

and

$$\omega_2 L - \frac{1}{\omega_2 C} = +R \tag{15-30b}$$

The quadratic equation (15-30a) is now solved for ω_1. Using the relationship $\omega_0^2 = 1/LC$ and rejecting a negative solution for ω, we obtain

$$\omega_1 = -\frac{R}{2L} + \sqrt{\left(\frac{R}{2L}\right)^2 + \omega_0^2} = -\alpha + \sqrt{\omega_0^2 + \alpha^2} \tag{15-31a}$$

Similarly, solving Eq. (15-30b) gives

$$\omega_2 = \frac{R}{2L} + \sqrt{\left(\frac{R}{2L}\right)^2 + \omega_0^2} = +\alpha + \sqrt{\omega_0^2 + \alpha^2} \tag{15-31b}$$

Thus the bandwidth in radians per second is

$$\text{Bandwidth} = \omega_2 - \omega_1 = \frac{R}{L} \quad \text{rad/sec} \tag{15-32}$$

If we form the ratio of resonant frequency to bandwidth, we obtain

$$\frac{\text{Resonant frequency}}{\text{Bandwidth}} = \frac{f_0}{f_2 - f_1} = \frac{\omega_0}{\omega_2 - \omega_1} = \frac{\omega_0 L}{R} = Q_0 \tag{15-33}$$

We see now that the quantity Q_0 has the geometrical interpretation of ratio of resonant frequency to bandwidth. The number Q_0 therefore determines the "selectivity" of the R-L-C circuit. The term selectivity arises from the application of resonant circuits in radio and television receivers. In this application several stations broadcast simultaneously with different frequencies. The equivalent circuit of the antenna may be visualized as an R-L-C circuit to which several voltage sources of about equal amplitude, but with different frequencies, are applied simultaneously. It is the function of the resonant circuit to permit large current flow only for the desired station (frequency). The circuit is therefore adjusted so that the bandwidth of the circuit is sufficiently large for the signal of the station which is desired to be within the half-power frequencies but for the adjacent station to have a signal which is so far from resonance that it does not contribute materially to the signal which the receiver amplifies. The number Q_0 associated with the resonant circuit determines the suitability of a given circuit for this application. Hence Q_0 is called the "selectivity" or "quality ratio" of the circuit.

We mention here that, in the application cited above, reasonably large values of Q_0 (say, 5 or more) are often desirable, but the reader should not infer that there are no applications in which low Q_0 is desirable.

While we have defined the Q of a series-resonant circuit as the ratio of resonant frequency to bandwidth, another interpretation which is associated with the ratio of stored to dissipated energy in the circuit is possible. We have shown that the stored energy in the circuit at resonance is constant and equal to LI_0^2. The power dissipated in the resistance is of course I_0^2R. The energy dissipated by the resistance in *one cycle* (see Chap. 14) is given by

$$W_R = \frac{2\pi}{\omega_0} I_0^2 R \quad \text{joules/cycle}$$

The ratio of the stored energy in the circuit to the energy dissipated per cycle is proportional to Q_0:

$$\frac{\text{Stored energy}}{\text{Energy dissipated/cycle}} = \frac{1}{2\pi} \frac{\omega_0 L I_0^2}{R I_0^2} = \frac{1}{2\pi} Q_0 \qquad (15\text{-}34)$$

In circuits other than series or parallel connection of R-L-C elements (whose Q's are $\omega_0 L/R$ and $R/\omega_0 L$, respectively) the quantity $\omega_0 L/R$ has no special significance. In such cases the Q of the circuit is defined by

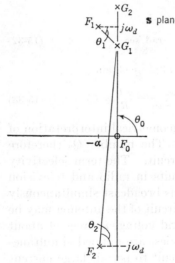

$$Q_0 = 2\pi \frac{\text{peak stored energy}}{\text{energy dissipated/cycle}}$$

15-7. Approximate Results Obtained by the Use of the Pole-Zero Diagram. We shall now show how some useful approximate results can be obtained from the pole-zero diagram. Let us start by assuming a high-Q ($Q_0 > 5$) R-L-C circuit whose admittance has the pole-zero diagram shown in Fig. 15-10. As discussed in Art. 15-4, in this diagram we assume that, as ω varies between G_1 and G_2, the distance ratio $F_0 G/F_2 G$ remains approximately constant. This is justified if $\alpha \ll \omega_0$ because then

Fig. 15-10. Pole-zero diagram for approximate admittance calculations in a highly oscillatory series R-L-C circuit.

$$F_0 G = \omega \qquad F_2 G \approx \omega_d + \omega$$

And, near resonance, $\omega \approx \omega_d$, $F_0 G/F_2 G \approx \frac{1}{2}$. (The radian frequency ω_0 differs very little from ω_d if $\alpha/\omega_0 \ll 1$. For example, if $\omega_0 = 1$, $\alpha = 0.1$, $Q_0 = 5$; $\omega_d = \sqrt{.99} \approx 1$.) Hence near resonance, if $Q_0 > 5$,

$$Y \approx \frac{(1/L) \times \frac{1}{2}}{F_1 G} \qquad (15\text{-}35)$$

Now, at $\omega = \omega_d$, $F_1G = \alpha$. Hence the admittance is obtained at $\omega = \omega_d$ as $Y = 1/2L\alpha = 1/R$. This is of course only approximate; we know that $Y = 1/R$ occurs at $\omega = \omega_0$, not at ω_d. If we assume that the ratio F_0G/F_2G remains fixed near $\omega = \omega_d$, then Y is proportional to F_1G. But at $\omega = \omega_d - \alpha$ and $\omega = \omega_d + \alpha$ the distance F_1G is $\sqrt{2}\,\alpha$; that is, the admittance has an absolute value which is $1/\sqrt{2}\,R$. Hence $\omega_d \pm \alpha$ are the half-power points. Again the results when compared with the exact analysis are seen to be in good agreement. If, for example, $\omega_0 = 1$, $\alpha = 0.1$, the half-power frequencies are from the exact equation (15-31)

$$\omega_{1,2} = \pm 0.1 + \sqrt{1.01} = 1.105,\ 0.905 \qquad (15\text{-}36)$$

while the approximate analysis from the pole-zero diagram gives answers

$$\omega_{1,2} = \pm 0.1 + \sqrt{0.99} = 1.095,\ 0.895 \qquad (15\text{-}37)$$

i.e., within about 1 per cent of the exact answers. Now we must be aware of the fact that this type of analysis is eventually applied to practical circuits so that the component values will be known only with finite precision. Hence the small error which is introduced when the simpler and more convenient approximate analysis is used is often insignificant.

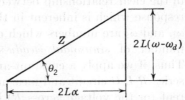

FIG. 15-11. Graphical interpretation of Eq. (15-41).

We note also that the bandwidth, as obtained from the approximate analysis, is $2\alpha = R/L$ rad. This is exactly the right answer. There is no particular significance in the fact that this answer is not approximate. It just happens that the error in F_0G and F_2G compensates at these points.

If we continue the approximate calculation, then

$$Y \approx \frac{1}{2L(F_1G)} \qquad (15\text{-}38)$$

or
$$Z \approx 2L(F_1G) \qquad (15\text{-}39)$$

Now $F_1G = \sqrt{\alpha^2 + (\omega_d - \omega)^2}$; moreover, the angle of Y is

$$\text{Angle } Y = \theta_0 - \theta_1 - \theta_2$$

Since $\theta_0 = \pi/2$ and $\theta_1 \approx \pi/2$, the angle of Y is $-\theta_2$. This angle is given by

$$\theta_2 = -\tan^{-1}\frac{\omega_d - \omega}{\omega} \qquad (15\text{-}40)$$

Hence
$$Z \approx 2L\,\sqrt{\alpha^2 + (\omega_d - \omega)^2}\ \underline{/-\theta_2} \qquad (15\text{-}41)$$

near resonance. We recognize this complex quantity from Fig. 15-11 in rectangular form,

$$Z \approx 2L\alpha + jL2(\omega_d - \omega)$$

Since $\alpha = R/2L$, $2L\alpha = R$; further, $L(\omega_d - \omega) \approx L(\omega_0 - \omega) = \omega_0 L[(\omega_0 - \omega)/\omega_0]$.

Hence
$$\mathbf{Z} \approx R(1 + j2Q_0\delta) \tag{15-42}$$

where $\delta = 1 - (\omega/\omega_0) = 1 - \mu$. Equation (15-42) is a useful approximation to the exact formula for $\mathbf{Z}$. It applies when $Q_0 > 5$ and $|\delta| \ll 1$. (The requirement $\delta \ll 1$ corresponds to the assumption that the ratio of F_0G to F_2G remains constant; $Q_0 > 5$ corresponds to the assumption $\alpha/\omega_0 < 0.1$.)

From Eq. (15-42) we also deduce that, if $|\delta| \ll 1$, the resonance curve is symmetrical about the resonant frequency. This is also evident if we recall that the arithmetic mean and the geometric mean of two numbers which differ by a sufficiently small amount are approximately equal.

To summarize the application of the pole-zero diagram to frequency response, we point out that in general a network function has a *maximum* when the source frequency is "near" a *pole* and a *minimum* when the source frequency is "near" a *zero* of the transform-network function.

The significance of the pole-zero analysis lies not only in the fact that approximate results can be obtained for the frequency response but also in the clear relationship between frequency response and free (transient) response which is inherent in the pole-zero diagram. The quantities ω_0, ω_1, and ω_2 are numbers which can be *measured* (and are derived) from a number of *sinusoidal steady-state conditions* at different frequencies. Thus, if we apply a constant-amplitude variable-frequency source to the series R-L-C circuit and measure the radian frequency at which the current (or the voltage across R) has the largest amplitude, we have measured ω_0. If we adjust the frequency to those values at which the current has 70.7 per cent of the resonant value, ω_1 and ω_2 can be determined. Using these values, we can now calculate

$$2\alpha = \omega_2 - \omega_1 \tag{15-43}$$

Knowing α and ω_0, we now have all the information which is needed to predict (i.e., calculate) the free component of the response and hence the complete response of the circuit! This possibility is one of the significant accomplishments which sinusoidal-steady-state calculations and experiments make possible. This indirect method for predicting transient components from sinusoidal-steady-state measurements is important because measurements of transient response are frequently more difficult to perform than sinusoidal-steady-state measurements.

15-8. Low-Q Circuit. Much of the discussion has revolved around highly oscillatory (high-Q) circuits. It should not be inferred that low-Q circuits are without significance. Let us therefore consider the R-L-C series circuit shown in Fig. 15-12. We know that for this circuit a constant-amplitude adjustable-frequency voltage source will produce maximum current amplitude at $\omega = \omega_0$. Since the voltage across the

resistance is proportional to the current, it is also a maximum at resonance. In many applications, however, the voltage across the capacitance, v_{mn}, or across the inductance, v_{nb}, is the desired response. We shall
now demonstrate that these voltages do not have their maximum ampli-

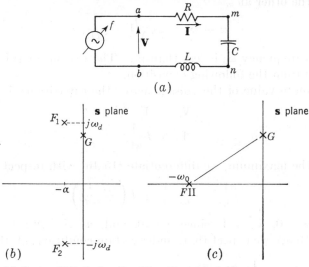

(a)

(b)   (c)

Fig. 15-12. (a) Series R-L-C circuit with adjustable-frequency constant-amplitude
voltage source. (b) Pole-zero diagram of the transform voltage-gain function which
relates v_{mn} to $v(t)$ in a highly oscillatory case. (c) Pole-zero diagram for the same
transform network function as in (b), but drawn for the critically damped case.

tude at the resonant frequency ω_0. This is immediately evident from the
pole-zero diagram. Consider the phasor ratio $\mathbf{V}_{mn}/\mathbf{V}$:

$$\frac{\mathbf{V}_{mn}}{\mathbf{V}} = \frac{1/j\omega C}{R + j\omega L + 1/j\omega C} = \frac{1}{(j\omega)^2 LC + j\omega RC + 1}$$

The transform network function (voltage gain function) of interest is

$$H(s) = \frac{1}{s^2 LC + sRC + 1} = \frac{1}{LC}\frac{1}{s^2 + (R/L)s + 1/LC}$$

Hence $$H(s) = \frac{\omega_0^2}{(s - s_1)(s - s_2)}$$

where $s_{1,2} = -\alpha \pm \sqrt{\alpha^2 - \omega_0^2}$, $\alpha = R/2L$, $\omega_0^2 = 1/LC$. This network
function, in contrast to the driving-point admittance, has no zero at
$s = 0$. The poles are as before. Now, in a high-Q circuit, the poles are
close to the imaginary axis as in Fig. 15-12b. Hence we still have F_1G
varying more rapidly than F_2G near $\omega = \omega_d$ so that v_{mn} will have maximum amplitude near $\omega = \omega_d \approx \omega_0$. Let us now turn to a low-Q circuit,
e.g., a critically damped circuit, $Q_0 = \frac{1}{2}$. In this case

$$s_1 = s_2 = -\omega_0 = -\alpha$$

and we have a double pole at $s = -\omega_0$ on the real axis as shown in Fig. 15-12c. In this case the denominator $(FG)^2$ increases with increasing ω, and the only maximum amplitude of v_{mn} occurs at $s = 0$. In general it can be shown that, if $Q_0 > 1/\sqrt{2}$, the voltage v_{mn} will have one maximum at $\omega = 0$, the other at

$$\omega = \omega_p = \omega_0 \sqrt{1 - \frac{1}{2Q_0{}^2}} \tag{15-44}$$

The radian frequency ω_p is less than ω_0. The reason for this is easy to understand from the following exposition.

The absolute value of the voltage across the capacitance is written as

$$|\mathbf{V}_c| = |\mathbf{I}|\,|X_c| \tag{15-45}$$

or

$$V_c = I \frac{1}{\omega C} \tag{15-46}$$

To locate the maximum, we differentiate (15-46) with respect to ω,

$$\frac{\partial V_c}{\partial \omega} = \frac{\partial I}{\partial \omega} \frac{1}{\omega C} + I\left(-\frac{1}{\omega^2 C}\right)$$

Now, at $\omega = 0$, $V_c = V$ since $I = 0$, and, at $\omega = \infty$, $V_c = 0$ since $X_c = 0$. Hence we expect that, under certain conditions of $\partial V_c/\partial \omega = 0$,

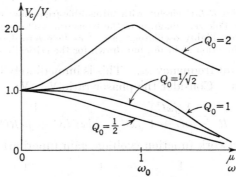

Fig. 15-13. Amplitude-response curves for the phasor ratio $\mathbf{V}_{mn}/\mathbf{V}$, illustrating that the maxima which occur for $Q_0{}^2 > \frac{1}{2}$ occur below the series resonant frequency.

between zero and infinite frequencies V_c has a maximum. We know already that *at resonance* I has a maximum, that is, $\partial I \left/ \partial \omega \right|_{\omega=\omega_0} = 0$. Hence at resonance $\partial V_c \left/ \partial \omega \right|_{\omega=\omega_0} = -I/\omega_0{}^2 C$ so that the maximum voltage across the capacitance does *not* occur at resonance. Since at resonance $\partial V_c/\partial \omega$ is negative, the point $\omega = \omega_0$ must be on the decreasing portion of the V_c versus ω curve (see Fig. 15-13). Therefore we expect that the maximum capacitance voltage occurs at a frequency below resonance. Four typical curves for V_c/V as a function of μ are shown in Fig. 15-13.

15-9. The Parallel R-L-C Circuit. The parallel R-L-C circuit is the dual of the series circuit, and we shall see that by using this fact *carefully* many results of the series circuit can be applied.

The *admittance* of the three elements R, L, and C in parallel has the form

$$\mathbf{Y}_{ab} = G + j\omega C + \frac{1}{j\omega L}$$

The magnitude of $\mathbf{Y}_{ab}$ is a minimum at the radian frequency $\omega_0 = 1/\sqrt{LC}$. This frequency defines the parallel or antiresonant frequency of the circuit. Since

$$\mathbf{Y}_{ab} = G + j\omega C \left(1 - \frac{1}{\omega^2 LC} \right)$$

we use the symbol ω_0 to denote $1/\sqrt{LC}$ and obtain

$$\mathbf{Y}_{ab} = G + j\omega C \left(1 - \frac{\omega_0^2}{\omega^2} \right)$$

If we normalize the admittance with respect to G and the frequency with respect to ω_0 (as before, let $\mu = \omega/\omega_0$), we write

$$\frac{\mathbf{Y}_{ab}}{G} = 1 + j\frac{\omega_0 \mu C}{G} \left(1 - \frac{1}{\mu^2} \right)$$

or

$$\frac{\mathbf{Y}_{ab}}{G} = 1 + j\frac{\omega_0 C}{G} \left(\mu - \frac{1}{\mu} \right)$$

We now *define* the number Q_0 *of a parallel-resonant circuit* as the ratio $\omega C/G$,

$$Q_0 \equiv \frac{\omega_0 C}{G} = \frac{R}{\omega_0 L}$$

so that the equation for the normalized admittance reads

$$\frac{\mathbf{Y}_{ab}}{G} = 1 + jQ_0 \left(\mu - \frac{1}{\mu} \right) \tag{15-47}$$

Equation (15-47) shows that the *admittance of the parallel R-L-C circuit* has a form which is identical to the *impedance of the series-resonant circuit*. All the results of the previous analysis are therefore applicable, as is seen from the tabulation below.

Series R-L-C circuit	*Parallel R-L-C circuit*
Resonance at $\omega = \omega_0 = \dfrac{1}{\sqrt{LC}}$	Resonance at $\omega = \omega_0 = \dfrac{1}{\sqrt{LC}}$
$Q_0 = \dfrac{\omega_0 L}{R}$	$Q_0 = \dfrac{\omega_0 C}{G} = \dfrac{R}{\omega_0 L}$
At resonance:	At resonance:
$\|\mathbf{Z}\|$ is minimum	$\|\mathbf{Y}\|$ is minimum
$\|\mathbf{Y}\|$ is maximum	$\|\mathbf{Z}\|$ is maximum
High Q if $\dfrac{\omega_0 L}{R} \geq 5$	High Q if $\dfrac{\omega_0 C}{G} \geq 5 \left(\dfrac{R}{\omega_0 L} \geq 5 \right)$

In every instance where the results of the series circuit are to apply, it must be remembered that an observation for the series circuit which describes the current if a voltage source is impressed corresponds to a result in the parallel case concerning the voltage if a current source is applied.

15-10. Comparison of Lossy and Lossless Circuits.   For an oscillatory R-L-C series circuit the admittance is

$$Y = \frac{1}{L}\frac{s}{(s - s_1)(s - s_2)}$$

where $s_{1,2} = \alpha \pm j\omega_d$.

For a series L-C circuit the admittance is

$$Y = \frac{1}{sL + 1/sC} = \frac{1}{L}\frac{s}{s^2 + \omega_0^2}$$

where $\omega_0^2 = 1/LC$.   In Fig. 15-14 the pole-zero diagrams for an R-L-C and an L-C circuit are shown.   It is assumed that in both these circuits $LC = 1$.   The difference between the two pole-zero diagrams is in the location of the poles.   In the lossless (L-C) case the poles are on the imaginary axis; hence a sinusoidal source, at the frequency of the pole ($s = j$), will produce a double pole so that the component of the response due to the source has the form $t \cos (t + \psi)$.   This component approaches infinity as t approaches infinity.   (This is verified by observing that $X = 0$ at $\omega = 1$.)   Comparing the R-L-C and the L-C circuit, we observe the following: At the frequency $\omega = \omega_0$ the lossless circuit results in "infinite" response, but the lossy circuit has maximum response.   Furthermore the effect of adding small damping to the L-C circuit moves the poles into the left half plane, off the $j\omega$ axis, but the resonant frequency remains approximately equal to the frequency of the damped oscillations ($\omega_0 \approx \omega_d$).

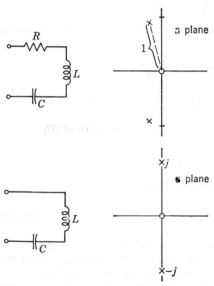

Fig. 15-14. Comparison of highly oscillatory and lossless circuits by means of admittance pole-zero diagrams.

The relationship between the L-C and the R-L-C circuit can be generalized as follows: If a circuit is slightly damped so that all the poles and zeros of its network functions are "near" the imaginary axis, then they can be located approximately by first ignoring the resistance. (The term near means that for every pole and zero at $s = s_1$ we require $|\operatorname{Re} s_1| \ll |\operatorname{Im} s_1|$.)   Thus in the slightly *damped* circuit the maxima and minima of response will occur near the poles and zeros of the lossless circuit.

It is noted that the circuit is slightly damped if the resistance in series with an L or C element is small compared with the element reactance at the zero-pole frequencies and if the resistance in parallel with an L or C element be large compared with the reactance at these frequencies.

Example 15-1. Determine the frequency response of the circuit shown in Fig. 15-15a. The source is an ideal current source. The response is v_{ab}. Use and justify approximate methods.

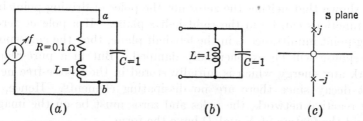

$$(a) \qquad\qquad (b) \qquad\qquad (c)$$

Fig. 15-15. Illustration of how the lossless circuit of (b) and its impedance pole-zero diagram (c) are used to obtain the frequency response of the slightly lossy circuit of (a).

Solution. Setting the series resistance to zero, we obtain the circuit of Fig. 15-15b. For this circuit $Y(s) = s + 1/s$ or $Y(s) = (s^2 + 1)/s$. Hence $Z(s) = s/(s^2 + 1)$, which corresponds to a zero at $s = 0$ and a pole pair at $s = \pm j$, as shown in Fig. 15-15c. We therefore expect maximum response at $s = j$, $\omega = 1$. At $\omega = 1, X_L = 1$, since $R = 0.1$, $R/X_L = 0.1$; hence the circuit of Fig. 15-15a is slightly damped, and we expect its Z_{ab} to have a maximum in the neighborhood of $\omega = 1$. This impedance at $s = j$ is

$$Z(j) = \frac{(0.1 + j)/j}{0.1} = 10 - j$$

Thus from the pole-zero diagram we conclude that Z has a maximum value $\sqrt{101}$ ohms at $\omega = 1$. This is an approximate result. To illustrate the value of the approximate method, the exact maximum of Z_{ab} is calculated. Consider the circuit of Fig. 15-15a.

$$Y(s) = s + \frac{1}{0.1 + s} = \frac{s^2 + 0.1s + 1}{s + 0.1}$$

or
$$Z(s) = \frac{s + 0.1}{s^2 + 0.1s + 1}$$

so that the poles of $Z(s)$ are at $s = -0.05 \pm j \sqrt{1 - 0.05^2}$ and the zero is at $s = -0.1$. We observe that the poles are very close to the values obtained by using $R = 0$ and that the zero is at $s = -0.1$ rather than zero. If we study $Z(j\omega)$,

$$Z(j\omega) = \frac{j\omega + 0.1}{1 - \omega^2 + 0.1j}$$

its absolute value is

$$Z(\omega) = \frac{\sqrt{0.01 + \omega^2}}{\sqrt{(1 - \omega^2)^2 + 0.01}}$$

We find after elaborate computation that $Z(\omega)$ is a maximum at $\omega = 1.00453$, within 0.5 per cent of 1.

15-11. Pure-reactance Networks.

In the preceding articles we have seen how a lossless network can be used to give approximate but sufficiently precise answers about slightly lossy circuits. For this reason the study of networks which contain no resistance is useful. Such circuits are called "pure-reactance" or "pure-susceptance" networks. In this article we shall discuss the properties of pure-reactance driving-point immittances.

In Chap. 13 it was shown that driving-point immittances have the form $H(s) = N(s)/D(s)$, where N and D are polynomials in s. Further it was shown that neither the zeros nor the poles of driving-point immittance functions can be in the right-half s plane. If a pole or zero of a driving-point immittance is in the left-half plane, then the corresponding free response will be exponentially damped. But in a pure-reactance network any energy which is initially stored in the source-free network cannot decay since there are no dissipating elements. Hence, for a purely reactive network, the poles and zeros must be on the imaginary axis, and the factors of N and D have the form

$$(s - j\omega_A)(s + j\omega_A) = s^2 + \omega_A{}^2$$

In addition we observe that the complex driving-point immittance must be imaginary because the average power input in the sinusoidal steady state must be zero. Hence for pure-reactance networks

$$Z(s) \Big|_{s=j\omega} = Z(j\omega) = \frac{1}{Y(j\omega)} = jX(\omega)$$

where X is a real function of the (radian) frequency. The factors $s^2 + \omega_A{}^2$ are real for $s = j\omega$, but $Z(s)$ itself is imaginary. It follows that $Z(s)$ must have a factor of s either in N or in D. Thus, for pure-reactance networks, the degree of the numerator polynomial *must* differ from the degree of the denominator polynomial by unity. This fact implies that such functions must have either a zero or a pole at $s = 0$. The same conclusion can be reached in another way. If there is a path from one input terminal of the terminal pair to the second terminal which does not pass through a capacitance, then the driving-point impedance at $s = 0$ is zero; if every path passes through a capacitance, then the driving-point impedance at $s = 0$ is infinity. Since these are the only two possibilities, s must be a factor of the numerator or denominator of the driving-point impedance.

The general form of the driving-point impedance for a purely reactive network is therefore

$$Z(s) = H s^{\pm 1} \frac{(s^2 + \omega_A{}^2)(s^2 + \omega_B{}^2) \cdots}{(s^2 + \omega_1{}^2)(s^2 + \omega_2{}^2) \cdots}$$

Another condition must be satisfied by the function $Z(s)$. This condition states that zeros and poles must alternate. Thus, if

$$Z(s) = s \frac{(s^2 + \omega_A{}^2)(s^2 + \omega_B{}^2) \cdots}{(s^2 + \omega_1{}^2)(s^2 + \omega_2{}^2) \cdots}$$

we have a zero at $s = 0$ and

$$\omega_1 < \omega_A < \omega_2 < \omega_B < \cdots$$

while if $Z(s)$ has the form

$$Z(s) = \frac{1}{s} \frac{(s^2 + \omega_A{}^2) \cdots}{(s^2 + \omega_1{}^2) \cdots}$$

it is necessary that

$$\omega_A < \omega_1 < \omega_B < \cdots$$

This property is called the *separation* property of zeros and poles and is part of a theorem which deals with the synthesis of pure-reactance driving-point immittances. This theorem, named after its discoverer R. M. Foster, is called Foster's reactance theorem. The proof of the separation property is beyond the scope of this book.

15-12. Reactance and Susceptance—Frequency Curves. Since, for a pure-reactance terminal pair a-b, $Z_{ab} = jX_{ab}$ and $Y_{ab} = jB_{ab}$, it follows that the driving-point reactance X_{ab} is always the negative reciprocal of the susceptance B_{ab}. Moreover, if X_{ab} is positive, this means that in the sinusoidal steady state v_{ab} leads i_{ab} by 90°; if X_{ab} is negative, v_{ab} lags i_{ab} by 90°. Hence a graph of X_{ab} or B_{ab} as a function of frequency shows not only the magnitude ratio V_{ab}/I_{ab} but also the phase relation between v_{ab} and i_{ab}. The latter is obtained from the sign of X_{ab} or B_{ab}. In this article we shall first study the curves of X and B for the two basic energy-storing elements and show how these curves can be applied to more elaborate circuits.

For an inductance L_{ab} the reactance is $X_{ab} = \omega L_{ab}$, and the susceptance is $-1/\omega L_{ab}$. A curve of reactance as a function of frequency is therefore a straight line, as shown in Fig. 15-16a. The curve of susceptance as a function of frequency for an inductance is the hyperbola shown in Fig. 15-16b.

For a capacitance C_{ab} we observe that the susceptance curve is a straight line and the reactance curve is a hyperbola as shown in Fig. 15-16c and d.

If we now desire to find the reactance-frequency curve of two series elements, we need only add the individual reactance curves, while to obtain the susceptance-frequency curve of two parallel elements we need only add the individual susceptance curves because series reactances and parallel susceptances add. In this procedure as well as in the subsequent examples we shall not be concerned with the values of the reactances at the various frequencies although the graphical method which will be described could be used in any numerical case. We shall rather concentrate on determining the sign of X or B and the shape of the curves.

Let us consider first the reactance-frequency curve of a series L-C circuit, shown in Fig. 15-17a. The reactance-frequency curves for these two elements are drawn in Fig. 15-17b and c. Since $X_{ab} = X_L + X_C$, by adding the two curves of Fig. 15-17b and c we note that, at $\omega = 0$, $X = -\infty$; at $\omega = \infty$, $X = +\infty$; and, at some point marked ω_0, $X = 0$. At that point $X_L + X_C = 0$ or $\omega_0 L = +1/\omega_0 C$. Hence the radian frequency at which the reactance changes sign is at $\omega_0 = 1/\sqrt{LC}$. The curve for X_{ab} is shown in Fig. 15-17d.

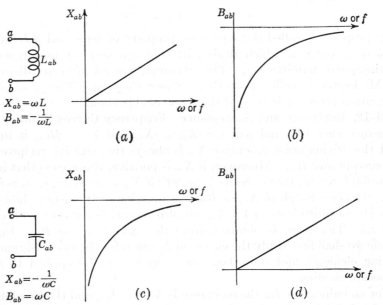

FIG. 15-16. Reactance- and susceptance-frequency curves for a single inductance and a single capacitance.

In Fig. 15-17 we observe that, at $\omega = \omega_0$, $X_{ab} = 0$. Hence at that frequency the impedance $Z_{ab} = 0$. It follows that $s = \pm j\omega_0$ are zeros of the driving-point impedance and poles of the admittance. Thus, if an ideal sinusoidal *current* source of radian frequency ω_0 is impressed on the circuit, the voltage response $v_{ab}(t)$ due to this source is zero. If on the other hand a voltage source of radian frequency ω_0 is impressed, the response component due to the source is $t \cos (\omega_0 t + \psi)$ since a pole of the admittance function corresponds to the pole of the source function. The reactance functions discussed above are special cases of network functions, and the terms zeros and poles which are applied to transform network functions are also applied to reactance functions. Thus ω_0 is a zero of the reactance of the series L-C circuit (Fig. 15-17).

The definitions that follow are used in the discussion of pure-reactance circuits:

Series-resonant frequency: A series-resonant frequency is a frequency at which the driving-point reactance has a zero.

Parallel- (or anti-) resonant frequency: A parallel-resonant frequency is a frequency at which the driving-point reactance has a pole.

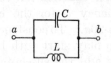

The reason for the definition of parallel-resonant frequency becomes

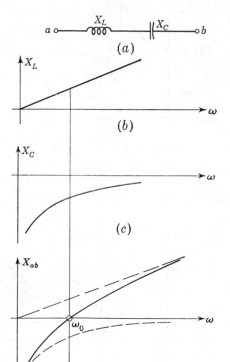

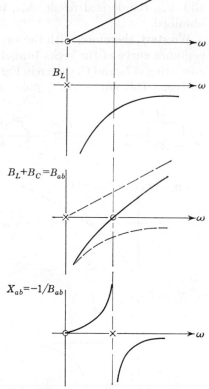

FIG. 15-17. Reactance-frequency curve of an L-C series circuit obtained by addition of the reactance curves for an inductance and a capacitance.

FIG. 15-18. Susceptance- and reactance-frequency curve constructed for a parallel L-C circuit.

clear if we study the parallel L-C circuit of Fig. 15-18. We note that at $\omega = \omega_0$ the reactance is infinite. It is also evident that the susceptance curve of the series L-C circuit is identical in shape to the reactance curve of the parallel L-C circuit, and vice versa. This is again a manifestation of the duality of the two circuits (see Fig. 15-19).

As an example of a circuit which consists of more than two elements, consider the pure-reactance circuit shown in Fig. 15-20a. Let it be required to sketch the shape of X_{ab} as a function of the radian frequency ω for the circuit of Fig. 15-20a. To construct these curves, we may start with branch mb. If we add the susceptance of branch mb to the susceptance of C_2, we obtain B_{db}. If we then find X_{db} and add X_{ad}, the desired result, X_{ab}, is obtained.

We start, therefore, with the susceptance curve of the series branch consisting of L_3 and C_3 shown in Fig. 15-20b. This curve has a pole at

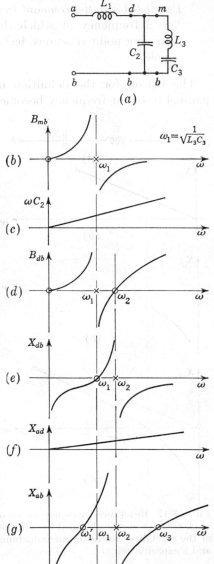

(a)

FIG. 15-20. Construction of the reactance-frequency curve for the four-element circuit shown.

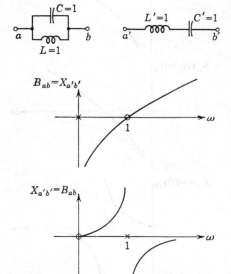

FIG. 15-19. Illustration of duality. In this example $L = C'$, and $C = L'$; hence the same curve applies to B_{ab} and $X_{a'b'}$. In general the shape of the susceptance-frequency graph of the parallel circuit is the same as the reactance-frequency curve of the series circuit, but the scales need to be changed.

$\omega = \omega_1$. To this curve we add the susceptance curve of C_2, which is shown in Fig. 15-20c. Adding the two curves, we note that the resulting susceptance-frequency curve for B_{db}, shown in Fig. 15-20d, has a pole at $\omega = \omega_1$ and also has a zero at $\omega = \omega_2$. Since the element values are not given, the curves cannot be drawn to scale but we note that ω_2 is larger than ω_1. To include the effect of L_1, we now need the reactance-frequency curve for X_{db}. This curve has been constructed in Fig. 15-20e. Note that the poles of the susceptance are zeros of the reactance, zeros and poles alternate, and the slope of the resulting curve is positive. To obtain X_{ab}, we add the reactance of L_1, X_{ad}, shown in Fig. 15-20f, to X_{db} and get the result shown in Fig. 15-20g. Note that, unless the value of the circuit elements is specified, the location of none of the zeros and poles is known except relative to ω_1. Thus the reactance zero ω_1' is below ω_1, ω_2 is above ω_1, and ω_3 above ω_2. The fact that several poles and zeros may occur in a reactance- (or susceptance-) frequency curve is sometimes referred to as the phenomenon of "multiple resonance." In a more advanced course the reader will learn that the creation of zeros or poles through the insertion of elements in a pure-reactance circuit is a very useful tool in the *design* of circuits, since it enables the designer to obtain minima and maxima of Z or Y with facility.

In the preceding examples we observe that zeros and poles of the reactance and susceptance function do indeed alternate, as predicted by Foster's reactance theorem. Moreover, as a result of this alternation, the slope of the reactance- or susceptance-frequency curve is always of the same sign, namely, positive.

15-13. Circuits with an Adjustable Element. Introduction. Since a change in the value of a single element in a circuit generally influences the location of *all* zeros and poles, it is often convenient to study the effect of adjustable elements on the value of the complex network function without reference to the pole-zero diagram. Let us introduce this subject by considering the variation of a complex driving-point immittance as a function of the element which is adjustable. In order to study such varying complex quantities, it will be convenient to inquire about the *locus* of the quantity in

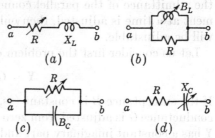

FIG. 15-21. Examples of adjustable two-element circuits.

the complex plane. (A locus is a collection of points which satisfy a specified condition. For example, the locus of all points in a plane which are equidistant from a given point is a circle.)

Considering first the two-element circuits shown in Fig. 15-21, we note that the impedances and admittances are of one of two forms,

$$\mathbf{Z}_{ab} = R + jX \qquad \text{and} \qquad \mathbf{Y}_{ab} = \frac{1}{R + jX}$$

or

$$\mathbf{Z}_{ab} = \frac{1}{G + jB} \qquad \text{and} \qquad \mathbf{Y}_{ab} = G + jB$$

In this article we consider either series or parallel combinations of R-L-C elements. At first we study the impedance of the series connections and

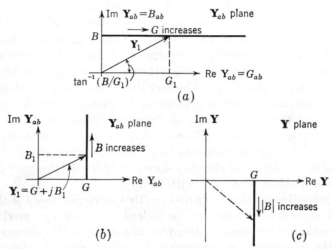

Fig. 15-22. Simple admittance loci. (a) Locus of admittance for fixed susceptance and adjustable conductance. (b) Locus of admittance for fixed conductance and adjustable positive susceptance. (c) Locus of admittance for fixed conductance and adjustable negative susceptance.

the admittance of the parallel connections of elements. If only one element at a time is adjusted, then only one of the values, R or $X(G$ or $B)$, will be adjustable.

Let us consider first the problem of an admittance which has the form

$$\mathbf{Y} = G + jB \tag{15-48}$$

If the susceptance B is constant (as, for example, in Fig. 15-21c) and the conductance G is adjusted from zero to infinity, then the complex number $\mathbf{Y}$ has a constant imaginary part and a real part which varies from zero to infinity. We now define the $\mathbf{Y}$ plane (complex admittance plane) as the set of cartesian axes in which the abscissas represent the real part of $\mathbf{Y}$ and the ordinates represent the imaginary part of $\mathbf{Y}$. Figure 15-22a shows the $\mathbf{Y}$ plane for the admittance of Eq. (15-48) if G is adjustable and B_c is positive (as in Fig. 15-21c). The horizontal line from B to the right in Fig. 15-22a is the locus of the admittance $\mathbf{Y}$ as G is adjusted from zero to infinity. *For any particular value of G, for example, $G = G_1$, the admit-*

tance $\mathbf{Y}_1$ *may be represented by the line from the origin to the linear locus as indicated in Fig. 15-22a.*

If, in Eq. (15-48), B is adjustable and G is fixed, then the locus of the admittance is shown in Fig. 15-22b. In Fig. 15-22b it is assumed that B is capacitive since the locus is the straight line in the first quadrant. Figure 15-22c shows the locus for the circuit indicated in Fig. 15-21b. Here B is a negative number because the adjustable element is an inductance.

Similarly, if we consider two series elements, for example, those indicated in Fig. 15-21a, then the locus of the complex impedance in the $\mathbf{Z}$ *plane* will also be a straight line. For the circuit shown in Fig. 15-21a X is constant and positive, and R is adjustable, so that the locus of the impedance will show a constant imaginary part. This locus is shown in Fig. 15-23a. In Fig. 15-23b the real part of $\mathbf{Z}$ is constant, and X is adjustable from 0 to $-\infty$. We may identify this locus with the circuit of Fig. 15-21d.

Note that on all the loci shown in Figs. 15-22 and 15-23 an arrow has been associated with each locus to show how an increase in the element value affects the value of $\mathbf{Z}$ or $\mathbf{Y}$.

15-14. Locus of Admittance of a Series R and X Connection When One of the Elements Is Adjustable. Inversion. In the previous article it

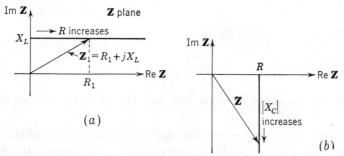

Fig. 15-23. Straight-line impedance loci. (a) Locus of $\mathbf{Z}_{ab}$ for the circuit of Fig. 15-21a. (b) Locus of $\mathbf{Z}_{ab}$ for the circuit of Fig. 15-21d.

was shown that for the circuit of Fig. 15-21d, the locus of the impedance $\mathbf{Z}_{ab}$ was a straight line, as shown in Fig. 15-23b. In the following articles, it will be shown that many a-c steady-state problems can be solved graphically in preference to an analytical solution. In such cases it is often necessary to know the locus of the admittance of a series connection of elements, such as that of Fig. 15-21d. In the complex plane of Fig. 15-23b the point $\mathbf{Z}_{ab}$ moves on a straight line as $|X_c|$ is varied from zero to infinity. The problem is to find the locus of $\mathbf{Y}_{ab}$ in the $\mathbf{Y}$ plane for the same range of variations of X_c.

Before continuing with the solution of this specific problem, consider the $\mathbf{Z}$ and $\mathbf{Y}$ planes shown in Fig. 15-24. In this figure the point $\mathbf{Z}_1 = 5\underline{/37°} = 4 + j3$ and the corresponding $\mathbf{Y}_1 = 1/\mathbf{Z}_1 = \frac{1}{5}\underline{/-37°}$ are shown in the $\mathbf{Z}$ and $\mathbf{Y}$ planes, respectively. In these planes the points $\mathbf{Z}_2 = \sqrt{32}\ \underline{/-45°} = 4 - j4$ and $\mathbf{Z}_3 = 4\underline{/0}$ and, correspondingly, $\mathbf{Y}_2 = (32)^{-\frac{1}{2}}\underline{/45°}$ and $\mathbf{Y}_3 = \frac{1}{4}\underline{/0}$ are also shown. From this example a general conclusion is drawn: For every point $\mathbf{Z} = Z\underline{/\theta}$ in the $\mathbf{Z}$ plane there exists a point $\mathbf{Y} = Y\underline{/-\theta} = (1/Z)\underline{/-\theta}$ in the $\mathbf{Y}$ plane. The procedure for finding a point $\mathbf{Y}$ in the $\overline{\mathbf{Y}}$ plane, corresponding to a point $\mathbf{Z}$ in the $\mathbf{Z}$ plane, should be clear from Fig. 15-24. In particular note that, if the point $\mathbf{Z}$ is in the first quadrant of the $\mathbf{Z}$ plane, then its corresponding $\mathbf{Y}$ point will be in the fourth quadrant of the $\mathbf{Y}$ plane. The length $OY = 1/OZ$. For example, $OY_1 = 1/OZ_1$, and the angle between OY and the G axis is the

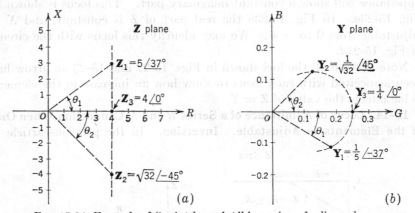

Fig. 15-24. Example of "point-by-point" inversion of a linear locus.

negative of the angle between OZ and the R axis. As an example, $\underline{/GOY_1} = -\underline{/ROZ_1}$.

The length of OY_1 in a given drawing will depend on the choice of scale for mhos. In Fig. 15-24 the R and G axes are calibrated in ohms and mhos, respectively, by a convenient choice of scales.

In Fig. 15-24a the points $\mathbf{Z}_1$, $\mathbf{Z}_2$, and $\mathbf{Z}_3$ were specially chosen such that they were on the straight line, shown dotted, $R = 4$. If we select many other points on the line $Z_1Z_2Z_3$ in the Z plane and find their corresponding Y points in the $\mathbf{Y}$ plane, the latter points will be on a curve, shown by dotted line $Y_2Y_3Y_1$.

The point $\mathbf{Y}_1 = 1/\mathbf{Z}_1$ is called the inversion of the point $\mathbf{Z}_1$, and the function $\mathbf{Y} = 1/\mathbf{Z}$ is said to *map* the line $Z_1Z_2Z_3$ in the $\mathbf{Z}$ plane into the curve $Y_1Y_2Y_3$ in the $\mathbf{Y}$ plane. It is noted that, in this type of mapping, the distance from $\mathbf{Z}_1$ to $\mathbf{Z}_2$ is not necessarily the same as the distance from $\mathbf{Y}_1$ to $\mathbf{Y}_2$. On the other hand, the points $\mathbf{Z}_1$ and $\mathbf{Z}_2$ are seen from the origin of the Z plane through an angle Z_1OZ_2 which is identical with the angle Y_2OY_1, which is the angle presented by Y_2 and Y_1 to the origin of the Y plane. In other words, the function $Y = 1/Z$ maps a curve in the Z plane into another curve in the Y plane, such that in the mapping the distances are not preserved but the angles as seen from the respective origins remain the same. In the process of inversion just described the points very far away from the origin of the Z plane are mapped into points close to the origin of the Y plane, and vice versa. In particular the point at infinity in the Z plane (i.e., any point at infinite distance from the origin) is mapped into the origin of the Y plane. In Fig. 15-24a, if the line $Z_1Z_3Z_2$ is extended both ways to infinity, the inversion of both points described by ($R = 4$, $X = +\infty$) and ($R = 4$, $X = -\infty$) will be at the origin of the Y plane. Thus the infinitely extended (in both directions)

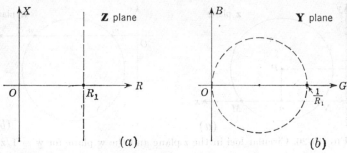

FIG. 15-25. Linear locus in the Z plane and its inversion. The point R_1, closest to the origin in the Z plane, is the most distant point from the origin in the Y plane, while the point at infinity in the Z plane maps into the origin of the Y plane.

straight line shown in Fig. 15-25a maps into a closed curve shown in Fig. 15-25b.

Returning now to the problem of locus of the admittance of the circuit of Fig. 15-21b, we note that the problem is solved if we find an analytical expression for the closed curve of Fig. 15-25b or if we identify the curve as a familiar geometrical shape. In the next article we shall show that the closed curve of Fig. 15-25b is a circle.

15-15. Inversion of Straight Lines and Circles. In the graphical solution of many problems the loci of the admittances and impedances of interest are usually straight lines or circles. In this article we shall study the inversion of such loci. It is noted that the complex immittance of any combination of circuit elements has a positive real part (negative resistance is not studied), and therefore the loci in which we shall be interested will lie in the first and fourth quadrants. In other words the immittances are located in the right half of the complex plane. To reduce the amount of work involved in the study of inversion of straight lines and circles, we note that a straight line can be considered a circle of infinite radius, and therefore it will be sufficient to study the inversion of a circle. Once this is found, the results can be extended to the case of the straight line.

The problem of inversion of circles is elegantly treated in geometry, and the reader is urged to refer to textbooks in geometry in order to gain a clear insight into the problem. There are various analytical approaches to this problem, and we have selected the procedure used in analytical geometry. For this reason we shall temporarily change notation, and, instead of the **Z** and **Y** planes with their respective axes of RX and GB, we shall discuss the equation of a circle in the **z** plane with the rectangular coordinates x and y and the inversion of this circle into the plane (which will be called the **w** plane) with the rectangular coordinates u and v as shown in Fig. 15-26.

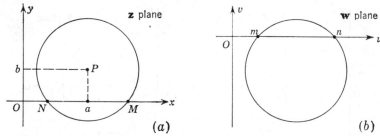

FIG. 15-26. Circular loci in the **z** plane and the **w** plane for **w** $= 1/\mathbf{z}$.

In the **z** plane the equation of a circle of radius r, whose center is at $x = a$ and $y = b$, is

$$(x - a)^2 + (y - b)^2 = r^2$$

Expanding this equation, we have

$$x^2 + y^2 - 2ax - 2by + a^2 + b^2 - r^2 = 0 \qquad (15\text{-}49)$$

We may write this equation in the general form

$$A(x^2 + y^2) + Bx + Cy + D = 0 \qquad (15\text{-}50)$$

The form (15-50) does not show the position of the center of the circle or its radius explicitly, although these values can easily be obtained from it by comparison with Eq. (15-49). The advantage of Eq. (15-50) lies in the ease of manipulation, which will be evident soon. We note that if in Eq. (15-50) the value of A is set to zero then the equation describes the straight line

$$Bx + Cy + D = 0$$

This confirms our previous remark that the straight line is a special case of the circle. Now the inversion of a point in the **z** plane, **z** $= x + jy$, into a point $\mathbf{w} = 1/\mathbf{z}$, where $\mathbf{w} = u + jy$ in the $\mathbf{w}$ plane, requires that

$$\mathbf{z} = x + jy - \frac{1}{u + jv} - \frac{u - jv}{u^2 + v^2}$$

$$x = \frac{u}{u^2 + v^2} = \frac{u}{w^2} \quad \text{and} \quad y = \frac{-v}{u^2 + v^2} = \frac{-v}{w^2} \quad (15\text{-}51)$$

Substituting for x and y from Eq. (15-51) into Eq. (15-50), we have

$$A\left(\frac{u^2}{w^4} + \frac{v^2}{w^4}\right) + \frac{Bu}{w^2} - \frac{Cv}{w^2} + D = 0 \quad (15\text{-}52)$$

Multiplying both sides of (15-52) by w^2 and noting that $w^2 = u^2 + v^2$, we have

$$D(u^2 + v^2) + Bu - Cv + A = 0 \quad (15\text{-}53)$$

Equation (15-53) describes a circle in the $\mathbf{w}$ plane. Thus we arrive at the general conclusion that *inversion of any circle results in another circle.* Although the form of Eq. (15-53) neither gives the radius nor indicates

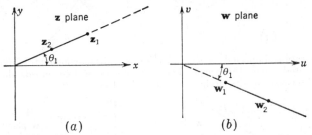

(a)   (b)

Fig. 15-27. The inversion of a straight line through the origin in the $\mathbf{z}$ plane gives a straight line through the origin in the $\mathbf{w}$ plane.

the position of the center of the circle in the $\mathbf{w}$ plane explicitly, it is important nonetheless because it assures us of the fact that the inversion of any circle is another circle. Furthermore, since a straight line is also a circle (of infinite radius), it follows that the inversion of a straight line is also a circle. In the special case of a line through the origin the inversion will be a circle of infinite radius, i.e., another straight line. This is shown in Fig. 15-27.

15-16. Determination of a Diameter of an Inverted Circle. The derivations of the previous article do not indicate explicitly how the center and the radius of the inverted circle are to be found. In general it will be sufficient to find the inversion of any three points on the original circle and pass another circle (by geometrical construction) through the inverted points. Figure 15-28 illustrates this procedure.

If the original circle cuts the real axis as in Fig. 15-28, then it is convenient to choose these points for inversion since their corresponding points in the $\mathbf{w}$ plane also lie on the real axis. An even more convenient

method is illustrated in Fig. 15-29.   Let the circle with center P be in the
z plane, and let it be required to find its inversion in the **w** plane.   If the
origin O of the **z** plane is joined to the center P and extended to cut the
circle at A and B, these will be the points on the circle nearest and
farthest from the origin, respectively.   Therefore the inversion of A in the

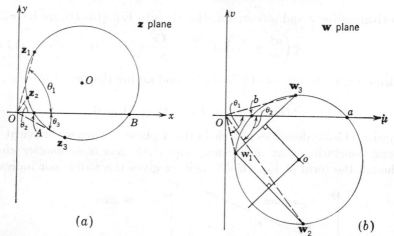

FIG. 15-28. Graphical method for the inversion of a circular locus: the inverse of three
points is located; then the perpendicular bisectors of two chords determine the
location of the center of the circle in the inverted locus.

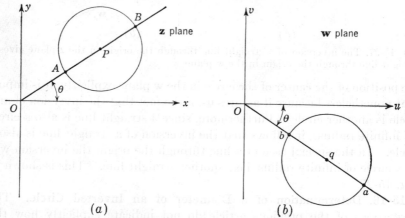

FIG. 15-29. Inversion of circle by location of inverse diameter.

w plane will be farthest away from the origin, and that of B will be closest
to the origin of the **w** plane.

If these points in the **w** plane are designated as a and b, respectively,
then they will both lie on a line abo such that the angle $\angle aou$ in the
w plane will be equal (in magnitude) to the angle $\angle AOx$ in the **z** plane.
Once the points a and b are found, then, a little thought will show that

the center of the circle in the **w** plane will be midway between a and b on the abo line.   The reader is warned that this center, *the point q, is not the inversion of the P, the center of the circle in the z plane, nor is the length ab equal to the reciprocal of the length AB.*   It is recalled that in the process of inversion only the angles subtended to the origin are maintained and that the distances will *not* be preserved.

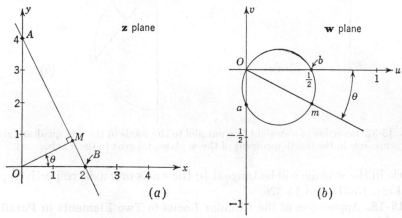

FIG. 15-30. Inversion of a straight line.

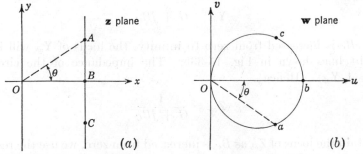

FIG. 15-31. Inversion of a straight line parallel to the y axis gives a circle tangent to the v axis.

15-17. Inversion of a Straight Line.   We have noted that the points at infinity on an extended straight line in the **z** plane map into the origin of the **w** plane.   In Fig. 15-30a a straight line AB is shown in the **z** plane. The line OM is perpendicular to AB.   The point M is the nearest point on AB to the origin O, and therefore, in the **w** plane, the point m (inversion of M) must be the farthest point on the inversion of AB from the origin O.   Thus, if om is made equal to $1/OM$ and the angle $\underline{/mou}$ in the **w** plane is made equal (in magnitude) to the angle $\underline{/MOx}$, then the line om is the diameter of the circle in the **w** plane.   In particular, if the line AB is parallel to the y or x axis, as in Fig. 15-31a or 15-32a, then the

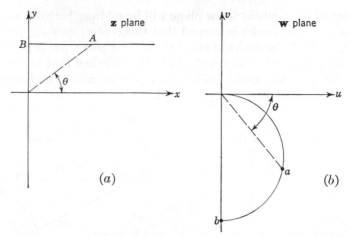

Fɪɢ. 15-32. Inversion of a straight line parallel to the x axis in the first quadrant gives the semicircle in the fourth quadrant of the **w** plane, tangent to the u axis.

circle in the **w** plane will be tangent to the v axis or u axis, respectively, as in Figs. 15-31b and 15-32b.

15-18. Application of the Circular Locus to Two Elements in Parallel. Consider the parallel circuit shown in Fig. 15-33a. The admittance of the circuit is

$$\mathbf{Y}_{ab} = G + jB_C$$

When B_C is increased from zero to infinity, the locus of $\mathbf{Y}_{ab}$ will be the straight line shown in Fig. 15-33b. The impedance of the circuit is $\mathbf{Z}_{ab} \ (= 1/\mathbf{Y}_{ab})$. Hence

$$\mathbf{Z}_{ab} = \frac{1}{G + jB_C}$$

To obtain the locus of $\mathbf{Z}_{ab}$ as B_C is increased from zero, we use the result of the previous article. We identify $\mathbf{Z}_{ab}$ with **w**, G with x, and B_C with y. As B_C is varied, the locus of $\mathbf{Z}_{ab}$ is seen to be a semicircle with its center at $\mathbf{Z}_{ab} = 1/2G$ and radius of $1/2G$. The result is shown in Fig. 15-33c. Note that the semicircle is in the fourth quadrant of the $\mathbf{Z}_{ab}$ plane. This corresponds to the relationship $\mathbf{Z} = 1/\mathbf{Y}$; for positive angles of the admittance the impedance angles are negative.

The correspondence between the two loci of Fig. 15-33 may be studied by considering an arbitrary value of B_C, say, $B_C = B_1$. For this value $\mathbf{Y}_{ab} = G + jB_1 = \mathbf{Y}_1$. The admittance $\mathbf{Y}_1$ is represented in Fig. 15-33b by a line from the origin to the point $G + jB_1$. The angle of $\mathbf{Y}_1$ is $\tan^{-1}(B_1/G)$. To find the point in the impedance plane which corresponds to $\mathbf{Y}_{ab} = \mathbf{Y}_1$, we need only recall that the angle associated with the impedance is the negative of the angle of the admittance. Hence $Z_1 = 1/Y$ if $\theta_1 = -\tan^{-1}(B_C/G)$ as shown in Fig. 15-33c.

As a second example, consider the parallel R-C circuit with adjustable conductance as indicated in Fig. 15-34a. The admittance locus is shown in Fig. 15-34b. Upon recalling that $Z_{ab} = 1/(G + jB_C)$, it is seen that the locus of Z_{ab}, as G varies, is the semicircle whose radius is $1/2B_C$, shown in

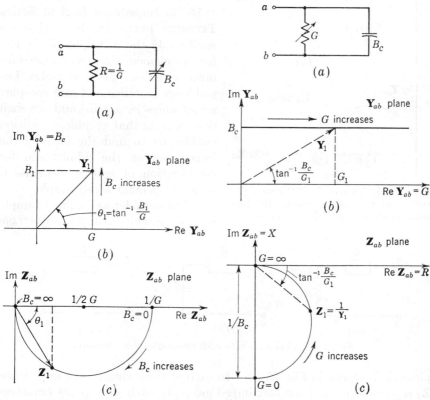

Fig. 15-33. Impedance and admittance loci for a particular circuit. (a) Circuit diagram, indicating adjustable element. (b) Admittance locus. (c) Impedance locus.

Fig. 15-34. Parallel R-C circuit with adjustable resistance. (a) Circuit diagram. (b) Admittance locus. (c) Impedance locus.

Fig. 15-34c. Two corresponding points on the two loci of Fig. 15-34 are indicated by the dotted lines representing Y_1 and $Z_1 = 1/Y_1$.

The relationship for the locus of w if $w = 1/(x + jy)$ is also useful for studying the admittance of a series circuit. Consider the series R-C circuit shown in Fig. 15-35a. Since the capacitance is adjustable, the *impedance* locus is the straight line shown in Fig. 15-35b. To obtain the *admittance* locus, note that $Y_{ab} = 1/Z_{ab} = 1/(R + jX_C)$. The semi-

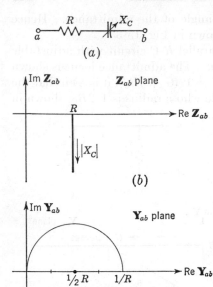

FIG. 15-35. Adjustable R-C series circuit. (a) Circuit diagram. (b) Impedance locus. (c) Admittance locus.

circular locus is shown in Fig. 15-35c. Further illustrations would involve adjustment of R in the series R-C circuit or adjustment of R, X_L, or B_L in R-L circuits. The construction of appropriate loci for such circuits is left as an exercise.

15-19. Impedance Loci of Series Terminal Pair. In this article we shall apply the principles of the loci for two-element circuits to more elaborate circuits. Since complex impedances in series add and complex admittances in parallel add, we shall demonstrate that graphical addition enables us to find the locus of the impedance or the admittance for combination of several elements if only *one* element is adjustable.

Let us consider as the first example a series circuit with an adjustable

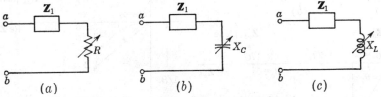

FIG. 15-36. Series circuits with one adjustable element.

element as shown in Fig. 15-36. In each of these circuits the impedance Z_1 represents a fixed complex impedance. In each case we set ourselves the problem of finding the locus of Z_{ab} (in the next article Y_{ab}) as the adjustable element is varied. We shall first consider the locus of Z_{ab}.

In Fig. 15-36a we may write

$$Z_{ab} = Z_1 + R$$

As R varies from zero to infinity, Z_{ab} moves from point Z_1 (see Fig. 15-37), where $R = 0$ on a line parallel to the R_{ab} axis. In the construction of Fig. 15-37 the point Z_1 was taken to be in the first quadrant. This cor-

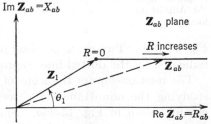

FIG. 15-37. Impedance locus for the circuit of Fig. 15-36a. It is assumed that the impedance Z_1 is inductive.

responds to assuming the angle of $\mathbf{Z}_1$, θ_1, to be positive or $\mathbf{Z}_1$ to be inductive. For Fig. 15-36b and c, assuming $\mathbf{Z}_1$ to be inductive, the corresponding loci for $\mathbf{Z}_{ab}$ are drawn as in Fig.
15-38a and b. In each case the
locus of jX is added to $\mathbf{Z}_1$ to give
the locus of $\mathbf{Z}_{ab}$.

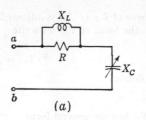

**15-20. Loci for Series-Parallel Cir-
cuits. Example 15-2.** Find the admittance locus for the series-parallel circuit
shown in Fig. 15-39a if X_c is adjustable.

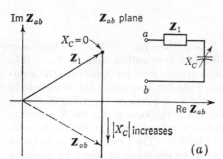

(a)

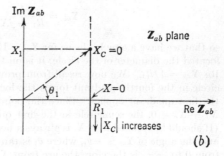

(b)

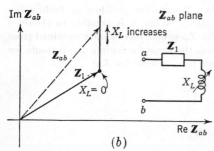

(b)

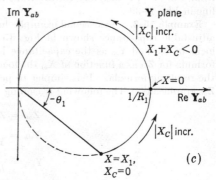

(c)

FIG. 15-38. Impedance loci for the series
circuits of Fig. 15-36b and c.

FIG. 15-39. Series circuit with adjustable
capacitance. (a) Circuit. (b) Impedance locus. (c) Admittance locus.

Solution. We shall first construct the impedance locus. We write

$$\mathbf{Z}_{ab} = \mathbf{Z}_1 + jX_c$$

where

$$\mathbf{Z}_1 = \frac{R(jX_L)}{R + jX_L}$$

or

$$\mathbf{Z}_1 = R_1 + jX_1$$

Where the equivalent series elements for the parallel combination of R and X_L are R_1
and X_1,

$$R_1 = \text{Re } \mathbf{Z}_1 = \frac{RX_L{}^2}{R^2 + X_L{}^2}$$

$$X_1 = \text{Im } \mathbf{Z}_1 = +\frac{X_L R^2}{R^2 + X_L{}^2}$$

We now have $\mathbf{Z}_{ab}$ in the form

$$\mathbf{Z}_{ab} = R_1 + jX_1 + jX_c$$

The locus of $\mathbf{Z}_{ab}$ as $|X_c|$ is adjusted from zero to infinity is shown in Fig. 15-39b. To obtain the locus of $\mathbf{Y}_{ab}$, we write

$$\mathbf{Y}_{ab} = \frac{1}{\mathbf{Z}_{ab}} = \frac{1}{R_1 + jX_1 + jX_c}$$

If we define

$$X = X_1 + X_c$$

then $\mathbf{Y}_{ab}$ has the general form

$$\mathbf{Y}_{ab} = \frac{1}{R_1 + jX}$$

so that we have a circular locus for $\mathbf{Y}_{ab}$. If $X = 0$, then $\mathbf{Y}_{ab} = 1/R_1$. We have now located the diameter of the circle; it is on the real axis extending from Re $\mathbf{Y}_{ab} = 0$ to Re $\mathbf{Y}_{ab} = 1/R_1$. We now recall from previous articles that for X positive the semicircle in the fourth quadrant forms the locus, while for X negative the semicircle in the first quadrant applies. Since the point $1/R_1$ corresponds to the value $X = 0$ or $X_1 + X_c = 0$, the semicircle in the first quadrant is the locus of $\mathbf{Y}_{ab}$ for X negative. (It should be recalled that X_c is always a negative number.) If $X_c = 0$, then $X = X_1$ and the angle of $\mathbf{Y}_{ab}$ is $-\theta_1$, where θ_1 is $\tan^{-1}(X_1/R_1)$. The locus of $\mathbf{Y}_{ab}$, as X_c varies from 0 to $-\infty$, is therefore the arc from $X = X_1$ to the origin as shown by the solid line in Fig. 15-39c.

Example 15-3. As a second example, let us consider the series-parallel circuit with adjustable capacitance shown in Fig. 15-40a. We set the problem of finding the locus of $\mathbf{Z}_{ab}$ and $\mathbf{Y}_{ab}$ as the capacitance is varied. While it is possible to obtain a formula for $\mathbf{Z}_{ab}$ as a function of X_c, the locus for $\mathbf{Z}_{ab}$ is not conveniently obtained from the resulting formula. It is simpler to perform the steps for finding the formula for $\mathbf{Z}_{ab}$ graphically. The following reasoning leads to a formula for $\mathbf{Z}_{ab}$:

$$\mathbf{Z}_{ab} = \mathbf{Z}_{aa'} + \mathbf{Z}_{a'b}$$

$$\mathbf{Z}_{a'b} = \frac{1}{\mathbf{Y}_{a'b}}$$

$$\mathbf{Y}_{a'b} = \frac{1}{R_2} + \mathbf{Y}_{a''b}$$

$$\mathbf{Y}_{a''b} = \frac{1}{\mathbf{Z}_{a''b}}$$

$$\mathbf{Z}_{a''b} = R + jX_c$$

We shall perform these five steps graphically, starting with the last step.

The locus of $\mathbf{Z}_{a''b}$ is a straight line in the fourth quadrant of the $\mathbf{Z}_{a''b}$ plane as shown in Fig. 15-40b. The admittance $\mathbf{Y}_{a''b}$ locus is the inversion of the impedance locus, i.e., the semicircle with diameter $1/R$ on the real axis as shown in Fig. 15-40c. To obtain the admittance $\mathbf{Y}_{a'b}$, we must add the parallel admittance $1/R_2$ to $\mathbf{Y}_{a''b}$. The resulting locus is the semicircle shifted to the right as shown in Fig. 15-40d. The reciprocal of the admittance locus $\mathbf{Y}_{a'b}$ is the impedance locus $\mathbf{Z}_{a'b}$. Since the reciprocal locus of a circle is also a circle, we need only locate a diameter to construct the impedance locus. Since the maximum admittance $Y_{a'b}$ is $1/R + 1/R_2$, the minimum impedance is $R_1R_2/(R_1 + R_2)$. The corresponding minimum admittance gives the other end of the diameter at $\mathbf{Z} = R_2$.

Since impedance and admittance have angles which are negatives of each other, the semicircular locus for $Z_{a'b}$ can be constructed as shown in Fig. 15-40e. The locus of the impedance Z_{ab} can now easily be constructed. We need only shift the axes so that $Z_{ab} = Z_{a'b} + Z_{aa'}$. Construction of the admittance locus for Y_{ab} is left as an exercise for the reader.

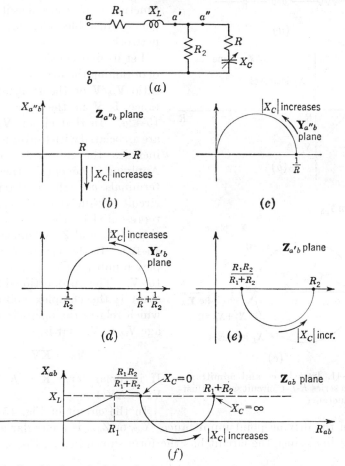

FIG. 15-40. Graphical method for obtaining the impedance locus of a series-parallel circuit with one adjustable element.

Example 15-4. Series R-L-C Circuit. As a third example, consider the series R-L-C circuit with adjustable inductance as shown in Fig. 15-41a. The impedance locus of Z_{ab} is shown in Fig. 15-41b. The admittance locus is known to be circular. The minimum impedance is R; the maximum impedance is infinite. Hence the diameter of the admittance locus will extend from the origin to $1/R + j0$. When $X_L = 0$, the angle of the impedance is $\tan^{-1}(X_c/R)$. Hence the admittance locus starts on the circle at the angle, $-\tan^{-1}(X_c/R)$. Since X_c is a negative number, this angle is in the first quadrant as shown in Fig. 15-41c.

15-21. Locus Diagrams of Transfer Functions. In the preceding articles we have shown that the locus of the complex driving-point immittance of a terminal-pair network in which there is one adjustable element

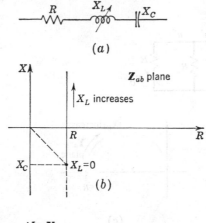

is circular. We shall now show that the locus of a complex transfer function is also circular if there is one adjustable element in the network.

Let us first consider the problem of obtaining the locus of the voltage ratio $\mathbf{V}_{ab}/\mathbf{V}$ or the transfer admittance $\mathbf{I}_2/\mathbf{V}$ in the circuit of Fig. 15-42a. In that circuit $\mathbf{V}_{ab}$ and $\mathbf{I}_2$ are associated with the branch which includes the adjustable element. Applying Thévenin's theorem at terminals a-b, the portion of the circuit within the dotted lines is represented by the series combination of $\mathbf{V}_0$ and $\mathbf{Z}_s$ as shown in Fig. 15-42b. In this circuit $\mathbf{V}_0$ is a complex number which is proportional to $\mathbf{V}$. The proportionality constant is the complex voltage gain which relates the open-circuit voltage $\mathbf{V}_{ab}$ to $\mathbf{V}$, that is,

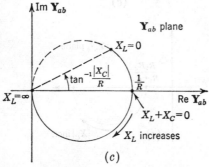

$$\mathbf{V}_0 = \mathbf{KV} \qquad (15\text{-}54)$$

If in polar form $\mathbf{K} = K\underline{/\phi}$, then $\mathbf{V}_0 = K\mathbf{V}(1\underline{/\phi})$.

In the circuit of Fig. 15-42b the

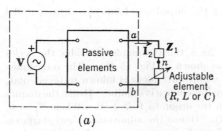

FIG. 15-41. Impedance and admittance loci for a series R-L-C circuit with adjustable inductance.

locus of the driving-point immittance ($\mathbf{Y}_{a'b}$ or $\mathbf{Z}_{a'b}$) is a circular arc (or a straight line) since the circuit has the form shown in Fig. 15-36. Hence

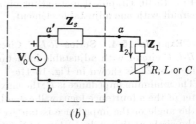

FIG. 15-42. (a) Generalized circuit to illustrate the transfer-function locus problem. (b) Thévenin's equivalent to (a) at terminals a-b.

we know that the locus of I_2/V_0 is circular (or linear). Since

$$\frac{I_2}{V} = \frac{I_2}{V_o}\frac{V_o}{V} = Y_{a'b}(K\underline{/\phi})$$

it follows that the locus of the transfer admittance I_2/V is circular since it is the product of the (circular) locus of $Y_{a'b}$ multiplied by K. Multiplication by a complex number means a scale change and a rotation of the axes, neither of which changes the shape of the locus.

In the circuit of Fig. 15-42b we observe that

$$\frac{V_{a'a}}{V} = \frac{I_2}{V} \cdot Z_s = Y_{a'b}KZ_s \tag{15-55}$$

Hence the locus of $V_{a'a}/V$ is circular since it is also related to the admittance locus $Y_{a'b}$ by scale change and rotation. Similarly the locus of V_{an}/V (Fig. 15-42a) is circular. Now since

$$\frac{V_{ab}}{V} = \frac{V_0}{V} - \frac{V_{a'a}}{V}$$

using Eqs. (15-54) and (15-55) we can write

$$\frac{V_{ab}}{V} = K(1 - Y_{a'b}Z_s)$$

Thus it is seen that the locus of V_{ab}/V is obtained from the locus of $Y_{a'b}$ by rotation, scale change, and translation of the axes.

We have now shown that the locus of the ratio of every phasor associated with the branch which includes the adjustable element to the source phasor is circular. Since all other phasors in the original circuit are related to these phasors by multiplication and addition (including division and subtraction), as used when the voltage- or current-division formulas are applied, the locus of all transfer functions in the circuit will be circular arcs. This follows from the fact that the operations enumerated above correspond to axis rotation, translation, and scale change and do not influence the shape of the locus.

Since it has been established that the transfer-function loci are circular arcs, it is not necessary to perform the operations described above in a particular example. The locus can be established by the three-point method described in Art. 15-16.

Example 15-5. In the circuit of Fig. 15-43a establish the locus of the phasor ratio V_{ab}/V as X_c is adjusted.

Solution. Using the three-point method, we calculate V_{ab}/V for three (convenient) values of X_c. Using the voltage-division formula, we have

X_c	0	Infinite	$-j2$
V_{ab}/V	$1 + j0$	$0.2 + j0$	$0.231 + j0.154$

The three points are located as in Fig. 15-43b, and the semicircular arc which is the desired locus is then obtained as shown.

By using the step-by-step method the locus of the driving-point admittance $\mathbf{Y}_{a'b}$ is established as in Fig. 15-43c to f. Since $\mathbf{V}_{ab} = 0.5\mathbf{I}_{ab} = 0.5\mathbf{V}\mathbf{Y}_{ab}$, the locus of $\mathbf{V}_{ab}/\mathbf{V}$ is

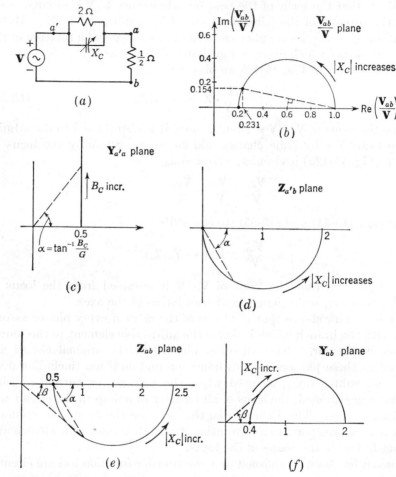

Fig. 15-43. (a) Circuit for Example 15-5. (b) Locus of $\mathbf{V}_{ab}/\mathbf{V}$ obtained by the three-point method. (c) Locus of $\mathbf{Y}_{a'a}$. (d) Locus of $\mathbf{Z}_{a'a}$. (e) Locus of $\mathbf{Z}_{a'b}$. (f) Locus of $\mathbf{Y}_{a'b}$. Since $\frac{1}{2}\mathbf{V}\mathbf{Y}_{a'b} = \mathbf{V}_{a'b}$, the locus shown in (b) can be obtained by scale change.

obtained immediately from Fig. 15-43f by a scale change (divide by 2) and the same result as before (Fig. 15-43b) is obtained.

Example 15-6.   In the circuit of Fig. 15-44a obtain the transfer impedance locus $\mathbf{V}_2/\mathbf{I}$ as X_L is adjusted.

Solution.   This example is used to illustrate the value of Norton's theorem.   We first establish the locus of $\mathbf{V}_{a'b}/\mathbf{I}$.   Since $\mathbf{V}_2 = \mathbf{V}_{a'b}\,[5/(5 - j5)]$, the desired locus is then obtained by scale change and axis rotation.   Upon removing the branch which includes the adjustable element the circuit of Fig. 15-44b results.   For this active

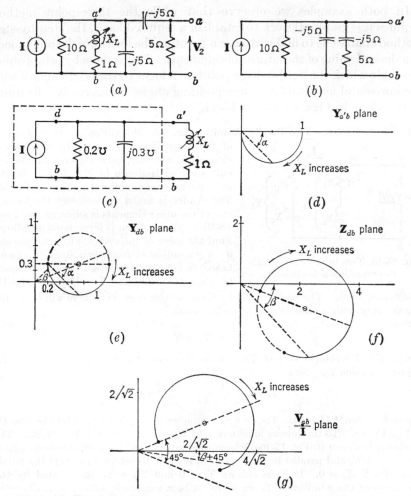

FIG. 15-44. (a) Circuit for Example 15-6.   (b) Circuit of (a) with the branch which includes the adjustable element removed.   (c) Norton's equivalent.   (d) Locus of $Y_{a'b}$.   (e) Locus of Y_{db}.   (f) Locus of Z_{db}.   (g) Locus of V_{ab}/I obtained from (f) by rotation and scale change.

terminal-pair network the short-circuit current $I_s = I$.   If I is set to zero, the driving-point admittance $Y_{a'b}$ is Y_s,

$$Y_s = \frac{1}{10} + \frac{1}{-j5} + \frac{1}{5 - j5} = 0.20 + j0.30$$

Connecting the branch whose impedance is $1 + jX_L$ to terminals a'-b, we obtain the circuit of Fig. 15-44c.   We observe that the transfer-function locus $V_{a'b}/I$ is identical to the driving-point impedance locus Z_{db}.   This locus is established in Fig. 15-44c to f.   Since $V_{ab}/I = (V_{a'b}/I)0.707\underline{/45^\circ}$, we rotate the locus of Fig. 15-44f through 45° and change the scale to obtain the desired locus as shown in Fig. 15-44g.

In both examples we observe that while the three-point method requires less graphical work to establish a required locus, the step-by-step method enables us to find with ease a point on the locus which corresponds to a desired value of the adjustable element. This is done by establishing the angle which the line joining a point on a locus to the origin makes with the horizontal and marking corresponding angles on successive diagrams as was done in Figs. 15-43 and 15-44.

15-22. Examples. Two Parallel Admittances.

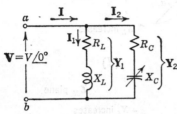

FIG. 15-45. Two branches in parallel with one adjustable element.

As illustration of the application of the locus diagrams in circuits in which one element is adjusted, we consider a parallel circuit such as is shown in Fig. 15-45. In this example we are assuming that X_c is adjustable. The reader is urged to construct the locus if one of the other elements is adjusted (see Prob. 15-40). The problem is formulated as follows: Find the locus of the end point of the phasor $\mathbf{I}$ if $|X_c|$ is adjusted from zero (infinite capacitance) to infinity (zero capacitance). It should be clear that the case $\mathbf{V} = 1\underline{/0}$ will give the admittance locus. The problem will be done for this case since there will be no loss in generality, only a scale change being involved.

Since

$$\mathbf{Y}_{ab} = \mathbf{Y}_1 + \mathbf{Y}_2$$

the graphical representation of $\mathbf{Y}_{ab}$ will be the sum of the fixed value $\mathbf{Y}_1$ and the adjustable value $\mathbf{Y}_2$. Now

$$\mathbf{Y}_1 = \frac{1}{R_L + jX_L} = \frac{1}{Z_1}\underline{/-\theta_1}$$

where $\theta_1 = \tan^{-1}(X_L/R)$. The complex number $\mathbf{Y}_1$ is represented by the line OA in Fig. 15-46a. To this line we must now add $\mathbf{Y}_2$. If $X_c = 0$, then $\mathbf{Y}_2 = 1/R_c$. This condition is shown in Fig. 15-46a, where the line AM has been constructed equal in length to $1/R_c$ and parallel to the G axis. Line OM therefore represents the admittance $\mathbf{Y}_{ab}$ if $X_c = 0$. If X_c is infinite $\mathbf{Y}_2 = 0$ and $\mathbf{Y}_{ab} = \mathbf{Y}_1$, represented by OA. The locus of the admittance $\mathbf{Y}_2$ we know to be a semicircle with AM as diameter. This semicircle has been constructed in Fig. 15-46a. If, for some value of X_c, line AD is drawn such that $\tan \theta_2 = |X_c|/R_c$, then AD represents $\mathbf{Y}_2$ and the line OD represents $\mathbf{Y}_{ab}$. We conclude that a line from the origin to a point on the semicircle will represent the admittance $\mathbf{Y}_{ab}$ for a value of X_c corresponding to θ_2. Of particular interest are lines OF and OF' because for these points $\mathbf{Y}_{ab}$ is real, the susceptances of $\mathbf{Y}_1$ and $\mathbf{Y}_2$ having canceled each other's effect. In this case the voltage $\mathbf{V}_{ab}$ and the current $\mathbf{I}$ will be in phase. This condition is the unity power-factor resonance (cos $\theta_{ab} = 0$) and is discussed further below. For the present we wish to point out that this unity-power-factor condition can be obtained only if $1/R_c$ is sufficiently large so that the semicircle will intersect the real axis.

Figure 15-46b shows a condition where R_c is so large ($1/R_c$ is so small) that unity power factor cannot be produced by adjustment of X_c. It is of interest to calculate the limits of R_c for which unity power factor can occur. The susceptance of $\mathbf{Y}_1$ is the projection of OA on the imaginary (B) axis. If unity power factor can be produced by adjustment of X_c, then the radius of the circle must at least be equal to OH (see

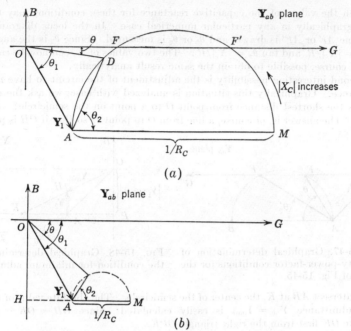

FIG. 15-46. Possible admittance loci for the circuit of Fig, 15-45.   (a) The resistance R_c is sufficiently small so that unity power factor can be achieved.   (b) The resistance R_c is so large that no unity-power-factor condition is possible.

Fig. 15-46b).   In this case the requirement would be

$$Y_1 \sin |\theta_1| \le \frac{1}{2R_c}$$

or, since $\sin \theta_1 = X_L/Z_1$ and $Y_1 = 1/\sqrt{R_L{}^2 + X_L{}^2}$,

$$\frac{X_L}{R_L{}^2 + X_L{}^2} \le \frac{1}{2R_c}$$

Hence we conclude that

One unity-power-factor condition is possible if $R_c = \dfrac{R_L{}^2 + X_L{}^2}{2X_L}$

No unity-power-factor condition is possible if $R_c > \dfrac{R_L{}^2 + X_L{}^2}{2X_L}$

Two unity-power-factor conditions are possible if $R_c < \dfrac{R_L{}^2 + X_L{}^2}{2X_L}$

It must be emphasized that the last condition does not ensure that unity power factor will occur in the circuit.   The condition states that unity power factor is *possible* by adjustment of X_c.

The above results can also be obtained analytically.   The condition $\cos \theta_{ab} = 1$ corresponds to Im $\mathbf{Y}_1 +$ Im $\mathbf{Y}_2 = 0$.   (See Prob. 15-39.)

Unity Power Factor and Minimum Current for Parallel Connection of Impedances. In Fig. 15-45, if R_c is sufficiently small so that unity power factor (resonance) is possible, then the values of the capacitive reactance for these conditions may be determined graphically in any particular numerical case. In the locus diagram of Fig. 15-47 line AF or AF' is drawn, and θ_2 or θ_2' is measured. Since θ_2 is the angle of Y_2, $\tan \theta_2 = |X_c|/R_c$ and $\tan \theta_2' = |X_c'|/R_c$. The two values of X_c can now be calculated. It is, of course, possible to obtain the same result analytically.

A second interesting possibility is the adjustment of the circuit to have minimum admittance. Graphically this situation is analyzed with ease; we ask the question: What is the shortest distance from point O to a point on the semicircle? (See Fig. 15-48.) The answer is, of course, a line from O to point H so that if OH is prolonged

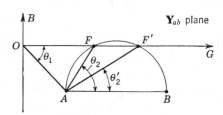

FIG. 15-47. Graphical determination of the unity-power-factor conditions for the circuit of Fig. 15-45.

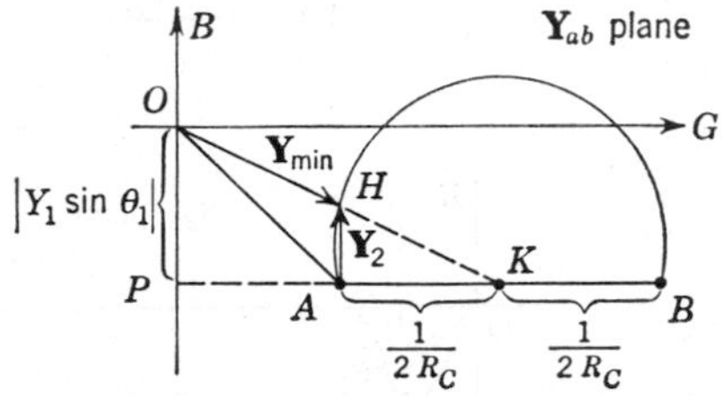

FIG. 15-48. Graphical determination of the condition for minimum admittance.

it will intersect AB at K, the center of the semicircle. The absolute value of the minimum admittance $Y_{ab} = Y_{min}$ is easily calculated. Since $OH = OK - HK$, we calculate OK first from the right triangle OPK,

$$OK = \sqrt{(Y_1 \sin \theta_1)^2 + \left(Y_1 \cos \theta_1 + \frac{1}{2R_c} \right)^2}$$

Since $HK = 1/2R_c$,

$$|\mathbf{Y}_{min}| = \sqrt{Y_1{}^2 \sin^2 \theta_1 + \left(Y_1 \cos \theta_1 + \frac{1}{2R_c} \right)^2} - \frac{1}{2R_c} \qquad (15\text{-}56)$$

While the above equation can be simplified, we shall not waste space doing so since in any numerical case the result is obtained from the construction immediately. This method of obtaining the minimum admittance (and therefore the maximum impedance) is a good example of the usefulness of the locus method of solution. Analytically the proof of Eq. (15-56) is quite involved. The reader should convince himself of this statement by setting up the problem analytically.

15-23. Power-factor Correction. Another application of the locus diagram is to the subject of power-factor adjustment, or power-factor correction. To understand the nature of the problem, consider a load receiving power from a source through cables which have resistance as shown in Fig. 15-49a. We shall assume that the power dissipated by the load, P_{ab}, and the magnitude of the voltage across the load, V_{ab}, must be a certain value. Since the circuit is a series circuit, $I = I_L$, the value of the current I is

$$|\mathbf{I}| = \frac{P_{ab}}{V_{ab} \cos \theta_L}$$

The power factor of the load, $\cos \theta_L$, has not yet been specified. Let us now calculate the power dissipated in the cable. This power is $I^2(R/2 + R/2)$. Hence

$$\text{Power dissipated in cable} = \left(\frac{P_{ab}}{V_{ab} \cos \theta_L} \right)^2 R$$

We note that, for cos $\theta_L = 1$, this quantity is less than for any other power factor. At a power factor of (cos $\theta_L =$) 0.5, for example, four times the power loss occurs in the cables than would occur at unity power factor. If the power factor of the load is small, this power loss may be excessive and often is accompanied by overheating of the cables (or of the generator if some part of R represents internal resistance of the generator). For these reasons it is often practical to connect a second admittance in parallel with the given load for the purpose of adjusting the power factor. If this second admittance is used to adjust the power factor only, then it should be a pure

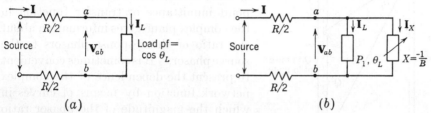

FIG. 15-49. Load receiving energy from a resistive source. (a) Without parallel admittance. (b) With parallel power-factor-correcting admittance.

susceptance; otherwise it will dissipate energy. Such a connection is shown in Fig. 15-49b; the added admittance has been labeled $X = -1/B$, to indicate an ideal power-factor-adjusting element.

If the load is inductive, then it can be represented as an admittance with a negative imaginary part such as the admittance $\mathbf{Y}_1$ in the circuit of Fig. 15-45. In order to increase the power factor, the element X must be a capacitive reactance. Figure 15-50 shows the locus of the total admittance $\mathbf{Y}_{ab}$ for adjustable capacitive reactance. Note that this locus is a special case of the diagram shown in Fig. 15-46a, when R_c is zero, so that the circle has become a straight line from A upward. One finite value of X_c only is possible for unity power factor. This value corresponds to the admittance represented by line AF (see Fig. 15-50). Note that the minimum admittance

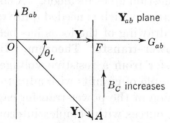

FIG. 15-50. Admittance locus for the circuit of Fig. 15-49, assuming that the load proper is inductive and that the element X is a capacitive reactance.

and unity-power-factor conditions coincide. Quantitatively, unity power factor is obtained when

$$\text{Im } \mathbf{Y}_1 = -Y_1 \sin \theta_L + B_c = 0$$

or

$$\omega C = \frac{X_L}{R^2 + X_L^2}$$

From another point of view (which is very popular in power-system study), we recall from Chap. 14 that the complex powers in circuits add. Adjusting the capacitance in the present example can therefore be regarded as adjustment of the reactive power. If the complex power for the load is $P_L + jQ_L$, then, for unity power factor, the reactive power of the parallel branch must be $-Q_L$. Figure 15-51 shows the complex-power diagram for two changed power-factor conditions. Note that, to raise the power factor from $\cos \theta$ to $\cos \theta'$, the capacitive reactive power needed is $Q' = P_L (\tan \theta - \tan \theta')$.

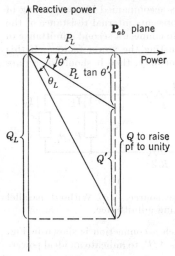

FIG. 15-51. Complex-power locus diagram corresponding to the admittance locus of Fig. 15-50.

15-24. Amplitude and Phase Curves. A study of the locus of the complex driving-point immittance or transfer function in the complex plane gives information about the ratio of the response phasors to the source phasor. It is sometimes convenient to present the dependence of the complex network function by means of curves in which the magnitude of the phasor ratio is plotted as a function of the adjustable element, as well as curves which show the phase difference between source and response. Such curves are called amplitude and phase curves, respectively.

If the locus has been constructed to scale, then the amplitude and phase curves can be obtained quite quickly. For each value of the adjustable element for which data are desired, we locate the corresponding point on the locus. The distance from the origin to the point in question gives the magnitude of the network function, and the angle of the line joining the origin to the point in question gives its angle. A compass, scale, and protractor give the information which is needed quite quickly and accurately if a reasonably careful drawing of the locus has been made.

15-25. Maximum-power-transfer Theorem. In Chap. 10 we discussed the power transfer from a resistive voltage source to a resistive load. As the final example of circuits with adjustable elements, we shall now consider the question of the power-transfer capabilities in the sinusoidal steady state, for sources with complex internal impedance.

Let us consider an ideal sinusoidal current source in parallel with admittance Y_S representing a practical current source (this source could be Norton's equivalent for an active terminal pair). Figure 15-52a shows such a source connected to an admittance Y_T. Since each admittance can be represented as the parallel combination of a conductance and susceptance, an equivalent circuit is shown in Fig. 15-52b.

To calculate the power delivered to the load, we note that this power is the power delivered to the conductance G_T. Letting P_T be the symbol for this power,

$$P_T = V_{ab}{}^2 G_T$$

But we may calculate $\mathbf{V}_{ab}$ from

$$\mathbf{V}_{ab}(\mathbf{Y}_S + \mathbf{Y}_T) = \mathbf{I}_s \tag{15-57}$$

Hence

$$\mathbf{V}_{ab} = \frac{\mathbf{I}_s}{\mathbf{Y}_S + \mathbf{Y}_T}$$

Since

$$\mathbf{Y}_S = G_S + jB_S \qquad \text{and} \qquad \mathbf{Y}_T = G_T + jB_T$$

$$Y_S = \sqrt{(G_T + G_S)^2 + (B_T + B_S)^2}$$

the magnitude of $\mathbf{V}_{ab}$ is

$$V_{ab} = \frac{I}{\sqrt{(G_T + G_S)^2 + (B_T + B_S)^2}}$$

and the expression for P_T becomes

$$P_T = \frac{I_s{}^2 G_T}{(G_T + G_S)^2 + (B_T + B_S)^2}$$

The maximum power which is transferred to G_T can be deduced with ease from above equation if we recall that susceptance may be either a positive

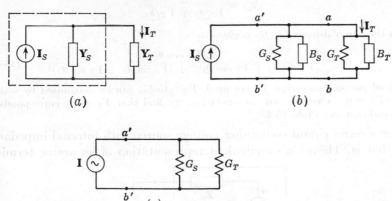

FIG. 15-52. Current source with an internal admittance Y_S connected to a load Y_T. (a) Circuit diagram. (b) Circuit diagram in which each admittance is represented by two elements. (c) Equivalent circuit if $B_S + B_T = 0$.

or a negative number. If we set the total susceptance to the right of a' and b' to zero,

$$B_T + B_S = 0 \qquad \text{or} \qquad B_T = -B_S$$

then

$$P_T = \frac{I_s{}^2 G_T}{(G_T + G_S)^2}$$

This equation gives the expression for maximum power transfer if the susceptances only are adjustable. For this condition the equivalent circuit is shown in Fig. 15-52c. But for this circuit we have shown, in Chap. 10, that the condition for maximum power transfer for a resistive current source *with any waveform* is $G_T = G_S$. Hence we conclude that maximum power transfer is achieved in the circuit of Fig. 15-52 if

$\mathbf{Y}_S = \mathbf{Y}_T^*$. In words: If a sinusoidal current source is represented as the parallel combination of an ideal source $\mathbf{I}_s$ and a parallel (source) admittance $\mathbf{Y}_S$, then in the sinusoidal steady state the maximum power is transferred to a load admittance $\mathbf{Y}_T$ if the source admittance and the load admittance are *conjugate* complex numbers.

An interesting theorem concerning power transfer deals with the case in which the magnitude but not the angle of $\mathbf{Y}_T$ is adjustable. To visualize such a case, we may imagine that $\mathbf{Y}_S$ is complex but $\mathbf{Y}_T$ is real, that is, a resistance. When the magnitude but not the angle of $\mathbf{Y}_T$ is adjustable, then the condition at which maximum power transfer takes place is expressed by

$$|\mathbf{Y}_T| = |\mathbf{Y}_S|$$

i.e., the magnitudes are adjusted to be equal. To prove this, we write

$$\mathbf{Y}_T = Y_T (\cos \theta_T + j \sin \theta_T) = Y_T \underline{/\theta_T}$$
$$\mathbf{Y}_S = Y_S \underline{/\theta_S}$$

and, substituting this form in Eq. (15-57),

$$\mathbf{V}_{ab} = \frac{\mathbf{I}_s}{Y_S \underline{/\theta_S} + Y_T \underline{/\theta_T}}$$

Then the power delivered to G_T is given by

$$P_T = \frac{I_s^2 Y_T \cos \theta_T}{(Y_S \cos \theta_S + Y_T \cos \theta_T)^2 + (Y_S \sin \theta_S + Y_T \sin \theta_T)^2} \tag{15-58}$$

Since all parameters except Y_T are fixed, Eq. (15-57) can be maximized by setting $\partial P_T / \partial Y_T = 0$. Carrying out the operation, we find that $Y_T = Y_S$ corresponds to this condition (see Prob. 15-45).

For a series circuit containing voltage source with internal impedance $\mathbf{Z}_S$ (that is, Thévenin's equivalent representation of an active terminal

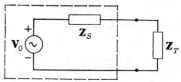

FIG. 15-53. Series circuit. For maximum power transfer to $\mathbf{Z}_T$, $\mathbf{Z}_S$ and $\mathbf{Z}_T$ are conjugate complex numbers.

pair) (Fig. 15-53) the condition for maximum power transfer to a load impedance $\mathbf{Z}_T$ is

$$\mathbf{Z}_T = \mathbf{Z}_S^*$$

The proof of this, as well as the condition $|\mathbf{Z}_T| = |\mathbf{Z}_S|$ when the angle of $\mathbf{Z}_T$ is fixed, is left as an exercise for the reader (see Prob. 15-44).

PROBLEMS

15-1. For the series circuit shown in Fig. P15-1 $v(t) = \sqrt{2}\ V \cos \omega t$, and in the steady state $i_{ab}(t) = \sqrt{2}\ I \cos (\omega t - \theta)$; calculate and sketch to scale the following frequency-response curves: (a) V/I; (b) I/V; (c) θ; (d) V_{ab}/V; (e) angle of $\mathbf{V}_{ab}$.

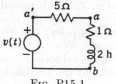

FIG. P15-1

15-2. In the circuit of Prob. 15-1 (Fig. P15-1) $v(t) = 12 + 12 \cos 3t$. Calculate and sketch as a function of time the steady-state functions (a) $i_{Q'a}(t)$; (b) $v_{ab}(t)$; (c) $v_{a'a}(t)$.

15-3. Calculate the complete response $i_{Q'a}(t)$ in the circuit of Prob. 15-1 (Fig. P15-1) if $v(t) = 12 + 12 \cos 3t$ and if $i(0^+) = 0$.

15-4. Discuss the integrating and differentiating properties of a series R-L circuit from the sinusoidal-steady-state viewpoint; in particular deduce the range of frequencies for which the above-named properties occur if it is assumed that any phase shift above 89.43° corresponds to 90°.

15-5. Use a pole-zero diagram to deduce the amplitude- and phase-response curves of the frequency response for I_1/I and for V_{ab}/I (Fig. P15-5).

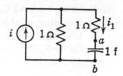

FIG. P15-5

15-6. In the circuit of Prob. 15-5 (Fig. P15-5) $i(t) = 2 + 2 \cos \frac{1}{2}t$; calculate and sketch the steady-state functions $i_1(t)$ and $v_{ab}(t)$.

15-7. A "discriminator" is a circuit in which the output-voltage amplitude is proportional to the frequency of the source. Show that in a series R-C circuit supplied by a voltage source the voltage amplitude across R is proportional to frequency if $\omega RC \ll 1$.

15-8. Show that in a series R-L-C circuit the value of Q_0 can be defined as the ratio of the rms value of the voltage across the capacitance to the rms value of the source voltage at resonance.

15-9. (a) Sketch to scale a curve of Y_{ab} as a function of frequency if between terminals a-b there is the series connection of 40 ohms, 10^{-3} henry, and 10^{-7} farad. Choose unequal frequency increments so that the Y_{ab} increments are approximately equal. *Hint:* Use normalized axes. (b) Sketch the angle of Y_{ab} for the circuit of (a) as a function of frequency.

15-10. The admittance of a series R-L-C circuit is a maximum at a frequency of 5 kc and 50 per cent of its maximum at a frequency of 4 kc. (a) At which other frequency is the admittance 50 per cent of its maximum value? (b) What is the angle of the complex admittance at 4 kc and at the frequency of (a)? (c) Calculate the upper and lower half-power frequencies of the circuit. (d) Calculate Q_0.

15-11. The lower and upper half-power frequencies of a series R-L-C circuit are 5 and 20 kc, respectively. (a) Calculate Q_0. (b) Calculate the frequencies at which the angle of the complex admittance is $\pm 10°$.

15-12. In the theory of oscillators R-L-C circuits are important; in particular the rate of change of the angle of the immittance with frequency is of significance in connection with stability. Start with the equation $\theta(\mu) = \tan^{-1} Q_0(\mu - 1/\mu)$. Show that $(d\theta/d\mu)_{\mu=1} = 2Q_0$.

15-13. The circuit shown in Fig. P15-13 is named, after its discoverer, the Wien bridge. (a) If $R_1 = 2$ and $R_2 = 1$, obtain the transform network function which relates v_{ab} to v. Locate the zeros and poles. (b) Plot the frequency-response curve for V_{ab}/V, using the values of R_1 and R_2 given in (a). (c) Show that, when $\omega = 1$, V_{ab} is in phase with V regardless of the values of R_2 and R_1. (d) Locate the zeros and poles for $R_2/(R_1 + R_2) = \frac{1}{2}$, and plot the amplitude and phase response for V_{ab}/V point by point. Normalize with respect to $(V_{ab}/V)_{min}$. (e) Repeat part (d) for $R_2/(R_1 + R_2) = \frac{1}{4}$, and plot the results on the same set of axes as are used in (d).

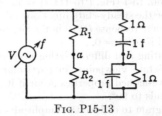

FIG. P15-13

15-14. It is known from experiment that a certain R-L-C series circuit has $Q_0 = 12$, $\omega_0 = 8,000$, and $R = 7$ ohms. (a) Calculate L and C. (b) Use the values of R, L, and C to calculate the driving-point impedance of this circuit at a radian frequency $\omega = 8,370$. Use the slide rule. (c) Use the pole-zero diagram to calculate the approximate driving-point impedance at $\omega = 8,370$ as explained in Art. 15-7. Use the slide rule. (d) Comment on the precision of the results obtained in (c) as compared with (b).

15-15. Prove Eq. (15-44).

15-16. In attempting to determine the parameters of a series-resonant circuit (Fig. P15-16) the voltage across R cannot always be obtained because the terminals of R

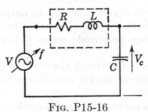

FIG. P15-16

may not be accessible. The frequency response V_c/V is therefore obtained. (a) Show that the maximum value of V_c/V is given by

$$\left(\frac{V_c}{V}\right)_{max} = Q_0 \frac{1}{\sqrt{1 - 1/(4Q_0^2)}} \qquad Q_0^2 > \frac{1}{2}$$

(b) Calculate the percentage errors in the half-power frequencies if the half-power frequencies are taken at $V_c = 0.707(V_c)_{max}$ rather than at $I = 0.707I_{max}$ when $Q_0 = 2$.

15-17. A constant-amplitude variable-frequency sinusoidal current source is impressed on a parallel R-L-C circuit. Let $\mu = \omega/\omega_0$, $Q_0 = \omega_0 C/G$, $\omega_0^2 = 1/LC$, and calculate the value of μ at which (a) the current through the inductance is a maximum; (b) the current through the capacitance is a maximum; (c) the current through the resistance is a maximum.

15-18. In the circuit of Fig. 15-15a the rms value of the source current is 1; calculate (a) the average value of energy stored by the capacitance if $\omega = 1$; (b) the energy dissipated in the 0.1-ohm resistance during one cycle if $\omega = 1$.

15-19. In the circuit of Fig. 15-15a change R from 0.1 to 1. (a) Is the approximate method used in Art. 15-10 now justified? (b) Calculate $Z(j)$ for $R = 1$. (c) Calculate the radian frequency at which $|Z(j\omega)|$ is a maximum.

15-20. In the circuit of Fig. 15-15a replace the 0.1-ohm resistance by an adjustable R. Calculate the maximum value of R so that the maximum impedance occurs at a value of ω which is within 5 per cent of 1.00.

15-21. A transform network function has poles at $s = -1 \pm j6$ and $s = -1 \pm j18$ and zeros at $s = 0$ and $s = -1 \pm j12$. When the source function is $10 \cos 6t$ the response amplitude is 5. (a) Calculate H. (b) Calculate *approximately* the maxima and minima of the complex network function as the frequency is varied, and sketch the amplitude-response curves.

15-22. A transform network function has simple poles at $s = -\alpha_1 \pm j9$ and $s = -\alpha_2 \pm j11$ and a double zero at $s = 0$. Sketch approximately the amplitude response using a point-by-point method from $\omega = 7$ to $\omega = 13$ if (a) $\alpha_1 = \alpha_2 = \frac{1}{2}$; (b) $\alpha_1 = \alpha_2 = 2$. Use $H = 100$.

15-23. For the driving-point impedance shown in Fig. P15-23 (a) sketch the reactance frequency curve if the circuit is made lossless; (b) locate the zeros and poles of the lossless $Z_{ab}(j\omega)$; (c) calculate the actual value Z_{ab} of the given lossy circuit at the frequencies of (b).

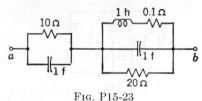

Fig. P15-23

15-24. Sketch the reactance and susceptance frequency curves for the reactive terminal-pair networks shown in Fig. P15-24. Assume that no special relationship between the parameters exists.

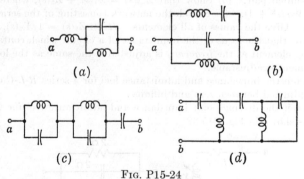

(a)   (b)

(c)   (d)

Fig. P15-24

15-25. In the circuit shown in Fig. P15-25 (a) assume that $R = 0$, and locate the zeros and poles of $Z_{ab}(s)$ with L as a parameter, if $LC = 1$ and the element marked X is a unit capacitance; (b) repeat (a) if the element marked X is a unit inductance.

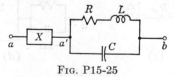

Fig. P15-25

15-26. In the circuit of Prob. 15-25 (Fig. P15-25) it is desired that Z_{ab} have a maximum at $\omega = 10^6$ and a minimum at $\omega = \omega' = \frac{1}{2} \times 10^{+6}$. It is also known that $R = 100$ and $L = 10^{-2}$ henry. (a) Calculate C, and show that the result, within slide-rule accuracy, is not affected by R. (b) Calculate $Z_{a'b}$ at $\omega = 10^6$. (c) Calculate $Z_{a'b}$ at $\omega = \omega'$. (d) Determine the element value of X (L or C) which results in minimum Z_{ab} at ω'. (e) Calculate Z_{ab} at $\omega = \omega'$, using the value of X from (d).

15-27. Repeat Prob. 15-26, using $\omega' = 2 \times 10^6$.

15-28. Foster's reactance theorem states that zeros and poles for *driving*-point reactances and susceptances must alternate. Locate the zeros and poles of the transform *transfer* functions v_2/v_1 (Fig. P15-28), and observe that the separation property does not apply to transfer functions.

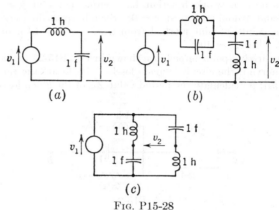

(a)   (b)

(c)

Fig. P15-28

15-29. A transform driving-point impedance function has the form $Z_{ab}(s) = 12[(s^2 + 1)/s(s^2 + 4)]$. (a) Show that this function is physically realizable as a pure-reactance terminal pair. (b) Show that $Z_{ab}(s) = Z_1(s) + Z_2(s)$, where $Z_1(s) = 3/s$ and $Z_2(s) = 9s/(s^2 + 4)$. (c) Sketch the network consisting of the series connection of Z_1 and Z_2. Give the values of all elements. *Hint:* $Z_2(s) = 1/Y_2(s)$.

15-30. Show that the locus of the immittance of a circuit which contains only one energy-storing element as the *frequency* is adjusted is the same as the locus obtained when the element is adjustable.

15-31. Sketch the impedance and admittance loci for a series R-L-C circuit as the *frequency* is adjusted between zero and infinity.

15-32. Sketch the driving-point impedance and admittance loci for the terminal-pair networks shown in Fig. P15-32.

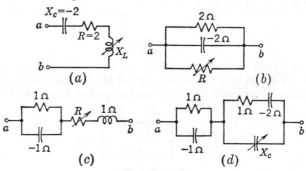

(a)   (b)

(c)   (d)

Fig. P15-32

15-33. The admittance locus $\mathbf{Y}_{ab}$ is given in Fig. P15-33; the adjustable element is R. Show that when $OB = \mathbf{Y}_{ab}$ the power ratio P_{db}/P_{ab} is the distance ratio DB/AB.

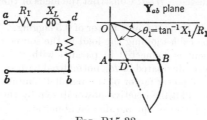

Fig. P15-33

15-34. From the admittance locus of Prob. 15-32d (Fig. P15-32d) obtain the value of $\mathbf{Y}_{ab}$ in polar form if $X_c = -\frac{1}{2}$, $-\frac{3}{4}$, -1, and -2.

15-35. In Fig. P15-35 (a) sketch the transfer-function locus $\mathbf{V}_2/\mathbf{V}_1$; ($b$) from the locus of ($a$) find the value of X_c for which the phase difference between $\mathbf{V}_2$ and $\mathbf{V}_1$ is a maximum.

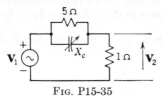

Fig. P15-35

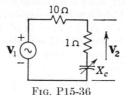

Fig. P15-36

15-36. In Fig. P15-36 (a) sketch the transfer-function locus $\mathbf{V}_2/\mathbf{V}_1$; ($b$) assume that $C = 1$, and use the result of (a) to find the frequency for which the phase difference between $\mathbf{V}_1$ and $\mathbf{V}_2$ is a maximum.

15-37. In the circuit of Prob. 15-13 (Fig. P15-13) assume that $R_1 = 1$ and R_2 is adjustable. (a) Sketch the transfer-function locus $\mathbf{V}_{ab}/\mathbf{V}$ for $\omega = 1$. (b) Repeat (a) if $\omega = 1.5$.

15-38. From the locus of Prob. 15-36 (Fig. P15-36), construct to scale a curve which gives the phase angle between $\mathbf{V}_2$ and $\mathbf{V}_1$ as a function of frequency.

15-39. In the circuit shown in Fig. P15-39 X_c is the adjustable element. Deduce analytically the inequalities which determine whether or not unity power factor can be achieved by adjustment of X_c.

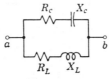

Fig. P15-39

15-40. In the circuit of Prob. 15-39 (Fig. P15-39) use an admittance-locus diagram to deduce the conditions for unity power factor at terminals a-b if all elements are fixed except (a) R_c; (b) R_L; (c) X_L.

15-41. In the circuit of Prob. 15-39 (Fig. P15-39) $R_L = 1$, $X_L = 2$. Use a locus diagram to calculate the minimum value of Y_{ab} and the corresponding $\mathbf{Y}_{ab}$ and X_c if (a) $R_c = 0$; (b) $R_c = 0.2$; (c) $R_c = 1$; (d) $R_c = 4$.

15-42. Two loads are connected in parallel. One load draws 100 kva at a power factor of 0.4 lagging; the second load draws 70 kva at an adjustable power factor

($-90° \leq \theta_2 \leq 90°$). Calculate (a) the power factor of the parallel combination if $\theta_2 = -90°$ (leading); (b) the maximum and minimum power factor of the parallel combination as θ_2 is adjusted. *Hint:* Construct the locus of the complex power of the combination.

15-43. A load draws 50 kw at a power factor of 0.5 lagging. The voltage across the load is 1,000 volts. The cables joining the load to the source have a total resistance R_0. A capacitive element is connected in parallel with the 50-kw load. (a) Plot carefully to scale the power dissipated in R_0, normalized with respect to the 0.5-pf condition as a function of the power factor of the parallel combination as the capacitive element is adjusted. (b) Plot the reactive power drawn by the capacitive element as a function of the power factor of the parallel combination.

15-44. Prove the maximum-power-transfer theorem for a (Thévenin) voltage source.

15-45. Show that, when a load Z_T is connected to a source whose internal impedance is Z_s, then, if the magnitude but not the angle of Z_T is adjustable, maximum power transfer occurs for $Z_T = Z_s$.

15-46. The Thévenin equivalent of an active terminal-pair network in the sinusoidal steady state is a voltage source $V_o = 24$ volts and an internal impedance $Z_s = 3 + j4$. Calculate the power delivered by this source to a load Z_T if (a) $Z_T = 3 - j4$; (b) $Z_T = 3 + j4$; (c) $Z_T = 5$; (d) $Z_T = 10$.

15-47. In Fig. P15-47 (a) calculate the value Z_T for which the active terminal pair delivers maximum power to Z_T; (b) for Z_T as in (a) calculate the power delivered by the ideal source V.

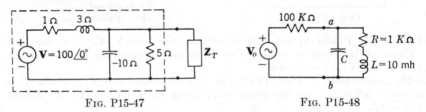

FIG. P15-47   FIG. P15-48

15-48. In the circuit shown in Fig. P15-48 the value of C is adjusted so that Im $Y_{ab} = 0$ at $\omega = 10^6$. (a) Calculate Re Y_{ab} at $\omega = 10^6$. (b) Obtain an expression for the power delivered to the 1,000-ohm resistance when $\omega = 10^6$. (c) Obtain an expression for the power delivered to the 1,000-ohm resistance when $\omega = 0$ (d-c).

CHAPTER 16

GENERAL ANALYSIS TECHNIQUES

A. SETTING UP NETWORK EQUATIONS

The circuits which have been discussed in the preceding chapters were all comparatively simple circuits in the sense that they contained only a few (i.e., four or five) elements connected in series, in parallel, or as series-parallel combinations. It is now our intention to consider the analysis of circuits which are composed of an arbitrary (but finite) number of active and passive elements and the determination of the voltages and currents associated with each element. Starting with series-parallel circuits, we shall demonstrate the logical development of systematic network analysis and arrive at three basic and useful results:

1. It will be shown how systematic procedures reduce the formulation of network equations and the corresponding network functions to the application of a set of (easily remembered) rules.

2. The solution of networks for the complete response or for any of its components will similarly be reduced to a "routine."

3. The basis of certain general theorems concerning networks will be developed.

16-1. Primitive Elements and Operational Elements. In Chap. 12 we showed that any series, parallel, or series-parallel combination of elements

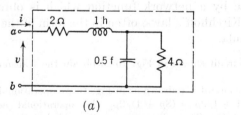
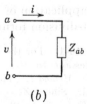

(a)   (b)

Fig. 16-1. A series-parallel circuit and its representation as a terminal-pair network.

between a pair of terminals can be described by means of its driving-point operational immittance. In doing so, we describe any single terminal pair a-b by means of the differential operator which relates v_{ab} to i_{ab}. Thus the series-parallel circuit shown in Fig. 16-1a may, with respect to

435

the terminals $a\text{-}b$, be represented by the "box" symbol given in Fig. 16-1b, provided that

$$Z_{ab}(p) = 2 + p + \frac{1}{\frac{1}{4} + \frac{1}{2}p} = \frac{2p^2 + 5p + 6}{2p + 1} \qquad (16\text{-}1)$$

The operational driving-point impedance is interpreted as representing the differential equation which relates v and i at a pair of terminals. For the circuit of Fig. 16-1 this equation is

$$(2p^2 + 5p + 6)i = (2p + 1)v \qquad (16\text{-}2)$$

If we deal with the sinusoidal steady-state response and if I is the phasor which represents the sinusoidal current $i(t) = \mathrm{Re}\ \sqrt{2}\ Ie^{j\omega t}$, then the phasor which represents the voltage $v(t) = \mathrm{Re}\ \sqrt{2}\ Ve^{j\omega t}$ is related to I through the equation

$$[2(j\omega)^2 + 5(j\omega) + 6]I = (2j\omega + 1)V \qquad (16\text{-}3)$$

It will be convenient to distinguish between the circuit elements R, L, and C and operational elements. For this reason we shall call the elements R, L, and C *primitive* elements, while the operational immittance associated with these elements or with any combination of these elements will be called the operational, or p, element as before.

16-2. Series-Parallel Circuits with One Source, Transfer Functions. Since operational impedances in series add and operational admittances in parallel add, any series-parallel combination of primitive elements can be reduced, with respect to two terminals, to a single operational element. If the terminals chosen are the terminals of the source (we have assumed only a single source in the network), then the relationship between the voltage across the source and the current through it will be given by the operational immittance of the network at the source terminals. The voltage and current associated with any element of the network can then be related to the source by a network function which is obtained by repeated application of Kirchhoff's laws, often in the form of the voltage- or current-division formula.

Example 16-1. For the circuit shown in Fig. 16-2a obtain the transfer function which relates $v_2(t)$ to $v(t)$.

Solution.   Method 1. The circuit is redrawn as in Fig. 16-2b, operational elements being used. Since $Z_5 = 4 + 1/2p = (8p + 1)/2p$, the operational admittance $Y_5(p) = 1/Z_5(p) = 2p/(8p + 1)$. This admittance can be added to the admittance of Z_4 ($Y_4 = 1/Z_4$) to obtain the circuit shown in Fig. 16-2c. The admittance of the parallel combination of Z_4 and Z_5 is denoted by $Y_6 = 1/Z_6$,

$$Y_6 = \frac{1}{1} + \frac{2p}{8p + 1} = \frac{10p + 1}{8p + 1}$$

or

$$Z_6 = \frac{8p + 1}{10p + 1}$$

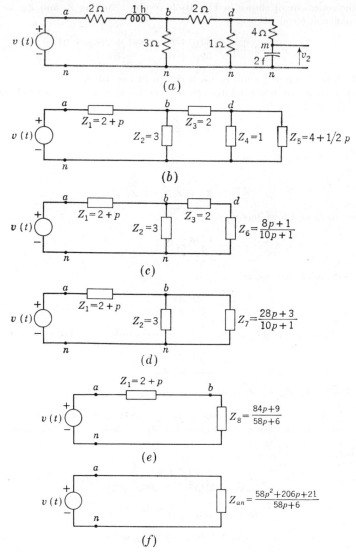

Fig. 16-2. Circuit to illustrate transfer function. The differential equation which relates v_2 to the source $v(t)$ is required.

The series combination of Z_3 and Z_6 is combined to give Z_7, where

$$Z_7 = \frac{8p + 1}{10p + 1} + 2 = \frac{28p + 3}{10p + 1}$$

so that the circuit shown in Fig. 16-2d can be drawn. Combining the admittances of Z_2 and Z_7 gives the admittance Y_8,

$$Y_8 = \frac{1}{3} + \frac{10p + 1}{28p + 3} = \frac{58p + 6}{84p + 9} = \frac{1}{Z_8}$$

so that the series circuit shown in Fig. 16-2e results.   Adding Z_1 and Z_8, we obtain the impedance at terminals a-n,

$$Z_{an}(p) = 2 + p + \frac{84p + 9}{58p + 6} = \frac{58p^2 + 206p + 21}{58p + 6}$$

The equivalent circuit at terminals a-n is shown in Fig. 16-2f.

To find the equation which relates $v(t)$ to $v_2(t)$, we first write v_{bn} in terms of $v_{an} = v(t)$ from Fig. 16-2e,

$$v_{bn}(t) = \frac{Z_8(p)}{Z_{an}(p)} v(t) \tag{16-4a}$$

Then we refer to Fig. 16-2c and write

$$v_{dn} = \frac{Z_6}{Z_3 + Z_6} v_{bn} = \frac{Z_6}{Z_7} v_{bn} \tag{16-4b}$$

From Fig. 16-2a and b we have

$$v_2 = \frac{1/2p}{Z_5} v_{dn} \tag{16-4c}$$

Using (16-4b) in (16-4c), we get

$$v_2 = \frac{1/2p}{Z_5} \frac{Z_6}{Z_7} v_{bn} \tag{16-4d}$$

and, using (16-4a) in (16-4d), we have the desired result in symbolic form,

$$v_2 = \frac{1/2p}{Z_5} \frac{Z_6}{Z_7} \frac{Z_8}{Z_{an}} v(t) \tag{16-4e}$$

Substituting for Z_5, Z_6, Z_7, Z_8, and Z_{an} in (16-4e),

$$v_2 = \frac{1/2p}{(8p + 1)/2p} \frac{(8p + 1)/(10p + 1)}{(28p + 3)/(10p + 1)} \frac{(84p + 9)/(58p + 6)}{(58p^2 + 206p + 21)/(58p + 6)} v(t) \tag{16-5a}$$

Simplifying,

$$v_2 = \frac{84p + 9}{(28p + 3)(58p^2 + 206p + 21)} v(t)$$

or

$$v_2 = \frac{3}{58p^2 + 206p + 21} v(t) \tag{16-5b}$$

and

$$(58p^2 + 206p + 21)v_2 = 3v \qquad\qquad Ans.$$

The operator $3/(58p^2 + 206p + 21)$ is the transfer function which relates v_2, a network variable, to the source $v(t)$.   The large number of common factors which occur in Eq. (16-5a) suggest that the work could have been carried out with symbols in place of numbers for the primitive elements.   However, the use of symbols does not really effect a saving in time since in any case all the numerical work is necessary to obtain the denominator of Eq. (16-5b).   Moreover, in problems of this type, the large number of algebraic symbols, together with subscripts, is cumbersome, and the use of numbers, where possible, recommends itself.

Method 2 (Branch Variables).   The method of solution illustrated above shows how the combination of primitive elements in the network of Fig. 16-2a can be used to reduce the network to a driving-point impedance, by means of which a given transfer function is obtained. However, this method is not the only possible procedure, and the same result may be arrived at by the direct application of Kirchhoff's laws to relate branch current and branch voltages. This method is illustrated below.

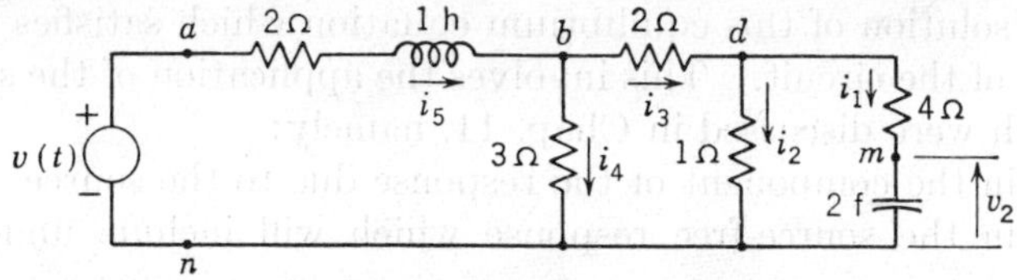

Fig. 16-3. Circuit of Fig. 16-2a, with branch-current symbols assigned to each element.

The network of Fig. 16-2a is redrawn in Fig. 16-3 with a current symbolically assigned to each branch. The voltage $v_2(t)$ is related to i_1 by the equation

$$i_1 = 2pv_2$$

Hence

$$v_{dn} = \left(4 + \frac{1}{2p}\right) i_1 = \frac{8p + 1}{2p} \times 2pv_2 = (8p + 1)v_2$$

The current i_2 is $v_{dn}/1 = v_{dn} = (8p + 1)v_2$. Since $i_3 = i_1 + i_2$,

$$i_3 = (8p + 1 + 2p)v_2 = (10p + 1)v_2$$

The voltage v_{bd} is given by $2i_3$,

$$v_{bd} = 2(10p + 1)v_2 = (20p + 2)v_2$$

Using Kirchoff's voltage law,

$$v_{bn} = v_{bd} + v_{dn}$$
$$= (20p + 2)v_2 + (8p + 1)v_2$$

or

$$v_{bn} = (28p + 3)v_2$$

Now $i_4 = v_{bn}/3$; therefore

$$i_4 = \frac{28p + 3}{3} v_2$$

Since $i_5 = i_4 + i_3$,

$$i_5 = \frac{28p + 3}{3} v_2 + (10p + 1)v_2$$
$$= \frac{58p + 6}{3} v_2$$

v_{ab} is related to i_5 through the equation

$$v_{ab} = (2 + p)i_5$$

or

$$v_{ab} = \frac{(2 + p)(58p + 6)}{3} v_2$$
$$= \frac{58p^2 + 122p + 12}{3} v_2$$

Now

$$v(t) = v_{ab} + v_{bn}$$

Hence

$$v(t) = \frac{58p^2 + 122p + 12}{3} v_2 + (28p + 3)v_2$$
$$= \frac{58p^2 + 206p + 21}{3} v_2$$

or

$$(58p^2 + 206p + 21)v_2 = 3v(t) \qquad \qquad Ans. \qquad (16\text{-}6)$$

16-3. Complete Response of a Series-Parallel Circuit with a Single Source. The transfer function which relates the desired circuit variable to the source function represents a (differential) equilibrium equation. The complete response of the network variable is obtained by finding that particular solution of this equilibrium equation which satisfies the initial conditions of the circuit. This involves the application of the same three steps which were discussed in Chap. 11, namely:

1. Obtain the component of the response due to the source.

2. Obtain the source-free response which will include undetermined constants.

3. Combine 1 and 2, and adjust the constants to satisfy the initial conditions.

We notice now that, in the absence of impulses, the initial conditions of the circuit problem are the continuity conditions which deal with the currents in inductances and the voltages across capacitances. In other words, the continuity conditions may not be directly applicable to the circuit variable in terms of which the equilibrium equation is established. Referring to Example 16-1 (circuit shown in Fig. 16-3), the continuity conditions require that $v_2(0^+) = v_2(0^-)$, because v_2 is the voltage across a capacitance, and $i_5(0^+) = i_5(0^-)$, because i_5 is the current through an inductance. Referring to the equilibrium equation (16-6), it is noted that this equation is a second-order differential equation so that the general solution (of the source free equation) will contain the necessary two constants to satisfy the two initial conditions. We have, however, the following dilemma: How can the initial value for the current i_5 be applied to solve for the voltage v_2? There are several methods which can be used to solve this problem.

1. We can solve for $v_2(t)$ and $i_5(t)$ simultaneously. This method will be explained in the latter parts of this chapter.

2. The situation is partially resolved by representing the initial conditions by sources (initial-condition generators). This procedure, however, still leads to either the method of (1) or to the method given in (3).

3. Derive initial conditions for the derivatives of the desired variable [in the case of Example 16-1 the initial value $(dv_2/dt)_{0^+}$ is needed] by *use of the Kirchhoff's-law relationships and the continuity conditions.*

The last-named procedure will be illustrated for the circuit of Fig. 16-3. Assume that, at the time $t = 0^+$, $v_{mn}(0^+) = V_0$ and $i_5(0^+) = I_0$. These are the continuity conditions. Now we refer to the circuit of Fig. 16-3 and note that $i_1 = 2 \, dv_2/dt$. Hence

$$\left(\frac{dv_2}{dt}\right)_{0^+} = \frac{i_1(0^+)}{2}$$

Hence we need $i_1(0^+)$. To relate $i_1(0^+)$ to I_0, we note that

$$v_{dn} = 4i_1 + v_2 = 1 \times i_2$$

or
$$i_2(0^+) = 4i_1(0^+) + V_0$$

Since $i_3 = i_2 + i_1$,

$$i_3(0^+) = 4i_1(0^+) + V_0 + i_1(0^+)$$

or
$$i_3(0^+) = 5i_1(0^+) + V_0$$

Thus
$$v_{bd}(0^+) = 2i_3(0^+) = 10i_1(0^+) + 2V_0$$

and
$$v_{bn}(0^+) = v_{bd}(0^+) + v_{dn}(0^+)$$
$$= 10i_1(0^+) + 2V_0 + 4i_1(0^+) + V_0$$
$$= 14i_1(0^+) + 3V_0$$

Hence
$$i_4(0^+) = \frac{14i_1(0^+) + 3V_0}{3}$$

and
$$i_5(0^+) = I_0 = i_4(0^+) + i_3(0^+)$$

or
$$I_0 = \tfrac{14}{3}i_1(0^+) + V_0 + 5i_1(0^+) + V_0$$

Therefore
$$I_0 - 2V_0 = \tfrac{29}{3}i_1(0^+)$$

so that
$$i_1(0^+) = \frac{3I_0 - 6V_0}{29}$$

and
$$\left(\frac{dv_2}{dt}\right)_{0^+} = \frac{3I_0 - 6V_0}{(2)(29)} = \frac{3I_0 - 6V_0}{58} \tag{16-7}$$

We observe that the derived initial condition (16-7) depends on the continuity conditions *and* on the values of the (primitive) elements in the circuit. Unfortunately no standard procedure for the calculation of derived initial conditions can be given; one can only restate that the Kirchhoff's-law equations at $t = 0^+$ must be combined with the continuity conditions to obtain derived initial conditions.

To show how the derived initial conditions are used, we shall continue the problem of Fig. 16-3. The equilibrium equation is

$$(58p^2 + 206p + 21)v_2 = 3v(t)$$

Let it be assumed that $(v_2)_s$, the component due to the source, is known. The source-free equilibrium equation is then

$$(58p^2 + 206p + 21)v_2 = 0$$

so that the characteristic equation is

$$58s^2 + 206s + 21 = 0$$

or
$$s^2 + 3.55s + 0.362 = 0$$
$$s_1 = -3.44 \qquad s_2 = -0.11$$

Hence the complete response has the form

$$v_2(t) = (v_2)_s + K_1 e^{-3.44t} + K_2 e^{-0.11t}$$

where $(v_2)_s$ is the response due to the source and its waveform depends on the waveform of $v(t)$ as well as on the network elements.

Using the initial conditions, we have the equations for K_1 and K_2,

$$V_0 = [v_2(0^+)]_s + K_1 + K_2$$
$$\left(\frac{dv_2}{dt}\right)_{0^+} = \frac{3I_0 - 6V_0}{58} = \left[\frac{d(v_2)_s}{dt}\right]_{0^+} - 3.44K_1 - 0.11K_2$$

16-4. Series–Parallel Circuits with Several Sources.

When several ideal sources are simultaneously impressed on a series-parallel circuit, the equilibrium equation which relates any circuit variable to the sources can be obtained either exactly as in the case of a single source, or by use of the superposition principle. If the former method is used, we start by assigning a symbol to the desired variable and then apply Kirchhoff's laws to the branches and nodes of the network until the desired equation is obtained. The use of the superposition method requires that the transfer function which relates each source acting *alone* (i.e., with the other sources set to zero) is first obtained and subsequently the components of the response due to the individual sources are added. It is also frequently possible to reduce the complexity of the circuit by repeatedly converting voltage to current sources, and vice versa. An example will serve to illustrate these procedures.

Example 16-2. In the circuit of Fig. 16-4a obtain the equilibrium equation which relates $v_{ab}(t)$ to $i(t)$, $v_1(t)$, and $v_2(t)$.

Solution. Method 1 (*Conversion of Sources*). The voltage source formed by the series branch to the left of terminals *b-d* and the 2-ohm–$v_2(t)$ combination are converted to current sources as shown in Fig. 16-4b. The parallel passive elements between terminals *d* and *b* are converted into a single operational element whose admittance is $(1 + 3p)$. The parallel passive elements between terminals *a-b* are converted into a single operational element whose admittance is $\frac{1}{2} + 1/(1 + 2p)$. The resulting circuit, which is equivalent to the original circuit with respect to the elements and terminals on the outside of the dotted lines, is shown in Fig. 16-4c. In this circuit

$$Z_1(p) = \frac{1}{1 + 3p} \quad \text{and} \quad Z_2(p) = \frac{2 + 4p}{3 + 2p}$$

The two current sources to the left of terminals *a-b* are now converted to voltage sources. The resulting circuit is shown in Fig. 16-4d. The circuit of Fig. 16-4d is equivalent to the original circuit only as far as the voltages v_{ad}, v_{ab}, and v_{db} are concerned. (Note, however, that knowledge of these voltages would allow us to calculate the currents in all the elements of the original circuit.) In the circuit of Fig. 16-4d, $Z_1(p)$ is combined with the $\frac{1}{2}$-ohm resistance to give $Z_3(p)$, where

$$Z_3(p) = \frac{1}{2} + \frac{1}{1 + 3p} = \frac{3 + 3p}{2 + 6p}$$

The two voltage sources, $(1 + p)v_1(t)/(1 + 3p)$ and $\frac{1}{2}i(t)$, are combined into a single source, and the arrangement shown in Fig. 16-4e results. This circuit is equivalent to the original circuit with respect to the (desired) terminals *a-b*. As the last step, the part of the circuit to the left of terminals *a-b* is converted to a current source, and we arrive at Fig. 16-4f. In this circuit

$$i_a(t) = \frac{1 + p}{1 + 3p}\frac{2 + 6p}{3 + 3p} v_1(t) + \frac{2 + 6p}{6 + 6p} i(t)$$

or
$$i_a(t) = \tfrac{2}{3}v_1(t) + \frac{1 + 3p}{3 + 3p} i(t) \tag{16-8a}$$

Application of the definition of operational impedance at terminals *a-b* in Fig. 16-4f gives the desired relationship,

$$v_{ab} = \frac{1}{Y_2(p) + Y_3(p)} [i_a + \tfrac{1}{2}v_2(t)] \tag{16-8b}$$

Now
$$Y_2(p) + Y_3(p) = \frac{3 + 2p}{2 + 4p} + \frac{2 + 6p}{3 + 3p} = \frac{30p^2 + 35p + 13}{12p^2 + 18p + 6}$$

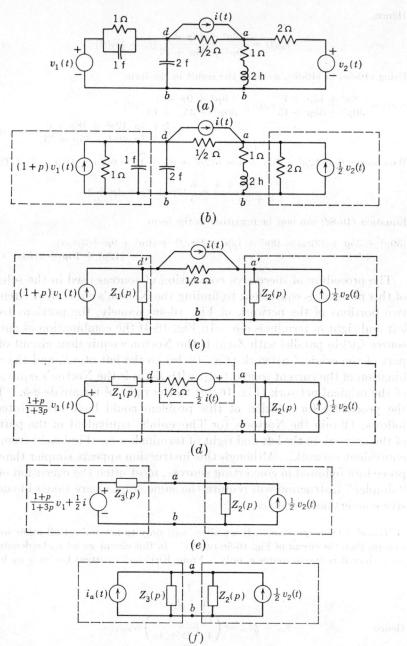

Fig. 16-4. Network containing several sources and equivalents with respect to various terminal pairs.

Hence

$$v_{ab}(t) = \frac{12p^2 + 18p + 6}{30p^2 + 35p + 13} [i_a + \tfrac{1}{2}v_2(t)] \tag{16-8c}$$

Using (16-8a) in (16-8c), we have the result in the form

$$v_{ab}(t) = \frac{8p^2 + 12p + 4}{30p^2 + 35p + 13} v_1(t) + \frac{6p^2 + 9p + 3}{30p^2 + 35p + 13} v_2(t)$$
$$+ \frac{1 + 3p}{3 + 3p} \frac{12p^2 + 18p + 6}{30p^2 + 35p + 13} i(t) \tag{16-8d}$$

We observe that $12p^2 + 18p + 6 = 6(2p^2 + 3p + 1) = 6(2p + 1)(p + 1)$. Thus

$$\frac{12p^2 + 18p + 4}{3 + 3p} = \frac{6}{3}(2p + 1) = 4p + 2$$

Equation (16-8d) can now be rewritten in the form

$$(30p^2 + 35p + 13)v_{ab} = (8p^2 + 12p + 4)v_1(t) + (6p^2 + 9p + 3)v_2(t)$$
$$+ (12p^2 + 10p + 2)i(t) \tag{16-9}$$

The procedure of successive conversion of sources used in the solution of this problem is equivalent to finding the Norton's equivalent circuit of two portions of the network of Fig. 16-4a, namely, the portions to the left and right of terminals a-b. In Fig. 16-4f the combination of current source $i_a(t)$ in parallel with $Z_3(p)$ is the Norton's equivalent circuit of the part of the original network (Fig. 16-4a) to the left of a-b, and the combination of the current source $\tfrac{1}{2}v_2(t)$ with $Z_2(p)$ is the Norton's equivalent of the original network (Fig. 16-4a) to the right of terminals a-b. Thus the procedure for solution of this problem could have been stated as follows: Obtain the Norton's (or Thévenin's) equivalent of the portions of the network to the left and right of terminals a-b. Find $v_{ab}(t)$ from this equivalent network. Although this instruction appears simpler than the procedure followed in converting sources, most often the execution of the "simpler" instruction will require the same steps as are taken in successive conversion of sources.

Method 2 (*Superposition*). If we allow $v_1(t)$ only to act and set all other sources to zero, then the circuit of Fig. 16-5a results. In this circuit we let v_{ab} be denoted by $(v_{ab})_1$ since it is due to source v_1 only. From Kirchhoff's current law at a we have

$$i_{da} = \tfrac{1}{2}(v_{ab})_1 + \frac{1}{1 + 2p}(v_{ab})_1$$

Hence

$$v_{da} = \tfrac{1}{2}i_{da} = \left(\frac{1}{4} + \frac{1}{2 + 4p}\right)(v_{ab})_1$$

and

$$v_{db} = v_{da} + v_{ab} = \left(\frac{5}{4} + \frac{1}{2 + 4p}\right)(v_{ab})_1$$

Then

$$i_b = 2pv_{db} = \left(\frac{5p}{2} + \frac{2p}{2 + 4p}\right)(v_{ab})_1$$

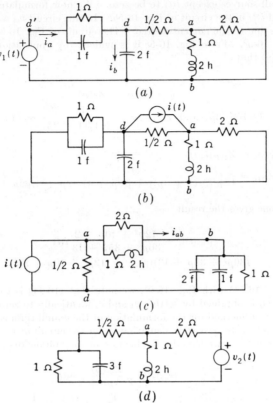

FIG. 16-5. (a) Circuit of Fig. 16-4 with only source $v_1(t)$ acting. (b) Circuit of Fig. 16-4 with only source $i(t)$ acting. (c) Equivalent to circuit of (b). (d) Circuit of Fig. 16-4 with only source $v_2(t)$ acting.

Since $i_a = i_b + i_{da}$,

$$i_a = \left(\frac{1 + 5p}{2} + \frac{1 + p}{1 + 2p}\right)(v_{ab})_1$$

and $v_{d'd} = [1/(1 + p)]i_a$; hence

$$v_{d'd} = \left(\frac{1 + 5p}{2 + 2p} + \frac{1}{1 + 2p}\right)(v_{ab})_1$$

Now $v_1(t) = v_{d'd} + v_{db}$, or

$$v_1(t) = \left(\frac{1 + 5p}{2 + 2p} + \frac{1}{1 + 2p} + \frac{5}{4} + \frac{1}{2 + 4p}\right)(v_{ab})_1$$

$$= \frac{30p^2 + 35p + 13}{8p^2 + 12p + 4}(v_{ab})_1$$

or $$(30p^2 + 35p + 13)(v_{ab})_1 = (8p^2 + 12p + 4)v_1(t) \qquad (16\text{-}10)$$

Note that Eq. (16-10) is the special form which Eq. (16-9) has if the sources $v_2(t)$ and $i(t)$ are made identical with zero. To obtain Eq. (16-9) by the superposition method, we next allow all sources except $i(t)$ to be zero. We now formulate the relationship between v_{ab} and $i(t)$ in the circuit of Fig. 16-5b. In this circuit v_{ab} will be denoted by $(v_{ab})_i$ since it is due to the current source. The circuit of Fig. 16-5b is redrawn, for clarity, in Fig. 16-5c. From Fig. 16-5c it is evident (by application of the current-division formula) that

$$i_{ab} = \frac{\frac{1}{2}}{\frac{1}{2} + Z_1(p) + Z_2(p)}\, i(t)$$

where $Z_1(p) = 1/(1 + 3p)$ and $Z_2(p) = \dfrac{1}{\frac{1}{2} + 1/(1 + 2p)} = (4p + 2)/(2p + 3)$.

Then

$$(v_{ab})_i = Z_2(p)i_{ab}(t)$$

Hence

$$(v_{ab})_i = \frac{1}{1 + [2/(1 + 3p)] + [(8p + 4)/(2p + 3)]}\, \frac{4p + 2}{2p + 3}\, i(t)$$

Clearing fractions gives the result

$$[v_{ab}(t)]_i = \frac{12p^2 + 10p + 2}{30p^2 + 35p + 13}\, i(t)$$

or

$$(30p^2 + 35p + 13)(v_{ab})_i = (12p^2 + 10p + 2)i \qquad (16\text{-}11)$$

Comparing Eq. (16-11) with Eq. (16-9), we note that (16-11) is the special case of Eq. (16-9), which is obtained by setting v_1 and v_2 identically to zero. The last step in the superposition method for the formulation of the equilibrium equations consists in setting $v_1(t)$ and $i(t)$ to zero and calculating v_{ab} for the circuit of Fig. 16-5d. Denoting v_{ab} in this case $(v_{ab})_2$, we have by application of the voltage division formula

$$(v_{ab})_2 = \frac{Z_{ab}(p)}{Z_{ab}(p) + 2}\, v_2(t)$$

where

$$Y_{ab}(p) = \frac{1}{1 + 2p} + \frac{1}{\frac{1}{2} + [1/(1 + 3p)]}$$

or

$$Y_{ab}(p) = \frac{12p^2 + 13p + 5}{6p^2 + 9p + 3}$$

Hence

$$(v_{ab})_2 = \frac{6p^2 + 9p + 3}{30p^2 + 35p + 13}\, v_2(t)$$

or

$$(30p^2 + 35p + 13)(v_{ab})_2 = (6p^2 + 9p + 3)v_2(t) \qquad (16\text{-}12)$$

We now note that Eq. (16-12) is obtained from (16-9) by setting $i(t)$ and $v_1(t)$ to zero. If we add Eqs. (16-10), (16-11), and (16-12) and define $v_{ab}(t) \equiv (v_{ab})_1 + (v_{ab})_2 + (v_{ab})_i$, then Eq. (16-9) is obtained as the equilibrium equation which relates the voltage $v_{ab}(t)$ to the source functions $v_1(t)$, $v_2(t)$, and $i(t)$ in the original circuit (Fig. 16-4a).

  Method 3 (*Direct Application of Kirchhoff's Laws to the Circuit*). Exactly as in the case of the circuit of Fig. 16-3, the equilibrium equation for the circuit of Fig. 16-4 with v_{ab} as the chosen variable can be obtained by starting with the symbol for v_{ab} and writing Kirchhoff's-law relationships until only v_{ab} and the sources are involved. The circuit is redrawn as shown in Fig. 16-6, and current reference directions are indicated for each p element. We could then write

$$v_{ab} = (1 + 2p)i_5 = 2i_4 + v_2(t)$$

Then

$$i_5 = \frac{1}{1 + 2p}\, v_{ab} \quad \text{and} \quad i_4 = \tfrac{1}{2}v_{ab} - \tfrac{1}{2}v_2(t)$$

Now we apply Kirchhoff's current law at junction a.

$$i(t) + i_3 = i_4 + i_5 \tag{16-13}$$

In Eq. (16-13) we now express i_4 and i_5 in terms of v_{ab}. Then Kirchhoff's current law at junction d is written and combined with expressions for v_{da} and v_{db} until the desired

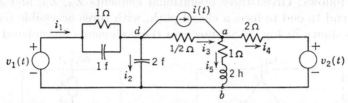

FIG. 16-6. Circuit of Fig. 16-4. A current has been designated symbolically for each p-element branch.

result is obtained. We shall not demonstrate the detailed procedure because it is not systematic and therefore not "standard"; i.e., it would apply only to this example.

The reason for this difficulty stems from the fact that when we get "stuck" we look for another junction or loop which leads to a "new" relationship. This type of procedure can easily lead to redundant relationships and vicious circles. In subsequent articles the *systematic* (and direct) application of Kirchhoff's laws will be discussed.

Before concluding this example one further remark is necessary. The equilibrium equation (16-9) is a second-order differential equation. Observe that in the *source-free circuit* there are only two independent energy-storing elements, namely, the 2-henry inductance and the combination of 1- and 2-farad capacitances since these are parallel when the sources [(in particular $v_1(t)$] are set to zero. In this circuit the continuity conditions do not apply to the capacitances because an impulse current can flow in the loop formed by $v_1(t)$ and the two capacitances. This matter of impulses and the associated initial conditions is discussed in another article of this chapter (Art. 16-23).

16-5. Passive Three-terminal Networks.

In the preceding articles we have shown how the equilibrium equation for any circuit variable in a series-parallel circuit can be formulated. Before discussing the simultaneous-equation methods (which apply to any network), we wish to extend the series-parallel circuit methods to certain networks in which there are elements which are connected neither in series nor in parallel. In particular

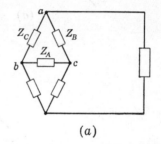

(a)

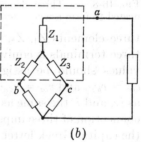

(b)

FIG. 16-7. (a) A circuit which consists of six elements; no two of these elements are either in series or in parallel. (b) By proper choice of the functions Z_1, Z_2, and Z_3 this circuit is equivalent to the circuit of (a) as far as the voltages and currents which are external to the dotted "box" are concerned.

the six elements shown in Fig. 16-7a are connected so that no two elements are either in series or in parallel with each other. We shall now show that the three elements Z_A, Z_B, and Z_C (which are passive) can be replaced, with respect to the three terminals a-b-c, by three elements Z_1, Z_2, and Z_3 connected as shown in Fig. 16-7b. Note that the circuit of Fig. 16-7b is a series-parallel circuit. We formulate the problem as follows: Given three operational elements Z_A, Z_B, and Z_C connected end to end to form a closed path, with three accessible terminals a-b-c as shown in Fig. 16-8a, how can these elements be replaced by the

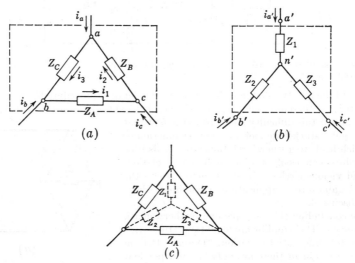

FIG. 16-8. (a) Three elements connected to form a delta. (b) Three elements connected to form a wye. (c) Diagram used in delta-wye conversion.

three elements Z_1, Z_2, and Z_3 of Fig. 16-8b so that the situation at the three terminals is equivalent for the two circuits? In other words, what values should be assigned to Z_1, Z_2, and Z_3 so that, when $v_{ab} = v_{a'b'}$, $v_{bc} = v_{b'c'}$, and $v_{ca} = v_{c'a'}$, the current i_a will be the same as $i_{a'}$, i_b the same as $i_{b'}$, and i_c the same as $i_{c'}$? The connection of Fig. 16-8a is called a *delta* connection of three impedances because (as drawn) the elements represent the capital Greek letter delta (Δ). The connection of Fig. 16-8b is called a *wye*, or *star*, connection because of the resemblance to the capital letter Y (upside down in Fig. 16-8b). The equivalence relationships which are to be deduced are called the *delta-wye* conversion formulas. These formulas will now be deduced by starting with the voltage-current relationships at the terminals of each circuit and selecting Z_1, Z_2, and Z_3 so that the same relationships apply in each circuit.[1]

[1] In an alternate approach to this problem, the equivalence can be established by equating the driving-point impedances in the two circuits as follows:

$$Z_{ab} = Z_{a'b'} \qquad Z_{bc} = Z_{b'c'} \qquad Z_{ca} = Z_{c'a'}$$

In each calculation of such a driving-point impedance the third terminal is ignored. Thus $Z_{ab} = (Z_A + Z_B)Z_C/(Z_A + Z_B + Z_C)$, $Z_{a'b'} = Z_1 + Z_2$, etc. From the three

In the delta of Fig. 16-8a

$$Z_A i_1 = v_{bc} \quad \text{or} \quad i_1 = Y_A v_{bc}$$

Thus the currents in the three immittances may be written as

$$i_1 = Y_A v_{bc} \qquad i_2 = Y_B v_{ca} \qquad i_3 = Y_C v_{ab} \qquad (16\text{-}14)$$

Application of Kirchhoff's current law at each junction a, b, and c gives the equations

$$i_a = i_3 - i_2 \quad \text{or} \quad i_a = Y_C v_{ab} - Y_B v_{ca} \qquad (16\text{-}14a)$$
$$i_b = i_1 - i_3 \quad \text{or} \quad i_b = Y_A v_{bc} - Y_C v_{ab} \qquad (16\text{-}14b)$$
$$i_c = i_2 - i_1 \quad \text{or} \quad i_c = Y_B v_{ca} - Y_A v_{bc} \qquad (16\text{-}14c)$$

Observe now that the addition of the three equations (16-14) gives the result

$$i_a + i_b + i_c = i_3 - i_2 + i_1 - i_3 + i_2 - i_1 \equiv 0 \qquad (16\text{-}15)$$

This result is also obtained by the application of Kirchhoff's current law at junction n' in Fig. 16-8b: $i_{a'} + i_{b'} + i_{c'} = 0$. We also conclude that the three equations (16-14) are not independent of each other since any one can be deduced from the other two. The voltages v_{ab}, v_{bc}, and v_{ca} will now be expressed as functions of the currents i_a, i_b, and i_c. Since $v_{ab} + v_{bc} + v_{ca} = 0$ (from Kirchhoff's voltage law), $v_{ca} = -v_{ab} - v_{bc}$. Introducing this relationship as well as (16-15) in (16-14a) and (16-14c), we have

$$i_a = (Y_C + Y_B)v_{ab} + Y_B v_{bc} \qquad (16\text{-}16a)$$
$$-i_a - i_b = i_c = (-Y_B)v_{ab} - (Y_A + Y_B)v_{bc} \qquad (16\text{-}16b)$$

Now v_{bc} can be eliminated by multiplying Eq. (16-16b) by Y_B, (16-16a) by $Y_A + Y_B$, and adding the resulting equations:

$$-Y_B i_a - Y_B i_b + (Y_A + Y_B)i_a = (Y_C + Y_B)(Y_A + Y_B)v_{ab} - Y_B^2 v_{ab}$$

or

$$Y_A i_a - Y_B i_b = (Y_A Y_B + Y_B Y_C + Y_C Y_A)v_{ab}$$

or, if $Y_A Y_B + Y_B Y_C + Y_C Y_A \neq 0$,

$$v_{ab} = \frac{Y_A}{Y_A Y_B + Y_B Y_C + Y_C Y_A} i_a - \frac{Y_B}{Y_A Y_B + Y_B Y_C + Y_C Y_A} i_b \qquad (16\text{-}17)$$

To obtain similar expressions for v_{bc} and v_{ca}, we could now introduce $v_{bc} = -v_{ca} - v_{ab}$ into (16-14a) and (16-14b) and proceed as with (16-16a) and (16-16b). We note from Eqs. (16-14), however, that the relationships are symmetrical in the sense that if we change a to b, b to c, and c to a in one of the equations another equation of this set is obtained. Applying this symmetry to the result (16-17), we have three relations [for convenience, (16-17) is repeated as (16-17a)],

$$v_{ab} = \frac{Y_A}{Y_A Y_B + Y_B Y_C + Y_C Y_A} i_a - \frac{Y_B}{Y_A Y_B + Y_B Y_C + Y_C Y_A} i_b \qquad (16\text{-}17a)$$

$$v_{bc} = \frac{Y_B}{Y_A Y_B + Y_B Y_C + Y_C Y_A} i_b - \frac{Y_C}{Y_A Y_B + Y_B Y_C + Y_C Y_A} i_c \qquad (16\text{-}17b)$$

$$v_{ca} = \frac{Y_C}{Y_A Y_B + Y_B Y_C + Y_C Y_A} i_c - \frac{Y_A}{Y_A Y_B + Y_B Y_C + Y_C Y_A} i_a \qquad (16\text{-}17c)$$

simultaneous equations which are obtained in this manner the relationship between the numbered and lettered impedance is deduced. This method is left as an exercise for the reader. It is pointed out that this approach shows that the results arrived at are necessary. The proof of necessity and sufficiency is as given in the text.

Turning now to the circuit of Fig. 16-8b, we apply Kirchhoff's voltage law three times and obtain

$$v_{a'b'} = Z_1 i_{a'} - Z_2 i_{b'} \tag{16-18a}$$

$$v_{b'c'} = Z_2 i_{b'} - Z_3 i_{c'} \tag{16-18b}$$

$$v_{c'a'} = Z_3 i_{c'} - Z_1 i_{a'} \tag{16-18c}$$

If we now set $v_{ab} = v_{a'b'}$, $v_{bc} = v_{b'c'}$, and $v_{ca} = v_{c'a'}$, then $i_a = i_{a'}$, $i_b = i_{b'}$, and $i_c = i_{c'}$ if

$$Z_1 = \frac{Y_A}{Y_A Y_B + Y_B Y_C + Y_C Y_A} = \frac{Z_B Z_C}{Z_A + Z_B + Z_C} \tag{16-19a}$$

$$Z_2 = \frac{Y_B}{Y_A Y_B + Y_B Y_C + Y_C Y_A} = \frac{Z_C Z_A}{Z_A + Z_B + Z_C} \tag{16-19b}$$

$$Z_3 = \frac{Y_C}{Y_A Y_B + Y_B Y_C + Y_C Y_A} = \frac{Z_A Z_B}{Z_A + Z_B + Z_C} \tag{16-19c}$$

The relations (16-19) are the formulas for *delta-to-wye conversion*. These formulas can easily be remembered by means of the following *rule*, which is evident from the formulas: Given the delta, to find the impedances of the equivalent wye, draw the wye inside the delta as shown dotted in Fig. 16-8c. We refer to each impedance of the delta as a "side" of the triangle formed by the delta. Hence any impedance of the wye is the ratio of the product of two *adjacent* sides of the delta to the sum of its sides. Alternatively, in terms of admittances, we first form the sum of the products: $S_\Delta = Y_A Y_B + Y_B Y_C + Y_C Y_A$. Then each admittance of the wye is found by dividing S_Δ by the admittance of the side of the delta which is *opposite* to the desired admittance of the wye.

It is also possible to replace a wye by a delta. To obtain the conversion formulas, we could start with Eqs. (16-18) and put them in a form analogous to (16-14). This procedure is left as an exercise for the reader. The wye-delta conversion formulas can also be deduced by starting with Eqs. (16-19) and solving for Z_A, Z_B, and Z_C in terms of Z_1, Z_2, and Z_3 (or Y_1, Y_2, and Y_3). We observe that the sum of the products $Z_1 Z_2 + Z_2 Z_3 + Z_3 Z_1$ is given by

$$Z_1 Z_2 + Z_2 Z_3 + Z_3 Z_1 = \frac{1}{Y_A Y_B + Y_B Y_C + Y_C Y_A} \equiv S_Y$$

and

$$Z_A = \frac{Z_1 Z_2 + Z_2 Z_3 + Z_3 Z_1}{Z_1} = \frac{Y_1 + Y_2 + Y_3}{Y_2 Y_3} \tag{16-20a}$$

$$Z_B = \frac{Z_1 Z_2 + Z_2 Z_3 + Z_3 Z_1}{Z_2} = \frac{Y_1 + Y_2 + Y_3}{Y_3 Y_1} \tag{16-20b}$$

$$Z_C = \frac{Z_1 Z_2 + Z_2 Z_3 + Z_3 Z_1}{Z_3} = \frac{Y_1 + Y_2 + Y_3}{Y_1 Y_2} \tag{16-20c}$$

A rule for wye-to-delta conversion can therefore be stated as follows: Draw the wye and the delta as in Fig. 16-8c. Each impedance of the delta is given by dividing S_Y by the *opposite* impedance of the wye. In terms of admittances each *impedance* of the delta is found by dividing the sum of the admittances of the wye by the product of the two wye admittances which are connected to the desired impedance of the delta. An important special case is the "symmetrical" delta or wye. A symmetrical delta or wye is one which is composed of three identical impedances. In this case

$$Z_A = Z_B = Z_C \equiv Z_\Delta = 3Z_Y \equiv 3Z_1 = 3Z_2 = 3Z_3 \qquad (16\text{-}21)$$

It must be emphasized that the conversion of a delta to a wye or a wye to a delta in the solution of a network problem applies only with respect to the three terminals chosen.   The voltage $v_{a'n'}$ in a wye which was obtained from a delta is meaningless in the original circuit which included the delta.   Similarly, if a wye is converted to a delta, then the currents in the elements of the delta have no meaning in the original circuit.   The use of delta-wye conversion will be illustrated in the next article.

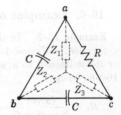

Fig. 16-9. Example of a delta-wye conversion which leads to nonphysical elements.

To conclude this introduction, it is necessary to point out that the conversion delta-wye (or wyedelta) is always possible on paper simply by applying the formulas (16-19) or (16-20) or the corresponding rules.   The elements of the converted circuit may, however, not be physically realizable in terms of primitive elements R, L, and C.

As an example of this problem, let us consider the delta shown in Fig. 16-9.   Suppose that it is desired to convert this delta to a wye.   The wye has been drawn inside the delta, and application of the rules given above yields

$$Z_1(p) = \frac{R/pC}{R + 2/pC} = \frac{R}{pRC + 2} \qquad \text{or} \qquad Y_1(p) = \frac{pRC + 2}{R} = pC + \frac{2}{R}$$

Hence the p element Z_1 is the parallel combination of a capacitance C and a resistance $R/2$.   Evidently $Z_1 = Z_3$.   The p element Z_2 is given by

$$Z_2(p) = \frac{(1/pC)^2}{R + 2/pC} = \frac{1}{(pC)^2 R + p2C}$$

Hence $$Y_2(p) = p^2 C^2 R + p2C$$

To interpret $Y_2(p)$, we should say that it is the sum of two admittances $p2C$ and $p^2 C^2 R$. The admittance $p2C$ is the admittance of a capacitance $2C$, but none of the three elements R, L, or C has a voltage-current relationship $(p^2 C^2 R)v = i$. Hence the element Z_2 is not physically realizable.

The fact that the admittance function $Y_2(p)$ is not physically realizable is also evident if we observe that $Y_2(p) = pC(pRC + 2)/1$. Hence it is a fraction of polynomials, with the numerator polynomial $pC(pRC + 2)$, a second-degree polynomial, and the denominator polynomial unity, a zero-degree "polynomial." Since in a physically realizable driving-point immittance the numerator and denominator polynomials cannot differ by more than one degree, $Y_2(p)$ is not physically realizable.

It must be emphasized that the physically nonrealizable elements which may be encountered in delta-wye and wye-delta conversion are no hindrance to the usefulness of the procedure *since the voltages or currents connected with the elements of the part of the circuit which has undergone conversion have no meaning in the original circuit.* The equivalence between delta and wye has been established only for the circuit with respect to the three terminals external to the delta or wye. The "impossible" elements which are obtained on paper will therefore still lead to the correct solution for any variable which is external to the "converted" part of the circuit.

16-6. Examples of Delta-Wye and Wye-Delta Conversion

Example 16-3. In the circuit of Fig. 16-10a calculate the current I_0.

Solution. Method 1. (By Delta-Wye Conversion.) Convert either the delta *adb* or the delta *dbn* to a wye. Choosing *adb*, the circuit with the wye is shown in Fig. 16-10b, where

$$R_1 = \frac{(8)(6)}{8+6+6} = \frac{48}{20} = 2.4 \text{ ohms} \qquad R_2 = \frac{(6)(6)}{20} = 1.8 \text{ ohms} \qquad R_3 = R_1$$

Hence, from Fig. 16-10c,

$$R_{an} = 2.4 + \frac{(4.4)(2.8)}{4.4+2.8} = 4.12 \text{ ohms} \qquad \text{and} \qquad R_{mn} = 7.12 \text{ ohms}$$

so that $I_0 = 10/7.12 = 1.41$ amp.

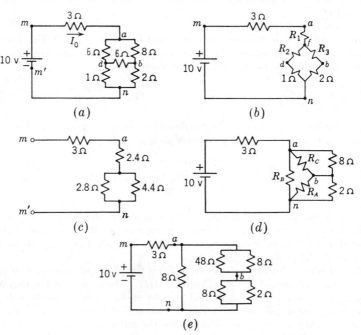

FIG. 16-10. A circuit used to illustrate delta-wye conversion.

Method 2. (*By Wye-Delta Conversion.*) There are four wyes in Fig. 16-10a. They are formed by the 6-, 8-, and 3-ohm resistances, the 6-, 8-, and 2-ohm resistances, the 6-, 6-, and 1-ohm resistances, and the 1-, 2-, and 3-ohm resistances (if the circuit is redrawn with the 3-ohm resistance between m' and n). If we were to choose the wye formed between m, d, and b, a series-parallel circuit would not result. We therefore choose the wye formed by the 6-, 6-, and 1-ohm resistances (the 6-, 8-, and 2-ohm resistances can also be used). If we convert the wye between a, b, and n, then the circuit of Fig. 16-10d results, where

$$R_A = \frac{(6)(6) + (6)(1) + (1)(6)}{6} = \frac{48}{6} = 8 \text{ ohms}$$

$$R_B = \frac{48}{6} = 8 \text{ ohms} \qquad R_C = \frac{48}{1} = 48 \text{ ohms}$$

We now draw the circuit of Fig. 16-10e. In this circuit

$$R_{abn} = \frac{(48 \times 8)}{48 + 8} + \frac{(2)(8)}{2 + 8} = 8.47 \text{ ohms}$$

Hence $\qquad R_{mn} = 3 + \frac{(8.47)(8)}{8.47 + 8} = 7.12$ ohms, as before

It is evident, even from this simple example, that when delta-wye or wye-delta conversion can be used there may well be a choice as to which elements to convert. While no rigid rule can be cited, we can call attention to several factors which influence the choice:

1. Does the conversion eliminate terminals which we wish to deal with? If, for example, in Fig. 16-10a, the voltage v_{db} were required, then Method 2 is unacceptable because terminal d does not appear in Fig. 16-10e.

2. Will further conversion be necessary? This is usually an undesirable situation. If the wye mdb in Fig. 16-10a is converted to a delta, subsequent delta-wye conversion is necessary.

3. Is there any symmetry? If two or three sides in a delta or wye are equal, then the numerical work is simplified because two or three sides in the corresponding wye or delta will also be equal.

As a guiding rule it is suggested that, before the conversion is carried out numerically, the new circuit which will be a result of the conversion be examined to see if any inconveniences result from the proposed conversion.

Example 16-4. In the circuit of Fig. 16-11a obtain the equilibrium equations which relate $v_{ab}(t)$ and $i_{ab}(t)$ to $v(t)$. Use delta-wye conversion.

Solution. Since we desire to deal with terminals a and b, neither of these terminals should disappear in the conversion process. Because $Z_{da} = Z_{db}$, we choose to convert the delta dab to a wye. The circuit of Fig. 16-11b results. In this circuit

$$Z_1(p) = \frac{(3 \times 3)}{3 + 3 + 1/p} = \frac{9p}{6p + 1}$$

and $\qquad Z_2(p) = Z_3(p) = \frac{3}{6p + 1}$

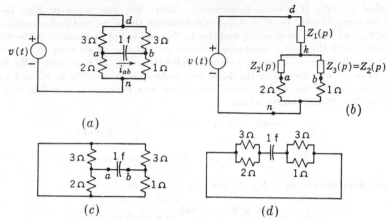

(a)

(b)

(c)

(d)

FIG. 16-11. A second circuit used to illustrate delta-wye conversion.

Now the voltage-division formula will be applied repeatedly.

$$v_{an} = \frac{2}{2 + Z_2(p)} v_{kn} = \frac{2}{2 + 3/(6p + 1)} v_{kn}$$

or

$$v_{an} = \frac{2(6p + 1)}{12p + 5} v_{kn}$$

and

$$v_{bn} = \frac{1}{1 + Z_2(p)} v_{kn} = \frac{6p + 1}{6p + 4} v_{kn}$$

Since $v_{ab} = v_{an} - v_{bn}$,

$$v_{ab} = \left(\frac{12p + 2}{12p + 5} - \frac{6p + 1}{6p + 4}\right) v_{kn}$$

$$= (6p + 1)\left(\frac{3}{(12p + 5)(6p + 4)}\right) v_{kn}$$

Now

$$v_{kn} = \frac{Z_{kn}(p)}{Z_{dn}(p)} v(t)$$

where

$$Y_{kn} = \frac{1}{Z_{kn}} = \frac{1}{2 + Z_2(p)} + \frac{1}{1 + Z_2(p)} = \frac{6p + 1}{12p + 5} + \frac{6p + 1}{6p + 4}$$

$$= (6p + 1)\frac{18p + 9}{(12p + 5)(6p + 4)}$$

$$Z_{kn} = \frac{(12p + 5)(6p + 4)}{(6p + 1)(18p + 9)}$$

and

$$Z_{dn}(p) = \frac{9p}{6p + 1} + Z_{kn}$$

$$Z_{dn} = \frac{9p(18p + 9) + (12p + 5)(6p + 4)}{(6p + 1)(18p + 9)}$$

Then

$$\frac{Z_{kn}}{Z_{dn}} = \frac{(12p + 5)(6p + 4)}{9p(18p + 9) + (12p + 5)(6p + 4)}$$

and

$$v_{ab} = \frac{3(6p + 1)}{(12p + 5)(6p + 4)} \frac{(12p + 5)(6p + 4)}{9p(18p + 9) + (12p + 5)(6p + 4)} v(t)$$

$$= \frac{(6p + 1) \times 3}{9p(18p + 9) + (12p + 5)(6p + 4)} v(t) \qquad (16\text{-}22)$$

Although Eq. (16-22) *appears* to state that v_{ab} and $v(t)$ are related by a second-order differential equation, we know that this is impossible with only one energy-storing element in the circuit. Hence we seek a common factor in the numerator and the denominator of Eq. (16-22),

$$9p(18p + 9) + (12p + 5)(6p + 4) = 234p^2 + 159p + 20 = (6p + 1)(39p + 20)$$

Thus

$$v_{ab} = \frac{3}{39p + 20} v(t)$$

or

$$(39p + 20)v_{ab} = 3v(t) \qquad\qquad Ans. \qquad (16\text{-}23)$$

[Equation (16-23) is checked at $p = 0$(d-c). For $v(t) = V = $ const, $v_{ab} = 3V/20$ from Eq. (16-23), and this result is checked by inspection of Fig. 16-11a. For direct current the capacitance is omitted, and $v_{ab} = (\frac{2}{5} - \frac{1}{4})V = \frac{3}{20}V$.] The time constant of the circuit can be found by inspection of the characteristic equation; if $v(t) = 0$, then

$$(39p + 20)v_{ab} = 0$$

If $v_{ab} = Ke^{st}$,

$$39s + 20 = 0 \qquad \text{or} \qquad s = -\frac{1}{T} = -\frac{20}{39}$$

The source-free circuit is drawn as in Fig. 16-11c or d. For this series-parallel R-C circuit, $R = \frac{6}{5} + \frac{3}{4} = \frac{39}{20}$, since $C = 1$, $T = RC = \frac{39}{20}$, which also checks.

As the last part of this example, $i_{ab}(t)$ (in the circuit of Fig. 16-11a) has to be related to $v(t)$. Now, since $v_{ab}(t)$ is the same function in both Fig. 16-11a and b, $v_{ab}(t)$ is related to $v(t)$ through Eq. (16-23). Hence $i_{ab}(t) = pv_{ab}(t)$, and

$$(39p + 20)\left(\frac{1}{p}\, i_{ab}\right) = 3v(t)$$

or

$$(39p + 20)i_{ab} = 3pv(t) \qquad\qquad Ans. \qquad (16\text{-}24)$$

In concluding this example it is hardly necessary to point out that the delta-wye conversion method is certainly not the fastest way of obtaining the desired result (see Prob. 16-4).

16-7. Solution of Networks Using Simultaneous Equations. Introduction.

In this article we shall introduce the notion of working with several circuit variables simultaneously with the purpose of eventually obtaining an equilibrium equation which relates one of these variables to the source functions. This method requires that a circuit variable (i.e., voltage or current) be assigned symbolically to each element (either primitive element or p element, depending on how the problem is formulated) and then that Kirchhoff's laws be applied until a sufficient number of independent simultaneous equations has been obtained (i.e., as many equations as there are variables) so that the problem is (uniquely) specified. This procedure raises the following questions: (1) In any given circuit how many variables should be chosen as unknowns? (2) How can we be sure that the formulated equations are independent? The remainder of this article will be devoted to an illustration which is intended to show how these questions arise. The following articles will illustrate *how these questions can be resolved.*

Consider the circuit of Fig. 16-12 as an example in which it is required to relate the current $i_3(t)$ to the source functions $v(t)$ and $i(t)$. It is clear that if we knew the current in each element then we should also know the voltage across each element because we know the voltage-current relationships for the elements. Similarly knowledge of the voltages across each element would give us the currents in the elements by means of the same basic equations. Now the waveforms of the ideal source $v(t)$ and the ideal current source are assumed to be known. There are four other elements, R_1, R, R_3, and C, all passive. We shall now symbolically associate a variable with each of these elements. The circuit variables

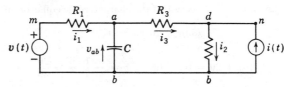

FIG. 16-12. A network and its branch variables.

chosen as the unknowns are $i_1(t)$, $i_2(t)$, $i_3(t)$, and $v_{ab}(t)$. To find the waveform of these variables, we need four independent equations. In this circuit we have three junctions, a, b, and d, so that Kirchhoff's current law can be applied three times, as follows:

> At junction a: $i_1 - pCv_{ab} - i_3 = 0$ (16-25a)
> At junction d: $i_3 - i_2 + i(t) = 0$ (16-25b)
> At junction b: $-i_1 + i_2 - i(t) + pCv_{ab} = 0$ (16-25c)

We observe that Eq. (16-25c) can be obtained by adding (16-25a) to (16-25b) and multiplying the resulting equation by -1. It is therefore clear that, although we have three junctions, Kirchhoff's current law can be applied fruitfully only twice. Any two of the three equations (16-25) can be chosen for further use. Since we have four circuit variables, we need two more equations. Clearly these equations must be obtained by application of Kirchhoff's voltage law since the current law has been "exhausted." Kirchhoff's voltage law states that the sum of the voltages in a closed path (loop) of the circuit is zero. A study of Fig. 16-12 shows that the following are some of the loops of the network: m-a-b-m; m-b-d-a-m; a-b-d-a; b-n-d-b; etc. Clearly we need information which will tell us which loops to choose so that application of Kirchhoff's voltage law will result in independent equations, without trial and error. An elementary introduction to network geometry answers the questions concerning the number of independent equations which can be written for a given network, and the next article deals with this subject.

16-8. Network Terminology ·and Geometry. *Terminology.* In discussing how the elements forming a network are interconnected certain terms were introduced in Chap. 5. It is convenient to restate the definitions of these terms here.

Node: A point in the network which is common to two or more elements.

Junction: A node formed by three or more elements.

Branch: An element or a series connection of elements between junctions. A branch is *active* if it includes one or more ideal sources; otherwise it is *passive*.

Loop: A closed path through the circuit elements of a network.

Mesh: In a given "planar" network diagram a loop which does not enclose or encircle another loop and which cannot be divided into other loops.

It is noted here that by redrawing a network diagram a mesh in the old diagram can be made to become a loop in the new diagram, and vice versa. We therefore talk about a mesh or a loop in connection with a specific drawing of the network diagrams. We pointed out at the beginning of this chapter that the term *element* may apply either to a primitive element or to an operational element. The definitions given above apply in any case.

Network Geometry (Topology).[1] Whether a network is shown with its primitive circuit elements or in the form of p elements, its geometry can be studied regardless of the nature of the circuit elements or p-element branches. Since all the elements dealt with so far, except mutual inductance, have two terminals and the latter can be represented by a combination of such elements (as will be shown in Chap. 18), then between these two terminals all circuit elements, as well as the p-element branches, can be geometrically represented by lines between two terminals.

Line elements: A line which represents a circuit element or a p element is called a line element.[2]

Graph of a network: When the elements of a network are replaced by line elements, the resulting structure is called the graph of the network.

Planar network: A network whose graph can be drawn on a plane, (e.g. a sheet of paper), so that no line elements cross, is called a planar network. In a nonplanar network the definition of meshes cannot be applied.

---

[1] For a detailed study of topology the reader is referred to E. A. Guillemin, "Introductory Circuit Theory," Chaps. 1 and 2, John Wiley & Sons, Inc., New York, 1953.

[2] Some authors restrict line elements to passive elements and examine the structure of the source-free network. In the ensuing discussion, active elements (ideal sources) are included as line elements.

Geometrical Representation. The representation of a network by its graph is called the geometrical representation of the network. In Fig. 16-13a and b a network and its geometrical representation are given. The small circles shown in the graph of a network are called nodes, and a node common to more than two elements is called a junction. A line element or a "series" connection of line elements between two junctions shall be called a branch. The definitions of loop and mesh are similarly extended to apply to the geometrical representation of the networks.

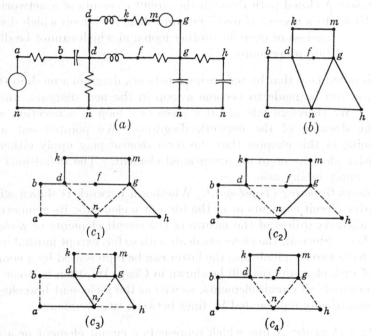

Fig. 16-13. (a) A circuit diagram. (b) Graph of the circuit diagram. (c) Trees and links of the graph.

Trees and Links. The graph of a network as shown in Fig. 16-13b is composed of a number of loops, in which currents flow. It is possible to remove some of the line elements from the graph in such a manner as to destroy (open) all loops and *leave all the nodes connected to each other.* Figure 16-13c shows several such arrangements, where the dotted lines indicate line elements which are removed, while all the nodes are joined by the solid lines.

The reader should sketch more of these arrangements. By removing the appropriate elements in each case the graph has lost its loops, and the corresponding network will be unable to allow passage of current in it, since a current presupposes a closed path through circuit elements.

Tree: A tree of a network is the graph made by a certain number of its line elements such that all the nodes of the network are connected but no closed path is formed. There are many trees[1] possible for a given network. In Fig. 16-13c some of the trees of the graph of network of Fig. 16-13a are shown in solid lines.

Link: For a given tree all the lines in the graph of a network which do not belong to the tree are called the links of the tree. In Fig. 16-13c the links of the graph are indicated by dotted lines.

Basic Properties of Trees and Links. Whereas the tree has the property of connecting all the nodes without forming a closed path, from Fig. 16-13 it is seen that the links have the following important property: Starting with a tree, every time a link is added to the graph, a new loop can be traced which is different from previous loops inasmuch as it includes the new link, not included in the previous loops. In this sense to each link there corresponds a loop which is "independent" from other loops. It can be shown that the number of meshes in a network is identical with the number of independent loops of the network, which, as stated above, is equal to the number of the links of the network. Furthermore it can be shown[2] that the application of Kirchhoff's voltage law to independent loops of the network will result in the maximum number of independent equations, which is equal to the number of the links of the network. These considerations are summarized in the form of the following rule: To obtain a set of independent equations which uniquely specify the network, it is sufficient to apply Kirchhoff's voltage law to the independent loops of the network. It is clear that the number of these equations will be the same as the number of the meshes of the network if the network is planar. If meshes cannot be defined as in nonplanar network, independent-loop equations are written. In the discussion below, we shall use the term *mesh* synonymously with *independent loop.*

Number of Line Elements in a Tree. It is seen that the number of line elements in all possible trees of a given network are equal (eight in Fig. 16-13). This can be proved by observing that in tracing a tree, starting with unconnected nodes, the first line element connects two nodes together, the second line element will connect three nodes and so on. Thus if

$$N = \text{total number of nodes}$$

then $\quad N - 1 = \text{number of line elements in the tree} \quad \quad (16\text{-}26)$

---

[1] See, for example, Louis Weinberg, Number of Trees in a Graph, *Proc. IRE*, vol. 46, no. 12, pp. 1954–1955, December, 1958.

[2] Guillemin, *op. cit.*

Similarly, if

$$E = \text{total number of line elements in graph}$$

and $l = \text{number of links} = \text{number of meshes}$

then $E = (N - 1) + l$

or $l = E - N + 1$ (16-27)

Equations (16-26) and (16-27) are used in the determination of the minimum (necessary and sufficient) number of equilibrium equations which are required for obtaining the response of a network.

16-9. Complexity of Network Graphs. It is intuitively clear that networks with many nodes, elements, and links are more complex than those which have only a few. The use of operational elements and the conversion of voltage to current sources, and vice versa, can simplify the network graph. Whether or not such simplification of the graph results in simplification of the ultimate network problem, i.e., the determination of response or response components, is not certain and depends on the nature of the problem.

The simplification of the network graph using p elements results from the fact that two or more primitive elements in series or in parallel can be represented as a single p element. If we therefore start with a network and its graph in which there are series connections of passive elements and represent such branches as single p elements the resulting graph will contain fewer nodes than the original graph. The representation of parallel combinations of elements as single p elements will result in a new graph in which there are fewer links (i.e., independent loops) than in the original graph. If active branches which contain voltage sources are converted to two branches which represent a current source in parallel with an operational element, then it is possible *to reduce the graph of the original network to a graph in which all nodes are junctions.* The advantages of these three suggested procedures appears evident. We are left with a network in which there are essentially fewer elements (albeit p elements) than in the original network, and as a result we expect that the solution of the new network may be easier. On the other hand, whenever elements are combined into operational elements or whenever sources are converted, the equivalent representation holds only with respect to the two terminals which remain accessible. Thus, in converting and combining elements we may "hide" what may turn out to be essential features of the original network, and thus the determination of certain responses may involve several steps. These statements will now be illustrated.

Let us start with the example of a series R-L-C circuit which has a voltage source $v(t)$ impressed as shown in Fig. 16-14a. This network has four nodes (a, d, f, b) and one mesh, as is seen from the graph shown in Fig. 16-14b. The series combination of R, L, and C can be represented as the operational element

$$Z_{ab}(p) = R + pL + \frac{1}{pC}$$ (16-28)

as shown in Fig. 16-14c.   The graph of the new network has only two nodes and two elements since one of the line elements in the new graph represents a p element.   However, in the new circuit (Fig. 16-14c) we can only relate the voltage v_{ab} to the current

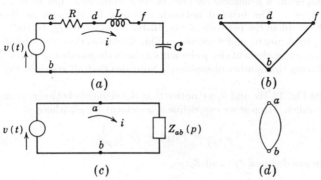

Fig. 16-14. A four-element one-mesh network can be reduced to a two-element network.

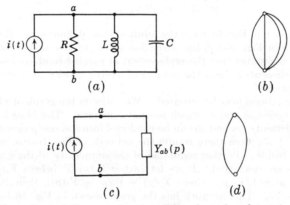

Fig. 16-15. A four-element three-mesh network can be reduced to a two-element network by use of p elements.

$i(t)$.   If the voltage v_{fb} is desired, then reference to the original circuit (Fig. 16-14a) must be made.   Moreover, if the complete response is required, two initial conditions $[i(0^+)$ and $v_{fb}(0^+)]$ are needed.   Since terminal f is no longer accessible in Fig. 16-14c, a derived initial condition $[(di/dt)_{0^+}]$ must be found before Fig. 16-14c can be used to obtain the complete response.

The parallel R-L-C circuit of Fig. 16-15a, which has three meshes, can be reduced by the combination of parallel admittances to the one-mesh circuit of Fig. 16-15c, where

$$Y_{ab}(p) = \frac{1}{R} + pC + \frac{1}{pL}$$ (16-29)

In this circuit (Fig. 16-15c) the three branch currents in the passive elements no longer appear.

As the last example, consider the elaborate circuit shown in Fig. 16-16a. The graph of this circuit is shown in Fig. 16-16b. This graph has 12 elements and 7 nodes. Hence there are $12 - 7 + 1 = 6$ links or 6 independent loops. Inspection of the graph reveals that there are 2 nodes which are not junctions, namely, d and h. We next examine the branches connected to these nodes and find that they are passive. Hence we can define a p element for each of these branches. Let $Z_1 = R_3 + pL_2$ and $Z_2 = R_4 + 1/pC_2$. The original network can now be redrawn as shown in Fig. 16-16c. The graph of the network of Fig. 16-16c is shown in Fig. 16-16d. This graph has 5 nodes, 10 elements, and 6 meshes. This illustrates that replacing a series combination of primitive elements by p elements reduces the number of nodes (from 7 to 5) without reducing the number of meshes. Note also that all nodes in Fig. 16-16d are junctions.

Examining Fig. 16-16c and d, we notice that the elements between m and a (R_1 and L_1) are in parallel. Hence we can define a p element $Z_3(p)$, where

$$\frac{1}{Z_3(p)} = Y_3(p) + \frac{1}{R_1} + \frac{1}{pL_1} \tag{16-30}$$

Similarly we can define $Z_4(p)$ and $Z_5(p)$,

$$\frac{1}{Z_4(p)} = pC_1 + \frac{1}{Z_1(p)} \tag{16-31}$$

and

$$\frac{1}{Z_5(p)} = \frac{1}{R_5} + \frac{1}{Z_2(p)} \tag{16-32}$$

The network shown in Fig. 16-16e is the result of these definitions. The graph of this network, shown in Fig. 16-16f, has seven line elements, five nodes, and hence three meshes. This illustrates that the replacement of parallel combinations of primitive elements by p elements reduces the number of meshes (from 6 to 3) without affecting the number of nodes.

The reducing process may be repeated. We notice in the graph of Fig. 16-16f that there are two nodes, m and a, which are not junctions. The branch mn is active; however, the elements ma and ab can be combined into a single p element. If we let $Z_6(p) = Z_3(p) + R_2$, then there results the network of Fig. 16-16g, whose graph is shown in Fig. 16-16h. Further reduction of the complexity of the graph is possible only if sources are converted. If we let $i_2(t) = Y_6(p)v(t)$ [where $Y_6(p) = 1/Z_6(p)$] and define $Z_7(p) = 1/Y_7(p)$ [where $Y_7(p) = Y_6(p) + Y_4(p)$], then the network of Fig. 16-16i results. This network has the graph shown in Fig. 16-16j. Note that this graph has only three nodes and that all of them are junctions. We observe in this example that the conversion of both current sources in Fig. 16-16i to voltage sources results in a series circuit, but only terminals b, f, and n in that circuit correspond to terminals in the original circuit. Hence only v_{bf}, v_{fn}, and v_{nb} can be obtained from the reduced circuit.

We can now point out several considerations which can be used as guides to determine whether the reduction of complexity of the network by use of p elements, conversion of sources, or both is desirable:

1. What is the circuit problem? If the reduction of the network eliminates terminals at which responses are to be found, the procedure may not be desirable.

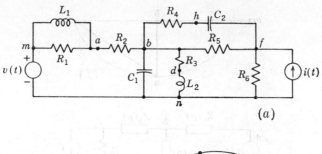

(a)

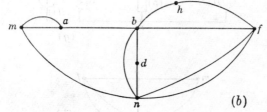

(b)

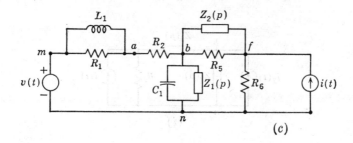

(c)

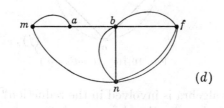

(d)

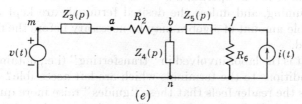

(e)

FIG. 16-16. Reducing the complexity of a graph by use of p elements and source conversion.

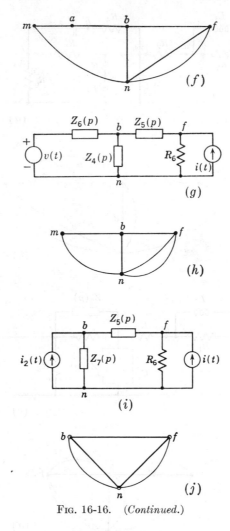

Fig. 16-16.   (*Continued.*)

2. How much algebra is involved in the reduction?   The combination of elements either in operational form or in complex form may be very time-consuming, and unless the desired terminals are kept accessible, a considerable amount of algebra may be necessary before the final solution is obtained.

3. What is the labor involved in "transferring" (i.e., obtaining derived) initial conditions to the terminals which are left accessible?

Perhaps the reader feels that these "guides" raise more questions than they answer.   Unfortunately no firm rules can be stated.   It will become evident, however, in subsequent articles that the reduction of networks is *usually* beneficial if steady-state responses are desired. If the complete response is desired, the reduction is sometimes useful.

16-10. The General Problem of Network Analysis. We shall formulate the general problem of network analysis as follows: (1) Given a network which contains sources and passive elements, relate the variables associated with the passive elements to the source functions. (It is a matter of indifference here whether p elements or primitive elements are used, because we deal with whatever variables are associated with the given elements.) (2) Find the complete response.

Note that we have not stated what is known and what is unknown in the circuit. For the purpose of explaining the analytical procedure, we shall assume that the source functions as well as the element values or operators are known. As we progress, it will become evident that the analytical procedure can sometimes be reversed so that the source functions for a required response or the element values can be the unknowns.

Assuming that the source functions and the network elements are known, then, if there are E passive elements, S_i current sources, and S_v voltage sources in the network, it appears that there are $2E + S_i + S_v$ unknowns. We arrive at this result as follows: We associate with each passive element two variables, namely, the voltage across the terminals of the element and the current which enters (or leaves) a terminal of the element. Hence there are $2E$ unknowns associated with the passive elements. Since, for each ideal voltage source, the voltage across the terminals is known, the current through the voltage source is the only unknown associated with each such source and there are S_v of these. For each ideal current source the voltage across its terminals is the only unknown, and this adds S_i unknowns. Hence we have $2E + S_i + S_v$ unknowns.

Now it is immediately evident that knowledge of the circuit elements means that we know the relationship between the current which enters the terminal of an element and the voltage across the terminals of the element because it is exactly this relationship which is used to define the circuit elements or p elements in the first place. We say, therefore, that, starting with $2E$ unknowns, E of them, either the voltages or the currents associated with each passive element, can be found in terms of the other E, and we shall take the number of these unknowns to be E. Next we shall show that the $S_v + S_i$ unknowns which are associated with the ideal sources are not independent unknowns but are known if the E unknowns associated with the passive elements are found. In the network there are several possible ways in which a source can be connected. We shall consider each of these in turn:

1. An ideal voltage source may be in series with another ideal voltage source as shown in Fig. 16-17a. If that is the case, then, by application

of the definition of a voltage source, the two sources can be represented as a single source. In Fig. 16-17a,

$$v_{ab} = v_{am} + v_{mb} \qquad (16\text{-}33)$$

2. An ideal current source, in parallel with another ideal current source, can be represented as a single current source as shown in Fig. 16-17b, where

$$i(t) = i_1(t) + i_2(t) \qquad (16\text{-}34)$$

3. Two ideal voltage sources $v_1(t)$ and $v_2(t)$ cannot be in parallel unless $v_1 \equiv v_2$. Similarly two ideal current sources $i_1(t)$ and $i_2(t)$ cannot be in series unless $i_1 \equiv i_2$. This follows from the definition of ideal sources.

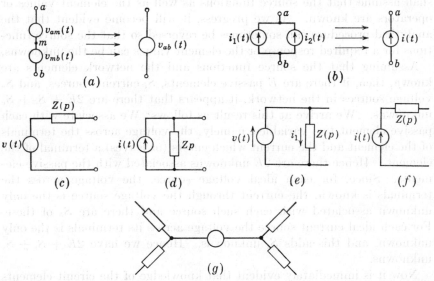

FIG. 16-17. An enumeration of the manner in which sources can appear in a network.

4. An ideal voltage source can be in series with a passive element as shown in Fig. 16-17c. In this case it is evident that, once the current in the passive element is known, the current in the source is known as well.

5. An ideal current source may be in parallel with a passive element as in Fig. 16-17d. In this case the voltage across the element is identical to the voltage across the current source.

6. An ideal voltage source may be in parallel with a passive element as in Fig. 16-17e. In this case the current in the element is immediately known, $i_1 = Y(p)v(t)$, so that one connection of this type in a network gives $E - 1$ unknowns associated with passive elements plus one additional unknown, the current in the voltage source, or, altogether, E unknowns. Although this case may occur "on paper," it does not represent a practical situation. (Why?)

7. An ideal current source may be in series with a passive element as in Fig. 16-17*f*. In this case the current in $Z(p)$ is known, and the voltage across the current source is not known. Again such an arrangement, which may occur on paper, does not represent a practical situation.

8. An ideal source may be connected between two junctions as in Fig. 17-17*g*. If the currents in all the passive elements are known, then the voltage across such a source is found by application of Kirchhoff's voltage law around any loop which includes the source, and the current in such a source is found by application of Kirchhoff's current law at either terminal of the source.

We conclude, therefore, that *the circuit is completely specified through E variables, where E is the number of passive elements in the circuit and only one variable, either voltage or current, is chosen for each passive element.*

For the present we shall restrict the discussion to networks in which all voltage sources have a passive element in series and all current sources have a passive element in parallel. (The other cases result in certain simplifications which will be illustrated in another article.) With this assumption we shall ask how many equilibrium equations are needed to describe the network and how these equations can be obtained.

Since for E passive elements there are E unknown variables, we need E equations. Since Kirchhoff's laws deal with voltages and currents in several elements (i.e., voltages in loops and currents at junctions), these E equations will be simultaneous equations. Since voltages and currents in elements are related through linear operations, the equations will be linear simultaneous equations. If all current sources which have admittances in parallel are converted to voltage sources, then the number of meshes in the network is equal to the links, namely, $E - N + 1$, where N is the number of nodes. Since meshes are geometrically independent loops, we can write $E - N + 1$ independent equations which will express Kirchhoff's voltage law. Hence we need $N - 1$ additional equations. We expect, therefore, that $N - 1$ independent equations can be obtained by application of Kirchhoff's current law. In the next several articles we shall discuss the simultaneous linear equations which are associated with networks. In this connection matrix notation is convenient. A brief résumé about linear equations, determinants, and matrices is given in the Appendix.

16-11. Formulation of Network Equations Using Branch Variables. From Art. 16-10 we know that in a circuit in which all the elements and source functions are known there are as many unknowns as there are passive elements. To obtain the equilibrium equations, we start by assigning, symbolically, a voltage or a current variable to each element. Kirchhoff's voltage law is then applied to each mesh and Kirchhoff's current law at each (independent) junction to result in the required number

of simultaneous equations to solve for the unknowns.   This method will
be illustrated by means of an example.

Example 16-5.   In the resistance network of Fig. 16-18a find the currents in all
resistances as a function of the source functions $v_A(t)$ and $i_B(t)$.

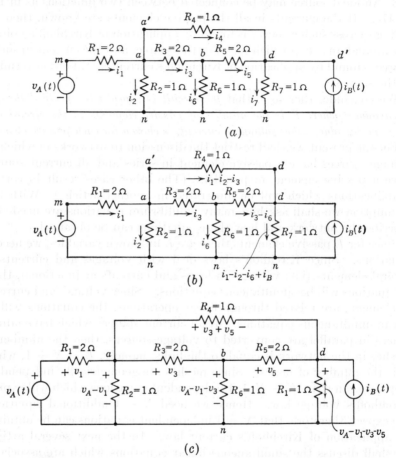

Fig. 16-18. Network used to illustrate the use of branch variables.   (a) A branch
current assigned to each element.   (b) Assignment of branch currents so that Kirchhoff's current law is satisfied by the choice of variables at every junction.   (c) Assignment of element voltages so that Kirchhoff's voltage law is satisfied for every loop.

Solution.   Since only one type of passive element (resistance) is involved, the relationship between the currents in the resistances and the source functions will be
algebraic.   We shall first illustrate the use of branch currents as variables.   The
circuit contains seven resistances; we have accordingly assigned the variables i_1 to i_7
to the resistances.   (The reference directions chosen are arbitrarily assigned.)   We
now seek seven independent relationships for finding the seven unknown currents.
The network graph shows five meshes and four junctions.   One of these meshes,
d-d'-n-d consists of a resistive current source which can be changed to a voltage source
and can therefore be eliminated.   Hence we shall have four Kirchhoff's-voltage-law

equations for the remaining four meshes and three Kirchhoff's-current-law equations. From the voltage law, using the numerical values of the elements, we have for

Mesh m-a-n-m: $2i_1 + i_2 = v_A(t)$ (16-35a)
Mesh a-b-n-a: $2i_3 + i_6 - i_2 = 0$ (16-35b)
Mesh b-d-n-b: $2i_5 + i_7 - i_6 = 0$ (16-35c)
Mesh a-b-d-a'-a: $2i_3 + 2i_5 - i_4 = 0$ (16-35d)

From the current law at

Junction a: $i_1 - i_2 - i_3 - i_4 = 0$ (16-35e)
Junction b: $i_3 - i_6 - i_5 = 0$ (16-35f)
Junction d: $i_5 - i_7 + i_B(t) + i_4 = 0$ (16-35g)

[Note that addition of Eqs. (16-35e), (16-35f), and (16-35g) gives the same result as application of Kirchhoff's current law at junction n.] Equations (16-35) can now be solved simultaneously for the seven unknowns i_1 to i_7.

It is possible to reduce the labor involved in solution and in setting up equations if, in the assignment of current symbols to the elements, the Kirchhoff's current law is satisfied at every junction. Thus at each junction we start assigning symbols to each branch current except one, where the symbol assigned to this branch will depend on the symbols assigned to other branches, such that the Kirchhoff's current law is satisfied. Referring to Fig. 16-18b (this circuit is identical to the circuit of Fig. 16-18a), we have assigned i_1 to R_1, i_2 to R_2, i_3 to R_3, but the current in R_4 is chosen to be $i_1 - i_2 - i_3$ so that the manner in which symbols are assigned to the branch variables assures that Kirchhoff's current law is satisfied at junction a. Proceeding to junction b, we assign i_6 to R_6 but call the current in R_5, $i_3 - i_6$, so that the current law is satisfied at junction b. At junction d Kirchhoff's current law is satisfied by assigning the current $i_1 - i_2 - i_6 + i_B(t)$ to R_7. We now have four unknowns, i_1, i_2, i_3, and i_6. Note, however, that when these currents are found the currents in R_4, R_5, and R_7 must be found through further algebraic operations.

Since Kirchhoff's current law is already satisfied at every junction, the four mesh equations are now written.

Mesh m-a-n-m: $2i_1 + i_2 = v_A(t)$ (16-36a)
Mesh a-b-n-a: $2i_3 + i_6 - i_2 = 0$ (16-36b)
Mesh b-d-n-b: $2(i_3 - i_6) + 1[i_1 - i_2 - i_6 + i_B(t)] - i_6 = 0$ (16-36c)
Mesh a-b-d-a' $=$ a: $2i_3 + 2(i_3 - i_6) - 1(i_1 - i_2 - i_3) = 0$ (16-36d)

Rewriting (16-36a) to (16-36d) and collecting terms, we have

$$2i_1 + i_2 \qquad\qquad\qquad = v_A(t)$$ (16-37a)
$$-i_2 + 2i_3 + i_6 = 0$$ (16-37b)
$$i_1 - i_2 + 2i_3 - 4i_6 = -i_B(t)$$ (16-37c)
$$-i_1 + i_2 + 5i_3 - 2i_6 = 0$$ (16-37d)

Solving for $i_1(t)$, by Cramer's rule we have

$$i_1 = \frac{\begin{vmatrix} v_A & +1 & 0 & 0 \\ 0 & -1 & +2 & +1 \\ -i_B & -1 & +2 & -4 \\ 0 & +1 & +5 & -2 \end{vmatrix}}{\begin{vmatrix} +2 & +1 & 0 & 0 \\ 0 & -1 & +2 & +1 \\ +1 & -1 & +2 & -4 \\ -1 & +1 & +5 & -2 \end{vmatrix}} = \frac{-35v_A + 9i_B}{-89} = \tfrac{35}{89}v_A - \tfrac{9}{89}i_B$$

Similarly
$$i_2 = \frac{-19v_A - 18i_B}{-89} = \tfrac{19}{89}v_A + \tfrac{18}{89}i_B$$
$$i_3 = \tfrac{6}{89}v_A + \tfrac{1}{89}i_B$$
$$i_6 = \tfrac{7}{89}v_A + \tfrac{16}{89}i_B$$

Using Kirchhoff's current law, at junctions a, b, and n in Fig. 16-18a we have the branch currents i_4, i_5, and i_7,

$$i_4 = i_1 - i_2 - i_3 = \tfrac{10}{89}v_A - \tfrac{28}{89}i_B$$
$$i_5 = i_3 - i_6 = -\tfrac{1}{89}v_A - \tfrac{15}{89}i_B$$
$$i_7 = i_1 - i_2 - i_6 + i_B = \tfrac{9}{89}v_A + \tfrac{46}{89}i_B$$

Use of Voltage Variables. If we symbolically assign a voltage to each resistance in Fig. 16-18a, then we can write the seven equations (16-35) as before. Exactly as in the case of current variables the number of equations can be reduced below seven. This is achieved if we assign voltage variables so that Kirchhoff's *voltage* law is satisfied by the manner in which the variables are chosen. Starting with R_1, the voltage v_1 is assigned to R_1 as in Fig. 16-18c. Now we note that the voltage across R_2 (with reference directions as chosen) must be $v_A(t) - v_1$ because Kirchhoff's voltage law around mesh m-a-n-m must be satisfied. Proceeding now to another mesh, say, mesh a-b-n-a, we assign v_3 to R_3 as shown. The voltage across R_6 is seen to be $v_A - v_1 - v_3$. Assigning v_5 to R_5, we have $v_A - v_1 - v_3 - v_5$ across R_7 and $v_3 + v_5$ across R_4 (all with arbitrarily chosen reference directions as indicated in the figure). Now Kirchhoff's voltage law around every mesh is satisfied by the manner in which the voltage variables have been assigned. We now proceed to satisfy Kirchhoff's current law.

At junction a: $\dfrac{v_1}{2} - \dfrac{v_A - v_1}{1} - \dfrac{v_3}{2} - \dfrac{v_3 + v_5}{1} = 0$

At junction b: $\dfrac{v_3}{2} - \dfrac{v_A - v_1 - v_3}{1} - \dfrac{v_5}{2} = 0$

At junction d: $\dfrac{v_5}{2} - \dfrac{v_A - v_1 - v_3 - v_5}{1} + i_B + \dfrac{v_3 + v_5}{1} = 0$

Collecting terms in each of these equations, we have

$$+\tfrac{3}{2}v_1 - \tfrac{3}{2}v_3 - v_5 = v_A \tag{16-38a}$$
$$+v_1 + \tfrac{3}{2}v_3 - \tfrac{1}{2}v_5 = v_A \tag{16-38b}$$
$$+v_1 + 2v_3 + \tfrac{5}{2}v_5 = v_A - i_B \tag{16-38c}$$

Solving for v_1, we have

$$v_1 = \frac{\begin{vmatrix} v_A & -\tfrac{3}{2} & -1 \\ v_A & +\tfrac{3}{2} & -\tfrac{1}{2} \\ v_A - i_B & 2 & +\tfrac{5}{2} \end{vmatrix}}{\begin{vmatrix} +\tfrac{3}{2} & -\tfrac{3}{2} & -1 \\ +1 & +\tfrac{3}{2} & -\tfrac{1}{2} \\ +1 & +2 & +\tfrac{5}{2} \end{vmatrix}} = \frac{35v_A/4 + 9i_B/4}{\tfrac{89}{8}} = \frac{70v_A}{89} - \frac{18i_B}{89}$$

Similarly
$$v_3 = \frac{6v_A/4 + i_B/4}{\tfrac{89}{8}} = \frac{12v_A}{89} + \frac{2i_B}{89}$$
$$v_5 = \frac{-v_A/4 - 15i_B/4}{\tfrac{89}{8}} = -\frac{2v_A}{89} - \frac{30i_B}{89}$$

The remaining voltages are found by application of the voltage law,

$$v_{an} = v_A(t) - v_1 \qquad v_{bn} = v_A(t) - v_1 - v_3$$
$$v_{ad} = v_3 + v_5 \qquad v_{dn} = v_A - v_1 - v_3 - v_5$$

The numerical result may be obtained by the reader by using direct substitution, and the results for the branch currents may then be checked.

In this example we have shown how the number of simultaneous equations can be reduced below E to either $E - (N - 1)$ or $N - 1$ by choice of current or voltage symbols such that either the current or the voltage law is satisfied "automatically." Two systematic procedures which accomplish the same aim (i.e., reducing the number of simultaneous equations below E) are the "node-voltage" and the "mesh-current" methods, which are treated in the next two articles.

16-12. The Method of Node Voltages. In this article we shall show how by the choice of certain voltages as the variables of a network simultaneous equations can be obtained by the application of Kirchhoff's current law alone. Furthermore it will be seen that, when these voltages are found, all other variables of the network can be found. Since we plan to obtain the simultaneous equations of the network by application of Kirchhoff's current law, the voltage variables must be chosen such that Kirchhoff's voltage law will be satisfied for every loop. For the present it will be *convenient* to assume that all voltage sources in the network have internal immittances and that the network has been drawn with all sources shown as (i.e., converted to) current sources. We shall further represent the network by use of operational elements but remember that the results hold when each operational element is a primitive element. The use of operational elements in the circuit reduces the network, as we have shown, so that all nodes are junctions.

To develop the node method, we assign a number or letter to all nodes in the network. In Fig. 16-19a a typical node, which is assigned the number 1, is shown. This node has the following connections to it:

1. The admittance $Y_A(p)$ connects node 1 to node 2.

2. The current source consisting of $i_B(t)$ and $Y_B(p)$ connects node 1 to node 3.

3. The current source consisting of $i_C(t)$ and $Y_C(p)$ connects node 1 to node 4.

4. The admittance $Y_D(p)$ connects node 1 to node R.

5. The admittance $Y_E(p)$ connects node 1 to node 5.

6. The admittance zero connects node 1 to node 6 (this means that there is no connection between node 1 and node 6).

7. The ideal current source $i_E(t)$ connects node 1 to node 7.

In Fig. 16-19a only those circuit elements which are connected to node 1 are shown. Nodes 2, 3, etc., are also interconnected, but we are now con-

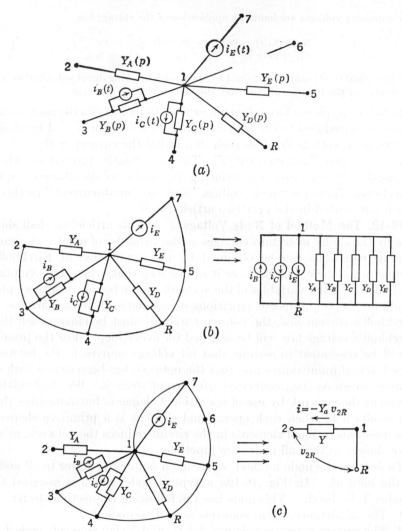

FIG. 16-19. (*a*) Portion of a network showing how node 1 can be connected to other nodes. (*b*) All nodes except node 1 are connected to the reference node when Y_{11} is determined. (*c*) All nodes except node 2 are connected to the reference node when Y_{12} is determined.

cerned only with the conditions at the "typical node," which we have numbered as node 1. We further assume that the network contains no mutual inductance. (Circuits with mutaul inductance will be treated in Chap. 18.)

Let us apply Kirchhoff's current law at node 1. The sum of the currents flowing into node 1 is given by the following equations (for v_{21} read

"v two one," not "v twenty-one," etc.):

$$Y_A(p)v_{21} + Y_B(p)v_{31} + i_B(t) + Y_C(p)v_{41} - i_C(t)$$
$$+ Y_D(p)v_{R1} + Y_E(p)v_{51} - i_E(t) = 0$$

or

$$Y_A(p)v_{21} + Y_B(p)v_{31} + Y_C(p)v_{41} + Y_D(p)v_{R1} + Y_E(p)v_{51}$$
$$= -i_B + i_C + i_E \quad (16\text{-}39a)$$

Multiplying (16-39a) by -1, we have

$$Y_A(p)v_{12} + Y_B(p)v_{13} + Y_C(p)v_{14} + Y_D(p)v_{1R} + Y_E(p)v_{15}$$
$$= i_B - i_C - i_E \quad (16\text{-}39b)$$

Reference Node and Node Voltages. In Eq. (16-39b) the currents which flow through passive elements into node 1 are expressed in terms of the voltage between node 1 and the other nodes. But these voltages can all be expressed by applying Kirchhoff's voltage law around loops in the circuit all of which include an arbitrarily chosen node, called the reference node. We have chosen node R to be the reference node, thus:

$$v_{12} = v_{1R} + v_{R2} = v_{1R} - v_{2R}$$
$$v_{13} = v_{1R} + v_{R3} = v_{1R} - v_{3R}$$
$$v_{14} = v_{1R} + v_{R4} = v_{1R} - v_{4R} \quad (16\text{-}40)$$
$$v_{15} = v_{1R} + v_{R5} = v_{1R} - v_{5R}$$
$$v_{1R} = v_{1R} + v_{RR} = v_{1R}$$

In the above equation the voltage associated with a branch (such as v_{12} associated with branch joining junctions 1 and 2) is determined in terms of the difference between the voltage between the nodes of that branch and a given reference node: $v_{12} = v_{1R} - v_{2R}$. The voltage of a given node with respect to a specified reference node is called the node voltage. Substituting Eqs. (16-40) into (16-39b), we may write

$$Y_A(v_{1R} - v_{2R}) + Y_B(v_{1R} - v_{3R}) + Y_C(v_{1R} - v_{4R}) + Y_D v_{1R}$$
$$+ Y_E(v_{1R} - v_{5R}) = i_B - i_C - i_E$$

or

$$[Y_A(p) + Y_B(p) + Y_C(p) + Y_D(p) + Y_E(p)]v_{1R} + [-Y_A(p)]v_{2R}$$
$$+ [-Y_B(p)]v_{3R} + [-Y_C(p)]v_{4R} + [-Y_E(p)]v_{5R}$$
$$= i_B - i_C - i_E \quad (16\text{-}41)$$

Now in Eq. (16-41) we note that the terms are arranged so that the right-hand side of the equation contains only the source functions. We observe that $i_B - i_C - i_E$ is equal to the sum of the currents from ideal sources *flowing into node* 1. If the reference arrow of the current source is away from the node, the source is assigned a negative sign in the summation.   We denote this sum as $i_1(t)$,

$$i_B - i_C - i_E = i_1(t)$$

Nodal Current Supply.   In general we denote the sum of the currents which flow from ideal current sources into node k as i_k and call it the current supply of node k.   Note that i_k is the sum of the currents from the *ideal* sources and does not include currents associated with the node k through passive elements.

Nodal Self-admittance.   Next we study the terms on the left-hand side of Eq. (16-41).   We observe that if we set

$$v_{2R} = v_{3R} = v_{4R} = v_{5R} \equiv 0$$

but $v_{1R} \neq 0$ i.e., if $v_{kR} = 0$, for $k \neq 1$,

then $[Y_A(p) + Y_B(p) + Y_C(p) + Y_D(p) + Y_E(p)] v_{1R} = i_1(t)$ (16-42)

Now v_{kR} can be made zero by connecting node k to node R.   In Fig. 16-19b the portion of the network shown in Fig. 16-19a is redrawn, but all nodes except node 1 are connected to node R.   We now define the *self-admittance of node k*, denoted by the symbol $Y_{kk}(p)$, as follows:

If all nodes except node k are connected to the reference node, then the application of Kirchhoff's current law at node k will result in an equation of the form $Y_{kk}(p)v_{kR}(t) = i_k(t)$. $Y_{kk}(p)$ is called the operational self-admittance of node k.

From Eq. (16-42) it is seen that in a network (which does not contain mutual inductance) the self-admittance of a node is given by the sum of the admittances between the node in question and the reference node if all nodes except the node in question are connected to the reference node. Hence in the above example $Y_{11}(p) = Y_A + Y_B + Y_C + Y_D + Y_E$.

Mutual Admittance between Two Nodes.   Observe that in Fig. 16-19a if all nodes except node 2 but including node 1 are connected to the reference node, as shown in Fig. 16-19c, then the current which flows *out of* node 1 owing to a voltage v_{2R} is $(-Y_A)v_{2R}$.   Based on this observation, we define the *mutual admittance between two nodes*, k and n, as follows:

If all nodes except node k are connected to the reference node, then the current which flows *out of* node n due to a voltage v_{kR} is $Y_{nk}v_{kR}$, where Y_{nk} is the operational mutual admittance between nodes n and k.

We observe from Eq. (16-41) that (in the absence of mutual inductance in the network) the mutual admittance between two nodes is given by the *negative* of the admittance of the element which directly connects these two nodes.

Setting $Y_{11} = Y_A + Y_B + Y_C + Y_D + Y_E$, $Y_{12} = -Y_A$, $Y_{13} = -Y_B$, $Y_{14} = -Y_C$, $Y_{15} = -Y_E$, Kirchhoff's current law at node 1 is expressed through the equation

$$Y_{11}(p)v_{1R} + Y_{12}(p)v_{2R} + Y_{13}(p)v_{3R} + Y_{14}(p)v_{4R} + Y_{15}(p)v_{5R} = i_1(t)$$

In a network which contains N nodes we have for node 1

$$Y_{11}(p)v_{1R} + Y_{12}(p)v_{2R} + \cdots + Y_{1n}v_{nR} + Y_{1N}v_{NR} = i_1(t)$$

where $n = N - 1$. If the node numbered N is the reference node, then $v_{NR} = v_{RR} = 0$. The term $Y_{1N}v_{NR}$ in the equation for node 1 can then be omitted. Moreover, from the definition of self-admittance it is seen that the self-admittance of the reference node is zero. Using the symbols defined above, we now write the equations which express Kirchhoff's current law at each node except at the reference node. This will result in $n = N - 1$ equations, where N is the total number of the nodes.

$$Y_{11}v_{1R} + Y_{12}v_{2R} + Y_{13}v_{3R} + \cdots + Y_{1n}v_{nR} = i_1(t)$$
$$Y_{21}v_{1R} + Y_{22}v_{2R} + Y_{23}v_{3R} + \cdots + Y_{2n}v_{nR} = i_2(t)$$

$$\qquad (16\text{-}43a)$$

$$Y_{n1}v_{1R} + Y_{n2}v_{2n} + Y_{n3}v_{3R} + \cdots + Y_{nn}v_{nR} = i_n(t)$$

The node equation for the reference node reads

$$Y_{R1}v_{1R} + Y_{R2}v_{2R} + Y_{R3}v_{3R} + \cdots + Y_{nR}v_{nR} = i_R \qquad (16\text{-}43b)$$

This equation is superfluous because we already have the n simultaneous equations (16-43a) for the n variables v_{1R} through v_{nR}, which completely specify the network. To show explicitly that Eq. (16-43b) is not independent of the system of Eqs. (16-43a), we observe that

$$Y_{R1} = -(Y_{11} + Y_{21} + \cdots + Y_{n1})$$

since Y_{R1} is the negative of the admittances connected between node R and node 1. In Fig. 16-19a,

$$Y_{R1} = -Y_D$$
$$= -(Y_A + Y_B + Y_C + Y_D + Y_E - Y_A - Y_B - Y_C - Y_E)$$

Hence

$$Y_{Rk} = -(Y_{kk} + Y_{k1} + Y_{k2} + \cdots + Y_{kn})$$

Hence the sum of Eqs. (16-43a) gives Eq. (16-43b), and the latter equation is not independent of the others.

Single-index Notation for Node Voltages. We have seen that the voltage of any node with respect to a specified reference node of the network is called the node voltage of that node. Since the node voltages in the network are always with respect to a specified reference node, these voltages can be referred to by means of a single index. Thus in place of v_{1R} we write v_1, in place of v_{2R}, v_2, etc. It is understood that the reference node will be marked on the circuit diagram so that the single-index notation is meaningful. Commonly the "ground symbol" $\perp$ is used to mark the reference node.

Further Discussion of the Node Equations. Using the single-index notation, the node equations have the form

$$Y_{11}v_1 + Y_{12}v_2 + \cdots + Y_{1n}v_n = i_1$$

$$\vdots \qquad\qquad\qquad \vdots \qquad (16\text{-}44a)$$

$$Y_{n1}v_1 + Y_{n2}v_2 + \cdots + Y_{nn}v_n = i_n$$

To represent this set of simultaneous equations, the matrix form is particularly convenient. We define the node admittance matrix $\|Y_{jk}\|$

$$\|Y_{jk}\| = \begin{Vmatrix} Y_{11} & Y_{12} & \cdots & Y_{1n} \\ Y_{21} & Y_{22} & \cdots & Y_{2n} \\ \cdot & \cdot & \cdots & \cdot \\ Y_{n1} & Y_{n2} & \cdots & Y_{nn} \end{Vmatrix} \qquad (16\text{-}44b)$$

so that the node equations are written as the matrix product

$$\|Y_{jk}\| \times \|v_j\| = \|i_j\| \qquad (16\text{-}44c)$$

where $\|v_j\|$ is the node-voltage column matrix and $\|i_j\|$ is the nodal supply-current column matrix. The solution for the node voltages is obtained by solution of these equations.

The Summation Notation for the Simultaneous Equations of Network. The set of equations given in Eq. (16-44a) can be written as

$$\sum_{k=1}^{k=n} Y_{jk}v_k = i_j \qquad j = 1, 2, 3, \ldots, n \qquad (16\text{-}44d)$$

where the subscript k is a subscript of summation and subscript j is called the parametric subscript. For every value of j from 1 through n, Eq. (16-44d) will be the result of the application of Kirchhoff's laws to the node corresponding to the chosen j. Thus Eq. (16-44d) represents a set of $n = N - 1$ simultaneous equations, where N is the total number of the nodes in the network.

Properties of the Node Admittance Matrix. The matrix (16-44b) has a principal diagonal which consists of the self-admittances at the nodes. We now note that $Y_{12}v_2$ is the current which flows out of node 1 (with node 1 and all nodes except 2 connected to the reference node) due to a voltage v_2 at node 2, and $Y_{21}v_1$ is the current out of node 2 due to a voltage v_1 at node 1 if all nodes except node 1 are connected to the reference node. Hence for admittances composed of the elements R, L, and C, $Y_{12} = Y_{21}$. Similarly $Y_{jk} = Y_{kj}$. (This property of the elements is called the "bilateral" property.) Consequently the node admittance matrix is symmetrical with respect to the principal diagonal.

In Part B several examples of the setting up of node equations are given. For the present, the following will suffice.

Example 16-6. Find the node equations for the circuit of Fig. 16-20.

Solution. The reference node is given, and the junctions are numbered. If we are not interested in the voltage across the inductance, the node between the 2-ohm

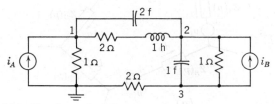

FIG. 16-20. Circuit used to illustrate setting up of node equations.

resistance and the 1-henry inductance may be eliminated by using a p element for that branch. Since there are three other nodes (in addition to the reference node), the equations are:

$$Y_{11}(p)v_1 + Y_{12}(p)v_2 + Y_{13}(p)v_3 = i_1$$
$$Y_{21}(p)v_1 + Y_{22}(p)v_2 + Y_{23}(p)v_3 = i_2$$
$$Y_{31}(p)v_1 + Y_{32}(p)v_2 + Y_{33}(p)v_3 = i_3$$

where the nodal current supplies are

$$i_1(t) = i_A(t) \qquad i_2(t) = i_B(t) \qquad i_3(t) = -i_B(t)$$

$$Y_{11}(p) = 1 + 2p + \frac{1}{2 + p} = \frac{2p^2 + 5p + 3}{2 + p}$$

$$Y_{22}(p) = 1 + 3p + \frac{1}{2 + p} = \frac{3p^2 + 7p + 3}{2 + p}$$

$$Y_{33}(p) = \left(\frac{3}{2} + p\right) = \frac{3 + 2p}{2}$$

$$Y_{12} = Y_{21} = -\left(2p + \frac{1}{2 + p}\right) = -\frac{2p^2 + 4p + 1}{2 + p}$$

$$Y_{13} = Y_{31} = 0$$

$$Y_{23} = Y_{32} = -(1 + p)$$

With matrix notation the node equations read

$$\left\| \begin{matrix} \dfrac{2p^2 + 5p + 3}{2 + p} & -\dfrac{2p^2 + 4p + 1}{2 + p} & 0 \\[2ex] -\dfrac{2p + 4p + 1}{2 + p} & \dfrac{3p^2 + 7p + 3}{2 + p} & -(1 + p) \\[2ex] 0 & -(1 + p) & \dfrac{3 + 2p}{2} \end{matrix} \right\| \times \left\| \begin{matrix} v_1 \\[2ex] v_2 \\[2ex] v_3 \end{matrix} \right\| = \left\| \begin{matrix} i_A \\[2ex] i_B \\[2ex] -i_B \end{matrix} \right\|$$

The Number of Necessary and Sufficient Node Equations. In Art. 16-8 dealing with network topology we noted that the number of the elements in the tree of a network is equal to $n = N - 1$, where N is the number of the nodes of the network. In this article we have seen that the node method uniquely describes the network by obtaining $n = N - 1$ nodal equations. This fact shows that the number of elements in the tree of a network determines the number of independent nodal equations required for unique description of the network. It is seen that this number is $n = N - 1$.

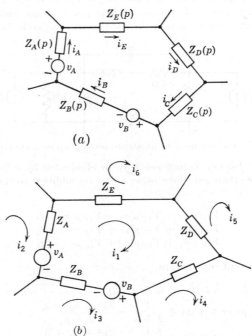

(a)

(b)

FIG. 16-21. A typical mesh in a network.

16-13. The Method of Mesh Currents.

In this article we shall show how the choice of certain currents as the variables in a network can be used in connection with Kirchhoff's voltage law alone to obtain a set of equations which uniquely describe the network. In other words, we shall assign current variables in such a manner that Kirchhoff's current law at every junction in the network is satisfied by the choice of variables. For the present it will be convenient to assume that all the current sources in the network have internal immittances and that the network has been drawn with such sources converted to voltage sources. We shall further assume that there is no mutual inductance in the network and that the elements are represented as operational elements. (The case with mutual inductance is discussed in Chap. 18.)

In Fig. 16-21a a typical mesh of the network is shown. The application of Kirchhoff's voltage law around this mesh (clockwise) gives the equation

$$-v_A + Z_A(p)i_A + Z_E(p)i_E + Z_D(p)i_D + Z_C(p)i_C + v_B + Z_B(p)i_B = 0$$

or

$$Z_A(p)i_A + Z_B(p)i_B + Z_C(p)i_C + Z_D(p)i_D + Z_E(p)i_E$$
$$= v_A(t) - v_B(t) \quad (16\text{-}45)$$

We observe that Eq. (16-45) is written with the branch currents i_A, i_B, i_C, i_D, and i_E as the variables.

Mesh Currents. We define six new variables which are dimensionally currents (see Fig. 16-21b) such that

$$i_A = i_1 - i_2$$
$$i_B = i_1 - i_3$$
$$i_C = i_1 - i_4 \quad\quad (16\text{-}46)$$
$$i_D = i_1 - i_5$$
$$i_E = i_1 - i_6$$

In other words each branch current has been taken as the *difference* between i_1 and another of the new numbered current variables. Equation (16-45), using the new variables, reads

$$(Z_A + Z_B + Z_C + Z_D + Z_E)i_1 + (-Z_A i_2) + (-Z_B i_3) + (-Z_C i_4)$$
$$+ (-Z_D i_5) + (-Z_E i_6) = v_A - v_B \quad (16\text{-}46a)$$

If we now associate each of the currents i_1 to i_6 with a *mesh* as indicated in Fig. 16-21b, then the relationships (16-46) are satisfied, and since each of the numbered currents *circulates* in a mesh it enters *and* leaves each node so that Kirchhoff's current law at every node or junction is satisfied. Hence if we choose these "new" variables, called *mesh* currents, as the circuit variables, we need only write the Kirchhoff-voltage-law equations for each mesh in the circuit. A typical mesh equation is Eq. (16-46a), the equation for mesh 1 in Fig. 16-21b. We note that all mesh currents are assigned clockwise; and once a choice has been made we associate that circulation not only with the mesh current but also with the geometric entity, namely, the mesh itself. The mesh equation (16-46a) has the form

$$Z_{11}(p)i_1 + Z_{12}(p)i_2 + Z_{13}(p)i_3 + Z_{14}(p)i_4 + Z_{15}(p)i_5 + Z_{16}(p)i_6 = v_1$$

where the Z_{ij} operators and v_1 are identified by comparison with Eq. (16-46a). We now introduce the following definitions.

Mesh Voltage Supply. The sum of voltage sources in the branches of a mesh, summed up in a direction *opposite* to the reference direction of the mesh current, is called the mesh voltage supply. The mesh voltage supply is denoted by letter v with a single subscript referring to its respective mesh. In Fig. 16-21b the mesh voltage supply of mesh number 1 is obtained by starting from a node and adding up voltage sources in a counterclockwise direction. This gives

$$v_1 = v_A - v_B$$

Self-impedance of a Mesh. If all meshes except mesh k are *opened* and a mesh current i_k flows in mesh k, then the sum of the voltages across the passive elements in mesh k summed up in the direction of the reference arrow of i_k is given by $Z_{kk}i_k$, where $Z_{kk}(p)$ is the self-impedance of mesh k. If the network contains no mutual inductance, then the sum of the impedances of the elements in the mesh is called the self-impedance of that mesh. In mesh 1 (Fig. 16-21b)

$$Z_{11} = Z_A + Z_B + Z_C + Z_D + Z_E$$

Mutual impedance of Two Meshes. If all currents except i_k are zero and if we add the voltages across the passive elements in mesh m due to i_k, the addition being done in the direction of the reference arrow of i_k, then the sum of these voltages is $Z_{mk}i_k$, where Z_{mk} is called the mutual imped-ance between the two meshes k and m. From this definition it is seen that if two meshes in a network have a common branch (which does not include a mutual inductance) the negative of impedance of the branch is the mutual impedance of the two meshes. This will be denoted by Z with two subscripts corresponding to the two meshes sharing the common branch. Thus in Fig. 16-21b $Z_{12} = -Z_A$, $Z_{13} = -Z_B$, etc. If the ele-ments are bilateral, then $Z_{mn} = Z_{nm}$.

The mesh equations for an m-mesh network can now be written in the form

$$\begin{aligned}
Z_{11}(p)i_1 + Z_{12}(p)i_2 + \cdots + Z_{1m}i_m &= v_1 \\
Z_{21}(p)i_1 + Z_{22}(p)i_2 + \cdots + Z_{2m}i_m &= v_2 \\
&\vdots \\
Z_{m1}(p)i_1 + Z_{m2}(p)i_2 + \cdots + Z_{mm}i_m &= v_m
\end{aligned} \qquad (16\text{-}47)$$

or in matrix form

$$\|Z_{jk}\| \times \|i_j\| = \|v_j\|$$

where $\|Z_{jk}\|$ is the mesh impedance matrix,

$$\|Z_{jk}\| = \begin{Vmatrix}
Z_{11} & Z_{12} & \cdots & Z_{1m} \\
Z_{21} & Z_{22} & \cdots & Z_{2m} \\
\cdot & \cdot & \cdots & \cdot \\
Z_{m1} & Z_{m2} & \cdots & Z_{mm}
\end{Vmatrix}$$

We observe that the mesh impedance matrix is symmetrical with respect to its principal diagonal if the elements in the network are bilateral.

Summation Notation for Mesh Equations. By analogy with the use of summation notation for node equations the mesh equations of Eq. (16-47) can be written as

$$\sum_{k=1}^{k=m} Z_{jk}i_k = v_j \qquad j = 1, 2, \ldots, m \qquad (16\text{-}48)$$

where m is the number of meshes in the network and the i_k and v_j are the mesh currents and mesh voltage supplies, respectively.

Example 16-7. Find the mesh equations for the network of Fig. 16-22.

Solution. For the three-mesh network shown the mesh equations in symbolic form are

$$Z_{11}(p)i_1 + Z_{12}(p)i_2 + Z_{13}(p)i_3 = v_1$$
$$Z_{21}(p)i_1 + Z_{22}(p)i_2 + Z_{23}(p)i_3 = v_2$$
$$Z_{31}(p)i_1 + Z_{32}(p)i_2 + Z_{33}(p)i_3 = v_3$$

where $\qquad v_1 = v_A \qquad v_2 = -v_B \qquad v_3 = v_B$

and $Z_{11} = 3 + 2p$, $Z_{22} = 3 + 2p + 1/p$, $Z_{33} = 2 + 1/p$, $Z_{12} = Z^{21} - 1 - 2p$, $Z_{23} = Z_{32} = -1/p$, $Z_{13} = Z_{31} = 0$.

The Number of Necessary and Sufficient Mesh Equations. In Art. 16-8 dealing with network topology we noted that the number of the links in the graph of a network is identical with the number of independent loops of that graph. Since meshes are independent loops, their number is equal to the number of links given by $E - N + 1$, where E and N are the number of passive elements and nodes of the network, respectively. Thus the number of

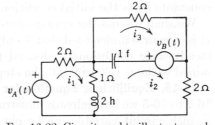

FIG. 16-22. Circuit used to illustrate mesh equations.

mesh equations required for the unique description of the network is $E - N + 1$.

B. SOLUTION OF THE NETWORK EQUATIONS

16-14. Formulation of the Problem. In the preceding paragraphs we have seen that the application of Kirchhoff's laws to a network results in equilibrium equations which are a set of simultaneous linear ordinary inhomogeneous differential equations with constant coefficients. The variables in these equations can be the node voltages or the mesh currents, or they can be currents and voltages which are associated with the elements of the network. After the network equations have been formulated, the remaining problem is to determine the complete response of the network. The term "complete response" is extended to apply to networks exactly as it is applied to simple circuits. The complete response for a network variable is that function which satisfies the equilibrium equations of the network as well as the initial conditions. While in general one can state that the determination of complete response of a network involves finding the functions which represent *all* the variables of the network, in practice it is usually required to solve not for *all* the voltages and currents in the network but only for selected variables. Thus, for example, in a 5-node network only the node voltages $v_1(t)$ and $v_3(t)$ may be of interest. If for the present we assume that appropriate initial conditions are given, then the procedure for obtaining the complete response is outlined as follows:

1. Obtain the equilibrium equations of the network.

2. Manipulate the equilibrium equations (for example, by the use of Cramer's rule) until the network functions which relate the desired variable to the source functions are obtained.

3. Obtain the free component of the response. This component will include undetermined constants.

4. Obtain the component of the response due to the source functions.

5. Formulate the complete response, and evaluate the undetermined constants from the initial conditions.

We shall discuss the various steps in this outline in the articles below. It is of course understood that if only a response component (for example, steady-state condition) is desired that component can often be determined without following all the steps in the outline.

16-15. Equilibrium Equation for a Single Circuit Variable. In Arts. 16-2 to 16-5 we have already illustrated how the equilibrium equation for a single circuit variable can be obtained by direct application of Kirchhoff's laws to the network. In those articles the use of simultaneous equations was avoided by repeated substitutions. In this article we shall show how simultaneous equations are manipulated to obtain the equilibrium equation for a single variable. While we shall use the notation of the node and mesh equations, it is expected that the reader will recognize the generality of the procedure so that the manipulation of linear simultaneous equations which result from the use of branch variables will also be clear.

Suppose that we have an n-node network which is specified through the node equations

$$\|Y_{jk}(p)\| \times \|v_j\| = \|i_j\| \tag{16-49}$$

or, in detail,

$$
\begin{aligned}
Y_{11}(p)v_1 + Y_{12}(p)v_2 + \cdots + Y_{1n}(p)v_n &= i_1(t) \\
Y_{21}(p)v_1 + Y_{22}(p)v_2 + \cdots + Y_{2n}(p)v_n &= i_2(t) \\
&\ \ \vdots \\
Y_{n1}(p)v_1 + Y_{n2}(p)v_2 + \cdots + Y_{nn}(p)v_n &= i_n(t)
\end{aligned}
\tag{16-50}
$$

We now make use of the quasi-algebraic character of the operators $Y_{jk}(p)$ and solve for a desired variable by Cramer's rule. If, for example, the equilibrium equation for $v_1(t)$ is desired, then

$$
v_1 = \frac{
\begin{vmatrix}
i_1 & Y_{12} & \cdots & Y_{1n} \\
i_2 & Y_{22} & \cdots & Y_{2n} \\
\cdot & \cdot & \cdots & \cdot \\
i_n & Y_{n2} & \cdots & Y_{nn}
\end{vmatrix}
}{
\begin{vmatrix}
Y_{11} & Y_{12} & \cdots & Y_{1n} \\
Y_{21} & Y_{22} & \cdots & Y_{2n} \\
\cdot & \cdot & \cdots & \cdot \\
Y_{n1} & Y_{n2} & \cdots & Y_{nn}
\end{vmatrix}
}
\tag{16-51}
$$

Now the determinant in the denominator of Eq. (16-51) is the determinant of the node admittance matrix, and this determinant is denoted by the symbol $D_y(p)$. Applying Laplace's expansion of determinants to the numerator of Eq. (16-51) and expanding about the first column, we obtain

$$
v_1 = \frac{
\begin{vmatrix}
Y_{22} & \cdots & Y_{2n} \\
\cdot & \cdots & \cdot \\
Y_{n2} & \cdots & Y_{nn}
\end{vmatrix}
}{D_y(p)} i_1 + (-1) \frac{
\begin{vmatrix}
Y_{12} & \cdots & Y_{1n} \\
\cdot & \cdots & \cdot \\
Y_{n2} & \cdots & Y_{nn}
\end{vmatrix}
}{D_y(p)} i_2 + \cdots
$$

$$
+ (-1)^{n+1} \frac{
\begin{vmatrix}
Y_{12} & \cdots & Y_{1n} \\
\cdot & \cdots & \cdot \\
Y_{(n-1)2} & \cdots & Y_{(n-1)n}
\end{vmatrix}
}{D_y(p)} i_n
$$

or, using the definition of cofactors and letting $(F_y)_{k1}$ be the cofactor of row k, column 1 of D_y,

$$
v_1 = \frac{1}{D_y(p)} [(F_y)_{11}i_1 + (F_y)_{21}i_2 + (F_y)_{31}i_3 + \cdots + (F_y)_{n1}i_n]
$$

This expression can be abbreviated to read

$$
v_1 = \frac{1}{D_y(p)} \sum_{k=1}^{n} (F_y)_{k1}i_k
\tag{16-52a}
$$

For any node voltage v_a

$$v_a = \frac{1}{D_y(p)} \sum_{k=1}^{n} (F_y)_{ka} i_k \tag{16-52b}$$

Equation (16-52b) is interpreted as

$$D_y(p)v_a = \sum_{k=1}^{n} (F_y)_{ka} i_k \tag{16-52c}$$

Equation (16-52c) is the operational form of the equlibrium equation which relates a node voltage v_a to the source functions i_k.

If we start with the mesh equations of a circuit, then the result for the relation between a mesh current i_a and the source functions v_k is

$$D_z(p)i_a = \sum_{k=1}^{m} (F_z)_{ka} v_k \tag{16-53}$$

where $D_z(p)$ is the determinant of the mesh-impedance matrix and $(F_z)_{ka}$ is its cofactor of row k, column a. Proof of Eq. (16-53) is left as an exercise for the reader.

16-16. Network Functions and Characteristic Determinants. A study of Eq. (16-52c) shows that the response (nodal voltage) v_a is related to a nodal current supply i_k through the network function

$$H(p) = \frac{(F_y)_{ka}}{D_y(p)}$$

Similarly, from Eq. (16-53), the response (a mesh current) i_a is related to a mesh voltage supply v_k through the network function

$$H(p) = \frac{(F_z)_{ka}}{D_z(p)}$$

It is recalled that network functions were defined for networks containing only one source. If the network contains more than one source, as implied by Eq. (16-52b), then the response (node voltage v_a) is the superposition (sum) of a number of components {such as $[(F_y)_{ka}/D_y(p)]i_k$} each of which is related to its respective source (nodal current supply i_k) by a different network function $(F_y)_{ka}/D_y(p)$. Each of these network functions differs in its numerator polynomial $(F_y)_{ka}$ but has the same denominator polynomial[1] $D_y(p)$.

In Chap. 13 we saw that the poles of the network function determine the source-free modes of response. These modes are thus characterized

---

[1] It is assumed that $D(s)$ has no factor which is also a factor of any of its minors.

by the roots of the characteristic equation

$$D_y(s) = 0 \qquad \text{or} \qquad D_z(s) = 0$$

corresponding to the source-free equilibrium equations of the form $D_y(p)v_a = 0$ or $D_z(p)i_a = 0$, respectively. There is a tendency to ask a question formulated as follows: What is the relationship between the roots of $D_y(s) = 0$ and $D_z(s) = 0$. Are they the same?

In its present form this question is vague. We could ask the question in a more precise fashion: If in a given network we solve for the complete response of a mesh current i_a, using mesh equations, we obtain in addition to the component of the response due to sources the source-free modes. If now in the same network we solve for a node voltage v_b, using the node equations, will the source-free modes of v_b be the same as the source-free modes of i_a? Before answering this question and in order to show why the first question is vague, we shall see that, starting with an active network, only one source-free network can be obtained from it. On the other hand, if we start with a source-free network, depending on the manner in which sources are inserted, different active networks, having different source-free responses, will be obtained.

Soldering-iron and Pliers Entries.[1] There are two ways in which an ideal source can be impressed on a source-free network. An ideal source can be connected between two nodes of a source-free network; this is called a "soldering-iron entry." Alternatively an ideal source may be inserted in a branch of the network; this is called a "pliers entry." The term soldering-iron entry is used since in this type of connection the entry does not disturb the existing branches of the source-free network, and the source is introduced by soldering its leads to the nodes of the network. The pliers entry implies cutting of existing leads of the source-free network by means of pliers and inserting the ideal source.

From the form of the mesh or node equations it should be clear that the general solution of the source-free equilibrium equations will form the source-free component of the complete response of the active network *if the insertion of the sources into the source-free network does not change either the mesh impedances or the node admittances.* This can be achieved by a soldering-iron entry of ideal current sources, as in Fig. 16-23*b*, or a pliers entry of an ideal voltage source, as in Fig. 16-23*c*, corresponding to the source-free network of Fig. 16-23*a*. The source-free equilibrium equation for the networks of Fig. 16-23*b* and *c* is identical to that of the network of Fig. 16-23*a*. If an ideal voltage source is inserted by a soldering-iron entry, as in Fig. 16-23*d*, then the source-free circuit corresponding to this situation is shown in Fig. 16-23*e*. In arriving at this figure it is recalled

---

[1] This terminology is introduced by Guillemin, *op. cit.*

that, in setting sources to zero, the ideal voltage sources are replaced by a short circuit. The soldering-iron entry of an ideal voltage source in Fig. 16-24d has eliminated an independent node, since v_{12} is now prescribed. Similarly pliers entry of an ideal current source will eliminate an independent mesh current, which will be prescribed by the waveform of the inserted current source. Thus, with such entries, the source-free component of the complete response of the active network will not be the same as the response of the source-free network, prior to the entry.

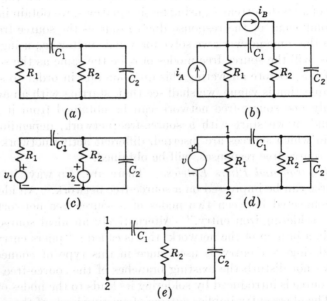

FIG. 16-23. (a) A source-free network. (b) Current sources added to the network by means of soldering-iron entries. (c) Voltage sources added by means of pliers entries. (d) Soldering-iron entry with an ideal voltage source. (e) The new source-free network corresponding to the entry made in (d).

We conclude that the correct procedure for obtaining the source-free component of the complete response of an active network is to set the sources (in the equilibrium equation or in the network) to zero and compute the resulting source-free response. The soldering-iron entry of an ideal voltage source or the pliers entry of an ideal current source in a source-free network will eliminate some of the natural modes of the original source-free network and change the values of the remaining modes.

From the above discussion we see that the source-free mode of any given response is always determined by the poles of its corresponding network function, but, starting with a source-free network, the network function may depend on whether a pliers entry or a soldering-iron entry is made by the source into the network.

Example 16-8. In Fig. 16-24a a source-free network is shown. Find the network function which relates the response v_{ba} to the source introduced by a pliers entry if (a) the source is a current source as in Fig. 16-24b; (b) the source is a voltage source as in Fig. 16-24c.

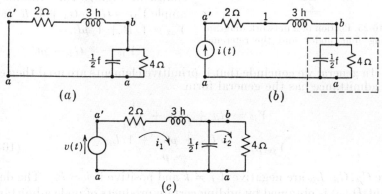

(a)   (b)

(c)

Fig. 16-24. (a) A source-free circuit. (b) Circuit of (a) with current-source pliers entry. (c) Circuit of (a) with voltage-source pliers entry.

Solution. In Fig. 16-24b the current $i(t)$ flows through a'-b and the terminal pair b-a.

$$v_{ba} = Z_{ba}(p)i(t) = \frac{4(2/p)}{4 + 2/p}\, i(t) = \frac{4}{2p + 1}\, i(t)$$

The pole of this network function is $s = -\frac{1}{2}$, corresponding to $(v_{ba})_f = A e^{-t/2}$. If the node a is taken as reference, then v_{ba} is a (node voltage) response with free mode $e^{-t/2}$. In Fig. 16-24c the modes of i_2 are the same as the modes of $4i_2 = v_{ba}$. From the voltage-division formula

$$v_{ba} = \frac{4/(2p + 1)}{(2 + 3p) + 4/(2p + 1)}\, v(t) = \frac{4}{6p^2 + 7p + 6}\, v(t)$$

The network (voltage gain) function relating v_{ba} to $v(t)$ is $4/(6p^2 + 7p + 6)$. This network function has two poles $s_{1,2} = -\frac{7}{12} \pm [(\frac{7}{12})^2 - 1]^{\frac{1}{2}}$, and therefore v_{ba} (and i_{ba}) will have two damped oscillatory free modes.

16-17. The Structure of Network Functions.

In Chap. 12 we stated that a network function is always a ratio of polynomials in p; that is, it has the form $\sum_n a_n p^n \big/ \sum_m b_m p^m$. In this article we prove this statement. We have seen that a network function is the ratio of a cofactor of the characteristic determinant of a network to the determinant itself. Let us assume that we have set up the node equations of a network *and that the node equations were written using primitive elements* when all the nodes are *not* junctions. Several typical nodes of a network are shown in Fig. 16-25. In this example $Y_{11} = G_1 + G_2 + 1/R + pC$, $Y_{22} = 1/R + 1/pL$,

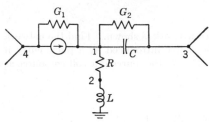

$$Y_{13} = -G_2 - pC$$

FIG. 16-25. Portion of a network diagram showing four nodes and the reference node.

etc. In general we conclude that if primitive elements are used then each node admittance has the general form

$$Y_{jk} = G_{jk} + pC_{jk} + \frac{1}{pL_{jk}}$$

or

$$Y_{jk}(p) = \frac{p^2 C_{jk} + pG_{jk} + 1/L_{jk}}{p} \qquad (16\text{-}54)$$

where C_{jk}, G_{jk}, L_{jk} are negative if $j \neq k$ and positive if $j = k$. The determinant $D_y(p)$ is obtained by adding certain products of node admittances in accordance with the rules of determinant manipulation. It therefore follows that $D_y(p)$ has the form

$$D_y(p) = \frac{b_0 + b_1 p + b_2 p^2 + \cdots + b_k p^k}{p^r} \qquad (16\text{-}55)$$

i.e., it is the ratio of a polynomial in p to p raised to a power r, where the value of k and r will depend on the "anatomy" of the network. Now any cofactor of the determinant $D_y(p)$ will also contain elements whose form is as shown in Eq. (16-54). Therefore such a cofactor will also be the ratio of a polynomial in p to a power of p,

$$F_y = \frac{a_0 + a_1 p + a_2 p^2 + \cdots + a_l p^l}{p^q} \qquad (16\text{-}56)$$

where the value of l and q will again depend on the structure of the network. From Eqs. (16-55) and (16-56) it is seen that the general form of a network function is

$$H(p) = \frac{F_y}{D_y} = \frac{\displaystyle\sum_{n=0}^{N} a_n p^n}{\displaystyle\sum_{m=0}^{M} b_m p^m} \qquad (16\text{-}57)$$

where N, M, a_n, and b_m are determined by the structure of the network.

16-18. Free Modes of Response. We have seen that, when the denominator of a transform network function is equated to zero, this equation constitutes the characteristic equation *whose roots* (poles of the network function) *characterize the source-free modes of that response which is associated with the particular network function under discussion.*

The characteristic equation is an algebraic equation; the roots of this equation give those values of s which allow the form Ae^{st} to satisfy the source-free equilibrium equation. We recall from Chap. 11 that, if the characteristic equation

$$s^k + b_{k-1}s^{k-1} + \cdots + b_2 s^2 + b_1 s + b_0 = 0 \qquad (16\text{-}58)$$

has the roots $s = s_1, s_2, \ldots, s_k$, then, if no two roots are equal, the general solution of the source-free equation can be written in the form

$$y_f = A_1 e^{s_1 t} + A_2 e^{s_2 t} + \cdots + A_k e^{s_k t} \qquad (16\text{-}59)$$

If the characteristic equation includes multiple roots, then the general solution is modified accordingly. For example, the general solution which corresponds to the characteristic equation

$$(s + 2)^2 (s + 3)^3 (s + 4) = 0$$

is $\qquad y_f = (A_1 + A_2 t)e^{-2t} + (A_3 + A_4 t + A_5 t^2)e^{-3t} + A_6 e^{-4t} \quad (16\text{-}60)$

If any of the roots is complex, then its conjugate is also a root and the two exponentials can be combined into real form. For example, the characteristic equation

$$(s + 2)(s + 3 - j4)(s + 3 + j4) = 0$$

results in the general solution

$$y_f = Ae^{-2t} + \text{Re}\,[\mathbf{K}e^{(-3+j4)t}]$$

We have seen that when the source-free response is written as the sum of exponential functions employing arbitrary constants, as in Eq. (16-60), then each term in this form is called a *mode* of the (source-) free response. Thus a term $Ae^{s_1 t}$ is a mode, a term $te^{s_1 t}$ is a mode, but a term of the form $Ae^{-at}\cos(\omega_d t + \varphi)$ represents *two* modes.

We shall now show that, *except under very special circumstances*, the source-free modes are the same for all network variables. Let us suppose that in a problem the source-free modes of node voltages are obtained. To obtain the voltage across any *element* in the network, we have two possibilities: either the element is connected between the reference node and another node, or the element is connected between two nodes neither of which is the reference node. Since we are using *primitive* elements in this entire discussion, all possibilities are shown in Fig. 16-26. Now the voltage across the elements R_1, L_1, and C_1 is the node voltage v_1, and therefore its free components consist of the sum of the modes which arise from the admittance characteristic equation. The voltage across R_2, L_2, and C_2 is the difference between the two node voltages. Now if

$$v_1 = A_1 e^{s_1 t} + \cdots$$

and

$$v_2 = B_1 e^{s_1 t} + \cdots$$

then

$$v_2 - v_1 = (A_1 - B_1)e^{s_1 t} + \cdots$$

so that

$$(v_2 - v_1) = D_1 e^{s_1 t} + \cdots$$

Hence the voltage across these elements will consist of the sum of the same modes as the node voltages. It must be pointed out here that we are dealing with the *general* solution of the homogeneous equation. To the reader who asks, "Cannot $A_1 - B_1 = 0$?" we answer that this may indeed happen if we use *special* initial conditions. In that case A_1 or B_1 may also be zero. We are not discussing particular cases at this time; we are rather concerned with the *general* form of the source-free response.

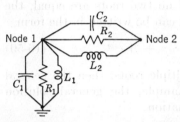

FIG. 16-26. Portion of a passive network showing how a node can be connected to another node.

Now we know that the *currents* in the elements are linearly related to the voltages. Since the voltages across the elements are exponential, the currents are also exponential in resistances and in capacitances. In inductances $i = (1/pL)v$, so that an exponential voltage gives a current which is an exponential plus a constant (of integration). (If the initial conditions are represented by the initial-condition generators, then the integration constant is zero.) At any rate the currents in the elements have the same modes as the node voltages except possibly for a constant. Since the mesh currents are related to the branch currents by addition (or subtraction), we conclude that the modes for the mesh currents are the same as the modes of the node voltages if only dynamic (i.e., time-varying) modes are considered.

Since free-response modes are characterized by the poles of the network function, the node and mesh methods may be considered as methods for locating the poles of network functions. Similarly the zeros of a transform network function can be obtained from the appropriate numerator determinant (cofactor) in the solution for a mesh current or a node voltage in the presence of a single source.

It is interesting to observe that the discussion in this article has revolved around the voltages and currents which are associated with the primitive elements in the network. In spite of the convenience which mesh or node variables introduce into the process of analysis, we must not forget that the element variables are the basic variables in the circuit.

16-19. Use of p Elements. We have shown that the node or mesh equations can be written by the use of p elements as well as primitive elements. Referring, for example, to the node equations, the case of p elements allows us to use only as many voltage variables as there are junctions. The use of p elements generally results in fewer equations than the use of primitive elements. It is therefore appropriate to ask how the characteristic equation can be obtained from the p-element form of the node-admittance or mesh-impedance matrix. The source-free equilibrium equation has the general form

$$D(p)x = 0$$

where $D = D_z$ when x is a mesh current and $D = D_y$ when x is a node voltage. Now, when primitive elements were used, then $D(p)$ was a polynomial in p, "divided" by p raised to a power. When p elements are used, $D(p)$ will be a function consisting of the ratio of two polynomials in p because each node admittance or each mesh impedance will be such a fraction. To obtain the characteristic equation, we start with

$$D(p)x = \frac{N(p)}{M(p)}x = 0$$

Hence

$$N(p)x = 0$$

Thus the characteristic equation is obtained by using the numerator polynomial in $D(p)$,

$$N(s) = 0$$

Now the question arises: Shall we get the same modes if p elements are used as when primitive elements are used? The answer is that we do get the same modes generally but that the variables which are used in conjunction with p elements may not include all the modes which are obtained with primitive elements. An example suffices to show how this can occur.

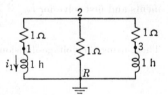

Fig. 16-27. A symmetrical source-free circuit.

Example 16-9. Study the modes of the source-free circuit shown in Fig. 16-27.

Solution. By using p elements the only node is node 2. Hence the node-admittance determinant is

$$Y_{22}(p) = \frac{1}{1+p} + \frac{1}{1+p} + 1$$

and, combining the first two terms,

$$Y_{22}(p) = \frac{2}{1+p} + 1 = \frac{3+p}{1+p}$$

Hence the characteristic equation is

$$D_y(s) = 0 \qquad \frac{3+s}{1+s} = 0 \qquad s = -3$$

Hence it appears that v_2 has only one source-free mode, namely, Ae^{-3t}. If primitive elements are used, then the characteristic equation is

$$D_y(s) = \begin{vmatrix} 1 + \dfrac{1}{s} & -1 & 0 \\ -1 & 3 & -1 \\ 0 & -1 & 1 + \dfrac{1}{s} \end{vmatrix} = 0$$

or

$$\frac{s+1}{s}\left(\frac{3s+3}{s} - 1\right) + 1\left(-\frac{s+1}{s}\right) = 0$$

or

$$\frac{s+1}{s^2}(2s + 3 - s) = 0$$

or

$$(s+1)(s+3) = 0$$

so that we have two modes, A_1e^{-t} and A_2e^{-3t}.

In order to explain what has happened in this example, consider the node voltage v_1 of the form

$$v_1 = A_1e^{-t} + A_2e^{-3t}$$

Since $i_1 = (1/p)v_1$

$$i_1 = -A_1e^{-t} - \tfrac{1}{3}A_2e^{-3t}$$

Hence the voltage $v_{21} = i_1(t) = -A_1e^{-t} - \tfrac{1}{3}A_2e^{-3t}$, and the node voltage v_2 is

$$v_2 = v_{21} + v_1$$

or

$$v_2 = -A_1e^{-t} - \tfrac{1}{3}A_2e^{-3t} + A_1e^{-t} + A_2e^{-3t}$$
$$= Ke^{-3t} \qquad K = A_2 - \tfrac{1}{3}A_2$$

We observe, therefore, that the node voltage v_2 will not have a mode Ae^{-t} regardless of the initial conditions. This is due to the special numerical relationship between the circuit elements in this example. The same final result is obtained if we use p elements and first solve for v_2,

$$v_2 = Ke^{-3t}$$

Then, using the voltage-division formula,

$$v_1 = \frac{p}{1+p}v_2$$

or

$$\frac{(1+p)v_1}{p} = v_2$$

v_1 is therefore the result of solving an *inhomogeneous* equation,

$$(1+p)v_1 = pKe^{-3t}$$

and the complementary solution of this equation is the solution of the homogeneous equation,

$$(1+p)v_1 = 0$$

or

$$v_1 = A_1e^{st} \qquad 1 + s = 0 \qquad s = -1$$

We conclude, therefore, that the use of operational elements will lead to the correct free response for the variables which are used in setting up the simultaneous equations but that the characteristic equation which is obtained from the p-element determinant does not necessarily give all modes for all the variables in the circuit. If the special numerical relationship (i.e., the fact that branches 2-1-R and 2-3-R are identical) is altered, then both primitive and p elements give the same characteristic equation. (See Prob. 16-26.)

16-20. The Component of the Response Due to the Source. Once the equilibrium equations for the desired circuit variables have been obtained, the procedure for determination of the component of the response due to each source is similar to the procedure which was used in simple series, parallel, or series-parallel circuits. For example, if the source is constant (e.g., if step functions are applied at $t = 0$ and we consider $t \geq 0^+$ only), then the component of the response due to the source is also constant. This constant (or constants if we deal with simultaneous equations) can be obtained either by setting $p = 0$ or by drawing the d-c circuit (in which inductances are replaced by short circuits and capacitances are replaced by open circuits) and solving. This method of drawing the d-c circuit usually results in a circuit with fewer meshes and/or nodes so that simultaneous equations either may not be needed or may be fewer in number than in the original circuit. *In any case, no matter what the source waveforms, the component of the response due to a source need not be determined by the same method as was used to obtain the characteristic equation.* Thus, for example, it may happen that the node-admittance matrix is used to obtain the characteristic equation but series-parallel circuit methods (i.e., branch variable methods) are used to obtain a steady-state component.

For a sinusoidal source we represent each circuit variable as well as the source by a phasor and replace p by $j\omega$ in the equilibrium equation to obtain the complex form of the equilibrium equation. Several examples will illustrate how the component of the response due to the source can be obtained.

Example 16-10. Find the d-c steady-state equivalent network of Fig. 16-28a.
Solution. By short-circuiting the inductances and open-circuiting the capacitances in Fig. 16-28a the d-c steady-state equivalent network shown in Fig. 16-28b is obtained.

Mutual and Self-admittances (or Impedances) in a D-C Network. The d-c steady-state equivalent of a network with inductances and capacitances which contain only d-c sources is a d-c network. The general formula for the node voltages and the mesh currents can be applied to d-c networks to obtain their d-c steady-state values. However, since there are no time-varying currents or voltages in a d-c network, the self- and mutual admittances (or impedances) will no longer be functions of the differential operator p but will contain conductances (or resistances) exclusively. For this reason the self-impedance of a mesh designated by b will be shown as R_{bb} instead of Z_{bb} and will be called the self-resistance of

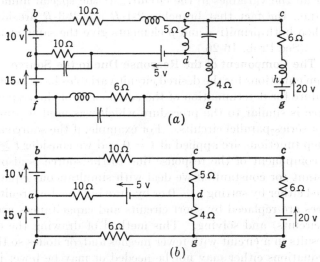

FIG. 16-28. A circuit and its d-c equivalent.

mesh b. The mutual impedance between meshes b and mesh k will be shown by R_{bk} rather than Z_{bk}. Similarly the symbols G_{aa} and G_{ak} will be used for the self- and mutual admittance of the nodes of a d-c network. The characteristic impedance and admittance determinants of the d-c network will be shown by D_R and D_G instead of $D_z(p)$ and $D_y(p)$. The following examples illustrate the application of node and mesh methods to d-c networks.

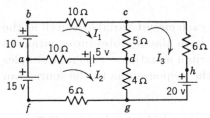

FIG. 16-29. A d-c network in which mesh currents have been assigned.

Example 16-11. For the network of Fig. 16-29 determine (a) the mesh currents I_1, I_2, and I_3; (b) the power delivered to each resistance; (c) the power furnished by each ideal voltage source.

Solution

$$R_{11} = 10 + 5 + 10 = 25 \text{ ohms}$$
$$R_{22} = 10 + 4 + 6 = 20 \text{ ohms}$$
$$R_{33} = 5 + 4 + 6 = 15 \text{ ohms}$$
$$R_{12} = -10 \text{ ohms} \qquad R_{13} = -5 \text{ ohms} \qquad R_{23} = -4 \text{ ohms}$$
$$V_1 = 10 + 5 = 15 \text{ volts}$$
$$V_2 = 15 - 5 = 10 \text{ volts}$$
$$V_3 = -20 \text{ volts}$$

The mesh equations are

$$25I_1 + (-10)I_2 + (-5)I_3 = 15$$
$$(-10)I_1 + 20I_2 + (-4)I_3 = 10$$
$$(-5)I_1 + (-4)I_2 + 15I_3 = -20$$

Hence
$$I_1 = \frac{N_1}{D_R} \qquad I_2 = \frac{N_2}{D_R} \qquad I_3 = \frac{N_3}{D_R}$$

where D_R is the characteristic impedance determinant and N_1, N_2, and N_3 are the appropriate numerator determinants. As a review example, these determinants are worked out in detail below.

$$D_R = \begin{vmatrix} 25 & -10 & -5 \\ -10 & 20 & -4 \\ -5 & -4 & 15 \end{vmatrix} = 10^3 \times \begin{vmatrix} 2.5 & -1 & -0.5 \\ -1 & 2.0 & -0.4 \\ -0.5 & -0.4 & 1.5 \end{vmatrix}$$

This may be evaluated at once by minors,

$$D_R = 10^3 \times \{2.5[(2)(1.5) - (-0.4)(-0.4)]$$
$$+ (-1)(-1)[(-1)(1.5) - (-0.4)(-0.5)]$$
$$+ (-0.5)[(-1)(-0.4) - (-0.5)(2.0)]\}$$
$$= 10^3 \times [(2.5)(2.84) + (-1.7) - (0.5)(1.4)]$$
$$= 4.7 \times 10^3$$

Alternatively columns or rows may be multiplied by constants and added to other columns or rows so that two zeros are produced in a column or row. (Note incidentally that the first column is identical to the first row, etc. Why?)

Thus multiply the third row by -2, and add to the second. Then

$$D_R = 10^3 \times \begin{vmatrix} 2.5 & -1 & -0.5 \\ 0 & 2.8 & -3.4 \\ -0.5 & -0.4 & 1.5 \end{vmatrix}$$

Now multiply the first row by 0.2, and add to the third,

$$D_R = 10^3 \times \begin{vmatrix} 2.5 & -1 & -0.5 \\ 0 & 2.8 & -3.4 \\ 0 & -0.6 & 1.4 \end{vmatrix}$$

and
$$D_R = 10^3 \times 2.5[(2.8)(1.4) - (-0.6)(-3.4)]$$
$$= 4.7 \times 10^3 \qquad\qquad Check$$

Now evaluate N_1,

$$N_1 = \begin{vmatrix} 15 & -10 & -5 \\ 10 & 20 & -4 \\ -20 & -4 & 15 \end{vmatrix} = 10^3 \times \begin{vmatrix} 1.5 & -1 & -0.5 \\ 1 & 2 & -0.4 \\ -2 & -0.4 & 1.5 \end{vmatrix}$$

Multiply the first column by -2, and add to the second,

$$N_1 = 10^3 \times \begin{vmatrix} 1.5 & -4 & -0.5 \\ 1 & 0 & -0.4 \\ -2 & 3.6 & 1.5 \end{vmatrix}$$

Now multiply the first column by 0.4, and add to the third,

$$N_1 = 10^3 \times \begin{vmatrix} 1.5 & -4 & 0.1 \\ 1 & 0 & 0 \\ -2 & 3.6 & 0.7 \end{vmatrix} = -1 \begin{vmatrix} -4 & 0.1 \\ 3.6 & 0.7 \end{vmatrix} \times 10^3$$

$$N_1 = 3.16 \times 10^3$$

Now evaluate N_2,

$$N_2 = 10^3 \times \begin{vmatrix} 2.5 & 1.5 & -0.5 \\ -1 & 1 & -0.4 \\ -0.5 & -2 & 1.5 \end{vmatrix} = 3.05 \times 10^3$$

$$N_2 = 3.05 \times 10^3$$

And finally

$$N_3 = 10^3 \times \begin{vmatrix} 2.5 & -1 & 1.5 \\ -1.0 & 2 & 1 \\ -0.5 & -0.4 & -2 \end{vmatrix} = -4.4 \times 10^3$$

$$N_3 = -4.4 \times 10^3$$

(a) Now we have the mesh currents within slide-rule accuracy,

$$I_1 = \frac{3.16 \times 10^3}{4.7 \times 10^3} = 0.672 \text{ amp}$$

$$I_2 = \frac{3.05}{4.7} = 0.648 \text{ amp}$$

$$I_3 = \frac{-4.4}{4.7} = -0.937 \text{ amp}$$

(b) The power delivered to the resistances is

$$P_{bc} = (0.672^2)(10) = 4.50 \text{ watts}$$
$$P_{cd} = (0.672 + 0.937)^2(5) = 12.9 \text{ watts}$$
$$P_{ad} = (0.672 - 0.648)^2(10) = 0.0058 \text{ watt}$$
$$P_{fg} = (0.648^2)(6) = 2.52 \text{ watts}$$
$$P_{dg} = (0.648 + 0.937)^2(4) = 10.0 \text{ watts}$$
$$P_{ch} = (-0.937^2)(6) = 5.28 \text{ watts}$$

The total power absorbed by all resistances is 35.2 watts.

(c) The power *delivered by* the sources is calculated,

For the 10-v source: $P_{ab} = (0.672)(10) = 6.72$ watts
For the 15-v source: $P_{fa} = (0.648)(15) = 9.72$ watts
For the 5-v source: $P = (0.672 - 0.648)(5) = 0.12$ watt
For the 20-v source: $P_{gh} = (-)(-0.937)(20) = 18.74$ watts

The power delivered by the ideal sources is 35.3 watts. This checks within slide-rule accuracy.

Example 16-12. For the circuit of Fig. 16-30 determine the current in every branch.

Solution. (a) Mesh currents have been assigned in the figure in accordance with the mesh-current convention.

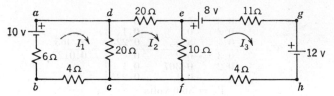

Fig. 16-30. The d-c network used in Example 16-12.

(b) Writing the mesh equations,

$$(6 + 4 + 20)I_1 + \qquad\qquad (-20)I_2 + \qquad\qquad (0)I_3 = +10$$
$$(-20)I_1 + (20 + 20 + 10)I_2 + \qquad\qquad (-10)I_3 = 0$$
$$(0)I_1 + \qquad\qquad (-10)I_2 + (10 + 11 + 4)I_3 = -12 - 8$$

These equations may be solved by any algebraic means (e.g., determinants).
(c) Solution for mesh currents,

$$I_1 = 0.306 \text{ amp}$$
$$I_2 = -0.0407 \text{ amp}$$
$$I_3 = -0.816 \text{ amp}$$

(d) Solution for branch currents,

$$I_{ab} = -I_1 = -0.306 \text{ amp}$$
$$I_{dc} = I_1 - I_2 = 0.347 \text{ amp}$$
$$I_{ef} = I_2 - I_3 = 0.775 \text{ amp}$$
$$I_{hf} = I_3 = -0.816 \text{ amp}$$

. . . .

Example 16-13. For the network shown in Fig. 16-31 use the node method to find the current I in the 15-ohm resistance.

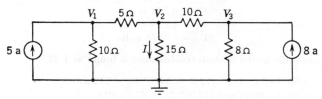

Fig. 16-31. The d-c circuit used in Example 16-13.

Solution. The node equations are to be solved for V_2. The nodal conductances are

$$G_{11} = \tfrac{1}{10} + \tfrac{1}{5} = 0.300 \text{ mho}$$
$$G_{22} = \tfrac{1}{5} + \tfrac{1}{15} + \tfrac{1}{10} = 0.367 \text{ mho}$$
$$G_{33} = \tfrac{1}{10} + \tfrac{1}{8} = 0.225 \text{ mho} \qquad G_{12} = -0.2 \text{ mho} \qquad G_{13} = 0 \qquad G_{23} = -0.1 \text{ mho}$$

The nodal supply currents are

$$I_1 = 5 \text{ amp} \qquad I_2 = 0 \qquad I_3 = 8 \text{ amp}$$

Hence

$$0.300V_1 + (-0.2)V_2 \qquad\qquad = 5$$
$$(-0.2)V_1 + 0.367V_2 + (-0.1)V_3 = 0$$
$$+ (-0.1)V_2 + 0.225V_3 = 8$$

and

$$V_2 = \frac{\begin{vmatrix} 0.3 & 5 & 0 \\ -0.2 & 0 & -0.1 \\ 0 & 8 & 0.225 \end{vmatrix}}{\begin{vmatrix} 0.3 & -0.2 & 0 \\ -0.2 & 0.367 & -0.1 \\ 0 & -0.1 & 0.225 \end{vmatrix}} = \frac{0.465}{0.0127}$$

$$V_2 = 36.6 \text{ volts}$$

and

$$I = \frac{36.6}{15} = 2.44 \text{ amp} \qquad\qquad Ans.$$

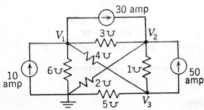

FIG. 16-32. The d-c circuit used in Example 16-14.

We note that the node method is not the fastest method of arriving at the solution. The reader is urged to solve this problem using Thévenin's theorem.

Example 16-14. In the circuit shown in Fig. 16-32 (*a*) calculate the node voltages V_1, V_2, V_3; (*b*) calculate the power dissipated by each conductance; (*c*) calculate the power delivered by each source, and check the power delivered with the power dissipated.

Solution. (*a*) Set up the nodal equations,

$$G_{11} = 6 + 4 + 3 = 13 \text{ mhos} \qquad I_1 = 10 - 30 = -20 \text{ amp}$$
$$G_{22} = 3 + 2 + 1 = 6 \text{ mhos} \qquad I_2 = 30 + 50 = 80 \text{ amp}$$
$$G_{33} = 1 + 4 + 5 = 10 \text{ mhos} \qquad I_3 = -50 \text{ amp}$$
$$G_{12} = -3 \text{ mhos}; \qquad G_{13} = -4 \text{ mhos}; \qquad G_{23} = -1 \text{ mho}$$

The equations are

$$13V_1 - 3V_2 - 4V_3 = -20$$
$$-3V_1 + 6V_2 - V_3 = 80$$
$$-4V_1 - V_2 + 10V_3 = -50$$

Solving,

$$V_1 = 0.342 \text{ volt}$$
$$V_2 = 12.9 \text{ volts}$$
$$V_3 = -3.58 \text{ volts}$$

(*b*) The power dissipated in each conductance is found as V^2G,

In the 1-mho conductance: $[12.9 + 3.58]^2(1) = 272$ watts
In the 2-mho conductance: $(12.9)^2(2) = 333$ watts
In the 3-mho conductance: $(12.9 - 0.342)^2(3) = 473$ watts
In the 4-mho conductance: $[0.342 - (-3.58)]^2(4) = 61.3$ watts
In the 5-mho conductance: $(3.58)^2(5) = 64$ watts
In the 6-mho conductance: $(0.342)^2(6) = 0.7$ watts

The total power dissipated by the conductances is 1,204 watts.

(*c*) The power delivered by the sources,

10-amp source: $(0.342)(10) = 3.42$ watts
30-amp source: $(12.9 - 0.342)(30) = 377$ watts
50-amp source: $[12.9 - (-3.58)](50) = 824$ watts

The total power delivered by the sources is 1,204 watts. (Within slide-rule accuracy.)

Example 16-15. For the circuit shown in Fig. 16-33*a* calculate the branch currents I_a, I_b, I_c, and I_d.

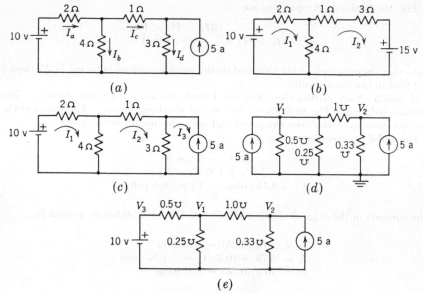

FIG. 16-33. (a) A d-c circuit (Example 16-15). (b) Circuit of (a) with current source replaced by a voltage source. (c) Illustrating the use of mesh currents with ideal current sources in the circuit. (d) Circuit of (a) with the voltage source converted to a current source. (e) Circuit of (a) illustrating the use of node voltages when an ideal voltage source is in the circuit.

Solution. *Method* 1 (*Mesh Method Converting the Current Source to a Voltage Source*). The circuit is redrawn in Fig. 16-33b with the converted current source.

The mesh equations are

$$6I_1 - 4I_2 = 10$$
$$-4I_1 + 8I_2 = -15$$

giving

$$I_1 = 0.625 \text{ amp}$$
$$I_2 = -1.56 \text{ amp}$$

The branch currents in the *original* circuit are

$$I_a = I_1 = 0.625 \text{ amp}$$
$$I_b = I_1 - I_2 = 2.19 \text{ amp}$$
$$I_c = I_2 = -1.56 \text{ amp}$$

The current in the 3-ohm resistance of the original circuit is *not* the same as the current in the 3-ohm resistance after the voltage source was introduced. This again illustrates that the equivalence between sources is with respect to their output terminals only. Since the 3-ohm resistance was internal to the current source, the currents are not the same. The current I_d is found by applying Kirchhoff's current law at the junction of the 1-ohm and the 3-ohm resistance in the original circuit,

$$I_d = I_c + 5 = 5 - 1.56 = 3.44 \text{ amp}$$

Method 2 (*Mesh Method Applied to the Original Circuit*). The circuit as given may be regarded as a three-mesh circuit in which one of the mesh currents is known,

$$I_3 = -5$$

In Fig. 16-33c the mesh equations are

$$6I_1 - 4I_2 = 10$$
$$-4I_1 + 8I_2 + (-3)(-5) = 0$$

Note that these equations are identical to the mesh equations obtained in Method 1 and lead to the same results.

Method 3 (*Node Method Converting the Voltage Source to a Current Source*). The circuit is redrawn in Fig. 16-33d with the converted voltage source. The values of the conductances have also been computed and are indicated on the diagram.

The nodal equations are

$$1.75V_1 - V_2 = 5$$
$$-V_1 + 1.33V_2 = 5$$
$$V_1 = 8.75 \text{ volts} \qquad V_2 = 10.3 \text{ volts}$$

The currents in the original circuit are calculated (within slide-rule accuracy),

$$I_b = (8.75)(0.25) = 2.19 \text{ amp}$$
$$I_c = (8.75 - 10.3)(1) = -1.55 \text{ amp}$$
$$I_d = (10.3)(0.33) = 3.41 \text{ amp}$$

As to I_a, it can be obtained from the relationship $I_a = I_b + I_c$ or from Fig. 16–33a,

$$I_a = \frac{10 - 8.75}{2} = 0.625 \text{ amp}$$

Method 4 (*Node Method Applied to the Original Circuit*). The original circuit may be regarded as a three-node circuit in which one of the node voltages is known: $V_3 = 10$ volts.

The nodal equations of Fig. 16-33e are

$$(-0.5)(10) + 1.75V_1 + (-1)V_2 = 0$$
$$-V_1 + 1.33V_2 = 5$$

Note that these equations are identical to the node equations obtained in Method 3 and lead to the same results.

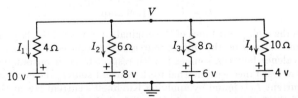

Fig. 16-34. A d-c circuit with three meshes but only one unknown node voltage.

Example 16-16. Example 16-15 was one in which the number of mesh equations needed for solution was the same as the number of nodal equations. In this example (Fig. 16-34) the number of nodal equations is smaller than the number of mesh equations. Calculate the current in each branch of this network.

Solution. By the mesh method three equations have to be solved. There is, however, only one unknown node, V. Thus

$$\frac{V - 10}{4} + \frac{V - 8}{6} + \frac{V - 6}{8} + \frac{V - 4}{10} = 0$$

or $\quad 2.50 + 1.33 + 0.75 + 0.40 = (0.100 + 0.125 + 0.167 + 0.250)V$

and $\qquad\qquad\qquad V = 7.76$ volts

Hence $\qquad\qquad I_1 = \dfrac{7.76 - 10}{4} = -0.560$ amp

$$I_2 = \frac{7.76 - 8}{6} = -0.040 \text{ amp}$$

$$I_3 = \frac{7.76 - 6}{8} = 0.220 \text{ amp}$$

$$I_4 = \frac{7.76 - 4}{10} = 0.376 \text{ amp}$$

Example 16-17. For the circuit shown in Fig. 16-35a obtain the component of the response due to the source for $v_3(t)$ for all time $t > 0$ if the source is (a) the unit step function; (b) a ramp function given by $v(t) = 3tU(t)$; (c) the function $(2 + 4t)U(t)$; (d) the sinusoidal function $v(t) = 3 \cos 1.5t$.

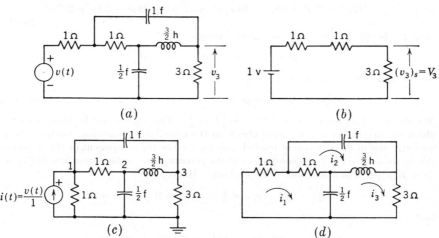

FIG. 16-35. Circuit diagrams used in Example 16-17.

Solution. (a) Since the step-function source is constant for $t \geq 0^+$, we have a d-c circuit. This circuit is shown in Fig. 16-35b. By application of the voltage-division formula we have $V_3 = (\frac{3}{5}) = 0.60$ volt.

(b) To obtain the ramp-function response, we need the equilibrium equation for $v_3(t)$. We shall illustrate the use of node and mesh equations. Using node equations with choice of reference node as in Fig. 16-35c and converting to a current source, the node equations are

$$(2 + p)v_1 + \qquad\qquad (-1)v_2 + \qquad\qquad (-p)v_3 = i(t)$$

$$(-1)v_1 + \left(1 + \tfrac{1}{2}p + \frac{2}{3p}\right)v_2 + \qquad\qquad \left(-\frac{2}{3p}\right)v_3 = 0$$

$$(-p)v_1 + \qquad\qquad \left(-\frac{2}{3p}\right)v_2 + \left(\frac{1}{3} + p + \frac{2}{3p}\right)v_3 = 0$$

By Cramer's rule

$$v_3 = \frac{\begin{vmatrix} 2+p & -1 & i(t) \\ -1 & 1+\dfrac{p}{2}+\dfrac{2}{3p} & 0 \\ -p & -\dfrac{2}{3p} & 0 \end{vmatrix}}{\begin{vmatrix} 2+p & -1 & -p \\ -1 & 1+\dfrac{p}{2}+\dfrac{2}{3p} & -\dfrac{2}{3p} \\ -p & -\dfrac{2}{3p} & \dfrac{1}{3}+p+\dfrac{2}{3p} \end{vmatrix}} = \frac{\dfrac{2}{3p}+p+\dfrac{p^2}{2}+\dfrac{2}{3}}{D_y(p)} i(t)$$

The determinant $D_y(p)$ is now evaluated. The result is

$$D_y(p) = \tfrac{7}{6}p^2 + 2p + \frac{17}{9} + \frac{10}{9p}$$

or $\qquad\qquad D_y(p) = \dfrac{1}{36p}(42p^3 + 72p^2 + 68p + 40)$

Hence $\quad \dfrac{1}{36p}(42p^3 + 72p^2 + 68p + 40)v_3(t) = \dfrac{1}{6p}(3p^3 + 6p^2 + 4p + 4)i(t)$

or $\qquad (42p^3 + 72p^2 + 68p + 40)v_3(t) = (18p^3 + 36p^2 + 24p + 24)i(t)$

$$(16\text{-}61)$$

Now $i(t)$ is $v(t)/1$ or $i(t) = 3t$ for $t > 0$. Hence

$$pi = 3 \qquad p^2 i = 0 \qquad p^3 i = 0$$

so that we need to consider the equation

$$(42p^3 + 72p^2 + 68p + 40)v_3 = (24)(3) + (24)(3t) \qquad (16\text{-}61a)$$

We observe that, for $i(t) = 1$, $[v_3(t)]_s = \frac{24}{40} = \frac{3}{5}$. This should not be regarded as a check for (a); rather it is a partial check on the equilibrium equation (16-61). Now we make use of the theorem of related sources. Since the component of the response due to the source 1 is $\frac{3}{5}$, the component of the response due to the source $3t$ is $3\int\frac{3}{5}\,dt = \frac{9}{5}t + K$ when K is a constant of integration. Hence, if

$$v_3 = \tfrac{9}{5}t + K \qquad pv_3 = \tfrac{9}{5} \qquad p^2 v_3 = 0 \qquad p^3 v_3 = 0$$

and, substituting in (16-61a),

$$(68)(\tfrac{9}{5}) + (40)(\tfrac{9}{5}t) + 40K = (24)(3) + (24)(3t)$$

or $\qquad\qquad (68)(\tfrac{9}{5}) + 72t + 40K = (24)(3) + 72t$

or $\qquad\qquad\qquad\qquad\quad 40K = 72 - 122.4$

$$K = -1.26$$

Hence $\qquad\qquad\qquad [v_2(t)]_s = 1.8t - 1.26 \qquad\qquad\qquad\qquad Ans. (b)$

The same result can be obtained from the mesh equations. If meshes are chosen as in Fig. 16-35d, then $v_3 = 3i_3$. The mesh equations are

$$\left(2+\frac{2}{p}\right)i_1 + \qquad\qquad (-1)i_2 + \qquad\qquad \left(-\frac{2}{p}\right)i_3 = v(t)$$

$$(-1)i_1 + \left(1+\frac{1}{p}+\frac{3p}{2}\right)i_2 + \qquad\qquad \left(-\frac{3p}{2}\right)i_3 = 0$$

$$\left(-\frac{2}{p}\right)i_1 + \qquad\qquad \left(-\frac{3p}{2}\right)i_2 + \left(3+\tfrac{3}{2}p+\frac{2}{p}\right)i_3 = 0$$

Hence, by Cramer's rule,

$$
i_3 = \frac{\begin{vmatrix} 2 + \dfrac{2}{p} & -1 & v(t) \\[2mm] -1 & 1 + \dfrac{1}{p} + \dfrac{3p}{2} & 0 \\[2mm] -\dfrac{2}{p} & -\dfrac{3p}{2} & 0 \end{vmatrix}}{\begin{vmatrix} 2 + \dfrac{2}{p} & -1 & -\dfrac{2}{p} \\[2mm] -1 & 1 + \dfrac{1}{p} + \dfrac{3p}{2} & -\dfrac{3p}{2} \\[2mm] -\dfrac{2}{p} & -\dfrac{3p}{2} & 3 + \tfrac{3}{2}p + \dfrac{2}{p} \end{vmatrix}} = \frac{\left(\dfrac{3p}{2} + \dfrac{2}{p} + \dfrac{2}{p^2} + 3\right)}{D_z(p)} v(t)
$$

The determinant $D_z(p)$ is now evaluated; the result is

$$
D_z(p) = \tfrac{21}{2}p + 18 + \frac{17}{p} + \frac{10}{p^2}
$$

or
$$
D_z(p) = \frac{1}{2p^2}(21p^3 + 36p^2 + 34p + 20)
$$

Hence $\dfrac{1}{2p^2}(21p^3 + 36p^2 + 34p + 20)i_3 = \dfrac{1}{2p^2}(3p^3 + 6p^2 + 4p + 4)v(t)$

and $(21p^3 + 36p^2 + 34p + 20)i_3 = (3p^3 + 6p^2 + 4p + 4)v(t)$ (16-62)

Comparing (16-62) and (16-61) shows that the same result has been obtained.   Since $v_3 = 3i_3$, we can write (16-62) in the form

$$
(21p^3 + 36p^2 + 34p + 20)v_3 = (9p^3 + 18p^2 + 12p + 12)v(t) \quad (16\text{-}62a)
$$

Equation (16-62a), except for the common factor of 2, is identical to Eq. (16-61).

(c) To obtain the component of the response due to the source $v(t) = 2 + 4t$, we use superposition.   If $v(t) = 1$, $(v_3)_s = \tfrac{3}{5}$.   Hence, if $v(t) = 2$, $(v_3)_s = \tfrac{6}{5}$.   If $v(t) = 3t$, $(v_3)_s = 1.8t - 1.26$.   Hence, if $v(t) = 4t$,

$$
(v_3)_s = \tfrac{4}{3}(1.8t - 1.26)
$$

It follows that the component of the response due to the source $2 + 4t$ is

$$
(v_3)_s = \tfrac{6}{5} + \tfrac{4}{3}(1.8t - 1.26)
$$
or $(v_3)_s = 2.4t - 0.48$ *Ans. (c)*

(d) To obtain the component of the response due to the source $v(t) = 3 \cos 1.5t$, we represent $v(t)$ by the amplitude phasor $V_m = 3\underline{/0°}$.   We can now use the equilibrium equation (16-61) or (16-62a) and solve for the phasor $\mathbf{V}_{3m}$ which represents $v_3(t)$ by also replacing p with $j1.5$,

$$
[(21)(j1.5)^3 + (36)(j1.5)^2 + (34)(j1.5) + 20]\mathbf{V}_{3m} =
$$
$$
[(9)(j1.5)^3 + (18)(j1.5)^2 + (12)(j1.5) + 12]3\underline{/0°}
$$
or $(-61 - j20)\mathbf{V}_{3m} = (-28.5 - j12.4)3\underline{/0°}$

or $\mathbf{V}_{3m} = 3\,\dfrac{28.5 + j12.4}{61 + j20} = 1.45\underline{/5.4°}$

Hence $[v_3(t)]_s = 1.45 \cos(1.5t + 5.4°)$

If the sinusoidal steady-state solution only had been required, then the mesh or node equations could have been set up by using complex immittances from the beginning. Example 16-18 will illustrate this procedure.

Example 16-18.   In the circuit of Fig. 16-36a find the mesh current $i_2(t)$ in the steady state.

Solution.   Since the two sinusoidal sources have the *same* frequency, we can replace the series and parallel combinations of elements by their complex impedances.   Thus

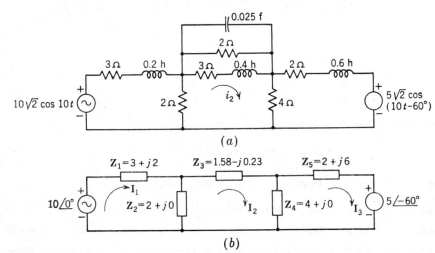

(a)

(b)

FIG. 16-36. Example of an a-c circuit using mesh currents.

the circuit of Fig. 16-36b is obtained.   In this circuit, voltages and current time functions have been replaced by the phasors which represent them.   (Effective phasors are used in this example.)   The impedances are calculated as follows:

$$\mathbf{Z}_1 = 3 + j(0.2)(10) = 3 + j2 \qquad \mathbf{Z}_2 = 2 + j0$$
$$\mathbf{Y}_3 = (0.025)(j10) + \frac{1}{2} + \frac{1}{3 + j0.4(10)} = 0.50 + j0.25 + \frac{1}{3 + j4}$$
or $\qquad \mathbf{Y}_3 = 0.62 + j0.09 \qquad \mathbf{Z}_3 = 1.58 - j0.23$
$$\mathbf{Z}_4 = 4 + j0 \qquad \mathbf{Z}_5 = 2 + j(0.6)(10) = 2 + j6$$

Assigning meshes as in Fig. 16-36b, we have

$$\mathbf{Z}_{11} = 5 + j2 \qquad \mathbf{Z}_{22} = 7.58 - j0.23 \qquad \mathbf{Z}_{33} = 6 + j6 \qquad \mathbf{Z}_{12} = \mathbf{Z}_{21} = -2$$
$$\mathbf{Z}_{23} = \mathbf{Z}_{32} = -4 \qquad \mathbf{Z}_{13} = \mathbf{Z}_{31} = 0$$

The phasor $\mathbf{I}_2$ is given by Cramer's rule,

$$\mathbf{I}_2 = \frac{\begin{vmatrix} 5 + j2 & 10\underline{/0} & 0 \\ -2 & 0 & -4 \\ 0 & -5\underline{/-60°} & 6 + j6 \end{vmatrix}}{\begin{vmatrix} 5 + j2 & -2 & 0 \\ -2 & 7.58 - j0.23 & -4 \\ 0 & -4 & 6 + j6 \end{vmatrix}} = \frac{35.4 + j186.6}{41.5 + j258}$$

Hence $\mathbf{I}_2 = 0.728\underline{/-1.6°}$ and $i_2(t) = 0.728\ \sqrt{2}\ \cos\ (10t - 1.6°)$.

Example 16-19. Calculate the ratio of the node voltage phasors $\mathbf{V}_3/\mathbf{V}_1$ in the circuit of Fig. 16-37a.

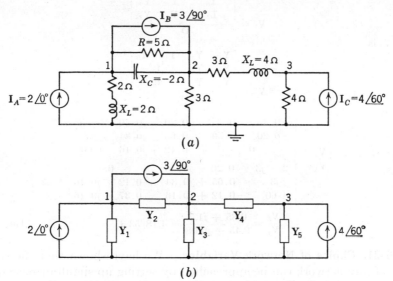

FIG. 16-37. Example of an a-c circuit using node voltages.

Solution. Since the reactances are given, we must find the complex admittances first. The circuit is redrawn as in Fig. 16-37b. The complex admittances are

$$\mathbf{Y}_1 = \frac{1}{2 + j2} = \frac{2 - j2}{8} = 0.25 - j0.25 \text{ mho}$$
$$\mathbf{Y}_2 = \tfrac{1}{5} + j\tfrac{1}{2} = 0.20 + j0.50 \text{ mho}$$
$$\mathbf{Y}_3 = \tfrac{1}{3} + j0 = 0.33 \text{ mho}$$
$$\mathbf{Y}_4 = \frac{1}{3 + j4} = \frac{3 - j4}{25} = 0.12 - j0.16 \text{ mho}$$
$$\mathbf{Y}_5 = \tfrac{1}{4} + j0 = 0.25 \text{ mho}$$

Hence the node admittances are

$$\mathbf{Y}_{11} = \mathbf{Y}_1 + \mathbf{Y}_2 = 0.45 + j0.25$$
$$\mathbf{Y}_{22} = \mathbf{Y}_2 + \mathbf{Y}_3 + \mathbf{Y}_4 = 0.65 + j0.34$$
$$\mathbf{Y}_{33} = \mathbf{Y}_4 + \mathbf{Y}_5 = 0.37 - j0.16$$
$$\mathbf{Y}_{12} = \mathbf{Y}_{21} = -\mathbf{Y}_2 = -0.20 - j0.50$$
$$\mathbf{Y}_{13} = \mathbf{Y}_{31} = 0$$
$$\mathbf{Y}_{23} = \mathbf{Y}_{32} = -\mathbf{Y}_4 = -0.12 + j0.16$$

The complex node equations are

$$\mathbf{Y}_{11}\mathbf{V}_1 + \mathbf{Y}_{12}\mathbf{V}_2 + \mathbf{Y}_{13}\mathbf{V}_3 = \mathbf{I}_A - \mathbf{I}_B$$
$$\mathbf{Y}_{21}\mathbf{V}_1 + \mathbf{Y}_{22}\mathbf{V}_2 + \mathbf{Y}_{23}\mathbf{V}_3 = \mathbf{I}_B$$
$$\mathbf{Y}_{31}\mathbf{V}_1 + \mathbf{Y}_{32}\mathbf{V}_2 + \mathbf{Y}_{33}\mathbf{V}_3 = \mathbf{I}_C$$

The phasor $\mathbf{V}_1$ is given by

$$\mathbf{V}_1 = \frac{\begin{vmatrix} \mathbf{I}_A - \mathbf{I}_B & \mathbf{Y}_{12} & \mathbf{Y}_{13} \\ \mathbf{I}_B & \mathbf{Y}_{22} & \mathbf{Y}_{23} \\ \mathbf{I}_C & \mathbf{Y}_{32} & \mathbf{Y}_{33} \end{vmatrix}}{\mathbf{D}_y}$$

and $\mathbf{V}_3$ is

$$\mathbf{V}_3 = \frac{\begin{vmatrix} \mathbf{Y}_{11} & \mathbf{Y}_{12} & \mathbf{I}_A - \mathbf{I}_B \\ \mathbf{Y}_{21} & \mathbf{Y}_{22} & \mathbf{I}_B \\ \mathbf{Y}_{31} & \mathbf{Y}_{32} & \mathbf{I}_C \end{vmatrix}}{\mathbf{D}_y}$$

Hence

$$\frac{\mathbf{V}_3}{\mathbf{V}_1} = \frac{\begin{vmatrix} 0.45 + j0.25 & -0.20 - j0.50 & 2 - j3 \\ -0.20 - j0.50 & 0.65 + j0.34 & j3 \\ 0 & -0.12 + j0.16 & 4\underline{/60^\circ} \end{vmatrix}}{\begin{vmatrix} 2 - j3 & -0.20 - j0.50 & 0 \\ j3 & 0.65 + j0.34 & -0.12 + j0.16 \\ 4\underline{/60^\circ} & -0.12 + j0.16 & 0.37 - j0.16 \end{vmatrix}}$$

$$\frac{\mathbf{V}_3}{\mathbf{V}_1} = \frac{0.85 + j1.7}{0.45 + j0.08} = 4.18\underline{/53.3^\circ} \qquad\qquad Ans.$$

16-21. Choice of Network Variables.

We have shown that the solution of any network can be approached by setting up simultaneous equilibrium equations. At this point the reader should ask: When a given network is to be analyzed, how can we tell whether to use the node voltages, the junction voltages, mesh currents, element voltages, or element currents as the variables? Unfortunately the answer to this question cannot be unequivocal, because the choice which is made depends on many factors and one cannot say which method will involve the least number of manipulations. Some of the factors which influence the decision will be discussed in this article.

First of all, we must point out that in the complete-response calculations the free component and the component of the response due to the source must be determined. These two subsidiary problems need not be approached by the same method. Thus it is entirely conceivable that we may choose the node voltages as the variables to obtain the characteristic equation of the network but use branch currents to determine the component of the response due to the source. If, for example, the sources are step-function sources, then the component of the response due to the source will be the d-c response. In such cases the equivalent circuit which is used to obtain the steady-state response can be much simpler than the given network because the influence of the energy-storing elements is already known (the steady-state current through capacitances will be zero and the steady-state voltage across inductances will be zero).

We may enumerate the factors which we consider before choosing the method of analysis as follows:

1. Is the complete response required? If so, should the same variables be used to obtain both response components? To some extent this depends on the number of simultaneous equations which arise from each method, but this is much less important than the novice generally believes.

2. How is the information concerning the network given? If, for example, the initial conditions for node voltages are given (or are obtained very easily), then the node method may be indicated.

3. In a sinusoidal steady-state problem how are the immittances specified? If, for example, the complex admittances are given (in rectangular form), then the complex number manipulations which are necessary to obtain the impedances may involve so much work that the mesh method ought not to be used.

4. Should p elements or primitive elements be used? With p elements there are fewer equations, but if the desired variable is an element variable, then more work is needed after the voltage or current associated with the p element is known.

These four items are not listed in any particular order of importance. In solving a network the reader should keep the entire problem in mind and plan ahead so that the solution is accomplished with the greatest economy of effort. The only general statement which can be made is that, all other things being equal, that method which results in the least number of simultaneous equations is indicated—but then all other things are rarely equal!

A Special Case. While we have said that the determination of the source-free component and the component of the response are two separate subsidiary problems, there is one special situation which requires separate discussion. This case occurs when the source function is exponential and is represented by a pole which is also a pole of the transform network function. In this case the component of the response due to the source has the form given in Art. 13-7. Hence, when a network includes a source which is an exponential function of time we must first ascertain whether or not this function is a mode of the source-free network. For this purpose the roots of the characteristic equation should be determined before the components of the response due to the source can be found.

16-22. Initial Conditions. On several occasions we have stated that the complete-response calculation for a network will require a knowledge of the "appropriate" initial conditions. In most practical cases the appropriate initial conditions are not explicitly specified and must be obtained from continuity or other specified conditions through the application of Kirchhoff's laws. Thus, in the absence of impulses, the continuity conditions for voltages across capacitances and for currents through inductances are used to find initial conditions related to other elements. If impulses occur (because the problem has been idealized), then the jumps which may be caused by impulses can be calculated. In this article we shall discuss the determination of the initial conditions.

Initial Conditions in the Absence of Impulses. Impulses can occur in a network only if there is an impulse-function source or if there is a loop in the network which consists of an ideal source and energy-storing elements only. We must emphasize that under these conditions impulses can occur; this implies also that impulses may not occur. For the present we shall assume that all sources in the circuit have a source impedance which includes a series resistance for voltage sources and a parallel resistance for current sources. As we have shown in Chap. 10, such sources can deliver only finite power.

The Continuity Conditions. As stated above, in the absence of impulses the current in each inductance and the voltage across each capacitance will be a continuous function of time. Consequently, if a switching operation occurs at $t = 0$, the values of these variables at $t = 0^+$ will be identical to their values at $t = 0^-$, independently of the equilibrium equations at $t = 0^+$. All other variables in the circuit at the instant $t = 0^+$ must satisfy both the equilibrium equations and the continuity conditions. We recall that the initial values of those variables which do *not* obey the general continuity conditions at $t = 0$ are called "derived initial conditions."

Example 16-20. The Direct Use of Continuity Conditions. The circuit shown in Fig. 16-38a is in the d-c steady state before $t = 0$. At $t = 0$ the switch S is suddenly thrown from position 1 to position 2. Solve for the mesh current $i_2(t)$ for all $t \geq 0^+$.

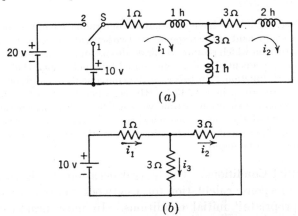

(a)

(b)

Fig. 16-38. (a) Switching operation in a circuit. (b) The d-c equivalent is used to determine the currents at $t = 0^-$.

Solution. 1. *Continuity Conditions.* With the switch in position 1, the d-c steady state is calculated from the circuit of Fig. 16-38b. Evidently

$$i_1 = I_1 = \frac{10}{1 + \frac{3}{2}} = 4.0 \text{ amp}$$
$$i_3 = i_2 = I_2 = \tfrac{1}{2}I_1 = 2.0 \text{ amp}$$

Hence we have $i_1(0^-) = 4.0$ amp, $i_2(0^-) = 2.0$ amp. Note that $i_3(0^-)$ (also 2.0 amp) is determined by the application of Kirchhoff's current law at the junction; this condition is not independent of the other two conditions. Since i_1 and i_2 are the currents in inductances, we have the continuity conditions

$$i_1(0^+) = i_1(0^-) = 4.0 \text{ amp}$$
$$i_2(0^+) = i_2(0^-) = 2.0 \text{ amp}$$

2. *Characteristic Equation.* The source-free circuit has the mesh impedances

$$Z_{11}(p) = 4 + 2p \qquad Z_{22}(p) = 6 + 3p \qquad Z_{12}(p) = -3 - p$$

Hence the characteristic equation is

$$\begin{vmatrix} 4 + 2s & -3 - s \\ -3 - s & 6 + 3s \end{vmatrix} = 0$$

or

$$s^2 + \tfrac{18}{5}s + 3 = 0$$

Hence the characteristic roots are

$$s_1 = -2.29 \qquad s_2 = -1.31$$

The free component of the response has the form

$$(i_1)_f = A_1 e^{-2.29t} + A_2 e^{-1.31t}$$
$$(i_2)_f = B_1 e^{-2.29t} + B_2 e^{-1.31t}$$

3. *Steady-state Component.* The d-c steady state in the circuit can be calculated from Fig. 16-38b if the 10-volt source is replaced by a 20-volt source. Thus

$$(i_1)_s = 8.0 \text{ amp} \qquad (i_2)_s = 4.0 \text{ amp}$$

4. *Complete Response.* We now have

$$i_1(t) = 8.0 + A_1 e^{-2.29t} + A_2 e^{-1.31t}$$
$$i_2(t) = 4.0 + B_1 e^{-2.29t} + B_2 e^{-1.31t}$$

At this point the *four constants* A_1, A_2, B_1, and B_2 need to be evaluated from the two initial conditions $i_1(0^+)$ and $i_2(0^+)$. We first observe that we need to consider both $i_1(t)$ and $i_2(t)$ although only the solution for $i_2(t)$ is desired. Second, we conclude that these four constants cannot be independent of each other, because there are only two modes. To obtain the relationship between the constants, we recall that *each mode must satisfy the source-free equilibrium equations.* Hence, using mesh 1,

$$(4 + 2p)A_1 e^{-2.29t} - (3 + p)B_1 e^{-2.29t} = 0$$
$$(4 + 2p)A_2 e^{-1.31t} - (3 + p)B_2 e^{-1.31t} = 0$$

(using mesh 2 results in redundant equations). Carrying out the operations, we have

$$(4 - 2 \times 2.29)A_1 - (3 - 2.29)B_1 = 0 \qquad (16\text{-}63a)$$
$$(4 - 2 \times 1.31)A_2 - (3 - 1.31)B_2 = 0 \qquad (16\text{-}63b)$$

In addition we have the continuity conditions

$$i_1(0^+) = 4 = 8 + A_1 + A_2 \qquad (16\text{-}63c)$$
$$i_2(0^+) = 2 = 4 + B_1 + B_2 \qquad (16\text{-}63d)$$

The four simultaneous equations (16-63a, 16-63b, 16-63c, 16-63d) are now solved for B_1 and B_2. Completion of this exercise is left for the reader.

We have seen in this example that the use of the continuity condition requires the simultaneous solution for both of the variables i_1 and i_2 for which independent continuity conditions exist. Since each of these variables contained two modes, it was necessary to solve for four constants. We can now generalize as follows: If a circuit contains E independent energy-storing elements, the direct application of the continuity conditions requires the solution of E^2 simultaneous algebraic equations for the desired constants even though we may not need to know the complete response for all (or even any) of the variables with which the continuity conditions are associated. We shall now show how the use of derived initial conditions allows us to solve for only one variable without simultaneous solution for other variables, even if there is no continuity condition for the desired network variable.

Derived Initial Conditions. Let us again consider that the solution of the network is started at $t = 0$ and that at $t = 0$ a switching operation has occurred. If we have written equilibrium equations for $t \geq 0^+$, then these equations and the derivatives of these equations must hold for all $t \geq 0^+$. By substituting the values of the continuity conditions and the values of the source functions at $t = 0^+$ into the equilibrium equations, (derived) initial conditions can be obtained. The general technique which is used in solving for only one circuit variable is to formulate the complete response for that one variable and evaluate the constants in the complete response by obtaining initial conditions for the derivatives of the variable. Two examples will illustrate this method.

Example 16-21. In the circuit of Example 16-20 (Fig. 16-38a) obtain the initial value $(di_2/dt)_{0^+}$.

Solution. The equilibrium equations for this circuit in terms of the mesh currents are, for $t \geq 0^+$,

$$4i_1 + 2\frac{di_1}{dt} - 3i_2 - \frac{di_2}{dt} = 20$$

$$-3i_1 - \frac{di_1}{dt} + 6i_2 + 3\frac{di_2}{dt} = 0$$

Setting $t = 0^+$, $\quad 4i_1(0^+) = (4)(4) = 16, \quad 3i_1(0^+) = 12, \quad 3i_2(0^+) = 6, \quad 6i_2(0^+) = 12$. Hence

$$16 + 2\left(\frac{di_1}{dt}\right)_{0^+} - 6 - \left(\frac{di_2}{dt}\right)_{0^+} = 20$$

$$-12 - \left(\frac{di_1}{dt}\right)_{0^+} + 12 + 3\left(\frac{di_2}{dt}\right)_{0^+} = 0$$

or

$$2\left(\frac{di_1}{dt}\right)_{0^+} - \left(\frac{di_2}{dt}\right)_{0^+} = 10$$

$$-\left(\frac{di_1}{dt}\right)_{0^+} + 3\left(\frac{di_2}{dt}\right)_{0^+} = 0$$

Hence $(di_2/dt)_{0^+} = 2$ amp/sec.

In the problem as stated in Example 16-20 we now "pick up" the solution after $i_2(t)$ has been formulated as

$$i_2(t) = 4 + B_1 e^{-2.29t} + B_2 e^{-1.31t}$$

and differentiate,

$$\frac{di_2}{dt} = 0 - 2.29B_1e^{-2.29t} - 1.31B_2e^{-1.31t}$$

Hence

$$i_2(0^+) = 2 = 4 + B_1 + B_2 \tag{16-64a}$$

$$\left(\frac{di_2}{dt}\right)_{0^+} = 2 = 0 - 2.29B_1 - 1.31B_2 \tag{16-64b}$$

Simultaneous solution of Eqs. (16-64a) and (16-64b) gives the constants B_1 and B_2.

Example 16-22. In the circuit of Fig. 16-38c it is known that

$$i_1(0^-) = 3 \qquad i_2(0^-) = 0 \qquad v_{ab}(0^-) = 6$$

Calculate $i_3(0^+)$, $(di_3/dt)_{0^+}$, $(d^2i_3/dt)_{0^+}$.

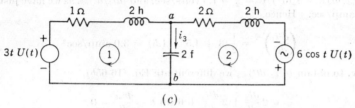

(c)

FIG. 16-38. (c) Another circuit used to illustrate derived initial conditions.

Solution. Since i_1 and i_2 are currents in inductances and since v_{ab} is the voltage across a capacitance, the given values are continuity conditions,

$$i_1(0^+) = 3 \qquad i_2(0^+) = 0 \qquad v_{ab}(0^+) = 6$$

Applying Kirchhoff's current law at junction a, we have

$$i_1 - i_2 = i_3$$

and, setting $t = 0^+$,

$$3 - 0 = i_3(0^+)$$

Hence $i_3(0^+) = 3$ amp.

To obtain $(di_3/dt)_{0^+}$, we observe that

$$\left(\frac{di_1}{dt}\right)_{0^+} - \left(\frac{di_2}{dt}\right)_{0^+} = \left(\frac{di_3}{dt}\right)_{0^+}$$

so that we set up the subsidiary problem of evaluating $(di_1/dt)_{0^+}$ and $(di_2/dt)_{0^+}$.

From mesh 1

$$3t = i_1 + 2\frac{di_1}{dt} + v_{ab} \qquad t \geq 0^+ \tag{16-65a}$$

Setting $t = 0^+$,

$$0 = 3 + 2\left(\frac{di_1}{dt}\right)_{0^+} + 6$$

Hence $(di_1/dt)_{0^+} = -4.5$ amp/sec.

From mesh 2

$$2i_2 + 2\frac{di_2}{dt} - 6\cos t - v_{ab} = 0 \tag{16-65b}$$

Hence, setting $t = 0^+$,

$$(2)(0) + 2\left(\frac{di_2}{dt}\right)_{0^+} - 6 - 6 = 0$$

and $(di_2/dt)_{0^+} = 6$ amp/sec, so that $(di_3/dt)_{0^+} = -4.5 - 6 = -10.5$ amp/sec. To obtain $(d^2i_3/dt^2)_{0^+}$, we write

$$\left(\frac{d^2i_3}{dt^2}\right)_{0^+} = \left(\frac{d^2i_1}{dt^2}\right)_{0^+} - \left(\frac{d^2i_2}{dt^2}\right)_{0^+}$$

Now, to obtain $(d^2i_1/dt^2)_{0^+}$, we differentiate (16-65a),

$$3 = \frac{di_1}{dt} + 2\frac{d^2i_1}{dt^2} + \frac{dv_{ab}}{dt} \qquad t \geq 0^+$$

and set $t = 0^+$,

$$3 = \left(\frac{di_1}{dt}\right)_{0^+} + 2\left(\frac{d^2i_1}{dt^2}\right)_{0^+} + \left(\frac{dv_{ab}}{dt}\right)_{0^+}$$

Now $(dv_{ab}/dt)_{0^+} = i_3(0^+)/C = \frac{3}{2} = 1.5$ volts/sec, and $(di_1/dt)_{0^+}$, as we have just found, is -4.5 amp/sec. Hence

$$\left(\frac{d^2i_1}{dt^2}\right)_{0^+} = \frac{1}{2}(3 + 4.5 - 1.5) = 3.0 \text{ amp/sec}^2$$

Similarly, to obtain $(d^2i_2/dt^2)_{0^+}$, we differentiate Eq. (16-65b),

$$2\frac{di_2}{dt} + 2\frac{d^2i_2}{dt^2} + 6\sin t - \frac{dv_{ab}}{dt} = 0$$

so that $(d^2i_2/dt^2)_{0^+} = \frac{1}{2}[-(2)(6) - 0 + 1.5] = -5.25$ amp/sec². Hence $(d^2i_3/dt^2)_{0^+}$ $= 3.0 - (-5.25) = 8.25$ amp/sec². The results are

$$i_3(0^+) = 3 \text{ amp} \qquad \left(\frac{di_3}{dt}\right)_{0^+} = -10.5 \text{ amp/sec} \qquad \left(\frac{d^2i_3}{dt^2}\right)_{0^+} = 8.25 \text{ amps/sec}^2$$

16-23. Complete-response Calculations. In this article, we present several examples of complete-response calculations. These examples are intended to show how the principles which are associated with such calculations are applied in the solution of numerical problems.

Example 16-23. The circuit shown in Fig. 16-39a is in the steady state with the switch S on source v_1. At $t = 0$ the switch is thrown to source v_2. Calculate $v_{ab}(t)$ for all $t \geq 0^+$.

Solution. 1. *The Continuity Conditions.* Since v_{ab} and v_{db} are voltages across capacitances, the continuity conditions are

$$v_{ab}(0^+) = v_{ab}(0^-) \qquad v_{db}(0^+) = v_{db}(0^-)$$

To determine the values of these voltages at $t = 0^-$, the steady-state functions of $v_{ab}(t)$ and $v_{db}(t)$ for all $t < 0$ must be determined. Representing $v_1(t)$ by the amplitude phasor $10\underline{/0^\circ}$, we draw the circuit diagram for $t < 0$ as in Fig. 16-39b. On this diagram the reactances of the capacitances at the radian frequency $\omega = 1$ are shown. Since this circuit is a ladder type, the (amplitude) phasors which represent v_{db} and v_{ab} can be found immediately by repeated application of the voltage-division formula,

$$(\mathbf{V}_{db})_m = 10\underline{/0^\circ}\frac{(-j)(1 - j2)/(1 - j3)}{1 + (-j)(1 - j2)/(1 - j3)} = 10\underline{/0^\circ}\frac{2 + j}{1 + j4}$$
$$= 3.54 - j4.12 \; (= 5.43\underline{/-49.4^\circ})$$

Hence $\qquad v_{db}(t) = \text{Re }(3.54 - j4.12)e^{jt} = 5.43\cos(t - 49.4^\circ) \qquad t < 0$

and $\qquad v_{db}(0^-) = \text{Re }(3.54 - j4.12) = 5.43\cos(-49.4^\circ) = 3.54$ volts

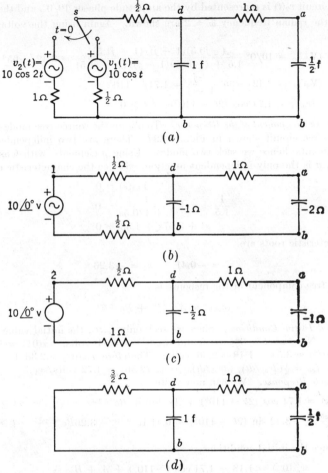

FIG. 16-39. Circuits used to illustrate complete-response calculations.

The phasor $(\mathbf{V}_{ab})_m$ is given by

$$(\mathbf{V}_{ab})_m = (\mathbf{V}_{db})_m \times \frac{-j2}{1 - j2} = 1.18 - j4.71$$

Hence
$$v_{ab}(t) = \mathrm{Re}\,(1.18 - j4.71)e^{it} \qquad t < 0$$
and
$$v_{ab}(0^-) = 1.18 \text{ volts}$$

The continuity conditions require that

$$v_{ab}(0^+) = 1.18 \text{ volts} \qquad v_{db}(0^+) = 3.54 \text{ volts}$$

2. *Steady-state Component for* $t \geq 0^+$. To obtain the steady-state component (component of the response due to the sources) for $t \geq 0^+$, the circuit of Fig. 16-39c is used.

In this circuit $v_2(t)$ is represented by the amplitude phasor $10\underline{/0°}$, and the reactance values at the radian frequency $\omega = 2$ are shown. Again using the voltage-division formula,

$$(\mathbf{V}_{db})_m = 10\underline{/0°}\ \frac{(-j0.5)(1-j)/(1-j1.5)}{1.5 + (-j0.5)(1-j)/(1-j1.5)} = 2.42\underline{/-65°}$$

$$(\mathbf{V}_{ab})_m = 2.42\underline{/-65°}\ \frac{-j}{1-j} = 1.71\underline{/-110°}$$

Hence $\qquad (v_{ab})_s = 1.71 \cos (2t - 110°) \qquad t \geq 0^+$

3. *The Free Component of the Response.* To obtain the source-free modes, we study the source-free circuit shown in Fig. 16-39d. There are two independent energy-storing elements; hence we seek two modes. Using p elements, with b as the reference node, d is the only independent junction. Hence the characteristic equation is

$$Y_{bd}(s) = 0$$

or $\qquad \dfrac{1}{1.5} + s + \dfrac{1}{1 + 1/0.5s} = 0$

$$s^2 + 3.67s + 1.33 = 0$$

The characteristic roots are

$$s_1 = -0.41 \qquad s_2 = -3.26$$

Hence the free component of the response is

$$(v_{ab})_f = Ae^{-0.41t} + Be^{-3.26t}$$

4. *Derived Initial Condition.* Since we seek only $v_{ab}(t)$, the initial value $(dv_{ab}/dt)_{0^+}$ is needed. Now at $t = 0^+$ we found $v_{db}(0^+) = 3.54$ volts, $v_{ab}(0^+) = 1.18$ volts. Hence $v_{da}(0^+) = 3.54 - 1.18 = 2.36$ volts. Therefore $i_{da}(0^+) = 2.36/1 = 2.36$ amp. Since $i_{da} = i_{ab} = \frac{1}{2}(dv_{ab}/dt)$, $(dv_{ab}/dt)_{0^+} = (2)(2.36) = 4.72$ volts/sec.

5. *Complete Response.* We can now write

$$v_{ab}(t) = 1.71 \cos (2t - 110°) + Ae^{-0.41t} + Be^{-3.26t} \qquad t \geq 0^+$$

$$\frac{dv_{ab}}{dt} = -3.42 \sin (2t - 110°) - 0.41Ae^{-0.41t} - 3.26Be^{-3.26t} \qquad t \geq 0^+$$

and introduce the initial conditions,

$$v_{ab}(0^+) = 1.18 = 1.71 \cos (-110°) + A + B$$

$$\left(\frac{dv_{ab}}{dt}\right)_{0^+} = 4.72 = -3.42 \sin (-110°) - 0.41A - 3.26B$$

The constants A and B are therefore determined from the two equations

$$A + B = 1.76$$
$$-0.41A - 3.26B = 1.51$$

Hence $A = 2.58$, $B = -0.82$. The complete response for $v_{ab}(t)$ is therefore given by the equation

$$v_{ab}(t) = 1.71 \cos (2t - 110°) + 2.58e^{-0.41t} - 0.82e^{-3.26t} \qquad t \geq 0^+$$

Example 16-24. The network in Fig. 16-40a has no initial energy stored. The source $v(t)$ is a rectangular pulse given by

$$v(t) = U(t) - U(t-1)$$

Calculate $v_{ab}(t)$ for all $t \geq 0^+$, and sketch the result.

Solution. 1. *The Initial Conditions.* From the continuity conditions we have $i_L(0^+) = i_L(0^-)$; $v_{ab}(0^+) = v_{ab}(0^-)$. Hence $v_{ab}(0^+) = 0$; $i_L(0^+) = 0$. Since $v_{ab}(0^+) = 0$, $i_R(0^+) = 0$. Because $i_L = i_R + i_C$, $i_C(0^+) = 0$. Hence $(dv_{ab}/dt)_{0^+} = 0$. We now have the two initial conditions $[v_{ab}(0^+)$ and $(dv_{ab}/dt)_{0^+}]$ which we shall need to solve for $v_{ab}(t)$.

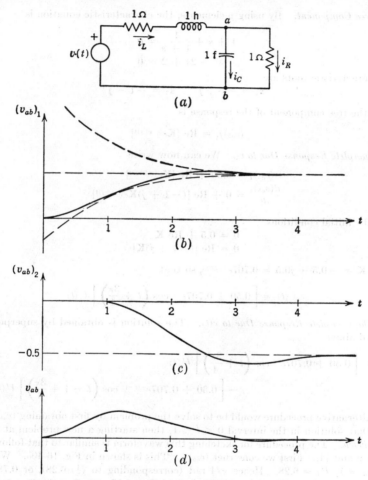

FIG. 16-40. Circuit and waveform sketches for Example 16-24.

2. *Component of the Response Due to the Source.* The source is a rectangular pulse and is therefore considered to be the sum of two sources, $v_1(t) + v_2(t)$, when

$$v_1(t) = U(t) \qquad v_2(t) = -U(t - 1)$$

The complete response will be of the form $(v_{ab})_1 + (v_{ab})_2$, where $(v_{ab})_1$ is the complete response due to $v_1(t)$ and $(v_{ab})_2$ is the complete response due to $v_2(t)$. Hence $v_{ab}(t)$ will be given by

$$v_{ab}(t) = [v_{ab}(t)]_1 - [v_{ab}(t - 1)]_1$$

This follows from the fact that $v_2(t) = -v_1(t - 1)$. Hence we need to find only the response due to the source $U(t)$. The component of the response due to this source is the d-c steady-state solution, which we obtain by application of the voltage-division formula to the d-c circuit,

$$(v_{ab})_{s1} = 0.50 \text{ volt}$$

3. *Free Component.* By using p elements, the characteristic equation is

$$1 + s + \frac{1}{1 + s} = 0$$

or

$$s^2 + 2s + 2 = 0$$

The characteristic roots are

$$s_1 = -1 + j \qquad s_2 = -1 - j$$

Hence the free component of the response is

$$(v_{ab})_{f_1} = \text{Re } [\mathbf{K}e^{(-1+j)t}]$$

4. *Complete Response Due to v_1.* We can now write

$$(v_{ab})_1 = 0.50 + \text{Re } [\mathbf{K}e^{(-1+j)t}]$$
$$\frac{d(v_{ab})_1}{dt} = 0 + \text{Re } [(-1 + j)\mathbf{K}e^{(-1+j)t}]$$

using the initial conditions

$$0 = 0.5 + \text{Re } \mathbf{K}$$
$$0 = \text{Re } [(-1 + j)\mathbf{K}]$$

Hence $\mathbf{K} = -0.5 + j0.5 = 0.707e^{+j3\pi/4}$, so that

$$v_{ab_1}(t) = \left[0.50 + 0.707e^{-t} \cos\left(t + \frac{3\pi}{4}\right) \right] U(t)$$

5. *The Complete Response Due to $v(t)$.* The solution is obtained by superposition as noted above.

$$v_{ab}(t) = \left[0.50 + 0.707e^{-t} \cos\left(t + \frac{3\pi}{4}\right) \right] U(t)$$
$$- \left[0.50 + 0.707e^{-(t-1)} \cos\left(t - 1 + \frac{3\pi}{4}\right) \right] U(t - 1)$$

An alternative procedure would be to solve the problem by first obtaining $(v_{ab})_1$ and using that solution in the interval $0 < t < 1$, then starting a new problem at $t = 1$.

6. *Sketch.* The procedure for sketching this waveform is similar to that followed in Chaps. 9 and 11. First we construct $(v_{ab})_1$. This is shown in Fig. 16-40b. We note that $\omega_d = 1$, $P_d = 6.28$. Hence $\pi/4$ rad (corresponding to $(\frac{1}{8})(6.28)$, or 0.78, sec) is the first t_e point. The first t_z point is $3.14/2 = 1.57$ sec after the first t_e point. This occurs at $t = 0.78 + 1.57 = 2.35$ sec. We also know that $(v_{ab})_1(0^+) = 0$ and $(dv_{ab}/dt)_{0^+} = 0$. Hence we can sketch $(v_{ab})_1$ as in Fig. 16-40b. To sketch $(v_{ab})_2$, we delay $(v_{ab})_1$ by 1 sec, turn it negative, and draw as in Fig. 16-40c. The result for v_{ab} is obtained by adding the waveforms of Fig. 16-40b and c. The result is shown in Fig. 16-40d.

Example 16-25. In the circuit of Fig. 16-40a, which was used in Example 16-24, the source $v(t)$ is a ramp function given by

$$v(t) = 3tU(t)$$

If the circuit has no initial-energy storage, find $v_{ab}(t)$ for all $t > 0^+$.

Solution. 1. *Results Used from Example* 16-24. Examining the discussion of Example 16-24 in connection with initial conditions, we find that in this particular case $(dv_{ab}/dt)_{0^+}$ was independent of the source $v(t)$. Hence we have again

$$v_{ab}(0^+) = 0 \qquad \left(\frac{dv_{ab}}{dt}\right)_{0^+} = 0$$

The source-free circuit is also identical to the one of Example 16-24. Hence

$$(v_{ab})_f = \text{Re } [\mathbf{K}e^{(-1+j)t}]$$

2. *Component of the Response Due to the Source.* We now need the equilibrium equation of the circuit. In this case we shall illustrate the use of the node method without converting the voltage source to a current source.

Since

$$i_R = \frac{v_{ab}}{1} \qquad i_C = 1\frac{dv_{ab}}{dt}$$

we have

$$i_L = (1 + p)v_{ab}$$

Also

$$v(t) - v_{ab} = (1 + p)i_L$$

Hence

$$\frac{1}{1 + p}[v(t) - v_{ab}] = (1 + p)v_{ab}$$

or

$$[(1 + p)^2 + 1]v_{ab} = v(t)$$

Thus

$$(p^2 + 2p + 2)v_{ab} = v(t) = 3t$$

[We check the characteristic equation: Setting $v(t) \equiv 0$, replacing p by s, we have $s^2 + 2s + 2 = 0$ as before.] To obtain $(v_{ab})_s$, we make use of the related-sources theorem. If $v(t) = 1$, $(v_{ab})_s = 0.5$; if $v = 3$, $(v_{ab})_s = 1.5$; and since $3t = \int 3\, dt$, we have

$$(v_{ab})_s = 1.5t + A$$

The constant (of integration) A is obtained by substituting in the equilibrium equation,

$$pv_{ab} = 1.5 \qquad p^2v_{ab} = 0$$

Hence

$$0 + (2)(1.5) + 2(1.5t + A) = 3t$$

or

$$3 + 2A = 0 \qquad A = -1.5$$

Therefore

$$(v_{ab})_s = 1.5(t - 1)$$

3. *Complete Response.* We now have

$$v_{ab} = 1.5(t - 1) + \text{Re } [\mathbf{K}e^{(-1+j)t}]$$

$$\frac{dv_{ab}}{dt} = 1.5 + \text{Re } [(-1 + j)\mathbf{K}e^{(-1+j)t}]$$

Using the initial conditions

$$0 = -1.5 + \text{Re } \mathbf{K}$$
$$0 = 1.5 + \text{Re } [(-1 + j)\mathbf{K}]$$

gives $\mathbf{K} = 1.5 + j0 = 1.5$. Hence

$$v_{ab}(t) = 1.5(t - 1 + e^{-t}\cos t) \qquad t \geq 0^+ \qquad\qquad Ans.$$

Example 16-26. The network shown in Fig. 16-41a is deenergized prior to $t = 0$. Obtain the equilibrium equation for the node voltage $v_2(t)$, and solve for $v_2(t)$ for all $t \geq 0^+$ if $i_1(t) = 3\cos 2t$ and $i_2(t) = 2e^{-t}\cos t$.

Solution. 1. *The Equilibrium Equation.* With node admittances, the equilibrium equations are

$$Y_{11}(p)v_1 + Y_{12}(p)v_2 = i_1(t)$$
$$Y_{21}(p)v_1 + Y_{22}(p)v_2 = i_2(t)$$

where $Y_{11}(p) = 1.5 + 1.5p$, $Y_{22}(p) = 0.75 + 1.5p$, $Y_{12}(p) = Y_{21}(p) = -(0.5 + 1.5p)$. The operational form for $v_2(t)$ is

$$v_2(t) = \frac{\begin{vmatrix} 1.5 + 1.5p & i_1(t) \\ -0.5 - 1.5p & i_2(t) \end{vmatrix}}{\begin{vmatrix} 1.5 + 1.5p & -0.5 - 1.5p \\ -0.5 - 1.5p & 0.75 + 1.5p \end{vmatrix}}$$

Simplifying, $$v_2(t) = \frac{(1.5 + 1.5p)i_2(t) + (0.5 + 1.5p)i_1(t)}{1.875p + 0.875}$$

so that the equilibrium equation is

$$(15p + 7)v_2(t) = (12 + 12p)i_2 + (4 + 12p)i_1$$

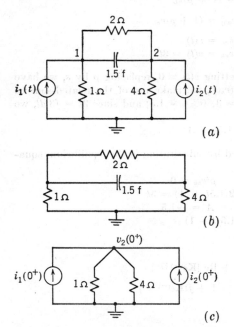

(a)

(b)

(c)

FIG. 16-41. Circuits for Example 16-26.

2. *The Characteristic Equation.* Setting $i_1 \equiv i_2 \equiv 0$, we have the source-free equilibrium equation

$$(15p + 7)(v_2)_f = 0$$

Hence the characteristic equation is

$$15s + 7 = 0 \qquad s = -\tfrac{7}{15} = -0.467$$

As a check, consider the source-free circuit shown in Fig. 16-41b. The time constant of this circuit is

$$T = 1.5[(2 \times 5)/(2 + 5)] = \tfrac{15}{7}$$

which is the reciprocal of the characteristic root. The source-free component of the response is therefore

$$[v_2(t)]_f = Ke^{-0.467t}$$

3. *The Component of the Response Due to $i_1(t)$.* If we set $i_2(t) \equiv 0$, then

$$(15p + 7)v_2(t) = (4 + 12p)i_1(t)$$

Since the source is sinusoidal, it can be represented by a phasor. Let $3\underline{/0^\circ}$ be the (amplitude) phasor which represents i_1. The component of v_2 due to i_1 will be represented by $\mathbf{V}_m$. Replacing p by $j2$ in the equilibrium equation, $\mathbf{V}_m$ is given by

$$[15(j2) + 7]\mathbf{V}_m = [4 + 12(j2)]3\underline{/0^\circ}$$

Hence $\mathbf{V}_m = 2.37 + j0.152 = 2.37\underline{/3.68^\circ}$. The component of v_2 due to i_1 is therefore

$$(v_2)_{s1} = 2.37 \cos (2t + 3.68^\circ)$$

4. *The Component of the Response Due to $i_2(t)$.* Setting $i_1(t) \equiv 0$, we have

$$(15p + 7)v_2 = 12(1 + p)i_2 \qquad \text{where } i_2 = 2e^{-t} \cos t$$

or
$$v_2 = \frac{12(1 + p)}{15p + 7} \text{ Re } [2e^{(-1+j)t}]$$

Hence the transform network function which relates an exponential source i_2 to v_2 is $12(1 + s)/(15s + 7)$. Since $(-1 + j)$ is not a pole of this network function, we have

$$v_{2_s} = \text{Re} \left\{ \frac{12[1 + (-1 + j)]}{15(-1 + j) + 7} 2e^{(-1+j)t} \right\}$$

or
$$v_{2_s} = \text{Re} \left[\frac{24j}{-8 + j15} e^{(-1+j)t} \right]$$

Since $24j/(-8 + j15) = 1.41\underline{/-28°}$,

$$(v_2)_{s2} = 1.41e^{-t} \cos (t - 28°)$$

5. *Complete Response.* Adding the three response components, the complete response $v_2(t)$ is

$$v_2(t) = 2.37 \cos (2t + 3.68°) + 1.41e^{-t} \cos (t - 28°) + Ke^{-0.467t}$$

To evaluate K, we need $v_2(0^+)$. Since the circuit is deenergized before $t = 0$, $v_{12}(0^+) = v_{12}(0^-) = 0$. The circuit shown in Fig. 16-41c is therefore equivalent to the given circuit at the *instant* $t = 0^+$. Hence

$$v_2(0^+) = [i_1(0^+) + i_2(0^+)] \times \tfrac{4}{5} = 4 \text{ volts}$$
Therefore
$$4 = 2.37 \cos 3.68° + 1.41 \cos (-28°) + K$$

and $K = 0.38$. The final solution reads

$$v_2(t) = 2.37 \cos (2t + 3.68°) + 1.41e^{-t} \cos (t - 28°) + 0.38e^{-0.467t}$$
$$t \geq 0^+ \quad Ans.$$

Example 16-27. The circuit shown in Fig. 16-42 is initially deenergized. Calculate $v_2(t)$ for all $t \geq 0^+$.

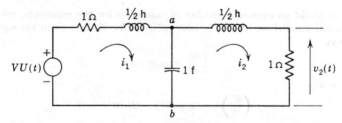

FIG. 16-42. Circuit for Example 16-27.

Solution. 1. *Equilibrium Equation.* We shall employ this circuit to illustrate the use of mesh analysis. Choosing mesh currents as in Fig. 16-42, we have

$$Z_{11}(p)i_1 + Z_{12}(p)i_2 = V \qquad t \geq 0^+$$
$$Z_{21}(p)i_1 + Z_{22}(p)i_2 = 0 \qquad t \geq 0^+$$

where $\quad Z_{11}(p) = Z_{22}(p) = 1 + \tfrac{1}{2}p + \dfrac{1}{p} \quad$ and $\quad Z_{12}(p) = Z_{21}(p) = -\dfrac{1}{p}$

We observe immediately that $Z_{11} = Z_{22}$; hence the network is symmetrical.   The solution for i_2 is, symbolically,

$$i_2 = \frac{-Z_{12}(p)V}{Z_{11}{}^2(p) - Z_{12}{}^2(p)}$$

or since $1 \cdot i_2 = v_2$,

$$[Z_{11}{}^2(p) - Z_{12}{}^2(p)]v_2 = -Z_{12}(p)V$$

2. *The Free Component of the Response.*   The characteristic equation is

$$Z_{11}{}^2(s) - Z_{12}{}^2(s) = 0$$

or

$$[Z_{11}(s) - Z_{12}(s)][Z_{11}(s) + Z_{12}(s)] = 0$$

Hence the characteristic roots satisfy the relationship

$$Z_{11}(s) = \pm Z_{12}(s)$$

or

$$1 + \tfrac{1}{2}s + \frac{1}{s} = \pm \frac{1}{s}$$

Thus the characteristic roots are the solutions of the two equations

$$1 + \tfrac{1}{2}s = 0 \qquad \text{and} \qquad 1 + \tfrac{1}{2}s + \frac{2}{s} = 0$$

giving three nonzero roots

$$s_1 = -2 \qquad s_{2,3} = -1 \pm j\sqrt{3}$$

The free component of the response has the form

$$(v_2)_f = K_1 e^{-2t} + \text{Re } [\mathbf{K}_2 e^{(-1+j\sqrt{3})t}]$$

3. *Component of the Response Due to the Source.*   Inspection of Fig. 16-42 reveals that the d-c steady-state response for v_2 is $(v_2)_s = 0.50$ volt.

4. *Initial Conditions.*   Since the initial-energy storage in the network is given as zero, the continuity conditions require that

$$i_1(0^+) = 0 \qquad i_2(0^+) = 0 \qquad v_{ab}(0^+) = 0$$

In order to avoid an excessive number of equations for the constants, we seek the derived initial conditions $(dv_2/dt)_{0^+}$, $(d^2v_2/dt^2)_{0^+}$. We observe from the equation for mesh 2 that

$$\frac{1}{2}\frac{di_2}{dt} + i_2 = v_{ab}$$

Setting $t = 0^+$,

$$\left(\frac{di_2}{dt}\right)_{0^+} = 2v_{ab}(0^+) - 2i_2(0^+) = 0$$

Since $v_2 = 1 \cdot i_2$, $v_2(0^+) = 0$ and $(dv_2/dt)_{0^+} = 0$. Differentiating the equation for mesh 2,

$$\frac{1}{2}\frac{d^2i_2}{dt^2} + \frac{di_2}{dt} = \frac{dv_{ab}}{dt}$$

Now the current in the capacitance i_{ab} is related to v_{ab} through $i_{ab} = 1(dv_{ab}/dt)$.   Hence

$$\frac{1}{2}\frac{d^2i_2}{dt^2} + \frac{di_2}{dt} = i_1 - i_2 = i_{ab} \qquad \text{in } C$$

Setting $t = 0^+$, we have $(d^2i_2/dt^2)_{0^+} = 0$; thus $(d^2v_2/dt^2)_{0^+} = 0$. We need to point out here that the special circuit arrangement and the specified initial conditions led to the *result* that v_2 and its first two derivatives are zero. There is some tendency to *assume* incorrectly that the condition of no initial-energy storage always leads to zero values for the derived initial conditions. In this example, had we solved for i_1 this would not be the case.

5. *Complete Response.* We now write for $t \geq 0^+$

$$v_2 = 0.50 + K_1 e^{-2t} + \mathrm{Re}\ [\mathbf{K}_2 e^{(-1+j\sqrt{3})t}]$$

$$\frac{dv_2}{dt} = 0 - 2K_1 e^{-2t} + \mathrm{Re}\ [(-1 + j\sqrt{3})\mathbf{K}_2 e^{(-1+j\sqrt{3})t}]$$

$$\frac{d^2v_2}{dt^2} = 0 + 4K_1 e^{-2t} + \mathrm{Re}\ [(-1 + j\sqrt{3})^2 \mathbf{K}_2 e^{(-1+j\sqrt{3})t}]$$

Introducing the initial conditions and writing $\mathbf{K}_2$ in rectangular form, $\mathbf{K}_2 = k_2 + jk_2'$, we have

$$0 = 0.50 + K_1 + \mathrm{Re}\ (k_2 + jk_2')$$
$$0 = -2K_1 + \mathrm{Re}\ [(-1 + j\sqrt{3})(k_2 + jk_2')]$$
$$0 = 4K + \mathrm{Re}\ [(-1 + j\sqrt{3})^2(k_2 + jk_2')]$$

or

$$K_1 - k_2 \qquad\qquad = -0.50$$
$$-2K_1 - k_2 - \sqrt{3}\,k_2' = 0$$
$$4K_1 - 2k_2 + 2\sqrt{3}\,k_2' = 0$$

Solving,

$$K_1 = -0.50 \qquad k_2 = 0 \qquad k_2' = \frac{1}{\sqrt{3}} \qquad \text{so that } \mathbf{K}_2 = \frac{j}{\sqrt{3}} = \frac{1}{\sqrt{3}}\, e^{j\pi/2}$$

and thus the complete response is

$$v_2(t) = 0.50 \left[1 - e^{-2t} - \frac{2}{\sqrt{3}}\, e^{-t} \sin\ (\sqrt{3}\,t) \right] \qquad t \geq 0^+$$

Example 16-28. An Attenuator. In many practical applications a "resistance voltage divider" as shown in Fig. 16-43a is placed into a circuit with the intention of obtaining a voltage $v_2(t)$ which is a predetermined fraction of $v_1(t)$ (that is, v_2 is "attenuated" with respect to v_1) regardless of the waveform of $v_1(t)$. Now, if all elements are ideal, then $v_2(t) = R_2 v_1/(R_1 + R_2)$ and the output waveform will be identical to the input waveform for all time. Unfortunately it often happens that a capacitance C_2 appears across R_2, unavoidably, because of the nature of the device which is placed across the terminals of R_2. This situation is represented by the circuit of Fig. 16-43b. Under these conditions the effect of the capacitance introduces a free response component. Assuming for the present that v_1 is generated by an ideal source, the effect of this capacitance is to introduce a time delay because the voltage across it cannot change abruptly even if the input voltage v_1 changes abruptly. To analyze the situation, we treat the series combination of v_1 and R_1 as a resistive voltage source, convert to a current source as shown in Fig. 16-43c, and observe that the free component of the response will be an exponential decay with a time constant $R_1 R_2 C_2/(R_1 + R_2)$. We recall that the time delays introduced by R-C circuits were discussed in detail in Chap. 11.

This circuit can be modified so that $v_2(t)$ is proportional to $v_1(t)$ [as long as $v_1(t)$ remains an ideal source] by placing a capacitance C_1 across R_1 as shown in Fig. 16-43d. In this new circuit the loop consisting of $v_1(t)$, C_1, and C_2 is lossless so that impulses of current can take place. Let us now assume that $v_1(t)$ is a step function, $v_1(t) = VU(t)$. Further assume that at $t = 0^-$ each capacitance is uncharged: $v_{am}(0^-) = 0$,

$v_{mb}(0^-) = 0$. Now, at $t = 0^+$, $v_{am}(0^+) + v_{mb}(0^+) = V$. Consequently the values of the voltages v_{am} and v_{mb} must change in zero time so that an impulse of current must flow through C_1 and C_2. Hence at $t = 0$ infinite current flows in the capacitances so that the current in the resistances (which must be finite) is at that instant neglected.

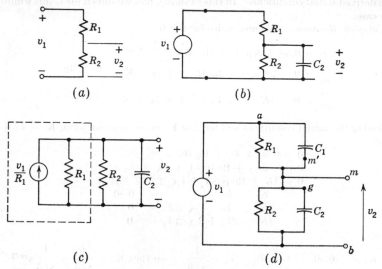

FIG. 16-43. Circuits for Example 16-28: compensation of an attenuator.

Consequently at $t = 0^+$ the voltage across the capacitances will be divided inversely as the capacitances,

$$v_{am}(0^+) = V\frac{C_2}{C_1 + C_2} \qquad v_{mb}(0^+) = V\frac{C_1}{C_1 + C_2}$$

The same initial conditions can be deduced from the equilibrium equation for $v_2 = v_{mb}$. Applying Kirchhoff's current law at junction m,

$$\left(\frac{1}{R_1} + pC_1\right)(v_1 - v_2) = \left(\frac{1}{R_2} + pC_2\right)v_2$$

or

$$\left[\frac{1}{R_1} + \frac{1}{R_2} + p(C_1 + C_2)\right]v_2 = \left(\frac{1}{R_1} + pC_1\right)v_1$$

Or let

$$R_p = \frac{R_1 R_2}{R_1 + R_2} \qquad C_p = C_1 + C_2$$

and substitute $v_1 = VU(t)$,

$$\frac{1}{R_p}v_2 + C_p\frac{dv_2}{dt} = \frac{1}{R_1}VU(t) + C_1V\,\delta(t)$$

Now integrate this equation from $t = 0^-$ to $t = 0^+$,

$$\frac{1}{R_p}\int_{0^-}^{0^+} v_2\,dt + C_p\int_{0^-}^{0^+}\frac{dv_2}{dt}\,dt = \frac{1}{R}V\int_{0^-}^{0^+} U(t)\,dt + C_1V$$

Since v_2 is always finite, $v_2\Delta t = 0$ if $\Delta t = 0$ as is the case in the interval 0^- to 0^+. Similarly $\int_{0^-}^{0^+} U(t)\,dt = 0$. Hence

$$C_p[v_2(0^+) - v_2(0^-)] = C_1V$$

Since $v_2(0^-) = 0$, we have, as before,

$$v_2(0^+) = \frac{C_1}{C_1 + C_2} V$$

Now, as time progresses, the d-c steady state is reached. Hence v_2 will approach the value $VR_2/(R_1 + R_2)$. If we now set

$$\frac{R_2}{R_1 + R_2} = \frac{C_1}{C_1 + C_2}$$

or $\qquad R_2C_1 + R_2C_2 = R_1C_1 + R_2C_1 \qquad$ or $\qquad R_1C_1 = R_2C_2$

then the initial value will be the same as the steady-state value and no transient occurs. The circuit with $R_1C_1 = R_2C_2$ is called a "compensated" attenuator.

We can reach the same conclusion by solution of the equilibrium equation. For $t \geq 0^+$, we have [because $\delta(t) = 0$ for $t > 0$]

$$\left(\frac{1}{R_p} + pC_p\right) v_2 = \frac{1}{R_1} V$$

Hence $\qquad\qquad v_2 = \frac{R_2}{R_1 + R_2} V + Ke^{-t/T} \qquad T = R_pC_p, \, t \geq 0^+$

Using the initial condition,

$$\frac{C_1}{C_1 + C_2} V = \frac{R_2}{R_1 + R_2} V + K$$

Thus $\qquad\qquad\qquad K = \frac{R_1C_1 - R_2C_2}{(C_1 + C_2)(R_1 + R_2)} V$

so that $K = 0$ for $R_1C_1 = R_2C_2$.

We have based this example on the assumption that $v_1(t)$ is generated by an ideal source. Calculating the improvement which the compensated attenuator furnishes with a resistive source (when no impulses can take place) is left as an exercise for the reader.

16-24. Impedance Level. The reader has undoubtedly noticed that the numerical values which were assigned to the circuit parameters in the numerical examples and in many of the problems at the ends of the chapters were not "practical." The magnitudes of the values which were chosen for the R, L, and C elements were between 0.1 and 10 (ohms, henrys, and farads, respectively). Now we recall from elementary physics that such values (for example, a 1-farad capacitance) may not correspond to practical devices. We have chosen these simple numbers for two reasons. First, the principles connected with the solutions of problems can be exhibited just as clearly with simple numbers as with annoying decimals, and the operations are easier to follow with small integral numbers. Second, as we shall show in this article, a change of the scale can often be used either to simplify the numbers in a problem or, more important, to *reinterpret* a problem in such a manner that the numbers are simple and still correspond to a problem with "practical" numbers.

Circuit problems can be formulated in a variety of ways. For example, mesh, node, or other equations may be used, but in every case we make use of the operational immittance. Thus the equations with which we deal have terms of the form

$$Z(p)i = v(t) \qquad \text{or} \qquad Y(p)v = i(t)$$

Now, if an operational impedance is multiplied by a constant, say, k_L (a constant for change of level), then

$$v(t) = k_L Z(p) \frac{1}{k_L} i(t) \tag{16-66}$$

Now we can interpret Eq. (16-66) in two ways. The obvious way is to state that one side was multiplied and divided by a constant and nothing has changed. Alternatively we may say that Eq. (16-66) states: If the operational impedance is multiplied by k_L, then $1/k_L$ times as much current is needed to produce the same voltage as before the multiplication. This interpretation is used to change the impedance level of a network.

Operational impedances are composed of products and quotients of terms which have the form

$$Z(p) = R + pL + \frac{1}{pC}$$

Hence
$$k_L Z(p) = k_L R + p k_L L + \frac{1}{pC/k_L} \tag{16-66a}$$

It follows that the impedance level of a network can be changed if every resistance is multiplied by a constant, every inductance is multiplied by the same constant, and every capacitance is divided by that constant. (For convenience we often choose $k_L = 10^n$, $n =$ positive or negative integer.) We also observe that such a change in impedance level does not influence the poles or zeros of the network function. Thus the waveshape of the response or the angle of any complex immittance is unchanged; only the magnitude is changed. This follows by observing that the roots of the equation $D(s) = 0$ are the same as the roots of $k_L D(s) = 0$.

Example 16-29. In the circuit of Fig. 16-44a it is desired that the value of no capacitance should exceed 1 μf. Draw a terminal pair whose immittance has the same poles and zeros (the same frequency response) as the terminal pair shown but which satisfies the limitation on capacitance values.

Solution. Since the specification deals with reducing capacitance values, $k_L > 1$. The larger capacitance controls. Choosing $k_L = 10^7$, a network that meets the requirement is shown in Fig. 16-44b.

16-25. Change of Time or Frequency Scale. In the preceding article we have seen that the multiplication of every resistance and inductance by a constant in a network, and the division of every capacitance value by that constant, will change the impedance level without changing the values of the poles or zeros of the network. Since the frequency response of a network is determined by the poles and zeros of the corresponding network function, a change in the impedance level does not change the frequency response of a network. Now it frequently happens that, using simple numbers, we obtain poles and zeros which are of the undesired order of magnitude. Thus, for example, we may have in the network a free mode with a time constant of 1 sec when we really desire a microsecond time constant. It is also possible that the frequency-response curve of a network function has the correct shape but not the desired frequency scale. For example, a series R-L-C circuit in which $R = 0.1$ ohm, $C = 1$ farad, $L = 1$ henry may have the (desired) $Q_0 = 10$ but a radian resonant frequency of 1. We may be satisfied with the value

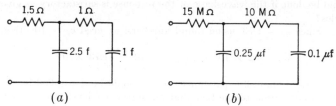

Fig. 16-44. Illustrating change of impedance level.

Q_0 but may desire a radian resonant frequency of 100,000. By choice of proper scale factors the results obtained by the use of analysis of circuits with simple numbers can be used.

The problem is then to modify the values of the elements in a network so that the shapes of its amplitude- and phase-frequency curves are unaltered but so that every aspect of these new curves occurs at a frequency k_F times the old frequency. To satisfy this requirement, we note that the frequency response of a network may be computed from the ratios of length of lines joining the zeros and poles of the network function to the pole $j\omega$ representing the source function. If the frequency response is to be unaltered, this ratio must be maintained when ω is changed to $k_F\omega$. This can be accomplished if all the poles and zeros are multiplied by k_F. The poles and zeros of a network function are the roots of expressions which have factors of the form $R_{ij} + sL_{ij} + 1/sC_{ij}$. The resulting poles and zeros are of the form

$$s_{1,2} = -\frac{R_{ij}}{2L_{ij}} \pm \sqrt{\left(\frac{R_{ij}}{2L_{ij}}\right)^2 - \frac{1}{L_{ij}C_{ij}}}$$

If in this expression the values of L_{ij} and C_{ij} are divided by k_F but the value of R_{ij} is left unaltered, the poles and zeros of the network will be multiplied by k_F.   Any aspect of the frequency response which occurred at frequency ω in the old network will now occur at frequency $k_F\omega$.   It is noted that in multiplying the value of poles and zeros of a network by k_F the time constants associated with the poles (free response) will be divided by the factor k_F.   Thus any change in the value of the elements which produces a desired effect in the steady state at $k_F\omega$ instead of ω changes the time constant of the free modes from T to T/k_F.   It must be noted that a change in frequency scale alters the value of complex imped-ance at any given frequency but is not a change in impedance level.

Example 16-30.   In a certain network function the poles are

$$s_1 = -2 \qquad s_{2,3} = -1 \pm j1.73$$

It is desired that the frequency of the transient oscillations be no less than 10^7 rad/sec. What should be done if the waveshape of the response is satisfactory as given by the original poles?

Solution.   Since $\omega_d = 1.73$, using round numbers, we need $k_T = 10^7$; then

$$s_1' = -2 \times 10^7 \qquad s_{2,3}' = -10^7 \pm j1.73 \times 10^7$$

Hence all inductance and all capacitance values should be multiplied by 10^{-7}.   It is necessary to call attention to the fact that an impedance-level change could also be used in conjunction with time scaling (see, e.g., Prob. 16-32).

C. NETWORK THEOREMS

In the preceding articles we have shown how the behavior of a linear network is determined by a system of linear (differential) equations.   So far we have concentrated on procedures for the determination of complete response.   We have seen that the use of mesh or node equations system-atizes the procedure for the solution of particular problems.   In this part of the chapter we shall discuss certain general statements about linear networks.   These statements, all of which are the result of the assump-tion of linearity, are formulated as "theorems" or "principles."   All of them apply to linear networks regardless of the source waveforms. These theorems will generally be deduced from the node or mesh equa-tions.   We anticipate two important results from a discussion of network theorems.   First, the use of these theorems will reduce the labor involved in the solution of particular examples because much of the work which is common to many problems has been done, once and for all, in the "deri-vation" of the theorem.   Second, the study of networks in the form of theorems can be expected to give new insight into the mechanisms which determine (the energy-transfer processes which are involved in) network response.

We have already discussed the following network theorems in the preceding chapters: complete-response theorem, conversion-of-sources theorem, Thévenin's theorem, initial-condition generators, and the maximum-power-transfer theorem for the sinusoidal and d-c steady states.

16-26. The Superposition Principle

In a network which is composed of linear elements the component of the response due to several ideal sources acting simultaneously is equal to the sum of the components of the response due to each source acting individually.

This statement has already been discussed several times. The superposition principle is the direct consequence of the linearity of the elements, i.e., a consequence of linear equations. Thus the assumption of linearity constitutes the proof of the superposition principle. Nevertheless we wish to duplicate some of the discussion concerning superposition before the discussion of other network theorems, because all these theorems are a consequence of the superposition property. As we have seen earlier in this chapter, the node and mesh formulation of network equations exhibits the superposition principle in a particularly useful and lucid fashion.

The node equations for an n-node network are

$$Y_{11}(p)v_1 + Y_{12}(p)v_2 + Y_{13}(p)v_3 + \cdots + Y_{1n}(p)v_n = i_1$$
$$Y_{21}(p)v_1 + Y_{22}(p)v_2 + Y_{23}(p)v_3 + \cdots + Y_{2n}(p)v_n = i_2$$
$$\vdots \qquad\qquad\qquad\qquad\qquad \vdots \qquad (16\text{-}67)$$
$$Y_{n1}(p)v_1 + Y_{n2}(p)v_2 + Y_{n3}(p)v_3 + \cdots + Y_{nn}(p)v_n = i_n$$

so that
$$v_1 = \frac{(F_y)_{11}}{D_y}\, i_1 + \frac{(F_y)_{21}}{D_y}\, i_2 + \cdots + \frac{(F_y)_{n1}}{D_y}\, i_n \qquad (16\text{-}68)$$

If in Eq. (16-68) all current sources are set to zero except i_1, then

$$v_1 \text{ due to } i_1 = \frac{(F_y)_{11}}{D_y}\, i_1$$

Similarly, if all sources except i_2 are set to zero, then

$$v_1 \text{ due to } i_2 = \frac{(F_y)_{21}}{D_y}\, i_2$$

Hence Eq. (16-68) is an expression of the principle of superposition since it reads

$$v_1 = (v_1 \text{ due to } i_1) + (v_1 \text{ due to } i_2) + \cdots + (v_1 \text{ due to } i_n)$$

If we had written the mesh equations of an m-mesh network, we should have solved for the mesh current i_k and obtained the result

$$i_k = \sum_{a=1}^{m} \frac{(F_z)_{ak}}{D_z} v_a$$

so that $i_k = (i_k$ due to $v_1) + (i_k$ due to $v_2) + \cdots + (i_k$ due to $v_m)$.

We have already presented many examples in which the response of particular networks was determined by applications of the superposition principle. At this point it is important to recognize a general result of superposition. If we wish to study networks in general form, it is quite sufficient that we study the network behavior under the influence of a single ideal source—moreover, we may assume that the network is initially deenergized. This follows first of all from the fact that the initial-energy storage in networks can be represented by ideal sources (initial-condition generators); hence assuming nonzero initial-energy storage corresponds to assuming that the network has several sources. Now, if we prove a statement with the assumption that the network contains only a single ideal source, then, by using the superposition principle, we can prove that statement for any number of sources acting simultaneously since the general procedure of proof will be the same for all sources.

16-27. Driving-point Immittance. If we wish to impress an ideal source on a source-free network without affecting its natural modes, then

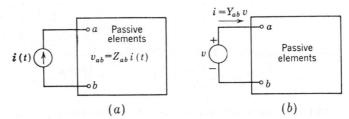

Fig. 16-45. Driving-point immittance functions.

there are two ways in which this can be done. Either we can connect an ideal current source to a node pair (soldering-iron entry), or we can insert an ideal voltage source (pliers entry). An operational driving-point immittance is then defined in connection with the terminals of the source as that operator which relates the voltage across the source to the current which the source furnishes. Thus, if a current source is impressed between two nodes a and b with reference direction as shown in Fig. 16-45a, the driving-point immittance at terminals a-b, $Z_{ab}(p)$, is given by the operational relationship $v_{ab}(t) = Z_{ab}(p)i(t)$. If a voltage source is inserted into a network between terminals a-b as shown in Fig. 16-45b, then the driving-point admittance $Y_{ab}(p)$ is defined through the relationship $i(t) = Y_{ab}(p)v_{ab}(t)$. It should be evident that the driving-point immittance of a given network depends on the terminals which are used to insert the source.

The use of node and mesh equations makes it possible to deduce a general formula for driving-point immittance. Suppose that a current source $i(t)$ is inserted between node 1 and the reference node such that $i(t)$ flows into node 1 and that this is the only source in the network. Then, from Eq. (16-68),

$$v_1(t) = \frac{(F_y)_{11}}{D_y} i(t)$$

so that the driving-point impedance between node 1 and the reference node, $Z_{1R}(p)$, is

$$Z_{1R}(p) = \frac{(F_y)_{11}}{D_y(p)} \tag{16-69}$$

If a voltage source $v(t)$ is inserted in mesh 1 such that only $i_1(t)$ flows in the source, then, if the reference direction for $v(t)$ is in the direction of mesh 1,

$$i_1(t) = \frac{(F_z)_{11}}{D_z} v(t)$$

Hence the driving-point admittance at the terminals of the source is $Y(p) = (F_z)_{11}/D_z(p)$.

At this point we suggest that the reader review Thévenin's theorem (Art. 12-9). In the proof of this theorem we assumed that a driving-point immittance for any passive terminal pair can always be formulated. In the light of the discussion just concluded we see that this assumption is justified since this immittance function can be determined from the node- (or mesh-) admittance (or impedance) matrix.

16-28. The Compensation Theorem. The compensation theorem (also called "substitution theorem") is so deceptively simple that it is often neglected as trivial. There are, however, several types of applications such as vacuum-tube circuits and circuits with mutual inductance (see Chap. 18) in which application of the compensation theorem is helpful. This theorem may be stated as follows:

Compensation Theorem. If a passive element or branch in a circuit is defined by the voltage-current relationship $v_{ab} = Z_{ab}(p)i_{ab}$ or $i_{ab} = Y_{ab}(p)v_{ab}$, then that element or branch may be replaced by a compensating voltage source whose waveform is given by $Z_{ab}(p)i_{ab}$ or a current source given by $Y_{ab}(p)v_{ab}$.

This theorem follows from Kirchhoff's laws. That is, it makes no difference which symbol is used to describe the voltage-current relationship for an element or branch. If the application of Kirchhoff's laws results in the correct equilibrium equations, then the circuit is correctly formulated.

In order to apply the theorem fruitfully, we must understand the difference (see Fig. 16-46) between an ideal source such as $v(t)$ and a source such as $v_{ab}(t)$. We recall that an ideal source is a source that generates a function $v(t)$ or $i(t)$ which is *independent* of the elements connected to the terminals of the source. Clearly the waveform of the compensating volt-

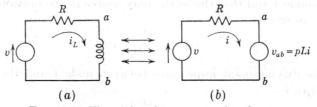

$$(a) \qquad\qquad (b)$$

FIG. 16-46. Illustrating the compensation theorem.

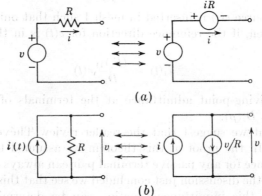

$$(a)$$

$$(b)$$

FIG. 16-47. Representation of resistive source as the combination of ideal and compensating sources.

age source $v_{ab}(t)$ discussed above is dependent on the circuit elements. Hence a source which is introduced into the circuit diagram as a result of applying the compensation theorem is not an ideal source. We shall call such a source a "compensating" or "dependent" source as distinguished from an "impressed," "independent," or ideal source. We note incidentally that a resistive source (as defined in Chap. 10) may be represented as the combination of an independent and a dependent source as shown in Fig. 16-47.

Example 16-31. Determine Thévenin's equivalent circuit with respect to terminals a-n in Fig. 16-48a.

Solution. In the given circuit v_s is an ideal source but μv_{gk} (μ = const) is a partially dependent source because $v_{gk} = v_{gn} + v_{nk} = v_s + v_{nk}$.

To obtain Thévenin's equivalent circuit, we need v_{an} in Fig. 16-48a. Since no current flows in that circuit, $v_{an} = v_o = -\mu v_s$.

Now we need the driving-point impedance at terminals a-n with *all ideal sources set to zero*. Setting $v_s = 0$ gives the circuit of Fig. 16-48b. Applying a voltage source v as indicated by the dotted portion of the circuit in Fig. 16-48b, we have

$$v = i(R_p + R_k) - \mu v_{gk} \qquad v_{gk} = v_{nk} = -iR_k$$

Hence
$$v = i[R_p + (\mu + 1)R_k]$$

so that the driving-point impedance at terminals a-n is

$$Z_{an} = R_p + (\mu + 1)R_k$$

Thévenin's equivalent circuit can now be drawn as in Fig. 16-48c.

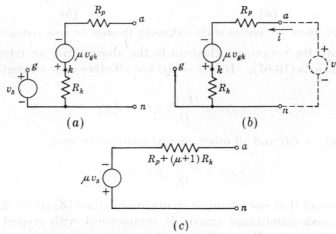

FIG. 16-48. Illustration of the application of Thévenin's theorem in a circuit in which there is a partially dependent source.

16-29. The Reciprocity Theorem.

All the theorems discussed so far deal with the behavior of a network at a terminal pair. The reciprocity theorem describes how certain voltages and currents in two different branches of a network are related. Thus it will deal with *two terminal pairs* of a network. The reciprocity theorem is most simply stated as follows:

> *Reciprocity Theorem.* If an ideal current source $i(t)$ is impressed between node 1 and the reference node [such that $i(t)$ enters node 1] of a passive network and if the resulting component of the node voltage $v_2(t)$ due to this source is $v_a(t)$, then impressing the same source current $i(t)$ between node 2 and the reference node [such that $i(t)$ enters node 2] will result in a contribution to the node voltage at node 1 which will be $v_a(t)$.

To understand this statement of the reciprocity theorem consider the circuit indicated in Fig. 16-49a. In this figure the component of $v_2(t)$ due to $i(t)$ is $v_a(t)$. Now in Fig. 16-49b we have the same passive elements, but $i(t)$ is applied between node 2 and the reference node. The reciprocity theorem tells us that now $[v_1(t)]_s = v_a(t)$.

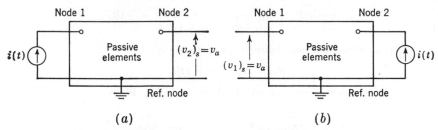

FIG. 16-49. Illustration of the reciprocity theorem for node voltages.

To prove the reciprocity theorem in the above form, we refer to the node equations (16-67). If $i_1(t) = i(t)$ but all other node current sources are zero,

$$v_2(t) = \frac{(F_y)_{12}}{D_y}\, i(t) \equiv v_a(t)$$

If now $i_2(t) = i(t)$ and all other current sources are zero,

$$v_1(t) = \frac{(F_y)_{21}}{D_y}\, i(t) \equiv v_b(t)$$

Now we recall that our circuit elements are bilateral $[Z_{ab}(p) = Z_{ba}(p)]$ so that the node-admittance matrix is symmetrical with respect to the principal diagonal. Hence $(F_y)_{21} = (F_y)_{12}$, and $v_b(t) \equiv v_a(t)$.

In the statement of the reciprocity theorem we have discussed the relationship between node voltages if a current source is connected between the reference node and either one of two other nodes. We can extend the reciprocity theorem so that it deals with any two node pairs. Consider the network represented by Fig. 16-50a, with a current source impressed between nodes 1 and 2. The node equations will be

$$Y_{11}v_1 + Y_{12}v_2 + Y_{13}v_3 + Y_{14}v_4 + \cdots + Y_{1n}v_n = i(t)$$
$$Y_{21}v_1 + Y_{22}v_2 + Y_{23}v_3 + Y_{24}v_4 + \cdots + Y_{2n}v_n = -i(t)$$
$$Y_{31}v_1 + Y_{32}v_2 + \cdots\cdots\cdots\cdots\cdots + Y_{3n}v_n = 0$$

$$Y_{n1}v_1 + \cdots\cdots\cdots\cdots\cdots\cdots\cdots + Y_{nn}v_n = 0$$

Hence

$$v_3(t) = \frac{(F_y)_{13}}{D_y}\, i + \frac{(F_y)_{23}}{D_y}\,(-i)$$

$$v_4(t) = \frac{(F_y)_{14}}{D_y}\, i + \frac{(F_y)_{24}}{D_y}\,(-i)$$

$$\text{(16-70)}$$

and

$$v_a = v_3 - v_4$$

Now if we connect the ideal source to the node pair 3-4 as shown in Fig. 16-50b, we obtain from the new node equations

$$v_1 = \frac{(F_y)_{31}}{D_y} i + \frac{(F_y)_{41}}{D_y} (-i)$$

$$v_2 = \frac{(F_y)_{32}}{D_y} i + \frac{(F_y)_{42}}{D_y} (-i)$$

(16-71)

and since $F_{kj} = F_{jk}$ as before, by comparing Eqs. (16-70) and (16-71), we have $v_1 - v_2 = v_a$.

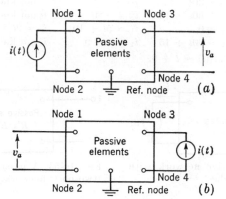

FIG. 16-50. Extension of the reciprocity theorem to node-pair voltages.

The reciprocity theorem can also be used when the network is active provided that we interpret the result as dealing only with the component of the response due to the external source $i(t)$.

It is also possible to state the reciprocity theorem in connection with a voltage source:

If an ideal voltage source $v(t)$ introduced in branch b_1 produces a component of current $i_a(t)$ due to $v(t)$ in branch b_2, then the same component of current $i_a(t)$ due to $v(t)$ will be produced in branch b_1 when the voltage source $v(t)$ is introduced in branch b_2.

(The proper reference directions for voltages and currents are illustrated in Fig. 16-51.)

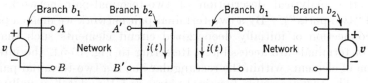

FIG. 16-51. Reference directions for the statement of the reciprocity theorem with voltage source.

In this ("voltage") form of the theorem, unless each of the two branches referred to belongs to one mesh only (but not the same mesh), the proof of this form is somewhat cumbersome.

Example 16-32. The "box" in Fig. 16-52 contains only resistances. It is known that, when $v_1(t) = 30t$, $v_2(t) \equiv 0$, $i_1(t) = 5t$, and $i_2(t) = 2t$. Calculate $i_1(t)$ when $v_1(t) = 30t + 60$ and $v_2(t) = 60t + 15$.

Solution. We shall tabulate as follows

				Reason
$v_1 = 30t$	$v_2 \equiv 0$	$i_1 = 5t$	$i_2 = 2t$	Given
$v_1 \equiv 0$	$v_2 = 30t$	$i_1 = -2t$	i_2 not known	Reciprocity
$v_1 \equiv 0$	$v_2 = 60t + 15$	$i_1 = -4t - 1$	i_2 not known	Superposition
$v_1 = 30t + 60$	$v_2 = 0$	$i_1 = 5t + 10$	$i_2 = 2t + 4$	Superposition
$v_1 = 30t + 60$	$v_2 = 60t + 15$	$i_1 = t + 9$	i_2 not known	Superposition

Hence the solution is $i_1(t) = t + 9$.

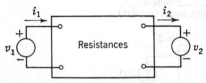
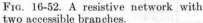

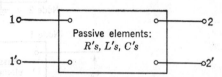

FIG. 16-52. A resistive network with two accessible branches.

FIG. 16-53. A passive two-terminal-pair (two-port) network.

16-30. Transfer Immittance.
In studying the reciprocity theorem we discussed the relationship between a source function and a response function. We found that for a passive two-terminal pair such as is shown in Fig. 16-53, the voltage at either terminal pair is related to a source current connected across the other terminal pair through the same transfer immittance,

$$(z_{tr})_{12} = (z_{tr})_{21}$$

From the preceding article it should be clear how the operational transfer immittance can be determined from the node-admittance or mesh-impedance matrix.

16-31. Introduction to Two-terminal-pair Networks.
We have discussed the relationship of driving-point or transfer immittances to the mesh or node formulation of network equations. In this article we shall study the analytical description of two-terminal-pair networks (also called "two-ports"). By a two-terminal-pair network we mean a passive interconnection of initially deenergized circuit elements such that two pairs of terminals are accessible. Referring to Fig. 16-54, the interconnection of elements within the rectangular box is a two-terminal-pair network. The two accessible terminal pairs are 1-1' and 2-2', usually called

the input and output terminals, respectively. In discussing such networks we deal with the relationship between v_1, i_1, v_2, i_2, that is, with the variables that are associated with the two terminal pairs; we do *not* consider such functions as v_{12}. In Fig. 16-54 we have indicated schematically a general problem of signal transmission. A two-terminal-pair network is interposed between a source and a load. How can the input voltage and current (v_1 and i_1) be related to load voltage and current

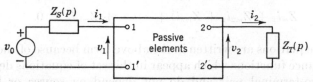

FIG. 16-54. A two-port supplied by a source with internal immittance terminated into an impedance Z_T.

(v_2 and i_2)? We know immediately that $v_2 = Z_T i_2$. On the other hand, the relationship between v_1 and i_2 depends on the elements of the two-terminal pair as well as on the load. A simple way of arriving at a useful result for the schematic of Fig. 16-54 is to apply mesh analysis (had the current-source equivalent for v_0 and Z_s been chosen, node analysis would be used). As indicated in Fig. 16-55, we assume that v_0 and Z_s are part of mesh 1 only, and no other mesh, and that Z_T is part of mesh 2 only, and no other mesh.

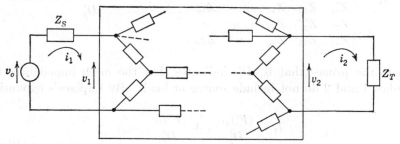

FIG. 16-55. Choice of mesh currents for the analysis of a two-port.

If we calculate the mesh impedances, all these except Z_{11} and Z_{22} are independent of source and load. For Z_{11} we may write $Z_{11} = Z_s + Z'_{11}$ and, for Z_{22}, $Z_{22} = Z_T + Z'_{22}$, where Z'_{11} and Z'_{22} are the contributions of the two-terminal pair to the mesh impedances of meshes 1 and 2, respectively. Hence the mesh equations for meshes 1 and 2, assuming m meshes, read

$$Z'_{11}i_1 + Z_s i_1 + Z_{12}i_2 + \cdots + Z_{1m}i_m = v_0$$
$$Z_{21}i_1 + Z'_{22}i_2 + Z_T i_2 + \cdots \cdots \cdots = 0$$

Since $v_0 - Z_s i_1 = v_1$ and $v_2 = Z_T i_2$, the m-mesh equations read

$$Z_{11}' i_1 + Z_{12} i_2 + Z_{13} i_3 + \cdots + Z_{1m} i_m = v_1$$
$$Z_{21} i_1 + Z_{22}' i_2 + Z_{23} i_3 + \cdots + Z_{2m} i_m = -v_2$$
$$Z_{31} i_1 + Z_{32} i_2 + Z_{33} i_3 + \cdots + Z_{3m} i_m = 0$$
$$\vdots \qquad\qquad\qquad\qquad\qquad \vdots$$
$$Z_{m1} i_1 + Z_{m2} i_2 + Z_{m3} i_3 + \cdots + Z_{mm} i_m = 0$$

The mesh equations are written in the above form because of the fact that the impedance functions which appear in this set of equations depend *only* on the two-terminal pair and do not depend on source or load. To obtain a relationship between the input and output variables which does not depend on Z_s and Z_T, we may solve the above equations for i_1 and i_2 only since none of the other currents are accessible.

Using Cramér's rule,

$$i_1 = \frac{\begin{vmatrix} v_1 & Z_{12} & \cdots & Z_{1m} \\ -v_2 & Z_{22}' & \cdots & Z_{2m} \\ 0 & \cdot & \cdots & \cdot \\ 0 & \cdot & \cdots & \cdot \\ 0 & \cdot & \cdots & Z_{mm} \end{vmatrix}}{\begin{vmatrix} Z_{11}' & Z_{12} & Z_{12} & \cdots & Z_{1m} \\ Z_{21} & Z_{22}' & Z_{23} & \cdots & \cdot \\ Z_{31} & Z_{32} & Z_{33} & \cdots & Z_{mm} \end{vmatrix}} = \frac{\begin{vmatrix} v_1 & Z_{12} & \cdots & Z_{1m} \\ -v_2 & Z_{22}' & \cdots & \cdot \\ 0 & \cdot & \cdots & \cdot \\ 0 & \cdot & \cdots & \cdot \\ 0 & \cdot & \cdots & Z_{mm} \end{vmatrix}}{D_z'}$$

where the prime (that is, D_z') indicates that the mesh impedances for meshes 1 and 2 do not include source or load. By Laplace's expansion

$$i_1 = \frac{(F_z')_{11}}{D_z'} v_1 + \frac{(F_z')_{21}}{D_z'} (-v_2)$$
$$i_2 = \frac{(F_z')_{12}}{D_z'} v_1 + \frac{(F_z')_{22}}{D_z'} (-v_2)$$

(16-72)

It follows that the relationship between the four variables associated with the two-terminal pairs is completely defined through the four operators $(F_z')_{11}/D_z'$, $(F_z')_{22}/D_z'$, $(F_z')_{21}/D_z'$, and $(F_z')_{12}/D_z'$. If the network is bilateral and obeys the reciprocity theorem, then $F_{21} = F_{12}$. Hence three operators are sufficient to specify the terminal relationships for a two-terminal-pair network!

Dimensionally each of the terms F_{ij}'/D_z' is an admittance function. We use lower-case letters to abbreviate,

$$y_{11}(p) = \frac{(F'_z)_{11}}{D'_z}$$

$$y_{22}(p) = \frac{(F'_z)_{22}}{D'_z}$$

$$y_{12}(p) = y_{21}(p) = \frac{(F'_z)_{12}}{D'_z}$$

Hence we can write

$$
\begin{aligned}
i_1 &= y_{11}(p)v_1 - y_{12}(p)v_2 \\
i_2 &= y_{12}(p)v_1 - y_{22}(p)v_2
\end{aligned}
\tag{16-73}
$$

Now our result so far can be stated in words as follows: The terminal relations of a two-terminal-pair network are specified through the three operators y_{11}, y_{22}, and y_{12}. These operators can be obtained from the mesh equations or the node equations as above. Even if this statement were the only conclusion from the above discussion, the results would be important. In addition, however, we shall now show that these operators can be determined, without study of the mesh or node equations, simply by calculation (or "measurement") of the terminal relationships under special conditions.

16-32. The Short-circuit Admittance Matrix. If we inspect Eqs. (16-73) we observe that, when $v_2 \equiv 0$,

$$
\begin{aligned}
i_1 &= y_{11}v_1 & v_2 &\equiv 0 \\
i_2 &= y_{12}v_1 & v_2 &\equiv 0
\end{aligned}
$$

Now setting $v_2 \equiv 0$ means short-circuiting terminal pair 2-2'. Hence y_{11} is the driving-point admittance at terminal pair 1-1' with terminal pair 2-2' short-circuited. Similarly, y_{12} is the transfer admittance from terminal pair 1-1' to 2-2' with v_2 short-circuited, and y_{22} is the driving-point admittance at terminal pair 2-2' with pair 1-1' short-circuited! Since, in matrix form, Eqs. (16-73) are written

$$
\begin{Vmatrix} y_{11} & y_{12} \\ y_{12} & y_{22} \end{Vmatrix} \times \begin{Vmatrix} v_1 \\ -v_2 \end{Vmatrix} = \begin{Vmatrix} i_1 \\ i_2 \end{Vmatrix}
$$

the matrix

$$
\begin{Vmatrix} y_{11}(p) & y_{12}(p) \\ y_{21}(p) & y_{22}(p) \end{Vmatrix} \equiv \|y\|
$$

is referred to as the *short-circuit admittance matrix* of the two-terminal-pair network. We again point out that the elements of the matrix need not be obtained from the mesh equations but are determined from transfer and driving-point admittances. By taking this view Eqs. (16-73) define the short-circuit admittance matrix.

16-33. The Open-circuit Impedance Matrix. If Eqs. (16-73) are solved for v_1 and v_2, we obtain

$$v_1 = \frac{y_{22}}{y_{11}y_{22} - y_{12}^2} i_1 + \frac{-y_{12}}{y_{11}y_{22} - y_{12}^2} i_2$$

$$v_2 = \frac{y_{12}}{y_{11}y_{22} - y_{12}^2} i_1 + \frac{-y_{11}}{y_{11}y_{22} - y_{12}^2} i_2$$

The terms $y_{ij}/(y_{11}y_{22} - y_{12}^2)$ are dimensionally impedance functions. Hence we can write

$$v_1 = z_{11}i_1 + z_{12}(-i_2)$$
$$v_2 = z_{12}i_1 + z_{22}(-i_2)$$

Exactly as before, the operators z_{11}, z_{22}, and z_{12} need *not* be considered as defined either through the short-circuit admittance matrix or through the mesh or node equations. We rather observe that

$$v_1 = z_{11}i_1 \text{ if } i_2 \equiv 0 \qquad v_2 = z_{12}i_1 \text{ if } i_2 \equiv 0$$
$$v_1 = -z_{12}i_2 \text{ if } i_1 \equiv 0 \qquad v_2 = -z_{22}i_2 \text{ if } i_1 \equiv 0$$

Hence these operators are determined as driving-point or transfer impedances under open-circuit conditions. The parameters in matrix form

$$\begin{Vmatrix} z_{11} & z_{12} \\ z_{12} & z_{22} \end{Vmatrix}$$

are referred to as the *open-circuit impedance matrix* of the two-terminal pair.

It should now be evident that the short-circuit admittance matrix and the open-circuit impedance matrix are not the only ways of describing a two-terminal pair. We can solve for any two of the four variables v_1, v_2, i_1, and i_2 in terms of the other two (see Prob. 16-47). The applications of such descriptions of two-terminal-pair networks are left for a more advanced treatment of network theory. For our purposes here, it is sufficient to state that first of all these matrices are very useful in the study of equivalent two-terminal pairs because they can be determined independently of the mesh or node equations and hence show how the terminal functions (driving-point and transfer immittances) influence the network behavior. Second, the reader will find, in more advanced treatments, that the two-terminal pair can be considered to be the basic "building block" in more complex networks or systems. We shall then find that the rules of matrix addition or multiplication can, under certain conditions, be applied to two-terminal-pair networks exactly as element addition is used in networks (i.e., addition of impedances in series and admittances in parallel). Thus in this book we have developed the subject of circuit analysis in accordance with the following scheme. We started with the primitive elements R, L, and C. After a study of these we introduced the immittance function or the p element as the basic "unit" of a network. Finally we arrived at an operational matrix as the basic building block of a system composed of networks. As we have said, a more advanced treatment of circuit analysis will deal with these matrices in detail.

PROBLEMS

16-1. (a) Obtain the operational transfer functions which relate v_{ab} to $v(t)$ and to $i(t)$. (b) Write the differential equation which relates v_{ab} to the source functions. (c) For $v(t) = 7 \cos \frac{1}{3}t$ and $i(t) = 3e^{-2t}$ calculate the complete response $v_{ab}(t)$ if $v_{ab}(0^+) = 0$. (d) For $v(t) = 3U(t)$ and $i(t) = e^{-2t} \cos 2t$ calculate the complete response $v_{ab}(t)$ if $v_{ab}(0^+) = 0$. The circuit is shown in Fig. P16-1.

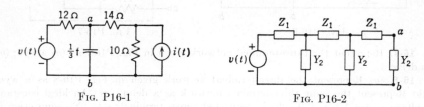

FIG. P16-1   FIG. P16-2

16-2. (a) Starting from the a-b terminals and by the application of Kirchhoff's laws, obtain the gain function which relates v_{ab} to v. (b) If $Z_1 = 1$ and $Y_2 = p$, deduce the radian frequency at which v_{ab} differs in phase from v by 180° in the sinusoidal steady state. (c) What is the amplitude ratio $(V_{ab})_m/V_m$ at the radian frequency of (b)? The circuit is shown in Fig. P16-2.

16-3. (a) Use repeated source conversion in Fig. P16-3 to obtain the equation which relates v_{ab} to the source functions. (b) Use the result of (a) to calculate the steady-state components of v_{ab} if $v(t) = 12$, $i_a(t) = 3 \sin t$, $i_c(t) = 2 \cos 2t$.

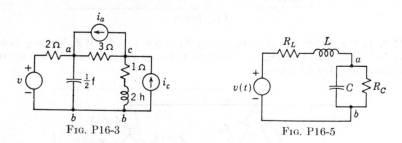

FIG. P16-3   FIG. P16-5

16-4. Use Thévenin's theorem in the circuit of Fig. 16-11 to obtain Eq. (16-24).

16-5. The initial energy stored in the inductance is zero and $v_{ab}(0^+) = 4$ volts. If $R_L = \frac{1}{2}$ ohm, $R_C = \frac{1}{6}$ ohm, $L = \frac{1}{2}$ henry, $C = 2$ farads, (a) calculate $(dv_{ab}/dt)_{0^+}$; (b) calculate the complete response v_{ab} if (1) $v(t) = 16U(t)$, (2) $v(t) = e^{-t}U(t)$, (3) $v(t) = 5 \cos t$. The circuit is shown in Fig. P16-5.

16-6. In the circuit shown in Fig. P16-6 the three p elements labeled Z_1 are identical to each other, and the three elements labeled Z_0 are identical to each other.   (*a*) Draw a circuit equivalent to the given circuit at terminals *a-b*, converting the three Z_0 elements to a wye.   (*b*) If $Z_0 = 30$ ohms and $Z_1 = 10$ ohms (i.e., all resistances), what is the numerical value of Z_{ab}?   (*c*) If the elements marked Z_0 are 3-farad capacitances and the elements labeled Z_1 are 1-farad capacitances, what is $Z_{ab}(p)$?   (*d*) $v_{ab} = 60 \cos 10{,}000t$. Z_0 is the series combination of a 3-ohm resistance and a 0.0003-henry inductance. Z_1 is the series combination of a 1-ohm resistance and a 100-μf capacitance.   Calculate (1) $i(t)$ in the steady state; (2) $v_{db}(t)$ in the steady state.

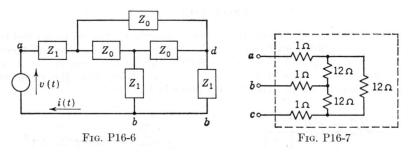

FIG. P16-6   FIG. P16-7

16-7. Represent the three-terminal network given in Fig. P16-7 as (*a*) a wye; (*b*) a delta.

16-8. (*a*) Represent the three-terminal network given in Fig. P16-8 as a wye. (*b*) Represent the same three-terminal network as a delta.   (*c*) An ideal constant voltage source $V_{ab} = 120$ volts is connected across terminals *a-b*.   No connection is made to terminal *c*.   Calculate the power delivered by this source.

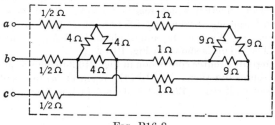

FIG. P16-8

16-9. In Fig. P16-9, at a given frequency $\mathbf{Z}_\Delta = 3.6 + j4.8$.   If $\mathbf{Z}_y$ is purely capacitive, find its value at this frequency such that the equivalent three-terminal network is a purely resistive delta or wye.

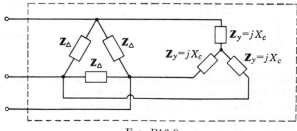

FIG. P16-9

16-10. Prove Eqs. (16-19) and (16-20) by the method suggested in the footnote on page 448.

16-11. Calculate the transform driving-point impedance $Z_{ab}(s)$ in Fig. P16-11.

16-12. (a) Show that in the circuit of Fig. P16-12 the application of delta-wye conversion leads to nonphysical elements. (b) Show that the driving-point admittance $Y_{mn}(s) = 1$.

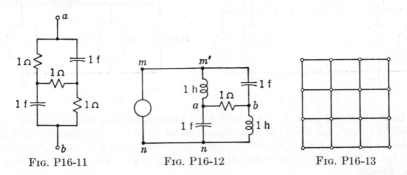

FIG. P16-11   FIG. P16-12   FIG. P16-13

16-13. The linear graph of a network is shown in Fig. P16-13. What is the number of (a) nodes; (b) junctions; (c) meshes; (d) line elements in a tree?

16-14. Draw five trees for the network graph of Prob. 16-13 (Fig. P16-13).

16-15. Draw the graph of a network which has 5 nodes, all junctions, and each junction connected to all other junctions. Is this network planar?

16-16. Why should a manufacturer of printed circuits be concerned with the planar or nonplanar character of a network?

16-17. (a) In Fig. P16-17 obtain two simultaneous equations for I_1 and V_{ab}. (b) Calculate I_1 and V_{ab}. (c) Calculate the power delivered by each source and the power dissipated by each resistance.

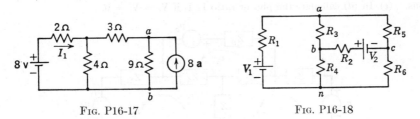

FIG. P16-17   FIG. P16-18

16-18. If $R_1 = R_2 = 1$, $R_3 = R_4 = 2$, $R_5 = 4$, $R_6 = 3$ (all in ohms), $V_1 = 10$ volts and $V_2 = 10$ volts, calculate the power delivered to each resistance and the power delivered by each source in Fig. P16-18, using (a) branch currents as variables; (b) voltages across elements as variables; (c) mesh currents as variables; (d) junction voltages as variables.

16-19. (a) Represent the combination of Z_2 and $v(t)$ (Fig. P16-19) as a current source, and write the node equations for v_1 and v_2. (b) Write the node equations for v_1 and v_2 if each of the p elements (Z_1 to Z_5) is a 1-ohm resistance. (c) Write the node equations if $Z_1 = Z_4 = 1$, $Z_2 = 1/2p$, $Z_3 = 3$, $Z_5 = p$, $i_a = U(t)$, $i_b = 3U(t)$, $v = 2tU(t)$. (d) Draw the circuit diagram which corresponds to the information given in (c). (e) If $v(t) = 0$ and $i_a(t) = 3 \cos(\frac{1}{2}t)$, calculate $i_b(t)$ so that $v_1(t) \equiv 0$ in the steady state; use the numerical values of the passive elements given in (c).   (f) If the circuit elements i_a and i_b are as in (e), calculate $v(t)$ so that $v_1(t) = 5 \cos \frac{1}{2}t$ in the steady state.

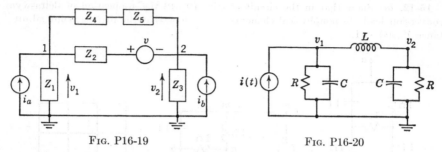

FIG. P16-19   FIG. P16-20

16-20. If $R = 2$ ohms, $L = 4$ henrys, $C = 2$ farads and if the elements are not energized at $t = 0^-$, (a) write the node equations for v_1 and v_2; (b) calculate the initial values $v_1(0^+)$, $(dv_1/dt)_{0^+}$, $(d^2v_1/dt^2)_{0^+}$, $v_2(0^+)$, $(dv_2/dt)_{0^+}$, $(d^2v_2/dt^2)_{0^+}$, and $(d^3v_2/dt^3)_{0^+}$ if (1) $i(t) = tU(t)$; (2) $i(t) = U(t)$; (3) $i(t) = \cos (t + \varphi)$. The circuit is shown in Fig. P16-20.

16-21. (a) Write the mesh equations for Fig. P16-21.   (b) If each element marked Z is a resistance whose numerical value is equal to the subscript (for example, $Z_3 = 3$ ohms), write the mesh equations employing numerical coefficients.   (c) Using the numerical values of (b), assume that the sources v_a, v_b, and v_c are all constant ideal sources.   If $v_a = V_a = 5$, calculate two sets of values of $v_b = V_b$ and $v_c = V_c$ so that $I_1 = 0$.   *Hint:* If two columns in a determinant are multiples of each other, the determinant is identically zero.   (d) The p elements in the circuit are defined as follows: Z_1 and Z_5, 4-ohm resistances; Z_2, parallel combination of 4-ohm resistance and $\frac{1}{16}$-farad capacitance; Z_3, 2-henry inductance; Z_4, series combination of 5-ohm resistance and 3-henry inductance; Z_6, $\frac{1}{3}$-farad capacitance.   The sources are sinusoidal, and all have the same radian frequency $\omega = 3$.   Write the complex mesh equations.   (e) In (d) calculate the phasor ratio $\mathbf{I}_3/\mathbf{I}_1$ if $\mathbf{V}_b = \mathbf{V}_c = 0$.

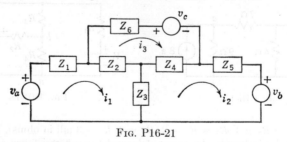

FIG. P16-21

16-22. In the circuit of Prob. 16-21 (Fig. P16-21), $v_b = v_c \equiv 0$, and $v_a = 141.4 \cos 1,000t$.   The elements are defined as follows: $Z_1 = R_1$, $Z_2 = R_2 + pL_2$, $Z_3 = 1/pC_3$, $Z_4 = R_4 + pL_4$, $Z_5 = R_5$, $Z_6 = 1/pC_6$.   The complex mesh equations are

$$
\begin{aligned}
(20 - j10)\mathbf{I}_1 + (j20)\mathbf{I}_2 \quad\quad + (-15 - j10)\mathbf{I}_3 &= 100 + j0 \\
(j20)\mathbf{I}_1 + (20 - j10)\mathbf{I}_2 \quad + (-10 - j10)\mathbf{I}_3 &= 0 \\
(-15 - j10)\mathbf{I}_1 + (-10 - j10)\mathbf{I}_2 + \quad (25 + j10)\mathbf{I}_3 &= 0
\end{aligned}
$$

(a) Calculate the values of R_1, R_2, R_4, R_5, L_2, L_4, C_3, and C_6.   (b) Calculate $i_1(t)$ in the steady state.   (c) Calculate the average power delivered by the source.

16-23. The simultaneous equations

$$5\frac{d^2x}{dt^2} + 8\frac{dx}{dt} + x + 6\frac{dy}{dt} + y = 4\cos 3t$$

$$6\frac{dx}{dt} + x + 6\frac{d^2y}{dt^2} + 6\frac{dy}{dt} + 4y = 0$$

have a solution of the form $x = A\cos(3t + \theta)$. Calculate A and θ.

16-24. (a) Write the transform node-admittance matrix. (b) Write the transform mesh-impedance matrix. (c) Show that the roots of $D_z(s) = 0$ are the same as the roots of $D_y(s) = 0$. (d) Calculate the characteristic roots of the free response of the mesh currents or node voltages. The circuit is shown in Fig. P16-24.

16-25. The circuit of Prob. 16-24 (Fig. P16-24) is deenergized at $t = 0^-$. Determine the form of the complete response (do not evaluate scale factors or constants) for $v_2(t)$ if (a) an ideal voltage source $v_a(t) = \cos tU(t)$ is impressed between node 1 and the reference node; (b) an ideal current source $i_b(t) = \cos tU(t)$ is impressed between node 1 and the reference node; (c) an ideal voltage source $v_a(t) = e^{-t}U(t)$ is impressed between node 1 and the reference node; (d) an ideal current source $i_b(t) = e^{-t}U(t)$ is impressed between node 1 and the reference node; (e) an ideal voltage source $v_a(t) = e^{-t}U(t)$ is introduced into mesh 1 by means of a pliers entry made between the 1-ohm resistance and node 1.

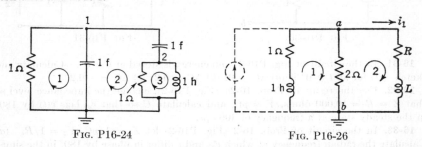

FIG. P16-24   FIG. P16-26

16-26. (a) In the circuit indicated in Fig. P16-26, show that the free modes obtained from the mesh-impedance matrix are the same as those obtained from the p-element node-admittance matrix if $L/R \ne 1$. (b) A current source $8U(t)$ is impressed as shown by the dotted portion of Fig. P16-26. Calculate the branch current $i_1(t)$ which is identical with the mesh current in mesh 2 for all $t \ge 0^+$ if the circuit stores no energy at $t = 0^-$ and if $R = 2$ ohms, $L = 1$ henry. (c) Repeat (b) if the current source is $i(t) = 2\sin 2tU(t)$.

16-27. In the circuit of Prob. 16-20 (Fig. P16-20) calculate the complete response $v_2(t)$ if the circuit is initially deenergized. The source is $i(t) = U(t)$, and the elements have the numerical values $R = 2$, $L = 4$, $C = \frac{1}{2}$. *Hint:* Note that the circuit is symmetrical, so that $Y_{11} = Y_{22}$.

16-28. (a) In the network given in Fig. P16-28 $Z_{11} = Z_{22}$ if the parallel combination of 1 farad and $\frac{1}{4}$ henry is treated as a p element. Use this method to locate the zeros and poles of the driving-point admittance $Y_{ab}(s)$ and of the transform transfer admittance which relates i_2 to v. (b) Assume that the circuit is built of capacitors with negligible losses and inductors which are

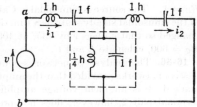

FIG. P16-28

represented as series R-L branches. Assume further that, at radian frequencies which exceed $\frac{1}{2}$, the inductive reactance of each nductor is imore than five times its resistance. Use these assumptions in conjunction with the pole-zero location of (a) to sketch the shape of the frequency-response curves for I_1/V and I_2/V in the sinusoidal steady state.

16-29. In a certain two-node circuit $Y_{11} = Y_{22} = (p^2 + 4p/R + 1)/p$, $Y_{12} = -(2/R + p)$. (a) Sketch such a circuit, giving numerical values for elements where possible. (b) Deduce the range of values of R for which the source-free modes are nonoscillatory.

16-30. This problem is intended to illustrate the effect of source resistance in the attenuator circuit of Fig. P16-30. (a) Calculate $v_{ab}(t)$. (b) Calculate $v_{ab}(t)$ if a unit capacitance is placed across terminals a-b and $v_{ab}(0^-) = 0$. (c) Calculate $v_{ab}(t)$ if a unit capacitance is connected across terminals a-b and a capacitance of value $\frac{1}{9}$ is placed across terminals a-d. Each capacitance is uncharged at $t = 0^-$.

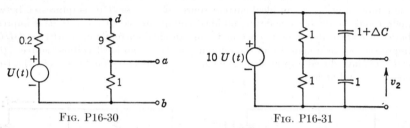

FIG. P16-30   FIG. P16-31

16-31. In the circuit of Fig. P16-31, no energy is stored at $t = 0^-$. Calculate and sketch $v_2(t)$ for all $t \geq 0^+$ if (a) $\Delta C = 0$; (b) $\Delta C = 0.2$; (c) $\Delta C = -0.2$.

16-32. Use the result of Prob. 16-2b (Fig. P16-2), change the impedance level so that $Z = R = 10,000$ ohms, $Y = pC$, and calculate C so that v_{ab} lags $v(t)$ by $180°$ in the steady state at a frequency of 400 cps.

16-33. In the circuit of Prob. 16-2 (Fig. P16-2) let $Z_1 = 1/pC$, $Y_2 = 1/R$. (a) Calculate the radian frequency at which v_{ab} and v differ in phase by $180°$ in the sinusoidal steady state. (b) Choose the scale so that $R = 10K$ and the phase condition of (a) is fulfilled at 550 cps. Calculate C. (c) What is the amplitude ratio V_{ab}/V of the network of (b) at 550 cps?

FIG. P16-34

16-34. (a) If $R = 1$, $L = 10$, and $C = 0.1$, locate the poles and zeros of $Z_{ab}(s)$, and compare the result with the pole-zero location for $R = 0$, $L = 10$, $C = 0.1$. (b) Use the pole-zero diagram of (a) to calculate the maximum value of $Z_{ab}(j\omega)$. (c) Use scale changes to calculate the values of R, L, and C if the maximum value of Z_{ab} has a real part which is 40,000 ohms at a frequency of 100 kcps. See Fig. P16-34.

16-35. (a) In the circuit of Prob. 16-5 (Fig. P16-5), $R_L = 1$, $L = \frac{1}{2}$, $C = 1$, $R_C = 1$. The source is sinusoidal. Calculate and sketch the angle by which v_{ab} lags v in the sinusoidal steady state as a function of frequency. (b) If the frequency scale is changed so that v_{ab} lags v by $135°$ at 400 cps and if the level is changed so that $R_L = R_C = 600$, calculate L and C.

16-36. The analysis of networks containing amplifiers is similar to the analysis of passive networks provided that the amplifiers are linear. In Fig. P16-36a the two-port marked A is an ideal voltage amplifier; that is, $v_2 = Av_1$. A source applied at terminal pair 2, however, does not produce a response at terminal pair 1 and the driving-point admittance at the terminals of v_1 is zero. This type of network is called a unilateral network. Show that for Fig. P16-36b (a) $[p/(p + 1)](v_2 - v_1) = (1 + p)v_1$; (b) $p^2v_1 + p(3 - A)v_1 + v_1 = 0$; (c) the network has a free response which is characterized by a pole pair in the right-half s plane if $A > 3$ (this fact makes it possible to use active networks as "oscillators").

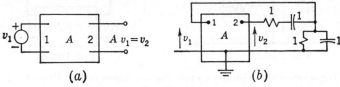

(a)   (b)

Fig. P16-36

16-37. Use mesh equations to calculate the driving-point immittance for the circuit of (a) Prob. 16-11 (Fig. P16-11); (b) Prob. 16-12 (Fig. P16-12).

16-38. Use node equations to calculate the driving-point immittance for the circuit of (a) Prob. 16-11 (Fig. P16-11); (b) Prob. 16-12 (Fig. P16-12).

16-39. When ideal source $v(t) = v_{11'}(t)$ is impressed on the terminal pair 1-1' in Fig. P16-39, then $v_{22'} = \frac{1}{2}v(t)$ if terminals 2-2' are left open and $v_{22'} = \frac{1}{3}v(t)$ when a 5-ohm resistance is connected between terminals 2-2'. (a) Calculate $v_{22'}$ when a 3 ohm resistance is connected to terminals 2-2'. (b) If $v_{11'}(t) = 3U(t)$, calculate the complete response $v_{22'}$ if the parallel combination of a 10-ohm resistance and a 0.15-farad, initially deenergized capacitance is connected between 2-2'.

Fig. P16-39

16-40. In the network of Prob. 16-39 (Fig. P16-39) an ideal current source $i_A(t)$ is connected between 1 and 1' (so that the reference arrow of i_A points toward terminal 1), and an ideal source $i_B(t)$ is connected between terminals 2 and 2' (so that its reference arrow points toward terminal 2). When $i_A \equiv 5$, $i_B \equiv 0$, $v_{11'} \equiv 100$ and $v_{22'} \equiv 30$. Calculate i_B so that $v_{11'} = 0$.

16-41. When $v_1(t) = 10 \cos \omega t$ and $v_2 = 0$, then in the steady state $i_1(t) = 2 \cos (\omega t - 36.9°)$ and $i_2(t) = 2.82 \sin (\omega t + 8.1°)$. Calculate the steady-state function $i_1(t)$ if (a) $v_2(t) = 10 \cos \omega t$, $v_1(t) \equiv 0$; (b) $v_2(t) = 10 \cos \omega t$, $v_1(t) = 10 \sin \omega t$. The circuit is shown in Fig. P16-41.

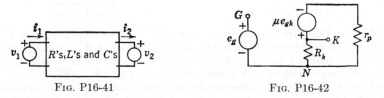

Fig. P16-41   Fig. P16-42

16-42. Obtain Thévenin's equivalent circuit with respect to terminals K-N in Fig. P16-42.

16-43. Obtain Norton's equivalent circuit with respect to terminals c-e in Fig. P16-43.

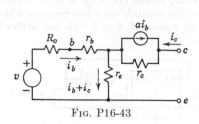

Fig. P16-43

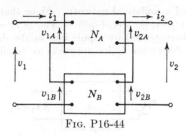

Fig. P16-44

16-44. The series connection of two two-ports is shown in Fig. P16-44. If the two-ports are specified by their open-circuit impedance matrices, show that the open-circuit impedance matrix which relates i_1, i_2, v_1, and v_2 is the sum of the open-circuit impedance matrices of N_A and N_B.

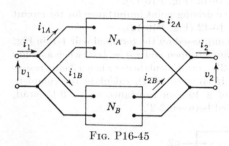

Fig. P16-45

16-45. The parallel connection of two two-ports is shown in Fig. P16-45. Show that the short-circuit admittance matrix which relates v_1, i_2, v_2, and i_2 is the sum of the short-circuit admittance matrices of N_A and N_B.

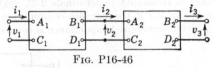

Fig. P16-46

16-46. The "cascade" connection of two two-ports is shown in Fig. P16-46. Show that, if $v_1 = A_1v_2 + B_1i_2$, $i_1 = C_1v_2 + D_1i_2$, $v_2 = A_2v_3 + B_2i_3$, $i_2 = C_2v_3 + D_2i_3$, then the matrix which relates v_1 and i_1 to v_3 and i_3 is the product $\begin{Vmatrix} A_1 & B_1 \\ C_1 & D_1 \end{Vmatrix} \times \begin{Vmatrix} A_2 & B_2 \\ C_2 & D_2 \end{Vmatrix}$.

16-47. As mentioned in the text, various other matrices in addition to the open-circuit impedance, short-circuit admittance, and cascade (A-B-C-D) matrices are used to describe two-ports. For each of the following matrices given state how the operators (elements of the matrix) are defined in terms of driving-point and transfer functions: (a) $v_1 = h_{11}i_1 + h_{12}v_2$, $i_2 = h_{21}i_1 + h_{22}v_2$; (b) $i_1 = g_{11}v_1 + g_{12}v_2$, $i_2 = g_{21}v_1 + g_{22}v_2$. Reference directions are shown in Fig. P16-47.

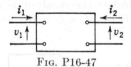

Fig. P16-47

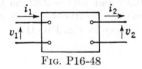

Fig. P16-48

16-48. If in Fig. P16-48 $v_1 = A(p)v_2 + B(p)i_2$, $i_1 = C(p)v_2 + D(p)i_2$, and if the two-port has an impedance Z_T across terminal pair 2, show that (a) the driving-point impedance at terminal pair 1 is $Z_1 = [A(p)Z_T + B(p)]/[C(p)Z_T + D(p)]$; (b) the transfer admittance relating i_2 to a source voltage v_1 is $1/(AZ_T + B)$.

16-49. In a two-port the following driving-point immittances are measured or calculated: driving-point impedance at terminal pair 1 with terminal pair 2 short-circuited, Z_{s1}; driving-point impedance at terminal pair 1 with terminal pair 2 open, Z_{01}; driving-point impedance at terminal pair 2 with terminal pair 1 short-circuited, Z_{s1}; driving-point impedance at terminal pair 2 with terminal pair 1 open, Z_{02}. Show that $Z_{s1}Z_{02} = Z_{01}Z_{s2}$. *Hint:* Use the A-B-C-D matrix.

CHAPTER 17

THREE-PHASE CIRCUITS

This chapter deals with circuits which are supplied by certain special combinations of sinusoidal sources. We shall be exclusively concerned with the sinusoidal steady-state conditions in such circuits. The discussion which is presented here will serve to illustrate the application of general principles of circuit analysis described in the preceding chapters. However, the circuits discussed are themselves of intrinsic importance, especially in power systems. We shall show that certain symmetrical connections of sources (and loads) are advantageous from the economical point of view, especially when large amounts of power are involved. All the circuits which we shall discuss contain several sources. We emphasize at the outset that all these sinusoidal sources will be assumed to operate at a single frequency. This assumption is true of the interconnected power systems. In the United States the power system operates at the frequency of 60 cps (with very few exceptions[1]).

17-1. Sources. A practical sinusoidal source of electrical energy can be represented as the series combination of an ideal voltage source and a complex impedance or as the parallel combination of an ideal current source and a complex admittance, as indicated in Fig. 17-1a and b.

If a passive combination of elements, forming a single-terminal-pair network and represented by impedance Z_T is connected to such a source (as indicated by the dotted portion of Fig. 17-1a and b), then one may, for purposes of calculating the circuit response in the steady state, choose the phase angle of the ideal source (ϕ or ψ) arbitrarily. A circuit which contains only one such source is distinguished by the fact that all phase relations between voltages and currents in every pair of points of the circuit can be related to the phase angle of this single source. For this reason a practical two-terminal sinusoidal source represented by an internal impedance (or admittance) and an ideal sinusoidal source is called a *single-phase source*.

If a circuit contains several sources (of like frequency), then three possibilities may occur:

---

[1] Air-borne equipment and other *isolated* systems are often operated at other frequencies.

1. The combination of sources may be equivalent to a single-phase source.

2. Special relationships may exist between the amplitude and/or phase of various sources.

3. Neither (1) nor (2) occurs.

In the next article we shall consider briefly circuits with a single-phase source. We recall here that all the circuits discussed in Chap. 14 have sources of this type. In subsequent articles we shall discuss those circuits with special combinations of sources which are called three-phase sources.

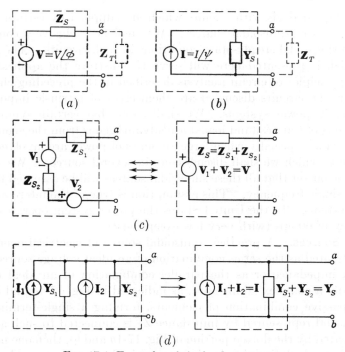

FIG. 17-1. Examples of single-phase sources.

We shall see that combinations of single-phase sources which do not involve special phase relationships are also of interest in this discussion. The circuit in which these sources occur receives its name from the type of source which is used. Thus, unless a special relationship between the sources exists, the circuit is called a "single-phase" circuit with one or several sources (as the case may be).

While circuits with several sources can always be analyzed by using the principle of superposition, so that the effect of each source can be accounted for separately, we shall see that the application of the network procedures which were developed in the previous chapters makes such a cumbersome scheme unnecessary.

17-2. Single-phase Circuits. *Sources in Series.* If two single-phase sources are connected in series as shown in Fig. 17-1c, then the combination of these sources is equivalent to the single-phase source shown in Fig. 17-1c. This statement follows immediately from application of Kirchhoff's voltage law between terminals a-b. In either circuit, if a current represented by the phasor $\mathbf{I}_{ab}$ flows through an external load connected to terminals a-b, the phasor $\mathbf{V}_{ab}$ is $\mathbf{V}_1 + \mathbf{V}_2 - \mathbf{I}_{ab}(\mathbf{Z}_{s1} + \mathbf{Z}_{s2})$ and therefore the two circuits are equivalent at the terminals a-b.

Sources in Parallel. If two practical single-phase sources are in parallel, we may represent them as current sources as shown in Fig. 17-1d. The combination of these two sources, with respect to terminals a-b, is equivalent to the single source shown in Fig. 17-1d. This follows from the application of Kirchhoff's current law at terminal a or b. For any voltage $\mathbf{V}_{ab}$ the current $\mathbf{I}_{ab}$ flowing through an external admittance is given by $\mathbf{I}_{ab} = \mathbf{I}_1 + \mathbf{I}_2 - \mathbf{V}_{ab}(\mathbf{Y}_{s1} + \mathbf{Y}_{s2})$, and therefore the two circuits are equivalent at the terminals a-b.

Three-wire Single-phase Circuit. The three-wire single-phase circuit is discussed here, not only because of its intrinsic importance but also because this connection is often confused with the three-phase connection, which will be discussed later. A three-wire single-phase source consists of two single-phase sources in which each source has its terminals accessibly connected, as shown in Fig. 17-2a. Such a source is a three-terminal or three-wire source.

In practically all instances an additional restriction is imposed on the three-terminal connection of Fig. 17-2a. In a *three-wire single-phase* source the two source voltages $\mathbf{V}_1$ and $\mathbf{V}_2$ are usually understood to be identical; i.e., they are to have the same amplitude, and they are to be in phase with each other. Moreover, the complex internal impedances of the sources must be identical. This situation is indicated in Fig. 17-2b. The internal common

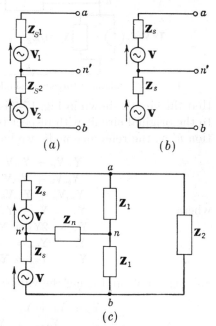

(a)   (b)

(c)

FIG. 17-2. Three-wire systems. (a) Three-wire source. (b) Three-wire single-phase source. (c) Balanced three-wire single-phase system.

point of the two sources is marked n' and is referred to as the "neutral" point of the source.

A typical application of a three-wire system is shown in Fig. 17-2c. In this circuit two identical complex loads Z_1 are connected together and joined through an impedance Z_n to the neutral point of the source. In addition an impedance Z_2 is connected across the terminals a-b (the impedance of the wires joining the loads to the a and b points of the source may be included in Z_s). With this special symmetry of the load impedances and the source the circuit forms a balanced three-wire *single-phase* system. By "balanced system" we mean that both the two sources and the loading of the sources are identical. We shall now show that with this balanced connection $V_{nn'} = 0$.

The voltage sources are converted to current sources, and the impedances are labeled with the values of the corresponding admittances so

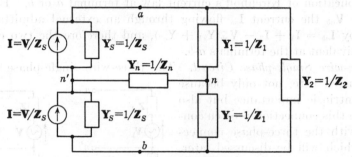

FIG. 17-3. Balanced three-wire single-phase system using current sources.

that the circuit shown in Fig. 17-3 is obtained. This circuit is equivalent to the original circuit with respect to terminals a, n', and b. Using junction n' as the reference node, we have the general node-pair equations

$$Y_{aa}V_a + Y_{ab}V_b + Y_{an}V_n = I$$
$$Y_{ba}V_a + Y_{bb}V_b + Y_{bn}V_n = -I$$
$$Y_{na}V_a + Y_{nb}V_b + Y_{nn}V_n = 0$$

where
$$Y_{aa} = Y_s + Y_1 + Y_2 = Y_{bb}$$
$$Y_{nn} = 2Y_1 + Y_n$$
$$Y_{ab} = Y_{ba} = -Y_2$$
$$Y_{an} = Y_{na} = Y_{bn} = Y_{nb} = -Y_1$$

Solving for V_n and using the values of the node admittances, we have

$$V_n = \frac{\begin{vmatrix} Y_s + Y_1 + Y_2 & -Y_2 & I \\ -Y_2 & Y_s + Y_1 + Y_2 & -I \\ -Y_1 & -Y_1 & 0 \end{vmatrix}}{D_y} \equiv \frac{N}{D_y} \qquad (17\text{-}1)$$

where D_y is the complex determinant of the admittance matrix.

In the numerator determinant of Eq. (17-1) we add rows 2 and 3 to row 1,

$$N = \begin{vmatrix} Y_s + Y_1 + Y_2 & -Y_2 & I \\ -Y_2 & Y_s + Y_1 + Y_2 & -I \\ -Y_1 & -Y_1 & 0 \end{vmatrix} = \begin{vmatrix} Y_s & Y_s & 0 \\ -Y_2 & Y_s + Y_2 & -I \\ -Y_1 & -Y_1 & 0 \end{vmatrix}$$

(17-2)

The determinant on the right-hand side of Eq. (17-2) is evaluated by expansion about column 3, row 2,

$$N = -(-I)[-Y_s Y_1 - (Y_s)(-Y_1)] \equiv 0$$

Hence $V_n = V_{nn'} \equiv 0$.

For a balanced three-wire single-phase circuit we conclude as follows:

1. Since $V_{nn'} = 0$, the current in the neutral $I_{nn'} = 0$. Hence the functioning of the circuit is independent of the admittance Y_n. This admittance may therefore be removed without affecting the circuit as long as the circuit remains balanced.

2. Since $I_{nn'} = 0$, $V_{an} = V_{nb}$; this is seen from the fact that the current in the two equal impedances Z_1 is the same current. Hence $V_{ab} = 2V_{an}$. This states that the voltage across the impedance Z_2 has twice the value of the voltage across Z_1. We have therefore a source which furnishes two voltages, one twice the other. Frequently two such voltages are needed. In a home if $|V_{an}|$ is, for example, 110 volts and $|V_{ab}| = 220$ volts, then terminal pairs a-n and b-n can be used for lighting while terminal pair a-b, where the higher voltage is available, may be used for a major appliance such as a clothes drier or an electric stove.

While the discussion has revolved around the balanced case, where the connection from n to n' is not needed, this connection is not omitted in practice because of the effect on the various voltages if the load becomes unbalanced ($Z_{an} \neq Z_{nb}$) (see Prob. 17-1).

17-3. Three-phase Sources. A source which can be represented as three single-phase voltage sources connected to form a wye or a delta as shown in Fig. 17-4 forms a balanced three-phase source provided that the following special relationships exist:

1. The three complex impedances are equal to each other.

$$Z_{s1} = Z_{s2} = Z_{s3}$$

2. The magnitudes of the source voltages are equal to each other.

In the wye: $|V_1| = |V_2| = |V_3| = V_y$
In the delta: $|V_a| = |V_b| = |V_c| = V_\Delta$

3. The source voltages add up to zero at every instant of time so that their phasor sum is zero.

In the wye: $\mathbf{V}_1 + \mathbf{V}_2 + \mathbf{V}_3 = 0$

or

In the delta: $\mathbf{V}_a + \mathbf{V}_b + \mathbf{V}_c = 0$

If three phasors have equal absolute values and add up to zero, they must differ in phase by exactly 120° because the graphical addition of

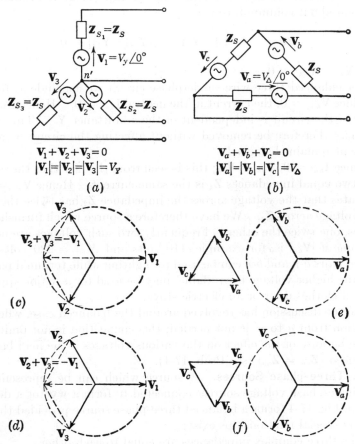

Fig. 17-4. Balanced three-phase sources. (a) Balanced three-phase wye-connected source. (b) Balanced three-phase delta-connected source. (c) Phasor diagram for 1-2-3 sequence in (a). (d) Phasor diagram for 1-3-2 sequence in (a). (e) Phasor diagram for a-c-b sequence in (b). (f) Phasor diagram for a-b-c sequence in (b).

these phasors by the polygon method must result in an equilateral triangle. In Fig. 17-4, if in the wye connection we choose $\mathbf{V}_1$ as the reference, we have

$$\mathbf{V}_1 = V_y\underline{/0°}$$

and either $\mathbf{V}_2 = V_y\underline{/+120°}$ and $\mathbf{V}_3 = V_y\underline{/-120°}$

or $\mathbf{V}_2 = V_y\underline{/-120°}$ and $\mathbf{V}_3 = V_y\underline{/+120°}$

Similarly, if in the delta connection we choose $\mathbf{V}_a$ as reference, we have

$$\mathbf{V}_a = V_\Delta\underline{/0^\circ}$$

and either $\quad \mathbf{V}_b = V_\Delta\underline{/+120^\circ} \quad$ and $\quad \mathbf{V}_c = V_\Delta\underline{/-120^\circ}$

or $\quad\quad\quad \mathbf{V}_b = V_\Delta\underline{/-120^\circ} \quad$ and $\quad \mathbf{V}_c = V_\Delta\underline{/+120^\circ}$

The possibilities are shown in Fig. 17-4c to f. For each source we have shown the two possible phase relations. The term used to describe the difference between the phase relations of Fig. 17-4c and d (or between Fig. 17-4e and f) is the *phase sequence* or *phase order*. By phase sequence we mean the order in which the three sources reach their maxima. For the relationship shown in Fig. 17-4c, if we observe the voltages $\mathbf{V}_1$, $\mathbf{V}_2$, and $\mathbf{V}_3$, we find the following:

$$v_1(t) \text{ is maximum at } t = 0$$

$$v_2(t) \text{ is maximum at } \omega t = \frac{2\pi}{3} \text{ or } 120^\circ$$

$$v_3(t) \text{ is maximum at } \omega t = \frac{4\pi}{3} \text{ or } 240^\circ$$

$$v_1(t) \text{ is maximum at } \omega t = 2\pi \text{ or } 360^\circ$$

$$\cdot\ \cdot\ \cdot\ \cdot\ \cdot\ \cdot\ \cdot\ \cdot\ \cdot\ \cdot\ \cdot\ \cdot\ \cdot\ \cdot\ \cdot\ \cdot\ \cdot\ \cdot\ \cdot$$

Hence the phase sequence is 1-2-3-1-2-3 $\cdot$ $\cdot$ $\cdot$ $\cdot$. Starting with the source labeled 1, the phase sequence is expressed as 1-2-3.

Similarly, if we start when v_a is a maximum in Fig. 17-4e, the phase order is *a-c-b*.

On *paper* the phase sequence appears to be a trivial matter because we can always renumber the sources to obtain either phase order. Practically we must point out that the three sources shown in Fig. 17-4 may represent a single physical device, i.e., a three-phase generator. Once we label the actual wires, the phase sequence is fixed. The direction of rotation of a three-phase motor will depend on the phase sequence of the three-phase source. Knowledge of the actual phase order in the physical generator may therefore be a matter of importance. We shall illustrate in a later article how phase sequence may be determined experimentally.

In the definition of a balanced three-phase source we have stated three requirements: equal internal impedances for the three sources, equal voltage amplitudes, and a phase difference of exactly 120° between the voltages. Lest the reader should wonder about the rigidity of these requirements, we point out that in practice these conditions can be approximated very closely, for example, by construction of a single rotating machine in which three separate windings are made identically (to ensure equal impedances and equal voltage magnitudes) and are placed symmetrically in the mechanical structure of the machine (to ensure the correct phase relationships).

When *any* of the conditions for balance is not satisfied, then the source is called an *unbalanced* (or unsymmetrical) three-phase source. We understand that for purposes of analysis an unbalanced three-phase source is merely an interconnection of single-phase sources.

17-4. Delta- and Wye-connected Sources.   *Equivalent Ideal Sources.* In order to show how delta- and wye-connected sources can replace each

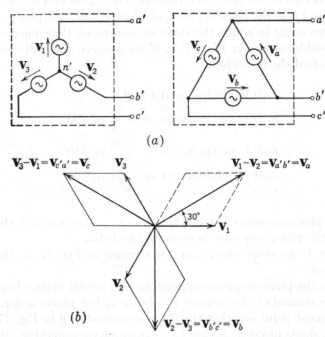

FIG. 17-5. Ideal three-phase voltage sources.   (a) Wye- and delta-connected sources. (b) Phasor diagram used to establish equivalence.

other, we shall first consider the ideal, balanced sources shown in Fig. 17-5a.   These sources are equivalent with respect to terminals a', b', c', provided that the voltages $\mathbf{V}_a$, $\mathbf{V}_b$, and $\mathbf{V}_c$ have a special relationship to $\mathbf{V}_1$, $\mathbf{V}_2$, and $\mathbf{V}_3$.   Note that the junction point of the sources in the equivalent wye connection (point n') is not accessible to the circuit external to the source.   To establish the conditions for equivalence, we note first that the voltages between a', b', and c' are independent of the currents which may be drawn by an external circuit connected to these points, because all sources are ideal.   Hence the two sources are equivalent if the voltages between any pairs of terminals correspond exactly as in the tabulation below.

$$Wye \qquad Delta$$

$$\mathbf{V}_{a'b'} = \mathbf{V}_1 - \mathbf{V}_2 = \mathbf{V}_a \qquad (17\text{-}3a)$$

$$\mathbf{V}_{b'c'} = \mathbf{V}_2 - \mathbf{V}_3 = \mathbf{V}_b \qquad (17\text{-}3b)$$

$$\mathbf{V}_{c'a'} = \mathbf{V}_3 - \mathbf{V}_1 = \mathbf{V}_c \qquad (17\text{-}3c)$$

Equations (17-3) show how the equivalent delta is obtained, given the voltages in the wye. Note that, since the balanced case was assumed,

$$|\mathbf{V}_1 - \mathbf{V}_2| = |\mathbf{V}_2 - \mathbf{V}_3| = |\mathbf{V}_3 - \mathbf{V}_1| = \sqrt{3}\,|\mathbf{V}_1| \qquad (17\text{-}4)$$

as can be seen from the phasor diagram shown in Fig. 17-5b. We conclude from this diagram that the magnitude of each equivalent source in the delta is $\sqrt{3}$ times the magnitude of a source in the wye. Both sources form a balanced system of voltages: in the delta each source has the same magnitude, and the sum of the phasors is zero. Hence no current flows in any of the delta-connected sources in the absence of external loading. Note that the condition for equivalence at the external terminals a', b', and c' causes the voltages $\mathbf{V}_a$, $\mathbf{V}_b$, $\mathbf{V}_c$ to be 30° displaced from $\mathbf{V}_1$, $\mathbf{V}_2$, and $\mathbf{V}_3$, respectively. Since in any particular example the phase differences between the various voltages can be obtained from a phasor diagram with ease, the principal conclusion here is the magnitude relationship. If V_y is the magnitude of a source voltage in the wye and V_Δ is the magnitude of a source voltage in its equivalent delta connection, then these magnitudes are related by the number $\sqrt{3}$; $V_\Delta = \sqrt{3}\,V_y$.

Equivalent Practical Sources. We shall now deduce the conditions under which the wye connection of three practical sources is equivalent to the delta connection of another set of three practical sources. In the following analysis no assumption is made about the sources being balanced or three-phase, and the results will apply to any three sinusoidal sources so long as the frequency of the sources is the same. In Fig. 17-6a and b the wye and delta connections of the sources are shown. We require a set of relations to give $\mathbf{V}_1$, $\mathbf{V}_2$, $\mathbf{V}_3$, $\mathbf{Z}_1$, $\mathbf{Z}_2$, and $\mathbf{Z}_3$ if $\mathbf{V}_a$, $\mathbf{V}_b$, $\mathbf{V}_c$, $\mathbf{Z}_a$, $\mathbf{Z}_b$, and $\mathbf{Z}_c$ are given, and vice versa.

If the delta connection of the voltage sources shown in Fig. 17-6b is converted into a delta connection of current sources, the arrangement of Fig. 17-6c results. In this figure the three admittances connected in delta between a-b-c can be converted into a wye, and the three delta-connected current sources can be converted into a wye. These two conversions are independent of each other, as shown in Fig. 17-6d.

The requirement for the transformation of current sources is that

$$\mathbf{I}_{a''a} = \mathbf{Y}_a\mathbf{V}_a - \mathbf{Y}_c\mathbf{V}_c = \mathbf{I}_\alpha \qquad (17\text{-}4a)$$

$$\mathbf{I}_{b''b} = \mathbf{Y}_b\mathbf{V}_b - \mathbf{Y}_a\mathbf{Y}_a = \mathbf{I}_\beta \qquad (17\text{-}4b)$$

$$\mathbf{I}_{c''c} = \mathbf{Y}_c\mathbf{V}_c - \mathbf{Y}_b\mathbf{V}_b = \mathbf{I}_\gamma \qquad (17\text{-}4c)$$

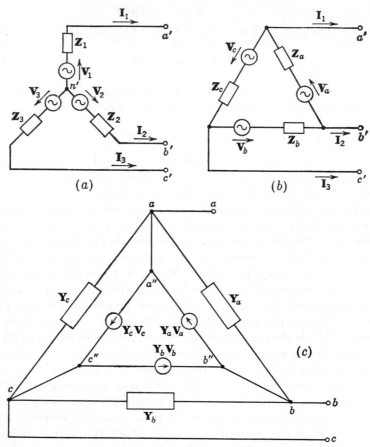

FIG. 17-6. (a) Wye-connected source with internal impedances. (b) Delta-connected source with internal impedances. (c) Current-source representation of (b).

and the requirement for the transformation of the admittances, from delta into wye connection, is given [see (Eq. 16-19)] by

$$Z_\alpha = \frac{Z_a Z_c}{Z_a + Z_b + Z_c} \tag{17-5a}$$

$$Z_\beta = \frac{Z_a Z_b}{Z_a + Z_b + Z_c} \tag{17-5b}$$

$$Z_\gamma = \frac{Z_b Z_c}{Z_a + Z_b + Z_c} \tag{17-5c}$$

In Fig. 17-6d the points n and n'' do not correspond to any terminals in Fig. 17-6c. The voltages of these points with respect to the terminals a, b, and c will depend on the external loads connected to the sources. In particular the voltage of n'' with respect to a, b, and c is undetermined as yet (the waveform of voltage across a current source is not specified, whereas its current waveform is specified). However, regardless of the external loads connected to terminals a, b, and c, from Eqs. (17-4) it is seen that $I_\alpha + I_\beta + I_\gamma = 0$. Therefore, if we join n to n'', there will be

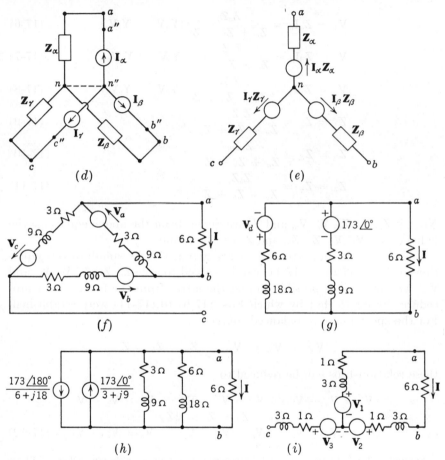

Fig. 17-6. (d) Wye connection equivalent to (c). (e) Voltage-source form of (d). (f) Circuit for Example 17-1. (g) Equivalent to (f). (h) Current-source form of (f). (i) Circuit of (f) after (source) delta-wye conversion.

no current through nn'', since the sum of currents leaving n'' must be zero. As there is no current in nn'', the current distribution in Z_α, Z_β, Z_γ (and external loads, if any) will not be disturbed if n is connected to n'' and therefore the voltage of n with respect to a, b, and c will not be changed. The only change brought about by connecting n to n'' is making $v_{nn''} = 0$, with no change in the voltages of "accessible" terminals a, b, and c. Thus such a connection is allowed. Once n and n'' are joined, the resulting three current sources and the impedances Z_α, Z_β, and Z_γ in parallel with them can be changed into the wye connection of Fig. 17-6e.

A comparison of Fig. 17-6e and a shows that if the two networks of Fig. 17-6a and b are to be equivalent then

$$V_1 = Z_\alpha I_\alpha = \frac{Z_a Z_c}{Z_a + Z_b + Z_c} (Y_a V_a - Y_c V_c) \qquad (17\text{-}6)$$

$$V_2 = Z_\beta I_\beta = \frac{Z_a Z_b}{Z_a + Z_b + Z_c} (Y_b V_b - Y_a V_a) \qquad (17\text{-}7)$$

$$V_3 = Z_\gamma I_\gamma = \frac{Z_b Z_c}{Z_a + Z_b + Z_c} (Y_c V_c - Y_b V_b) \qquad (17\text{-}8)$$

$$Z_1 = Z_\alpha = \frac{Z_a Z_c}{Z_a + Z_b + Z_c} \qquad (17\text{-}9)$$

$$Z_2 = Z_\beta = \frac{Z_a Z_b}{Z_a + Z_b + Z_c} \qquad (17\text{-}10)$$

$$Z_3 = Z_\gamma = \frac{Z_b Z_c}{Z_a + Z_b + Z_c} \qquad (17\text{-}11)$$

Now, if Z_a, Z_b, Z_c, V_a, V_b, and V_c are given, from the above equations the value of V_1, V_2, V_3, Z_1, Z_2, and Z_3 can be found.

Conversely, if the latter values are given, the six simultaneous equations of Eqs. (17-6) to (17-11) can be solved to give Z_a, Z_b, Z_c, V_a, V_b, and V_c. Of course it is possible to find the latter from the former by a procedure similar to that by which Eqs. (17-6) to (17-11) were established. For the special case of balanced sources

$$|V_a| = |V_b| = |V_c| \qquad Z_a = Z_b = Z_c$$

these relationships can be reduced to

$$V_1 = V_a - V_c \qquad V_2 = V_b - V_a \qquad V_3 = V_c - V_b$$
$$Z_1 = Z_2 = Z_3 = \tfrac{1}{3} Z_a$$

or $\qquad V_a = V_1 - V_2 \qquad V_b = V_2 - V_3 \qquad V_c = V_3 - V_1 \qquad (17\text{-}12)$

Example 17-1. In the balanced delta-connected generator shown in Fig. 17-6f

$$|V_a| = |V_b| = |V_b| = 173 \text{ volts}$$

and $\qquad V_a + V_b + V_c = 0$

Calculate the absolute value of the current phasor I, in the 6-ohm resistance.

To illustrate the usefulness of conversion of the delta source to a wye source, this problem is first done without conversion of the source.

Solution. Method 1 (With Original Source). Using V_a as reference and assuming a-b-c phase order, we write

$$V_a = 173 \underline{/0°}$$
$$V_b = 173 \underline{/-120°}$$
$$V_c = 173 \underline{/+120°}$$

Since terminal c is not connected to any external elements, we may combine the two branches containing V_c and V_b into a single branch as shown in Fig. 17-6g.

Since $V_d = V_b + V_c$, $V_d = 173\underline{/-120°} + 173\underline{/+120°} = 173\underline{/180°}$. Converting the voltage sources to current sources, we obtain the circuit of Fig. 17-6h. Hence we may calculate

$$V_{ab} = \left(\frac{173\underline{/0°}}{3 + j9} - \frac{173\underline{/180°}}{6 + j18}\right) Z_{ab}$$

where Z_{ab} is the impedance of the three parallel branches shown in Fig. 17-6h;

$$Y_{ab} = \frac{1}{6} + \frac{1}{6 + j18} + \frac{1}{3 + j9} = \frac{1}{6} + \frac{1}{2 + j6}$$

and

$$Z_{ab} = \frac{(6)(2 + j6)}{8 + j6}$$

Since

$$\frac{173\underline{/0°}}{3 + j9} - \frac{173\underline{/180°}}{6 + j18} = \frac{173}{2 + j6}$$

$$V_{ab} = \frac{173\underline{/0}}{2 + j6} \frac{(6)(2 + j6)}{8 + j6} \qquad |V_{ab}| = \left|\frac{(173)(6)}{8 + j6}\right| = \frac{(173)(6)}{10}$$

Hence $\qquad\qquad\qquad\qquad I = 17.3$ amp $\qquad\qquad\qquad\qquad\qquad Ans.$

Method 2 (*By Conversion of the Delta Source*). The delta source can be replaced by a balanced wye source in which each single-phase source generates an amplitude of $173/\sqrt{3} = 100$ volts and has an internal impedance of $(3 + j9)/3 = 1 + j3$ ohms as shown in Fig. 17-6i.

The magnitude of the current I is given by

$$|I| = \frac{|V_1 - V_2|}{|2 + j6 + 6|} = \left|\frac{V_1 - V_2}{8 + j6}\right| = \frac{|V_1 - V_2|}{10}$$

Since the source is balanced, the difference between V_1 and V_2 has the absolute value $V_1 \sqrt{3}$. Hence we have the solution immediately,

$$I = \frac{100 \sqrt{3}}{10} = 17.3 \text{ amp} \qquad\qquad\qquad Ans.$$

It is seen that conversion from delta into wye reduces the amount of work entailed in this particular problem.

Reconnection of Sources. A problem quite different from equivalent three-phase sources is posed by the relationship between a delta- and a wye-connected source, which may be formed by connecting three single-phase sources. We shall term this problem the "reconnection" of sources. Consider the three single-phase sources shown in Fig. 17-7a. Since the internal impedances of the three sources are equal and the source voltages are equal and add up to zero, balanced three-phase sources may be formed by connecting these single-phase sources properly.

A study of the phasor diagram shows that a wye-connected source may be formed by joining points a, c, and e to form the neutral. This connection is shown in Fig. 17-7b. Since $V_{ab} + V_{cd} + V_{ef} = 0$, a balanced delta-connected source may be formed by joining points bc, de, and fa as shown in Fig. 17-7c.

We note now that in the wye-connected source the voltage between any two of the three terminals of the source (*b-d*, *d-f* and *f-b*) is in magnitude $\sqrt{3}\ V$, while the corresponding terminals in the delta connection make available the open-circuit voltage V.   In return for the higher voltage which the wye connection furnishes, we shall show later, the current "capacity" of this source is less.   Qualitatively this can be seen by noting that in the wye any current which flows from one of the terminals, say, terminal *b*, flows directly through one of the single-phase sources, while

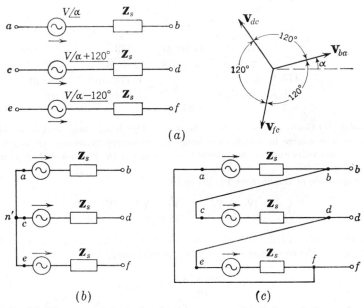

(*a*)

(*b*)   (*c*)

Fig. 17-7. (*a*) Three special single-phase sources.   (*b*) Balanced three-phase wye-connected source formed with the sources of (*a*).   (*c*) Balanced three-phase delta-connected source formed from (*a*).

the corresponding current in the delta connection may flow through either of two paths (that is, *a-b* and *c-b*).

Phase Generators, Line and Phase Voltages.   Each of the three single-phase sources which is used to form a three-phase source is called a phase generator.   The magnitude of voltage associated with each phase generator in a balanced source is called the phase voltage of the source.   The magnitude of the voltage which is available between any two of the three line terminals is called a "line-to-line" voltage, or, for brevity, a "line" voltage.   For an ideal wye-connected balanced three-phase source the ratio of line to phase voltage is the *square root of* 3.

17-5. Balanced Three-phase Circuits.   *Balanced Load.*   Three *equal complex impedances*, connected in delta or in wye, form a balanced three-phase load.   Exactly as in the case of three-phase sources, the representation of a three-phase load as three separate terminal pairs does not mean that the physical device which is so represented actually consists of three separate units.   In the case of loads it is possible for a single unit (such as a "three-phase motor") to have an equivalent circuit which is represented by a delta or a wye; it is also possible to form a wye or delta load from separate units.

Three-phase balanced loads are shown in Fig. 17-8a and b.   Since every delta can be converted to a wye, any three-phase load can be represented as either a wye or a delta.   We have seen that in the balanced case the transformation between delta and wye reduces to

$$\mathbf{Z}_Y = \tfrac{1}{3}\mathbf{Z}_\Delta \tag{17-13}$$

In the three-phase loads of Fig. 17-8 terminals a, b, and c are referred to as the "line terminals" of the load.   In the wye-connected load of Fig.

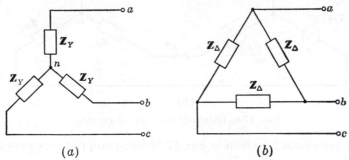

(a)   (b)

FIG. 17-8. Balanced three-phase loads.

17-8a the junction of the three impedances (point n) is referred to as the "neutral point" of the load.   In each load each of the impedances $\mathbf{Z}_Y$ or $\mathbf{Z}_\Delta$ is called a "phase impedance."

Balanced Circuit.   If a balanced load is supplied by a balanced three-phase source, then the combination is referred to as a *balanced three-phase circuit.*   If either source or load is unbalanced, then the circuit is unbalanced.   In practice, the generator is usually balanced, but the load may be unbalanced.   We shall first study, in detail, balanced circuits.

In Fig. 17-9a a balanced three-phase wye-connected source is shown connected to a balanced wye load by means of three cables connecting the line terminals of the load to those of the source.   Since the cables have equal impedances $\mathbf{Z}_L$, an equivalent circuit is shown in Fig. 17-9b.   In this circuit the internal impedances of the source and the line impedances have been added to the impedances of the load so that the resulting circuit consists of an ideal three-phase wye-connected source connected to a balanced wye load.   We shall see that every balanced circuit can be

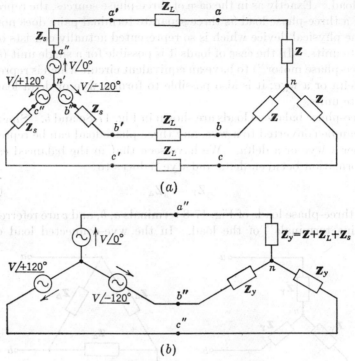

(a)

(b)

Fig. 17-9. Balanced three-phase circuits.

reduced to a circuit as shown in Fig. 17-9b by appropriate use of delta-wye conversion.

We shall now show how every balanced three-phase circuit can be solved by solving an equivalent single-phase circuit. The problem we set ourselves is the calculation of the relationship between the currents which flow from the source to the load, the line voltages, and the power transferred.

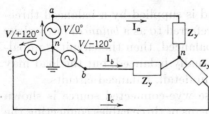

17-6. The Representative Single-phase Problem.

Since every balanced circuit can be represented as the combination of a balanced wye-connected load and an ideal wye-connected three-phase source,

Fig. 17-10. Balanced three-phase circuit showing reference directions.

we shall first study this circuit in detail. Examples of how the results which are obtained in this case apply to other balanced circuits will be cited in subsequent articles.

Consider, therefore, the balanced three-phase circuit shown in Fig. 17-10. Let it be required to solve for the line currents $\mathbf{I}_a$, $\mathbf{I}_b$, and $\mathbf{I}_c$ in terms of the phase voltages of the source, $\mathbf{V}_{an'}$, $\mathbf{V}_{bn'}$, $\mathbf{V}_{cn'}$. We note that the circuit has only two junction points; hence it can be solved by means of a single node equation: If the voltage $V_{nn'}$ is known, then the currents can be calculated by the application of Kirchhoff's voltage law. Although each voltage source in series with $\mathbf{Z}_y$ can be converted to a current source, we need not apply this formalism. At junction n Kirchhoff's current law reads

$$\mathbf{I}_a + \mathbf{I}_b + \mathbf{I}_c = 0 \qquad (17\text{-}14)$$

but
$$\mathbf{I}_a = \frac{\mathbf{V}_{an}}{\mathbf{Z}_y} \qquad \mathbf{I}_b = \frac{\mathbf{V}_{bn}}{\mathbf{Z}_y} \qquad \mathbf{I}_c = \frac{\mathbf{V}_{cn}}{\mathbf{Z}_y} \qquad (17\text{-}15)$$

and
$$\mathbf{V}_{an} = \mathbf{V}_{an'} - \mathbf{V}_{nn'} \qquad (17\text{-}16a)$$
$$\mathbf{V}_{bn} = \mathbf{V}_{bn'} - \mathbf{V}_{nn'} \qquad (17\text{-}16b)$$
$$\mathbf{V}_{cn} = \mathbf{V}_{cn'} - \mathbf{V}_{nn'} \qquad (17\text{-}16c)$$

Substituting (17-16) in (17-15) and applying (17-14), we obtain

$$\frac{\mathbf{V}_{an'}}{\mathbf{Z}_y} + \frac{\mathbf{V}_{bn'}}{\mathbf{Z}_y} + \frac{\mathbf{V}_{cn'}}{\mathbf{Z}_y} = \frac{3\mathbf{V}_{nn'}}{\mathbf{Z}_y} \qquad (17\text{-}17)$$

or
$$\mathbf{V}_{an'} + \mathbf{V}_{bn'} + \mathbf{V}_{cn'} = 3\mathbf{V}_{nn'} \qquad (17\text{-}17a)$$

But in a balanced three-phase source the sum of the phase voltages (with respect to n') is zero; hence

$$\mathbf{V}_{an'} + \mathbf{V}_{bn'} + \mathbf{V}_{cn'} = 3\mathbf{V}_{nn'} = 0 \qquad (17\text{-}18)$$

and
$$\mathbf{V}_{nn'} = 0$$

We conclude that in a balanced three-phase circuit the voltage between the neutral point of the source and the neutral point of the generator is zero.

Since the voltage between points n and n' is always zero, no current will flow between these points if they are connected together through any impedance. The circuit shown in Fig. 17-11a is therefore equivalent to the circuit shown in Fig. 17-10. It follows that the two neutral points may be joined by a wire of zero impedance, as shown in Fig. 17-11b. We now observe that the current $\mathbf{I}_a$ may be calculated by application of Kirchhoff's voltage law in loop $a\text{-}n\text{-}n'\text{-}a$: $\mathbf{I}_a = \mathbf{V}_{an'}/\mathbf{Z}_y$. Similarly $\mathbf{I}_b = \mathbf{V}_{bn'}/\mathbf{Z}_y$, and $\mathbf{I}_c = \mathbf{V}_{cn'}/\mathbf{Z}_y$. If we now separate the three parts of the circuit, as shown in Fig. 17-11c, each current in each of the three single-phase circuits will be identical to the current in one of each of the three line currents in the three-phase circuit. To solve the three-phase circuit, it is necessary only to solve any *one* of these single-phase circuits shown in Fig. 17-11c. For example, if $\mathbf{Z}_y = Z_y\underline{/\theta}$, then

$$\mathbf{I}_a = \frac{V\underline{/0}}{Z\underline{/\theta}} = \frac{V\underline{/-\theta}}{Z}$$

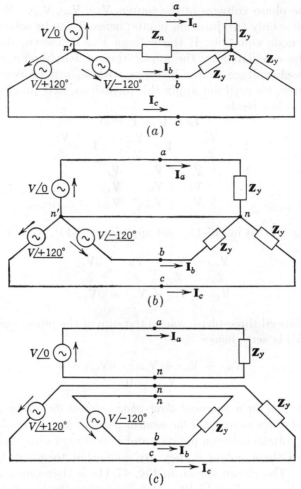

FIG. 17-11. (a) Equivalent to Fig. 17-10. (b) Equivalent to (a). (c) The three single-phase circuits shown are equivalent to the balanced three-phase circuit.

Since the voltages are symmetrical, the currents will also differ in phase by 120° so that for the circuits of Fig. 17-11

$$\mathbf{I}_a = \frac{\mathbf{V}}{\mathbf{Z}_y}$$
$$\mathbf{I}_b = \mathbf{I}_a(1\underline{/-120°})$$
$$\mathbf{I}_c = \mathbf{I}_a(1\underline{/+120°})$$

Example 17-2. Calculate the magnitude of a line current in the circuit shown in Fig. 17-12a.

We immediately recognize the circuit as balanced and separate one-phase, as shown in Fig. 17-12b.   Hence

$$|\mathbf{I}_a| = \left| \frac{100}{4 + j6} \right| = 13.85 \text{ amp}$$

Since $|\mathbf{I}_a| = |\mathbf{I}_b| = |\mathbf{I}_c|$

the solution is complete.

17-7. Line and Phase Quantities.

The Square Root of 3.   If a three-phase load is represented by a three-terminal box marked "load" as shown in Fig. 17-13a, then, in view of the delta-wye equivalence, the internal connections of the impedances in the box are immaterial with respect to the three accessible terminals.   For purposes of calculating the currents entering the terminals we may, if we choose, assume either delta or wye

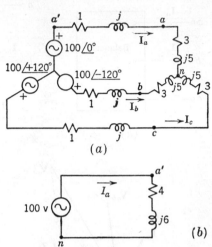

Fig. 17-12. (a) A balanced three-phase circuit. (b) A representative phase of (a).

connection internally.   The voltages across the individual impedances and the current through them are, however, of interest.   We shall now relate the internal voltages and currents in the balanced delta and wye to the quantities at the line terminals.   The voltages $\mathbf{V}_{ab}$, $\mathbf{V}_{bc}$, and $\mathbf{V}_{ca}$ at the terminals of the load are referred to as the line voltages.   Since, in the balanced *circuit*, they are all equal in magnitude, we shall designate their magnitude by the symbol V_L,

$$V_L = |\mathbf{V}_{ab}| = |\mathbf{V}_{bc}| = |\mathbf{V}_{ca}|$$

The currents entering the terminals of the load are equal in magnitude, and this magnitude is called the line current, denoted by the symbol I_L,

$$I_L = |\mathbf{I}_a| = |\mathbf{I}_b| = |\mathbf{I}_c|$$

In a balanced load the magnitudes of the voltages across each impedance are equal, and the magnitude of the current through each impedance is the same.   These magnitudes are called the phase voltage and phase current, respectively, and will be identified by the subscript p.   Thus in the balanced *wye*

$$V_p = |\mathbf{V}_{an}| = |\mathbf{V}_{bn}| = |\mathbf{V}_{cn}| \qquad I_p = |\mathbf{I}_{an}| = |\mathbf{I}_{bn}| = |\mathbf{I}_{cn}|$$

and in the balanced *delta*

$$V_p = |\mathbf{V}_{ab}| = |\mathbf{V}_{bc}| = |\mathbf{V}_{ca}| \qquad I_p = |\mathbf{I}_{ab}| = |\mathbf{I}_{bc}| = |\mathbf{I}_{ca}|$$

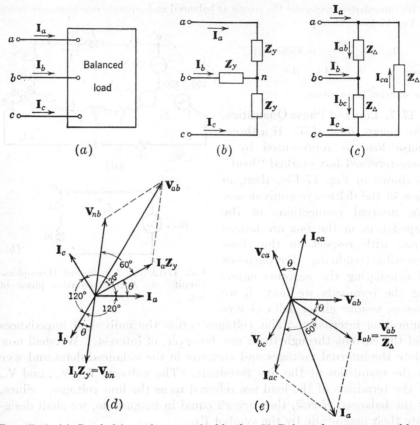

Fig. 17-13. (a) Symbol for a three-terminal load. (b) Balanced wye-connected load. (c) Balanced delta-connected load. (d) Phasor addition of phase voltages in the wye connection to give a line voltage. (e) Phasor addition of phase currents in the delta to give a line current.

Evidently a line current in a wye is identical to a phase current,

In the wye:
$$I_L = I_p$$

while, in a delta, line and phase voltages are identical,

In the delta:
$$V_L = V_p$$

To relate the line and phase voltages (*magnitudes*) in a balanced wye, with a-b-c sequence, let, $I_a = I_p\underline{/0°}$, $I_b = I_p\underline{/-120°}$, and $I_c = I_p\underline{/+120°}$. A line voltage, such as V_{ab}, may be obtained by the application of Kirchhoff's voltage law,

$$V_{ab} = V_{an} + V_{nb} \qquad V_{an} = I_a Z_y \qquad V_{nb} = -I_b Z_y$$

(Evidently $|\mathbf{V}_{an}| = |\mathbf{V}_{bn}| = V_p$.)   Hence

$$\mathbf{V}_{ab} = (\mathbf{I}_a - \mathbf{I}_b)\mathbf{Z}_y$$

but $\qquad \mathbf{I}_a - \mathbf{I}_b = I_p(1\underline{/0°} - 1\underline{/-120°}) = I_p \sqrt{3} \underline{/30°}$

Thus $\qquad \mathbf{V}_{ab} = \sqrt{3} \, I_p \mathbf{Z}_y \underline{/30°}$

or, using only absolute values,

In the balanced wye: $|\mathbf{V}_{ab}| = \sqrt{3} \, V_p = V_L$

This result, illustrated by the phasor diagram shown in Fig. 17-13d, could also be obtained by assuming a balanced wye-connected source, joining the neutral points, and noting that for the source $V_p \sqrt{3} = V_L$, as was shown in Art. 17-4.

To find the relationship between line and phase currents in a balanced delta, as shown in Fig. 17-13c, let

$$\mathbf{V}_{ab} = V_L\underline{/0}$$

and $\qquad \mathbf{V}_{ca} = V_L\underline{/+120°}$

Then $\qquad \mathbf{I}_{ab} = \dfrac{V_L\underline{/0}}{\mathbf{Z}_\Delta} \qquad \mathbf{I}_{ac} = -\dfrac{V_L\underline{/+120°}}{\mathbf{Z}_\Delta}$

Now, the line current $\mathbf{I}_a$ is given by Kirchhoff's current law at point a,

$$\mathbf{I}_a = \mathbf{I}_{ab} + \mathbf{I}_{ac}$$

or $\qquad \mathbf{I}_a = \dfrac{V_L}{\mathbf{Z}_\Delta} (1 - 1\underline{/+120°}) = \sqrt{3} \dfrac{V_L}{\mathbf{Z}_\Delta} \underline{/-30°}$

But since $|\mathbf{V}_L/\mathbf{Z}_\Delta| = I_p$, we have the result

In a balanced delta: $\sqrt{3} \, I_p = I_L$

This result is illustrated by the phasor diagram shown in Fig. 17-13e.

It must be emphasized that the relationships

For a balanced wye: $V_L = \sqrt{3} \, V_p$

For a balanced delta: $I_L = \sqrt{3} \, I_p$

are magnitude relationships.   If the phase relationships between the various currents and voltages are required, they are easily obtained from a phasor diagram or by analytical application of Kirchhoff's laws.

17-8. Power Relationships.   Since every balanced three-phase circuit can be represented as three individual single-phase circuits as in Fig. 17-11c, the total power delivered to the balanced three-phase load equals three times the power delivered to each phase.   Denoting the power per phase by P_p, we have

$$P_p = V_p I_p \cos \theta$$

where θ *is the angle of a phase impedance.* Hence the total power delivered to the balanced three-phase load is given by

$$P = 3V_pI_p \cos \theta \qquad (17\text{-}19)$$

In three-phase circuit applications it is preferable to express, where possible, all final results in terms of *line* quantities. In the case of Eq. (17-19) we note that for both delta- and wye-connected loads

$$V_pI_p = \frac{1}{\sqrt{3}} V_LI_L \qquad (17\text{-}20)$$

Because in a delta

$$V_p = V_L \qquad \text{and} \qquad I_p = \frac{1}{\sqrt{3}} I_L$$

and in a wye

$$V_p = \frac{1}{\sqrt{3}} V_L \qquad \text{and} \qquad I_p = I_L$$

the expression for the power delivered to a three-phase load may be written

$$P = \sqrt{3}\, V_LI_L \cos \theta \qquad \text{watts} \qquad (17\text{-}21a)$$

Note that θ is the angle between a *phase voltage* and the corresponding *phase current,* i.e., the angle of an (equivalent) phase impedance.

Similarly the total reactive power delivered to the three-phase load is given by

$$Q = -\sqrt{3}\, V_LI_L \sin \theta \qquad \text{var} \qquad (17\text{-}21b)$$

Since the complex power per phase is $P_p + jQ_p$, we define the complex power for a three-phase load as

$$\mathbf{P}_a = \text{complex power} = 3P_p + j3Q_p$$
$$\mathbf{P}_a = \sqrt{3}\, V_LI_L (\cos \theta - j \sin \theta) \qquad (17\text{-}21c)$$

In a *single-phase* circuit the absolute value of the complex power is the apparent power for the circuit. We now extend this definition to a balanced three-phase circuit. For a balanced three-phase circuit the apparent power is

$$P_a = \sqrt{3}\, V_LI_L \qquad \text{va} \qquad (17\text{-}21d)$$

The definition of power factor is also retained,

$$\text{pf} = \frac{P}{P_a} = \cos \theta \qquad (17\text{-}21e)$$

Thus the power factor for a balanced three-phase load is equal to the power factor of one of the phases, i.e., the cosine of the angle of an (equivalent) phase impedance.

We recall here that the use of complex power simplified many single-phase problems (such as combinations of parallel loads and power-factor correction). Since we can always reduce a balanced three-phase problem to an equivalent single-phase problem by using a representative phase, the method of complex-power addition (discussed in Chaps. 14 and 15) for single-phase circuits can be applied to balanced three-phase circuits.

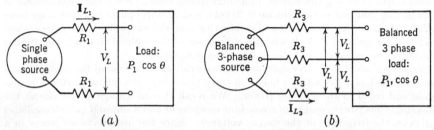

FIG. 17-14. A single-phase and a balanced three-phase circuit.

17-9. Balanced Three-phase Compared with Single-phase. We shall now discuss some advantages which make three-phase circuits preferable to single-phase circuits. This discussion will also serve to illustrate how some of the results of the previous articles are applied. Additional examples will be presented in the next article.

Power Transmission. Suppose that a certain load requires a power P, at a power factor cos θ, and at a line voltage V_L. This load is to be connected to a generator by means of cables. Let us assume that we have the option of connecting the load as a single-phase load as shown in Fig. 17-14a or as a balanced three-phase load as shown in Fig. 17-14b. We shall compare the power loss in the cables for the two cases. For the single-phase connection (Fig. 17-14a) we have called the resistance of each of the two cables R_1, and for the balanced three-phase load (Fig. 17-14b) each of the three cables has a resistance R_3.

In the *single-phase* connection the line current I_{L1} is given by

$$I_{L1} = \frac{P}{V_L \cos \theta}$$

Since the power loss in the two cables is $2(I_{L1}{}^2 R_1)$, we have

$$\text{Power loss in single phase} = \frac{P^2}{V_L{}^2 \cos^2 \theta} 2R_1$$

In the balanced *three-phase* connection the magnitude of a line current is given by

$$I_{L3} = \frac{P}{\sqrt{3} \ V_L \cos \theta}$$

Since the power loss in the three cables is $3(I_{L3}{}^2 R_3)$, we have

$$\text{Power loss in three-phase} = \frac{P^2}{3V_L{}^2 \cos^2 \theta} \times 3R_3$$

Hence, if we divide the two results for comparison,

$$\frac{\text{Power loss in three-phase transmission}}{\text{Power loss in single-phase transmission}} = \frac{R_3}{2R_1} \qquad (17\text{-}22)$$

If we use identical cables, then the power loss in three-phase transmission is only half the loss in the cables for the single-phase connection. If we *allow* the same power loss in either case, then each of the three cables in the three-phase connection may have twice the resistance of a cable in the single-phase case. Now, the resistance of a cable varies inversely with the cross-sectional area, and the length of the cables is the same in either case. The volume of the conducting material used therefore compares as follows: If $R_3 = 2R_1$ (equal loss in transmission), the volume $(\text{Vol})_3$ of a three-phase cable is half of $(\text{Vol})_1$, the volume of a single-phase cable. Since the total volume of conducting material in three-phase is $3(\text{Vol})_3$ and in single-phase is $2(\text{Vol})_1$, we have $(\text{Vol})_3/(\text{Vol})_1 = \frac{3}{4}$. This saving of conducting material and weight is of importance. While this example has dealt with the advantage of three-phase transmission, similar savings occur in weight and size of three-phase machines.

Instantaneous Power. We shall now demonstrate that the *sum* of the *instantaneous* powers which is delivered to a balanced three-phase load in a balanced circuit is *constant* and equal to the average power. We recall that in a single-phase circuit the instantaneous power consists of a constant component and a sinusoid (which oscillates at twice the frequency of the source voltage). Since the instantaneous power in a three-phase circuit is constant, if the load is a three-phase motor this motor will develop a constant torque, while a single-phase motor develops a pulsating torque.

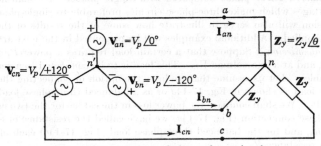

FIG. 17-15. A balanced three-phase circuit.

To obtain the expression for the instantaneous power delivered to all three phases of a balanced three-phase load from a balanced source, consider the circuit shown in Fig. 17-15. The total power delivered to all three phases at any instant of time is

$$p(t) = p_{an}(t) + p_{bn}(t) + p_{cn}(t)$$

where

$$p_{an}(t) = v_{an}i_{an} = \text{power to phase } a$$
$$p_{bn}(t) = v_{bn}i_{bn} = \text{power to phase } b$$
$$p_{cn}(t) = v_{cn}i_{cn} = \text{power to phase } c$$

Since $\mathbf{V}_{an} = V_p\underline{/0}$, we may write

$$v_{an}(t) = \sqrt{2}\,V_p\cos\omega t \qquad v_{bn} = \sqrt{2}\,V_p\cos(\omega t - 120°) \qquad v_{cn} = \sqrt{2}\,V_p\cos(\omega t + 120°)$$

Hence

$$i_{an}(t) = \sqrt{2}\,I_p\cos(\omega t - \theta) \qquad \text{where } I_p = \frac{V_p}{Z_y}$$

$$i_{bn}(t) = \sqrt{2}\,I_p\cos(\omega t - \theta - 120°)$$
$$i_{cn} = \sqrt{2}\,I_p\cos(\omega t - \theta + 120°)$$

Then

$$p_{an} = 2V_pI_p\cos\omega t\cos(\omega t - \theta) = V_pI_p\cos\theta + V_pI_p\cos(2\omega t - \theta)$$
$$p_{bn} = 2V_pI_p\cos(\omega t - 120°)\cos(\omega t - \theta - 120°)$$
$$= V_pI_p\cos\theta + V_pI_p\cos(2\omega t - 240° - \theta)$$

$$p_{cn} = 2V_p I_p \cos (\omega t + 120°) \cos (\omega t - \theta + 120°)$$
$$= V_p I_p \cos \theta + V_p I_p \cos (2\omega t + 240° - \theta)$$

Since $\cos (2\omega t - \theta) + \cos (2\omega t - 240° - \theta) + \cos (2\omega t + 240° - \theta) \equiv 0$

we have
$$p(t) = p_{an} + p_{bn} + p_{cn} = 3V_p I_p \cos \theta = P \qquad (17\text{-}23)$$

as was stated at the beginning of the discussion.

17-10. Examples of Balanced Three-phase Calculations. Example 17-3. Two balanced three-phase loads are connected in parallel (see Fig. 17-16a). Load 1 draws 20 kw at a lagging power factor of 0.85; load 2 draws 15 kw at a lagging power factor of 0.5. The line voltage at the terminals of the load is 440 volts. The load terminals are connected to the source terminals by means of cables which have an impedance of $1 + j3$ ohms each. Calculate (a) the line current drawn by the combination of the two loads; (b) the line voltage at the terminals of the source; (c) the power factor at the load terminals and at the source terminals.

Solution. A variety of methods for solving this problem is possible. We shall illustrate one very convenient method in which complex power is used. The two loads in parallel may be replaced by an equivalent load with respect to the load terminals by addition of complex power.

For load 1: $P_1 = 20$ kw $\qquad \cos \theta_1 = 0.85 \qquad \theta_1 = 31.7°$

Hence $\qquad Q_1 = -P_1 \tan \theta_1 = (-20)(0.614) = -12.3$ kvar

For load 2: $P_2 = 15$ kw $\qquad \cos \theta_2 = 0.5 \qquad \theta_2 = 60°$

Hence $\qquad Q_2 = -P_2 \tan \theta_2 = (-15)(1.73) = -26$ kvar

The combination draws

$$P = P_1 + P_2 = 20 + 15 = 35 \text{ kw}$$
and $\qquad Q = Q_1 + Q_2 = -12.3 - 26 = -38.3$ kvar

The equivalent balanced three-phase circuit is shown in Fig. 17-16b.

We now formulate the representative single-phase problem, assuming a wye connection for source and load. Each phase draws $P/3$ and $Q/3$. The phase voltage for a wye connection is $1/\sqrt{3}$ times the line voltage. Hence the representative single-phase circuit is as shown in Fig. 17-16c. In this circuit the apparent power for the load is

$$P_a = \sqrt{11.7^2 + 12.8^2} = 17.4 \text{ kva}$$

The magnitude of the line current is now calculated,

$$I_L = \frac{17.4 \times 10^3}{255} = 68 \text{ amp} \qquad\qquad Ans. \ (a)$$

This result can also be obtained without referring to the equivalent single-phase problem. For the three-phase load $P = 35$ kw, $Q = -38.3$ kvar. Hence

$$\sqrt{3} \ V_L I_L = \sqrt{35^2 + 38.3^2} = 52.5 \text{ kvar}$$
Thus $\qquad I_L = \frac{52.2 \times 10^3}{1.73 \times 440} = 68 \text{ amp}$

We have chosen to show the single-phase method first, in view of the following parts of the problem. To calculate the line voltage V' at the terminals of the source, we calculate first the phase voltage V'_p in the representative single-phase problem. Since $V'_p = |\mathbf{V}_{a'n}|$, we apply Kirchhoff's voltage law,

$$\mathbf{V}_{a'n} = \mathbf{V}_{a'a} + \mathbf{V}_{an}$$

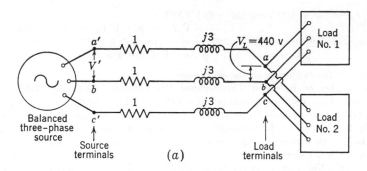

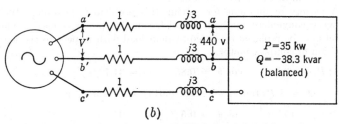

$$(b)$$

FIG. 17-16. (a) Balanced loads in parallel fed through cables from a balanced source. (b) Representing the two balanced loads as a single equivalent load.

To carry out this phasor addition, we may choose any reference. For this series circuit it is convenient to write

$$\mathbf{I}_{an} = I_L/\underline{0} = 68/\underline{0°}$$

Hence $\mathbf{V}_{an}$ will be given as

$$\mathbf{V}_{an} = 255/\underline{\theta}$$

where θ is the power-factor angle of the single-phase load. Because $\tan \theta = -Q/P$, we have

$$\tan \theta = \frac{12.8}{11.7} \qquad \theta = 47.6°$$

The voltage $\mathbf{V}_{a'a}$ is given by $\mathbf{I}_{an}\mathbf{Z}_{a'a}$,

$$\mathbf{V}_{a'a} = (68/\underline{0°})(1 + j3) = 68 + j204$$

Hence $\mathbf{V}_{a'n} = 68 + j204 + 255/\underline{47.6°}$

or $\mathbf{V}_{a'n} = 68 + j204 + 172 + j188 = 240 + j392 = 460/\underline{58.5°}$

This phasor addition is illustrated by Fig. 17-16d. We need the magnitude of $\mathbf{V}_{a'n}$, since this value is V_p',

$$V_p' = 460 \text{ volts}$$

Thus $V' = 460 \sqrt{3} = 796 \text{ volts.}$ *Ans. (b)*

Note that we do not know the angle of V' (with respect to I_{an}) since line and phase voltages are not in phase. This angle, if required, could be obtained from a phasor diagram of line and phase voltages if the phase sequence were specified.

The power factor at the load terminals is immediately obtained either as the cosine of the angle between $\mathbf{V}_{an}$ and $\mathbf{I}_{an}$,

$$\text{pf at load terminals} = \cos 47.6°$$
$$= 0.674 \text{ lagging} \qquad \textit{Ans. (c)}$$

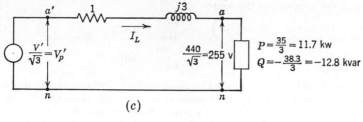

$$\frac{V'}{\sqrt{3}} = V_p'$$

$$\frac{440}{\sqrt{3}} = 255 \text{ v}$$

$$P = \frac{35}{3} = 11.7 \text{ kw}$$

$$Q = -\frac{38.3}{3} = -12.8 \text{ kvar}$$

(c)

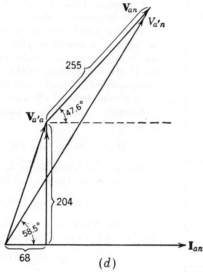

(d)

FIG. 17-16. (c) The representative single-phase problem for (b).   (d) Voltage phasor addition in the circuit of (c).

or as the ratio of the power to the apparent power,

$$\text{pf} \Big)_{\text{load}} = \frac{P}{P_a} = \frac{11.7}{17.4} = \frac{35}{52.5} = 0.67 \text{ lagging} \qquad \textit{Check}$$

At the generator terminals, the power factor is given by

$$\text{pf} \Big)_{gen} = \cos \overset{\mathbf{V}_{a'n}}{\underset{\mathbf{I}_{a'n}}{\Big\rangle}} = \cos 58.5° = 0.523 \text{ lagging} \qquad \textit{Ans. (c)}$$

The results can be checked by the use of complex power,

$$P_{a'n} = P_{a'a} + P_{an} = I_L{}^2 \times 1 + 11.7 \times 10^3$$
$$P_{a'n} = 4.6 + 11.7 = 16.3 \text{ kw}$$
$$-Q_{a'n} = \frac{(I_L)^2 \times 3}{1,000} + 12.8 = 26.6 \text{ kvar}$$

We now write

$$|\mathbf{V}_{a'n}\mathbf{I}_{a'n}| = \sqrt{16.3^2 + 26.6^2} = 31.2 \text{ kva}$$

Hence at the terminals of the source

$$\text{pf}\Big)_{gen} = \frac{16.3}{31.2} = 0.522 \qquad\qquad Check$$

and

$$V'_p = \frac{31,200}{68} = 460 \qquad\qquad Check$$

The reader should not be concerned by the unrealistically large energy dissipation and energy storage in the cables.   The numbers were purposely chosen so that these results are unrealistically large and none of the quantities are negligible.

Example 17-4.   The balanced three-phase load shown in Fig. 17-17 draws 20 kw at a lagging power factor of 0.4.   The frequency is 60 cps.   Calculate (a) the total kva rating of three capacitances which when connected in delta or in wye in parallel with the load will raise the power factor of the combination to 0.9 lagging. (b) If the line voltage at the load terminals is 1,300 volts, calculate the value of each capacitance of (a) for (1) delta connection; (2) wye connection.

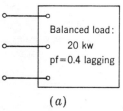

(a)

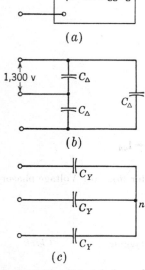

(b)

(c)

FIG. 17-17.   (a) A balanced load.   (b) Delta-connected capacitances.   (c) Wye-connected capacitances.

Solution.   The reactive power drawn by the load alone is

$$Q = -20 \tan (\cos^{-1} 0.4) = -45.8 \text{ kvar}$$

If the power factor were 0.9 lagging, the reactive power drawn by the load would be Q',

$$Q' = -20 \tan (\cos^{-1} 0.9) = -9.8 \text{ kvar}$$

Hence the three capacitances combined must draw $45.8 - 9.8$ kvar or, calling this quantity Q_c,

$$Q_c = +36.0 \text{ kvar} \qquad\qquad Ans.$$

Each capacitance draws

$$Q_p = +\frac{36.0}{3} = 12.0 \text{ kvar} \qquad\qquad Ans.$$

If the capacitances are delta-connected, as shown in Fig. 17-17b, the voltage across each is a line voltage V_L given as 1,300 volts.

Since the capacitances draw no average power, the apparent power in each equals, numerically, the magnitude of the reactive power.   The magnitude of a phase current in a capacitance is given by

$$V_L I_c = Q_p = 12,000$$

or

$$I_c = \frac{12,000}{1,300} = 9.23 \text{ amp}$$

Hence

$$\omega C_\Delta = Bc\Big)_\Delta = \frac{9.23}{1,300} = 7.10 \times 10^{-3} \text{ mho}$$

and

$$C_\Delta = \tfrac{1}{377} \times 7.10 \times 10^{-3} = 18.8 \; \mu\text{f} \qquad\qquad Ans. (b_1)$$

If the capacitances are wye-connected, as shown in Fig. 17-17c, then, by delta-wye conversion,

$$(Bc)_y = 3(Bc)_\Delta$$

Thus

$$C_y = 56.4 \; \mu\text{f} \qquad\qquad Ans. (b_2)$$

This result can be obtained independently. The voltage across each capacitance in the wye is $1{,}300/\sqrt{3} = 752$ volts. Hence a phase current I'_c in a wye-connected capacitance is given by

$$I'_c = \frac{12{,}000}{752} = 16 \text{ amp}$$

and
$$(B_C)_y = \tfrac{16}{752} = 21.3 \times 10^{-3} \text{ mho}$$
$$C_y = \frac{21.3}{0.377} \times 10^{-6} = 56.4 \ \mu\text{f}$$

17-11. Unbalanced Three-phase Circuits.

As was stated earlier, the calculation of an unbalanced three-phase circuit is carried out by node (or mesh) analysis because the special symmetry, which allows us to replace a balanced three-phase problem by a representative single phase, no longer exists. It should also be evident that the advantages of three-phase over single-phase are lost if the circuit becomes severely unbalanced. In this article we shall illustrate the calculation of several unbalanced circuits.

The Open-delta (V) Connection. Consider the unbalanced three-phase load shown in Fig. 17-18. The two impedances are equal, but a third impedance, which, if equal to the others, would form a balanced delta when connected across terminals a-b,

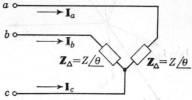

FIG. 17-18. The open-delta (V) connection.

is omitted. The line voltages at the load terminals are assumed balanced and of a-b-c sequence. Hence

$$\mathbf{V}_{ab} = V_L \underline{/0°}$$
$$\mathbf{V}_{bc} = V_L \underline{/-120°}$$
$$\mathbf{V}_{ca} = V_L \underline{/+120°}$$

We shall calculate the line currents $\mathbf{I}_a$, $\mathbf{I}_b$, and $\mathbf{I}_c$. Since the voltage across each impedance is known, we have

$$\mathbf{I}_{bc} = \frac{\mathbf{V}_{bc}}{\mathbf{Z}_\Delta} = \frac{V_L}{Z} \underline{/-120° - \theta}$$

$$\mathbf{I}_{ca} = \frac{\mathbf{V}_{ca}}{\mathbf{Z}_\Delta} = \frac{V_L \underline{/+120° - \theta}}{Z}$$

Hence
$$\mathbf{I}_a = -\mathbf{I}_{ca} = \frac{V_L}{Z} \underline{/-60° - \theta}$$

and
$$\mathbf{I}_b = \mathbf{I}_{bc} = \frac{V_L}{Z} \underline{/-120° - \theta}$$

Since
$$\mathbf{I}_c = -\mathbf{I}_b - \mathbf{I}_a$$

the line current $\mathbf{I}_c$ is given by

$$\mathbf{I}_c = \frac{V_L}{Z}\,(-1\underline{/-60° - \theta} - 1\underline{/-120° - \theta})$$

The phasor addition is illustrated in Fig. 17-19 for an acute positive angle θ. The result is

$$\mathbf{I}_c = \sqrt{3}\,\frac{V_L}{Z}\,\underline{/90° - \theta}$$

Since the three line currents are unequal, if this load is connected to a

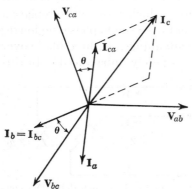

source by means of cables the power loss in the c cable would be three times the loss in the a or b cable. In addition the voltage across the cable impedances would be unequal and unbalanced. Consequently, if the source furnishes balanced voltages, then the assumption of balanced load voltage may be unjustified.

Unbalanced Wye. Consider next the unbalanced circuit shown in Fig. 17-20a. Assuming the source voltages to be known, the line current can be calculated if the voltage of a, b, and c with respect to the neutral

Fig. 17-19. Phasor diagram for Fig. 17-18.

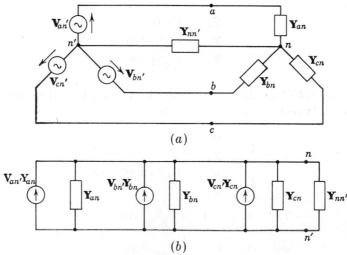

(a)

(b)

Fig. 17-20. (a) An unbalanced three-phase circuit. (b) Current-source equivalent with respect to terminals n-n' for the circuit of (a).

point of the load is known. The voltage $\mathbf{V}_{nn'}$ is easily calculated by using the node method. An equivalent circuit with respect to terminals n and n' can be obtained by converting each voltage source to a current source. This circuit is shown in Fig. 17-20b. Application of Kirchhoff's current law at junction n gives

$$\mathbf{V}_{an'}\mathbf{Y}_{an} + \mathbf{V}_{bn'}\mathbf{Y}_{bn} + \mathbf{V}_{cn'}\mathbf{Y}_{cn} = \mathbf{V}_{nn'}(\mathbf{Y}_{an} + \mathbf{Y}_{bn} + \mathbf{Y}_{cn} + \mathbf{Y}_{n'n})$$

or

$$\mathbf{V}_{nn'} = \frac{\mathbf{V}_{an'}\mathbf{Y}_{an} + \mathbf{V}_{bn'}\mathbf{Y}_{bn} + \mathbf{V}_{cn'}\mathbf{Y}_{cn}}{\mathbf{Y}_{an} + \mathbf{Y}_{bn} + \mathbf{Y}_{cn} + \mathbf{Y}_{n'n}}$$

If the neutrals n and n' are joined through a zero impedance (infinite admittance), then $\mathbf{V}_{nn'}$ is zero and the voltage across any phase impedance ($\mathbf{Z}_{an}$, $\mathbf{Z}_{bn}$, or $\mathbf{Z}_{cn}$) is not dependent on the other impedance. If, however, $\mathbf{Z}_{n'n}$ is appreciable, then the voltages across the individual phase impedances will influence each other.

As a numerical example consider the balanced voltage with a-b-c phase order,

$$\mathbf{V}_{an'} = V\underline{/0} \qquad \mathbf{V}_{bn'} = V\underline{/-120} \qquad \mathbf{V}_{cn'} = V\underline{/+120°}$$

and the unbalanced load admittances

$$\mathbf{Y}_{an} = 1 + j0 \text{ mho} \qquad \mathbf{Y}_{bn} = -j1 \text{ mho} \qquad \mathbf{Y}_{cn} = 0.5 + j0 \text{ mho}$$

and let the admittance of the neutral line be $0 - j3$ mhos. Then

$$\mathbf{V}_{an'}\mathbf{Y}_{an} = V(1 + j0)$$
$$\mathbf{V}_{bn'}\mathbf{Y}_{bn} = V(1\underline{/-120°})(-j) = V(-0.866 + j0.5)$$
$$\mathbf{V}_{cn'}\mathbf{Y}_{cn} = V(1\underline{/+120°})(0.5) = V(-0.25 + j0.433)$$

Hence

$$\mathbf{V}_{an'}\mathbf{Y}_{an} + \mathbf{V}_{bn'}\mathbf{Y}_{bn} + \mathbf{V}_{cn'}\mathbf{Y}_{cn} = V(0.116 + j0.933)$$
$$= 0.937V\underline{/82.9°}$$

Also

$$\mathbf{Y}_{an} + \mathbf{Y}_{bn} + \mathbf{Y}_{cn} + \mathbf{Y}_{n'n} = 1.5 - j4 = 4.28\underline{/-69.5°}$$

Thus

$$\mathbf{V}_{nn'} = \frac{0.937V}{4.28} \underline{/82.9° + 69.5°}$$
$$= 0.219V\underline{/152.4°}$$

Therefore

$$\mathbf{V}_{an} = \mathbf{V}_{an'} - \mathbf{V}_{nn'} = V\underline{/0} - 0.219V\underline{/152.4°}$$
$$= V\underline{/0} + V(0.194 - j0.103)$$

Similarly

$$|\mathbf{V}_{an}| = 1.2V$$
$$|\mathbf{V}_{bn}| = 1.02V$$
$$|\mathbf{V}_{cn}| = 0.788V$$

We conclude that the load voltages are unbalanced. The line currents will be given by

$$|\mathbf{I}_{an}| = |\mathbf{V}_{an}|\,|\mathbf{Y}_{an}| = 1.2V \qquad \text{amp}$$
$$|\mathbf{I}_{bn}| = |\mathbf{V}_{bn}|\,|\mathbf{Y}_{bn}| = 1.02V \qquad \text{amp}$$
$$|\mathbf{I}_{cn}| = |\mathbf{V}_{cn}|\,|\mathbf{Y}_{cn}| = 0.394V \qquad \text{amp}$$

The current in the neutral is

$$|\mathbf{I}_{n'n}| = |\mathbf{V}_{n'n}|\,|\mathbf{Y}_{nn}| = 0.657V \qquad \text{amp}$$

so that the currents are unbalanced.

If we now assume the *opposite* phase order,

$$\mathbf{V}_{an'} = V\underline{/0} \qquad \mathbf{V}_{bn'} = V\underline{/+120°} \qquad \mathbf{V}_{cn'} = V\underline{/-120°}$$

then
$$\mathbf{V}_{an'}\mathbf{Y}_{an} = V(1 + j0)$$

But
$$\mathbf{V}_{bn'}\mathbf{Y}_{bn} = (V\underline{/+120°})(-j) = V(0.866 + j0.5)$$

$$\mathbf{V}_{cn'}\mathbf{Y}_{cn} = (V\underline{/-120°})(0.5) = V(-0.25 - j0.433)$$

Hence in this case

$$\mathbf{V}_{an'}\mathbf{Y}_{an} + \mathbf{V}_{bn'}\mathbf{Y}_{bn} + \mathbf{V}_{cn'}\mathbf{Y}_{cn} = V(1.61 + j0.07)$$
and
$$|\mathbf{V}_{n'n}| = 0.377V$$

This result differs from the previous result.

We conclude that in an unbalanced circuit the magnitudes of the line currents depend on the phase order.

17-12. An Application of Unbalanced Circuits. Phase Sequence. We have just seen that line currents (and therefore phase voltage in a wye) depend on the phase sequence in unbalanced three-phase circuits. This result may be used to build a circuit which has the function of indicating the phase sequence for a balanced source. Such a phase-sequence indicator is shown in Fig. 17-21. We shall show that the magnitude V_{bn} is either larger or smaller than the line voltage V_L, depending on the phase sequence. The magnitude of V_{bn} for the two possible phase orders is easily obtained from a phasor diagram drawn for each case. Since $\mathbf{V}_{ab} + \mathbf{V}_{bc} + \mathbf{V}_{ca} = 0$, the three phasors which represent these voltages form an equilateral triangle as in Fig. 17-22a for the *ab-bc-ca* sequence and in Fig. 17-22b for the *ab-ca-bc* sequence. In either case $\mathbf{I}_{ac}$ leads $\mathbf{V}_{ac}$ by $\theta = \tan^{-1}|X_c|/R$ as shown in the phasor diagrams in Fig. 17-22.

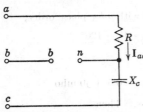

FIG. 17-21. A phase-sequence indicator.

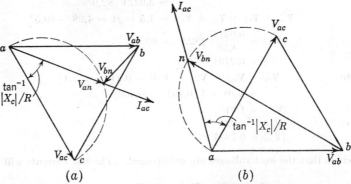

(a)   (b)

FIG. 17-22. Phasor diagrams for the circuit of Fig. 17-21, showing conditions for the two possible phase orders.

Since $\mathbf{V}_{an}$ is in phase with $\mathbf{I}_{ac}$ and $\mathbf{V}_{nb}$ lags $\mathbf{I}_{ac}$ by 90°, point n is located on the phasor diagrams so that angle $\underline{/anc}$ is a right angle. For any ratio of X_c to R the locus of point n is on the dashed semicircle. Since in Fig. 17-22a the distance from b to n, which represents the magnitude $|V_{bn}|$, is less than V_L, while in Fig. 17-22b $|V_{bn}| > V_L$, this device can be used to indicate phase sequence.

Other unblanced circuits can also be used to indicate phase sequence (see Prob. 17-16).

17-13. Wattmeters. We assume that the reader is familiar with the principles involved in the operation of a wattmeter. In this article we shall give an expression for the reading of an a-c wattmeter in terms of the voltages and currents applied to its voltage and current coils, respectively. A wattmeter is symbolically shown as in Fig. 17-23a. In this representation the symbol of inductance is used to represent the current coil, and the symbol of resistance represents the voltage coil of the meter. For an ideal meter the inductance (impedance) of the current coil is assumed to be

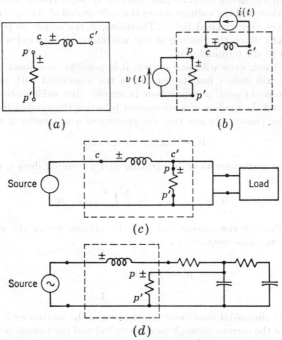

(a) (b) (c) (d)

FIG. 17-23. Wattmeter connections. (a) Symbolic representation of a wattmeter. (b) Separate sources excite voltage and current coils. (c) A wattmeter connected to read single-phase power. (d) A wattmeter connection in a single-phase circuit. The wattmeter reading does not correspond to the power delivered to the circuit.

zero ($v_{cc'} = 0$ for any $i_{cc'}$), and the resistance (impedance) of the voltage coil is assumed infinite ($i_{pp'} = 0$ for any $v_{pp'}$).

The mechanism of an a-c wattmeter is such that if a current source $i(t)$ is applied to the current coil with the reference arrow of the source pointing to the terminal marked $\pm$, as shown in Fig. 17-23b, and if a voltage source $v(t)$ is applied to the voltage coil with its reference arrow pointing to the terminal marked $\pm$, and if the functions $v(t)$ and $i(t)$ are periodic with period T, then the wattmeter reading will be

$$W = \frac{1}{T} \int_0^T v(t)i(t)\, dt$$

Two points are to be noted here:

1. Although the meter is called an a-c wattmeter, the voltages and currents associ-

ated with it need not be sinusoidal and the above expression is valid so long as $v(t)$ and $i(t)$ are periodic and have the same period.

2. The reading of the meter is not necessarily the average power delivered to a load. For example, in Fig. 17-23b for given $v(t)$ and $i(t)$ there is no power involved, but the meter will still read $W = (1/T) \int_0^T vi\, dt$. The only time that the reading of the meter is to be interpreted as power (delivered to a terminal pair) is when $i(t)$ and $v(t)$ applied to the current and voltage coils of the meter are those associated with a (load) terminal pair.   In Fig. 17-23c the meter is connected so that the current through its current coil is the same as current in the terminal pair (current through voltage coil of the meter is assumed to be zero), and the voltage across the voltage coil of the meter is the same in the voltage across the terminal pair.   Therefore, if the source is periodic and the circuit is in steady state, the reading of the wattmeter is identical with the average power delivered to the terminal pair.

On the other hand, even with one source, it is possible to connect a wattmeter so that the needle will deflect but its reading is not associated with power.   In Fig. 17-23d an example of such a connection is given.   We shall distinguish between average power and the reading of a wattmeter by using the symbol W for wattmeter reading and P for power.   In any case the reading of a wattmeter is given by

$$W = (i_{\text{current coil}} v_{\text{volt coil}})_{\text{av}}$$

In this sense the wattmeter is an integrating and averaging device, defined by the expression

$$W = (v_{pp'} i_{cc'})_{\text{av}} = \frac{1}{T} \int_0^T v_{pp'} i_{cc'}\, dt$$

If the current through the current coil and the voltage across the voltage coil are sinusoidal with the same frequency, then

$$W = I_c V_p \cos \begin{smallmatrix} \mathbf{V}_p \\ \diagup \\ \diagdown \\ \mathbf{I}_c \end{smallmatrix}$$

In words: Under sinusoidal conditions the reading of the wattmeter is the product of the rms values of the current through its current coil and the voltage across its voltage coil multiplied by the cosine of the angle between those two phasors.   In this interpretation the reference arrows of the voltage and current must be pointing to the polarity signs $\pm$ of their respective coils.

17-14. Measurement of Three-phase Power.   It should be evident that the connections shown in Fig. 17-24 can be used to measure the power in either a delta- or a wye-connected load.   We have shown a wattmeter for each leg of the delta or wye; hence each wattmeter reads the power delivered to the load which is correspondingly numbered.   Each of these connections employs three wattmeters and represents what is referred to as the "three-wattmeter method" and for the following reasons is generally not useful.   In the case of a delta load the current coils of the wattmeters must be inserted in series with each phase impedance, and these may not be accessible. In the case of the wye-connected load each voltage coil is connected to the neutral point, and this point may not be accessible.   In the case of parallel connections of delta- and wye-connected loads the number of wattmeters which this method requires makes this scheme hopelessly inadequate.

In Fig. 17-25 the two-wattmeter method used in connection with three-wire systems is shown.   We shall now demonstrate that the (algebraic) sum of the readings of the two meters is the average power delivered to the three-terminal load. This is true so long as the sources in the network are periodic, with the same period, and the network is in steady state. In Fig. 17-25 the load is shown as wye-connected. This is for convenience and does not affect the generality of the following arguments.

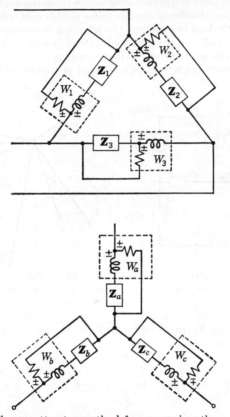

Fig. 17-24. Three-wattmeter method for measuring three-phase power.

In accordance with the definition of the wattmeter readings and the polarities shown in Fig. 17-25

$$W_1 + W_2 = \frac{1}{T} \int_0^T (v_{ac}i_a + v_{bc}i_b) \, dt$$

$$v_{ac} = v_{an} + v_{nc} \qquad v_{bc} = v_{bn} + v_{nc}$$

$$W_1 + W_2 = \frac{1}{T} \int_0^T [(v_{an} + v_{nc})i_a + (v_{bn} + v_{nc})i_b] \, dt$$

Adding and subtracting $v_{cn}i_c$ inside the integral sign and noting that $v_{cn} = -v_{nc}$, we have

$$W_1 + W_2 = \frac{1}{T} \int_0^T [v_{an}i_a + v_{bn}i_b + v_{cn}i_c + v_{nc}(i_c + i_b + i_a)] \, dt$$

In this expression, $i_a + i_b + i_c$ is the sum of the currents entering n and is identically zero. It is noted that this sum is zero regardless of the waveform of the currents.

We have assumed that there is no voltage across the current coils and therefore $v_{an} = v_{a'n}$, $v_{bn} = v_{b'n}$, and $v_{cn} = v_{c'n}$, but $1/T \int_0^T v_{a'n} i_a \, dt$ is the average power delivered to the load $a'n$, with similar interpretation for other terms in the integral. This shows that $W_1 + W_2$ is the total power delivered to the three-terminal load.

Although the two-wattmeter method requires neither that voltages and currents be sinusoidal nor that the load be balanced, the following discussion shows that, when the system given in Fig. 17-25 is a three-phase balanced system, then from the readings of W_1 and W_2 the reactive power as well as the average power can be computed. In Fig. 17-26 the phasor diagram of a three-phase balanced system, with the load angle θ, is

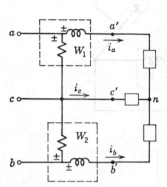

FIG. 17-25. The two-wattmeter method for measuring three-phase power.

FIG. 17-26. Phasor diagram for the two-wattmeter method in a balanced three-phase circuit.

shown, such that $\mathbf{I}_a$ lags $\mathbf{V}_{an}$ by θ and $\mathbf{I}_b$ lags $\mathbf{V}_{bn}$ by the same angle. From this phasor diagram it is seen that

$$W_1 = V_{ac} I_a \cos \underline{/V_{ac}, I_a} = V_L I_L \cos (30° - \theta) \tag{17-24}$$

$$W_2 = V_{bc} I_b \cos \underline{/V_{bc}, I_b} = V_L I_L \cos (30° + \theta) \tag{17-25}$$

where V_L and I_L are line voltage and line currents, respectively.

$$W_1 + W_2 = V_L I_L [\cos (30° - \theta) + \cos (30° + \theta)] = V_L I_L (2 \cos \theta \cos 30°)$$
$$= \sqrt{3} \, V_L I_L \cos \theta = P \tag{17-26}$$

$$W_1 - W_2 = V_L I_L [\cos (30° - \theta) - \cos (30° + \theta)] = V_L I_L (2 \sin \theta \sin 30°)$$
$$= V_L I_L \sin \theta = -\frac{1}{\sqrt{3}} Q \tag{17-27}$$

$$\tan \theta = -\sqrt{3} \frac{W_1 - W_2}{W_1 + W_2} \tag{17-28}$$

Equations (17-26) to (17-28) show that, from the values of W_1 and W_2, the average power, reactive power, and power factor of the load can be computed. From Eq. (17-25) it is seen that if $\theta < 60°$ then (with the polarities shown in Fig. 17-25) the value of $\cos (30 + \theta)$ and therefore W_2 will be positive. At $\theta = 60°$, $W_2 = V_L I_L \cos 90° = 0$, and, for $\theta > 60°$, $30° + \theta > 90°$ and W_2 will be negative. In such cases the meter polarity must be reversed (to read upscale) and then $P = |W_1| - |W_2|$.

PROBLEMS

17-1. In Fig. P17-1 calculate v_{an}/v_{nb} if $R_s = \frac{1}{2}$, $R_1 = 5$, $R_3 = 10$, $v = V = 100$, and (a) $R_2 = 5$; (b) $R_2 = 10$, $R_n = 20$; (c) $R_2 = 10$, $R_n = 0$; (d) $R_2 = 10$, $1/R_n = 0$.

17-2. In Prob. 17-1, $v(t) = \text{Re } \sqrt{2}\ 100e^{j\omega t}$. Calculate the phasor ratio $\mathbf{V}_{an}/\mathbf{V}_{nb}$ if $R_s = \frac{1}{2}$ and R_1 is replaced by $\mathbf{Z}_1 = 3 + j4$, R_3 is replaced by $6 + j8$, and (a) R_2 is replaced by $\mathbf{Z}_2 = 3 + j4$; (b) $R_n = 0$ and $R_2 = 5$; (c) $1/R_n = 0$ and $R_2 = 6$.

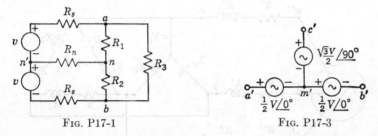

FIG. P17-1　　　　　　　　　FIG. P17-3

17-3. In Fig. P17-3 use a voltage phasor diagram drawn to scale of V volts = 2 in. to show that the three-terminal source a'-b'-c' is a balanced three-phase source. (Is m' the "neutral" of the three-phase source?)

17-4. Three ideal sources are given in Fig. P17-4 whose phasors are $\mathbf{V}_{ab} = V\underline{/0°}$, $\mathbf{V}_{cd} = V\underline{/60°}$, $\mathbf{V}_{ef} = V\underline{/-60°}$. How should these sources be connected to form a balanced three-phase source which is (a) wye-connected; (b) delta-connected? In each case state the phase sequence.

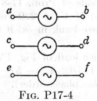

FIG. P17-4

17-5. A balanced three-phase load consists of three equal impedances. When these impedances are connected in wye across balanced three-phase lines, line voltage V_L, the line current is 1. Complete the following table for the line and phase quantities indicated, assuming that the line voltage remains V_L as the connections are changed.

Connection		Generator		Line	Load	
Generator	Load	V_p	I_p	I_L	V_p	I_p
Wye	Wye	$V_L/\sqrt{3}$	1	1	$V_L/\sqrt{3}$	1
Wye	Delta					
Delta	Delta					
Delta	Wye					

17-6. A balanced three-phase circuit consists of a delta-connected ideal source furnishing line voltages of 173 volts and three load impedances of $5 + j5$ ohms each. Calculate the phase voltage and phase current in the load and generator if the three impedances form a load which is (a) delta-connected; (b) wye-connected.

17-7. In the balanced three-phase circuit shown in Fig. P17-7, $R = 12$ ohms, $X_L = 18$ ohms, $X_C = -10$ ohms, $R' = 0.5$ ohms, $X' = 1.25$ ohms, $V_{ab} = 220$ volts. Calculate the magnitude of the line-to-line voltage at the generator terminals.

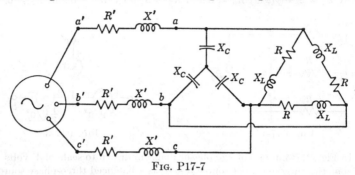

FIG. P17-7

17-8. Two balanced three-phase loads are connected in parallel across balanced three-phase lines. One load draws 50 kw at a lagging power factor of 0.4; the second load draws 50 kw at a lagging power factor of 0.707. (a) Calculate the power factor of the combination. (b) Calculate the magnitude of a line current if $V_L = 220$ volts.

17-9. (a) Calculate the kva size of a three-phase capacitance bank which when connected in parallel with the loads of Prob. 17-8 results in a power factor of 0.8 lagging for the combination. (b) If $V_L = 220$ volts, calculate the susceptance of each capacitance of the three-phase bank in (a) if this bank is (1) delta-connected; (2) wye-connected.

17-10. The balanced three-phase load of Fig. P17-10 is connected to a balanced source. It is known that $\mathbf{V}_{ab} = 173\underline{/0°}$, $\mathbf{I}_{an} = 5\underline{/-45°}$. (a) Calculate the complex value $\mathbf{Z}_y$ if $\mathbf{V}_{bc} = 173\underline{/-120°}$ (a-b-c phase order). (b) Calculate the complex value $\mathbf{Z}_y$ for the phase order a-c-b.

(c) For (a) and (b) draw a phasor diagram showing the nine phasors $\mathbf{V}_{ab}$, $\mathbf{V}_{bc}$, $\mathbf{V}_{ca}$, $\mathbf{V}_{an}$, $\mathbf{V}_{bn}$, $\mathbf{V}_{cn}$, $\mathbf{I}_{an}$, $\mathbf{I}_{bn}$, and $\mathbf{I}_{cn}$.

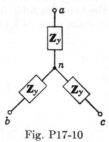

Fig. P17-10

17-11. Assume that the open-delta (V) load of Fig. P17-11 is connected to a balanced three-phase source. (a) If the maximum line current allowed in any one line is I_L, obtain an expression for maximum power delivered to the two impedances. (b) If $I_{L\text{max}}$ is the same as in (a), compare the result of (a) to the power delivered to three impedances $\mathbf{Z}$ connected in delta.

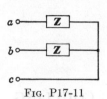

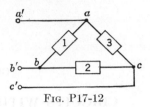

FIG. P17-11

FIG. P17-12

17-12. If $\mathbf{V}_{ab} = 200\underline{/0}$, $\mathbf{V}_{bc} = 200\underline{/-120°}$, $\mathbf{V}_{ca} = 200\underline{/+120°}$, and if the three loads are specified as follows, calculate $\mathbf{I}_{a'a}$, $\mathbf{I}_{b'b}$, and $\mathbf{I}_{c'c}$: load 1, 20 kw, unity power factor; load 2, 12 kw, 0.6 power factor lagging; load 3, 16 kw, 0.8 power factor leading. The circuit is shown in Fig. P17-12.

17-13. Calculate $\mathbf{I}_{a'a}$, $\mathbf{I}_{b'b}$, and $\mathbf{I}_{c'c}$ if $\mathbf{V}_{a'b'} = 200\underline{/0°}$, $\mathbf{V}_{b'c'} = 200\underline{/-120°}$, and $\mathbf{V}_{c'a'} = 200\underline{/+120°}$. The circuit is shown in Fig. P17-13.

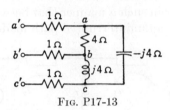

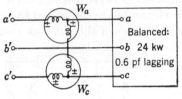

FIG. P17-13

FIG. P17-14

17-14. Calculate the reading of W_a and W_c if the phase sequence is (a) a-b-c; (b) a-c-b. The circuit is shown in Fig. P17-14.

17-15. In the circuit of Prob. 17-14 a wattmeter is connected so that the current in the current coil is $\mathbf{I}_{a'a}$ and the voltage across the voltage coil is $\mathbf{V}_{bc}$. Show that the magnitude of the reading of this wattmeter is proportional to reactive power.

17-16. Terminals a-b-c are connected to a balanced three-phase source. Show that the magnitude of the ratio $\mathbf{V}_{an}/\mathbf{V}_{bn}$ is more or less than unity depending only on the phase order. The circuit is shown in Fig. P17-16.

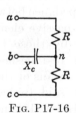

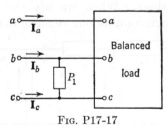

FIG. P17-16

FIG. P17-17

17-17. The combination of the three-phase and single-phase loads in Fig. P17-17 forms an unbalanced load. The line voltages are balanced and are given by $\mathbf{V}_{ab} = 220\underline{/0}$, $\mathbf{V}_{bc} = 220\underline{/-120°}$, $\mathbf{V}_{ca} = 220\underline{/+120°}$. The balanced load draws 50 kw at a lagging power factor of 0.500; the single-phase load P_1 draws 30 kw at unity power factor. (a) Calculate $\mathbf{I}_a$, $\mathbf{I}_b$, and $\mathbf{I}_c$. (b) Two wattmeters are connected to read total power. One of these wattmeters is in line a, the other in line c. Calculate the reading of each wattmeter.

CHAPTER 18

CIRCUITS WITH MAGNETIC COUPLING

In our study of networks we have made extensive use of the concept of two-terminal elements called terminal pairs. All the networks so far studied have been distinguished by one common feature, namely, that their elements are connected to each other in such a manner that between any two nodes of the network there exists an uninterrupted path made of

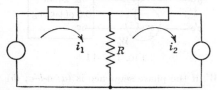

FIG. 18-1. Two meshes which are coupled conductively through a resistance.

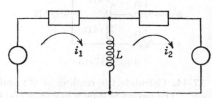

FIG. 18-2. Two meshes which are coupled conductively through an inductance.

network elements. The nodes and meshes of such networks are said to be coupled together by "conduction." The equilibrium equations of the coupled networks are in the form of "simultaneous," or "coupled," equations. When we say that the coupling between two meshes is through conduction, we mean that the mutual impedance between meshes

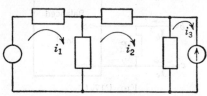

FIG. 18-3. Meshes 1 and 3 are coupled "indirectly" through conduction.

consists of passive elements which are shared by those two meshes. Thus in Fig. 18-1 meshes 1 and 2 are coupled by means of the resistance R and are said to be resistively coupled. In Fig. 18-2 meshes 1 and 2 are coupled inductively through conduction. In Fig. 18-3 meshes 1 and 3 are coupled (indirectly) through conduction because each of these two meshes shares an element with mesh 2 (although not the same element).

Now at the outset of this book we stated that the purpose of circuit analysis is to provide "models" of the basic electromagnetic field problems. In this chapter we shall study the circuit representation of the transfer of energy from one region of space to another through a magnetic field, a problem we have so far ignored. In circuit analysis this

586

phenomenon is represented by a two-terminal-pair network called "mutual inductance." Two loops coupled by a mutual inductance are said to be coupled by induction. In contrast to coupling through conduction (where two loops share a branch), with coupling through induction there is no common element between the two coupled loops (either directly or indirectly).

18-1. Mutual Inductance. In Chap. 1 we mentioned that, if a charge is accelerated in one region of space, a force will be exerted on charges located in other regions. From this we concluded that, when a charge moves with nonuniform velocity, an electric field will be established all over space, owing to the acceleration of this charge. To say that a charge moves with nonuniform velocity in space is analogous in circuit language to saying that $d^2q/dt^2 = di/dt$ is not zero in a terminal pair. Therefore, when a current i flows in a terminal pair such that di/dt is not zero, in addition to the magnetic energy stored in the space and given by $\frac{1}{2}Li^2$ we have to account for the electric field intensity established in other regions of space. This phenomenon is accounted for by introducing a dependent source in one terminal pair to represent the effect of the variation of the current in another terminal pair.

In saying that a current $i_1(t)$ flows in a terminal pair we have implicitly assumed that there exists a closed path (circuit) through which the current flows. The magnetic energy associated with the flow of current in this path is represented by an inductance L_1. The reader is reminded that this inductance represents the magnetic energy associated with the "entire closed path" in which $i_1(t)$ flows, and therefore L_1 is a property of a closed path, although it is symbolically shown in a "lump" by a terminal pair. Any path of current will also have a resistance R_1. We may assume that the current i_1 is caused by a voltage source $v(t)$ as shown in Fig. 18-4a. For convenience of reference, we shall call the closed path of Fig. 18-4a, which includes the source, the "primary." Now consider another closed path, which need not, to begin with, contain any material medium and may be thought of as a closed line drawn through space. We shall call this closed path the "secondary."

Because of the variations of i_1 in the primary, an electric field will exist at every point in the secondary. In conformity with the circuit concept we shall lump the whole effect of this electric field around the secondary (the line integral of the electric-field intensity around the closed path) into a dependent voltage source. Theoretical considerations, as well as experimental evidence, show that the waveform of this dependent voltage source is proportional to di_1/dt and that the constant of proportionality depends on the "geometry" of the primary and secondary paths. The proportionality constant is called the *mutual inductance* between the two paths and is designated by letter M. Thus the effect of variation of i_1 in a primary as observed in the secondary will be accounted for by a dependent source $v_{i_2} = M(di_1/dt)$ as shown in Fig. 18-4b. This voltage is called the *voltage induced in the secondary due to i_1 in the primary*. Although the voltages pL_1i_1 or R_1i_1 can also be represented as dependent sources, we do not choose to do so at this time.

In Fig. 18-4b we have not as yet shown a closed circuit, but only the induced voltage in the form of a dependent source. Suppose that the secondary path was such that a current could flow in it. Then, because of the induced voltage v_{i_2}, a current i_2 will flow in the secondary path. The magnetic energy associated with i_2 flowing in the secondary is accounted for by associating an inductance L_2 with this path. Similarly

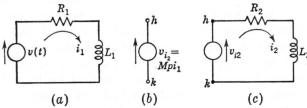

(a)   (b)   (c)

FIG. 18-4. Circuit interpretation of mutual inductance. (a) Current in a mesh. (b) Dependent source between two terminals not in the mesh of i_1, induced by i_1. (c) The energy transferred to the circuit elements in mesh 2 represents the energy which is transferred through the magnetic field.

a resistance R_2 must account for the dissipation of electromagnetic energy into heat.

Thus, to a good degree of approximation, the secondary path can be represented by a series connection of the dependent source v_{i_2}, R_2, and L_2, as shown in Fig. 18-4c. In this figure the reference arrow of i_2 is drawn arbitrarily from h to k through the R_2-L_2 combination. (We could have chosen the opposite direction if we wished.) Because a time-varying current i_2 flows in the secondary, an electric field will be created at every point of the primary. The effect of this field must be represented in the primary by a dependent voltage source whose waveform will be proportional to di_2/dt. The constant of proportionality will depend on the geometry of the two paths. Theoretical and experimental considerations show that this constant is the same M as discussed above. Therefore, to account for the effect of variation of i_2, we include a dependent source $v_{i_1} = M(di_2/dt)$ in the primary.

Coefficient of Coupling, k. We have said that the value of the mutual inductance between two paths (circuits) depends on the geometry of these paths. We remember that the inductance of each path, L_1 and L_2, also depended on the geometry of the individual paths. Analytical as well as experimental studies show that the value of M between two circuits is related to the inductances of those circuits, L_1 and L_2, through the relation

$$M = k \sqrt{L_1 L_2} \qquad (18\text{-}1)$$

where k is dimensionless and depends again on the geometry of the paths. In the following paragraphs we shall show that $|k| \leq 1$. The factor k in Eq. (18-1) is called the coupling coefficient of the two paths. The unit of mutual inductance is the same as the unit of inductance (the henry in the mks system). From Eq. (18-1) it is seen that the mutual inductance presupposes the inductive property of the two paths.

The energy-storing characteristic of a circuit in a magnetic field is designated by the symbol associated with L. Since mutual inductance

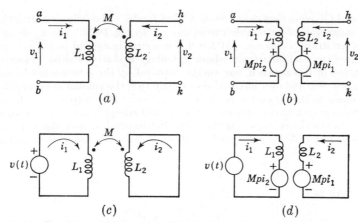

FIG. 18-5. (a) Circuit symbol for mutual inductance between two paths which have self-inductances L_1 and L_2. (b) The assumed current directions together with the reference dots in (a) result in the indicated polarities for the two compensating sources which represent the effect of mutual inductance. (c) Circuit used to study the range of values of k. (d) Circuit of (c) with compensating sources used to represent the effect of mutual inductance.

represents transfer of energy through a magnetic field, the symbol chosen for mutual inductance is, by convention, made up of symbols for the inductances of the primary and the secondary.

Symbol and Polarity of Mutual Inductance. Once we have chosen reference directions for the currents i_1 and i_2, the reference directions for the compensating sources pMi_1 and pMi_2 must conform to the geometry of the paths of the current.

In circuit diagrams the information about the geometry of the two paths is shown by "polarity dots" (or other marks such as $\pm$) on the inductances associated with the paths. The conventional symbol of mutual inductance between two paths of current whose inductances are L_1 and L_2 is shown in Fig. 18-5a. In this figure the dots imply that dependent sources are in series with L_1 and L_2 in such a manner that, with no current in L_2, the voltage of its dotted point with respect to its undotted point is equal to Mpi_1, where i_1 is the current whose reference arrow goes from the dotted point to the undotted point in L_1. A similar relationship is understood for the voltage across L_1 when there is no current flowing through it. This interpretation is shown in Fig. 18-5b. It is seen that in the explicit representation of Fig. 18-5b the reference directions for the dependent sources are obtained exactly in the manner described above. In Fig. 18-5b the dependent source Mpi_2 represents contribution to the voltage v_{ab} due to the magnetic coupling between the paths represented by L_1 and L_2. Similarly Mpi_1 represents the contribution to v_{hk} due to this magnetic coupling.

Proof that Coupling Coefficient Cannot Exceed Unity. The following analysis shows that the magnitude of k can never exceed unity. In Fig. 18-5c, $v(t)$ is a voltage source with any arbitrary waveform. At $t = 0$ this source is applied to the primary of a (deenergized) mutual inductance whose secondary is short-circuited. Since there is no resistance in this network, any energy supplied by the source must be stored in the magnetic field and over any period of time 0 to t_1 the amount of energy delivered by the source to the network must be nonnegative. This is true since the network itself is passive and, having started with no stored energy, cannot deliver an amount of energy to the source exceeding the value it has received from the source. With reference to Fig. 18-5c the energy delivered by the source to the network, in time zero to t_1, is

$$w(t_1) = \int_0^{t_1} vi_1 \, dt \tag{18-2}$$

From Fig. 18-5d

$$v = L_1 \frac{di_1}{dt} + M \frac{di_2}{dt} \tag{18-2a}$$

$$M \frac{di_1}{dt} = -L_2 \frac{di_2}{dt} \tag{18-2b}$$

Substituting for di_2/dt from Eq. (18-2b) in Eq. (18-2a), we have

$$v = L_1 \frac{d}{dt} i_1 - \frac{M^2}{L_2} \frac{d}{dt} i_1 = \frac{1}{L_2} (L_1 L_2 - M^2) \frac{d}{dt} i_1 \tag{18-2c}$$

Substituting for v from Eq. (18-2c) in Eq. (18-2), we have

$$\begin{aligned}
w(t_1) &= \int_0^{t_1} \left[\frac{1}{L_2} (L_1 L_2 - M^2) \frac{d}{dt} i_1 \right] i_1 \, dt \\
&= \frac{L_1 L_2 - M^2}{L_2} \int_{i_1=0}^{i_1=i_1(t_1)} i_1 \, di_1 \\
&= \frac{L_1 L_2 - M^2}{2L_2} [i_1(t_1)]^2
\end{aligned}$$

Since $w(t_1)$ cannot be negative and $[i_1(t_1)]^2$ is always positive,

$$L_1 L_2 - M^2 = L_1 L_2 (1 - k^2) \geq 0 \qquad k^2 \leq 1$$

which proves that the magnitude of k is less than or equal to unity.

Mutual Inductance as a Two-port. A study of Fig. 18-5*b* shows that the two equations representing the mutual inductance of Fig. 18-5*a* are

$$v_1 = pL_1i_1 + pMi_2 = z_{11}i_1 + z_{12}i_2$$
$$v_2 = pMi_1 + pL_2i_2 = z_{21}i_1 + z_{22}i_2$$

Recalling the definition of a two-port (two-terminal pair) from Chap. 16, we observe that a mutual inductance can be considered a two-port defined by the above equations.

18-2. Series Connection of Mutual Inductance. The terminals of the two-port representing a mutual inductance can be connected in different

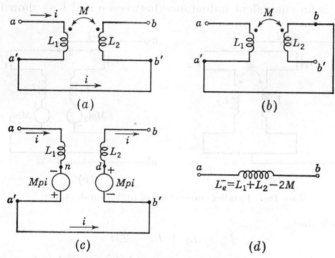

Fig. 18-6. (*a, b*) Series connection of mutual inductance. (*c*) Circuit of (*a*) with compensating sources representing the effect of mutual inductance. (*d*) Equivalent inductance between terminals *a-b* for the circuit of (*a*).

manners, changing the two-port into a terminal pair. Such connections are referred to as series or parallel connections of mutual inductance and will be discussed in this and the following articles.

If one of the output terminals of the two-port representing a mutual inductance is connected to a terminal in the input side, as shown in Fig. 18-6*a* and *b*, then the resulting circuit is a terminal pair. This terminal pair behaves as an inductance, whose value will now be found. In Fig. 18-6*c* the effect of mutual inductance is shown explicitly by compensating sources for the connection of Fig. 18-6*a*. Since both the input and output currents are the same $i(t)$, the waveforms of the two compensating sources will be identical and given by $pMi(t)$. The polarity of the compensating sources is determined by observing that in L_1 the reference arrow of current goes *from* the dotted point *through* L_1; therefore, with no current in L_2, pMi is the voltage of the dotted point of L_2 (point *b*) with respect to its undotted point (point b').   But, with no current in L_2, $v_{bd} = 0$, and $v_{bb'} = v_{db'}$.   Therefore $pMi = v_{db}$, as shown in Fig. 18-6c.

In L_2 the reference arrow of the current points *through* L_2 *to* the dotted point; therefore, with no current in L_1, $-pMi$ is the voltage of the dotted point of L_1 (point a) with respect to its undotted point (point a').   With no current in L_1, $-pMi = v_{aa'} = v_{na'}$ or $v_{a'n} = pMi$, as shown in Fig. 18-6c.

Now if, in Fig. 18-6c, v_{ab} is expressed in terms of i, we shall have

$$v_{ab} = pL_1i - pMi - pMi + pL_2i$$
$$= p(L_1 + L_2 - 2M)i = pL_e^-i$$

where L_e^- is an equivalent inductance between a and b as shown in Fig.

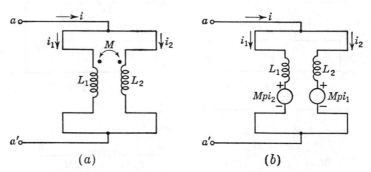

$$(a) \qquad\qquad (b)$$

Fig. 18-7. Parallel connection of mutual inductance.

18-6d, such that

$$L_e^- = L_1 + L_2 - 2M$$

In this case the two undotted terminals of the mutual inductance were connected together.   If a dotted point and undotted point were connected as shown in Fig. 18-6b, the resulting equivalent inductance would be

$$L_e^+ = L_1 + L_2 + 2M$$

The reader should verify this relationship.

The two series connections are useful because they furnish a means of measuring mutual inductance between coils.   We need measure only the equivalent inductances for each connection; then

$$\tfrac{1}{4}(L_e^+ - L_e^-) = M$$

or, if the measurements are carried out in the sinusoidal steady state,

$$\tfrac{1}{4}(\omega L_e^+ - \omega L_e^-) = \omega M \equiv X_m$$

where X_m is called the *mutual reactance* of M at the radian frequency ω (see Prob. 18-1).

In another application two coils are made so that the mutual inductance between them can be adjusted.   The series connection is then used to make a variable inductor.

18-3. Parallel Connection of Mutual Inductance.   When the output-input terminals of the mutual inductance are connected as shown in Fig. 18-7a, the connection is referred to as a parallel connection.   In this case, from the explicit representation of Fig. 18-7b we have

$$v_{aa'} = pL_1i_1 + pMi_2$$
$$v_{aa'} = pMi_1 + pL_2i_2$$

Solving for i_1 and i_2 and adding, we have

$$i_1 + i_2 = \frac{L_1 + L_2 - 2M}{p(L_1L_2 - M^2)} \, v_{aa'} = i$$

$$v_{aa'} = p \frac{L_1L_2 - M^2}{L_1 + L_2 - 2M} \, i = pL_\pi^+ i$$

where L_π^+ is the equivalent parallel inductance and is given by

$$L_\pi^+ = \frac{L_1L_2 - M^2}{L_1 + L_2 - 2M}$$

If a dotted point were connected to an undotted point, the resulting equivalent inductance would be

$$L_\pi^- = \frac{L_1L_2 - M^2}{L_1 + L_2 + 2M}$$

The reader should verify this expression.

18-4. Mutual Inductance in Multielement Networks.   Since the compensating sources which are used to represent the effect of mutual inductance are dependent on the currents, the natural method for the formulation of the equilibrium equation of circuits with mutual inductance is the method of mesh currents.   If meshes 1 and 2 are coupled through the mutual inductance M_{12}, then the induced voltages are

$$v_{i_2} = \pm pM_{12}i_1 \qquad \text{and} \qquad v_{i_1} = \pm pM_{12}i_2$$

where the choice of sign depends on the relative location of the dots. Consequently mutual inductance between meshes 1 and 2 will introduce the term $\pm pM_{12}$ into the mesh impedances Z_{12} and Z_{21}.   Mutual inductance within a mesh will also affect the mesh impedance of such a mesh. An illustrative example will serve to clarify these statements.

Example 18-1.   Let it be required to formulate the mesh equations for the circuit shown in Fig. 18-8.   Note that in this circuit mesh 1 is magnetically coupled to mesh 2 through both M_1 and M_2 and that there is magnetic coupling within mesh 1 due to M_1.   The mesh equations for this two-mesh circuit read

$$Z_{11}(p)i_1 + Z_{12}(p)i_2 = v_1(t)$$
$$Z_{21}(p)i_1 + Z_{22}(p)i_2 = -v_2(t)$$

To find the mesh impedances, we use the definitions for mesh impedance given in Chap. 16, so that the effect of mutual inductance can be taken into account correctly.

$Z_{11}(p)i_1 =$ sum of voltages in mesh 1 due to i_1 ($i_2 \equiv 0$), added in the direction of mesh 1

$Z_{12}(p)i_2 =$ sum of voltages in mesh 1 due to i_2 ($i_1 \equiv 0$), added in the direction of mesh 1

$Z_{21}(p)i_1 =$ sum of voltages in mesh 2 due to i_1 ($i_2 \equiv 0$), added in the direction of mesh 2

$Z_{22}(p)i_2 =$ sum of voltages in mesh 2 due to i_2 ($i_1 \equiv 0$), added in the direction of mesh 2

To apply these definitions, it is convenient to redraw the circuit, replacing the effect of the mutual inductances by compensating sources. This circuit is shown in Fig.

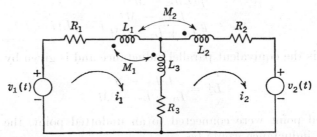

FIG. 18-8. A two-mesh circuit in which the coupling between the two meshes is partially by conduction and partially by induction.

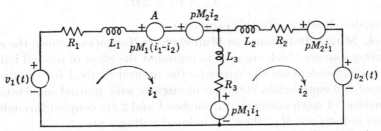

FIG. 18-9. Equivalent to Fig. 18-8. The effect of the mutual inductances is represented by compensating sources.

18-9. Note that the source A depends on the branch current $i_1 - i_2$ which flows in L_3. To obtain the mesh impedances, we now apply the definitions given above for the self- and mutual impedances. If $i_2 \equiv 0$, then in mesh 1

$$R_1 i_1 + pL_1 i_1 + pM_1 i_1 + pL_3 i_1 + pM_1 i_1 + R_3 i_1 = \Sigma \text{ voltages in mesh 1}$$

Hence $\qquad\qquad Z_{11}(p) = R_1 + R_3 + p(L_1 + L_3 + 2M_1)$

This result could also have been obtained by noting that the equivalent series inductance in mesh 1 is $L_1 + L_3 + 2M_1$ (M_2 has no effect, since we set $i_2 \equiv 0$).

If $i_1 \equiv 0$, then in mesh 1

$$-pL_3 i_2 + pM_2 i_2 - R_3 i_2 - pM_1 i_2 = \Sigma \text{ voltages in mesh 1}$$

so that $\qquad\qquad Z_{12}(p) = -R_3 - p(L_3 - M_2 + M_1)$

If $i_2 \equiv 0$, then in mesh 2

$$-R_3 i_1 - pL_3 i_1 + pM_2 i_1 - pM_1 i_1 = \Sigma \text{ voltages in mesh 2}$$

so that
$$Z_{21}(p) = Z_{12}(p)$$

Finally in mesh 2, if $i_1 \equiv 0$,

$$(R_2 + R_3)i_2 + p(L_2 + L_3) = \Sigma \text{ voltages in mesh 2}$$

so that
$$Z_{22}(p) = R_2 + R_3 + (pL_2 + pL_3)$$

The mesh equations for the circuit of Fig. 18-8 therefore read

$$[(R_1 + R_3) + p(L_1 + L_3 + 2M_1)]i_1 + [-R_3 - p(L_3 + M_1 - M_2)]i_2 = v_1(t)$$
$$[-R_3 - p(L_3 + M_1 - M_2)]i_1 + [R_2 + R_3 + p(L_2 + L_3)]i_2 = -v_2(t)$$

18-5. The Linear Transformer.

A two-mesh circuit in which the coupling between meshes is entirely magnetic is shown in Fig. 18-10. Such a circuit is called a linear-transformer circuit. We shall use the term *linear* because, in practice, such circuits are often representations of coils coupled together through an iron core. In such cases the equivalent representation is an approximation, since the inductance of iron-cored coils is a function of the current through the coils. In Fig. 18-10

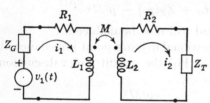

FIG. 18-10. Linear-transformer circuit.

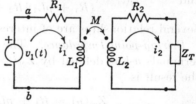

FIG. 18-11. Linear transformer with ideal source and arbitrary loading.

it is assumed that the elements are linear (such circuits are sometimes called "air-core" transformers). In the illustration R_1 and L_1 can be interpreted as the equivalent circuit of the coil which is magnetically coupled to a second coil represented by R_2 and L_2. Z_T is a load impedance, and the series combination of Z_G and $v_1(t)$ forms the (Thévenin) equivalent circuit of a nonideal source. For the assumed current directions relative to the dots the mesh equations are

$$Z_{11}(p)i_1 + Z_{12}(p)i_2 = v_1(t)$$
$$Z_{21}(p)i_1 + Z_{22}(p)i_2 = 0$$

where $\quad Z_{11}(p) = Z_G + R_1 + pL_1 \qquad Z_{22}(p) = Z_T + R_2 + pL_2$
$$Z_{12}(p) = Z_{21}(p) = -pM$$

In the sinusoidal steady state, if $v_1(t)$ is represented by the phasor $\mathbf{V}_1$, the complex mesh equations are

$$(R_1 + j\omega L_1 + \mathbf{Z}_G)\mathbf{I}_1 \qquad\qquad + (-j\omega M)\mathbf{I}_2 = \mathbf{V}_1$$
$$(-j\omega M)\mathbf{I}_1 + (R_2 + j\omega L_2 + \mathbf{Z}_T)\mathbf{I}_2 = 0$$

To study some relationships in the linear transformer, it is convenient to consider the circuit shown in Fig. 18-11, where a source $v_1(t)$ is applied directly to the terminals of the coil represented by R_1 and L_1. The results which we shall obtain can be applied when a nonideal source is impressed at these terminals, because the function $v_1(t)$ can then be reinterpreted as the sum of the ideal source and the compensating source which accounts for the internal impedance of the nonideal source. At present, however, we are concerned with the voltage-current relationship of the transformer considered as a two-port, so that $v_1(t)$ will be treated as an ideal source.

For the circuit of Fig. 18-11 the mesh equations are

$$(R_1 + pL_1)i_1 \qquad\qquad - pMi_2 = v_1(t)$$
$$-pMi_1 + [R_2 + pL_2 + Z_T(p)]i_2 = 0$$

so that in operational form

$$i_1(t) = \frac{R_2 + pL_2 + Z_T}{(R_1 + pL_1)[R_2 + pL_2 + Z_T(p)] - p^2M^2}\, v_1(t)$$

and $\qquad i_2(t) = \dfrac{pM}{(R_1 + pL_1)[R_2 + pL_2 + Z_T(p)] - p^2M^2}\, v_1(t)$

Several relationships are of interest and will now be deduced.

Driving-point Impedance. The operational driving-point impedance at terminals *a-b* is defined by $Z_{ab}i_1 = v_1$. For the circuit under discussion the result is

$$Z_{ab}(p) = R_1 + pL_1 + \frac{-p^2M^2}{R_2 + pL_2 + Z_T(p)}$$

We note that $Z_{ab} = Z_{11} - Z_{12}{}^2/Z_{22}$; if $i_2 \equiv 0$, $Z_{ab} = Z_{11}$. The term $-Z_{12}{}^2/Z_{22}$ which adds to Z_{11} is referred to as the *impedance of the secondary reflected into the primary.* For the sinusoidal steady state the complex driving-point impedance is

$$\mathbf{Z}_{ab} = R_1 + j\omega L_1 + \frac{\omega^2M^2}{R_2 + j\omega L_2 + \mathbf{Z}_T}$$

We note in passing that for "small" values of ωM this quantity depends only very slightly on $\mathbf{Z}_T$, the load impedance.

Current Ratio. From the equation of mesh 2 the ratio of the currents in operational form is

$$\frac{i_2}{i_1} = \frac{pM}{R_2 + pL_2 + Z_T(p)}$$

Voltage Ratio. The ratio of the voltage across the load impedance to the input voltage is, in operational form,

$$\frac{v_2}{v_1} = \frac{i_2 Z_T}{v_1} = \frac{pMZ_T(p)}{(R_1 + pL_1)(R_2 + pL_2 + Z_T) - p^2M^2}$$

18-6. The Ideal Transformer. A two-port shown in Fig. 18-12a, such that

$$v_2(t) = nv_1(t)$$

$$i_2(t) = \frac{1}{n} i_1(t)$$

where n is a positive number, is called an ideal transformer. If n is larger than unity, the transformer is called an ideal step-up transformer; otherwise it is called a step-down transformer.

If we wish to represent an ideal transformer by a mutual inductance, as shown in Fig. 18-12b, then we begin with the defining equations of

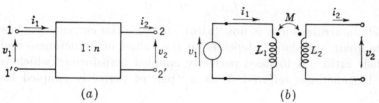

(a)   (b)

FIG. 18-12. (a) Symbol for an ideal transformer.   (b) Pertinent to the representation of an ideal transformer by mutual inductance.

mutual inductance,

$$v_1 = L_1 p i_1 - M p i_2$$

$$-v_2 = -M p i_1 + L_2 p i_2$$

Imposing the conditions $v_2 = nv_1 \quad i_2 = \frac{1}{n} i_1$

it is seen that with a source v_1 applied to the input of the two port, then with open-circuited output i_1 must be zero since i_1 is made proportional to i_2 (and for open circuit at the output port $i_2 \equiv 0$). But from the defining equations for mutual inductance we have $v_1 = L_1 p i_1$ when i_2 is zero. It follows that L_1 must be infinite so that i_1 be zero with nonzero v_1.

With a similar argument it can be shown that L_2 must also be infinite and the coefficient of coupling must be unity.

Those readers who are familiar with transformer theory will note that, if L_1 is infinite, then the magnetizing current will be zero and, since we have not included any resistance in the circuit representation of the ideal transformer, the losses must also be zero, resulting in a fixed ratio between the currents and voltages at the input and output sides of the ideal transformer.

Lossless Transformer. The transformer of Fig. 18-11 is lossless if $R_1 = R_2 = 0$, but is not ideal. For the lossless transformer the driving-point impedance, and the voltage and current ratios, by the results of the preceding articles, are

$$Z_{ab}(p) = pL_1 + \frac{-p^2 M^2}{pL_2 + Z_T(p)}$$

Current ratio: $\dfrac{i_2}{i_1} = \dfrac{pM}{pL_2 + Z_T(p)}$

Voltage ratio: $\dfrac{v_2}{v_1} = \dfrac{pM Z_T(p)}{p^2(L_1 L_2 - M^2) + pL_1 Z_T(p)}$

Perfectly Coupled and Lossless Transformer. A transformer is perfectly coupled and lossless (but not ideal) if

$$R_1 = R_2 = 0$$

and
$$L_1 L_2 - M^2 = 0$$

Such an arrangement is not "ideal" because the current ratio, as well as the input impedance, depends on the values of inductances and not on their ratio. A lossless, perfectly coupled transformer which is not ideal is sometimes referred to as a "pair of perfectly coupled lossless coils."

The three significant expressions for this case are

$$Z_{ab}(p) = \frac{pL_1 Z_T}{pL_2 + Z_T}$$

$$\frac{i_2}{i_1} = \frac{p\sqrt{L_1 L_2}}{pL_2 + Z_T}$$

$$\frac{v_2}{v_1} = \frac{p\sqrt{L_1 L_2}}{pL_1} = \sqrt{\frac{L_2}{L_1}}$$

Note that for the perfectly coupled lossless transformer the voltage ratio is independent of the waveform.

Ideal Transformer. We have stated in effect that an ideal transformer is a lossless, perfectly coupled transformer whose inductances are infinite. To obtain its properties, we therefore take the following limits:

$$L_2 \to \infty \qquad L_1 \to \infty \qquad \text{but } \frac{L_1}{L_2} \to \text{finite}$$

If we examine the operational expressions which were deduced for the preceding cases, then the limits stated above will give $Z_T(p)$ negligible when compared with pL_2. In the sinusoidal steady state this means that the condition $|Z_T| \ll |j\omega L_2|$ will approximate the conditions for an ideal transformer if the resistance and coupling conditions are approximately fulfilled. Theoretically, however, the two-port "ideal transformer" is defined with infinite inductance because then the expressions which are to be deduced will be independent of the impressed waveforms.

For the ideal transformer, the driving-point impedance and the voltage and current ratios are seen to be

Current ratio: $\qquad \dfrac{i_2}{i_1} = \sqrt{\dfrac{L_1}{L_2}} = \dfrac{1}{n}$

Voltage ratio: $\qquad \dfrac{v_2}{v_1} = \sqrt{\dfrac{L_2}{L_1}} = n$

Driving-point impedance: $Z_{ab}(p) = \dfrac{L_1}{L_2} Z_T(p) = \dfrac{1}{n^2} Z_T(p)$

(Note that $v_2 i_2 = v_1 i_1$.)   The symbol shown in Fig. 18-13 will be used to represent an ideal transformer.   The transformer in this illustration is marked with the symbol $n_1 : n_2 (= 1/n)$. From the above it is seen that

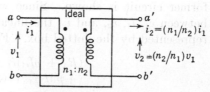

$$\frac{n_1}{n_2} = \sqrt{\frac{L_1}{L_2}} = \frac{1}{n}$$

To have the polarity dots on the ideal transformer symbol of Fig. 18-13 consistent with the definition of Fig. 18-12a, it is necessary that the reference arrows for both voltages and both currents be as shown in the two figures.   However if in Fig. 18-13 the reference arrow for v_1 is chosen in the opposite direction to that shown, that is, if $v_1 = v_{ba}$ instead of v_{ab}, then $v_2 = v_{a'b'} = -(n_2/n_1)v_1$.   Analogous statements apply to the reference arrows for currents.

FIG. 18-13. Another symbol for an ideal transformer. This symbol is intended to be suggestive of the use of mutual inductance to achieve the properties of an ideal transformer.

Example 18-2.   In the circuit shown in Fig. 18-14 determine Z_{ab}, I_1, and I_2.

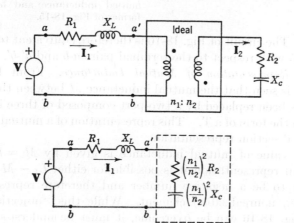

FIG. 18-14. Circuit to illustrate calculation with ideal transformer.

Solution. The driving-point impedance at the input terminals of the ideal transformer is

$$\mathbf{Z}_{a'b} = (R_2 + jX_c)\left(\frac{n_1}{n_2}\right)^2$$

Hence

$$\mathbf{Z}_{ab} = R_1 + \left(\frac{n_1}{n_2}\right)^2 R_2 + jX_L + jX_c\left(\frac{n_1}{n_2}\right)^2$$

and

$$\mathbf{I}_1 = \frac{\mathbf{V}}{\mathbf{Z}_{ab}} \qquad \mathbf{I}_2 = -\frac{n_1}{n_2}\mathbf{I}_1$$

18-7. Equivalent Circuit for the Nonideal Transformer. In this article the mesh equations of a nonideal transformer will be studied for the purpose of arriving at several equivalent circuits. In Fig. 18-15 a transformer circuit is shown. Since we are interested in the relationships between v_1, i_1, v_2, and i_2, the linear transformer is shown as a two-port represented by the dotted box. For this circuit the mesh equations are

$$(R_1 + pL_1)i_1 + (+pM)i_2 = v_1 \qquad (18\text{-}3a)$$
$$(+pM)i_1 + (R_2 + pL_2)i_2 = v_2 \qquad (18\text{-}3b)$$

If we have Eqs. (18-3a) and (18-3b), *then the circuit shown in Fig. 18-16 can be drawn to fit these equations* without regard to the original circuit since we are concerned only with voltages and currents on the outside

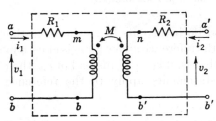

FIG. 18-15. A (nonideal) transformer as a two-port.

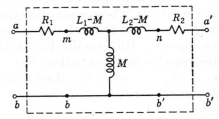

FIG. 18-16. T-section representation of mutual inductance and of the transformer of Fig. 18-15.

of the box. The circuit of Fig. 18-16 is therefore equivalent to the circuit of Fig. 18-15 with respect to the terminal pairs a-b and a'-b'.

T-section Representation of Mutual Inductance. From Figs. 18-15 and 18-16 it is seen that the mutual inductance M between the terminals m-b, n-b' has been replaced by a two-port composed of three inductances connected in the form of a T. This representation of a mutual inductance is called its T-section representation.

Since the value of mutual inductance is given by $M = k(L_1L_2)^{\frac{1}{2}}$, in the T-section representation it is possible for either $L_1 - M$ or $L_2 - M$ (Fig. 18-16) to be a negative number and therefore represent a nonphysical (i.e., nonrealizable) element. While this "objection" to the circuit of Fig. 18-16 can be overcome, it must be understood that the circuit in question is *on paper* equivalent to the original circuit, with respect to the two pairs of terminals, because it satisfies the same mesh equations as the circuit of Fig. 18-15.

A second remark concerning the equivalent circuit of Fig. 18-16 is necessary. In the original circuit of the transformer the input terminals a-b are isolated from the output terminals a'-b' because the coupling between the meshes is entirely by induction. In the equivalent circuit of Fig. 18-16 the coupling between the two meshes is through the inductance of value M so that the isolating property of the transformer has not been preserved.

The two objections mentioned above can be overcome (artificially) by manipulating the mesh equations (18-3a) and (18-3b) and using an ideal transformer.

Let us start by supposing that $L_1 - M$ is negative. Then $L_2 - M$ is positive because M is at most the geometric mean between L_1 and L_2. Let us choose a number a, less than unity, so that $L_1 - aM$ is positive. The mesh equations (18-3a) and (18-3b) may now be written as follows:

$$(R_1 + pL_1)i_1 + paM\,\frac{i_2}{a} = v_1 \qquad (18\text{-}4a)$$

$$(paM)i_1 + (R_2a^2 + pL_2a^2)\,\frac{i_2}{a} = av_2 \qquad (18\text{-}4b)$$

Equation (18-4a) is identical to Eq. (18-3a), and Eq. (18-4b) is a times Eq. (18-3b). Note now that the following four quantities are related in Eqs. (18-4): i_1, v_1, i_2/a, and av_2. We can therefore interpret the mesh equations (18-4) as representing the circuit shown in Fig. 18-17a. If we wish to make an equivalent circuit in which the current i_2 and the voltage v_2 appear, an ideal transformer whose turns ratio is a can be introduced. Hence with respect to the two terminal pairs a-b and a'-b' the circuit shown in Fig. 18-17b is equivalent for all values of the "number" a. Note that the "number" a can be chosen so that each element within the dotted box in Fig. 18-17b is physically realizable and that the use of the ideal transformer preserves the isolating property of the actual transformer.

The most popular value chosen for the "number" a is the turns ratio which the actual transformer has. Then, if

$$a = \left(\frac{L_1}{L_2}\right)^{\frac{1}{2}}$$

we have $aM = (L_1/L_2)^{\frac{1}{2}}k(L_1L_2)^{\frac{1}{2}} = kL_1 \le L_1$, and the equivalent circuit contains the elements with values as shown in Fig. 18-18. Note that, for $k = 1$, $R_1 = R_2 = 0$, and L_1 infinite, only the ideal transformer is left. The arrangements of the elements R_1, $L_1(1 - k)$, R_2L_1/L_2 in Fig. 18-18

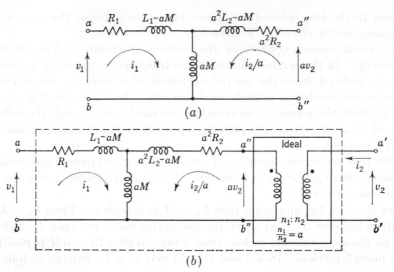

FIG. 18-17. (*a*) The mesh equations for this two-port are the same as the equation for the two-port of Fig. 18-15, but the current and voltage in the second mesh do not correspond. (*b*) The two-port shown is equivalent to the two-port of Fig. 18-15 at the accessible terminal pairs *a-b* and *a'-b'*.

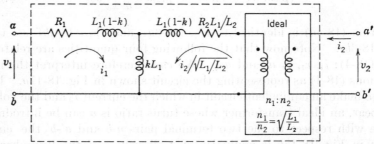

FIG. 18-18. In this equivalent circuit of a (nonideal) transformer the elements are physically realizable, and the isolating property of the transformer has been retained.

therefore conveniently represent the "imperfections" of the actual transformer.

18-8. Adjustable Circuits with Mutual Inductance. Introduction. In Chap. 13 it was shown how transform network functions are related to sinusoidal steady-state response and complete response through the pole-zero diagram. In Chap. 15 this relationship was explored for simple series, parallel, and series-parallel R-L-C circuits. In the remaining parts of this chapter the frequency response of circuits with mutual inductance is discussed. In addition the influence of adjusting the coefficient of coupling is studied. The problem is formulated as follows: In a two-mesh network the meshes are coupled through mutual inductance *only*; how does variation of the coefficient of coupling affect the responses of the circuit, and what is the frequency response of certain commonly used networks? As the various circuits are studied, the possible applications will be pointed out. In general we observe that each voltage induced by magnetic coupling is proportional to the *rate of change* of a current. Hence, if a source which is the sum of a constant and a time function is impressed in mesh 1 of the circuit, the constant source, in the steady state, has no effect in mesh 2 since constant sources produce only constant steady-state currents.

To fix the basic idea, a pair of coupled inductors, represented by the circuit of Fig. 18-19a, are first studied. (Each inductor is represented as a series R-L circuit.) An ideal source is placed in series with R_1 and L_1 to form mesh 1; mesh 2 is left open. Since mesh 1 includes the only source in the circuit, it is referred to as the primary. Mesh 2 is the secondary. We shall study the transform voltage-gain function, which relates $v_2(t)$ to $v_1(t)$, and the transform transfer impedance, which relates $v_2(t)$ to $i_1(t)$. In the former case the source in the primary is an ideal voltage source; in the latter case it is an ideal current source.

Since the secondary is open, $i_2 \equiv 0$; hence $v_{i1} \equiv 0$. The effect of the mutual inductance is therefore represented by the single source $v_{i_2} = pMi_1$ as shown in Fig. 18-19b. From Fig. 18-19b we observe that $(pL_1 + R_1)i_1 = v_1$ so that

$$v_2 = \frac{pM}{pL_1 + R_1} v_1 = \frac{pk \sqrt{L_1 L_2}}{pL_1 + R_1} v_1 \tag{18-5}$$

or

$$v_2 = \sqrt{\frac{L_2}{L_1}} \frac{pk}{p + R_1/L_1} v_1 \tag{18-6}$$

The transform voltage gain is

$$H(s) = \sqrt{\frac{L_2}{L_1}} k \frac{s}{s + R_1/L_1}$$

It is convenient to study the ratio $H(s)/\sqrt{L_2/L_1}$ since $\sqrt{L_2/L_1}$ is the voltage gain of an ideal transformer. Thus

$$K(s) \equiv \frac{H(s)}{\sqrt{L_2/L_1}} = k \frac{s}{s + R_1/L_1}$$

Hence the coefficient of coupling influences only the scale factor; i.e., for any value $s = s_g$, $K(s)$ is proportional to k. This result is shown for $s_g = j\omega$ in Fig. 18-19c. The frequency-response curve is obtained from the pole-zero diagram of Fig. 18-19d: $K(s)$ has a zero at $s = 0$ and a pole at $s = -R_1/L_1$. Hence in terms of the indicated distances

$$K(j\omega) = k \frac{OG}{PG} \underline{/90° - \varphi_1}$$

The amplitude-response curve is seen to be zero at $\omega = 0$ and approaches k as $\omega \to \infty$. Analytically, let $x = \omega L_1/R_1$; then

$$\frac{H}{\sqrt{L_2/L_1}} = k \frac{x}{\sqrt{1 + x^2}}$$

This curve is shown in Fig. 18-19e. The corresponding phase response is

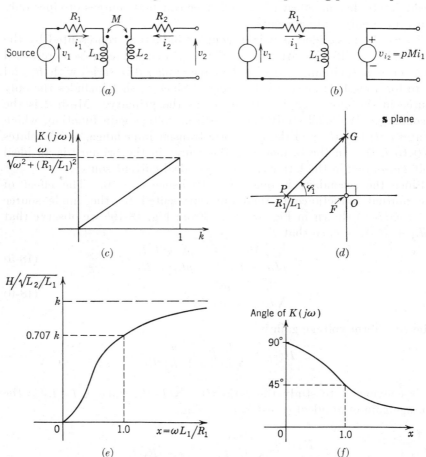

$$(a)$$

$$(b)$$

$$(c)$$

$$(d)$$

$$(e)$$

$$(f)$$

FIG. 18-19. (a) Circuit representation of a pair of magnetically coupled coils. (b) Equivalent circuit of (a) with secondary open-circuited. (c) Normalized open-circuit voltage gain as a function of coupling for the circuit of (a) in the sinusoidal steady state. (d) Pole-zero diagram for the transform voltage gain. (e) Amplitude response as a function of frequency. (f) Phase response as a function of frequency.

shown in Fig. 18-19f. We observe that this network may find application as a "high-pass filter." If the voltage source $v_1(t)$ is nonideal but is represented as the series combination of R_s–L_s–ideal voltage source, then the results obtained above are applicable, provided that R_1 includes R_s

and L_1 includes L_s.   The value of k must then be chosen (reduced) to give the correct value of M (see Prob. 18-21).

If terminals c-d are short-circuited and if the source is an ideal current source $i(t) = i_1(t)$, as shown in Fig. 18-20, then, from the mesh equation for mesh 2,

$$(R_2 + pL_2)i_2 = -pMi_1 \qquad (18\text{-}7)$$

Equation (18-7) is of the same form as (18-6); we observe that the frequency response for the current ratio I_2/I_1 in the short-circuit case is identical to the frequency response of the voltage ratio V_2/V_1 in the open-circuit case.   Thus the result shown in Fig. 18-19e is applicable to the current ratio if x is redefined as $\omega L_2/R_2$ and the current gain is normalized with respect to $\sqrt{L_1/L_2}$.

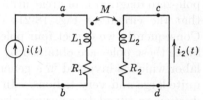

FIG. 18-20. Circuit of Fig. 18-19a with short-circuited secondary.

18-9. Introduction to Tuned Transformer Circuits.   In many applications of coupled inductors, capacitances appear across the input and output terminals as shown in Fig. 18-21c.   Either or both of these capacitances may appear in the circuit diagram to represent elements which have been placed into the actual circuit intentionally or to represent the effect of "stray capacitances" (e.g., due to wiring).   The frequency responses of the transfer functions which can be associated with such circuits (called "tuned transformer circuits") are of interest because these circuits find wide application as bandpass filters.

In the transmission of signals it is often necessary to design a two-port which has the following characteristics:

1. In a certain band of radian frequencies ω_1 to ω_2 all sinusoidal signals are to be passed with the *same* gain (or attenuation) and must suffer the same *time* delay.   Thus if an input is $v_1(t) = V_m \cos \omega t$, the output v_2 in that band is to be $v_2(t) = HV_m \cos [\omega(t - t_d)]$ where H and t_d are constants.   In terms of a complex transfer function this means that

$$\frac{\mathbf{V}_2(j\omega)}{\mathbf{V}_1(j\omega)} = H \underline{/-\omega t_d} \qquad \omega_1 < \omega < \omega_2$$

2. For frequencies outside of the band ω_1 to ω_2 it is desired that all sinusoids be attenuated (reduced in amplitude) as much as possible.

The reasons for the above requirements are discussed in Art. 19-17. In Fig. 19-20c an "ideal" bandpass-filter characteristic is shown.   In Art. 15-6 we discussed an example of a bandpass filter, namely, the series R-L-C circuit.   Comparison of Fig. 15-8a with Fig. 19-20c shows that in the R-L-C circuit the rate at which the amplitude response diminishes with frequency outside the passband (half power points), depends on the parameter Q_0. In the R-L-C circuit, therefore, if the radian resonant frequency ω_0 as well as the half power frequencies ω_1 and ω_2 are specified, then, since $Q_0 = \omega_0/(\omega_2 - \omega_1)$, we have no element which can be adjusted to "control" the attenuation outside the half power frequencies.

A tuned transformer circuit, such as the circuit shown in Fig. 18-21c, is one example of bandpass filters in which the required flexibility of adjustment is available and frequency-response curves of the shape shown in Fig. 18-27c can be obtained.

The principles which are used to study the frequency response of circuits are discussed in Chaps. 13 and 15. We recall that the use of the pole-zero diagram is of great utility in this connection. Now we observe that the circuit of Fig. 18-21c contains four energy-storing elements. Consequently we expect four poles to characterize its transfer functions. Since these poles are obtained by factoring a polynomial, the amount of labor which is involved in a general study of the circuit of Fig. 18-21c is quite large and very tedious. In this as in subsequent articles an introduction to tuned transformer circuits is presented; in this introduction certain simplifying assumptions concerning the relationship between the parameters is made. The use of these simplifying assumptions reduces the labor involved in the analysis and yet gives practical results because the assumed conditions are often (nearly) fulfilled.

The following analysis shows the necessity for optimizing certain network parameters to fulfill the above specifications. We start with the circuit shown in Fig. 18-21a, where a capacitance appears only across the "output" terminals. This circuit is called the "singly" tuned circuit. The sinusoidal steady-state conditions, using compensating sources, are shown in Fig. 18-21b. From mesh 2 we have

$$\frac{\mathbf{I}_2}{\mathbf{I}_1} = \frac{-j\omega M}{R_2 + j(\omega L_2 - 1/\omega C_2)}$$

and

$$\frac{\mathbf{V}_2}{\mathbf{I}_1} = \frac{-\mathbf{I}_2/j\omega C_2}{\mathbf{I}_1} = \frac{M/C_2}{R_2 + j(\omega L_2 - 1/\omega C_2)} \tag{18-8}$$

From Eq. (18-8) we conclude that, if an ideal current source is inserted in the primary, V_2 is a maximum at the frequency at which

$$\omega L_2 - \frac{1}{\omega C_2} = 0$$

independently of M. Thus $\mathbf{V}_2/\mathbf{I}_1 = M/R_2 C_2$ when $\omega^2 = 1/L_2 C_2$. At this frequency $V_2/I_1 = M/C_2 R_2$. Hence, if I_1 is kept constant (i.e., if the source is an ideal current source), the smallest possible value of R_2 and the largest possible value of M is "favorable." Once these have been obtained, V_2 is proportional to I_1. Now, if an ideal current source furnishes the current whose phasor is $\mathbf{I}$, it is possible to use a second

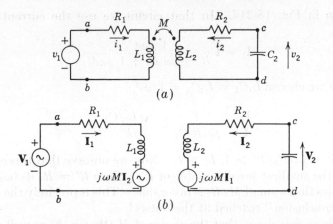

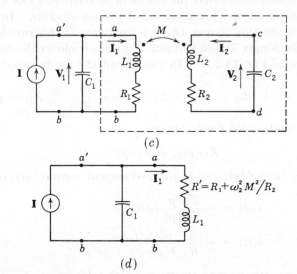

Fig. 18-21. (a) Singly tuned transformer circuit. (b) Circuit of (a) in the sinusoidal steady state. The effect of the mutual inductance is represented by the dependent sources. (c) Doubly tuned transformer circuit. (d) Equivalent circuit of the primary mesh of (c) at the resonant frequency of the secondary.

capacitance C_1 in the primary to increase I_1 above I, as shown in Fig. 18-21c. We shall now discuss the requirements for M and R_2 which with C_1 in the circuit would maximize V_2. We recall, from Art. 18-5, that

$$\mathbf{Z}_{ab} = R_1 + j\omega L_1 + \frac{\omega^2 M^2}{\mathbf{Z}_{22}}$$

and, in the present discussion ($\omega = 1/\sqrt{L_2 C_2} \equiv \omega_2$), $\mathbf{Z}_{22} = R_2$. Hence

$$\mathbf{Z}_{ab} = R' + j\omega_2 L_1 \qquad R' = R_1 + \frac{\omega_2{}^2 M^2}{R_2}$$

as shown in Fig. 18-21d. In that circuit we use the current-division formula,

$$\mathbf{I}_1 = \mathbf{I}\,\frac{1/j\omega_2 C_1}{R' + j\omega_2 L_1 + 1/j\omega_2 C_1}$$

Hence, if we choose $L_1 C_1 = L_2 C_2 = 1/\omega_2{}^2$,

$$\frac{\mathbf{I}_1}{\mathbf{I}} = \frac{1}{j\omega_2 R' C_1} = \frac{\sqrt{L_1/C_1}}{jR'}$$

so that, if $\sqrt{L_1/C_1}/R' > 1$, $I_1 > I$. Now we observe that this condition requires the smallest possible value of R'. Since $R' = R_1 + (\omega_2 M)^2/R_2$, this implies that a small M/R_2 is favorable. This is precisely the opposite of the "conclusion" reached at the outset!

This discussion shows that the choice of M (that is, k) as well as of the other circuit parameters for maximum V_2 is not obvious. In the articles below an introduction to quantitative treatment of this problem is given.

18-10. The Singly Tuned Circuit. In this article we discuss the singly tuned circuit of Fig. 18-22a. In this circuit the mesh impedances are

$$Z_{11}(p) = R_1 + pL_1 \qquad Z_{22} = R_2 + pL_2 + \frac{1}{pC_2} \qquad Z_{12} = pk\,\sqrt{L_1 L_2}$$

The mesh equation for mesh 2 gives

$$Z_{12}(p)i_1 + Z_{22}(p)i_2 = 0$$

If the source in the primary is an ideal current source $i_1(t)$, then

$$i_2(t) = -\,\frac{Z_{12}(p)}{Z_{22}(p)}\,i_1(t)$$

or
$$i_2(t) = -\,\frac{pk\,\sqrt{L_1 L_2}}{R_2 + pL_2 + 1/pC_2}\,i_1(t)$$

The transform current gain function which relates i_2 to i_1 is denoted by $H_i(s)$,

$$H_i(s) = -\,\sqrt{\frac{L_1}{L_2}}\,\frac{s^2 k}{s^2 + (R_2/L_2)s + 1/L_2 C_2} \tag{18-9}$$

We now define the radian resonant frequency of mesh 2 as $\omega_0 = 1/(L_2 C_2)^{\frac{1}{2}}$ and its quality factor (its Q) as $Q_2 = \omega_0 L_2/R_2 = \sqrt{L_2/C_2}/R_2$ and write

$$H_i(s) = -\,\sqrt{\frac{L_1}{L_2}}\,\frac{s^2 k}{s^2 + (\omega_0/Q_2)s + \omega_0{}^2}$$

We observe that the current gain is proportional to the coefficient of coupling. The frequency response for any value of k is found from the pole-zero pattern. The function $H_i(s)$ has a double zero at $s = 0$ and poles at $s = s_{1,2}$, where s_1 and s_2 are the roots of the equation

$$s^2 + \frac{\omega_0 s}{Q_2} + \omega_0^2 = 0$$

Assuming the oscillatory case ($Q_2 > \frac{1}{2}$), a typical pole-zero diagram is shown in Fig. 18-22b. We now recall that for a series R-L-C circuit the

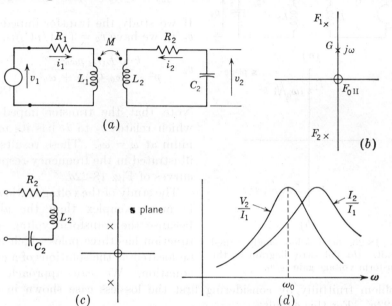

(a)

(b)

(c)

(d)

FIG. 18-22. (a) Singly tuned circuit. (b) Pole-zero diagram for the transform current gain, i_2/i_1, assuming $Q_2 > \frac{1}{2}$. (c) Series R-L-C circuit and the pole-zero diagram of its transform driving-point admittance. (d) Frequency-response curves of the singly tuned circuit.

transform driving-point admittance is (Fig. 18-22c)

$$Y_{ab}(s) = \frac{(1/L_2)s}{s^2 + (R_2/L_2)s + 1/L_2C_2}$$

The pole pattern which corresponds to this function is shown in Fig. 18-22c. In Chap. 15 it was shown that $Y_{ab}(j\omega)$ has a maximum at $\omega = \omega_0 = 1/\sqrt{LC}$. Since $H_i(j\omega)$ is proportional to the product of $j\omega$ and $Y_{ab}(j\omega)$, the maximum for $H_i(j\omega)$ will occur not at $\omega = \omega_0$ but at a frequency above this value. This follows by observing that

$$|H_i(j\omega)| = A\omega|Y_{ab}|$$

where A is a proportionality constant. Hence

$$\frac{\partial|H_i|}{\partial\omega} = A|Y_{ab}| + \omega A\frac{\partial|Y_{ab}|}{\partial\omega}$$

Since $\partial|Y_{ab}|/\partial\omega$ at $\omega = \omega_0$ is zero, $\partial|H_i|/\partial\omega$ is positive at that frequency. Hence the derivative $\partial H_i/\partial\omega$ is zero at a frequency at which $\partial|Y_{ab}|/\partial\omega$ is negative; this point will be after the peak of Y_{ab}, that is, for $\omega > \omega_0$. Detailed analysis shows that $|H_i(j\omega)|$ has a maximum when

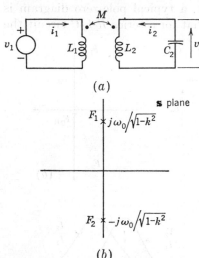

(a)

(b)

FIG. 18-23. (a) Lossless singly tuned circuit. (b) Pole-zero diagram of the transform voltage gain v_2/v_1.

$$\frac{\omega^2}{\omega_0^2} = \frac{2Q_2^2}{2Q_2^2 - 1} \qquad Q_2^2 > \tfrac{1}{2}$$

If we study the transfer impedance v_2/i_1, we have $v_2 = (-1/pC_2)i_2$, or

$$v_2 = \frac{k\sqrt{L_1 L_2}\, p\omega_0^2}{p^2 + (\omega_0/Q_2)p + \omega_0^2} i_1$$

$$(18\text{-}10)$$

Note that the transfer impedance which relates v_2 to i_1 has its maximum at $\omega = \omega_0$. These results are illustrated in the frequency-response curves of Fig. 18-22d.

The study of the voltage ratio v_2/v_1 is more complex than the above because the transform voltage-gain function has three poles which must be located as the solutions of a cubic equation. We can approach this problem fruitfully by considering first the lossless case shown in Fig. 18-23a. For this circuit

$$pL_1 i_1 + pM i_2 = v_1$$

$$pM i_1 + \frac{L_2}{p}(p^2 + \omega_0^2)i_2 = 0$$

where $\omega_0^2 = 1/L_2 C_2$. We also have $i_2 = -pC_2 v_2$. Hence

$$v_2 = \frac{k\sqrt{L_1 L_2}/C_2}{L_1 L_2(p^2 + \omega_0^2) - k^2 p^2 L_1 L_2} v_1$$

or

$$v_2 = \sqrt{\frac{L_2}{L_1}} \frac{k\omega_0^2}{p^2(1 - k^2) + \omega_0^2} v_1 \qquad (18\text{-}11)$$

The corresponding transform network function has a pole pair at

$$s = \frac{\pm j\omega_0}{\sqrt{1 - k^2}}$$

as shown in Fig. 18-23b. Hence in the low-loss case ($R_{1,2} \ll \omega_0 L_{1,2}$) we expect maximum response near the frequencies $\omega_0/\sqrt{1 - k^2}$. Thus the frequency at which V_2/V_1 has a maximum value in general depends on the coefficient of coupling k.

Let us now consider the phasor ratio $\mathbf{V}_2/\mathbf{V}_1$ at any radian frequency $\omega = \mu\omega_0$. We have from Eq. (18-11)

$$\frac{\mathbf{V}_2}{\mathbf{V}_1} = \sqrt{\frac{L_2}{L_1}}\, \frac{k}{(1 - \mu^2) + \mu^2 k^2} \qquad (18\text{-}12)$$

Hence, for every value $\mu > 1$, there exists a special value of k which gives maximum response ratio (the "maximum" is infinite in the lossless case). In particular, if we choose $k = \sqrt{1 - 1/\mu^2}$, the expression (18-12) is infinite.

We now apply the ideas of the above discussion to the lossy case, Fig. 18-22a. For convenience in analysis we choose to find the value of k for which the voltage gain is a maximum at the resonant frequency of the secondary mesh. When $\omega = \omega_0 = 1/\sqrt{L_2 C_2}$, $\mathbf{Z}_{11} = R_1 + j\omega_0 L_1$, $\mathbf{Z}_{22} = R_2$, $\mathbf{Z}_{12} = j\omega_0 k \sqrt{L_1 L_2}$. Hence

$$\frac{\mathbf{V}_2}{\mathbf{V}_1} = \frac{-\mathbf{I}_2/j\omega_0 C_2}{\mathbf{V}_1} = \frac{k\,\sqrt{L_1 L_2}/C_2}{R_1 R_2 + j\omega_0 L_1 R_2 + \omega_0^2 k^2 L_1 L_2}$$

or $\qquad \dfrac{\mathbf{V}_2}{\mathbf{V}_1} = \sqrt{\dfrac{L_2}{L_1}}\, \dfrac{k}{1/Q_1 Q_2 + k^2 + j/Q_2} \qquad (18\text{-}13)$

where $Q_2 = \omega_0 L_2/R_2 = \sqrt{L_2/C_2}/R_2$, is the quality factor of the secondary mesh and Q_1 is the reactance-resistance ratio of the primary at $\omega = \omega_0$. Differentiating V_2/V_1 with respect to k and setting the result equal to zero, we obtain $k = k_c$, where

$$k_c = \left(\frac{1}{Q_2}\sqrt{1 + \frac{1}{Q_1^2}}\right)^{\frac{1}{2}} \qquad (18\text{-}14)$$

The value of k_c given by Eq. (18-14) is called the "critical coupling of the singly tuned circuit." It is that value of coupling which gives maximum voltage gain *at the resonant frequency of the secondary.*

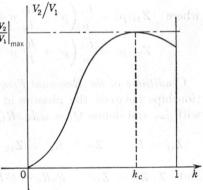

FIG. 18-24. Voltage gain of the singly tuned circuit at the resonant frequency of the secondary as a function of coefficient of coupling.

The value given in Eq. (18-14) applies only when Q_2 and Q_1 are sufficiently large so that $k_c < 1$. If Eq. (18-14) gives $k_c > 1$, then maximum voltage gain at ω_0 can be obtained with (as close to) unity coupling (as possible). A curve for $k_c < 1$ is shown in Fig. 18-24.

18-11. The Doubly Tuned Circuit. We now turn to the doubly tuned circuit, excited by an ideal current source as shown in Fig. 18-25a. By representing this current source in parallel with C_1 as a voltage source the circuit shown in Fig. 18-25b results.   In order to simplify the analysis, we assume that $1/L_1C_1 = 1/L_2C_2 = \omega_0^2$; that is, the resonant frequency of both primary and secondary is the same frequency.   (This assumption

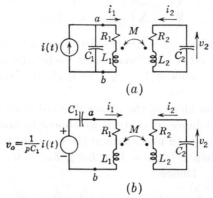

(a)

(b)

FIG. 18-25. (a) Doubly tuned circuit excited by an ideal current source.   (b) Circuit of (a) using voltage-source representation for $i(t)$-C_1 combination.

is fulfilled in many practical circuits.)   The mesh equations are

$$Z_{11}i_1 + Z_{12}i_2 = v_0(t)$$
$$Z_{12}i_1 + Z_{22}i_2 = 0$$

where $Z_{11}(p) = \dfrac{L_1}{p}\left(p^2 + \dfrac{R_1}{L_1}\,p + \omega_0^2\right)$ $Z_{12}(p) = pk\,\sqrt{L_1L_2}$

$\qquad Z_{22}(p) = \dfrac{L_2}{p}\left(p^2 + \dfrac{R_2}{L_2}\,p + \omega_0^2\right)$ $v_0(t) = \dfrac{1}{pC_1}\,i(t)$

Conditions at the Resonant Frequency $f_0 = \omega_0/2\pi$.   To study the relationships between the phasors at the resonant frequency, we replace p with $j\omega_0$ and define $Q_1 = \omega_0 L_1/R_1$, $Q_2 = \omega_0 L_2/R_2$.   Then

$$\mathbf{Z}_{11} = R_1 \qquad \mathbf{Z}_{22} = R_2 \qquad \mathbf{Z}_{12} = jk\,\sqrt{R_1R_2Q_1Q_2} \qquad \mathbf{V}_o = \frac{1}{j\omega_0 C_1}\,\mathbf{I}$$

and $\mathbf{Z}_{11}\mathbf{Z}_{22} - \mathbf{Z}_{12}{}^2 = R_1R_2 + k^2R_1R_2Q_1Q_2 = R_1R_2(1 + k^2Q_1Q_2)$

Hence $$\frac{\mathbf{I}_2}{\mathbf{I}} = -\sqrt{\frac{L_1}{L_2}}\,\frac{k}{1/Q_1Q_2 + k^2} \tag{18-15}$$

Differentiating Eq. (18-15) with respect to k and setting the result to zero gives $k = k_c$, where

$$k_c = \frac{1}{\sqrt{Q_1Q_2}} \tag{18-16}$$

The value k_c given by Eq. (18-16) is that value of coupling which produces maximum current gain at the resonant frequency and which is called "critical coupling for the doubly tuned circuit." Since $V_2 = -I_2/j\omega_0 C_2$, this value of coupling also gives maximum transfer impedance V_2/I at $\omega = \omega_0$.

Frequency Response. Before considering the general case, the lossless circuit of Fig. 18-26a is analyzed. We again assume $L_1C_1 = L_2C_2$; then

$$Z_{11}(p) = (L_1/p)(p^2 + \omega_0^2) \qquad Z_{22}(p) = (L_2/p)(p^2 + \omega_0^2)$$
$$Z_{12}(p) = pk \sqrt{L_1 L_2}$$

Solving the mesh equations:

$$i_2 = \frac{-p^2 k \sqrt{L_1 L_2}/C_1}{L_1 L_2 (p^2 + \omega_0^2)^2 - p^4 k^2 L_1 L_2} \, i$$

or $\qquad i_2 = -k \sqrt{\dfrac{L_1}{L_2}} \, \omega_0^2 \dfrac{p^2}{(p^2 + \omega_0^2)^2 - p^4 k^2} \, i$

Thus $\qquad i_2 = -k \sqrt{\dfrac{L_1}{L_2}} \, \omega_0^2 \dfrac{p^2}{(p^2 + \omega_0^2 + p^2 k)(p^2 + \omega_0^2 - p^2 k)} \, i \qquad (18\text{-}17)$

and $\qquad v_2 = -\dfrac{1}{pC_2} i_2$

Both these network functions have poles at

$$s^2(1 \pm k) + \omega_0^2 = 0$$

or, if $k \neq 1$,

$$s = \pm \frac{j\omega_0}{\sqrt{1 + k}} \qquad s = \pm \frac{j\omega_0}{\sqrt{1 - k}}$$

The transform current gain which relates i_2 to i has a double zero at $s = 0$, while the transfer impedance v_2/i has a simple zero. The pole-zero diagram for the current gain is shown in Fig. 18-26b. We observe that the response of the lossless circuit is maximum (infinite) at the pole frequencies. In the slightly (high-Q) lossy case we expect that the poles move off the $j\omega$ axis and maxima occur near the pole frequencies of the lossless circuit. In addition we note that the current ratio will have its maxima at frequencies above those of the transfer impedance because of the double zero at the origin in the former case. The results for the lossless case are illustrated in Fig. 18-26c. We note that as $k \to 0$ a double pole forms at $s = \pm j\omega_0$. Thus critical coupling for the lossless case ($Q_1 Q_2 = \infty$) is zero coupling.

While at first glance it may seem strange that maximum response does not occur at ω_0, the following physical reasoning explains this phenomenon. At resonance, $Z_{22} = 0$ in the lossless case. Hence the impedance of the secondary, reflected into the primary, $\omega_0^2 M^2/Z_{22}$, is infinite. Thus i_1 can only be infinitesimal so that an infinitesimal voltage pMi_1 is induced in the secondary. This produces finite current in the zero impedance.

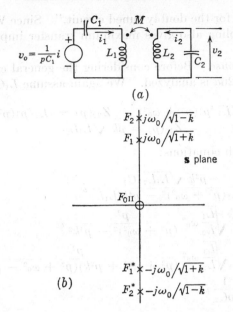

$$v_o = \frac{1}{pC_1} i$$

(a)

$$F_2 \times j\omega_0 / \sqrt{1-k}$$
$$F_1 \times j\omega_0 / \sqrt{1+k}$$

s plane

$$F_{0\text{II}}$$

(b)

$$F_1^* \times -j\omega_0 / \sqrt{1+k}$$
$$F_2^* \times -j\omega_0 / \sqrt{1-k}$$

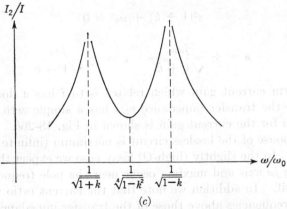

(c)

FIG. 18-26. (a) Lossless version of the circuit of Fig. 18-25b. (b) Pole-zero diagram for the transform current gain, i_2/i, of the lossless doubly tuned circuit. (c) Current gain as a function of frequency for the pole-zero pattern of (b).

We now apply this result to the lossy case. The expected pole-zero diagram is shown in Fig. 18-27a for the current-gain function. For any frequency the source is represented by a pole as at G. We now assume that, near ω_0, $F_1^* G$, $F_0 G$, and $F_2^* G$ are constant. Hence, near ω_0, the current gain function H_i [$i_2 = H_i(p)i$] is proportional to $1/(F_1 G)(F_2 G)$. In Fig. 18-27b an enlarged portion of the pole-zero diagram, showing the region near $s = j\omega_0$, is given. Now, as ω moves from ω_A to ω_B, $F_1 G_1$

increases and F_2G_1 decreases.   It follows that α_1 and α_2 as well as k (which determines $\omega_B - \omega_A$) will determine whether the product $(F_1G_1)(F_2G_1)$ decreases or increases between ω_A and ω_B.   We therefore conclude that the frequency-response curve for I_2/I and V_2/I may have a maximum

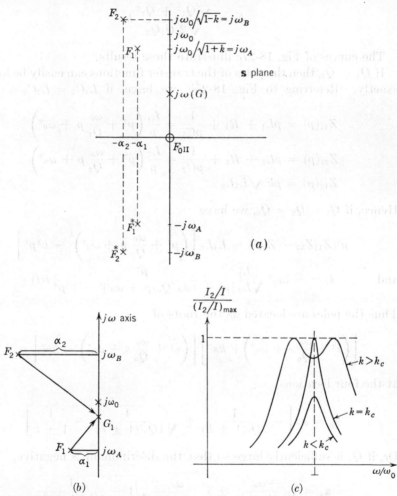

FIG. 18-27. (a) Pole-zero diagram for the transform current gain in a low-loss (high-Q) doubly tuned circuit: $\alpha_1/\omega_0 \ll 1$, and $\alpha_2/\omega_0 \ll 1$.   (b) Region of the s plane near $\mathbf{s} = j\omega_0$ (c). Current gain as a function of frequency with coefficient of coupling as a parameter for the high-Q case, $Q_1 = Q_2 \gg 1$.

or a minimum between ω_A and ω_B.   If a maximum occurs it is the only maximum.   It can be shown that, in the lossy case (finite Q), the frequency-response curve for I_2/I has only one peak and that that peak is at ω_0 if

1. The coefficient of coupling is less than or equal to the value of k_c given in Eq. (18-16), provided that $Q_1 = Q_2$; that is, $k_c \leqq 1/Q_1 = 1/Q_2$.

2. The coefficient of coupling is less than (or equal to) a value k_t (called "transitional coupling") if $Q_1 \neq Q_2$. The value of k_t is given by

$$k_t = \frac{\sqrt{Q_1^2 + Q_2^2}}{\sqrt{2\,Q_1Q_2}}\,k_c$$

The curves of Fig. 18-27c illustrate these results.

If $Q_1 = Q_2$, then the poles of the transfer functions can easily be located exactly. Referring to Fig. 18-25b, we have, if $L_1C_1 = L_2C_2 = 1/\omega_0^2$,

$$Z_{11}(p) = pL_1 + R_1 + \frac{1}{pC_1} = \frac{L_1}{p}\left(p^2 + \frac{\omega_0}{Q_1}\,p + \omega_0^2\right)$$

$$Z_{22}(p) = pL_2 + R_2 + \frac{1}{pC_2} = \frac{L_2}{p}\left(p^2 + \frac{\omega_0}{Q_2}\,p + \omega_0^2\right)$$

$$Z_{12}(p) = pk\,\sqrt{L_1L_2}$$

Hence, if $Q_1 = Q_2 = Q_0$, we have

$$p^2(Z_{11}Z_{22} - Z_{12}^2) = L_1L_2\left[\left(p^2 + \frac{\omega_0}{Q_0}\,p + \omega_0^2\right)^2 - k^2p^4\right]$$

and

$$i_2 = -k\omega_0^2\,\sqrt{\frac{L_1}{L_2}}\,\frac{p^2}{[p^2 + (\omega_0/Q_0)p + \omega_0^2]^2 - k^2p^4}\,i(t)$$

Thus the poles are located as the roots of

$$\left[\left(s^2 + \frac{\omega_0}{Q_0}\,s + \omega_0^2\right) + ks^2\right]\left[\left(s^2 + \frac{\omega_0}{Q_0}\,s + \omega_0^2\right) - ks^2\right] = 0$$

at the four locations:

$$s_p = \omega_0\left[-\frac{1}{2Q_0(1 \pm k)} \pm \sqrt{\frac{1}{4Q_0^2(1 \pm k)^2} - \frac{1}{1 \pm k}}\right]$$

Or, if Q_0 is sufficiently large so that the discriminant is negative,

$$\mathbf{s}_p = \frac{-\omega_0}{2Q_0(1 \pm k)} \pm j\,\frac{\omega_0}{\sqrt{1 \pm k}}\sqrt{1 - \frac{1}{4Q_0^2(1 \pm k)}}$$

Hence for this case in Fig. 18-27b

$$\alpha_1 = \frac{-\omega_0}{2Q_0(1 + k)} \qquad \omega_A = \frac{\omega_0}{\sqrt{1 + k}}\sqrt{1 - \frac{1}{4Q_0^2(1 + k)}}$$

$$\alpha_2 = \frac{-\omega_0}{2Q_0(1 - k)} \qquad \omega_B = \frac{\omega_0}{\sqrt{1 - k}}\sqrt{1 - \frac{1}{4Q_0^2(1 - k)}}$$

We observe again that the values ω_A and ω_B correspond very closely to the values obtained in the lossless case (Fig. 18-26b) if $Q_0 \gg 1$. The frequency-response curves can now be obtained by the method illustrated in Chap. 15, that is, by solving the geometry of Fig. 18-27b. This matter and related topics such as calculation of bandwidth is not pursued here because the main object of the preceding discussion has been to show how the principles of the preceding chapters can be applied to explain the behavior (e.g., double peaks) of the tuned circuits. Further details (relative height of the two peaks, bandwidth, etc.) are found in more advanced literature.[1]

PROBLEMS

18-1. In the circuit shown in Fig. P18-1 a 100-volt (rms) sinusoidal source is applied between terminals as indicated in the tabulation below. Connections are made as indicated, and the results of several measurements at the input terminals are also given. The polarity dots are omitted and their location may be deduced from the data below.

Apply source between	Connect	Rms, amp	Av power, watts
a-a'	b to b'	7.07	500
a-b'	b to a'	0.90	Not measured
a-b	a' and b' not connected	4.90	96

(a) Calculate R_1, R_2, and the coefficient of coupling k.   (b) Calculate L_1 and L_2 if the frequency is 60 cps.

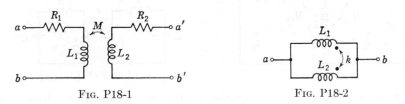

FIG. P18-1   FIG. P18-2

18-2. For the terminal pair shown in Fig. P18-2 (a) calculate the equivalent inductance L_{ab} as a function of the coefficient of coupling k.   (b) Let L_0 be the value of L_{ab} when $k = 0$. Plot the ratio L_{ab}/L_0 as a function of k for (1) $L_2 = L_1$; (2) $L_2 = 2L_1$; (3) $L_2 = 10L_1$ for $-1 \leq k \leq +1$. (What do negative values of k mean?)

---

[1] See, e.g., F. E. Terman, "Radio Engineering," chap. 3, particularly secs. 3–4, McGraw-Hill Book Company, Inc., New York, 1947; E. J. Angelo, Jr., "Electronic Circuits," pp. 350–375, McGraw-Hill Book Company, Inc., New York, 1958; or G. E. Valley, Jr., and H. Wallman (eds.), "Vacuum Tube Amplifiers," vol. 18, Massachusetts Institute of Technology Radiation Laboratory Series, chap. 5, pp. 201–221, McGraw-Hill Book Company, Inc., New York, 1948.

18-3. Sketch the reactance- and susceptance-frequency curves for the pure reactance network given in Fig. P18-3.

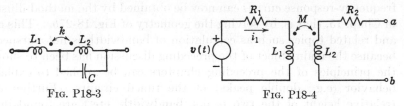

FIG. P18-3   FIG. P18-4

18-4. If $v(t)$ is the ramp function $v(t) = Vt/T_1U(t)$, (a) calculate v_{ab} for all $t \geq 0^+$, assuming no initial-energy storage; (b) discuss the usefulness of this circuit as a differentiator. The circuit is shown in Fig. P18-4.

18-5. Calculate $v_{ab}(t)$ for the circuit of Prob. 18-4 in the steady state if $v(t) = V_m \cos \omega t$.

18-6. In the circuit of Prob. 18-4 terminals a-b are short-circuited. It is known that $L_1/R_1 = L_2/R_2 = 1$. Solve for the complete response $i_{ab}(t)$ (current through the short circuit) for $t \geq 0^+$ if $|k| < 1$ and if the initial-energy storage is zero. The source is a unit step function.

18-7. In the circuit of Prob. 18-4 terminals a-b are short-circuited. The current in each mesh at $t = 0^-$ is zero. Let $R_1 = 1$, $R_2 = 2$, $L_1 = L_2 = 2$, $k = 1$. The source is $U(t)$. (a) Show that $i_{ab}(0^+) \neq 0$ and calculate its value. *Hint:* Obtain an expression for the total stored energy. (b) Calculate $i_1(0^+)$. (c) Obtain the complete response for $i_1(t)$ and $i_{ab}(t)$ for $t \geq 0^+$.

18-8. In the circuit of Fig. P18-8 (a) calculate the mesh impedances $Z_{11}(p)$, $Z_{12}(p)$, $Z_{22}(p)$. (b) If $L_1 = L_2 = 0.1$ henry, $L_3 = 0.2$ henry, $M_{12} = 0.05$ henry, $M_{23} = 0.1$ henry, $M_{13} = -0.10$ henry, $R_1 = R_2 = R_3 = 50$ ohms, calculate the complex mesh impedances at a radian frequency of 1,000/sec.

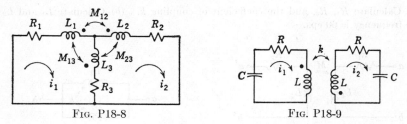

FIG. P18-8   FIG. P18-9

18-9. Write the characteristic equation for the mesh currents, and deduce the condition(s) for nonoscillatory transient components in the circuit of Fig. P18-9. ($M = kL$, $0 < k < 1$.)

18-10. In the circuit of Fig. P18-10, $R_1 = 1.0$ ohm, $R_2 = 10$ ohms, $X_{L1} = 9.0$ ohms, $X_{L2} = 90$ ohms, $k = 0.8$, $X_c = -50$ ohms, $R_T = 50$ ohms. Calculate $\mathbf{V}_{ab}$.

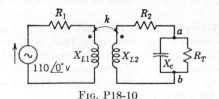

FIG. P18-10

18-11. The circuit shown in Fig. P18-11 is in the sinusoidal steady state. Calculate (a) I_1, I_2; (b) the power delivered to R_1 and the power delivered to R_2; (c) the power delivered by each ideal source.

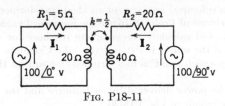

Fig. P18-11

18-12. In the circuit of Prob. 18-4 $R_1 = 2$ ohms, $L_1 = 0.01$ henry, $R_2 = 20$ ohms, $L_2 = 0.1$ henry, $M = 0.03$ henry. A load whose equivalent circuit is the parallel combination of a 100-ohm resistance and a 12.5μf capacitance is connected across terminals a-b. If $v_{ab} = 100\sqrt{2}\cos 400t$, calculate the source function $v(t)$.

18-13. In the circuit of Prob. 18-4, $R_1 = 2$ ohms, $L_1 = 0.01$ henry, $R_2 = 20$ ohms, $L_2 = 0.1$ henry, $M = 0.03$ henry. If $v(t) = 100\sqrt{2}\cos 400t$, deduce Thévenin's equivalent circuit for sinusoidal steady-state analysis (V_o and Z_s) with respect to terminals a-b.

18-14. If $L_1 = 9L_2$ and if $k = 1$, obtain Thévenin's equivalent circuit with respect to terminals c-d in the "autotransformer" circuit of Fig P18-14.

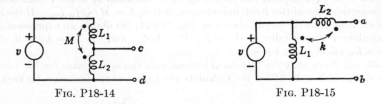

Fig. P18-14   Fig. P18-15

18-15. In the (induction regulator) shown in Fig. P18-15 k is adjustable. Obtain Thévenin's equivalent circuit with respect to terminals a-b.

18-16. In the circuit shown in Fig. P18-16 $R = 10$ ohms, $L = 0.001$ henry, $C = 10^{-6}$ farad, $n_1/n_2 = a$. Calculate the value of a so that the circuit is (a) critically

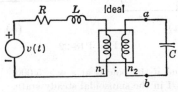

Fig. P18-16

damped; (b) oscillatory, with two cycles of decaying oscillations per time constant of envelope decay; (c) overdamped, with one root of the characteristic equation equal to twice the undamped (natural) radian frequency.

18-17. A voltage source has an internal resistance of 10,000 ohms. It is to supply a load resistance, value 100 ohms. Calculate (a) the turns ratio of an ideal transformer which will ensure that maximum power is transferred to the 100-ohm resistance; (b) the ratio of the power transferred in (a) to the power which would be transferred to the 100-ohm resistance if this resistance were connected directly across the terminals of the resistive generator.

18-18. What is a mechanical analogue of an ideal transformer?

18-19. (a) In the circuit of Prob. 18-16 use the numerical values $R = 0.2, L = 0.1$, $C = 1.25$, $n_1/n_2 = \frac{1}{2}$, and calculate the complete response for $v_{ab}(t)$ if no energy is stored at $t = 0^-$ and if the source is $v(t) = U(t)$. (b) Calculate the value of a resistance to be placed in parallel with C across terminals a-b so that the circuit is critically damped.

18-20. Calculate the power delivered by each source and the power dissipated by each resistance in the circuit of Fig. P18-20.

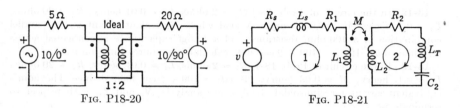

FIG. P18-20   FIG. P18-21

18-21. While the coefficient of coupling is usually defined as the ratio of mutual inductance to the geometric mean of two inductances ("coil self-inductances"), that is, $k = M/\sqrt{L_1L_2}$, one can also define k as the ratio of mutual inductance to the geometric mean of two mesh inductances, that is, $k = M/\sqrt{L_{11}L_{22}}$. If the latter definition is used in the circuit shown in Fig. P18-21, (a) obtain an expression for k; (b) calculate k numerically if $4L_1 = L_2$, $M = 1.5L_1$, and (1) $L_s = L_T = 0$, (2) $L_s = L_T = L_1$, (3) $L_s = L_1$, $L_T = L_2$.

18-22. (a) Show that the transform current gain i_2/i is the same for the two networks shown in Fig. P18-22. (b) Calculate the values of the elements for each net-

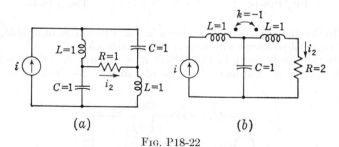

(a)   (b)

FIG. P18-22

work if $R = 600$ ohms and if the pole is at $s = -5,000$. (c) Sketch the amplitude and phase response for I_2/I in the sinusoidal steady state.

18-23. Calculate the transform driving-point impedance for each of the networks of Prob. 18-22 (Fig. P18-22).

18-24. In the text, critical coupling is defined as that condition which maximizes the absolute value of a transfer function at resonance. It is the purpose of this problem to show that this definition, while useful, is arbitrary because in general the value of k which maximizes a transfer function depends on the frequency. (a) Consider a complex transfer function of the form $\mathbf{H} = \mathbf{A}[k/(\mathbf{B} + k^2)]$, where k is adjustable, and show that $H_{\max}$ is obtained when $k^2 = B$. (b) Show that the form given in (a) applies to a singly or doubly tuned circuit if an ideal voltage source of radian frequency ω, whose phasor is $\mathbf{V}$, is impressed and if the response is either $\mathbf{V}_2$ or $\mathbf{I}_2$. Find $\mathbf{A}$ and $\mathbf{B}$ for these cases. (c) Show that the form given in (a) applies to a doubly tuned circuit with an ideal current source impressed. Find $\mathbf{A}$ and $\mathbf{B}$ for the transfer functions $\mathbf{V}_2/\mathbf{I}$ and $\mathbf{I}_2/\mathbf{I}$.

18-25. To explain why the coupling for maximum gain is a function of frequency (see Prob. 18-24), consider the lossless singly tuned circuit shown in Fig. P18-25. (a) Use the numerical values $L_1 = 1 = L_2$, $C_2 = 1$, and locate the zeros and poles of the transform transfer function which relates v_2 to v. (b) If the circuit is low-loss, how is the coefficient of coupling related to the frequency at which V_2/V is a maximum? (c) Calculate the location of the poles and the value of C_2 if the resonant frequency of the secondary is 455 kc, if $L_1 = L_2 = 1.0$ mh, and if (1) $k = 0.8$ (2) $k = 0.1$.

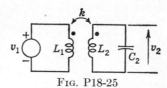

FIG. P18-25

18-26. In the singly tuned circuit of Prob. 18-25 (Fig. P18-25), $L_1 = L_2 = 1$, $C_2 = 1$, and a resistance $R_2 = 0.02$ is in series with L_2. The voltage source is replaced by a current source i in parallel with a 50-ohm resistance. The circuit is in the sinusoidal steady state. (a) Use the result of Prob. 18-24 to determine the relationship between k and ω so that at each frequency V_2/I is a maximum (assume $\mathbf{Z}_{11} = 50$). (b) Calculate approximately the range of frequencies for which a value of k which is less than unity gives maximum transfer impedance V_2/I.

18-27. Consider the geometry given in Fig. P18-27. It is shown in Prob. 18-28 that this geometry can be used to deduce the frequency response of a high-Q doubly tuned circuit. (a) Show that the square of the product of the distances $(P_1G)^2(P_2G)^2$ is given by $(P_1G)^2(P_2G)^2 = \alpha^4 + 2\alpha^2(k^2/4 + x^2) + (k^2/4 - x^2)^2$. (b) Show that, if $\alpha > k/2$, the product $(P_1G)(P_2G)$ is a minimum at $x = 0$. (c) Show that, if $\alpha < k/2$, the product $(P_1G)(P_2G)$ is a maximum at $x = 0$ and has two minima at

$$x = \pm \left(\frac{k^2}{4} - \alpha^2\right)^{\frac{1}{2}}$$

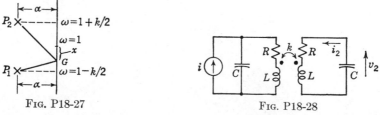

FIG. P18-27   FIG. P18-28

18-28. (a) In the symmetrical, doubly tuned circuit of Fig. P18-28 show that, if $L = 1$, $C = 1$, $R < 1$, the poles of the transform transfer functions, i_2/i and v_2/i, are at

$$s = -\frac{R/2}{1 \pm k} \pm \sqrt{\frac{R^2/4}{(1 \pm k)^2} - \frac{1}{1 \pm k}}$$

(b) Show that, for $R \ll 1$ and $k \ll 1$, the poles are approximately at $s = -R/2 \pm j(1 \mp k/2)$. (c) Use the approximate pole-zero diagram and the result of Prob. 18-27 to show that the frequency-response curves for V_2/I and I_2/I have two peaks at approximately $\omega = 1 \pm \frac{1}{2}k$ if $k > R$ and only one peak at $\omega = 1$ for $k < R$. (d) Show that the condition $k = R$ gives the value of critical coupling $k = k_c = 1/\sqrt{Q_1 Q_2}$. (e) Calculate the two radian frequencies at which the I_2/I has the same magnitude as at $\omega = 1$ if $k = 2R = 0.1$.

18-29. In the doubly tuned circuit of Prob. 18-28 the coefficient of coupling is 0.03, and $R = 0.02$. (a) Calculate the location of the poles of the transform network function v_2/i. (b) Calculate the two radian frequencies at which V_2/I has the same value as at $\omega = 1$. (c) Change the frequency scale and the impedance level so that the resonant frequency is 455 kc and $L = 1.0$ mh (calculate C and R). (d) Calculate for the circuit of (c) the two frequencies at which the response ratios are the same as at 455 kc.

CHAPTER 19

HARMONIC ANALYSIS AND FOURIER SERIES

In this chapter we shall show that a function which is the sum of sinusoidal functions whose frequencies are integral multiples of each other is a periodic function and that (under certain conditions) a periodic function can be represented as the sum of a finite or infinite number of sinusoidal functions. Because of this formulation we shall be able to represent periodic source functions as the sum of sinusoidal source functions. Hence the component of the response due to periodic source functions can be obtained as the sum (superposition) of sinusoidal functions. In addition we shall find that the concept of representing a waveform as the sum of a number of sinusoidal functions can be developed into a powerful mathematical tool which will shift the emphasis from the time variation of waveforms (time-domain analysis) to its frequency components (frequency-domain analysis).

19-1. Periodic Functions. If two sinusoidal functions $f_1(t) = B_1 \sin \omega t$ and $f_2(t) = B_2 \sin 2\omega t$ are added to give $f(t)$,

$$f(t) = B_1 \sin \omega t + B_2 \sin 2\omega t$$

then $f(t)$ is periodic with period $T = 2\pi/\omega$, because

$$f\left(t + \frac{2\pi}{\omega}\right) = B_1 \sin (\omega t + 2\pi) + B_2 \sin (2\omega t + 4\pi) = f(t)$$

In Fig. 19-1 this addition is illustrated for the case $B_1 = 3$, $B_2 = 1$. The function $f(t)$ is seen to be periodic with period $2\pi/\omega$, but not sinusoidal. A little thought will show that the function

$$f(t) = C_0 + C_1 \cos (\omega t + \varphi_1) + C_2 \cos (2\omega t + \varphi_2) \\ + \cdots + C_n \cos (n\omega t + \varphi_n) \quad (19\text{-}1)$$

is also periodic with period $2\pi/\omega$ if n is an integer. In the following articles we shall show that periodic functions can be represented as the sum of sinusoidal functions in the form of Eq. (19-1); this sum can have an infinite or a finite number of terms. For practical purposes a finite number of terms can be used to approximate a given periodic function to any desired degree of accuracy. Thus, for example, the waveform of

Fig. 19-2a can be approximated by the sum of a constant term and the four sinusoidal terms given in Eq. 19-2.

Before discussing the procedure which is followed when it is desired to represent a periodic function in the form of Eq. (19-1), it is important to realize the purpose of such a procedure. Let us therefore assume that

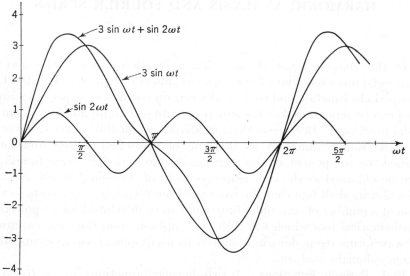

FIG. 19-1. The addition of the functions $3 \sin \omega t$ and $\sin 2\omega t$. The resultant has the period $2\pi/\omega$.

the waveform of Fig. 19-2a is the waveform of an ideal voltage source and is approximated by

$$v(t) = \frac{3}{2} - \frac{3}{\pi}\left(\sin\frac{2\pi}{3}t + \frac{1}{2}\sin\frac{4\pi}{3}t + \frac{1}{3}\sin\frac{6\pi}{3}t + \frac{1}{4}\sin\frac{8\pi}{3}t\right) \quad (19\text{-}2)$$

where the period of the waveform is 3. Suppose that this waveform is applied to the series combination of a 1-ohm resistance and a $3/\pi$-henry inductance. Let it be required to find the steady-state current in this circuit.

From the superposition theorem we know that the response to several sources is the sum of the responses to the individual sources. Now we write Eq. (19-2) in the form

$$v(t) = V_0 + \sum_{k=1}^{4} v_k(t) \qquad v_k = -\frac{3}{k\pi}\sin k\frac{2\pi}{3}t \qquad V_0 = \frac{3}{2} \quad (19\text{-}3)$$

and calculate the steady-state response due to each source.

The response to $V_0 = \frac{3}{2}$ volts is $I_0 = \frac{3}{2}$ amp.

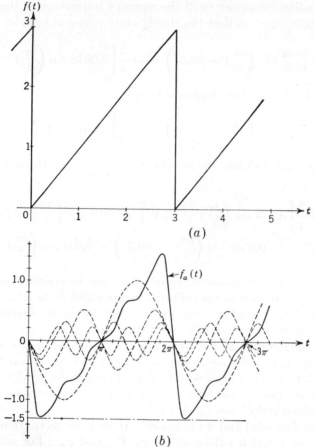

FIG. 19-2. (a) A periodic triangular waveform.   (b) The waveform $f_a(t)$ can be used to approximate the triangular waveform of (a) if the $f = 0$ axis is shifted to -1.5 and if the time scales are matched.   The equation for $f_a(t)$ is $f_a(t) = -(\sin t + \frac{1}{2}\sin 2t + \frac{1}{3}\sin 3t + \frac{1}{4}\sin 4t)$.

At the radian frequency $\omega_1 = 2\pi/3$,

$$R + j\omega_1 L = 1 + j2 = 2.24\underline{/63.4°} \text{ ohms}$$

hence the component of the steady-state response due to the source $v_1(t)$, denoted by $i_1(t)$, is

$$i_1(t) = -\frac{3/\pi}{2.24} \sin\left(\frac{2\pi}{3}t - 63.4°\right) = -\frac{3}{\pi}\left[0.446 \sin\left(\frac{2\pi}{3}t - 63.4°\right)\right]$$

At the radian frequency $\omega_2 = 4\pi/3$ the complex impedance of the circuit is $R + j\omega_2 L = 1 + j4 = 4.13\underline{/76°}$ so that the response due to v_2 is

$$i_2(t) = -\frac{3/2\pi}{4.13} \sin\left(\frac{4\pi}{3}t - 76°\right) = -\frac{3}{\pi}\left[0.121 \sin\left(\frac{4\pi}{3}t - 76°\right)\right]$$

At the radian frequency $6\pi/3$ the complex impedance of the circuit is $1 + j6 = 6.08/\underline{80.5°}$ so that the steady-state response to v_3 is

$$i_3(t) = -\frac{3/3\pi}{6.08} \sin\left(\frac{6\pi}{3} t - 80.5°\right) = -\frac{3}{\pi}\left[0.0548 \sin\left(\frac{6\pi}{3} t - 80.5°\right)\right]$$

Similarly the steady-state response to v_4 is

$$i_4(t) = -\frac{3/4\pi}{8.07} \sin\left(\frac{8\pi}{3} t - 82.9°\right) = -\frac{3}{\pi}\left[0.031 \sin\left(\frac{8\pi}{3} t - 82.9°\right)\right]$$

By using superposition, the steady-state response of the R-L circuit to $v(t)$ is

$$i(t) = \frac{3}{2} - \frac{3}{\pi}\left[0.446 \sin\left(\frac{2\pi}{3} t - 63.4°\right) + 0.121 \sin\left(\frac{4\pi}{3} t - 76°\right)\right.$$
$$\left. + 0.0548 \sin\left(\frac{6\pi}{3} t - 80.5°\right) + 0.031 \sin\left(\frac{8\pi}{3} t - 82.9°\right)\right]$$

The steady-state response waveform can now be constructed point by point by superposition of the different terms which form $i(t)$. From the expressions for $v(t)$ and $i(t)$ we observe that *the source function and the response function do not have the same waveform.*

19-2. Fundamental and Harmonics. Corresponding to a specified radian frequency ω the sinusoidal function $C_1 \cos(\omega t + \varphi_1)$ is called a fundamental function or fundamental. For any integral value n the sinusoidal function $C_n \cos(n\omega t + \varphi_n)$ is said to be a harmonic (function) of the fundamental $C_1 \cos(\omega t + \varphi_1)$.

For a fundamental and its harmonics there is no restriction placed on the values or relative values of C_1, φ_1, C_n, and φ_n. For example, the functions $1.8 \cos(2\omega t - 23°)$ and $15.1 \cos(2\omega t + 57°)$ are both second harmonics of the fundamental $2.3 \cos(\omega t + 11°)$. For this fundamental $2.1 \cos(3\omega t + 25°)$ is a third harmonic, but $\cos(3.1\omega t + 36°)$ is not a harmonic of $\cos(\omega t + 11°)$ since the ratio of the two frequencies is not an integer. It is seen that $\cos \omega t$ and $\cos 3.1\omega t$ are both harmonics of $\cos 0.1\omega t$, the former being its tenth harmonic and the latter its 31st. We observe that whenever the ratio of frequencies of two sinusoids is a rational number then the two functions are both harmonics of a common fundamental. If the ratio of the two frequencies is not a rational number, the two functions are not harmonically related and may be said to be *incommensurate.* For example, the functions $\cos t$ and $\cos \sqrt{5}\, t$ are incommensurate since the ratio of their frequencies is $\sqrt{5}$, which is an irrational number.

Sum of a Fundamental and Its Harmonics. In Art. 19-1 we saw that the sum of a fundamental and its second harmonic is a periodic function whose period is that of the fundamental. We now generalize that statement by observing that if the infinite sum

$$f(t) = \sum_{k=0}^{k=\infty} C_k \cos{(k\omega t + \varphi_k)} \tag{19-4}$$

exists (i.e., converges) then this sum represents a periodic function with period $2\pi/\omega$. This is seen from the fact that every term in the sum has the period $2\pi/\omega$, and therefore their sum has the period $2\pi/\omega$ such that $f(t) = f(t + 2\pi/\omega)$.

In Fig. 19-2b the sum of four terms

$$f_a(t) = -(\sin t + \tfrac{1}{2}\sin 2t + \tfrac{1}{3}\sin 3t + \tfrac{1}{4}\sin 4t)$$

or $$f_a(t) = -\sum_{n=1}^{n=4} \frac{1}{n} \sin nt \tag{19-5}$$

is shown. In Eq. (19-5) the fundamental is $\sin t$ with radian frequency $\omega = 1$ and the period $T = 2\pi/\omega = 2\pi$. The summation contains the fundamental $\sin t$ and the first three harmonics. From Fig. 19-2b it is seen that the result of the summation is a periodic function with period $T = 2\pi$.

Two points are noted in connection with the sum of a number of sinusoidal functions:

1. If a summation includes a number of harmonics but no fundamental, then the sum is still periodic with the period of the fundamental. This is seen from the fact that in the summation of Eq. (19-4) no restriction is placed on the C_n, and C_1 can be equal to zero.

2. If a sum of sinusoidal functions contains an incommensurate term, the sum is not periodic.

We have now established the fact that the sum of a number of harmonic functions is periodic. It is natural to ask whether *any* periodic function can be written as the sum of a fundamental of the same period as the periodic function and its harmonics. This question has been answered by mathematicians, and the answer is presented below under the name of the Fourier-series Theorem.[1]

19-3. Fourier-series Theorem. Any periodic function $f(t)$ with period T, such that, in an interval T, $f(t)$ is always finite but not necessarily continuous (i.e., "piecewise continuous"), can be represented by the sum of a constant, a fundamental of period T, and its harmonics. This sum is

---

[1] Named after its discoverer, the French mathematician Jean Baptiste Joseph Fourier (1758–1830).

called a Fourier series and has the form

$$f(t) = f(t + T) = \sum_{k=0}^{k=\infty} C_k \cos \left(k \frac{2\pi}{T} t + \varphi_k \right) \qquad (19\text{-}6)$$

If, at a point $t = t_1$, $f(t)$ is discontinuous, then the summation results in the value

$$\sum_{k=0}^{\infty} C_k \cos \left(k \frac{2\pi}{T} t_1 + \varphi_k \right) = \frac{1}{2} [f(t_1^+) + f(t_1^-)] \qquad (19\text{-}6a)$$

The proof of this theorem will not be given here. We note, however, that this theorem is by no means self-evident and requires proof. The fact that the sum of a fundamental and its harmonics is a periodic function does not prove that a periodic function can be written as the sum of a fundamental and its harmonics. The conditions regarding the finiteness of the function and the requirement of piecewise continuity are met by all functions of interest in circuit analysis, i.e., all periodic source and response functions.[1]

Assuming the theorem to be true, we now have to study the evaluation of the amplitudes C_n and the phase angles φ_n of the harmonics which correspond to any periodic function $f(t)$. The calculation of these quantities is based on a certain property of sinusoidal functions referred to as their *orthogonality* property. This property is most easily discussed when the sinusoidal functions are written in exponential form. For this reason we discuss the various forms of the Fourier series before discussing the evaluation of the coefficients C_k and the phase angles φ_k.

19-4. Trigonometric and Exponential Form of the Fourier Series. The general term in the Fourier series, Eq. (19-6), can be written in exponential form,

$$C_k \cos \left(k \frac{2\pi}{T} t + \varphi_k \right) = \tfrac{1}{2} C_k e^{i[k(2\pi/T)t + \varphi_k]} + \tfrac{1}{2} C_k e^{-i[k(2\pi/T)t + \varphi_k]}$$

or $\quad C_k \cos \left(k \frac{2\pi}{T} t + \varphi_k \right) = (\tfrac{1}{2} C_k e^{i\varphi_k}) e^{jk(2\pi/T)t} + (\tfrac{1}{2} C_k e^{-i\varphi_k}) e^{-jk(2\pi/T)t}$

$$(19\text{-}7)$$

---

[1] If it is desired to express a function which is not periodic but which is piecewise continuous in an interval t_1 to t_2 by a Fourier series, it is possible to do so by assuming that the function has a period $T = t_2 - t_1$ and expanding. The result, which has the form of Eq. 19-6, is then used only in the interval t_1 to t_2. This technique is commonly used in boundary-value problems (where, incidentally, space coordinates, not time, are the variables).

Hence the series (19-6) can be written as follows:

$$f(t) = C_0 + \sum_{k=1}^{\infty} (\tfrac{1}{2}C_k e^{j\varphi_k})e^{jk(2\pi/T)t} + \sum_{k=1}^{\infty} (\tfrac{1}{2}C_k e^{-j\varphi_k})e^{-jk(2\pi/T)t} \quad (19\text{-}8)$$

Now we define the complex quantity $\mathbf{D}_k$,

$$\mathbf{D}_k \equiv \tfrac{1}{2}C_k e^{j\varphi_k} \qquad k = 1, 2, 3, \ldots$$

and the real quantity

$$D_0 \equiv C_0$$

Then Eq. (19-8) can be written in the form

$$f(t) = D_0 + \sum_{k=1}^{\infty} \mathbf{D}_k e^{jk(2\pi/T)t} + \sum_{k=1}^{\infty} \mathbf{D}_k^* e^{-jk(2\pi/T)t}$$

We now define

$$\mathbf{D}_{-k} \equiv \mathbf{D}_k^* = \tfrac{1}{2}C_k e^{-j\varphi}$$

then

$$\sum_{k=1}^{\infty} \mathbf{D}_k^* e^{-jk(2\pi/T)t} = \sum_{k=1}^{\infty} \mathbf{D}_{-k} e^{-jk(2\pi/T)t} = \sum_{k=-1}^{-\infty} \mathbf{D}_k e^{jk(2\pi/T)t}$$

Hence $f(t)$ can be written as the sum

$$f(t) = \sum_{k=-\infty}^{k=+\infty} \mathbf{D}_k e^{jk(2\pi/T)t} \qquad (19\text{-}9)$$

Note that the summation in Eq. (19-9) extends from $-\infty$ to $+\infty$, that is,

$$f(t) = D_0 + \mathbf{D}_1 e^{j(2\pi/T)t} + \mathbf{D}_2 e^{j(4\pi/T)t} + \cdots$$
$$+ \mathbf{D}_{-1} e^{-j(2\pi/T)t} + \mathbf{D}_{-2} e^{-j(4\pi/T)t} + \cdots$$

The form (19-9) is called the *exponential*, or *complex*, form of the Fourier series and is particularly useful because one (complex) quantity, $\mathbf{D}_k$, contains both the amplitude and the phase angle of each harmonic.

Another (trigonometric) form of the Fourier series is obtained by expanding

$$\cos\left(k\,\frac{2\pi}{T}\,t + \varphi_k\right) = \cos k\,\frac{2\pi}{T}\,t \cos\varphi_k - \sin k\,\frac{2\pi}{T}\,t \sin\varphi_k$$

We define

$$A_0 \equiv C_0$$
$$A_k \equiv C_k \cos\varphi_k = 2\,\mathrm{Re}\,\mathbf{D}_k \qquad k = 1, 2, 3, \ldots$$
$$B_k \equiv -C_k \sin\varphi_k = -2\,\mathrm{Im}\,\mathbf{D}_k \qquad k = 1, 2, 3, \ldots$$

and rewrite Eq. (19-6) in the form

$$f(t) = A_0 + \sum_{k=1}^{\infty} \left(A_k \cos k\,\frac{2\pi}{T}\,t + B_k \sin k\,\frac{2\pi}{T}\,t\right) \qquad (19\text{-}10)$$

Conversion of Series from One Form to Another. The three forms in which the Fourier series can be expressed are summarized in Table 19-1. The formulas which are used in conversion from one form to another are also listed in that table.

Example 19-1. Convert the Fourier series

$$f(t) = \sum_{k=-\infty}^{+\infty} \frac{1}{1+jk} e^{jkt}$$

to both trigonometric forms.

Solution. $D_0 = 1$, hence $C_0 = 1$, $A_0 = 1$. Since $\mathbf{D}_k = 1/(1 + jk)$,

$$\mathbf{D}_k = \left(\frac{1}{\sqrt{1+k^2}} \right) \underline{/-\tan^{-1} k},$$

$$f(t) = 1 + \sum_{k=1}^{\infty} \frac{2}{\sqrt{1+k^2}} \cos{(kt - \tan^{-1} k)}$$

Also

$$\mathbf{D}_k = \frac{1}{1+jk} = \frac{1}{1+k^2} - \frac{jk}{1+k^2}$$

Hence

$$A_k = \frac{2}{1+k^2} \qquad B_k = \frac{2k}{1+k^2}$$

and

$$f(t) = 1 + 2 \sum_{k=1}^{\infty} \frac{\cos kt + k \sin kt}{1+k^2}$$

19-5. The Orthogonality Property of Sinusoidal Functions.

A number of functions with one or more common characteristics which distinguish them from other functions is called a set of functions. As an example, periodic functions form a set of functions whose distinguishing characteristic is that they are periodic. A particular set of functions which is of special interest in analysis is called an *orthogonal* set. To define the property of orthogonality, we first define a useful symbol, δ_{mn}, called Kronecker's delta.[1] This symbol is zero or unity depending on whether the subscripts m and n are unequal or equal,

$$\delta_{mn} = \begin{cases} 0 & m \neq n \\ 1 & m = n \end{cases}$$

For example $\delta_{12} = 0$, and $\delta_{44} = 1$.

Definition of Orthogonal Functions. If the members of a set of complex functions[2] are designated by $\mathbf{f}_1(t), \mathbf{f}_2(t), \ldots, \mathbf{f}_m(t), \ldots, \mathbf{f}_n(t), \ldots$ and if there exists an interval $a < t < b$ and a function $w(t)$ called the

---

[1] Named after the mathematician Leopold Kronecker (1823–1891).

[2] Real functions are considered special cases of complex functions whose imaginary part is zero.

TABLE 19-1. THE THREE FORMS OF A FOURIER SERIES

Complex form	Trigonometric form 1	Trigonometric form 2
$$f(t) = \sum_{k=-\infty}^{+\infty} \mathbf{D}_k e^{jk(2\pi/T)t}$$	$$f(t) = C_0 + \sum_{k=1}^{\infty} C_k \cos\left(k\frac{2\pi}{T}t + \varphi_k\right)$$ $$= D_0 + \sum_{k=1}^{\infty} 2\,\mathrm{Re}\,[\mathbf{D}_k e^{jk(2\pi/T)t}]$$	$$f(t) = A_0 + \sum_{k=1}^{\infty} \left(A_k \cos k\frac{2\pi}{T}t + B_k \sin k\frac{2\pi}{T}t\right)$$

Conversion formulas for $k = 1, 2, 3, \ldots$

$$\mathbf{D}_k = \tfrac{1}{2}C_k \underline{/\varphi_k} \qquad \mathbf{D}_{-k} = \mathbf{D}_k^* \qquad \mathbf{D}_k = \tfrac{1}{2}A_k - j\tfrac{1}{2}B_k$$

$$C_k = 2D_k \qquad \varphi_k = \text{angle } \mathbf{D}_k \qquad C_k = \sqrt{A_k^2 + B_k^2} \qquad \varphi_k = -\tan^{-1}\frac{B_k}{A_k}$$

$$A_k = 2\,\mathrm{Re}\,\mathbf{D}_k \qquad B_k = -2\,\mathrm{Im}\,\mathbf{D}_k \qquad A_k = C_k \cos\varphi_k \qquad B_k = -C_k \sin\varphi_k$$

For $k = 0$,

$$D_0 = C_0 = A_0 \qquad B_0 \equiv 0$$

"weighting function" such that

$$\int_a^b \mathbf{f}_m(t)\mathbf{f}_n^*(t)w(t)\ dt\ =\ A_{mn}\delta_{mn}$$

where A_{mn} is a constant, then in the interval $a < t < b$ the set of functions is said to be orthogonal with respect to the chosen weighting function.

We shall not discuss orthogonal functions in general but shall state that the harmonic functions are orthogonal over a period of the fundamental with respect to the weighting function $w(t) = 1$. To illustrate this property, consider

$$\mathbf{f}_m(t)\ =\ e^{jm(2\pi/T)t}$$
$$\mathbf{f}_n^*(t)\ =\ e^{-jn(2\pi/T)t}$$

We have

$$\int_0^T \mathbf{f}_m(t)\mathbf{f}_n^*(t)\ dt\ =\ \int_0^T e^{j(m-n)(2\pi/T)t}\ dt \tag{19-11}$$

Now in the integral (19-11), if $m = n$, we have

$$\int_0^T dt\ =\ T\ =\ \text{const}$$

and if $m \neq n$,

$$\int_0^T e^{j(m-n)(2\pi/T)t}\ =\ \frac{e^{j(m-n)(2\pi/T)T} - 1}{j(m - n)(2\pi/T)}\ =\ 0$$

Since $e^{j(m-n)2\pi} = 1$ for integral values of m and n,

$$\int_0^T e^{jm(2\pi/T)t}e^{-jn(2\pi/T)t}\ dt\ =\ T\delta_{mn}$$

Hence the set of functions $e^{jm(2\pi/T)t}$ is *orthogonal* in an interval $0 < t < T$.

Similarly it can be shown that sinusoidal functions which are harmonically related are orthogonal because

$$\int_0^{2\pi} \sin\ mx\ \sin\ nx\ dx\ =\ \pi\delta_{mn}$$
$$\int_0^{2\pi} \sin\ mx\ \cos\ nx\ dx\ =\ 0$$
$$\int_0^{2\pi} \cos\ mx\ \cos\ nx\ dx\ =\ \pi\delta_{mn}$$

19-6. Evaluation of Fourier Coefficients. The set of complex values $\mathbf{D}_k$ or the set A_k, B_k is referred to as the Fourier coefficients. We shall now show how these coefficients are related to the periodic function $f(t)$ which the Fourier series represents. If we start with the complex form

$$f(t)\ =\ \sum_{k=-\infty}^{+\infty} \mathbf{D}_k e^{jk(2\pi/T)t} \tag{19-12}$$

and multiply both sides of Eq. (19-12) by $e^{-jn(2\pi/T)t}$, then

$$f(t)e^{-jn(2\pi/T)t} = \sum_{k=-\infty}^{+\infty} \mathbf{D}_k e^{j(k-n)(2\pi/T)t} \tag{19-13}$$

Now, if both sides of Eq. (19-13) are integrated between the limits $t = 0$ to $t = T$ with respect to t, we have

$$\int_0^T f(t)e^{-jn(2\pi/T)t}\,dt = \int_0^T \left(\sum_{k=-\infty}^{+\infty} \mathbf{D}_k e^{j(k-n)(2\pi/T)t} \right) dt$$

Interchanging summation and integration,[1]

$$\sum_{k=-\infty}^{+\infty} \int_0^T \mathbf{D}_k e^{j(k-n)(2\pi/T)t}\,dt = \sum_{k=-\infty}^{\infty} \mathbf{D}_k T \delta_{kn} = \mathbf{D}_n T$$

since in the above summation all the δ_{kn} except for $k = n$ are zero. Hence

$$\mathbf{D}_k = \frac{1}{T} \int_0^T f(t)e^{-jk(2\pi/T)t}\,dt \tag{19-14}$$

Using the conversion formulas from Table 19-1,

$$A_0 = D_0 = \frac{1}{T} \int_0^T f(t)\,dt = [f(t)]_{\text{av}} \tag{19-15a}$$

$$A_k = 2\,\text{Re}\,\mathbf{D}_k = \frac{2}{T} \int_0^T f(t) \cos k\frac{2\pi}{T} t\,dt \tag{19-15b}$$

$$B_k = -2\,\text{Im}\,\mathbf{D}_k = \frac{2}{T} \int_0^T f(t) \sin k\frac{2\pi}{T} t\,dt \tag{19-15c}$$

Thus the problem of representing a given waveform as a Fourier series is reduced to the "routine" problem of evaluating the integral (19-14) or the equivalent forms (19-15).

Before presenting examples of the evaluation of Fourier coefficients, we shall discuss some interesting aspects of this procedure. First, we observe that because of the orthogonality property of the sinusoidal functions the formulas which we obtained allow us to find any one term in the Fourier series without finding all the other terms. Moreover it can be shown (as we stated above) that the infinite Fourier series will converge to the value of the function at any point of continuity. To understand fully what this implies, we shall consider another method of using trigonometric series to approximate a periodic function. Suppose that it is known that a function $f(t)$ whose period is 2π can be approxi-

---

[1] Such interchanges are not always possible. The procedure can be justified in the present instance.

mated by the series

$$f_a(t) = A_1 \cos t + A_2 \cos 2t + A_3 \cos 3t$$

[i.e., suppose that we have evaluated A_0, B_1, B_2, B_3 from (19-15a) and (19-15c) and obtained zero as the answer].

For this approximation how shall we choose A_1, A_2, and A_3? One method is of course to apply Eq. (19-15b) and find the Fourier coefficients. An alternate method is the following: Choose three points in the interval $0 < t < T$, the points t_1, t_2, and t_3, and then choose A_1, A_2, and A_3 so that $f_a(t) = f(t)$ at the three chosen points; i.e., let

$$f_a(t_1) = f(t_1) = A_1 \cos t_1 + A_2 \cos 2t_1 + A_3 \cos 3t_1$$
$$f_a(t_2) = f(t_2) = A_1 \cos t_2 + A_2 \cos 2t_2 + A_3 \cos 3t_2$$
$$f_a(t_3) = f(t_3) = A_1 \cos t_3 + A_2 \cos 2t_3 + A_3 \cos 3t_3$$

and now solve these three simultaneous equations for A_1, A_2, and A_3. The disadvantages of this method compared with Fourier's method are clear. First, we need to solve simultaneous equations, which means that the coefficients cannot be determined independently of each other. Second, if we have found A_1, A_2, and A_3 and sketched $f_a(t)$ [which is supposed to approximate $f(t)$], if the approximation is not accurate enough and we desire another harmonic, this other harmonic (for example, A_4) cannot be determined without recalculating A_1, A_2, and A_3. Finally, this alternate method assures us only that f_a corresponds to $f(t)$ at the three chosen instants t_1, t_2, and t_3. We have no information about the nature of the approximation at other instants during the cycle. In the next article we shall discuss the nature of the approximation which is implied when the Fourier coefficients are used and when a finite number of terms in the series is used to approximate a given periodic function.

19-7. Squared-error Property of Fourier Series. If a periodic function $f(t)$ with period[1] 2π is expressed as the Fourier series

$$f(t) = C_0 + \sum_{k=1}^{\infty} C_k \cos (kt + \varphi_k)$$

then in practice we use a finite number of terms, i.e., the first N terms of the Fourier series, to approximate $f(t)$,

$$f(t) \approx f_N(t) = \sum_{k=0}^{N} C_k \cos (kt + \varphi_k)$$

Now the actual value of $f(t)$ differs from the values obtained by use of the

---

[1] Choosing the period as 2π does not detract from the generality of the discussion because a time-scale change can always be used to apply the result to arbitrary period T.

first N terms in the sum $f_N(t)$ by a function $\epsilon(t)$ which is called the error,

$$\epsilon(t) = f(t) - f_N(t)$$

In one period the average error is

$$E_{\text{av}} = \frac{1}{2\pi} \int_0^{2\pi} \epsilon(t)\, dt$$

The average error is not a useful number in determining the "quality" of the approximation because positive errors will tend to cancel negative errors. Thus, if in the interval 0 to 2π the function $f(t) = t$ is approximated by $f_N(t) = \pi$, $\epsilon = t - \pi$ and

$$\int_0^{2\pi} (t - \pi)\, dt = \left[\frac{t^2}{2} - \pi t \right]_0^{2\pi} = 2\pi(\pi - \pi) = 0$$

so that the average error is zero for this (gross) approximation.

To avoid this difficulty, Gauss[1] introduced the idea of mean squared error M,

$$M = \frac{1}{2\pi} \int_0^{2\pi} \epsilon^2(t)\, dt \qquad (19\text{-}16)$$

It can be shown that choice of the coefficients in the Fourier series is such that the mean squared error $(1/2\pi) \int_0^{2\pi} [f(t) - f_N(t)]^2\, dt$ is minimized for any given N. In other words, if we wish to approximate a periodic function by means of, say, five harmonics, then using the Fourier coefficients will result in the smallest possible mean squared error; any other choice of coefficients results in a larger mean squared error. Moreover, as we have already stated, the mean squared error will become zero if the Fourier series is allowed to become infinite.

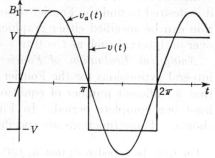

FIG. 19-3. The square wave $v(t)$ is to be approximated by the sine wave $v_a(t)$.

Example 19-2. The function $v_a(t) = B_1$ sin t is to be used to approximate the periodic function $v(t)$ shown in Fig. 19-3 so that the mean squared error is a minimum. Show that the value of B_1 for this condition is the Fourier coefficient given by Eq. (19-15c).

Solution. Since

$$v(t) = +V \qquad 0 < t < \pi$$
$$v(t) = -V \qquad \pi < t < 2\pi$$

[1] Karl Friedrich Gauss (1777–1855).

the error ϵ is given by

$$\epsilon = V - B_1 \sin t \qquad 0 < t < \pi$$
$$\epsilon = -V - B_1 \sin t \qquad \pi < t < 2\pi$$

Hence the mean squared error M is given as

$$M = \frac{1}{2\pi} \left[\int_0^\pi (V - B_1 \sin t)^2 \, dt + \int_\pi^{2\pi} (-V - B_1 \sin t)^2 \, dt \right]$$

Integrating and substituting the limits,

$$M = V^2 - \frac{4}{\pi} V B_1 + \frac{B_1^2}{2}$$

In order to make M a minimum, $\partial M / \partial B_1$ is formed and set to zero,

$$\frac{\partial M}{\partial B_1} = -\frac{4V}{\pi} + B_1 \qquad \frac{\partial M}{\partial B_1} = 0 \text{ gives } B_1 = \frac{4V}{\pi}$$

Since $\partial^2 M / \partial B_1^2 = +1$, a positive number, the value $B_1 = 4V/\pi$ gives minimum mean squared error. The Fourier coefficient B_1 is found by use of Eq. (19-15c), by using $2\pi / T = 1$,

$$B_1 = \frac{1}{\pi} \int_0^{2\pi} v(t) \sin t \, dt$$

or

$$B_1 = \frac{1}{\pi} \left[\int_0^\pi V \sin t \, dt + \int_\pi^{2\pi} (-V) \sin t \, dt \right] = 4V/\pi$$

exactly as was obtained by minimizing the mean squared error.

19-8. Evaluation of Fourier Coefficients, Examples.   In Art. 19-6 the complex and real Fourier coefficients were given as definite integrals.   If it is desired to find the Fourier series for a given function, then the function can be specified either graphically by its waveform or analytically over an interval such as $t = 0$ to $t = T$ by means of equations.

Analytical Evaluation of Fourier Coefficients.   In order to use the integral expressions for the Fourier coefficients correctly, it is necessary that a sufficient number of equations be written to specify $f(t)$ over at least one complete period.   In Fig. 19-4 three periodic functions are shown.   These functions are specified analytically as follows.

For $f_a(t)$ the period is 3; that is, $f_a(t) = f_a(t + 3)$.   The equations which define this function are

$$f_a(t) = t + 1 \qquad -1 < t < 2$$
$$f_a(t) = t - 2 \qquad 2 < t < 5$$
$$f_a(t) = t - 5 \qquad 5 < t < 8$$

We observe that the equation $f_a(t) = t - 2$ is valid only in the stated interval $2 < t < 5$; a different analytical expression is required to specify the function in each 3-sec interval.

For the function $f_b(t)$ the following five equations specify the function in the interval from $t = 0$ to $t = T$:

$$f_b(t) = 0 \qquad 0 < t < T_1$$

$$f_b(t) = A \qquad T_1 < t < \left(\frac{T}{2} - T_1\right)$$

$$f_b(t) = 0 \qquad \left(\frac{T}{2} - T_1\right) < t < \left(\frac{T}{2} + T_1\right)$$

$$f_b(t) = -A \qquad \left(\frac{T}{2} + T_1\right) < t < (T - T_1)$$

$$f_b(t) = 0 \qquad (T - T_1) < t < T$$

The function $f_c(t)$, for $A = 1$, is given as

or
$$
\begin{aligned}
f_c(t) &= |\sin t| \\
f_c(t) &= \sin t & 0 < t < \pi \\
f_c(t) &= \sin (t - \pi) & \pi < t < 2\pi \\
f_c(t) &= \sin (t - 2\pi) & 2\pi < t < 3\pi
\end{aligned}
$$

Clearly the expression $\sin t$ is not valid in the interval $\pi < t < 2\pi$; we observe that $f_c(t)$ has only positive values, while the function $\sin t$ in the interval $\pi < t < 2\pi$ has negative values. Note, however, that $\sin (t - \pi)$ does give the correct answer for $f_c(t)$ in that interval.

When a function is specified by means of several equations over one period, then the integral which defines the Fourier coefficients must be

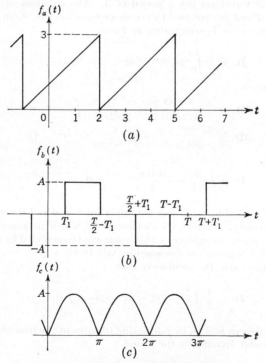

FIG. 19-4. Three periodic waveforms.

expressed as the sum of several integrals. For example, the complex coefficients $\mathbf{D}_k$ are given by

$$\mathbf{D}_k = \frac{1}{T} \int_0^T f(t) e^{-jk(2\pi/T)t} \, dt$$

To evaluate D_k for the waveform $f_a(t)$, for example, we write

$$D_k = \frac{1}{T} \left[\int_0^2 (t + 1) e^{-jk(2\pi/T)t} \, dt + \int_2^3 (t - 2) e^{-jk(2\pi/T)t} \, dt \right]$$

Example 19-3. Find the Fourier series for the saw-tooth waveform of Fig. 19-5.

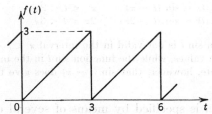

Fig. 19-5. Periodic saw-tooth waveform.

Solution. This waveform has a period of 3. The equation of the waveform in the interval 0 to T can be expressed by the single equation $f(t) = t$, $0 < t < 3$. Using the complex form of the Fourier series, we have

$$\mathbf{D}_k = \tfrac{1}{3} \int_0^3 t e^{-jk(2\pi/3)t} \, dt$$

Integrating by parts,

$$3\mathbf{D}_k = \frac{t e^{-jk(2\pi/3)t}}{-jk(2\pi/3)} \Big]_0^3 + \frac{1}{jk(2\pi/3)} \int_0^3 e^{-jk(2\pi/3)t} \, dt$$

or

$$3\mathbf{D}_k = \frac{3 e^{-jk2\pi} - 0}{-jk(2\pi/3)} + \frac{1}{k^2(4\pi^2/9)} (e^{-jk2\pi} - 1)$$

Since $e^{-jk2\pi} = 1$,

$$\mathbf{D}_k = j \frac{3}{2\pi k} = j \frac{0.478}{k} \qquad k \neq 0 \tag{19-17}$$

We observe first that this result does not apply for $k = 0$ and the value D_0 will have to be found separately. Second, the coefficients $\mathbf{D}_k$, which are generally complex, are, for this example, purely imaginary. This result can be predicted by certain symmetry considerations of $f(t)$ which are discussed in Art. 19-11.

To calculate the value D_0, we observe that

$$D_0 = \frac{1}{T} \int_0^T f(t) \, dt = \text{av value of } f(t)$$

In this example we can find D_0 by calculating the area of the triangular pulse between $t = 0$ and $t = 3$ and dividing by the period,

$$D_0 = (\tfrac{1}{2})(3)(3)(\tfrac{1}{3}) = \tfrac{3}{2} = 1.5$$

Hence we can write $f(t)$ in complex form,

$$f(t) = 1.5 + j0.478 \left(e^{j(2\pi/3)t} + \tfrac{1}{2}e^{j(4\pi/3)t} + \tfrac{1}{3}e^{j(6\pi/3)t} + \cdots \right.$$
$$\left. + -e^{-j(2\pi/3)t} + \frac{1}{-2}e^{-j(4\pi/3)t} + \frac{1}{-3}e^{-j(6\pi/3)t} + \cdots \right)$$

This series can be converted to real form either by use of the formulas in Table 19-1 or by "pairing" the terms $e^{j[k(2\pi/3)]t}$ with the terms $e^{-jk(2\pi/3)t}$; using the latter method, we write

$$f(t) = 1.5 + 0.478 \left(\frac{e^{j(2\pi/3)t} - e^{-j(2\pi/3)t}}{-j} + \frac{e^{j(4\pi/3)t} - e^{-j(4\pi/3)t}}{-j2} \right.$$
$$\left. + \frac{e^{j(6\pi/3)t} - e^{-j(6\pi/3)t}}{-j3} + \cdots \right)$$

or

$$f(t) = 1.5 - 0.956 \left(\sin \frac{2\pi}{3}t + \frac{1}{2}\sin \frac{4\pi}{3}t + \frac{1}{3}\sin \frac{6\pi}{3}t + \cdots + \frac{1}{k}\sin \frac{2\pi k}{3}t + \cdots \right)$$

This result shows that, for this function, the real coefficients are

$$A_0 = 1.5 \qquad A_k = 0, \; k = 1, 2, 3, \ldots \qquad B_k = -\frac{0.956}{k}$$

The reader should verify this result by application of the formulas (19-15) which define A_k and B_k.

With reference to this example the following observations can be made:

1. A periodic waveform has been written as the sum of a constant value and an infinite number of sinusoidal functions. The constant value is the average value of the function and is referred to as the "d-c" component of the function.

2. In the real (trigonometric) form of the Fourier series there are only *sine* terms; the cosine terms are zero (except for A_0). This is not a general result and applies only to certain types of functions, which are studied below.

3. The amplitude of the higher harmonics, B_n, decreases with n, the order of the harmonic. This is not always so. For example, it is possible that for a given periodic function the amplitude of the fifth harmonic is greater than the amplitude of the fourth harmonic. It is, however, always true that the amplitude of the nth harmonic approaches zero as n approaches infinity. In other words, although the amplitude of successive harmonics may "go up and down" as n increases, they will all tend to zero as n increases. This property of the Fourier coefficients (amplitudes of harmonics) can be proved by use of the conditions stated in the Fourier-series theorem.

4. Since, in this example, the amplitude of the kth harmonic decreases as $1/k$, for most practical purposes it will be sufficient to represent such a function as the sum of a finite number of terms of the Fourier series. In

Fig. 19-2b the sum of a fundamental and the first four harmonics is shown for a series in which the harmonic amplitudes decrease as $1/k$. A comparison of Fig. 19-2a and b shows that, except for the difference in their average values and a scale factor $2\pi/3$ in their period, the two functions are similar in waveform, f_a being a fairly good approximation to $f(t)$. If more harmonics are added to $f_a(t)$ (with proper amplitudes, of course), the resulting waveshape will resemble the saw-tooth waveform more and more closely.

Graphical Determination of Fourier Coefficients. It frequently happens that a periodic function is specified graphically (e.g., by means of an oscillogram). To find the Fourier series for such a function, it may not be convenient to use "curve fitting" for the purpose of obtaining equations which describe the function over one period. It is however possible to evaluate the real Fourier coefficients A_k and B_k graphically by evaluating the corresponding integrals graphically.

Example 19-4. Evaluate graphically the Fourier coefficient B_1 for the waveform of Fig. 19-5. (The waveform of Fig. 19-5 is identical to that of Fig. 19-7a below.) *Solution.* From Eq. (19-15c) we have

$$B_1 = \frac{2}{3} \int_0^3 t \sin \frac{2\pi}{3} t \, dt \tag{19-18}$$

To evaluate B_1 graphically, we plot the integrand $t \sin (2\pi/3)t$ and evaluate the area under this graph between $t = 0$ and $t = 3$. The graph of $t \sin (2\pi/3)t$ is shown in Fig. 19-6.

The area under the curve $t \sin (2\pi/3)t$ in the interval $t = 0$ to $t = 3$ may be found by counting the number of "positive" and "negative" squares in Fig. 19-6.

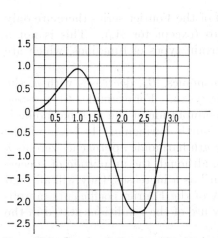

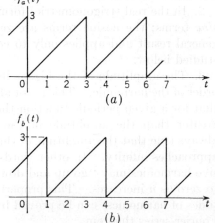

FIG. 19-6. Graph of the function $t \sin (2\pi t/3)$ used in the graphical evaluation of the coefficient B_1 for the waveform of Fig. 19-5.

FIG. 19-7. (a) Saw-tooth waveform. (b) Waveform of (a) delayed by one unit of time.

In Fig. 19-6 each square is $(\frac{1}{4})(\frac{1}{4}) = \frac{1}{16}$. There are approximately 11.4 squares above the line $f(t) = 0$ and about 34.5 squares below the $f(t) = 0$ line; therefore the area under the curve is $(11.4 - 34.5)/16$, and from Eq. (19-18)

$$B_1 = \frac{\frac{2}{3}(11.4 - 34.5)}{16} = -0.96$$

The value of B_1 obtained by analytical means was $B_1 = -3/\pi = -0.955$, which agrees closely with the above value. To find B_2, a plot of the function $t \sin (4\pi/3)t$ is made, and from the graph of this function the area under the curve is found. The value of B_2 is two-thirds of this area. The other Fourier coefficients are similarly found.

In order to evaluate the integrals $f(t) \sin k(2\pi/3)t$ or $f(t) \cos k(2\pi/3)t$ graphically, systematic tabulations which introduce short cuts into the calculations can be devised (see Probs. 19-11 and 19-12).

19-9. Time Displacement. We have seen that the Fourier series for the saw-tooth function shown in Fig. 19-7a is

$$f_a(t) = 1.5 - \frac{3}{\pi} \sum_{k=1}^{\infty} \frac{1}{k} \sin \left(k \frac{2\pi}{3} t \right)$$

$$= 1.5 - \frac{3}{\pi} \sum_{k=1}^{\infty} \frac{1}{k} \cos \left(k \frac{2\pi}{3} t - \frac{\pi}{2} \right) \quad (19\text{-}19)$$

The function $f_b(t)$ shown in Fig. 19-7b has the same waveform as $f_a(t)$ but is delayed in time by one unit with respect to $f_a(t)$, that is,

$$f_b(t) = f_a(t - 1)$$

Thus the Fourier series for $f_b(t)$ can be obtained from the Fourier series for $f_a(t)$ [Eq. (19-19)] by replacing t with $t - 1$ in Eq. (19-19).

$$f_b(t) = 1.5 - \frac{3}{\pi} \sum_{k=1}^{\infty} \frac{1}{k} \cos \left[k \frac{2\pi}{3} (t - 1) - \frac{\pi}{2} \right] \quad (19\text{-}20a)$$

or

$$f_b(t) = 1.5 - \frac{3}{\pi} \sum_{k=1}^{\infty} \frac{1}{k} \cos \left[k \frac{2\pi}{3} t + \left(-\frac{2\pi k}{3} - \frac{\pi}{2} \right) \right] \quad (19\text{-}20b)$$

Now Eq. (19-20b) is the Fourier series for the function $f_b(t)$ in the form

$$f_b(t) = C_0 + \sum_{k=1}^{\infty} C_k \cos \left(k \frac{2\pi}{T} + \varphi_k \right) \quad (19\text{-}21)$$

while Eq. (19-19) is the corresponding trigonometric form for the function

$f_a(t)$. A comparison of Eqs. (19-19) and (19-20b) shows that the time displacement leaves the value of the coefficients C_k unchanged but changes the angle φ_k of each harmonic. This result, illustrated for a particular example, can be proved in general in the form of the following theorem.

Time-displacement Theorem. If a function $f_a(t)$ has the Fourier series

$$f_a(t) = \sum_{k=-\infty}^{+\infty} \mathbf{D}_k e^{jk(2\pi/T)t} = C_0 + \sum_{k=1}^{\infty} C_k \cos\left(k\, \frac{2\pi}{T}\, t + \varphi_k \right) \quad (19\text{-}22)$$

then this function delayed in time by t_1 has the Fourier series

$$f_a(t - t_1) = \sum_{k=-\infty}^{+\infty} \left[\mathbf{D}_k e^{-jk(2\pi/T)t_1} \right] e^{jk(2\pi/T)t}$$

$$= C_0 + \sum_{k=1}^{\infty} C_k \cos\left(k\, \frac{2\pi}{T}\, t + \varphi_k - \frac{2\pi t_1}{T}\, k \right) \quad (19\text{-}23)$$

Since (19-23) was obtained from Eq. (19-22) by replacing t with $t - t_1$, the proof of the statement is evident. We observe that the effect of a time delay t_1 on the original complex coefficients $\mathbf{D}_k$ is the change in phase angle by the amount $k2\pi t_1/T$. Thus

$$(\mathbf{D}_k)_{\text{delayed function}} = (\mathbf{D}_k)_{\text{original function}} e^{-jk(2\pi t_1/T)} \quad (19\text{-}24)$$

We summarize this discussion as follows: If the function $f_b(t)$ has the same waveform as $f_a(t)$ but is delayed in time by t_1, then the harmonic amplitudes of the two functions are identical and the phase angle of the kth harmonic of f_b is $k2\pi t_1/T$ rad less than the phase angle of the corresponding harmonic of $f_a(t)$.

The most important application of this theorem deals with the converse: If two functions have the same harmonic amplitudes and if the phase angle differs so that the phase shift between corresponding harmonics is proportional to the frequency of the harmonic, then the two functions have the same waveform.

To illustrate the importance of this statement, we recall that networks which contain energy-storing elements have their own characteristic frequency response, as discussed in Chaps. 13, 15, and 18. Suppose now that the source function which is impressed on a network is periodic so that it can be expressed as a Fourier series. The steady-state response to such a source function can be calculated by superposition, i.e., by using phasor representation for each harmonic. Thus the response for each harmonic has an amplitude which is determined by the absolute value of the complex network function at the frequency of the harmonic. The phase angle of a harmonic of the response waveform will differ from the phase angle of the corresponding harmonic of the source waveform by the angle of the network function at the frequency of the harmonic. A little thought will show that the steady-state response waveform has the same shape as the source waveform only if all response harmonics have the same relative amplitudes as the source harmonics *and* if the phase angles of the response harmonics differ from those of the source harmonics proportionally to the frequency of the harmonics. For this condition it is necessary that the *network* function have the *same* absolute value for all frequencies and a *phase angle which is proportional to frequency*.[1] This matter was mentioned in Art. 18-9 and is discussed further in the article on Ideal Filters (Art. 19-18). When generalized, it becomes a cornerstone in the theory of transmission of signals.

19-10. Symmetry Properties of Certain Waveforms. For the waveform of Fig. 19-7a, the Fourier series has a constant and sine terms only, while, for Fig. 19-7b,

$$f_b(t) = 1.5 - \frac{3}{\pi} \sum_{k=1}^{\infty} \frac{1}{k} \cos\left[k \frac{2\pi}{3} t - \left(\frac{2\pi k}{3} + \frac{\pi}{2}\right) \right]$$

or $\quad f_b(t) = 1.5 - \dfrac{3}{\pi} \displaystyle\sum_{k=1}^{\infty} \left[\dfrac{1}{k} \cos\left(\dfrac{2\pi k}{3} + \dfrac{\pi}{2}\right) \cos k \dfrac{2\pi t}{3} \right.$

$$\left. - \frac{1}{k} \sin\left(\frac{2\pi k}{3} + \frac{\pi}{2}\right) \sin k \frac{2\pi}{3} t \right]$$

i.e., for $f_a(t)$, $A_0 = 1.5$, $A_k = 0$ $(k > 1)$, $B_k = -3/\pi k$; and for $f_b(t)$, $A_0 = 1.5$, $A_k = -(3/\pi k) \cos(2\pi k/3 + \pi/2)$ if $k > 1$,

$$B_k = -\left(\frac{3}{\pi k}\right) \sin\left(\frac{2\pi k}{3} + \frac{\pi}{2}\right)$$

The fact that $f_a(t)$ has a simpler form is the result of certain symmetry properties of $f_a(t)$. Such symmetry properties will now be considered in general.

Even Function. A function $f(t)$ is said to be "even" with respect to the axis $t = a$ if $f(a + t) = f(a - t)$. In particular, if the axis of symmetry is $t = 0$ so that $f(t) = f(-t)$, the function is said to be an *even function*. The term even function is used because the Maclaurin series for such a function contains only even powers of the independent variable. As an example of an even function, we cite $f(t) = at^2$ or $f(t) = A \cos t$. Since $(-t)^2 = t^2$ and $\cos t = \cos(-t)$, these two functions are even functions. Inspection of Fig. 19-8a shows that the function shown, $f_1(t)$, is an even

---

[1] Such networks are called "linear-phase networks."

function.   In Fig. 19-8*b*, $f_2(t)$ is symmetrical with respect to $t = 2$.   In general, if $f(t)$ is an even function, then $f(t - a)$ is even with respect to $t = a$.   It is left to the reader to show that sums and products of even functions are even functions.   An even function can be identified by

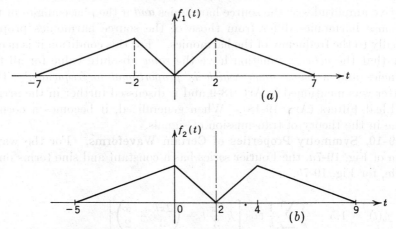

Fig. 19-8. (*a*) The function $f_1(t)$ is an even function.   (*b*) The function $f_2(t)$ is even with respect to (the axis) $t = 2$.

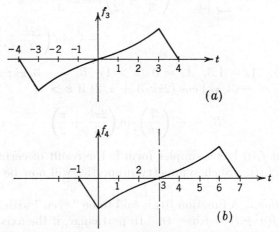

Fig. 19-9. (*a*) The function $f_3(t)$ is an odd function.   (*b*) The function $f_4(t)$ is odd with respect to (the axis) $t = 3$.

observing that the graph of the function for positive t is the mirror image of the graph for negative t.   If a mirror is placed at $t = 0$ perpendicular to the t axis, then the waveform of $f(t)$ for negative values of t will be the image of its waveform for positive values of t.   For this reason even functions are said to have "zero-axis" symmetry.

Odd Function.   A function is said to be odd with respect to an axis $t = b$ if $f(b + t) = -f(b - t)$.   In particular, if $b = 0$ so that

$$f(t) = -f(-t)$$

then the function is said to be an *odd function*.   The functions t^3 and $\sin t$ are examples of odd functions.   In Fig. 19-9a an odd function is shown.   The function $f_4(t)$ shown in Fig. 19-9b is odd with respect to $t = 3$ because $f_4(t + 3) = -f_4(-t + 3)$.

The sum of two odd functions is an odd function, but the product of two odd functions is an even function.   To prove the latter, let $f_5(t)$ and $f_6(t)$ be two odd functions.   Let $f(t) = f_5(t)f_6(t)$.   Then $f(-t) = f_5(-t)f_6(-t)$. Since f_5 and f_6 are odd, $f_5(-t)f_6(-t) = (-)f_5(t)(-)f_6(t) = f_5(t)f_6(t) = f(t)$. Hence the product f_5f_6 is even.

Expression of Arbitrary Function in Terms of Its Even and Odd Components.   Let $f(t)$ be an arbitrary function.   We can write

$$2f(t) = f(t) - f(-t) + f(t) + f(-t)$$

or $f(t) = \frac{1}{2}[f(t) + f(-t)] + \frac{1}{2}[f(t) - f(-t)] = \phi_1(t) + \phi_2(t)$

In this equation $\phi_1(t) = \frac{1}{2}[f(t) + f(-t)]$ is an even function since

$$\phi_1(-t) = \frac{1}{2}[f(-t) + f(t)] = \phi_1(t)$$

Similarly it can be shown that $\phi_2(t)$ is an odd function.   Thus an arbitrary function is expressed as the sum of an even and an odd function.

Integration of Even and Odd Functions.   In evaluating Fourier coefficients, integrals of the form

$$\int_{-a}^{+a} f(x) \sin x \, dx = \int_{-a}^{+a} F(x) \, dx$$

occur.   We shall now show that if $F(x)$ is an odd function then

$$\int_{-a}^{+a} F(x) \, dx \equiv 0$$

independently of the value of a.   To show this, we write

$$\int_{-a}^{+a} F(x) \, dx = \int_{-a}^{0} F(x) \, dx + \int_{0}^{a} F(x) \, dx$$

Now in the integral $\int_{-a}^{0} F(x) \, dx$ let $y = -x$; then

$$\int_{-a}^{0} F(x) \, dx = - \int_{a}^{0} F(-y) \, dy = \int_{0}^{a} F(-y) \, dy$$

Therefore $\int_{-a}^{+a} F(x) \, dx = \int_{0}^{a} F(-y) \, dy + \int_{0}^{a} F(x) \, dx$

Since x and y are ("dummy") variables of integration,

$$\int_0^a F(-y)\,dy = \int_0^a F(-x)\,dx$$

Hence

$$\int_{-a}^a F(x)\,dx = \int_0^a [F(x) + F(-x)]\,dx \tag{19-25}$$

If $F(x)$ is an odd function, then $F(x) + F(-x) = 0$ and the integral (19-25) is zero. If $F(x)$ is an even function, then $F(x) + F(-x) = 2F(x)$. Hence

$$\int_{-a}^{+a} F(x)\,dx = \begin{cases} 0 & \text{if } F(x) \text{ is odd} \\ 2\int_0^a F(x)\,dx & \text{if } F(x) \text{ is even} \end{cases} \tag{19-26}$$

Half-wave Symmetry. If $f(t)$ is periodic with period T so that

$$f(t) = f(t + T)$$

and if in addition

$$f(t) = -f\left(t + \frac{T}{2}\right)$$

then the periodic function is said to have *half-wave* symmetry. In Fig. 19-10a a waveform with half-wave symmetry is shown.

Quarter-wave Symmetry. If a periodic function has half-wave symmetry and in addition is either an even or an odd function, then it is said to have even or odd quarter-wave symmetry. In Fig. 19-10b a waveform with odd quarter-wave symmetry is shown.

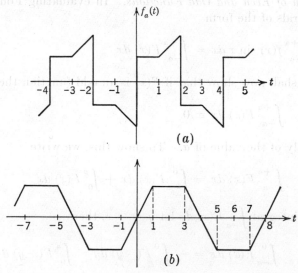

FIG. 19-10. (a) A waveform with half-wave symmetry. (b) A waveform with odd quarter-wave symmetry.

It will be shown in the next article that the calculation of the real Fourier coefficients is simplified if the periodic function has any of the symmetry properties discussed above.

19-11. Fourier Coefficient of Symmetrical Waveforms. *Odd Functions.* If $f(t)$ is an odd periodic function with period T, then its Fourier series consists of sine terms only, i.e.,

$$f(t) = \sum_{k=1}^{\infty} B_k \sin k \frac{2\pi}{T} t \qquad f(t) = -f(-t) \qquad (19\text{-}27a)$$

where
$$B_k = \frac{4}{T} \int_0^{T/2} f(t) \sin k \frac{2\pi}{T} t \, dt \qquad f(t) = -f(-t) \qquad (19\text{-}27b)$$

Proof. In general,

$$A_k = \frac{2}{T} \int_0^T f(t) \cos k \frac{2\pi}{T} t \, dt$$

$$B_k = \frac{2}{T} \int_0^T f(t) \sin k \frac{2\pi}{T} t \, dt$$

Since $f(t)$ is periodic, $f(t) = f(t - T)$; hence the limits in the integrals which define A_k and B_k can be taken as $-T/2$ to $T/2$. Hence in general

$$A_k = \frac{2}{T} \int_{-T/2}^{T/2} f(t) \cos k \frac{2\pi}{T} t \, dt \qquad (19\text{-}28a)$$

$$B_k = \frac{2}{T} \int_{-T/2}^{T/2} f(t) \sin k \frac{2\pi}{T} t \, dt \qquad (19\text{-}28b)$$

If $f(t)$ is an odd function, the integrand in Eq. (19-28a) is also odd because $\cos (2\pi kt/T)$ is an even function and the product of an even and an odd function is odd. From Eq. (19-26) we conclude that $A_k = 0$. Since the product of two odd functions is an even function, we conclude from Eq. (19-26) that Eq. (19-27b) is a simplified formula for B_k if $f(t)$ is odd.

Even Functions. If $f(t)$ is an even periodic function, then

$$f(t) = \sum_{k=0}^{\infty} A_k \cos k \frac{2\pi}{T} t \, dt \qquad f(t) = f(-t) \qquad (19\text{-}29a)$$

where
$$A_k = \frac{4}{T} \int_0^{T/2} f(t) \cos k \frac{2\pi}{T} t \, dt \qquad k > 0 \qquad (19\text{-}29b)$$

$$A_0 = \frac{2}{T} \int_0^{T/2} f(t) \, dt \qquad (19\text{-}29c)$$

The proof of Eqs. (19-29) is left as an exercise for the reader.

Half-wave Symmetry. If a function has half-wave symmetry (also called "mirror" symmetry), $f(t) = -f(t + T/2)$. Then its Fourier coefficients will not include even *harmonics* and

$$f(t) = \sum_{k=1}^{\infty} A_{2k-1} \cos (2k - 1) \frac{2\pi}{T} t + B_{2k-1} \sin (2k - 1) \frac{2\pi}{T} t \quad (19\text{-}30a)$$

where

$$A_{2k-1} = \frac{4}{T} \int_0^{T/2} f(t) \cos (2k - 1) \frac{2\pi}{T} t \, dt \quad (19\text{-}30b)$$

$$B_{2k-1} = \frac{4}{T} \int_0^{T/2} f(t) \sin (2k - 1) \frac{2\pi}{T} t \, dt \quad (19\text{-}30c)$$

Proof. In general

$$\tfrac{1}{2} A_k - j\tfrac{1}{2} B_k = \mathbf{D}_k = \frac{1}{T} \int_0^T f(t) e^{-jk(2\pi/T)t} \, dt$$

or

$$\mathbf{D}_k = \frac{1}{T} \int_0^{T/2} f(t) e^{-jk(2\pi/T)t} \, dt + \frac{1}{T} \int_{T/2}^T f(t) e^{-jk(2\pi/T)t} \, dt$$

$$(19\text{-}31)$$

In the integral

$$\int_{T/2}^T f(t) e^{-jk(2\pi/T)t} \, dt$$

let $x = t - T/2$; then

$$\int_{T/2}^T f(t) e^{-jk(2\pi/T)t} \, dt = \int_0^{T/2} f\left(x + \frac{T}{2}\right) e^{-jk(2\pi/T)(x+T/2)} \, dx$$

If the function f has half-wave symmetry, then $f(x + T/2) = -f(x)$. Hence

$$\int_0^{T/2} f\left(x + \frac{T}{2}\right) e^{-jk(2\pi/T)(x+T/2)} \, dx = - \int_0^{T/2} f(x) e^{-jk(2\pi/T)(x+T/2)} \, dx$$

$$= - \int_0^{T/2} f(t) e^{-jk(2\pi/T)(t+T/2)} \, dt$$

Hence, substituting in Eq. (19-31),

$$\mathbf{D}_k = \frac{1}{T} \int_0^{T/2} f(t) e^{-jk(2\pi/T)t}(1 - e^{-jk\pi}) \, dt$$

Now $e^{-jk\pi} = (-1)^k$. Hence $\mathbf{D}_k = 0$ for k even and

$$\mathbf{D}_k = \frac{2}{T} \int_0^{T/2} f(t) e^{-jk(2\pi/T)t} \, dt \qquad \text{for } k \text{ odd}$$

Further simplification of the integral formulas for the Fourier coefficients results if the function has quarter-wave symmetry. The corresponding formulas are given in Table 19-2; proof is left as an exercise for the reader. In the examples below we show how the use of symmetry properties simplifies the calculation of Fourier coefficients.

TABLE 19-2. FOURIER COEFFICIENTS OF SYMMETRICAL PERIODIC WAVEFORMS

Type of symmetry	Conditions	Form of the Fourier series	Formulas for the coefficients
Odd function	$f(t) = -f(-t)$	$f(t) = \displaystyle\sum_{k=1}^{\infty} B_k \sin k \frac{2\pi}{T} t$	$A_k = 0; \quad B_k = \dfrac{4}{T} \displaystyle\int_0^{T/2} f(t) \sin k \frac{2\pi}{T} t \, dt$
Even function	$f(t) = f(-t)$	$f(t) = \displaystyle\sum_{k=0}^{\infty} A_k \cos k \frac{2\pi}{T} t$	$B_k = 0; \quad A_k = \dfrac{4}{T} \displaystyle\int_0^{T/2} f(t) \cos k \frac{2\pi}{T} t \, dt; \quad A_0 = \dfrac{2}{T} \displaystyle\int_0^{T/2} f(t) \, dt$
Half wave	$f(t) = -f\left(t + \dfrac{T}{2}\right)$	$f(t) = \displaystyle\sum_{k=1}^{\infty} \left[A_{2k-1} \cos (2k-1) \frac{2\pi}{T} t + B_{2k-1} \sin (2k-1) \frac{2\pi}{T} t \right]$	$\left.\begin{array}{c} A_{2k-1} \\ B_{2k-1} \end{array}\right\} = \dfrac{4}{T} \displaystyle\int_0^{T/2} f(t) \begin{array}{c} \cos \\ \sin \end{array} (2k-1) \frac{2\pi}{T} t \, dt$
Odd quarter wave	$f(t) = -f(-t)$ and $f(t) = -f\left(t + \dfrac{T}{2}\right)$	$f(t) = \displaystyle\sum_{k=1}^{\infty} B_{2k-1} \sin (2k-1) \frac{2\pi}{T} t$	$A_k = 0; \quad B_{2k-1} = \dfrac{8}{T} \displaystyle\int_0^{T/4} f(t) \sin (2k-1) \frac{2\pi}{T} t \, dt$
Even quarter wave	$f(t) = f(-t)$ and $f(t) = -f\left(t + \dfrac{T}{2}\right)$	$f(t) = \displaystyle\sum_{k=1}^{\infty} A_{2k-1} \cos (2k-1) \frac{2\pi}{T} t$	$B_k = 0; \quad A_{2k-1} = \dfrac{8}{T} \displaystyle\int_0^{T/4} f(t) \cos (2k-1) \frac{2\pi}{T} t \, dt$

Example 19-5. Find the Fourier series for the periodic odd function shown in Fig. 19-11.

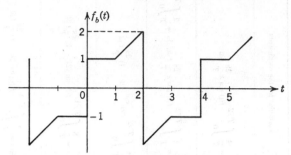

FIG. 19-11. An odd function.

Solution. The period T is 4. The function $f(t)$ is defined by the four equations

$$
\begin{aligned}
f(t) &= 1 & 0 < t < 1 \\
f(t) &= t & 1 < t < 2 \\
f(t) &= -4 + t & 2 < t < 3 \\
f(t) &= -1 & 3 < t < 4
\end{aligned}
$$

If no use of the symmetry properties is made, four integrals must be evaluated to determine D_k or eight integrals to evaluate A_k and B_k. Since $f(t)$ is odd, we know immediately that $A_k = 0$. The general term B_k is then given by

$$
B_k = \frac{4}{4} \int_0^1 (1) \sin k \frac{2\pi}{4} t \, dt + \frac{4}{4} \int_1^2 t \sin k \frac{2\pi}{4} t \, dt
$$

Integrating and substituting the limits we have

$$
B_k = \frac{2}{\pi} \left[\frac{1 - 2(-1)^k}{k} - \frac{2}{\pi k^2} \sin k \frac{\pi}{2} \right]
$$

Enumerating,

$$
B_1 = \frac{2}{\pi} \left[1 - 2(-1) - \frac{2}{\pi} \sin \frac{\pi}{2} \right] = \frac{2}{\pi} \left[3 - \frac{2}{\pi} \right]
$$

$$
B_2 = \frac{2}{\pi} \left[\frac{1 - 2(-1)^2}{2} - \frac{2}{4\pi} \sin \pi \right] = -\frac{1}{\pi}
$$

. . . .

Thus

$$
f(t) = \frac{2}{\pi} \sum_{k=1}^{\infty} \left[\frac{1 - 2(-1)^k}{k} - \frac{2}{\pi k^2} \sin k \frac{\pi}{2} \right] \sin k \frac{\pi}{2} t
$$

Example 19-6. Find the Fourier series for the function $f_a(t)$ shown in Fig. 19-12a, and use the result to obtain the Fourier series for $f_b(t)$ shown in Fig. 19-12b.

Solution. Since $f_a(t)$ has even quarter-wave symmetry, we need the formulas for f_a only in the interval $t = 0$ to $t = T/4 = 0.5$. In this interval

$$
f_a(t) = 1 - 2t \qquad 0 < t < 0.5
$$

Since f_a is an even function, $B_k = 0$. Since f_a has half-wave symmetry, $A_0 = 0$,

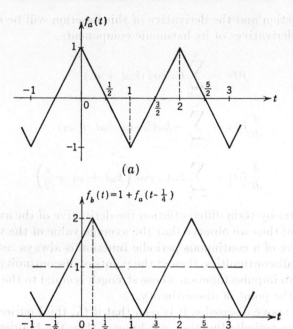

FIG. 19-12. (a) An even function. (b) The function $f_b(t)$, as obtained from $f_a(t)$ by translation of the origin of coordinates, is neither even nor odd.

$A_k = 0$, and k is even. Hence

$$A_{2k-1} = \frac{8}{2} \int_0^{0.5} (1 - 2t) \cos (2k - 1)\pi t \, dt$$

or

$$A_{2k-1} = \frac{8}{(2k - 1)^2 \pi^2}$$

Hence

$$f_a(t) = \frac{8}{\pi^2} \sum_{k=1}^{\infty} \frac{1}{(2k - 1)^2} \cos (2k - 1)\pi t$$

Since $f_b(t) = f_a(t - \frac{1}{4}) + 1,$

$$f_b(t) = 1 + \frac{8}{\pi^2} \sum_{k=1}^{\infty} \frac{1}{(2k - 1)^2} \cos \left[(2k - 1)\pi \left(t - \frac{1}{4} \right) \right]$$

or

$$f_b(t) = 1 + \frac{8}{\pi^2} \sum_{k=1}^{\infty} \frac{1}{(2k - 1)^2} \cos \left[(2k - 1)\pi t - (2k - 1) \frac{\pi}{4} \right]$$

19-12. Differentiation and Integration of Fourier Series.

The Fourier-series theorem states that, for any value of the independent variable t, the Fourier series converges to the value of its corresponding periodic function $f(t)$, except at points of discontinuity of $f(t)$, where the series converges to $\frac{1}{2}[f(t^-) + f(t^+)]$. When the periodic function has no discontinuities, then the series converges everywhere to the value of the periodic function and the derivative of this function will be equal to the sum of the derivatives of its harmonic components,

$$f(t) = \sum_{k=0}^{\infty} C_k \cos (k\omega t + \varphi_k)$$

$$\frac{d}{dt} f(t) = \sum_{k=1}^{\infty} -k\omega C_k \sin (k\omega t + \varphi_k)$$

or

$$\frac{d}{dt} f(t) = \sum_{k=1}^{\infty} k\omega C_k \cos \left(k\omega t + \varphi_k + \frac{\pi}{2} \right)$$

In this term-by-term differentiation the derivative of the average value of $f(t)$ is zero; thus we observe that the average value of the waveform of the derivative of a continuous periodic function is always zero.

If $f(t)$ has discontinuities, then at the points of discontinuity the derivative will be an impulse function whose strength is equal to the jump of the function at the point of discontinuity.

From the above discussion it is seen that if C_k, the Fourier coefficients of continuous periodic function, are known, then the Fourier coefficients of the derivative of that waveform are known and are equal to $k\omega C_k$.

Integration. The integral of a periodic waveform whose average value is nonzero, will not be a periodic function. This is seen from

$$\int f(t) \, dt = \int \left[A_0 + \sum_{k=1}^{\infty} C_k(k\omega t + \varphi_k) \right] dt$$

$$= A_0 t + \int \sum_{k=1}^{\infty} C_k \cos (k\omega t + \varphi_k) \, dt$$

The term $A_0 t$ is not periodic, and therefore the integral is not periodic. However, if the average value of $f(t)$ is zero, then the integral $\int f(t) \, dt$ will be periodic and its Fourier coefficients are related to those of $f(t)$ by

$$\int f(t) \, dt = \sum_{k=1}^{\infty} \int C_k \cos (k\omega t + \varphi_k) \, dt$$

$$= K + \sum_{k=1}^{\infty} \frac{C_k}{k\omega} \cos \left(k\omega t + \varphi_k - \frac{\pi}{2} \right)$$

In Fig. 19-13a a periodic waveform is shown whose Fourier series is

$$f(t) = -\frac{3}{\pi} \sum_{k=1}^{\infty} \frac{1}{k} \sin k \frac{2\pi}{3} t \qquad (19\text{-}32)$$

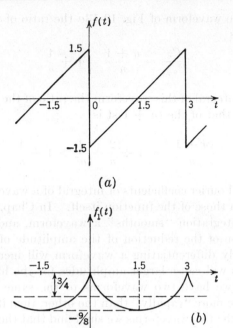

FIG. 19-13. (a) A periodic waveform $f(t)$. (b) The function $f_1(t)$ is an integral of $f(t)$, chosen so that $f_1(0) = 0$.

In Fig. 19-13b an integral of this waveform, $f_1(t)$, is shown. The Fourier series of $f_1(t)$ is given by

$$f_1(t) = \int_{-\infty}^{t} f(\tau)\, d\tau = K - \frac{3}{\pi} \sum_{n=1}^{\infty} \int \frac{1}{n} \sin n \frac{2\pi}{3} t = K + \frac{9}{2\pi^2} \sum_{n=1}^{\infty} \frac{1}{n^2} \cos n \frac{2\pi}{3} t$$

The value of K for the particular function $f_1(t)$ is obtained by observing that

$$f_1(0) = 0 = K + \frac{9}{2\pi^2} \sum_{n=1}^{\infty} \frac{1}{n^2}$$

$$K = -\frac{9}{2\pi^2} \sum_{n=1}^{\infty} \frac{1}{n^2}$$

The value of K can also be found from the waveform of $f(t)$. In the range $0 < t < 3$, $f(t) = t - 1.5$,

$$f_1(t) = 0.5t^2 - 1.5t \qquad 0 < t < 3$$

which checks at $t = 0$, that is, $f_1(0) = 0$.

$$K = \frac{1}{1.5} \int_0^{1.5} (0.5t^2 - 1.5t)\, dt = -0.75$$

From the above discussion it is seen that the effect of integration of a waveform is to reduce the relative magnitude of the higher harmonics.

In the case of the waveform of Fig. 19-13a the ratio of the amplitude of adjacent terms is

$$\frac{C_n}{C_{n+1}} = \frac{n+1}{n} = 1 + \frac{1}{n}$$

whereas for the integral of this waveform the ratio of the amplitude of the nth harmonic to that of the $(n+1)$st is

$$\frac{(n+1)^2}{n^2} = 1 + \frac{2}{n} + \frac{1}{n^2} > 1 + \frac{1}{n}$$

In general the Fourier coefficients of integral of a waveform decrease at a faster rate than those of the function itself. In Chap. 2 we noted that the process of integration "smooths" a waveform, and this smoothing effect is the cause of the reduction of the amplitude of the higher harmonics. Similarly differentiating a waveform will increase its "sharpnesses," and this will cause larger amplitudes for the higher harmonics.

In general, if we have two waveforms of the same period, but one changing its value more "rapidly" than the other, then if we compare the Fourier series of the two waveforms we shall find that the one corresponding to the waveform with rapid variation will have "larger" relative amplitudes for its higher harmonics.

Use of Differentiation for Evaluation of Fourier Coefficients.[1] For certain types of waveforms it is possible to compute the Fourier coefficients with little or no integration. In Fig. 19-14a a trapezoidal waveform is shown. To find the complex Fourier coefficients of this waveform from the formula

$$\mathbf{D}_k = \frac{1}{T} \int_0^T f(t) e^{-ik\omega t} \, dt$$

three separate integrals must be evaluated in the regions $0 < t < 1$, $1 < t < 2$, $2 < t < 4$. This is a somewhat long and tedious procedure. However, if the waveform of Fig. 19-14a is differentiated twice, the waveforms of Fig. 19-14b and c are obtained. Let

$$f(t) = \sum_{n=-\infty}^{+\infty} \mathbf{D}_n e^{jn\omega t}$$

Then

$$\frac{d}{dt} f(t) = f'(t) = \sum_{n=-\infty}^{+\infty} jn\omega \mathbf{D}_n e^{jn\omega t} = \sum_{n=-\infty}^{+\infty} \mathbf{D}_n' e^{jn\omega t}$$

$$\frac{d^2}{dt^2} f(t) = f''(t) = \sum_{n=-\infty}^{+\infty} -\omega^2 n^2 \mathbf{D}_n e^{jn\omega t} = \sum_{n=-\infty}^{+\infty} \mathbf{D}_n'' e^{jn\omega t}$$

[1] See J. F. Gibbons, A Simplified Procedure for Finding Fourier Coefficients, *Proc. I.R.E.*, vol. 45, no. 2, p. 243.

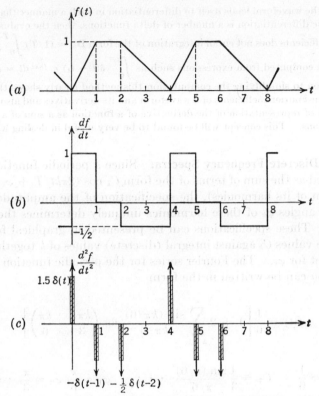

FIG. 19-14. A periodic waveform and the waveforms of its first two derivatives.

where the $\mathbf{D}_n''$ are the Fourier coefficients of the function $f''(t)\,dt$ and

$$\mathbf{D}_n = -\frac{1}{\omega^2 n^2}\,\mathbf{D}_n''$$

In the interval of time $0 \le t < 4^-$ the function $f''(t)$ can be written as

$$f''(t) = 1.5\,\delta(t) - \delta(t-1) - \tfrac{1}{2}\,\delta(t-2)$$

Now if we find $\mathbf{D}_n''$ from $f''(t)$, we have

$$\mathbf{D}_n'' = \frac{1}{T}\int_{0^-}^{T^-} f''(t)e^{-jn\omega t} = \frac{1}{4}\int_{0^-}^{4^-} [1.5\,\delta(t) - \delta(t-1) - \tfrac{1}{2}\,\delta(t-2)]e^{-jn\omega t}\,dt$$

But we know that

$$\int_{t=x^-}^{t=x^+} \delta(t-x) = 1 \qquad \text{and} \qquad \int_{t=x^-}^{x^+} e^{at}\,\delta(t-x)\,dt = e^{ax}$$

Therefore $\mathbf{D}_n'' = \tfrac{1}{4}(1.5 - e^{-jn\omega} - \tfrac{1}{2}e^{-j2n\omega})$
In this case $\omega = 2\pi/4 = \pi/2$,

$$\mathbf{D}_n'' = \tfrac{1}{4}(1.5 - e^{-jn\pi/2} - \tfrac{1}{2}e^{-jn\pi}) = \tfrac{1}{4}[1.5 - (-j)^n - \tfrac{1}{2}(-j)^{2n}]$$

and $$\mathbf{D}_n = -\frac{1}{\omega^2 n^2}\,\mathbf{D}_n'' = -\frac{1}{\pi^2 n^2}[1.5 - (-j)^n - \tfrac{1}{2}(-j)^{2n}]$$

Thus, if the waveform lends itself to differentiation in such a manner that the result of successive differentiation is a number of delta functions, then the evaluation of the Fourier coefficients does not entail integration of the form $\mathbf{D}_n = (1/T) \int_0^T f(t) e^{-in\omega t} \, dt$ but may be computed from expressions such as $\int_{0^-}^{t_1^+} \delta(t - t_1) \, e^{-in\omega t} \, dt = e^{-j\omega n t_1}$.

In addition to simplifying the computation this method clearly shows the relationship between Fourier coefficients of a waveform and its derivatives and also introduces the concept of representation of the derivative of a function as a sum of a number of delta functions. This concept will be found to be very useful in dealing with Fourier integrals.

19-13. Discrete Frequency Spectra. Since a periodic function can be represented as the sum of terms of the form $C_k \cos (2\pi kt/T + \varphi_k)$ (that is, as the sum of its harmonics), the specification of the amplitudes C_k and the phase angles φ_k of these harmonics uniquely determines the periodic function. These specifications can be presented in graphical form by a plot of the values C_k against integral (discrete) values of k together with a similar plot for φ_k. The Fourier series for the periodic function shown in Fig. 19-15a can be written in the form

$$f(t) = \frac{1}{6} \left[1 + 2 \sum_{k=1}^{\infty} \frac{\sin (k\pi/6)}{k\pi/6} \cos \left(\frac{k\pi t}{3} - \frac{k\pi}{6} \right) \right] \qquad (19\text{-}33)$$

Hence

$$C_0 = \frac{1}{6} \qquad C_1 = \frac{1}{3} \frac{\sin (\pi/6)}{\pi/6} \cdot \cdot \cdot ; \qquad \varphi_1 = \frac{\pi}{6}, \varphi_2 = \frac{\pi}{3}, \cdot \cdot \cdot$$

In Fig. 19-15b the values of C_k are shown as a function of k, and in Fig. 19-15c the corresponding values of φ_k are presented. (Note that C_k is negative for k between 6 and 12; it is often customary to plot the absolute values, $|C_k|$, which are of course positive. Since $- \cos x = \cos (x \pm \pi)$, a phase angle of π is then added or subtracted from φ_k when C_k is negative.) We observe that C_k and φ_k have values only for integral values of k, that is, at those frequencies which are integral multiples of the fundamental frequency. Hence the spectra are referred to as "discrete" frequency spectra.

For the waveform of Fig. 19-16a we obtain

$$C_k = 2 \frac{\tau}{T} \frac{\sin (k\pi\tau/T)}{k\pi\tau/T} \qquad \varphi_k = - \frac{k\pi\tau}{T} \qquad (19\text{-}34)$$

Proof of these relations is left as an exercise for the reader.

In Eq. (19-34) if we let $k\pi\tau/T = x_k$, then we have

$$C_k = 2 \frac{\tau}{T} \frac{\sin x_k}{x_k} \qquad (19\text{-}35)$$

In the above equation we have changed the (discrete) variable k to the (discrete) variable x_k. In frequency analysis terms of the form $(\sin x)/x$ appear so frequently that it is useful to become acquainted with its graph. Because of the usage of this

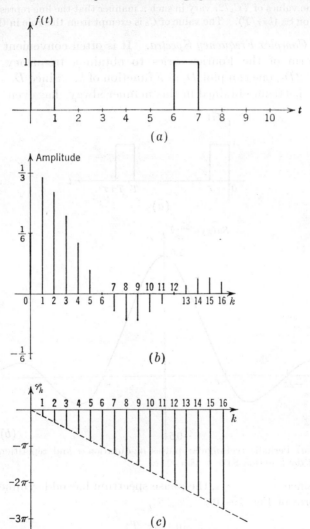

Fig. 19-15. (a) Periodic rectangular pulses. (b) Plot of C_k as a function of k for the pulses of (a). (c) Plot of φ_k as a function of k for the pulses of (a).

function in sampling problems, it is called the sampling function, and the symbol Sa x is assigned to it; Sa $x \equiv (\sin x)/x$.

Figure 19-16b shows Sa x plotted against x. In plotting this waveform x is dimensionless (radians). This plot is made for continuous variations of x, but in our present applications we are interested only in *selected (discrete)* values of x, such as $x_k = k\pi\tau/T$. Since $-1 \leq \sin x \leq +1$, it is seen that Sa x goes to zero as x goes to infinity. However, as x increases, sin x oscillates between positive and negative values and this is reflected in the variation of Sa x. It is noted that $(\sin x)/x$ is unity for $x = 0$.

In the discrete frequency spectrum of the waveform shown in Fig. 19-16a, given by Eq. 19-34, the values of $TC_k/2\tau$ vary in such a manner that the line representing them always ends on Sa $(k\pi\tau/T)$. The value of C_0 is exempt from this rule in this instance.

Discrete Complex Frequency Spectra. It is often convenient to use the complex form of the Fourier series to obtain a frequency spectrum. Since $C_k = 2D_k$, one can plot D_k as a function of k. Since $D_k = D_{-k}$, the amplitude spectrum obtained in this manner always has even symmetry.

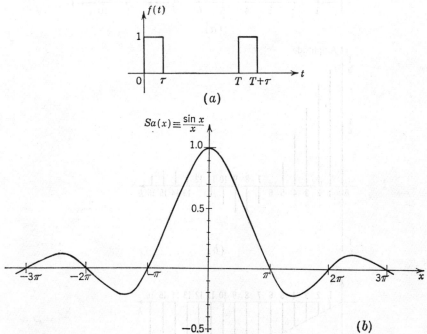

FIG. 19-16. (a) Periodic rectangular pulses of duration τ and repetition rate $1/T$. (b) Graph of the function Sa $x \equiv (\sin x)/x$.

Similarly, since $\varphi_k = -\varphi_{-k}$, the phase spectrum has odd symmetry. For the waveform of Fig. 19-16a

$$D_k = \frac{\tau}{T} \frac{\sin (k\pi\tau/T)}{(k\pi\tau/T)} e^{-j(k\pi\tau/T)}$$

Hence $D_k = |\text{Sa } x_k|$, where $x_k = k\pi\tau/T$ and $\varphi_k = -x_k$, except that where Sa x_k is negative an odd multiple of π is added to φ_k so that no information is lost. The spectra obtained in this manner for the waveform of Fig. 19-16a in the case $\tau/T = \frac{1}{6}$ are shown in Fig. 19-17a and b.

The reader recognizes that each of the lines in the spectrum of Fig. 19-15b corresponds to the amplitude of a harmonic. For example, in

Fig. 19-15b the line corresponding to $k = 3$ is $C_3 = 0.287$, the amplitude of the third harmonic in the Fourier series of the waveform of Fig. 19-15a. In Fig. 19-17a we have "amplitudes" corresponding to both positive and negative values of k or $k\omega$. For example, $D_{-3} = D_3 = 0.143$. This is

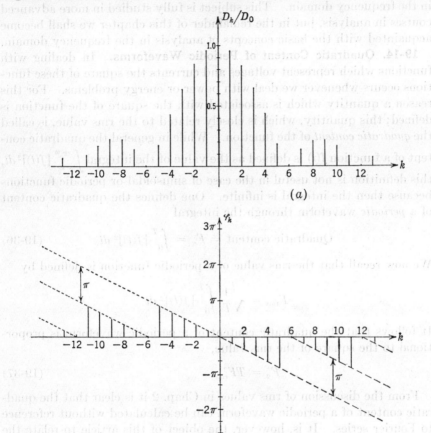

FIG. 19-17. (a) Values of D_k/D_0 for the waveform of Fig. 19-16a, where $\tau T = \frac{1}{6}$. This waveform corresponds to that shown in Fig. 19-15a. (b) Phase spectrum corresponding to the amplitude spectrum shown in (a). Note that an odd multiple of π has been introduced for $6 < k < 12$ because absolute values are shown in (a).

caused by the fact that in obtaining the complex Fourier series the identity

$$C_k \cos (k\omega t + \varphi_k) = \tfrac{1}{2}\mathbf{D}_k e^{jk\omega t} + \tfrac{1}{2}\mathbf{D}_{-k} e^{-jk\omega t}$$

was used and both $\mathbf{D}_k$ and $\mathbf{D}_{-k}$ refer to the same harmonic, namely, $C_k \cos (k\omega t + \varphi_k)$.

It is noted that a periodic function can be specified by giving its waveform in the time domain or its complex spectrum (i.e., both the amplitude and the phase) in the frequency domain. In this book we have so far been chiefly concerned with the time-domain analysis of network variables. In this chapter we have already shown the advantage of analysis in the frequency domain. This subject is fully studied in more advanced courses in analysis, but in the remainder of this chapter we shall become acquainted with the basic concepts of analysis in the frequency domain.

19-14. Quadratic Content of Periodic Waveforms. In dealing with functions which represent voltages and currents the square of these functions occurs whenever we deal with power or energy problems. For this reason a quantity which is associated with the square of the function is defined; this quantity, which is closely related to the rms value, is called the *quadratic content* of the function. While in general the quadratic content of a function $f(t)$ is defined as the value of the integral $\int_{-\infty}^{+\infty} [f(t)]^2 dt$, this definition is not useful in the case of sinusoidal or periodic functions because then the integral is infinite. One defines the quadratic content of a *periodic* waveform through the integral

$$\text{Quadratic content} = F_q = \int_0^T [f(t)]^2 dt \qquad (19\text{-}36)$$

We now recall that the rms value of a periodic function is defined by

$$F_{\text{rms}} = \sqrt{\frac{1}{T} \int_0^T [f(t)]^2 dt}$$

It follows that the quadratic content of a periodic waveform is proportional to the square of the rms value,

$$F_q = T F_{\text{rms}}^2 \qquad (19\text{-}37)$$

From the discussion of rms values in Chap. 2 it is clear that the quadratic content of a periodic waveform can be calculated without reference to Fourier series. It is, however, the object of this article to relate the value of F_q to the Fourier coefficients. In particular we shall show that

$$F_q = T \sum_{-\infty}^{+\infty} \mathbf{D}_k \mathbf{D}_k^* \qquad (19\text{-}38)$$

Proof. Let the periodic function $f(t)$ be written as the Fourier series

$$f(t) = D_0 + \mathbf{D}_1 e^{j\omega t} + \mathbf{D}_2 e^{j2\omega t} + \cdots + \mathbf{D}_k e^{jk\omega t} + \cdots$$
$$+ \mathbf{D}_{-1} e^{-j\omega t} + \mathbf{D}_{-2} e^{-j2\omega t} + \cdots + \mathbf{D}_{-k} e^{-jk\omega t} + \cdots$$

Then

$$[f(t)]^2 = D_0 \sum_{-\infty}^{+\infty} \mathbf{D}_k e^{jk\omega t} + \mathbf{D}_1 e^{j\omega t} \sum_{-\infty}^{+\infty} \mathbf{D}_k e^{jk\omega t} + \cdots$$

or

$$[f(t)]^2 = \sum_{k=-\infty}^{+\infty} \sum_{m=-\infty}^{+\infty} \mathbf{D}_k \mathbf{D}_m e^{j(k+m)\omega t} \tag{19-39}$$

Integrating both sides of Eq. (19-39) with respect to t between the limits 0 and $T = 2\pi/\omega$, and using the orthogonality property

$$\int_0^T e^{j(k+m)\omega t}\, dt \begin{cases} = 0 & k + m \neq 0 \\ = T & k + m = 0 \end{cases}$$

we have the result

$$\int_0^T [f(t)]^2\, dt = F_q = T \sum_{k=-\infty}^{+\infty} \mathbf{D}_k \mathbf{D}_k^*$$

Since

$$\sum_{k=-\infty}^{+\infty} \mathbf{D}_k \mathbf{D}_k^* = \mathbf{D}_0{}^2 + \mathbf{D}_1 \mathbf{D}_{-1} + \mathbf{D}_{-1} \mathbf{D}_1 + \cdots$$

we can also write

$$F_q = T D_0{}^2 + 2T \sum_{k=1}^{\infty} D_k{}^2 \tag{19-40a}$$

Using the relationships between $\mathbf{D}_k$, C_k, A_k, and B_k, we have the alternate forms

$$F_q = T C_0{}^2 + \frac{T}{2} \sum_{k=1}^{\infty} C_k{}^2 = T A_0{}^2 + \frac{T}{2} \sum_{k=1}^{\infty} (A_k{}^2 + B_k{}^2) \tag{19-40b}$$

We now observe that

$$\frac{1}{T} F_q = F_{\text{rms}}{}^2 = C_0{}^2 + \sum_{k=1}^{\infty} \left(\frac{C_k}{\sqrt{2}}\right)^2 = \sum_{k=0}^{\infty} (\text{rms value of } k\text{th harmonic})^2$$

Thus the mean squared value of a waveform is given as the sum of the mean squared values of its harmonics.

Example 19-7. The current in a 5-ohm resistance is given by

$$i(t) = 5 + 14.14 \cos t + 7.07 \cos 2t$$

Calculate the average power delivered to the resistance.

Solution. For the given waveform the amplitudes of the harmonics and the corresponding rms values are

$$I_0 = 5 \qquad I_{1m} = 14.14 \qquad I_1 = 10 \qquad I_{2m} = 7.07 \qquad I_2 = 5$$

Hence
$$I_{\text{rms}} = I = \sqrt{5^2 + 10^2 + 5^2} = \sqrt{150}$$

and since $P = I^2 R$, $P = (150)(5) = 750$ watts.

The term "energy content" can also be associated with quadratic content. We observe that two current (or voltage) functions which have the same quadratic content will deliver the same average energy to the same resistance during one period. Using this term, we can say that the energy content associated with a periodic waveform is the sum of the energy contents of its Fourier component. We have already observed that the Fourier coefficients are "frequency-domain" characteristics of the time function $f(t)$. In this sense Eq. (19-38) and its equivalents relate a time-domain property of a waveform to its frequency-domain characteristics.

Application to Steady-state-power Calculations. If at the terminals a-b of a network the voltage v_{ab} is defined by the Fourier series

$$v_{ab}(t) = \sum_{k=0}^{\infty} V_{k_m} \cos (k\omega t + \varphi_k)$$

and the current entering terminal a is $i(t)$ defined similarly as

$$i(t) = \sum_{k=0}^{\infty} I_{k_m} \cos (k\omega t + \psi_k)$$

then the power input as a function of time is given by the double sum

$$p_{ab}(t) = \sum_{n=0}^{\infty} \sum_{k=0}^{\infty} V_{k_m} I_{m_n} \cos (k\omega t + \varphi_k) \cos (n\omega t + \psi_k)$$

Using the orthogonality property of sinusoidal functions in the integral $\int_0^T p_{ab}\, dt$, we obtain the following expression for the *average* power, P_{ab}

$$\frac{1}{T} \int_0^T p_{ab}\, dt = P_{ab} = V_0 I_0$$
$$+ \frac{1}{2} [V_{1m} I_{1m} \cos (\varphi_1 - \psi_1) + V_{2m} I_{2m} \cos (\varphi_2 - \psi_2) + \cdots] \quad (19\text{-}41)$$

or, if we let $\varphi_k - \psi_k = \theta_k$, that is, the angle by which the kth-harmonic voltage leads the kth-harmonic current, and if we express the amplitudes V_{km} and I_{km} by means of their rms values (for example, $I_{km} = \sqrt{2}\, I_k$), then we have the result

$$P = P_0 + P_1 + P_2 \cdots = \sum_{k=0}^{\infty} P_k \quad (19\text{-}42)$$

where
$$P_k = V_k I_k \cos \theta_k$$

In words: The average power delivered to a terminal pair is the sum of the average powers delivered by the individual harmonics.

This remarkable "superposition of average power" property is an exceedingly attractive feature of Fourier analysis as applied to circuit problems. We note that in general power is not a linear function of voltage or current and cannot be super-posed; yet the orthogonality property of sinusoids which are harmonically related permits the superposition of the average powers delivered by the harmonics to give total average power.

Example 19-8. The voltage at terminals a-b of a terminal pair is

$$v_{ab} = 100 + 100 \cos t + 50 \cos 2t + 30 \cos 3t$$

and the current entering terminal a is

$$i(t) = 10 \cos (t - 60°) + 2 \cos (3t - 135°)$$

Calculate the average power delivered to the terminal pair a-b.

Solution. $V_0 = 100$, $I_0 = 0$, and hence $P_0 = 0$. Since $V_1 = (100)(0.707)$ and $I_1 = (10)(0.707)$, $V_1 I_1 = 500$. For the fundamental the phase difference between voltage and current is $60°$, $\cos 60° = 0.5$, and hence $P_1 = 250$ watts. Because $i_2 = 0$, $P_2 = 0$. For the third harmonic $V_3 I_3 = 30$, and $\cos \theta_3 = -0.707$; hence $P_3 = -21.2$, $P = 250 - 21.2 = 228.8$ watts.

19-15. Energy Content in a Given Frequency Range.

We have seen that the energy content of a periodic waveform is associated with the sum of the squares of its Fourier coefficients. The systems or devices studied in communication problems respond differently to different frequencies. In Chaps. 13, 15, and 18 this phenomenon was discussed in terms of the band-width of the circuit representing the device. For this reason it is often of interest to know the energy content of a waveform in a specified range (band) of frequencies.

The energy content of a periodic waveform, whose fundamental fre-quency is f_0, in the band of frequencies from f_1 to f_2 is

$$\frac{T}{2} \sum_{k=m}^{k=n} C_k{}^2$$

where m is the next largest integer to the number f_1/f_0 and n is the next smallest integer to the number f_2/f_0. Thus, for example, if a periodic waveform has a fundamental frequency of 5, then the energy content in the band $f_1 = 7$ to $f_2 = 21$ is

$$\left(\tfrac{1}{2}\right)\left(\tfrac{1}{5}\right) \sum_{k=2}^{k=4} C_k{}^2 = \frac{C_2{}^2 + C_3{}^2 + C_4{}^2}{10}$$

For the saw-tooth waveform of Fig. 19-13a,

$$f(t) = -\frac{3}{\pi} \sum_{k=1} \frac{1}{k} \sin k \frac{2\pi t}{3} \tag{19-43}$$

the quadratic content is

$$F_q = \int_0^3 (-1.5 + t)^2 \, dt = 2.25 = \frac{3}{2} \sum_{k=1}^{\infty} \left(-\frac{3}{k\pi}\right)^2$$

and the energy content in the band $f = 1.1$ to $f = 2$ is

$$\frac{3}{2} \sum_{k=4}^{k=6} \left(-\frac{3}{k\pi}\right)^2 = \frac{27}{2\pi^2} \left(\frac{1}{16} + \frac{1}{25} + \frac{1}{36}\right) = 0.178$$

Hence, in the band $1.1 < f < 2$, the energy content is 7.91 per cent of the total (since $7.91 = 17.8/2.25$).

19-16. Frequency-selective Networks. If a network contains energy-storing elements, then in general the steady-state response waveform due

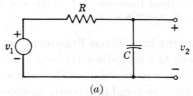

(a)

Fig. 19-18. (a) An R-C two-port.

to a nonsinusoidal periodic source will not be the same as the source waveform. We may explain this by observing that the network responds differently to the individual harmonics of the input waveform. To illustrate this approach, consider the R-C network shown in Fig. 19-18a as a two-port. Let the input waveform be given by the finite Fourier series

$$v_1(t) = 100(\cos t + \cos 3t + \cos 5t)$$

as shown in Fig. 19-18b.

For the R-C two-port of Fig. 19-18a the phasor ratio $\mathbf{V}_2/\mathbf{V}_1$ at any radian frequency ω is

$$\frac{\mathbf{V}_2}{\mathbf{V}_1} = \frac{1/j\omega C}{R + 1/j\omega C} = \frac{1}{j\omega RC + 1}$$

$$= \frac{1}{\sqrt{\omega^2 R^2 C^2 + 1}} \underline{/-\tan^{-1}\omega RC} \qquad (19\text{-}44)$$

Since the fundamental radian frequency of the input $v_1(t)$ is unity, the phasor ratio for the kth harmonic is

$$\left.\frac{\mathbf{V}_2}{\mathbf{V}_1}\right|_k = \frac{1}{\sqrt{k^2 R^2 C^2 + 1}} \underline{/-\tan^{-1} kRC} \qquad (19\text{-}45)$$

It follows from the principle of superposition that the output waveform in

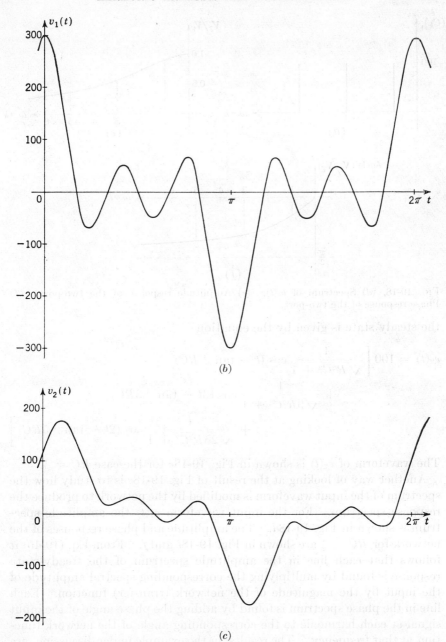

(b)

(c)

FIG. 19-18. (b) Graph of $v_1(t) = 100(\cos t + \cos 3t + \cos 5t)$. (c) Graph of the steady-state response $v_2(t)$ when $RC = \frac{1}{2}$.

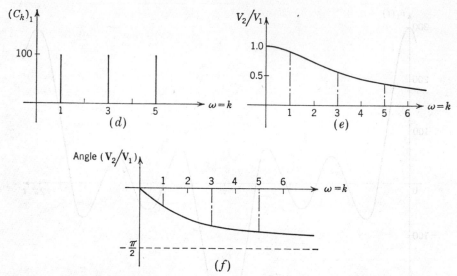

FIG. 19-18. (d) Spectrum of $v_1(t)$. (e) Amplitude response of the two-port. (f) Phase response of the two-port.

the steady state is given by the equation

$$v_2(t) = 100 \left[\frac{1}{\sqrt{R^2C^2 + 1}} \cos (t - \tan^{-1} RC) \right.$$

$$+ \frac{1}{\sqrt{9R^2C^2 + 1}} \cos (3t - \tan^{-1} 3RC)$$

$$\left. + \frac{1}{\sqrt{25R^2C^2 + 1}} \cos (2t - \tan^{-1} 5RC) \right]$$

The waveform of $v_2(t)$ is shown in Fig. 19-18c for the case $RC = \frac{1}{2}$.

Another way of looking at the result of Fig. 19-18c is to study how the spectrum of the input waveform is modified by the network to produce the response spectrum. For the input waveform $v_1(t)$ the amplitude spectrum is shown in Fig. 19-18d. The amplitude and phase responses of the network for $RC = \frac{1}{2}$ are shown in Fig. 19-18e and f. From Eq. (19-45) it follows that each line in the amplitude spectrum of the steady-state response is found by multiplying the corresponding spectral amplitude of the input by the magnitude of the network (transfer) function. Each line in the phase spectrum is found by adding the phase angle of the input signal at each harmonic to the corresponding angle of the network function at that frequency. The results, in the example under discussion, are shown dotted in Fig. 19-18e and f. Thus in general

$$\begin{pmatrix} \text{complex spectrum} \\ \text{of response} \end{pmatrix} = \begin{pmatrix} \text{complex network} \\ \text{function} \end{pmatrix} \begin{pmatrix} \text{complex spectrum} \\ \text{of input} \end{pmatrix}$$

19-17. Distortionless Transmission. If the relationship between the source function $v_1(t)$ and a response function $v_2(t)$ is of the form

$$v_2(t) = h_0 v_1(t - T_0)$$

then the network transmits the input signal without distortion. In the above expression it is seen that the waveform of the response is delayed in time by T_0 with respect to the input and that the magnitude of the output is h_0 times the magnitude of a corresponding phase of the input. If h_0 exceeds 1, it is referred to as the "gain" of the network; if h_0 is less than 1, it is called the "attenuation."

If $v_1(t)$ is a periodic signal whose fundamental radian frequency is ω_0 and if its spectrum is given by $\mathbf{D}_k = \frac{1}{2} C_k e^{j\varphi_k}$, from the definition of distortionless transmission it follows that the amplitude coefficients in the

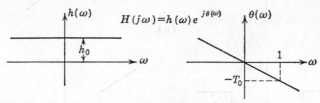

Fig. 19-19. Amplitude and phase characteristics of a network which transmits signals without distortion.

response v_2 must be $h_0 D_k$ and the phase angles in the response must be $\varphi_k - k\omega_0 T_0$. We conclude that for distortionless transmission the transfer function of the network, $H(j\omega)$, must have the form

$$H(j\omega) = \frac{\mathbf{V}_2}{\mathbf{V}_1} = h(\omega)e^{j\theta(\omega)} = h_0 e^{-j\omega T_0}$$

i.e., the amplitude response $h(\omega)$ (which in general varies with frequency) must be the constant h_0, and the phase response must be proportional to frequency. If this condition is met, then

Complex Fourier coefficient in the response $= h_0 \mathbf{D}_k e^{-jk\omega_0 T_0}$

where $\mathbf{D}_k$ is the corresponding Fourier coefficient in the input. The required frequency response of a network for distortionless transmission is shown in Fig. 19-19.

19-18. Ideal Filters. From the frequency-response curve of the R-C network of Fig. 19-18a shown in Fig. 19-18e, we observe that the network passes the low frequencies with little change in amplitude and with almost linear phase shift ($\tan^{-1} \omega RC \approx \omega RC$ if $\omega RC \ll 1$), while the high frequencies ($\omega RC > 1$) are attenuated to a greater degree. We recall that this discrimination is called "filtering action" and that in this sense the R-C two-port of Fig. 19-18a is called a "low-pass filter." Similarly an R-L-C circuit or the tuned transformer circuits are referred to as a "bandpass filters."

Now in practice no network can satisfy the requirements for distortionless transmission at all frequencies. Because of ever-present "stray" capacitance between input terminals and output terminals and because of lead inductance, the high frequencies will eventually be attenuated. To discuss distortionless transmission, therefore, we restrict the discussion to a *band of frequencies*. In this connection it is useful to define an

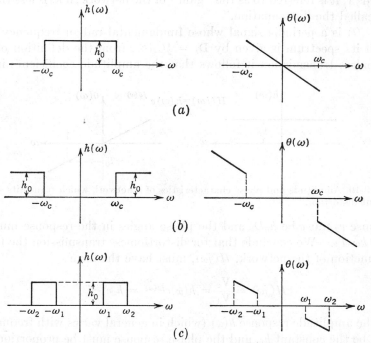

FIG. 19-20. Frequency-domain characteristics of ideal filters. $H(j\omega) = h(\omega)e^{j\theta(\omega)}$.
(a) Ideal low-pass filter. (b) Ideal high-pass filter. (c) Ideal bandpass filter.

"ideal" filter as a filter which passes a band of frequencies with uniform attenuation (gain) and with linear phase characteristics within this band; moreover an ideal filter must furnish infinite attenuation outside the passband. The frequency characteristics of some ideal filters are shown in Fig. 19-20. (Note that both "negative" and "positive" frequencies are shown; this is done as a convenience when the complex Fourier coefficients are used.)

Examining the transfer characteristics of the ideal filters, we observe that the "cutoff" is with infinite slope so that, for example, in the case of the low-pass filter (Fig. 19-20a) $h(\omega) = h_0$ at $\omega = \omega_c^-$ and $h(\omega) = 0$ at $\omega = \omega_c^+$. It can be shown that in any network the frequency-response curve must be a continuous function of ω with continuous derivatives and that the infinite slope shown cannot be attained with a finite number of R-L-C elements.[1] Although ideal filters are not physically attainable, it is frequently possible to obtain useful results by approximating a frequency-response curve with "sharp" cutoff, with ideal filter characteristics such as are shown in Fig. 19-20.

19-19. Sampling Theorem. *Band-limited Signals.* A periodic function is a *band-limited* function if in its (discrete) spectrum the values of $\mathbf{D}_n$ are identically zero for $|n| > N$, where N is a finite integer. For example, the function

$$v_1(t) = 100(\cos t + \cos 3t + \cos 5t)$$

shown in Fig. 19-18b is band-limited because the harmonics for $n > 5$ are identically zero. From the above definition it follows that an ideal low-pass or bandpass filter whose input is an arbitrary periodic function has an output which is a band-limited periodic function. For many practical purposes the output of nonideal filters (transmission systems) may be considered band-limited.

According to the above definition a band-limited periodic function has the form

$$f(t) = \sum_{k=-N}^{+N} \mathbf{D}_k e^{jk\frac{2\pi}{T}t} = C_0 + \sum_{k=1}^{N} C_k \cos\left(k\,\frac{2\pi}{T}\,t + \varphi_k\right) \quad (19\text{-}46)$$

We observe from Eq. (19-46) that if T is known we need only the $2N + 1$ *numbers*

$$C_0, C_1, \ldots, C_N; \quad \varphi_1, \varphi_2, \ldots, \varphi_N$$

to specify the *function* $f(t)$.

Sampling Theorem. A band-limited periodic function with no harmonics of order higher than N is uniquely specified by its value at $2N + 1$ instants within one period.

The proof of the theorem follows from Eq. (19-46). If we substitute the $2N + 1$ values $f(t_1), f(t_2), \ldots, f(t_{2N+1})$, referred to as samples of f, in Eq. (19-46) we obtain $2N + 1$ simultaneous equations for the unknowns

$$C_0, C_1, \ldots, C_N \qquad \varphi_1, \ldots, \varphi_N$$

or $\quad D_0 \quad \mathrm{Re}\,\mathbf{D}_1, \ldots, \mathrm{Re}\,\mathbf{D}_N \qquad \mathrm{Im}\,\mathbf{D}_1, \ldots, \mathrm{Im}\,\mathbf{D}_N$

The solution of these equations uniquely specifies the Fourier series and therefore specifies $f(t)$.

[1] It can also be shown that the use of an infinite number of elements can result in infinite $dh/d\omega$ provided that infinite time delay is associated with the filter.

Uniform Sampling. We observe that the instants $t_1, \ldots, t_{2N+1}$ can in principle be chosen arbitrarily. Most often one chooses these instants at equal intervals of $T/(2N + 1)$. This type of sampling is called *uniform* sampling. This theorem may be used to evaluate Fourier coefficients of a band-limited function by sampling. However the sampling procedure is not merely used for evaluation of Fourier coefficients but has the following practical applications.

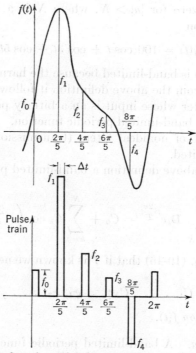

FIG. 19-21. The periodic function $f(t)$ is known to have no harmonics of higher order than the second. Shown are five uniform samples, $f_0 \cdots f_4$. The pulse train has five pulses per period and the height of the pulses corresponds to the sampled values of f.

Pulse Amplitude Modulation. In Fig. 19-21 is illustrated a function $f(t)$ whose period is 2π and is known to be band-limited with $N = 2$. Five uniform samples are marked at $t = 0$, $2\pi/5$, $4\pi/5$, $6\pi/5$, $8\pi/5$. Below $f(t)$ a pulse train is shown. This pulse train is periodic with the same period as $f(t)$, each period consisting of five pulses whose amplitude and spacing corresponds to the sampled values of $f(t)$. Fourier analysis of the pulse train shows (see Prob. 19-32) that it is not band-limited but that for the pulse train D_0, D_1 and D_2 are proportional to the corresponding coefficients of $f(t)$.

If the pulse train is passed through an "ideal" low-pass filter which passes its second but not third and higher harmonics, then the output of the low-pass filter will be proportional to $f(t)$. We conclude that to transmit the band-limited signal it is sufficient to transmit the pulse train. The comparative economy in power required to transmit the train of pulses, while evident, may not be an important factor. More important is the fact that in the interval between the sampled pulses the transmission channel may be used for transmitting other signals. The term used to describe the use of one "communication channel" for several "messages" is *multiplexing*. Special filter networks and techniques are used to interlace and separate signals for multiplex transmission.

19-20. Applications to Nonlinear Circuits. In the entire book so far we have discussed only linear circuits, i.e., circuits composed of linear elements which are described by linear equilibrium equations. As a consequence the treatment of circuit analysis has in fact been a study of the superposition principle and its consequences. Indeed the idea of Fourier series stems directly from the idea of superposition, i.e., the representation of source and response function as the sum of sinusoids so that each response component can be calculated individually.

When a circuit includes one (or more) nonlinear elements, then the equilibrium equation is not linear and, as is illustrated in Chaps. 3 and 11, the superposition principle does not apply. In spite of this it is possible to use the concept of Fourier series to discuss certain properties of nonlinear circuits. It is the object of this article to illustrate in a very elementary and introductory fashion some of these properties.

In a *linear* circuit the component of the response due to the source will include a harmonic for every harmonic of the input. For a given signal the amplitude and phase of these harmonics depend only on the network; they are unique and independent of the initial conditions.

In a *nonlinear* circuit the following possibilities exist:

1. *Harmonics which are not present in the input signal occur in the steady-state response.* Thus, for example, in a rectifier the input may be sinusoidal, while the output will contain a d-c component and an infinite number of harmonics. As a second example, consider an electronic oscillator. The input is a constant voltage, while the output may be sinusoidal.

2. *Subharmonics may be present in the output.* In certain nonlinear circuits the fundamental frequency in the response may be a proper fraction of the fundamental frequency of the source function.

3. *The response amplitudes may not be a unique function of the network parameters.* In certain nonlinear circuits the response depends on how the steady state is approached. Thus, for a given input signal, the network may have a different steady-state response depending on the initial

conditions. This property also illustrates that no free and forced response components can be superposed.

While the analysis (and design) of linear circuits (i.e., circuits which are to be realized by "sufficiently" linear elements) can be systematized and standardized, as indeed we have shown in the preceding chapters, no such standardization is possible in the case of nonlinear circuits. Each problem must be examined individually, and solutions, usually approximate, must be worked out for special numerical cases. In fact many times it is necessary to use experimental evidence as the starting point in an analytical solution.

PROBLEMS

19-1. Make careful freehand sketches of the following functions: (a) $f_a(x) = 10 \cos x + 5 \cos 2x$; (b) $f_b(x) = 10 \sin x + 5 \cos 2x$; (c) $f_c(x) = 10 \cos (x - \pi/4) + 5 \cos 2x$; (d) $f_d(x) = 10 \cos x + 5 \cos 3x$; (e) $f_e(x) = 10 \cos x - 5 \sin 3x$.

19-2. A voltage source $v(t) = 10 + 10 \cos \omega t + 5 \cos 2\omega t$ is impressed on the series R-C circuit as shown in Fig. P19-2. It is known that $R = 1/\omega C$. Calculate (a) the steady-state functions v_{am} and v_{mb}; (b) the complete responses v_{am} and v_{mb} if $\omega = 1/RC = 10$ and if (1) $v_{mb}(0^+) = 0$, (2) $v_{mb}(0^+) = 25$.

19-3. In the circuit of Prob. 19-2 (Fig. P19-2) the source is given by $v(t) = 10 \cos \omega t + 10 \cos n\omega t$. If $\omega RC = 1$, calculate the smallest integral value of n so that, in the steady-state component of v_{mb}, the amplitude of the nth harmonic is less than 5 per cent of the amplitude of the fundamental.

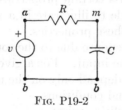

FIG. P19-2

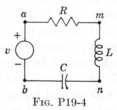

FIG. P19-4

19-4. A voltage source $v(t) = 10 + 10 \cos \omega t + 10 \cos 2\omega t + 10 \cos 3\omega t$ is impressed on the series R-L-C circuit shown in Fig. P19-4. Calculate the steady-state functions v_{am}, v_{mn}, and v_{nb} if $\omega L = 1.5$, $1/\omega C = 6.0$, and (a) $R = 3.0$; (b) $R = 0.60$. (c) For each case calculate Q_0 of the circuit, and use the result of this example to explain the bandpass filter property of this circuit.

19-5. The polynomial functions $P_0(x) = 1$, $P_1(x) = x$, $P_2(x) = \frac{1}{2}(3x^2 - 1)$, $P_3(x) = \frac{1}{3}(5x^3 - 3x)$, $P_4(x) = \frac{1}{8}(35x^4 - 30x^2 + 3)$ are the first five members of a set of functions (termed Legendre polynomials) which are orthogonal in the interval $-1 \le x \le 1$ with respect to the weighting function $w(x) = 1$. Verify this statement by application of the definition of orthogonality.

19-6. The set of functions $T_n(x) = (1/2^{n-1}) \cos (n \cos^{-1} x)$, called Tchebycheff polynomials, are orthogonal in the interval $-1 \le x \le +1$ with respect to the weighting function $w(x) = (1 - x^2)^{-\frac{1}{2}}$. (a) Prove the orthogonality with the aid of the substitution $\cos^{-1} x = \theta$. (b) Expand $T_n(x)$ for $n = 1, 2, 3,$ and 4, and show that the results are polynomials in x.

19-7. (a) Show that $\int_0^{2\pi} \left(\sum_{-n}^{+n} \mathbf{D}_k e^{jkx} \right)^2 dx = 2\pi \sum_{-n}^{+n} \mathbf{D}_k \mathbf{D}_{-k}.$ (b) If a periodic func-

tion $f(x)$ with period 2π, $f(x) = f(x + 2\pi)$, is approximated by $f_a(x)$ such that $f_a(x) = \sum_{-n}^{+n} \mathbf{D}_k e^{jkx}$, then the error in using the approximation is $\epsilon = f(x) - f_a(x)$. Use the result of (a) to show that the mean squared error M is given by

$$ M = \frac{1}{2\pi} \int_0^{2\pi} [f(x)]^2 \, dx - \frac{1}{\pi} \int_0^{2\pi} \left[f(x) \sum_{-n}^{+n} \mathbf{D}_k e^{jkx} \right] dx + \sum_{-n}^{+n} \mathbf{D}_k \mathbf{D}_{-k} $$

(c) Show that the mean squared error is a minimum if $\mathbf{D}_k$ is calculated as the complex Fourier coefficient according to Eq. (19-14).

19-8. The periodic function shown in Fig. 19-3, which is defined by the formula $v(t) = V$, $0 < t < \pi$, $v(t) = -V$, $\pi < t < 2\pi$, and $v(t) = v(t + 2\pi)$ is to be approximated by the finite Fourier series $v_a(t)$ as given below. Calculate the mean squared error if (a) $v_a(t) = B_1 \sin t$; (b) $v_a(t) = B_1 \sin t + B_3 \sin 3t$.

19-9. Obtain the Fourier series in complex form for the waveforms given in Fig. P19-9, and express the answer in the form of Eq. (19-6).

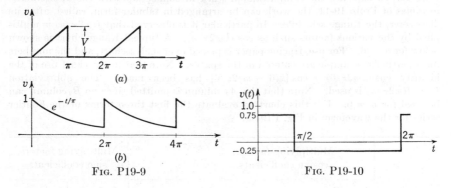

FIG. P19-9   FIG. P19-10

19-10. (a) Show that the Fourier series for the waveform given in Fig. P19-10 is

$$ v(t) = \frac{1}{\pi} \sum_{k=1}^{\infty} \left[\frac{\sin k\pi/2}{k} \cos kt + \frac{(1 - \cos k\pi/2)}{k} \sin kt \right] $$

(b) Use the result of (a) to calculate the value of $v(t)$ *as given by the Fourier series* at the points of discontinuity $t = 0$ and $t = \pi/2$. *Hint:* Recall that the Maclaurin series for $\tan^{-1} x$ is $\tan^{-1} x = \sum_1^{\infty} \frac{(-1)^{k+1} x^{2k-1}}{2k - 1}$.

19-11. (a) Assume that the time scale for a periodic function $f(t)$ has been normalized so that the period is 2π. Show, by use of the trapezoidal rule, dividing the period into n equal intervals, that the coefficients of the Fourier series in trigonometric form can be obtained approximately by use of the formulas

$$A_0 = \frac{1}{n} \sum_{m=0}^{n-1} f\left(m \frac{2\pi}{n}\right)$$

$$A_k = \frac{2}{n} \sum_{m=0}^{n-1} f\left(m \frac{2\pi}{n}\right) \cos\left(km \frac{2\pi}{n}\right)$$

$$B_k = \frac{2}{n} \sum_{m=0}^{n-1} f\left(m \frac{2\pi}{n}\right) \sin\left(km \frac{2\pi}{n}\right)$$

(b) Show that the formulas given for A_k and B_k are ambiguous unless they are used only to calculate the harmonic coefficients for $0 < k < n/2$ for waveforms which are known to have negligible harmonics for $k > n/2$. To show this, first let $n = 6$, and expand the formula for A_1; then use the same formula for A_5, and compare the result. Do the same for A_2 and A_4. Finally show in general that the use of the formula for A_k and A_{n-k} gives $A_k = A_{n-k}$, and discuss the resulting ambiguity. Repeat for B_k. (c) Use the formulas of (a) to calculate B_1 and B_3 for the waveform of Prob. 19-8 (Fig. 19-3). Use $n = 8$. (When f is discontinuous at $m2\pi/n$, use its average value.) Compare your result with the exact values. (d) Calculate A_0 for the waveforms of Prob. 19-9 (Fig. P19-9), using (1) $n = 4$, (2) $n = 6$, (3) $n = 8$, and compare the result with the exact values.

19-12. To expedite the computational work in connection with the approximate formulas of Prob. 19-11, the work can be arranged in tabular form, called, after its discoverer, the Runge schedule. In particular it is observed that $f(m2\pi/n)$ is multiplied by the various factors such as $\cos(km2\pi/n)$. A typical Runge chart is shown below for $n = 6$. For use, tracing paper is placed over such a chart, and the numbers for a particular example are entered in the spaces. Note that in the chart use of the identity $\cos(km2\pi/6) = \cos[k(6 - m)2\pi/6]$ has been made. The abbreviation $f_m = f(m2\pi/n)$ is used. Note that the A_3 column is omitted since no B_3 column can be used for $n = 6$. Use this chart to evaluate the first three terms of the Fourier series for the waveform in Fig. P19-9a.

	Multiplying factors, cosine coefficients				Multiplying factors, sine coefficients	
	A_0	A_1	A_2		B_1	B_2
f_0	1.00	1.00	1.00	$f_1 - f_5$	0.87	0.87
$f_1 + f_5$	1.00	0.50	−0.50	$f_2 - f_4$	0.87	−0.87
$f_2 + f_4$	1.00	−0.50	−0.50		Add column above	Add column above
f_3	1.00	−1.00	1.00			
	Add column above	Add column above	Add column above	*Ans.:*	Divide by 3	Divide by 3
Ans.:	Divide by 6	Divide by 3	Divide by 3			

19-13. Construct a chart similar to that given in Prob. 19-12 for $n = 12$. Use it to calculate the first three terms of the Fourier series for the waveform of Prob. 19-9a (Fig. P19-9a), and compare the result with that obtained in Prob. 19-12.

19-14. (a) Prove that $\sum_{k=0}^{n-1} e^{jk2\pi/n} = 0$ where n is an integer. *Hint:* $e^{jk2\pi/n} = (e^{j2\pi/n})^k$

so that the series given is a finite geometric series. (b) Prove that $\sum_{k=0}^{n-1} \cos (k2\pi/n) = 0$ and $\sum_{k=0}^{n-1} \sin (k2\pi/n) = 0$.

19-15. (a) Use the result of Prob. 19-14 to prove that

$$\sum_{m=0}^{n-1} \cos m \frac{k2\pi}{n} = \begin{cases} 0 & \text{if } \dfrac{k}{n} \text{ is not an integer} \\ n & \text{if } \dfrac{k}{n} \text{ is an integer} \end{cases}$$

(b) Given an even function whose Fourier series has no constant term, that is, $f(x) = \sum_{k=1}^{\infty} A_k \cos kx$, show that

$$\sum_{k=1}^{\infty} A_{nk} = \frac{1}{n} \sum_{m=0}^{n-1} f\left(m \frac{2\pi}{n}\right)$$

(c) Show that the result of (b) applies when the function is neither even nor odd. (d) Use this result to evaluate A_3, A_2, and A_1 for the waveform of Prob. 19-10 (Fig. P19-10), assuming that $A_k = 0$ for $k \geq 4$.

Note: This problem is an introduction to the "method of selected ordinates." Details may be found in Richard H. Frazier, "Elementary Electric Circuit Theory," pages 279 to 286, McGraw-Hill Book Company, Inc., New York, 1945.

19-16. For the waveform shown in Fig. P19-16 (a) obtain the Fourier series analytically if the point $t = 0$ is at A. (b) Use the result of (a) to write the Fourier series if $t = 0$ is at (1) B; (2) C.

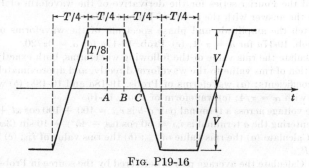

FIG. P19-16

19-17. Referring to Fig. P19-17 (a) obtain analytically the Fourier series for $f_a(x)$. (b) Use the result of (a) to obtain the Fourier series for $f_b(x)$ by superposition.

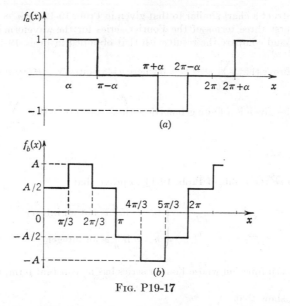

FIG. P19-17

19-18. (a) A function is defined through $f_a(x) = V_m \sin (x/2)$, $0 \leq x \leq 2\pi$, $f_a(x) = f_a(x + 2\pi)$ as shown in Fig. P19-18. Find, analytically, the Fourier series for $f_a(x)$. (b) Sketch the function $(V_m/2) \sin (x/2) + \frac{1}{2} f_a(x)$, and write its Fourier series. (c) Write the Fourier series for the waveforms of (a) and (b) if the variable is changed to $\omega t = x/2$.

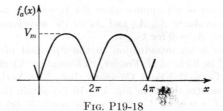

FIG. P19-18

19-19. Find the Fourier series for the derivative of the waveform of Prob. 19-16, and correlate the answer with the result of Prob. 19-17a.

19-20. Sketch the amplitude and phase spectrum of the waveforms of (a) Prob. 19-16; (b) Prob. 19-17a for $\alpha = \pi/4$; (c) Prob. 19-17a for $\alpha = 9\pi/20$.

19-21. Calculate the rms value of the following waveforms, both exactly by applying the definition of rms value to the waveform directly, and approximately by use of the Fourier coefficients: (a) waveforms of Probs. 19-18a and 19-18b; (b) waveform of Prob. 19-17a with $\alpha = \pi/4$; (c) waveform of Prob. 19-16.

19-22. The voltage across a terminal pair a-b is $v_{ab} = 100 + 100 \cos \omega t + 30 \cos 3\omega t$. The current entering the a terminal is $i_{ab} = 50 \cos (\omega t - 45°) + 10 \sin (3\omega t - 60°) + 20 \cos 5\omega t$. Calculate (a) the rms value of v_{ab}; (b) the rms value of i_{ab}; (c) the average power input P_{ab}.

19-23. (a) Calculate the average power delivered by the source in Probs. 19-4a and 19-4b (Fig. P19-4). (b) In Prob. 19-4a calculate the average value of the energy stored in L and in C if $\omega = 100$ rad/sec.

19-24. An amplitude-modulated signal is defined through the equation $f(t) = [1 + m(t)] \cos \omega_c t$. Obtain the frequency spectrum if (a) $m(t) = m_0 \cos \omega_s t$; (b) $m(t) = m_0 \cos \omega_s t + \frac{1}{2} m_0 \cos 2\omega_s t$. For each case sketch the amplitude spectrum, using $\omega_c = 2,000\omega_s$.

19-25. For the waveforms of Prob. 19-24 assume that $\omega_c = 1,000\omega_s$, and calculate the quadratic content of the waveforms with m_0 as a parameter. What fraction of the quadratic content is contributed by the harmonic at ω_c?

19-26. In Prob. 19-24a let $\omega_s = 0.001$, $\omega_c = 1$. Calculate the steady-state voltage across the resistance in an R-L-C circuit if $f(t)$ is a voltage source, $LC = 1$, and Q_0 is (a) 10; (b) 50; (c) 200. Use $m_0 = 1$.

19-27. A certain active nonlinear device has an output voltage v_o which is related to the input v_i through the equation $v_o = v_i + v_i^2$. Obtain the amplitude spectrum of the output voltage if (a) $v_i = \sin \omega t$; (b) $v_i = \sin \omega_1 t + \sin \omega_2 t$; (c) $v_i = 1 + \sin \omega t$.

19-28. Show that the function shown in Fig. P19-28—$f(t) = \displaystyle\sum_{n=1}^{\infty} U(t - 2n\pi)$—can be written in the form

$$f(t) = \left[\frac{t}{2\pi} - \frac{1}{2} + \frac{1}{\pi} \sum_{k=1}^{\infty} \frac{\sin kt}{k} \right] U(t)$$

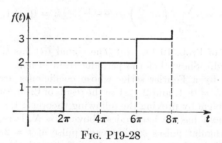

FIG. P19-28

19-29. If the function of Prob. 19-28 is a source function, what are the corresponding pole locations in the **s** plane?

19-30. The periodic signal $v(t)$ shown in Fig. P19-30 is applied to the input of an ideal low-pass filter whose cutoff frequency is 2.1 cps. Sketch the amplitude spectrum of the output voltage if (a) $T = 2$ sec; (b) $T = 4$ sec; (c) $T = 8$ sec.

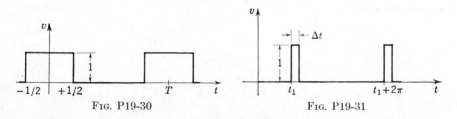

FIG. P19-30　　　　　　　　FIG. P19-31

19-31. (a) The periodic pulses shown in Fig. P19-31 form the input to an ideal low-pass filter whose cutoff frequency f_c is such that the highest harmonic passed is the Nth. The time delay caused by the filter is negligible. Show that the Fourier series of the output voltage v_0 is

$$v_0 = \frac{\Delta t}{2\pi} \sum_{k=-N}^{k=+N} \frac{\sin (k\, \Delta t/2)}{k\, \Delta t/2} e^{jk(t-t_1-\Delta t/2)}$$

(b) Show that if Δt is sufficiently small, so that $N\, \Delta t/2 \ll 1$, the result of (a) can be approximated by

$$v_0 \approx \frac{\Delta t}{2\pi} \sum_{k=-N}^{k=+N} e^{-jk(t-t_1)}$$

19-32. The signal shown in Fig. 19-21 is known to consist of a d-c component and the first two harmonics only, that is, $f(t) = D_0 + \mathbf{D}_1 e^{jt} + \mathbf{D}_{-1} e^{-jt} + \mathbf{D}_2 e^{j2t} + \mathbf{D}_{-2} e^{-j2t}$. (a) Show that

$$5D_0 = \sum_{m=0}^{4} f\left(m\, \frac{2\pi}{5} \right)$$

$$5\mathbf{D}_1 = \sum_{m=0}^{4} f\left(m\, \frac{2\pi}{5} \right) e^{-jm2\pi/5}$$

$$5\mathbf{D}_k = \sum_{m=0}^{4} f\left(m\, \frac{2\pi}{5} \right) e^{-jk2\pi m/5} \qquad k = 0, \pm 1, \pm 2$$

Hint: Use the result of Prob. 19-14. (b) The signal $f(t)$ has the values $f(m2\pi/5)$ at the instants indicated. Show that the periodic train of narrow pulses shown in Fig. 19-21 is represented by a Fourier series whose coefficients are proportional to the coefficients of $f(t)$ for $k = 0, 1$, and 2. (Use the result of Prob. 19-31.) (c) Generalize the result of this problem by proving the following theorem: If a periodic function $f(t)$, whose period is 2π and has no harmonics above $k = N$, is represented by $2N + 1$ equally spaced rectangular pulses so that each pulse at $t = 2\pi m/(2N + 1)$ has the amplitude $f[m2\pi/(2N + 1)]$, then these pulses, if passed through a low-pass filter which passes the Nth but not the $(N + 1)$st harmonic, will result in a filter output which has the same waveform as $f(t)$.

19-33. A periodic signal $m(t)$ has no harmonics above the frequency f_m. Hence, if $m(t)$ is passed through an ideal low-pass filter with cutoff of f_m, of unit gain and no time delay, the output is $m(t)$. Show that the signal $[1 + m(t)] \cos 2\pi f_c t$, $f_c \gg f_m$, will pass through an ideal bandpass filter with passband from $f_c - f_m$ to $f_c + f_m$ without distortion.

MATRICES AND DETERMINANTS

A-1. Matrices. In the study of systems, such as electric power systems, communication systems, and other systems characterized by sets of simultaneous equations, we deal with a set of numbers (coefficients), operators (time or space and other differential operators), and functions whose proper combinations determine the behavior of the system (the solution of the problem). In a systematic analysis of such problems these numbers, operators, or functions, which we shall refer to as "elements," often occur in the form of an "array" of "rows" and "columns," which can be manipulated in accordance with certain specified rules. Such an array of elements is called a matrix. With this in mind we define a matrix to be a "table" of elements arranged in a *rectangular* array of rows and columns, subject to certain rules of manipulation.

In the following articles we define certain terms associated with matrices. These definitions may seem arbitrary, and the purpose of a definition may not be immediately clear, but later experience will justify them. Some definitions are made to facilitate precision in statements about the properties of matrices.

A-2. Subscript Notation. We may designate a "typical" element of a matrix by a letter such as a and show its position in the array by two subscripts indicating its row and its column, respectively. For example, a_{25} denotes the element whose position is at the "intersection" of the second row and fifth column and a_{ij} denotes the element whose position is at the "intersection" of ith row and jth column. Consider the matrix given in the tabular form

$$
\begin{array}{c|c|c}
2 & R & L\dfrac{d}{dt} \\
\hline
-1 & -M\dfrac{d}{dt} & 4
\end{array}
\tag{A-1}
$$

This matrix has two rows and three columns; its elements are $a_{11} = 2$, $a_{12} = R$, $a_{13} = L(d/dt)$, $a_{21} = -1$, $a_{22} = -M(d/dt)$, $a_{23} = 4$. A matrix is designated by a capital letter such as A and is written as

$$
A = \|a_{ij}\|
\tag{A-2}
$$

679

where i takes up all the row numbers and j the column numbers of the matrix. The matrix of Eq. (A-1) can be written as

$$A = \left\| \begin{array}{ccc} a_{11} & a_{12} & a_{13} \\ a_{21} & a_{22} & a_{23} \end{array} \right\| = \|a_{ij}\| \qquad \begin{array}{l} i = 1, 2 \\ j = 1, 2, 3 \end{array}$$

A-3. Order of a Matrix. A matrix is called an m-by-n matrix, where m is the number of its rows and n the number of its columns. The matrix of Eq. (A-1) is a two-by-three (2×3) matrix.

A-4. Matrix Algebra. A matrix is not a "number," and it does not have a "value." It is simply an arrangement of "elements" ordered in rows and columns. Furthermore no restriction is placed on the nature (dimensions) of the elements; they can have varied dimensions. Although we have said that matrices are not numbers in the ordinary sense of the word, we may define certain rules for manipulations of matrices, analogous to those defined for algebraic numbers. Such rules may be stated quite arbitrarily, but it is doubtful that arbitrary rules would result in manipulations which are useful (in the study of physical systems). Therefore the rules for manipulation of matrices are drawn up in such a manner that their use simplifies the study and analysis of practical problems.

A-5. Equal Matrices. If two matrices have the same order and each element in one matrix is identical with its corresponding element (in the same row and column) in the other matrix, the two matrices are said to be equal.

A-6. Addition of Matrices. If the matrices $A = \|a_{ij}\|$ and $B = \|b_{kl}\|$ are of the same order, the matrix $C = \|c_{mn}\|$ is said to be the sum of the matrices A and B if $c_{mn} = a_{mn} + b_{mn}$.

Example A-1. Let

$$A = \left\| \begin{array}{cccc} 2 & \dfrac{d}{dt} & 0 & \dfrac{d}{dx} \\ \dfrac{d}{dy} & 3 & 1 & 0 \end{array} \right\|$$

$$B = \left\| \begin{array}{cccc} 1 & 1 & 1 & 1 \\ 2 & 2 & 2 & 2 \end{array} \right\|$$

Then

$$A + B = \left\| \begin{array}{cccc} 2+1 & \dfrac{d}{dt}+1 & 0+1 & \dfrac{d}{dx}+1 \\ \dfrac{d}{dy}+2 & 3+2 & 1+2 & 0+2 \end{array} \right\|$$

The addition is defined only for matrices of the same order. Subtraction can be considered as a special case of addition. It is noted that $A + B = B + A$.

The rules of addition and subtraction of matrices are easily understood. To define other matrix operations, we give an example from common experience; and, based on the manipulations in this example, generalizations and definitions will be made.

A-7. Item, Price, and Payment Matrices. Consider two customers making purchases from a supermarket. Customer X purchases 2 loaves of bread, 6 cans of orange juice, and $\frac{1}{2}$ lb of butter, and customer Y buys 3 loaves of bread, 0 cans of orange juice, and $\frac{3}{4}$ lb of butter. The purchases of the two customers can be set up as a matrix of 2×3 (2 customers and 3 items) as follows:

	Loaves of bread	Cans of juice	Pounds of butter
X	2	6	$\frac{1}{2}$
Y	3	0	$\frac{3}{4}$

We may add as many items or customers to this matrix and change the order of the matrix, but the above example suffices for our purpose. We call this matrix the "items" matrix. Now at the cash desk the clerk has a price list as follows:

Bread.............. 23 cents per loaf
Orange juice........ 11 cents per can
Butter.............. 72 cents per lb

This can be considered as a 3×1 unit price matrix. Customer X pays

$$2 \times 23 + 6 \times 11 + \tfrac{1}{2} \times 72 = 148 \text{ cents}$$

Notice that 148 cents is arrived at from a summation whose first term is obtained by taking the first element of the first row in the items matrix

$$\left\| \begin{array}{ccc} 2 & 6 & \tfrac{1}{2} \\ 3 & 0 & \tfrac{3}{4} \end{array} \right\| \tag{A-3}$$

and multiplying it by the first element of the first column in the price matrix

$$\left\| \begin{array}{c} 23 \\ 11 \\ 72 \end{array} \right\| \tag{A-4}$$

thus getting 2×23. The second term in the summation is obtained by taking the second element in the first row of the items matrix and multiplying by the second element of the price matrix, which gives 6×11. The third term in the summation is the product of the third term in the first row of the items matrix multiplied by the third term of the price matrix, giving $\frac{1}{2} \times 72$.

Customer Y must pay $3 \times 23 + 0 \times 11 + \frac{3}{4} \times 72 = 123$ cents. The value 123 cents is arrived at in a similar manner to that of 148 cents, except that the terms of the summation are obtained by multiplying the proper elements of the second row of the items matrix by those of the price matrix.   Thus the payments made to the cash clerk are

$$\text{Payment, cents}$$

$$X \ldots \ldots \ldots 148$$
$$Y \ldots \ldots \ldots 123$$

This is a 2×1 matrix, which we call the payment matrix.

$$\left\| \begin{matrix} 148 \\ 123 \end{matrix} \right\| \tag{A-5}$$

The elements of the payment matrix are obtained from elements of the items and price matrices through a definite procedure, which is now generalized in the following rules for matrix multiplication.

A-8. Compatible Matrices.   If the matrix A is of the order $m \times n$ (for example, $m = 5$, $n = 3$) and matrix B is of the order $n \times k$ ($n = 3$, and, for example, $k = 7$), the matrix B is said to be compatible with matrix A.   Thus, for B to be compatible with A, the number of rows of B must be identical with the number of columns of A.   In the above numerical examples B is compatible with A, since the number of rows of B is the same (three) as that of columns of A.   But A is not compatible with B, since the number of rows of A is 5 and the number of columns of B is 7.   In the example of purchases from the supermarket the price matrix is compatible with the items matrix, since the number of rows in the price matrix is the same (three) as the number of columns of the items matrix.   But the items matrix is not compatible (two rows) with the price matrix (one column).

A-9. Matrix Multiplication.   If the matrix $B = \|b_{ij}\|$ with n rows and q columns is compatible with matrix $A = \|a_{ij}\|$ of p rows and n columns, the matrix $C = \|c_{ij}\|$ is said to be the product $A \times B$, if

$$c_{ij} = \sum_{k=1}^{n} a_{ik} b_{kj}$$

$C = A \times B$, where the parametric subscript i assumes the values 1, 2, . . . , p and the parametric subscript j assumes the values 1, 2, . . . , q.

From this definition the following points are to be noted:

1. It is possible for the product $A \times B$ to exist without $B \times A$ existing. This happens when B is compatible with A but A is not compatible with B.

2. Even when both $A \times B$ and $B \times A$ exist, in general

$$A \times B \neq B \times A$$

3. If A is of the order $p \times n$ and B is of the order $n \times q$, then

$$A \times B = C$$

is a matrix of the order $p \times q$; that is, C has as many rows as A and as many columns as B.

4. The element c_{11} of $C = A \times B$ is obtained by taking the sum of a number of terms obtained from the product of "proper" elements of A and B.

$$c_{11} = \sum_{k=1}^{n} a_{1k}b_{k1} = a_{11}b_{11} + a_{12}b_{21} + a_{13}b_{31} + \cdots + a_{1n}b_{n1}$$

$$c_{21} = \sum_{k=1}^{n} a_{2k}b_{k1} = a_{21}b_{11} + a_{22}b_{21} + a_{23}b_{31} + \cdots + a_{2n}b_{n1}$$

$$c_{12} = \sum_{k=1}^{n} a_{1k}b_{k2} = a_{11}b_{12} + a_{12}b_{22} + a_{13}b_{32} + \cdots + a_{1n}b_{n2}$$

Note that the inner subscripts such as 2 in $a_{12}b_{21}$ or 3 in $a_{13}b_{32}$ are always equal.

With the above definition it is seen that the payment matrix of the supermarket example is the product of the items matrix and the unit price matrix,

$$\|\text{items matrix}\| \times \|\text{unit price matrix}\| = \|\text{payment matrix}\|$$

$$\left\| \begin{matrix} 2 & 6 & \frac{1}{2} \\ 3 & 0 & \frac{3}{4} \end{matrix} \right\| \times \left\| \begin{matrix} 23 \\ 11 \\ 72 \end{matrix} \right\| = \left\| \begin{matrix} (2 \times 23) + (6 \times 11) + (\frac{1}{2} \times 72) \\ (3 \times 23) + (0 \times 11) + (\frac{3}{4} \times 72) \end{matrix} \right\| = \left\| \begin{matrix} 148 \\ 123 \end{matrix} \right\|$$

We may extend the example of the supermarket purchase and say that the prices are given as 23 cents per loaf, 11 cents per can, and 72 cents per pound if paid for in cash and 24 cents per loaf, 12 cents per can, and 76 cents per pound if charged to account. In this case the unit price matrix will be a 3×2 matrix,

	Cash price, cents	Credit price, cents
Loaf of bread..............	23	24
Can of juice..............	11	12
Pound of butter..........	72	76

Now the product of the items matrix and the new price matrix is

$$\left\| \begin{matrix} 2 & 6 & \frac{1}{2} \\ 3 & 0 & \frac{3}{4} \end{matrix} \right\| \times \left\| \begin{matrix} 23 & 24 \\ 11 & 12 \\ 72 & 76 \end{matrix} \right\|$$

$$= \left\| \begin{matrix} (2 \times 23 + 6 \times 11 + \frac{1}{2} \times 72) & (2 \times 24 + 6 \times 12 + \frac{1}{2} \times 76) \\ (3 \times 23 + 0 \times 11 + \frac{3}{4} \times 72) & (3 \times 24 + 0 \times 12 + \frac{3}{4} \times 76) \end{matrix} \right\|$$

$$= \left\| \begin{matrix} 148 & 158 \\ 123 & 129 \end{matrix} \right\|$$

The new payment matrix is composed of elements which are the prices that X must pay, cash or credit (148 or 158), and Y must pay, cash or credit (123 or 129). The relationship $c_{ij} = \sum_{k=1}^{n} a_{ik} b_{kj}$ indicates the operation of taking the kth element of the ith row in A (items matrix) and multiplying it by the kth element of the jth column in B (price matrix) and adding the results for all k (all items) to give the c_{ij} element (the payment customer $i = X$ or $i = Y$ must make, if he pays $j = $ cash or $j = $ charge account).

A-10. Square Matrix. If the number of the rows and columns of a matrix are identical, the matrix is called a square matrix.

Principal Elements of a Square Matrix. In the square matrix

$$A = \|a_{jk}\|$$

the terms a_{jj} are called the principal elements of the matrix. Thus, in a square matrix of order 4, the terms a_{11}, a_{22}, a_{33}, and a_{44} are the principal elements.

Principal Diagonal of a Square Matrix. The "diagonal" formed by the principal elements of a square matrix is called the principal diagonal of the matrix.

Symmetrical Matrix. If in a square matrix $a_{jk} = a_{kj}$, that matrix is called symmetrical. Network matrices (mesh or node) of passive networks are symmetrical, since $Y_{21} = Y_{12}$, etc.

A-11. Fundamental Products of Elements of a Square Matrix. At the beginning of this Appendix we noted that for the purpose of precision of statement we must define certain terms. In the following paragraphs some of these terms are defined. A square matrix A of order n (n rows and n columns) has n^2 elements. Consider a term obtained by multiplication of n of such elements; a variety of such terms is possible, and the number increases as n increases. Among such products a particular set is of particular interest. The members of this set are chosen in such a manner that, for example, if a_{23} is one of the elements in the product, none of the other elements are chosen from row 2 or column 3 of the matrix.   Or, in general, if a_{ij} is one of the elements in the product, none of the other elements are chosen from the ith row or jth column.   We call such products the "fundamental" products of the square matrix.

As a specific example, we consider a fourth-order square matrix (four rows and four columns, with $n = 4$), $A = \|a_{ij}\|$.   We may ask ourselves: How many fundamental products exist for such a matrix?   The answer to this question is found if we systematize the problem by noting that, since not more than one element can be taken from one row, each of the elements in a fundamental product must be taken from a different row. Therefore a typical product can be written as $a_{1x}\, a_{2y}\, a_{3z}\, a_{4r}$, where x, y, z, and r refer to the column position of the various elements.   Now, if $x = 2$, then y, z, and r can no longer be 2.   We may start by giving x the choice of all the possible number of columns (one to four for a fourth-order matrix).   Once the value of x is selected, y can assume (in this example) three values, z two values, and r one value.   Thus, there will be $4 \times 3 \times 2 \times 1 = 4! = 24 = n!$ different products of the form $a_{1x}\, a_{2y}\, a_{3z}\, a_{4r}$, where no two elements belong to the same column or the same row. These products can be obtained by ordering the elements in accordance with their rows, that is, $a_{1\_}\, a_{2\_}\, a_{3\_}\, a_{4\_}$, and then filling the blanks by the order chosen for the columns.   These orders are given in Table A-1.

TABLE A-1

x	y	z	r	x	y	z	r	x	y	z	r	x	y	z	r
1	2	3	4	2	1	3	4	3	1	2	4	4	1	2	3
1	2	4	3	2	1	4	3	3	1	4	2	4	1	3	2
1	3	2	4	2	3	1	4	3	2	1	4	4	2	1	3
1	3	4	2	2	3	4	1	3	2	4	1	4	2	3	1
1	4	2	3	2	4	1	3	3	4	1	2	4	3	1	2
1	4	3	2	2	4	3	1	3	4	2	1	4	3	2	1

The corresponding products are $a_{11}\, a_{22}\, a_{33}\, a_{44}$, $a_{12}\, a_{21}\, a_{33}\, a_{44}$, $a_{13}\, a_{21}\, a_{32}\, a_{44}$, $a_{14}\, a_{21}\, a_{32}\, a_{43}$, with the remaining rows found from Table A-1.

A-12. Assignment of Positive or Negative Signs to Fundamental Products.   A fundamental product of a (numerical) matrix may be either a positive or a negative number.   Besides this sign, which will depend on the value of the elements in the product, we associate a positive or negative sign with the product (we polarize the product) in accordance with a rule illustrated in the following example.

If, in the example of a fourth-order matrix, the elements of the fundamental products are ordered in accordance with their row numbers and the sequence of the column numbers of the elements examined, one of the sequences given in Table A-1 will result.   Any of these (column numbers) sequences can be changed into a 1 2 3 4 (ordered) sequence by successive interchange of *adjacent* numbers. For example, 2143 can be changed to 2134 and then to 1234, a total of two changes of *adjacent* numbers. The sequence 1243 can be changed into 1234 in one step. If for a product the number of such changes is odd, the negative of that fundamental product will be called a "polarized product." If the number of changes is even, the polarized product is identical with the fundamental product. Thus the polarized product corresponding to $a_{11} a_{22} a_{34} a_{43}$ is $-a_{11} a_{22} a_{34} a_{43}$, and the polarized product corresponding to $a_{12} a_{21} a_{34} a_{43}$ is this product itself.

A-13. Determinant of a Square Matrix. The sum of the polarized products of a square matrix is called the determinant of that matrix. If the square matrix is $A = \|a_{ij}\|$, the determinant is shown as $D_A = |a_{ij}|$.

The determinant of a matrix is defined in the above manner, because of its use in the solution of a set of simultaneous equations. This will become apparent as we treat such equations.

Example A-2. Find the determinant of $A = \begin{Vmatrix} 1 & 2 \\ 3 & 4 \end{Vmatrix}$.

Solution. The fundamental products of A are $1 \times 4 = 4$ and $3 \times 2 = 6$. The polarized products are 4 and -6. The sum of these two gives

$$D_A = \begin{vmatrix} 1 & 2 \\ 3 & 4 \end{vmatrix} = 4 - 6 = -2$$

A-14. Properties of Determinants. 1. *Interchange of Rows and Columns.* A determinant is a "quantity" (number, operator, function) associated with a square array of elements. If the rows and columns of a determinant are interchanged, the value of the new determinant is identical with the value of the original determinant.

Example A-3. $\begin{vmatrix} 1 & 2 \\ 3 & 4 \end{vmatrix} = \begin{vmatrix} 1 & 3 \\ 2 & 4 \end{vmatrix}$.

The reason for this is that changing the rows and columns of determinants does not change the value of the polarized products. In Example A-3 the polarized products of the original determinant are 4 and -6, and those of the new determinant are also 4 and -6. A detailed study of any determinant will show the generality of the argument.

Because of this property any statement made about rows also applies to columns. For the sake of brevity, in such statements we shall not repeat "rows or columns"; rather, we shall simply make the statement about rows with the implicit understanding that the statement is equally applicable to columns.

2. *Interchange of Rows.* An interchange of adjacent rows of a determinant forms a new determinant. The fundamental products of the new

determinant are identical with those of the original determinant but will have the opposite polarity. For example, the fundamental products of each of the two determinants

$$\begin{vmatrix} 1 & 2 \\ 3 & 4 \end{vmatrix} \quad \text{and} \quad \begin{vmatrix} 3 & 4 \\ 1 & 2 \end{vmatrix}$$

are $1 \times 4 = 4$ and $3 \times 2 = 6$. The polarized products of the first determinant are 4 and -6. The polarized products of the second determinant are 6 and -4.

A detailed study of the general form of a determinant will show that this change of polarity takes place whenever adjacent rows of a determinant are interchanged. Since the value of a determinant is the sum of its polarized products, an interchange of adjacent rows of a determinant reverses the sign of the determinant. Thus

$$\begin{vmatrix} 1 & 2 \\ 3 & 4 \end{vmatrix} = -2 \quad \text{and} \quad \begin{vmatrix} 3 & 4 \\ 1 & 2 \end{vmatrix} = +2$$

3. *Identical Rows.* If two rows of a determinant are identical (their corresponding elements are identical), the value of the determinant is zero.

Proof. We first consider the case when the two adjacent rows are identical. Then an interchange of the adjacent rows must reverse the sign of the determinant. But such an interchange does not change the determinant because the two rows are identical. A quantity whose negative is equal to itself must be zero.

Example A-4. From property (2),

$$\begin{vmatrix} 1 & 2 & 3 \\ 1 & 2 & 3 \\ 4 & 5 & 6 \end{vmatrix} = - \begin{vmatrix} 1 & 2 & 3 \\ 1 & 2 & 3 \\ 4 & 5 & 6 \end{vmatrix}$$

The second determinant is obtained by interchanging the position of the first and second rows in the first determinant, but no change in the array results. The above determinant is equal to the negative of itself and must be zero.

The proof, for the case when the rows are not adjacent, is left to the reader as an exercise.

4. *Multiplication of Elements of a Row by a Constant.* If all the elements in a row of a determinant are multiplied by a constant, the value of the determinant is multiplied by the constant.

Proof. Each fundamental product contains one and only one element from the row which is multiplied by the constant. Therefore all the products are multiplied by the constant, and thus the resulting sum of polarized products is multiplied by the constant.

Before studying other properties of determinants we shall define a few terms.

A-15. Minors, Cofactors, and Complements. If in a determinant $D_A = |a_{mn}|$ the rth row and cth column are deleted, the remaining determinant is called the *minor* of the element a_{rc} and is denoted by $(M_A)_{rc}$. In the determinant

$$D_B = \begin{vmatrix} b_{11} & b_{12} & b_{13} \\ b_{21} & b_{22} & b_{23} \\ b_{31} & b_{32} & b_{33} \end{vmatrix}$$

there are nine possible minors among which are

$$(M_B)_{11} = \begin{vmatrix} b_{22} & b_{23} \\ b_{32} & b_{33} \end{vmatrix} \qquad (M_B)_{23} = \begin{vmatrix} b_{11} & b_{12} \\ b_{31} & b_{32} \end{vmatrix}$$

If the minor M_{rc} is multiplied by $(-1)^{r+c}$, the result is called the *cofactor* of row r and column c. Thus, if $r + c$ is an even number, the cofactor is identical to the minor; and if $r + c$ is an odd number, the cofactor is the negative of the minor. We denote the cofactor associated with row r and column c of the determinant D_B by $(F_B)_{rc}$. Thus

$$(F_B)_{rc} = (-1)^{r+c}(M_B)_{rc} \tag{A-6}$$

The element a_{rc} is called the *complement* of the cofactor F_{rc}.

A-16. Evaluation of Determinant by Laplace's Development. A systematic and convenient method for evaluating determinants is by Laplace's development. According to this method the value of a determinant may be found as follows:

Select either a row or a column of the determinant. Obtain all the cofactors for that row or column. The value of the determinant is the sum of all the products of the cofactors multiplied by their complements. Thus the third-order determinant

$$D_A = \begin{vmatrix} a_{11} & a_{12} & a_{13} \\ a_{21} & a_{22} & a_{23} \\ a_{31} & a_{32} & a_{33} \end{vmatrix}$$

may be written as

$$D_A = a_{11} \begin{vmatrix} a_{22} & a_{23} \\ a_{32} & a_{33} \end{vmatrix} + (-1)a_{21} \begin{vmatrix} a_{12} & a_{13} \\ a_{32} & a_{33} \end{vmatrix} + a_{31} \begin{vmatrix} a_{12} & a_{13} \\ a_{22} & a_{23} \end{vmatrix}$$

or $\quad D_A = (-1)a_{21} \begin{vmatrix} a_{12} & a_{13} \\ a_{32} & a_{33} \end{vmatrix} + a_{22} \begin{vmatrix} a_{11} & a_{13} \\ a_{31} & a_{33} \end{vmatrix} + (-1)a_{23} \begin{vmatrix} a_{11} & a_{12} \\ a_{31} & a_{32} \end{vmatrix}$

or, in general, if a column c is used,

$$D_A = a_{1c}(F_A)_{1c} + a_{2c}(F_A)_{2c} + a_{3c}(F_A)_{3c} \qquad c = 1 \text{ or } 2 \text{ or } 3$$

and if a row r is used,

$$D_A = a_{r1}(F_A)_{r1} + a_{r2}(F_A)_{r2} + a_{r3}(F_A)_{r3} \qquad r = 1 \text{ or } 2 \text{ or } 3$$

The general form for Laplace's development gives

$$D_A = \sum_{j=1}^{n} a_{jc}(F_A)_{jc} = \sum_{j=1}^{n} a_{rj}(F_A)_{rj}$$

where n is the order of the determinant.

Using column 1 in the following numerical example,

$$D = \begin{vmatrix} 8 & 2 & -4 \\ 3 & 6 & 2 \\ 1 & 2 & 3 \end{vmatrix} = 8 \begin{vmatrix} 6 & 2 \\ 2 & 3 \end{vmatrix} - 3 \begin{vmatrix} 2 & -4 \\ 2 & 3 \end{vmatrix} + 1 \begin{vmatrix} 2 & -4 \\ 6 & 2 \end{vmatrix}$$

Applying Laplace's development to a two-column two-row determinant,

$$\begin{vmatrix} a_{11} & a_{12} \\ a_{21} & a_{22} \end{vmatrix} = a_{11}a_{22} - a_{21}a_{12}$$

We observe, therefore, that repeated application of Laplace's development to the evaluation of the cofactors eventually results in a determinant of order 2, which is evaluated as above. It is evidently advantageous to choose the column or row for Laplace's development such that (where possible) as many complements are zero as is possible.

Example A-5.

$$D_1 = \begin{vmatrix} 8 & 2 & -4 \\ 3 & 6 & 2 \\ 0 & 2 & 3 \end{vmatrix} = 8(18 - 4) - 3(6 + 8) + 0(4 + 24) = 70$$

This value is identical to the sum of the polarized products of the matrix. The proof of Laplace's development is not given here. It may be proved by tabulation of the polarized products in groups where the first elements of the products are the same. The sum of such a group is the product of a complement with its cofactor.

A-17. Properties of Cofactors. From Laplace's development we have seen that

$$D_A = |a_{ij}| = \sum_{m=1,2,3,\dots,n} a_{mc}(F_A)_{mc} = \sum_{m=1,2,3,\dots,n} a_{rm}(F_A)_{rm} \qquad \text{(A-7)}$$

where n is the order of the determinants. In this summation each cofactor $(F_A)_{mc}$ is multiplied by its own complement a_{mc}. We now show that, if the respective cofactor of row 1 [that is, $(F_A)_{1m}$ is multiplied by complements taken from other rows (such as a_{2m}) and the results added, zero results; i.e.

$$\sum_{m=1,2,3,\ldots,n} a_{2m}(F_A)_{1m} = \sum_{m=1,2,3,\ldots,n} a_{m2}(F_A)_{m1} = \cdots = 0$$

To prove this, consider the determinant D'_A obtained from D_A by replacing its first row with its second row, but keeping the second row unchanged.

$$D'_A = \begin{vmatrix} a_{21} & a_{22} & a_{23} & \cdots & a_{2n} \\ a_{21} & a_{22} & a_{23} & \cdots & a_{2n} \\ a_{31} & a_{32} & \cdot & \cdots & \cdot \\ \cdot & \cdot & \cdot & \cdots & \cdot \\ a_{n1} & a_{n2} & \cdot & \cdots & a_{nn} \end{vmatrix}$$

Since two rows of D'_A are identical, $D'_A \equiv 0$. Laplace's development of D'_A gives

$$D'_A = a_{21}(F_A)_{11} + a_{22}(F_A)_{12} + a_{23}(F_A)_{13} + \cdots + a_{2n}(F_A)_{1n} = 0$$

This can be written as

$$\sum_{m=1,2,\ldots,n} a_{2m}(F_A)_{1m} = 0$$

which proves the above statement. If the first row is replaced by the third row and the third row is left unchanged, we arrive at

$$\sum_{m=1,2,\ldots,n} a_{3m}(F_A)_{1m} = 0 = \sum_{\substack{m=1,2,\ldots,n \\ i \neq j}} a_{im}(F_A)_{jm}$$

By a similar procedure we can show that

$$\sum_{m=1,2,\ldots,n} a_{mi}(F_A)_{mj} = 0 \qquad \text{for } i \neq j \tag{A-8}$$

A-18. Properties of Determinants (Continued). In Art. A-14 four of the properties of determinants were studied. By the use of Laplace's development and the properties of the cofactors the following properties of determinants can be examined:

5. *Any row of a determinant may be added to another row without changing the value of determinant.*

Proof. Consider the determinant $D_A = |a_{ij}| = \displaystyle\sum_{j=1}^{n} a_{ij}(F_A)_{ij}$. Let D'_A be obtained from D_A by adding the second row of D_A to its first row. Then

$$D'_A = \sum_{j=1}^{n} (a_{1j} + a_{2j})(F_A)_{1j} = \sum_{j=1}^{n} a_{1j}(F_A)_{1j} + \sum_{j=1}^{n} a_{2j}(F_A)_{1j}$$

In Art. A-17 it is shown that $\displaystyle\sum_{j=1}^{n} a_{2j}(F_A)_{1j} = 0$, which shows that

$$D_A = D'_A$$

6. *If all terms except those on the principal diagonal of a determinant are zero, the value of the determinant is equal to the product of the terms on the principal diagonal.*

Proof. The statement that the terms of the principal diagonal are zero can be expressed as

$$a_{ij} = \delta_{ij} a_{ij}$$

where δ_{ij} is Kronecker's delta, defined as

$$\delta_{ij} = 1 \qquad i = j$$
$$\delta_{ij} = 0 \qquad i \neq j$$

$$D_A = \sum_{j=1}^{n} a_{1j}(F_A)_{1j} = \sum_{j=1}^{n} \delta_{1j} a_{1j}(F_A)_{1j} = a_{11}(F_A)_{11}$$

A similar argument shows that $(F_A)_{11}$ is equal to the product of a_{22} by another factor which is a_{33} times a_{44}, and so on. Thus

$$D_A = a_{11}a_{22}a_{33} \cdots a_{nn}$$

To illustrate some of these properties, consider the three-column three-row determinant D,

$$D = \begin{vmatrix} 8 & 2 & -4 \\ 3 & 6 & 2 \\ 1 & 2 & 3 \end{vmatrix}$$

This determinant is evaluated by application of various properties of determinants given in rules 1 to 6 in Arts. A-14 and A-18.

Apply rule 4, multiplying row 1 by $\frac{1}{2}$,

$$\tfrac{1}{2}D = \begin{vmatrix} 4 & 1 & -2 \\ 3 & 6 & 2 \\ 1 & 2 & 3 \end{vmatrix}$$

Apply rule 5, adding row 1 to row 2,

$$\tfrac{1}{2}D = \begin{vmatrix} 4 & 1 & -2 \\ 7 & 7 & 0 \\ 1 & 2 & 3 \end{vmatrix}$$

Now multiply column 2 by -1, and add to column 1,

$$\tfrac{1}{2}D = \begin{vmatrix} 3 & 1 & -2 \\ 0 & 7 & 0 \\ -1 & 2 & 3 \end{vmatrix}$$

Now multiply column 1 by 2, and add to column 2,

$$\tfrac{1}{2}D = \begin{vmatrix} 3 & 7 & -2 \\ 0 & 7 & 0 \\ -1 & 0 & 3 \end{vmatrix}$$

Now subtract row 2 from row 1,

$$\tfrac{1}{2}D = \begin{vmatrix} 3 & 0 & -2 \\ 0 & 7 & 0 \\ -1 & 0 & 3 \end{vmatrix}$$

Now multiply row 1 by $\tfrac{1}{3}$, and add to row 3,

$$\tfrac{1}{2}D = \begin{vmatrix} 3 & 0 & -2 \\ 0 & 7 & 0 \\ 0 & 0 & \tfrac{7}{3} \end{vmatrix}$$

Finally multiply row three by $\tfrac{6}{7}$, and add to row 1,

$$\tfrac{1}{2}D = \begin{vmatrix} 3 & 0 & 0 \\ 0 & 7 & 0 \\ 0 & 0 & \tfrac{7}{3} \end{vmatrix}$$

Hence, using rule 6,

$$\tfrac{1}{2}D = 3 \times 7 \times \tfrac{7}{3} = 49$$

or

$$D = 98$$

A-19. Application to Linear Equations. The system of n simultaneous linear equations

$$\begin{aligned} a_{11}x_1 + a_{12}x_2 + \cdots + a_{1n}x_n &= y_1 \\ a_{21}x_1 + a_{22}x_2 + \cdots + a_{2n}x_n &= y_2 \\ & \vdots \\ a_{n1}x_1 + a_{n2}x_2 + \cdots + a_{nn}x_n &= y_n \end{aligned} \qquad \text{(A-9)}$$

can be written as the product of the matrices

$$\begin{Vmatrix} a_{11} & a_{12} & a_{13} & \cdots & a_{1n} \\ a_{21} & a_{22} & a_{23} & \cdots & a_{2n} \\ \cdot & \cdot & \cdot & \cdots & \cdot \\ a_{n1} & a_{n2} & a_{n3} & \cdots & a_{nn} \end{Vmatrix} \times \begin{Vmatrix} x_1 \\ x_2 \\ \cdot \\ x_n \end{Vmatrix} = \begin{Vmatrix} y_1 \\ y_2 \\ \cdot \\ y_n \end{Vmatrix}$$

If we denote the matrix of the coefficients by $\|a_{rc}\|$, then Eqs. (A-9) can be expressed as

$$\|a_{rc}\| \times \|x_r\| = \|y_r\|$$

where $\|a_{rc}\|$ is always a square matrix, while $\|x_r\|$ and $\|y_r\|$ have one column only and are called column matrices.

A-20. Cramer's Rule.   Cramer's rule concerns the solution of linear equations by determinants.   This rule states that the solution for any variable x_m in the system of equations

$$a_{11}x_1 + a_{12}x_2 + \cdots + a_{1m}x_m + \cdots + a_{1n}x_n = y_1$$
$$a_{21}x_1 + a_{22}x_2 + \cdots + a_{2m}x_m + \cdots + a_{2n}x_n = y_2$$
$$a_{31}x_1 + a_{32}x_2 + \cdots + a_{3m}x_m + \cdots + a_{3n}x_n = y_3$$
$$\vdots$$
$$a_{n1}x_1 + a_{n2}x_2 + \cdots + a_{nm}x_m + \cdots + a_{nn}x_n = y_n$$

is given by

$$x_m = \frac{\begin{vmatrix} a_{11} & a_{12} & \cdots & y_1 & \cdots & a_{1n} \\ a_{21} & a_{22} & \cdots & y_2 & \cdots & a_{2n} \\ & & \cdots & & \cdots \\ a_{n1} & a_{n2} & \cdots & y_n & \cdots & a_{nn} \end{vmatrix}}{D_A}$$

with the mth column replaced by the y's (column indicated above the determinant as "mth column").

i.e., $x_m = \dfrac{\text{determinant of the } a\text{'s with column } m \text{ replaced by the } y\text{'s}}{\text{determinant of the } a\text{'s}}$

Thus, for example, the set of equations

$$5i_1 - 2i_2 - i_3 = 4$$
$$-2i_1 + 10i_2 - 3i_3 = 2$$
$$-i_1 - 3i_2 + 4i_3 = 0$$

has the solutions

$$i_1 = \frac{\begin{vmatrix} 4 & -2 & -1 \\ 2 & 10 & -3 \\ 0 & -3 & 4 \end{vmatrix}}{D} \qquad i_2 = \frac{\begin{vmatrix} 5 & 4 & -1 \\ -2 & 2 & -3 \\ -1 & 0 & 4 \end{vmatrix}}{D} \qquad i_3 = \frac{\begin{vmatrix} 5 & -2 & 4 \\ -2 & 10 & 2 \\ -1 & -3 & 0 \end{vmatrix}}{D}$$

where

$$D = \begin{vmatrix} 5 & -2 & -1 \\ -2 & 10 & -3 \\ -1 & -3 & 4 \end{vmatrix}$$

The proof of Cramer's rule is quite straightforward.   We show that Cramer's rule applies for the solution x_1.   Since we can rearrange the column in Eq. (A-9) to call any unknown x_1, this proof is general.   Now let us multiply the first of the equations by the cofactor $(F_A)_{11}$, the second by the cofactor $(F_A)_{21}$, the third by $(F_A)_{31}$, etc.   The equations now read

$$a_{11}(F_A)_{11}x_1 + a_{12}(F_A)_{11}x_2 + a_{13}(F_A)_{11}x_3 + \cdots + a_{1n}(F_A)_{11}x_n = (F_A)_{11}y_1$$
$$a_{21}(F_A)_{21}x_1 + a_{22}(F_A)_{21}x_2 + a_{23}(F_A)_{21}x_3 + \cdots + a_{2n}(F_A)_{21}x_n = (F_A)_{21}y_2$$
$$\cdot$$
$$\cdot$$
$$\cdot$$
$$a_{n1}(F_A)_{n1}x_1 + a_{n2}(F_A)_{n1}x_2 + a_{n3}(F_A)_{n1}x_3 + \cdots + a_{nn}(F_A)_{n1}x_n = (F_A)_{n1}y_n$$

Now we add all the equations, and the result reads

$$[a_{11}(F_A)_{11} + a_{21}(F_A)_{21} + a_{31}(F_A)_{31} + \cdots + a_{n1}(F_A)_{n1}]x_1$$
$$+ [a_{12}(F_A)_{11} + a_{22}(F_A)_{21} + a_{32}(F_A)_{31} + \cdots + a_{n2}(F_A)_{n1}]x_2 + \cdots$$
$$= (F_A)_{11}y_1 + (F_A)_{21}y_2 + (F_A)_{31}y_3 + \cdots + (F_A)_{n1}y_n$$

But from the properties of cofactors given in Eq. (A-8) and the above equation we see that the coefficient of x_1 is D_A and the coefficients of x_2, x_3, . . . , x_n are identically zero. Therefore

$$D_A x_1 = y_1(F_A)_{11} + y_2(F_A)_{21} + \cdots + (F_A)_{n1}y_n$$

$$x_1 = \frac{\displaystyle\sum_{m=1,2,\ldots,n} y_m(F_A)_{m1}}{D_A} \tag{A-10}$$

We can show that for other x such as x_b

$$x_b = \frac{\displaystyle\sum_{m=1,2,\ldots,n} y_m(F_A)_{mb}}{D_A}$$

which proves Cramer's rule.

A-21. Inverse Matrix. We can now restate the problem posed by n simultaneous linear equations in a slightly different fashion. Equation (A-10) states how the $\|y_r\|$ matrix is obtained if the $\|a_{rc}\|$ and the $\|x_r\|$ matrix is given. In other words, the multiplication $\|a_{rc}\| \times \|x_r\|$ transforms the x's into the y's through linear combinations. The problem of finding the x's, given the y's (that is, solving the simultaneous equations), is then the problem of finding the transformation which transforms the y's into x's; or given

$$\|a_{rc}\| \times \|x_r\| = \|y_r\|$$

we wish to find a matrix $\|b_{rc}\|$ such that

$$\|b_{rc}\| \times \|y_r\| = \|x_r\|$$

But we know, from Cramer's rule and from Laplace's development, that

$$x_e = y_1 \frac{(F_A)_{1e}}{D_A} + y_2 \frac{(F_A)_{2e}}{D_A} + \cdots + y_n \frac{(F_A)_{ne}}{D_A}$$

Hence the $\|b\|$ matrix has the elements $b_{rc} = (F_A)_{cr}/D_A$.

We now define the $\|b_{rc}\|$ matrix as the *inverse* of the $\|a_{rc}\|$ matrix. Note that $D_A \neq 0$ is a necessary condition for the existence of the $\|b\|$ matrix. In general, then,

$$\text{Inverse of } \|a_{rc}\| = \|a_{rc}\|^{-1} = \left\| \frac{(F_A)_{cr}}{D_A} \right\|$$

For example,

$$\left\| \begin{matrix} a_{11} & a_{12} \\ a_{21} & a_{22} \end{matrix} \right\|^{-1} = \left\| \begin{matrix} \dfrac{a_{22}}{a_{11}a_{22} - a_{12}a_{21}} & \dfrac{-a_{12}}{a_{11}a_{22} - a_{12}a_{21}} \\ \dfrac{-a_{21}}{a_{11}a_{22} - a_{21}a_{12}} & \dfrac{a_{11}}{a_{11}a_{22} - a_{12}a_{21}} \end{matrix} \right\|$$

if $a_{11}a_{22} - a_{12}a_{21} \neq 0$. For $A = \left| \begin{matrix} 1 & 2 \\ 3 & 4 \end{matrix} \right|$

$$A^{-1} = \left\| \begin{matrix} \dfrac{4}{4 - 6} & \dfrac{-2}{4 - 6} \\ \dfrac{-3}{4 - 6} & \dfrac{1}{4 - 6} \end{matrix} \right\| = \left\| \begin{matrix} \left(-\dfrac{1}{2}\right)(4) & \left(+\dfrac{1}{2}\right)(2) \\ \left(+\dfrac{1}{2}\right)(3) & \left(-\dfrac{1}{2}\right)(1) \end{matrix} \right\|$$

INDEX

697